$7.95

FUZZY LOGIC
AND
NEURAL NETWORK
HANDBOOK

Computer Engineering Series

Chen · COMPUTER ENGINEERING HANDBOOK, 0-07-010924-9
Chen · FUZZY LOGIC AND NEURAL NETWORK HANDBOOK, 0-07-073020-2
Devadas, Keutzer, Ghosh · LOGIC SYNTHESIS, 0-07-016500-9
Howland · COMPUTER HARDWARE DIAGNOSTICS FOR ENGINEERS, 0-07-030561-7
Leiss · PARALLEL AND VECTOR COMPUTING, 0-07-037692-1
Perry · VHDL, Second Edition, 0-07-049434-7
Pick · VHDL TECHNIQUES, EXPERIMENTS, AND CAVEATS, 0-07-049906-3
Rosenstark · TRANSMISSION LINES IN COMPUTER ENGINEERING, 0-07-053953-7
Zomaya · PARALLEL AND DISTRIBUTED COMPUTING HANDBOOK, 0-07-073020-2

Related Titles of Interest

Kielkowski · INSIDE SPICE, 0-07-911525-X
Kielkowski · SPICE PRACTICAL PARAMETER MODELING, 0-07-911524-1
Massabrio, Antognetti · SEMICONDUCTOR DEVICE MODELING WITH SPICE, Second
   Edition, 0-07-002469-3

FUZZY LOGIC AND NEURAL NETWORK HANDBOOK

C. H. Chen Editor in Chief

University of Massachusetts Dartmouth

McGraw-Hill, Inc.

New York San Francisco Washington, D.C. Auckland Bogotá
Caracas Lisbon London Madrid Mexico City Milan
Montreal New Delhi San Juan Singapore
Sydney Tokyo Toronto

Library of Congress Cataloging-in-Publication Data

Fuzzy logic and neural network handbook / C.H. Chen.
     p.   cm.—(Computer engineering series)
     Includes index.
     ISBN 0-07-011189-8 (hb)
     1. Intelligent control systems.   2. Fuzzy systems.   3. Neural
networks (Computer science)   I. Chen, C. H. (Chi-hau), date.
II. Series.
TJ217.5.F9   1996
006.3—dc20   95-38128
                                          CIP

McGraw-Hill

A Division of The **McGraw·Hill** *Companies*

1 2 3 4 5 6 7 8 9 0 DOC/DOC 9 0 0 9 8 7 6 5

ISBN 0-07-011189-8

*The sponsoring editor for this book was Steve Chapman, the editing
supervisor was David E. Fogarty, and the production supervisor was
Pamela A. Pelton. It was set in Times Roman by North Market Street
Graphics.*

Printed and bound by R. R. Donnelley & Sons Company.

This book is printed on acid-free paper.

CONTENTS

Part 3   Architectures and Systems

Chapter 29. Chaotic Neural Network Architecture
Harold Szu, Charles Hsu, and Mona Zaghloul   **29.1**

Chapter 30. Artificial Neural Systems Based on Free-Space Optical
Interconnects   *Ashok V. Krishnamoorthy, Gokce Yayla, Matthias Blume, and Sadik C. Esener*   **30.1**

Chapter 31. A General-Purpose Analog Neural Computer for
Real-Time Spatiotemporal Pattern Analysis: Visual Motion Estimation
Jan Van der Spiegel, Ralph Etienne-Cummings, Christopher Donham, Alyssa Apsel, Paul Mueller, and David Blackman   **31.1**

Index follows Chapter 31

CONTRIBUTORS

Shigeo Abe   *Hitachi Research Laboratory, Hitachi, Ltd.* (CHAP. 7)

Nirwan Ansari   *Center for Communications and Signal Processing, New Jersey Institute of Technology, Newark* (CHAP. 17)

Alyssa Apsel   *Moore School of Electrical Engineering, Center for Sensor Technologies, University of Pennsylvania, Philadelphia* (CHAP. 31)

Shoichi Araki   *Central Research Laboratories, Matsushita Electric Industrial Co., Ltd., Kyoto, Japan* (CHAP. 21)

James C. Bezdek   *Department of Computer Science, University of West Florida, Pensacola* (CHAP. 2)

David Blackman   *Corticon Incorporated, Philadelphia* (CHAP. 31)

P. Bolland   *London Business School, Department of Decision Science* (CHAP. 19)

Elisabetta Binaghi   *ITIM—Istituto per le Tecnologie Informatiche Multimediali—C.N.R., Milano, Italy* (CHAP. 25)

Matthias Blume   *Department of Electrical and Computer Engineering, University of California, San Diego* (CHAP. 30)

J. Bremont   *Center for Automation Research, Henri Poincaré University, Nancy, France* (CHAP. 8)

Gail A. Carpenter   *Center for Adaptive Systems and Department of Cognitive and Neural Systems, Boston University, Boston, Massachusetts* (CHAP. 1)

Iacopo Cerrani   *Dipartimento di Scienze dell' Informazione, Università degli Studi di Milano, Milano, Italy* (CHAP. 25)

C. H. Chen   *Electrical and Computer Engineering Department, University of Massachusetts, Dartmouth* (EDITOR; CHAP. 20)

Ralph Etienne-Cummings   *Moore School of Electrical Engineering, Center for Sensor Technologies, University of Pennsylvania, Philadelphia* (CHAP. 31)

Taher Daud   *Center for Space Microelectronics Technology, Jet Propulsion Laboratory, California Institute of Technology, Pasadena* (CHAP. 27)

J. DeWitte, Jr.   *The George Washington University, Washington, D.C.* (CHAP. 6)

Christopher Donham   *Moore School of Electrical Engineering, Center for Sensor Technologies, University of Pennsylvania, Philadelphia* (CHAP. 31)

Mark E. Dreier   *Bell Helicopter Textron, Inc., Fort Worth, Texas* (CHAP. 22)

G. Dubois   *Center for Automation Research, Henri Poincaré University, Nancy, France* (CHAP. 8)

Tuan A. Duong   *Center for Space Microelectronics Technology, Jet Propulsion Laboratory, California Institute of Technology, Pasadena* (CHAP. 27)

Silvio P. Eberhardt *Center for Space Microelectronics Technology, Jet Propulsion Laboratory, California Institute of Technology, Pasadena; now with Department of Engineering, Swarthmore College, Swarthmore, Pennsylvania* (CHAP. 27)

Sadik C. Esener *Department of Electrical and Computer Engineering, University of California, San Diego* (CHAP. 30)

Qiang Gan *Department of Biomedical Engineering, Southeast University, Nanjing, China* (CHAP. 16)

Filson H. Glanz *Robotics Laboratory, University of New Hampshire, Durham* (CHAP. 26)

R. Paul Gorman *AlliedSignal Microelectronics and Technology Center, Columbia, Maryland* (CHAP. 13)

Stephen Grossberg *Center for Adaptive Systems and Department of Cognitive and Neural Systems, Boston University, Boston, Massachusetts* (CHAP. 1)

Jean-Paul Haton *Université Henri Poincaré, CRIN/INRIA-Nancy, France* (CHAP. 14)

Simon Haykin *Communications Research Laboratory, McMaster University, Hamilton, Ontario, Canada* (CHAP. 12)

Charles Hsu *Department of Electrical Engineering and Computer Science, The George Washington University, Washington, D.C.* (CHAP. 29)

Donald L. Hung *Department of Electrical Engineering, Gannon University, Erie, Pennsylvania; now with Electrical Engineering and Computer Science Department, Washington State University—Tri Cities, Richland, Washington* (CHAP. 23)

Casimir C. Klimasauskas *NeuralWare, Inc., Pittsburgh, Pennsylvania* (CHAP. 11)

Bart Kosko *Signal and Image Processing Institute, Electrical Engineering Department, University of Southern California, Los Angeles* (CHAP. 9)

Ashok V. Krishnamoorthy *Advanced Photonics Research Department, AT&T Bell Laboratories, Holmdel, New Jersey* (CHAP. 30)

M. Lamotte *Center for Automation Research, Henri Poincaré University, Nancy, France* (CHAP. 8)

Ming-Shong Lan *Science Center, Rockwell International Corporation* (CHAP. 7)

E. Levrat *Center for Automation Research, Henri Poincaré University, Nancy, France* (CHAP. 8)

William L. McKeown *Bell Helicopter Textron, Inc., Fort Worth, Texas* (CHAP. 22)

Gary S. May *Microelectronics Research Center, Georgia Institute of Technology, Atlanta* (CHAP. 18)

W. Thomas Miller, III *Robotics Laboratory, University of New Hampshire, Durham* (CHAP. 26)

Maria Grazia Montesano *ITIM—Istituto per le Tecnologie Informatiche Multimediali—C.N.R., Milano, Italy* (CHAP. 25)

Paul Mueller *Corticon Incorporated, Philadelphia* (CHAP. 31)

Hiroyoshi Nomura *Central Research Laboratories, Matsushita Electric Industrial Co., Ltd., Kyoto, Japan* (CHAP. 21)

Yoh-Han Pao *Electrical Engineering and Applied Physics, Case Western Reserve University and AI WARE, Inc., Cleveland, Ohio* (CHAP. 10)

Anna Rampini *ITIM—Istituto per le Tecnologie Informatiche Multimediali—C.N.R., Milano, Italy* (CHAP. 25)

A. N. Refenes *London Business School, Department of Decision Science* (CHAP. 19)

Fabio Roli *DIBE, University of Genoa, Italy* (CHAP. 15)

L. Rondeau *Center for Automation Research, Henri Poincaré University, Nancy, France* (CHAP. 8)

Enrique H. Ruspini *Artificial Intelligence Center, SRI International, Menlo Park, California* (CHAPS. 5; 24)

H. Wayne Scott *Bell Helicopter Textron, Inc., Fort Worth, Texas* (CHAP. 22)

Sebastiano B. Serpico *DIBE, University of Genoa, Italy* (CHAP. 15)

Donald F. Specht *Lockheed Martin Missiles & Space, Palo Alto Research Laboratories, Palo Alto, California* (CHAP. 3)

Jan Van der Spiegel *Moore School of Electrical Engineering, Center for Sensor Technologies, University of Pennsylvania, Philadelphia* (CHAP. 31)

Ching Y. Suen *Centre for Pattern Recognition and Machine Intelligence (CENPARMI), Concordia University, Montreal, Canada* (CHAP. 16)

Harold Szu *Naval Surface Warfare Center DD, Silver Spring, Maryland; now with The Center for Advanced Computer Studies, University of Louisiana, Lafayette* (CHAPS. 6; 29)

Anil Thakoor *Center for Space Microelectronics Technology, Jet Propulsion Laboratory, California Institute of Technology, Pasadena* (CHAP. 27)

Andrew Ukrainec *Communications Research Laboratory, McMaster University, Hamilton, Ontario, Canada* (CHAP. 12)

Gianni Vernazza *DIEE, University of Cagliari, Italy* (CHAP. 15)

Noboru Wakami *Central Research Laboratories, Matsushita Electric Industrial Co., Ltd., Kyoto, Japan* (CHAP. 21)

Gangsheng Wang *Center for Communications and Signal Processing, New Jersey Institute of Technology, Newark* (CHAP. 17)

Jun Wang *Department of Industrial Technology, University of North Dakota, Grand Forks and Mechanical and Automation Engineering Department, The Chinese University of Hong Kong, Shatin, New Territories, Hong Kong* (CHAP. 4)

Stephen S. Wilson *Applied Intelligent Systems, Inc., Ann Arbor, Michigan* (CHAP. 28)

Gokce Yayla *Department of Electrical and Computer Engineering, University of California, San Diego* (CHAP. 30)

Percy P. C. Yip *Electrical Engineering and Applied Physics, Case Western Reserve University and AI WARE, Inc., Cleveland, Ohio* (CHAP. 10)

Mona Zaghloul *Department of Electrical Engineering and Computer Science, The George Washington University, Washington, D.C.* (CHAP. 29)

PREFACE

In the past ten years there has been strong and renewed interest in fuzzy logic and neural networks motivated largely by the need for better management of uncertain information, the availability of VLSI implementation, and improved performance in wide areas of applications over the existing methods. Modern scientists and engineers must have some knowledge about fuzzy logic and neural networks which hold the key to intelligent systems and information processing. Computer engineers in particular must be familiar with the parallel computer architecture of neural networks that can play a dominant role in future computer systems. The effort to make computer-based systems more intelligent and more human certainly is centered on the use of fuzzy logic. A book on fuzzy logic and neural networks that presents algorithms, applications and architecture therefore is certainly essential for scientists and engineers in the near and more distant future. The fact that interest in fuzzy logic and neural networks is growing rapidly can be seen from the conferences on fuzzy logic and neural networks sponsored by IEEE, the International Neural Network Society, and other societies, with well over a thousand participants in most conferences. Applications of neural networks and fuzzy logic have appeared in almost every area of science, engineering, business, and technology. In this handbook leading researchers present concise and comprehensive reports on the major activities in fuzzy logic and neural networks. Particular focus is on the applications and systems that are of interest to computer engineers. Each chapter will focus on the most important activity of a specific topic. Although a growing number of books have provided different coverages of the activities and many more books will be published, we believe this handbook will give the readers not only an overview but also an in-depth understanding of the *major* results in fuzzy logic and neural networks. As a handbook, it is not an encyclopedia or a dictionary, and no attempt is made to cover all topics in this area.

The book has three parts. Part 1, "Principles and Algorithms," begins with a chapter by Carpenter and Grossberg on Fuzzy ARTMAP which is a self-organizing neural system that is capable of learning recognition categories and prediction in both supervised and unsupervised modes. Fuzzy logic provides a way for Fuzzy ARTMAP to adaptively categorize analog as well as binary input patterns occurring in a nonstationary time series. The second chapter by Bezdek, which is the only reprint chapter in the book, provides a comprehensive review of statistical, fuzzy, and neural models for pattern recognition. Chapter 3 by Specht covers both the basic and adaptive forms of probabilistic neural networks (PNN) for classification and the general regression neural networks (GRNN) for prediction. The algorithms for both networks are presented. Detailed examples are provided to compare accuracies. Reduction of network complexity by clustering is also examined. Chapter 4 by J. Wang presents various recurrent networks for solving optimization problems and in particular a recurrent neural network for convex programming is discussed. Chapter 5 by Ruspini approaches a different theoretical area in that available information can be imprecise and uncertain, and possible world semantics can provide a perspective into approximate reasoning problems and methods. Chapter 6 by DeWitte and Szu deals with another fuzzy logic topic concerning the development of automatic data-driven adaptive controllers which are suitable for nonstationary environments. The chapter focuses on a general noncentroidal form of defuzzification that can be used in data-driven adaptive fuzzy logic controllers.

Chapter 7 by Abe and Lan is devoted to algorithms for fuzzy rule extraction from numerical data for pattern classification using a direct method and a neural network–based method, as well as a fuzzy system for function approximation. Detailed examples for performance evaluation are given for vehicle license plate recognition and blood cell classification. Chapter 8 by Levrat, Dubois, Rondeau, Lamotte, and Bremont presents fuzzy relational equations, various types of compositions and equations, and inverted inverse equations, as well as solution methods. Chapter 9 by Kosko is on additive fuzzy systems and their uses from function approximation to learning. The last two chapters of Part 1 again deal with neural networks. Neural networks are useful to learn a computational model, and such a model can be crucial to process monitoring and control. Chapter 10 by Pao and Yip is concerned with neural net process monitoring and optimal control. The model building is also useful in database application. Chapter 11 by Klimasauskas discusses key techniques and issues in neural networks for database applications.

Part 2, "Applications," presents a number of important applications of neural networks and fuzzy logic. Chapter 12 by Ukrainec and Haykin presents a nonlinear neural network based on radial basis functions along with a training algorithm that minimizes the mutual information between the outputs for radar signal processing. Chapter 13 by Gorman and Chapter 14 by Haton provide an overview of sonar signal processing and automatic speech recognition, respectively, using neural networks. In addition to an overview of neural networks for remote sensing images, Chapter 15 by Roli, Serpico, and Vernazza also presents a treelike network structure for classification. Chapter 16 by Gan and Suen presents the state of art in off-line handwritten character recognition. Neural networks have been successfully applied to telecommunications in recent years. Chapter 17 by Ansari and G. Wang presents broadcast scheduling in telecommunications. Chapter 18 by May is on applying neural networks in semiconductor manufacturing processes. There has been strong interest in recent years in the use of neural networks and fuzzy logic in various financial market problems. Chapter 19 by Refenes and Bolland focuses specifically on the quantitative investment management using neural networks. Chapter 20 by Chen provides an overview of applications in nondestructive evaluation of materials. Though we have heard of smart home appliances using fuzzy logic through news media, little in-depth reporting in English is available. Chapter 21 by Wakami, Nomura, and Araki presents the mathematical principles of fuzzy logic for home appliances. Chapter 22 by Dreier, McKeown, and Scott is concerned with the use of fuzzy logic in the difficult manufacturing task of drilling small lubrication holes into hardened transmission gears. Although only major applications are presented in the book, the growing importance of fuzzy logic and neural networks applications to industry is quite evident.

Part 3, "Architectures and Systems," begins with Chapter 23 on hardware fuzzy inference systems by Hung and Chapter 24 on reactive control using fuzzy logic by Ruspini. Chapter 25 by Binaghi, Cerrani, Montesano, and Rampini is concerned with a hybrid fuzzy expert system shell for the acquisition and representation of medical knowledge and automated medical diagnosis. Chapter 26 by Miller and Glanz discusses the Cerebellar Model Arithmetic Computer, CMAC, a neural network based on the concept of sensory encoding using local receptive fields. Chapter 27 by Duong, Eberhardt, Daud, and Thakoor presents in detail the VLSI implementation

strategies of neural network learning. Chapter 28 by Wilson is on morphological networks. Morphological networks operate on image spaces and consist of a massive number of inputs to a massive network of iconic cells. The computational requirements and programming strategies of morphologcal networks differ from those encountered in the commonly used network architectures. Chapter 29 by Szu, Hsu, and Zaghloul is concerned with the chaotic neural network architecture. Chapter 30 by Krishnamoorthy, Yayla, Blume, and Esener examines the use of free-space optoelectronic technology in implementing artificial neural networks. Examples are presented of architectures and systems for implementing specific neural network models using these optoelectronic devices. Finally in Chapter 31 by Van der Spiegel, Etienne-Cummings, Donham, Apsel, Mueller, and Blackman, a large scale analog neural
computer with programmable architecture is presented. Spatiotemporal filters implemented are useful for real-time dynamic pattern analysis and the chapter is concentrated on using the computer for visual motion estimation.

In organizing the chapters which deal with different aspects of fuzzy logic and neural networks and which present both introductory and tutorial material as well as research results, effort has been made to arrange them in a coherent manner as much as possible. Effort is also made to provide a balanced coverage of both fuzzy logic and neural networks though a separate discussion of the two closely related fields is not always possible. Furthermore a significant percentage of the chapters were prepared by contributors from industry, which is an important departure from many conference proceedings and journals. It is my strong belief that fuzzy logic and neural networks have now reached a level of maturity, and thus a handbook publication like this is timely and useful as a permanent reference book in these dynamic fields. It has been my great pleasure to work with leaders in the fields in preparing this book and I am grateful to all contributors whose great contributions have made this book possible.

C. H. Chen

FUZZY LOGIC
AND
NEURAL NETWORK
HANDBOOK

PRINCIPLES AND ALGORITHMS

CHAPTER 1

LEARNING, CATEGORIZATION, RULE FORMATION, AND PREDICTION BY FUZZY NEURAL NETWORKS

Gail A. Carpenter[†] and Stephen Grossberg[‡]

Center for Adaptive Systems and
Department of Cognitive and Neural Systems
Boston University, Boston, Massachusetts

1.1 A SYNTHESIS OF PRODUCTION SYSTEMS, NEURAL NETWORKS, AND FUZZY LOGIC

For many years, the subjects of *artificial intelligence (AI)*, neural networks, and fuzzy logic were developed by separate intellectual communities. This was due more, perhaps, to social and institutional barriers to communication than to inherently different research goals and results. One manifestation of these barriers came in the form of claims, especially from the AI community, that the other approaches could not succeed at solving certain problems, despite progress to the contrary. This divisive period is fortunately substantially behind us. A growing number of models now computationally synthesize properties of expert production systems, neural networks, and fuzzy logic. Fuzzy ARTMAP, the topic of this chapter, is one such model. *Fuzzy ARTMAP* is a family of self-organizing neural architectures that are capable of rapidly learning to recognize, test hypotheses about, and predict consequences of analog or binary input patterns occurring in a nonstationary time series.

Fuzzy ARTMAP is the class of *adaptive resonance theory (ART)* architectures designed for supervised learning. Since the introduction of ART as a cognitive and neur-

[†]Supported in part by Advanced Research Project Agency (ARPA) (ONR N00014-92-J-4015), the National Science Foundation (IRI 94-01659), and the Office of Naval Research (ONR N00014-91-J-4100).
[‡]Supported in part by ARPA (AFOSR 90-0083 and N00014-92-J-4015) and the Office of Naval Research (ONR N00014-91-J-4100).
Acknowledgments: The authors wish to thank Cynthia E. Bradford and Diana J. Meyers for their valuable assistance in the preparation of the manuscript.

al theory (Grossberg, 1976a, 1976b), an ever-expanding family of ART neural network architectures have been progressively developed at Boston University. These models include ART 1, ART 2, ART 2-A, ART 3, Fuzzy ART, ARTMAP, Fuzzy ARTMAP, and Fusion ARTMAP (Asfour et al., 1993; Carpenter and Grossberg, 1987a, 1987b, 1990, 1991; Carpenter et al., 1991a to c, 1992b, 1993, 1995). Variants of these models have also been developed by a number of other investigators.

ART systems from the outset incorporated properties of production systems and fuzzy logic; e.g., see Grossberg (1980, 1982). However, Fuzzy ARTMAP provides a mathematically precise realization of ART concepts that is computationally powerful enough to outperform many expert systems, genetic algorithms, and other neural networks in benchmark studies (Tables 1.1 to 1.3) and to help solve outstanding technological problems (Bachelder et al., 1993; Caudell et al., 1991; Dubrawski and Crowley, 1994a, 1994b; Escobedo et al., 1993; Gan and Lua, 1992; Gopal et al., 1993; Ham and Han, 1993; Harvey, 1993; Kasperkiewicz et al., 1994; Keyvan et al., 1993; Kumara et al., 1995; Johnson, 1993; Mehta et al., 1993; Moya et al., 1993; Suzuki et al., 1993; Wienke, 1993, 1994; Wienke and Kateman, 1994; Wienke et al., 1994). A self-organizing neural architecture, called *VIEWNET* (Bradski and Grossberg, 1994), that can learn to recognize 3-D (three-dimensional) objects from sequences of their 2-D (two-dimensional) views is reviewed to show how Fuzzy ARTMAP can be embedded into larger systems. Another simulation example of 3-D object recognition illustrates how the ART-EMAP architecture (Carpenter and Ross, 1993, 1994, 1995) uses distributed network activity to improve noise tolerance while retaining the speed advantage of fast learning; and how temporal evidence accumulation can augment ARTMAP capabilities.

TABLE 1.1   ARTMAP Benchmark Studies

---

1. Medical database—mortality following coronary bypass grafting (CABG) surgery. Fuzzy ARTMAP significantly outperforms:
   Logistic regression
   Additive model
   Bayesian assignment
   Cluster analysis
   Classification and regression trees
   Expert panel–derived sickness scores
   Principal-component analysis

2. Mushroom database
   Decision trees (90–95% correct)
   ARTMAP (100% correct)
   Training set an order of magnitude smaller

3. Letter recognition database
   Genetic algorithm (82% correct)
   Fuzzy ARTMAP (96% correct)

4. Circle-in-the-square task
   Back propagation (90% correct)
   Fuzzy ARTMAP (99.5% correct)

5. Two-spiral task
   Back propagation (10,000–20,000 training epochs)
   Fuzzy ARTMAP (1–5 training epochs)

Source: Reprinted with permission from Carpenter and Grossberg (1993).

TABLE 1.2   Fuzzy ARTMAP Applied to Landsat Image Database

With the exception of k-NN, Fuzzy ARTMAP test set performance exceeded that of other neural network and machine learning algorithms. Compared to k-NN, Fuzzy ARTMAP showed a 6:1 code compression ratio.

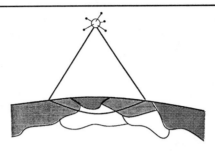

Algorithm	Accuracy(%)
k-N-N	91
fuzzy ARTMAP	89
RBF	88
Alloc80	87
INDCART	86
CART	86
Backprop	86
C4.5	85

Algorithm	Accuracy(%)
NewID	85
CN2	85
Quadra	85
SMART	84
LogReg	83
Discrim	83
CASTLE	81

	Test (%)	Compression
k-NN	91%	1:1
fuzzy ARTMAP	89%	6:1

Source: Feng et al. (1993).

One useful property of Fuzzy ARTMAP is that it can learn recognition categories and predictions in an unsupervised mode, yet can also use predictive disconfirmations to supervise learning of categories that fit the statistics of the input-output environment. Such a supervised architecture is capable of learning complex mappings from m-dimensional euclidean space to n-dimensional euclidean space, given arbitrary finite dimensions m and n.

There are several ways in which Fuzzy ARTMAP embodies fuzzy concepts. The most general way concerns how the architecture autonomously calibrates the degree of compression, or generalization, that should occur in each category to fit the statistics of the environment. More general categories embody more "fuzziness" in the range of feature values accepted by the category. Category choice by the network embodies a decision process that discovers which learned ranges of fuzzy features best match the input pattern.

Fuzzy logic enters this learned recognition process in a more precise sense as well. The fuzzy AND, or min, operator and the fuzzy OR, or max, operator are used to define

TABLE 1.3   Pima Indian Diabetes (PID) Database Studies

Fuzzy ARTMAP test set performance was similar to that of the ADAP algorithm (Smith et al., 1988) but with far fewer rules and faster training. An ARTMAP pruning algorithm (Carpenter and Tan, 1994) further reduces the number of rules by an order of magnitude and boosts test set accuracy to 79 percent.

Supervised learning: Training, 576; test, 192

1. ADAP (Smith et al., 1988)
   100,000 rules
   On test set 76% correct
   Slow learning

2. Fuzzy ARTMAP
   (Carpenter et al., 1992)
   50 to 80 rules
   On test set 76% correct
   Fast learning (6–15 epochs)

the range of mathematical values that are tolerated by a category for each linguistic variable, or feature. The features of "hat on head" and "hair on head" are illustrative as applied to the heads of men and dogs. Men sometimes wear hats and usually have at least some hair on their heads. Dogs very rarely wear hats but almost always have some hair on their heads. To express this mathematically, let each feature's values lie in the interval $[0, 1]$, where value 0 means *never*, value 1 means *always*, and intermediate values range from *rarely* through *sometimes* to *frequently*. Then "hair on head" is represented for a man's head by a wide interval $[A, 1]$, with A intermediate between 0 and 1. The variable of "hat on head" also translates to a wide interval $[0, B]$ of expectations, with B intermediate between 0 and 1. For a dog, "hair on head" is represented by a narrow interval $[C, 1]$ with C close to 1, whereas "hat on head" becomes a narrow interval $[0, D]$ with D close to 0. Simultaneous representation of both fuzzy features is achieved by category rectangles whose sides have a length and location that represent the fuzziness tolerated for the corresponding feature, as in Fig. 1.1. Hyperrectangles in $\Re^n$ code categories that represent n fuzzy features.

The min operator ($\wedge$) defines features that are *critically present* with intervals such as $[C, 1]$, whereas the max operator ($\vee$) defines features that are *critically absent* with intervals such as $[0, D]$. As shown below, the min operator may be realized by the on cells of a neural network—namely, the nodes that are turned on by an input feature—whereas the max operator is realized by the off cells of a neural network—namely, the nodes that are turned off by an input feature. Thus the duality between min and max in fuzzy logic translates to a duality between on and off in neural networks. The hypothesis that on and off cell pairs, or opponent processes, can represent fuzzy concepts has been part of ART heuristics since their inception (Grossberg, 1976b, 1980) and indeed part of the earliest modern tracts on neural networks (Grossberg, 1964, section 170). Fuzzy ART and Fuzzy ARTMAP develop fuzzy concepts into a computationally effective algorithm.

Fuzzy ARTMAP also computationally incorporates the operation of fuzzy subsethood (Kosko, 1986; Zadeh, 1965). Carpenter et al. (1991c) observed that the ART 1 computations of choice, match, and search naturally map into corresponding fuzzy operations. (See Sec. 1.8.) In particular, the ART 1 choice function that determines category selection can be interpreted in terms of the degree to which a learned category representation is a fuzzy subset of the current input.

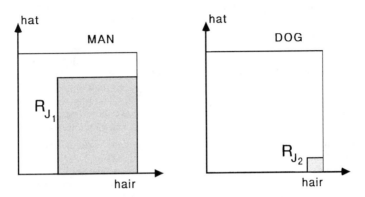

EXAMPLE: Features = hair, hat

man's head (category J_1)   dog's head (category J_2)
hair: usually   hair: almost always
hat: sometimes   hat: almost never

COMPLEMENT CODING: WITHOUT complement coding:
   a - present features   hat feature (usually absent)
   a^c - absent features   →   0 in both cases.

FIGURE 1.1   Representation of fuzzy categories using feature rectangles and, in higher dimensions, hyperrectangles. [*Reprinted with permission from Carpenter and Grossberg (1994).*]

Fuzzy logic provides a way for Fuzzy ARTMAP to adaptively categorize analog, as well as binary, input patterns. In particular, Fuzzy ARTMAP can autonomously learn, recognize, and make predictions with the following properties:

1. *Fast learning of rare events.* A successful autonomous agent must be able to learn about rare events that have important consequences, even if these rare events are similar to a surrounding cloud of frequent events that have different consequences. *Fast learning* is needed to categorize a rare event before it is supplanted by more frequent subsequent events. Many traditional learning schemes use a form of slow learning that tends to average over similar event occurrences. In contrast, Fuzzy ARTMAP can rapidly learn a rare event that predicts different consequences from a cloud of similar events in which it is embedded.

2. *Stable learning of large nonstationary databases.* Rare events often occur in a nonstationary environment whose event statistics may change rapidly and unexpectedly through time. Individual events may also occur with variable probabilities and durations, and arbitrarily large numbers of events may need to be processed. Each of these factors tends to destabilize the learning process within traditional algorithms. New learning in such algorithms tends to unselectively wash away the memory traces of old, but still useful, knowledge. Use of such an algorithm, e.g., learning a new face-to-name association, could erase the memory of a parent's face-to-name association. More generally, learning new facts could erase the memory of previous expert knowledge. Fuzzy ARTMAP contains a *self-stabilizing memory* that permits accumulating knowledge to be stably stored in response to arbitrarily many events in a nonstationary environment under incremental learning conditions, until the algorithm's full memory capacity, which can be chosen arbitrarily large, is exhausted.

3. *Efficient learning of morphologically variable events.* The morphological variability of information often changes through time, with some information coarsely defined whereas other information is precisely characterized. For example, it may be necessary only to recognize that an object is a face or that it is the face of one's own father. It may be necessary to recognize that an object is a vehicle or that it is a particular type of tank that is manufactured by a particular country. Under autonomous learning conditions, no teacher is generally available to instruct a system about how coarse its generalization, or compression, of particular types of data should be. Multiple scales of generalization, from fine to coarse, need to be available on an as-needed basis. Fuzzy ARTMAP automatically adjusts its scale of generalization to match the morphological variability of the data by using a *minimax learning rule* that conjointly *mini*mizes predictive error and *max*imizes generalization, using only information that is locally available under incremental learning conditions. The minimax learning rule enables Fuzzy ARTMAP to autonomously calibrate how much fuzziness should be tolerated on each feature dimension of a category in order to achieve accurate predictive generalization.

4. *Associative learning of many-to-one and one-to-many maps.* Many-to-one learning includes both categorization and associative prediction (Fig. 1.2). For example, during categorization of printed letter fonts, many similar instances of the same printed letter may establish a single recognition category, or compressed representation. Different printed letter fonts or written versions of the letter may establish additional categories. Each of these categories carries out a many-to-one map of input into category. During prediction, all the categories that represent the same letter may be associatively mapped into the letter name, or prediction. This is a second, distinct type of many-to-one map, since there need be no relationship between the visual features that define a printed letter A and a written letter A, yet both categories may have the same name for cultural reasons. The symbol that represents this name may, in turn, be transformed through learning into an arbitrary output pattern.

This two-stage many-to-one, or compressive, transformation, followed by a learned output transformation, is what enables Fuzzy ARTMAP to learn essentially arbitrary maps from $\Re^m$ to $\Re^n$. Individual recognition categories may be compared to the hidden units in the back propagation model (Parker, 1982; Rumelhart et al., 1986; Werbos, 1974). Fuzzy ARTMAP discovers on its own the number of categorical "hidden units" that it needs to achieve minimax learning, unlike back propagation where a human operator decides by trial and error how many hidden units are needed.

One-to-many learning is used to discover and accumulate expert knowledge about an object or event (Fig. 1.3). For example, a computerized record of a patient's medical checkup may lead to a series of predictions about the patient's health. A chemical assay of a sample of coal or petroleum may lead to many predictions about its uses as an energy source or structural material. In many learning algorithms, including back propagation, the attempt to learn more than one prediction about an event leads to unselective forgetting of previously learned predictions, for the same reason that these algorithms become unstable in response to nonstationary data.

1.2 ATTENTION, HYPOTHESIS TESTING, MATCH LEARNING, AND CONFIDENCE ESTIMATION

Fuzzy ARTMAP achieves properties 1 to 4 of Sec. 1.1 by implementing the following types of processes:

1. *Paying attention and top-down priming.* A Fuzzy ARTMAP system can learn top-down expectations (also called *primes,* or *queries*) that can bias the system to ignore

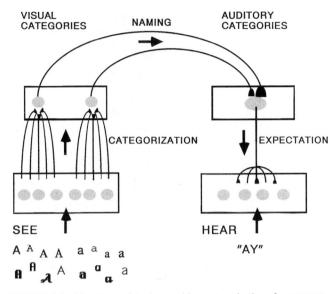

FIGURE 1.2 Many-to-one learning combines categorization of many exemplars into one category and labeling of many categories with the same name. [*Reprinted with permission from Carpenter and Grossberg (1994).*]

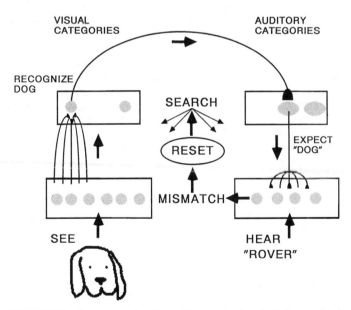

FIGURE 1.3 One-to-many learning enables one input vector to be associated with many output vectors. If the system predicts an output that is disconfirmed at a given stage of learning, the predictive error drives a memory search for a new category to associate with the new prediction, without degrading its previous knowledge about the input vector. [*Reprinted with permission from Carpenter and Grossberg (1994).*]

masses of irrelevant data. A large mismatch between a bottom-up input vector and a top-down expectation can suppress features in the input pattern that are not confirmed by the top-down prime and thereby drive an adaptive memory search that carries out a bout of hypothesis testing.

2. *Hypothesis testing and match learning.* The system hereby selectively searches for recognition categories, or hypotheses, whose top-down expectations provide an acceptable match to bottom-up data. Each top-down expectation begins to focus attention upon, and bind, that cluster of input features which are part of the prototype that it has already learned, while suppressing features that are not. The search continues if the current match is not good enough. If no previously learned category, or hypothesis, provides a good enough match, then selection and learning of a new category and top-down expectation are automatically initiated. When the search discovers an old or new category that provides an acceptable match, the system locks into an attentive resonance during which learning occurs. The input pattern hereby refines the adaptive weights of the category prototype based on any new information that the pattern contains.

Unlike many learning systems, such as back propagation, the Fuzzy ARTMAP system carries out match learning, rather than mismatch learning. A category modifies its previous learning only if its top-down expectation matches the input vector well enough to risk changing its defining characteristics. Otherwise, hypothesis testing selects a new category on which to base learning of a novel event.

3. *Choosing the globally best answer without recursive search.* In many learning algorithms, as learning proceeds, local minima or less-than-optimal solutions may be selected to represent the data. In Fuzzy ARTMAP, at any stage of learning, an input pattern first selects the category whose top-down expectation provides the globally best match. It is in this sense that a top-down expectation acts as a *prototype* for the class of all input patterns that its category represents. After learning self-stabilizes, every input directly selects and resonates with the globally best-matching category without triggering a recursive search. Familiar events directly resonate with the globally best category without recursive search, even if they are interspersed with unfamiliar events that drive recursive hypothesis testing for better matching categories.

4. *Learning both prototypes and exemplars.* The prototype represents the cluster of input features that the category learns based upon its past experience. The prototype represents the features to which the category "pays attention." In cognitive psychology, an input pattern is called an *exemplar.* A classical issue in cognitive psychology concerns whether the brain learns prototypes or exemplars. It sometimes seems that the brain learns prototypes, or abstract types of knowledge, such as being able to recognize that a particular object is a face or an animal. At other times, the brain appears to learn individual exemplars, or concrete types of knowledge, such as recognizing a particular face or a particular animal. What sort of hybrid system can learn both types of knowledge (Smith, 1990)? Fuzzy ARTMAP is such a hybrid system. It uses the minimax learning rule to control how abstract or concrete—how fuzzy—a category can become in order to conjointly minimize predictive generalization and maximize predictive generalization. The next section indicates how this is accomplished.

5. *Controlling vigilance to calibrate confidence.* A confidence measure, called *vigilance,* calibrates how well an exemplar needs to match the prototype that it reads out in order for the corresponding category to resonate with it and be chosen. In other words, vigilance calibrates how well the hypothesis represented by the category matches the data. If vigilance is low, even poor matches are accepted. Many different exemplars can then be incorporated into one category, so compression and generalization by that category are high. If vigilance is high, then even good matches may be rejected, and hypothesis testing may be initiated to select a new category. In this case, few exemplars activate the same category, so compression and generalization are low. A very high vigilance can select a unique category for a rare event that predicts an outcome different from that of any of the similar exemplars that surround it. In this limiting case, the prototype of the category learns the unique exemplar that the category represents, so that prototype learning reduces to exemplar learning.

The minimax learning rule is realized by adjusting the vigilance parameter in response to a predictive error. Vigilance is increased just enough to initiate hypothesis testing to discover a better category, or hypothesis, with which to match the data. In this way, a minimum amount of generalization is sacrificed to correct the error. This process is called *match tracking* because vigilance tracks the degree of match between exemplar and prototype in response to a predictive error. How this is computed is described below.

6. *Rule extraction and fuzzy reasoning.* At any stage of learning, a user can translate the state of a Fuzzy ARTMAP system to a fuzzy set of rules. These rules evolve as the system is exposed to new inputs. Suppose, e.g., that n categories are associated with the mth prediction of the network. Backtrack from prediction m along the associative pathways whose adaptive weights have learned to connect the n categories to this prediction (Fig. 1.2). Each of these categories codes a "reason" for making the mth prediction. The prototype of each category embodies the set of features, or constraints, whose binding together constitutes that category's "reason." The if-then rule takes the form: If the features of any of these n categories are found bound together, within the fuzzy constraints that lead to selection of that category, then the mth prediction holds. This is an example of such a rule: If feature 1 falls in interval $[a_1, b_1]$ *and* feature 7 falls in interval $[a_7, b_7]$, *or* feature 3 falls in interval $[a_3, b_3]$, feature 8 falls in interval $[a_8, b_8]$, *and* feature 94 falls in interval $[a_{94}, b_{94}]$, then prediction 7 is made. Fuzzy ARTMAP is thus a type of self-organizing fuzzy production system (Laird et al., 1987) that evolves adaptively from its unique input-output experiences.

The if-then rules of Fuzzy ARTMAP can be read off from the learned adaptive weights of the system at any stage of the learning process. This property is particularly important in applications such as medical diagnosis from a large database of patient records, where doctors may want to study the rules by which the system reaches its diagnostic decisions. Tables 1.1 to 1.3 summarize some medical and other benchmark studies that compare the performance of Fuzzy ARTMAP with alternative recognition and prediction models. These and other benchmarks are described elsewhere in greater detail (Carpenter et al., 1991a, 1992a, 1992b).

7. *Properties scale to arbitrarily large databases.* One of the most serious weaknesses of traditional artificial intelligence algorithms is that their desirable properties tend to break down as small toy problems are generalized to large-scale problems. In contrast, all the desirable properties of Fuzzy ARTMAP scale to arbitrarily large problems. On the other hand, Fuzzy ARTMAP helps to solve only learned categorization and prediction problems. These problems are, however, core problems in many intelligent systems, and they have been technological bottlenecks for many alternative approaches.

A summary is now given of adaptive resonance theory (ART) networks for unsupervised learning and categorization. The connection between ART systems and fuzzy logic is noted in an exposition of Fuzzy ART networks for unsupervised learning and categorization. Fuzzy ART modules are then combined into a Fuzzy ARTMAP system that is capable of supervised learning, recognition, and prediction.

1.3 UNSUPERVISED SELF-ORGANIZING FEATURE MAP AND ART SYSTEMS

As noted above, adaptive resonance theory was introduced as a theory of human cognitive information processing (Grossberg, 1976b, 1980). Theoretical development has continued to explain and predict ever-larger cognitive and neural databases to the present; see Carpenter and Grossberg (1991, 1993), Grossberg (1987a, 1987b, 1988, 1994), Grossberg and Merrill (1992), and Grossberg et al. (1994a) for illustrative contributions. In addition, an evolving series of self-organizing neural network models have been developed for applications to adaptive pattern recognition and prediction. These self-organizing models can operate in either an unsupervised or a supervised mode. Unsupervised learning occurs when network predictions do not generate environmental feedback. Supervised learning occurs when prediction-contingent feedback is available. This option does not occur in many supervised learning algorithms, such as back propagation, which can learn only when feedback is available. Unsupervised ART models learn stable recognition categories in response to arbitrary input sequences with either fast or slow learning. These model families include ART 1 (Carpenter and Grossberg, 1987a), which can stably learn to categorize binary input patterns presented in an arbitrary order; ART 2, ART 2-A, and Fuzzy ART (Carpenter and Grossberg, 1987b; Carpenter et al., 1991b, 1991c), which can stably learn to categorize either analog or binary input patterns presented in an arbitrary order; and ART 3 (Carpenter and Grossberg, 1990), which can carry out parallel search, or hypothesis testing, of distributed recognition codes in a multilevel network hierarchy. Variations of these models adapted to the demands of individual applications have been developed by a number of authors.

Figure 1.4 illustrates one example from the family of ART 1 models, and Fig. 1.5 illustrates a typical ART search cycle. Level F_1 in Fig. 1.4 contains a network of nodes, each of which represents a particular combination of sensory features. Level F_2 contains a network of nodes that represent recognition codes which are selectively activated by patterns of activation across F_1. The activities of nodes in F_1 and F_2 are also called *short-term memory (STM) traces*. STM is the type of memory that can be rapidly reset without leaving an enduring trace. For example, it is easy to reset the STM of a list of numbers that a person has just heard once by distracting the person with an unexpected event. STM is distinct from *long-term memory (LTM)* which is the type of memory that we usually ascribe to learning. For example, we do not forget our parents' names when we are distracted by an unexpected event.

As shown in Fig. 1.5a, an input vector $\mathbf{I}$ registers itself as a pattern $\mathbf{X}$ of activity across level F_1. The F_1 output vector $\mathbf{S}$ is then transmitted through the multiple converging and diverging adaptive filter pathways emanating from F_1. This transmission event multiplies the vector $\mathbf{S}$ by a matrix of adaptive weights, or LTM traces, to generate a net input vector $\mathbf{T}$ to level F_2. The internal competitive dynamics of F_2 contrast-enhance vector $\mathbf{T}$. Whereas many F_2 nodes may receive inputs from F_1, competition or lateral inhibition between F_2 nodes allows only a much smaller set of F_2 nodes to store their activation in STM. A compressed activity vector $\mathbf{Y}$ is thereby generated across F_2. In ART 1, the competition is tuned so that the F_2 node that receives the maximal $F_1 \rightarrow F_2$ input is selected. Only one component of $\mathbf{Y}$ is nonzero after this choice is made. Activation of such a winner-take-all node defines the category, or symbol, of input pattern $\mathbf{I}$. Such a category represents all the inputs $\mathbf{I}$ that maximally activate the corresponding node. So far, these are the rules of a *self-organizing feature map* (SOFM), also called *competitive learning, self-organizing feature maps,* or *learned vector quantization*.

In a self-organizing feature map, only the F_2 nodes that win the competition and store their activity in STM can influence the learning process. STM activity opens a learning gate at the LTM traces that abut the winning nodes. These LTM traces can then approach, or track, the input signals in their pathways by a process of steepest descent. This learning law is thus often called *gated steepest descent,* or *instar learning.* It was introduced to neural network models in Grossberg (1969) and is the learning law that was used to introduce ART (Grossberg, 1976b). Such an LTM trace can either increase or decrease to track the signals in its pathway. Since it is thus not a strictly Hebbian asso-

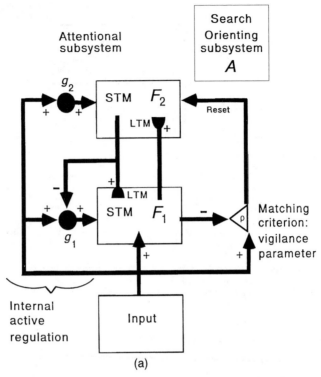

(a)

FIGURE 1.4   Interactions between the attentional and orienting subsystems of an adaptive resonance theory (ART) circuit: Level F_1 encodes a distributed representation of an event to be recognized via a short-term memory (STM) activation pattern across a network of feature detectors. Level F_2 encodes the event to be recognized, using a more compressed STM representation of the F_1 pattern. Learning of these recognition codes takes place at the long-term memory (LTM) traces within the bottom-up and top-down pathways between levels F_1 and F_2. The top-down pathways can read out learned expectations whose prototypes are matched against bottom-up input patterns at F_1. Mismatches in response to novel events activate the orientation subsystem $\mathscr{A}$, thereby resetting the recognition codes that are active in STM at F_2 and initiating a memory search for a more appropriate recognition code. Output from subsystem $\mathscr{A}$ can also trigger an orienting response. (a) Block diagram of circuit. (b) Individual pathways of circuit, including the input level F_0 that generates inputs to level F_1. The gain control input to level F_1 helps to instantiate the two-thirds rule (see text). Gain control to level F_2 is needed to instate a category in STM. [*Reprinted with permission from Carpenter and Grossberg (1987a).*]

ciative law, which allows traces only to increase, the instar law is sometimes said to be both Hebbian and anti-Hebbian. It has been used to model neurophysiological data about hippocampal LTP (Levy, 1985; Levy and Desmond, 1985) and adaptive tuning of cortical feature detectors during the visual critical period (Rauschecker and Singer, 1979; Singer, 1983), lending support to ART predictions that these two systems would employ such a learning law (Grossberg, 1976b).

Self-organizing feature map models were introduced and computationally characterized in the early 1970s (Grossberg, 1972, 1976a, 1978; Malsburg, 1973). In brief, a

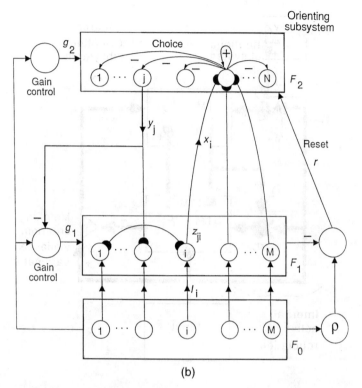

(b)

FIGURE 1.4 (*Continued*)

model for learned classification by an instar network was introduced in Grossberg
(1972). Malsburg (1973) modified the model equations used in that paper to introduce the
first biologically motivated self-organizing feature map (SOFM). The Malsburg model
used a nonlocal adaptive weight equation and did not operate in real time. The Grossberg
(1976a) model (Fig. 1.6) showed how to modify the Malsburg (1973) model to introduce
the first locally defined real-time SOFM, whose rules have been used in essentially all
such subsequent models. This model achieves L^1 normalization of its input patterns and
adaptive weights. Rumelhart and Zipser (1985) used this version of the SOFM model in
their computer simulations of competitive learning. Grossberg (1978) noted how a
euclidean, or L^2, norm achieves unbiased learning and more generally considered L^P
norms. Kohonen (1984/1989) popularized the L^2 version through his influential book.
Other contributions and applications of the SOFM model include those of Amari and
Takeuchi (1978), Bienenstock et al. (1982), Cohen and Grossberg (1987), Grossberg and
Kuperstein (1986/1989), Linsker, (1986), and Willshaw and Malsburg (1976).

By now, there are many hundreds of papers that develop variants of the SOFM
model, either mathematically or in applications. That is because they exhibit many useful properties, especially if not too many input patterns, or clusters of input patterns,
perturb level F_1 relative to the number of categorizing nodes in level F_2. Under these
sparse environmental conditions, category learning is provably stable: The LTM traces
track the statistics of the environment, are self-normalizing, and oscillate a minimum
number of times; and the classifier has bayesian properties (Grossberg, 1976a, 1978).

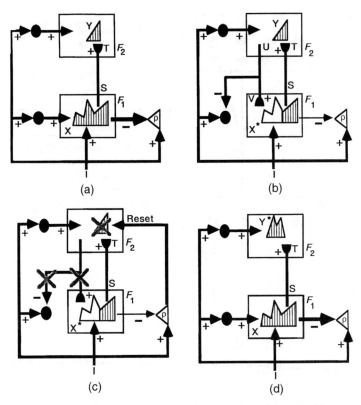

FIGURE 1.5   ART search for an F_2 recognition code. (*a*) Input pattern **I** generates the specific STM activity pattern **X** at F_1 as it nonspecifically activates the orienting subsystem $\mathcal{A}$. Pattern **X** is shown by the hatched pattern across F_1. Pattern **X** both inhibits $\mathcal{A}$ and generates output pattern **S**. Pattern **S** is transformed by the LTM traces into input pattern **T**, which activates STM pattern **Y** across F_2. (*b*) Pattern **Y** generates the top-down output pattern **U** which is transformed to the prototype pattern **V**. If **V** mismatches **I** at F_1, then a new STM activity pattern **X*** is generated at F_1. Pattern **X*** is represented by the hatched pattern. Inactive nodes corresponding to **X** are not hatched. The reduction in total STM activity which occurs when **X** is transformed to **X*** causes a decrease in the total inhibition from F_1 to $\mathcal{A}$. (*c*) If the vigilance criterion fails to be met, $\mathcal{A}$ releases a nonspecific arousal wave to F_2, which resets the STM pattern **Y** at F_2. (*d*) After **Y** is inhibited, its top-down prototype signal is eliminated, and **X** can be reinstated at F_1. Enduring traces of the prior reset leads **X** to activate a different STM pattern **Y*** at F_2. If the top-down prototype due to **Y*** also mismatches **I** at F_1, then the search for an appropriate F_2 code continues until a more appropriate F_2 representation is selected. Then an attentive resonance develops, and learning of the attended data is initiated. [*Reprinted with permission from Carpenter and Grossberg (1987a).*]

These are the key properties that Kohonen (1984/1989) discussed and applied. It was also proved, however, that under arbitrary environmental conditions, learning becomes unstable (Grossberg, 1976b). Such a model could forget its parents' faces. Although a gradual switching off of plasticity, or very slow learning, can partially overcome this problem, such a mechanism cannot work in a recognition learning system whose plasticity is maintained throughout adulthood.

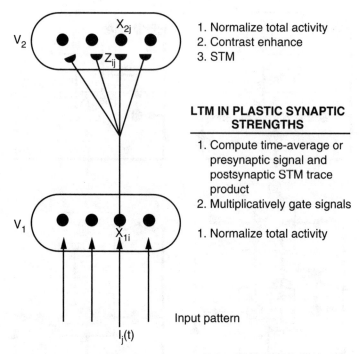

1. Normalize total activity
2. Contrast enhance
3. STM

LTM IN PLASTIC SYNAPTIC STRENGTHS

1. Compute time-average or presynaptic signal and postsynaptic STM trace product
2. Multiplicatively gate signals

1. Normalize total activity

Input pattern

FIGURE 1.6   The computational rules for the self-organizing feature map model were established in 1976. [*Reprinted with permission from Grossberg (1976a).*]

This memory instability is due to basic properties of feedforward associative learning networks. An analysis of this instability, as well as of behavioral and neural data about categorization, learning, and attention, led to the introduction of ART top-down feedback, or expectation, that stabilizes the memory of SOFM models in response to an arbitrary stream of input patterns (Grossberg, 1976b). Thus ART models were introduced as examples of how internal control mechanisms can *self-stabilize* SOFM learning. Learning in SOFM models has also been partially stabilized by external control of the learning rate. One theme of considerable research interest still today is whether, and how, external or internal controllers are used to stabilize SOFM learning.

1.4 HYPOTHESIS TESTING, ATTENTION, AND RESONANCE

The ART scheme for self-stabilizing its embedded SOFM model incorporates heuristics that are also used in expert production systems and fuzzy systems. In particular, ART systems carry out a form of hypothesis testing to discover new recognition categories and to stabilize learning. Thus in an ART model (Carpenter and Grossberg, 1987a, 1991), learning does not occur whenever some winning F_2 activities are stored in STM. Instead activation of F_2 nodes may be interpreted as "making a hypothesis" about an input **I**. When **Y** is activated (Fig. 1.5a), it generates an output vector **U** that is sent top-down through the second adaptive filter. After multiplication by the adaptive weight matrix of the top-down filter, a net vector **V** inputs to F_1 (Fig. 1.5b). Vector **V** plays the role of a learned top-down expectation. Activation of V by Y may be interpreted as "testing the hypothesis" Y, or "reading out the category prototype" V. The ART 1 network is designed to match the "expected prototype" V of the category against the active input pattern, or exemplar, I. Nodes that are activated by I are suppressed if they do not correspond to large LTM traces in the prototype pattern V (Fig. 1.5c). Thus F_1 features that are not "expected" by V are suppressed. Expressed in a different way, the matching process may change the F_1 activity pattern X by suppressing activation of all the feature detectors in I that are not "confirmed" by hypothesis Y. The resultant pattern X^* encodes the cluster of features in I that the network deems relevant to hypothesis Y based upon its past experience. Pattern X^* encodes the pattern of features to which the network "pays attention."

If expectation V is close enough to input I, then a state of *resonance* develops as the attentional focus takes hold. The pattern X^* of attended features reactivates hypothesis Y which, in turn, reactivates X^*. The network locks into a resonant state through the mutual positive feedback that dynamically links X^* with Y. In ART, the resonant state, rather than bottom-up activation, drives the learning process. The resonant state persists long enough, at a high enough activity level, to activate the slower learning process, hence the term *adaptive resonance* theory. ART systems learn prototypes, rather than exemplars, because the attended feature vector X^*, rather than input I itself, is learned. These prototypes may, however, also be used to encode individual exemplars, as described below.

1.5   PATTERN MATCHING, STABLE LEARNING, AND PHONEMIC RESTORATION

The ART attentive matching process may be realized in several ways (Carpenter and Grossberg, 1987a). In one instantiation, three different types of inputs are combined at level F_1 (Fig. 1.4): bottom-up inputs, top-down expectations, and attentional gain control signals. The attentional gain control channel sends the same signal to all F_1 nodes; it is a *nonspecific*, or modulatory, channel. This sort of attentive matching is said to obey a *two-thirds rule* (Carpenter and Grossberg, 1987a): An F_1 node can be fully activated only if two of the three input sources that converge upon it send positive signals at a given time.

The two-thirds rule allows F_1 nodes to generate suprathreshold outputs in response to bottom-up inputs, since an input directly activates its target F_1 features and indirectly activates them via the nonspecific gain control channel to satisfy the two-thirds rule (Fig. 1.5a). After the input instates itself at F_1, leading to selection of hypothesis Y and top-down prototype V, the two-thirds rule ensures that only those F_1 nodes that are confirmed by the top-down prototype can remain active and be attended at F_1 after an F_2 category is selected, since top-down feedback shuts off the attentional gain control signals.

ART matching rules like the two-thirds rule enable an ART network to realize a self-stabilizing learning process. Carpenter and Grossberg (1987a) proved that ART learning and memory are stable in arbitrary environments, but become unstable when the ART matching rule is eliminated. They also defined several circuits that generate the desired matching properties. Thus a type of matching that guarantees stable learning also enables the network to selectively pay attention to feature combinations that are confirmed by a top-down expectation.

ART matching in the brain is illustrated by experiments on phonemic restoration (Repp, 1991; Samuel, 1981a, 1981b; Warren, 1984; Warren and Sherman, 1974). Suppose that a noise spectrum replaces a letter sound in a word heard in an otherwise unambiguous context. Then subjects hear the correct letter sound, not the noise, to the extent that the noise spectrum includes the letter formants. If silence replaces the noise, then only silence is heard. Top-down expectations thus amplify expected input features while suppressing unexpected features, but do not create activations not already in the input.

ART matching rules also show how an ART system can be primed, or biased, to respond differently based upon prior short-term activation. This property has been used to explain paradoxical reaction time and error data from priming experiments during lexical decision and letter gap detection tasks (Grossberg and Stone, 1986; Schvaneveldt and MacDonald, 1981). Although priming is often thought of as a residual effect of previous bottom-up activation, a combination of bottom-up activation and top-down ART matching was needed to explain the complete data pattern. This analysis combined bottom-up priming with a type of top-down priming, namely, the top-down activation that prepares a network for an expected event that may or may not occur. ART matching rules clarify why top-down priming, by itself, has subthreshold (and in the brain unconscious) effects, even though it can facilitate suprathreshold processing of a subsequent expected event.

1.6 VIGILANCE, HYPOTHESIS TESTING, AND CONTROL OF CATEGORY GENERALIZATION

The criterion of an acceptable match is defined by a parameter ρ called *vigilance* (Carpenter and Grossberg, 1987a, 1991). The vigilance parameter is computed in the orienting subsystem $\mathcal{A}$. Vigilance weighs how similar an input exemplar must be to a top-down prototype in order for resonance to occur. Resonance occurs if $\rho|I| - |X^*| \leq 0$, where $0 \leq \rho \leq 1$. This inequality says that the F_1 attentional focus X^* inhibits $\mathcal{A}$ more than input I excites it. If $\mathcal{A}$ remains quiet, then an $F_1 \leftrightarrow F_2$ resonance can develop.

Vigilance calibrates how much novelty the system can tolerate before activating $\mathcal{A}$ and searching for a different category. If the top-down expectation and the bottom-up input are too different to satisfy the resonance criterion, then hypothesis testing, or memory search, is triggered. Memory search leads to selection of a better category at level F_2 with which to represent the input features at level F_1. During search, the orienting subsystem interacts with the attentional subsystem, as in Fig. 1.5c and d, to rapidly reset mismatched categories and to select other F_2 representations with which to learn about novel events, without risking unselective forgetting of previous knowledge. Search may select a familiar category if its prototype is similar enough to the input to satisfy the vigilance criterion. The prototype may then be refined by top-down attentional focusing. If the input is too different from any previously learned prototype, then an uncommitted population of F_2 cells is selected and learning of a new category is initiated.

Because vigilance can vary across learning trials, recognition categories capable of encoding widely differing degrees of generalization or abstraction can be learned by a single ART system. Low vigilance leads to broad generalization and abstract prototypes since then $\rho|I| - |X^*| \leq 0$ for all but the poorest matches. High vigilance leads to narrow generalization and to prototypes that represent fewer input exemplars, even a single exemplar. Thus a single ART system may be used, say, to recognize abstract categories of faces and dogs as well as individual faces and dogs. A single system can learn both, during supervised learning, by increasing vigilance just enough to activate $\mathcal{A}$ if a previous categorization leads to a predictive error (Carpenter and Grossberg, 1992; Carpenter et al., 1991a, 1992b). ART systems hereby provide a new answer to whether the brain learns prototypes or exemplars. Various authors have realized that neither alternative is satisfactory and that a hybrid system is needed (Smith, 1990). ART systems can perform this hybrid function in a manner that is sensitive to environmental demands.

1.7 MEMORY CONSOLIDATION AND DIRECT ACCESS TO THE GLOBALLY BEST CATEGORY

As inputs are practiced over learning trials, the search process eventually converges upon stable categories. The process whereby search is automatically disengaged may be interpreted as a form of memory consolidation. Inputs familiar to the network access their correct category directly, without the need for search. The category selected is the one whose prototype provides the globally best match to the input pattern. If both familiar and unfamiliar events are experienced, familiar inputs can directly activate their learned categories, while unfamiliar inputs continue to trigger adaptive memory searches for better categories, until the network's memory capacity is fully utilized (Carpenter and Grossberg, 1987a).

These ART properties have been used to explain and predict cognitive and brain data that have, as yet, received no other theoretical explanation (Carpenter and Grossberg, 1991; Grossberg, 1987a, 1987b). For example, a formal lesion of the orienting subsystem creates a memory disturbance that remarkably mimics properties of medial temporal amnesia (Carpenter and Grossberg, 1987c, 1993; Grossberg and Merrill, 1992). These and related data correspondences to orienting properties (Grossberg and Merrill, 1992) have led to a neurobiological interpretation of the orienting subsystem in terms of the hippocampal formation of the brain. In applications to visual object recognition, interactions within the F_1 and F_2 levels of the attentional subsystem are interpreted in terms of data concerning the prestrate visual cortex and the inferotemporal cortex (Desimone, 1992), with the attentional gain control pathway interpreted in terms of the pulvinar region of the brain.

1.8 NATURAL LINK BETWEEN ART SYSTEMS AND FUZZY LOGIC

Fuzzy ART is a generalization of ART 1 that incorporates operations from fuzzy logic (Carpenter et al., 1991c). Although ART 1 can learn to classify only binary input patterns, fuzzy ART can learn to classify both analog and binary input patterns. Moreover, fuzzy ART reduces to ART 1 in response to binary input patterns. As shown in Fig. 1.7, the generalization to learning both analog and binary input patterns is achieved simply by replacing appearances of the binary intersection operator ($\cap$) in ART 1 by the analog min operator ($\wedge$) of fuzzy set theory. The min operator reduces to the intersection operator in the binary case. Of particular interest is the fact that as parameter α approaches 0, the function T_j which controls category choice through the bottom-up filter (Fig. 1.5a) then measures the degree to which the adaptive weight vector $\mathbf{w}_j$ is a fuzzy subset (Kosko, 1986) of input vector $\mathbf{I}$. The network first chooses the category j that maximizes T_j.

In fuzzy ART, input vectors are L^1 normalized at a preprocessing stage (Fig. 1.8). This normalization procedure, called *complement coding,* leads to a symmetric theory in which the min operator ($\wedge$) and the max operator ($\vee$) of fuzzy set theory (Zadeh, 1965) play complementary roles. Geometrically, the categories formed by fuzzy ART are then hyperrectangles. Figure 1.9 illustrates how min and max define these rectangles in the 2-D case, with the min and max values defining the acceptable range of feature variation in each dimension. Complement coding uses on-cell (with activity $\mathbf{a}$ in Fig. 1.8) and off-cell (with activity $\mathbf{a}^c$ in Fig. 1.8) opponent processes to represent the input pattern. This representation preserves individual feature amplitudes while normalizing the total on-cell/off-cell vector. The on-cell portion of a prototype encodes features that are critically present in category exemplars, while the off-cell portion encodes features

| ART 1
(BINARY) | FUZZY ART
(ANALOG) |

CATEGORY CHOICE

$$T_j = \frac{|\,I \cap w_j\,|}{\alpha + |\,w_j\,|} \qquad T_j = \frac{|\,I \wedge w_j\,|}{\alpha + |\,w_j\,|}$$

MATCH CRITERION

$$\frac{|\,I \cap w_j\,|}{|\,I\,|} \geq \rho \qquad \frac{|\,I \wedge w_j\,|}{|\,I\,|} \geq \rho$$

FAST LEARNING

$$w_J^{(new)} = I \cap w_J^{(old)} \qquad w_J^{(new)} = I \wedge w_J^{(old)}$$

$\cap$ = logical AND $\wedge$ = fuzzy AND
   intersection   minimum

FIGURE 1.7 Comparison of ART 1 and fuzzy ART. [*Reprinted with permission from Carpenter et al. (1991c).*]

that are critically absent (Fig. 1.8). Each category is then defined by an interval of expected values for each input feature (Fig. 1.9). Thus, as noted in Sec. 1.1, for the category "man," fuzzy ART would encode the feature of "hair on head" by a wide interval ([A, 1]) and the feature "hat on head" by a wide interval ([0, B]) (Fig. 1.1). For the category "dog," two narrow intervals—[C, 1] for hair and [0, D] for hat—correspond to narrower ranges of expectations for these two features.

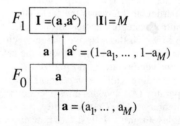

FIGURE 1.8 Complement coding uses on-cell and off-cell pairs to normalize input vectors. [*Reprinted with permission from Carpenter et al. (1991c).*]

Learning in fuzzy ART is stable because all adaptive weights can only decrease in time. Decreasing weights correspond to increasing sizes of category "boxes." Smaller vigilance values lead to larger category boxes. Learning stops when the input space is covered by boxes. The use of complement coding works with the property of increasing box size to prevent a proliferation of categories. With fast learning, constant vigilance, and a finite input set of arbitrary size and composition, learning stabilizes after just one presentation of each input pattern. A fast-commit slow-recode option combines fast learning with a forgetting rule that buffers system memory against noise. By using this option, rare events can be rapidly learned, yet previously learned memories are not rapidly erased in response to statistically unreliable input fluctuations. The equations that define the Fuzzy ART and ARTMAP algorithms are listed in App. 1A.

When the supervised learning of Fuzzy ARTMAP controls category formation, a predictive error can force the creation of new categories that could not otherwise be learned. Supervised learning permits the creation of complex categorical structures without a loss of stability.

1.9 FUZZY ARTMAP

Each Fuzzy ARTMAP system includes a pair of fuzzy ART modules (ART_a and ART_b), as seen in Fig. 1.10. During supervised learning, ART_a receives a stream $\{\mathbf{a}^{(p)}\}$ of input patterns and ART_b receives a stream $\{\mathbf{b}^{(p)}\}$ of input patterns, where $\mathbf{b}^{(p)}$ is the correct prediction given $\mathbf{a}^{(p)}$. These modules are linked by an associative learning network and an internal controller that ensures autonomous system operation in real time. The controller

$\wedge$ Fuzzy AND (conjunction)

$\vee$ Fuzzy OR (disjunction)

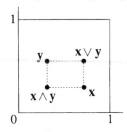

$$\mathbf{x} = (x_1, x_2) \qquad \mathbf{y} = (y_1, y_2)$$
$$(\mathbf{x} \wedge \mathbf{y})_1 = \min(x_1, y_1) \qquad (\mathbf{x} \wedge \mathbf{y})_2 = \min(x_2, y_2)$$
$$(\mathbf{x} \vee \mathbf{y})_1 = \max(x_1, y_1) \qquad (\mathbf{x} \vee \mathbf{y})_2 = \max(x_2, y_2)$$

FIGURE 1.9 Fuzzy AND and OR operations generate category hyperrectangles. [*Reprinted with permission from Carpenter et al. (1991c).*]

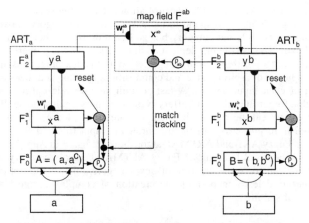

FIGURE 1.10 Fuzzy ARTMAP architecture. The ART_a complement coding preprocessor transforms the M_a vector **a** to the $2M_a$ vector $\mathbf{A} = (\mathbf{a}, \mathbf{a}^c)$ at the ART_a field F_0^a. Vector **A** is the input vector to ART_a field F_1^a. Similarly, the input to F_1^b is the $2M_b$ vector $(\mathbf{b}, \mathbf{b}^c)$. When a prediction by ART_a is disconfirmed at ART_b, inhibition of map field activation induces the match-tracking process. Match tracking raises the ART_a vigilance ρ_a to just above the F_1^a/F_0^a match ratio $|\mathbf{x}^a|/|\mathbf{A}|$. This triggers an ART_a search which leads to activation of either an ART_a category that correctly predicts **b** or to a previously uncommitted ART_a category node. [*Reprinted with permission from Carpenter et al. (1992b).*]

is designed to create the minimal number of ART_a recognition categories, or *hidden units,* needed to meet accuracy criteria. As noted above, this is accomplished by realizing a minimax learning rule that conjointly minimizes predictive error and maximizes category generalization. This scheme automatically links predictive success to category size on a trial-by-trial basis, using only local operations. It works by increasing the vigilance parameter ρ_a of ART_a by the minimal amount needed to correct a predictive error at ART_b (Fig. 1.11).

Parameter ρ_a calibrates the minimum confidence that ART_a must have in a recognition category, or hypothesis, that is activated by an input $\mathbf{a}^{(p)}$ in order for ART_a to accept that category, rather than search for a better one through an automatically controlled process of hypothesis testing. As in ART 1, lower values of ρ_a enable larger categories to form. These lower ρ_a values lead to broader generalization and higher code compression. A predictive failure at ART_b increases the minimal confidence ρ_a by the least amount needed to trigger hypothesis testing at ART_a, using a mechanism called *match tracking* (Carpenter et al., 1991a). Match tracking sacrifices the minimum amount of generalization necessary to correct the predictive error. Intuitively, match track embodies the idea that the criterion confidence level which permitted selection of the active hypothesis needs to be raised to satisfy the demands of the current environment. Match tracking increases the criterion confidence just enough to trigger hypothesis testing. Hypothesis testing leads to the selection of a new ART_a category, which focuses attention on a new cluster of $\mathbf{a}^{(p)}$ input features that is better able to predict $\mathbf{b}^{(p)}$. The combination of match tracking and fast learning allows a single ARTMAP system to learn a different prediction for a rare event than for a cloud of similar frequent events in which it is embedded. The equations for Fuzzy ART and Fuzzy ARTMAP are given in App. 1A in algorithmic form.

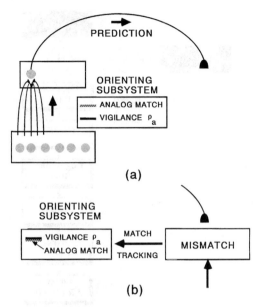

FIGURE 1.11   Match tracking. (*a*) A prediction is made by ART$_a$ when the baseline vigilance ρ_a is less than the analog match value. (*b*) A predictive error at ART$_b$ increases the baseline vigilance value of ART$_a$ until it just exceeds the analog match value, and thereby triggers hypothesis testing that searches for a more predictive bundle of features to which to attend. [*Reprinted with permission from Carpenter and Grossberg (1994).*]

The next two sections illustrate how variants of Fuzzy ARTMAP can be embedded into larger neural architectures.

1.10   VIEWNET: A NEURAL ARCHITECTURE FOR LEARNING TO RECOGNIZE 3-D OBJECTS FROM SEQUENCES OF 2-D VIEWS

This section shows how a Fuzzy ARTMAP network can be incorporated into a self-organizing neural architecture for invariant 3-D object recognition (Bradski and Grossberg, 1994). This architecture is called *VIEWNET* because it uses *view* information encoded *with net*works (Fig. 1.12). VIEWNET accumulates evidence across sequences of possibly noisy or incomplete 2-D views of a 3-D object in order to generate more accurate object identifications than would otherwise be possible. VIEWNET processes individual 2-D views of 3-D objects, using the CORT-X 2 filter (Carpenter et al., 1989; Grossberg and Wyse, 1991), which discounts the illuminant, regularizes and completes figure boundaries, and removes noise from the images. A log-polar transform is taken with respect to the centroid of the resulting figure and then recentered to achieve 2-D scale and rotation invariance. The invariant images are coarse-coded to further reduce noise, reduce foreshortening effects, and increase generalization. These compressed codes are input to a variant of the Fuzzy ARTMAP algorithm which learns 2-D view cat-

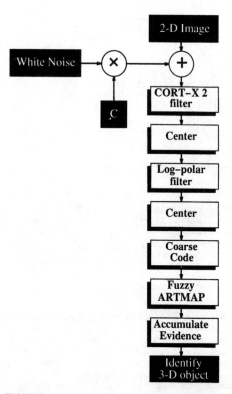

FIGURE 1.12 The image processing flowchart of the VIEWNET system, from presenting a 2-D image in the image database until the readout of the predicted 3-D object.

egories. Evidence from sequences of 2-D view categories is stored in a working memory. Voting based on the unordered set of stored categories determines object recognition. Recognition performance was tested with noisy and clean images, using slow and fast learning on an MIT Lincoln Laboratory database of 2-D views of aircraft with and without additive noise. A recognition rate of up to 90 percent was achieved with one 2-D view category and of up to 98.5 percent correct with three 2-D view categories.

Seibert and Waxman (1990a, 1990b, 1991, 1992) pioneered the use of 2-D view sequences for 3-D object recognition by adaptive neural networks. Seibert and Waxman developed their neural architecture based on the Koenderink and van Doorn (1979) concept of aspect graphs. The VIEWNET model is inspired by the Seibert-Waxman model, but uses a different preprocessor, adaptive pattern classifier, and evidence accumulation scheme to achieve better compression and higher accuracy on the same database from MIT Lincoln Laboratory, which was generously shared.

Seibert and Waxman used an unsupervised ART 2 network to classify coarse-coded maximal curvature image data. This approach generated unambiguous recognition based on one category only 25 percent of the time, using 41 categories, as compared to VIEWNET's 90 percent accuracy using 33 categories.

To compensate for the general categories formed in their model, Seibert and Waxman used in their model ordered view transitions between pairs of view categories to supplement individual recognition categories. For example, to recognize multiple views of an F-16 aircraft, 70 view transitions were learned. VIEWNET used only the unordered set of 2-D view categories, stored in a working memory, to vote for a best object. No view transitions were used, and it was shown that they do not improve accuracy. Two views achieved up to 94 percent accuracy, and three views up to 98.5 percent accuracy. These results suggest that the selection of preprocessor, classifier, and evidence accumulation scheme may substantially alter predictive accuracy. A number of issues, including the possible utility of ordered view transitions, remain open for further study.

The image database used to test the VIEWNET architecture consists of multiple 2-D images of three jets. Video images were taken of three airplane models: an F-16, an F-18, and an HK-1. Each airplane was painted black and suspended by string against a light background to aid in segmentation. The camera was mounted anywhere in an arc around the jets that started at 0.0° above horizontal and went in increments of 4.5° to a maximum of 72.0° above horizontal. For each camera angle, the airplanes were spun and frames covering one full revolution (an average of 88 frames) were retained, resulting in 1200 to 1400 images per object. The images themselves were 128×128 pixel gray scale. The images were then thresholded and binarized into a SUN raster format to form the "raw" database. For our processing, data were turned into a floating-point format scaled between 0.0 and 1.0, and an additive noise process was introduced. The noise consisted of 128×128 pixel images with each pixel taken from a uniform distribution between 0.0 and 1.0 scaled by a constant $C \geq 0.0$. These scaled, 128×128 noise images were then added to the 128×128 jet images prior to preprocessing. Thus, both noise-free and noisy 2-D views covering a half-sphere surrounding the 3-D object were collected, keeping their spatial relationships intact.

Even-numbered rotation images from each camera angle were taken as the training set with the odd-numbered images forming the test set. The system was trained by using random walks over the half-sphere of training images. Testing was done by using random walks over the half-sphere of test images so that the paths taken and views seen were never the same between the training and test sets.

The CORT-X 2 filter (Grossberg and Wyse, 1991, 1992) discounts the illuminant and normalizes image contrasts, regularizes and completes figure boundaries, and suppresses image noise. Alternative filters could have been used on the present data. CORT-X 2 was used because it is also capable of preprocessing more complex noisy images. The processing stages of CORT-X 2 are shown in Fig. 1.13. They embody a one-shot feedforward simplification of a model of the boundary segmentation process that takes place in the visual cortex (Grossberg et al., 1989).

The 2-D boundary segmentation is centered by dividing its first moments by its 0th moment to find the figure centroid, subtracting off the center of the image, and then shifting the figure by this amount. A log-polar transform is then taken with respect to the center of the image. Each point (x, y) is represented as $re^{i\theta}$. Taking the logarithm yields coordinates of log radial magnitude and angle. As is well known (Schwartz, 1977), figure sizes and rotations of a centered image are converted to figure shifts under log-polar transformation. Using these shift parameters to center the log-polar transformed image leads to a figure representation that is invariant under 2-D changes in position, size, and rotation.

Coarse coding, or data reduction, reduces memory requirements as it helps to compensate for inaccuracies of figure alignment, 3-D viewpoint-specific foreshortening, and self-occlusions. Too much coarse coding can, however, obscure critical input features and thereby harm recognition performance. These effects were balanced to maximize the benefits of coarse coding.

Coarse coding used a spatial averaging method that convolved the original image I with a function Ψ and then sampled the resultant image with delta functions $\delta(x - nT, y - kT)$ spaced every T pixels. For simplicity, in one dimension this is

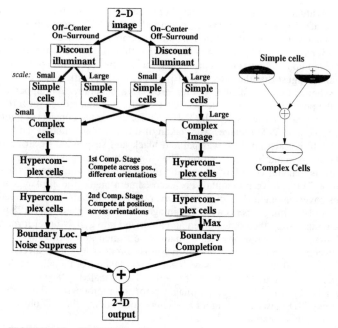

FIGURE 1.13   CORT-X 2 flowchart.

$$(I * \Psi) \cdot \sum_{n=-\infty}^{\infty} \delta(x - nT) \tag{1.1}$$

If the Fourier transform of I is $\hat{I}$, and that of Ψ is $\hat{\Psi}$, then the Fourier transform of Eq. (1.1) is

$$(\hat{I} \cdot \hat{\Psi}) * \frac{2\pi}{T} \sum_{k=-\infty}^{\infty} \delta(\Omega - k\Omega_s) \tag{1.2}$$

where $\Omega_s = 2\pi/T$ and T is the sampling period in pixels. If Ω_N is the highest frequency in the image, then for the image to be uniquely determined by its samples, by the Nyquist sampling theorem we must have

$$\Omega_s = \frac{2\pi}{T} > 2\Omega_N \tag{1.3}$$

Two simple spatial averaging functions Ψ are (1) the uniform averaging of the input image so that all pixels in a window of some width are summed and divided by the number of pixels in the window and (2) Gaussian averaging of the input image so that a normalized Gaussian weighted sum of all pixels is taken over a window of some width. Both approaches were investigated by Bradski and Grossberg (1994). Method 1 has the problem that uniform averaging is a rectangular filter in the space domain and a sinc function in the frequency domain which introduces high-frequency aliasing ("ringing") in the resultant image. The Gaussian function of method 2 is a "smoother" low-pass filter and so does not suffer from this problem. A Gaussian function is also an eigenfunction of a Fourier transform, which simplifies calculation.

To best set the standard deviation σ of the Gaussian functions, we define two standard deviations away from the Gaussian function midpoint to be essentially zero. The cutoff frequency of such a low-pass filter is then $\pi/(2\sigma)$, which by Eq. (1.3) yields at equality

$$\sigma = \frac{T}{2} \qquad (1.4)$$

Thus, the zero point of each Gaussian function just touches the center of the next Gaussian function. Figure 1.14 summarizes the preprocessing: Fig. 1.14a shows the output of CORT-X 2; Fig. 1.14b shows the centered log-polar transform of Fig. 1.14a; Fig. 1.14c depicts gaussian coarse coding according to Eq. (1.4); and Fig. 1.14d to f shows

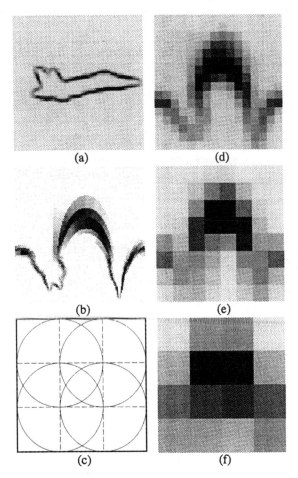

FIGURE 1.14 Preprocessing summary. (a) Output of CORT-X 2 preprocessing. (b) Centered log-polar image. (c) Gaussian coarse-coding pattern. (d–f) Coarse-coding reduction from 128×128 pixels to 16×16, 8×8, and 4×4 pixels.

TABLE 1.4 VIEWNET Recognition Results on Noisy Data ($C = 1$) with Slow Learning to the Map Field ($\beta_{ab} = 0.2$, $\rho_{max} = 0.95$)

Due to the low levels of noise surviving CORT-X 2 preprocessing, the recognition results here are not substantially different from those found by using fast learning in noise. As noise increases, slow learning becomes more important for maintaining good recognition scores.

		Coarse code using spatial average/Gaussian average		
CORT-X 2 filter set	Data presentation	4×4	8×8	16×16
Small	Ordered	79.9/83.1	84.0/85.6	84.7/89.9
Small	Unordered	78.8/83.3	83.2/85.7	84.9/89.1
Large	Ordered	76.3/78.2	78.5/81.5	77.0/78.8
Large	Unordered	77.4/80.2	79.6/80.41	75.8/79.2

coarse coding down to 16×16, 8×8, and 4×4 pixels. The best results, as summarized in Table 1.4, were achieved with 16×16 coarse coding.

A modified version of Fuzzy ARTMAP was used in the VIEWNET architecture. First the network was simplified, as in Carpenter et al. (1992a), to consist of a Fuzzy ART module (Carpenter et al., 1991c) ART_a and a field of output nodes F^b, rather than an ART_b module, linked to ART_a by an associative memory F^{ab} that is called the *map field* (see App. 1A). Fuzzy ARTMAP was modified to allow for on-line slow learning from ART_a 2-D view category nodes F_2^a to the map field nodes (Carpenter et al., 1993, 1994). A maximal ART_a vigilance level $\bar{\rho}_{max}$ was introduced such that an error at the map field triggers match tracking only if match tracking leads to a vigilance $\rho_a \leq \bar{\rho}_{max}$. If $\rho_a > \bar{\rho}_{max}$, learning takes place instead of memory search. By setting the map field learning rate β_{ab} and baseline ($\bar{\rho}_a$) and maximal ($\bar{\rho}_{max}$) vigilance levels appropriately, weights from F_2^a nodes to the map field approximate the conditional probability of the true class given the selected F_2^a category (Table 1.4).

For the airplane data set as processed by VIEWNET, the average overall length of an error sequence was 1.31 two-dimensional views with a standard deviation of 0.57 view. Thus, when an error occurs, collecting evidence from, and voting over, two more views will usually be sufficient to correct the error. This can be done most simply in VIEWNET by adding an integration field F^{int}, or working memory, to accumulate evidence between the map field F^{ab} and the winner-take-all (wta) field F^{wta}. The equation for the integrator field is stepped once each time ART_a chooses a category:

$$(x_k^{int})^{new} = \beta_{int} x_k^{ab} + (1 - \beta_{int})(x_k^{int})^{old} \tag{1.5}$$

where x_k^{int} is an integrator node for the kth object, β_{int} is the integration rate each time the equation is stepped, and x_k^{ab} is the kth map field category. The maximal integration node is chosen by the winner-take-all field F^{wta} as the network's identification of the 3-D object. Thus VIEWNET recognition is based upon the unordered winner of a temporal voting scheme.

The Fuzzy ARTMAP architecture computes goodness-of-fit information that may be used to enhance its power in various applications. For example, the algorithm's match or choice of equation may be used to measure the *quality* of the recognition. Thus if VIEWNET recognizes a 3-D object, but its ART_a category prototype provides a poor fit to the input vector, then the goodness-of-fit information could be used to cause VIEWNET to collect more data before a final recognition decision is made. Likewise, if VIEWNET is embedded in an active vision system, then a poorly fitting view could be used to trigger the system to move to get a better perspective.

1.11　ART-EMAP: OBJECT RECOGNITION BY SPATIAL AND TEMPORAL EVIDENCE ACCUMULATION

ART-EMAP (Fig. 1.15) uses spatial and temporal evidence accumulation to recognize target objects and pattern classes in noisy or ambiguous input environments (Carpenter

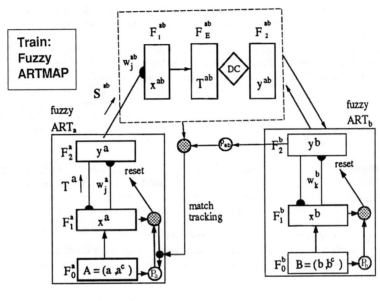

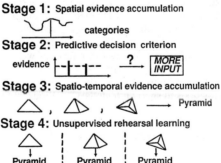

Stage 1: Spatial evidence accumulation

categories

Stage 2: Predictive decision criterion

evidence ⊢-╀-╀-- → ? → | MORE INPUT |

Stage 3: Spatio-temporal evidence accumulation

△ , ◁ , ◁ ——— Pyramid

Stage 4: Unsupervised rehearsal learning

△　　△　　◁
↓　　↓　　↓
Pyramid ¦ Pyramid ¦ Pyramid

FIGURE 1.15　ART-EMAP synthesizes adaptive resonance theory (ART) and spatial and temporal evidence integration for dynamic predictive mapping (EMAP). The network extends the capabilities of Fuzzy ARTMAP in four incremental stages. Stage 1 introduces distributed pattern representation at a view category field. Stage 2 adds a decision criterion to the mapping between view and object categories, delaying identification of ambiguous objects when faced with a low-confidence prediction. Stage 3 augments the system with a field where evidence accumulates in medium-term memory (MTM). Stage 4 adds an unsupervised learning process to fine-tune performance after the limited initial period of supervised network training. Simulations of the four ART-EMAP stages demonstrate performance on a difficult 3-D object recognition problem. [*Reprinted with permission from Carpenter and Ross (1993).*]

and Ross, 1993, 1995). During performance, ART-EMAP integrates spatial evidence distributed across recognition categories to predict a pattern class. During training, ART-EMAP is equivalent to Fuzzy ARTMAP and so inherits the advantages of fast on-line incremental learning, such as speed, stability, and the ability to encode rare cases (Sec. 1.1). Distributed activation during performance also endows the network with the advantages of slow learning, including noise tolerance and error correction. When a decision criterion determines the pattern class choice to be ambiguous, additional input from the same unknown class may be sought. Evidence from multiple inputs accumulates until the decision criterion is satisfied, and the system makes a high-confidence prediction. Accumulated evidence can also fine-tune performance during unsupervised rehearsal learning.

In four incremental stages, ART-EMAP improves predictive accuracy of Fuzzy ARTMAP and extends its domain to include spatiotemporal recognition and prediction. ART-EMAP applications include a vision system that samples 2-D perspectives of 3-D objects. In this scenario, a sensor generates an organized database of inputs that are views of each object from different perspectives or noisy samples of fixed views. Evidence accumulation has been successfully used in neural network machine vision applications, as in the aspect network (Baloch and Waxman, 1991; Seibert and Waxman, 1990b). ART-EMAP further develops this strategy.

3-D Object Recognition. Simulations illustrate the performance of Fuzzy ARTMAP and ART-EMAP (stages 1 to 4) on a recognition problem that requires a system to identify three similar 3-D objects (pyramid, prism, house). Inputs consist of ambiguous 2-D views taken from various angles (Fig. 1.16). The problem is made difficult by the similarity of views across objects and by several test set views that do not resemble any training set view of the same object. Fuzzy ARTMAP correctly identifies only 65 percent of the objects from noise-free test set images. Stage 1 ART-EMAP raises performance accuracy to 71 percent, while stage 2 and stage 3 both boost performance to 98.0 percent (Fig. 1.17).

Database Inputs. The simulation database was constructed by using Mathematica to generate shaded 2-D projections of 3-D objects illuminated by an achromatic point light source. For each of the three objects, 24 training set views were obtained from perspectives spaced 30° to 60° apart around a viewing hemisphere (Fig. 1.16 top). For each object, 17 test set views, spaced at 45° intervals, were obtained from perspectives between those of the training set (Fig. 1.16 bottom). Each 2-D view was then preprocessed, using Gabor filters (Gabor, 1946; Daugman, 1988) to recover boundaries, competitive interactions to sharpen boundary locations and orientations (Grossberg and Mingolla, 1985), and coarse coding to yield a 100-component input vector **a**. The preprocessing algorithm is a typical feature extractor, chosen to illustrate the comparative performance of different recognition systems, and was not selected to optimize performance of any one of these systems.

Training Regime. Fuzzy ARTMAP and ART-EMAP stage 1 through stage 4 were evaluated by using both a noise-free test set and a noisy test set. The noisy test set was constructed by adding gaussian noise [standard deviation (SD) = 0.2] to each input component. Each system was initially trained under one standard supervised learning protocol, with the training set presented once. Since the training set views were selected to be sparse and nonredundant, a situation of minimal code compression was simulated during training. This was achieved by assigning a high value to the ARTMAP baseline vigilance ($\bar{\rho}_a = 0.9$), which established 58 ART$_a$ recognition categories for the 72 training set pairs.

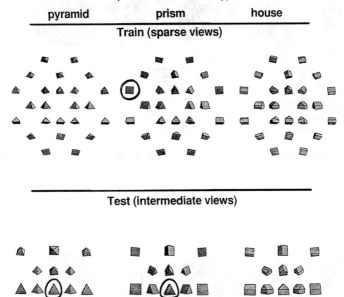

ART-EMAP SIMULATIONS
3-D object recognition from 2-D views
(noise-free and noisy)

pyramid	prism	house

Train (sparse views)

Test (intermediate views)

FIGURE 1.16 3-D object recognition training and test set images for ART-EMAP simulations. Circled exemplars indicate that single-view object identification may be difficult because a training set view of one object can be the same as a test set view of a different object; and because test set views of two different objects can be the same. [*Reprinted with permission from Carpenter and Ross (1994).*]

Fuzzy ARTMAP Simulation. Performance measures of Fuzzy ARTMAP and ART-EMAP on the 3-D object recognition database are summarized in Fig. 1.17, for noise-free test set inputs (plots in Fig. 1.17a to c) and for noisy test set inputs (plots in Fig. 1.17d to f). The prediction of each test set view is represented graphically, on shaded viewing hemispheres. Each hemisphere shows 17 faces, which correspond to the 17 test set viewing angles (Fig. 1.16 bottom). For each simulation, three hemispheres show object class predictions made by the system in response to the corresponding input, with shading of a face indicating a prediction of pyramid (black), prism (gray), or house (white).

Fuzzy ARTMAP made only 64.7 percent correct object class predictions on the noise-free test set (Fig. 1.17a) and 60.8 percent correct predictions on the noisy test set (Fig. 1.17d). This poor performance indicates the difficult nature of the problem when prediction must be made on the basis of a single view. Note, e.g., that many of the test set inputs from the lower left part of the pyramid view hemisphere were incorrectly identified as prism views. The reason for these errors can be inferred from the correspondence between certain pyramid test set views and similar prism training set views (Fig. 1.16).

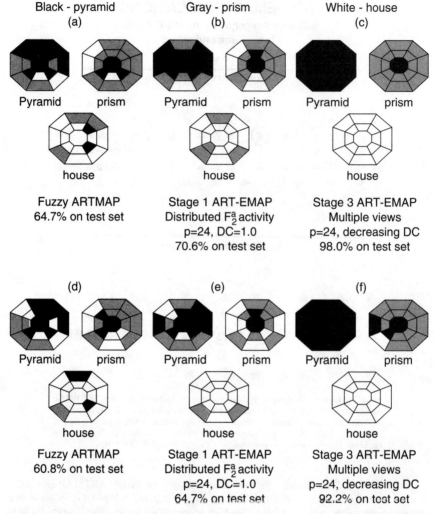

FIGURE 1.17   3-D object simulations. Response viewing hemispheres for each object show predictions from each test set view. A window in the hemisphere corresponds to one of the 17 test views (Fig. 1.16*b*). Plots (*a*) to (*c*) show noise-free test set results, and plots (*d*) to (*f*) show noisy test set results. Plots (*a*) and (*d*) show Fuzzy ARTMAP performance, using the F_2^a choice rule. Plots (*b*) and (*e*) show stage 1 ART-EMAP performance using the power rule (1.8) with $p = 24$. Plots (*c*) and (*f*) show stage 3 ART-EMAP performance with $p = 24$ plus temporal evidence accumulation with the decreasing decision criterion (1.14) and multiple views. [*Reprinted with permission from Carpenter and Ross (1994).*]

1.11.1   ART-EMAP Stage 1: Spatial Evidence Accumulation

ART-EMAP employs a spatial evidence accumulation process that integrates a distributed pattern of activity across coded category nodes to help disambiguate a noisy or novel test set input. In contrast, previous ART and ARTMAP simulations chose only the most highly activated, winner-take-all category node at field F_2^a as the basis for recognition and prediction.

In the fast-learn Fuzzy ARTMAP system, the input from F_1^a to the jth F_2^a node (Fig. 1.15) is given by

$$T_j^a = \frac{|\mathbf{A} \wedge \mathbf{w}_j^a|}{\alpha + |\mathbf{w}_j^a|} \tag{1.6}$$

as in Fig. 1.7. Fuzzy ARTMAP uses a binary choice rule:

$$y_j^a = \begin{cases} 1 & \text{if } T_J^a > T_j^a \quad \text{for all } j \neq J \\ 0 & \text{otherwise} \end{cases} \tag{1.7}$$

Then only the F_2^a category J that receives maximal $F_1^a \rightarrow F_2^a$ input predicts the ART_b output.

ART-EMAP also uses the binary choice rule (1.7) during the initial period of supervised training. However, during performance, F_2^a output $\mathbf{y}^a$ is determined by less extreme contrast enhancement of the $F_1^a \rightarrow F_2^a$ input pattern $\mathbf{T}^a$. Limited contrast enhancement extracts more information from the relative activations of F_2^a categories than does the all-or-none choice rule (1.7).

Power Rule.   Raising the input T_j^a of the jth F_2^a category to a power $p > 1$ is a simple way to implement contrast enhancement. Equation (1.8) defines a normalized power rule:

$$y_j^a = \frac{(T_j^a)^p}{\displaystyle\sum_{n=1}^{N_a} (T_n^a)^p} \tag{1.8}$$

Normalization constrains the F_2^a output values to a manageable range without altering relative values or subsequent predictions. The power rule (1.8) approximates the dynamics of a shunting competitive short-term-memory (STM) network that contrast-enhances its input pattern (Grossberg, 1973). The power rule is equivalent to the choice rule (1.7) when p is large. For smaller p, the distributed activity pattern (1.8) uses information from the relative F_2^a category activations to improve test set predictive performance at ART_b. In all ART-EMAP 3-D object simulations, $p = 24$.

After contrast enhancement, the F_2^a output $\mathbf{y}^a$ is filtered through the weights w_{jk}^{ab} to activate the EMAP field F_1^{ab}. The input S_k^{ab} from F_2^a to the kth F_1^{ab} node obeys the equation

$$S_k^{ab} = \sum_{j=1}^{N_a} w_{jk}^{ab} y_j^a \tag{1.9}$$

Since distributed F_2^a activity generally determines distributed EMAP field F_1^{ab} input, some means of choosing a winning prediction at the EMAP field is required. The simplest method is to choose the EMAP category K that receives maximal input from F_2^a. This can be implemented by letting $x_k^{ab} = S_k^{ab}$ and defining F_2^{ab} activity by

$$y_K^{ab} = \begin{cases} 1 & \text{if } x_K^{ab} > x_k^{ab} \quad \text{for all } k \neq K \\ 0 & \text{otherwise} \end{cases} \tag{1.10}$$

Other methods for predicting an ART_b category will be discussed below.

Stage 1 Simulation. Like Fuzzy ARTMAP, stage 1 ART-EMAP, with its spatially distributed activity pattern at F_2^a, is required to make a prediction from each single test set view. Nevertheless, predictive accuracy improves significantly, from 64.7 to 70.6 percent on the noise-free test set (Fig. 1.17b) and from 60.8 to 64.7 percent on the noisy test set (Fig. 1.17e).

1.11.2   Stage 2: EMAP Predictive Decision Criterion

An alternative to the stage 1 predictive choice rule (1.10) uses a *decision criterion (DC)* at the EMAP field F_2^{ab}. The decision criterion permits ART$_b$ choice only when the most active category K becomes a minimum proportion more active than the next most active EMAP category. Thus

$$y_K^{ab} = \begin{cases} 1 & \text{if } x_K^{ab} \gt (DC)x_k^{ab} \quad \text{for all } k \neq K \\ 0 & \text{otherwise} \end{cases} \tag{1.11}$$

where $DC \geq 1$. With $DC = 1$, the stage 2 decision criterion rule (1.11) reduces to the first-stage F_2^{ab} choice rule (1.10). With $DC > 1$, the decision criterion prevents prediction when multiple EMAP categories are about equally activated at F_1^{ab}, representing ambiguous predictive evidence. As the DC increases, both accuracy and the number of required input samples per decision tend to increase. When the decision criterion fails, and Eq. (1.11) implies that $y_k^{ab} = 0$ for all k, additional input is sought to resolve the perceived ambiguity. In an application, additional inputs might correspond to multiple views or to multiple samples of a single view.

Stage 2 Simulation. Stage 1 spatial evidence accumulation improves performance by causing a novel view to activate categories of two or more nearby training set views, which then strongly predict the correct object. However, many single-view errors, caused by similar views across different objects, remain. Stage 2 or stage 3 corrects most of these errors, when multiple views of the unknown object are available. With a high fixed decision criterion (DC = 5.0) and an average of 4.8 test set views, stage 2 ART-EMAP achieves 98.0 percent accuracy on the noise-free test set. Even on the noisy test set, object identification remains 90.2 percent accurate, with an average of 6.8 test set views. Both performance and the average number of views decrease as the fixed decision criterion decreases from 5 to 1.

1.11.3   Stage 3: Temporal Evidence Accumulation

The predictive DC strategy (stage 2 ART-EMAP) searches multiple views or samples until one input satisfies the decision criterion. However, any single noisy input vector **a** might produce map field activity that satisfies a given decision criterion but still make an incorrect prediction. The stage 2 strategy does not benefit from the partial evidence provided by all the views that failed to meet the decision criterion. Further performance improvement in a noisy input environment is achieved through the application of a decision criterion to *time-integrated* predictions that are generated by multiple inputs. Stage 3 ART-EMAP accumulates evidence at a *map evidence accumulation field* F_E^{ab} (Fig. 1.15). The time scale of this *medium-term memory (MTM)* process is longer than that of the STM field activations resulting from the presence of a single view, but shorter than the long-term memory stored in adaptive weights.

Additive Evidence Integration. A straightforward way to implement evidence accumulation at the EMAP module is to sum a sequence of F_1^{ab} map activations at the evidence accumulation field F_E^{ab}:

$$(T_k^{ab})^{\text{new}} = (T_k^{ab})^{\text{old}} + x_k^{ab} \tag{1.12}$$

At F_E^{ab}, evidence accumulating in MTM (T_k^{ab}) starts at zero and is reset to zero when the decision criterion is met. Activities y_k^{ab} at field F_2^{ab} obey

$$y_K^{ab} = \begin{cases} 1 & \text{if } T_K^{ab} > (\text{DC}) \, T_k^{ab} \qquad \text{for all } k \neq K \\ 0 & \text{otherwise} \end{cases} \tag{1.13}$$

A decision will eventually be made if the DC starts large and gradually decreases toward 1. As in stage 2, larger DC values tend to covary with both greater accuracy and longer input sequences. In simulations, the DC decreased exponentially from 6 to 1:

$$\text{DC}(l) = 5(1.0 - r)^{l-1} + 1 \tag{1.14}$$

where $\mathbf{a}(l)$ is the lth input in a same-class sequence ($l = 1, 2, \ldots$). The decay rate r was set equal to 0.2. Additive integration is equivalent to applying the decision criterion to a running average of map field activations $\mathbf{x}^{ab}$ rather than to $\mathbf{x}^{ab}$ itself.

Stage 3 Simulation. For a two-class prediction problem, evidence accumulation improves performance primarily by averaging across noisy inputs. Stage 3 ART-EMAP becomes increasingly useful as the number of predicted classes increases, since evidence accumulation can also help solve the difficult problem of disambiguating nearly identical views of different objects. With three or more object classes, when equal predictive evidence may exist for both the correct object and an incorrect one, the identity of the erroneous class tends to vary from one input to the next. As the sequence of views grows, erroneous evidence is quickly overwhelmed by evidence for the correct object. In the stage 3 ART-EMAP three-object simulations, with the decreasing DC function in Eq. (1.14), an average of 9.2 views was needed to reach 98.0 percent correct performance on the noise-free test set (Fig. 1.17*c*). On the noisy test set, an average of 11.3 views allowed the system to reach 92.2 percent correct performance (Fig. 1.17*f*).

1.11.4 Stage 4: Unsupervised Rehearsal Learning

Temporal evidence accumulation allows the stage 3 ART-EMAP system to recognize objects from a series of ambiguous views. However, the system learns nothing from the final outcome of this decision process. If, e.g., an input sequence $\mathbf{a}^{(1)}, \ldots, \mathbf{a}^{(L)}$ predicted an ART_b category K, by Eqs. (1.12) and (1.13), the entire sequence would need to be presented again before the same prediction would be made.

Unsupervised rehearsal learning (stage 4) fine-tunes performance by feeding back to the system knowledge of the final prediction. Specifically, after input $\mathbf{a}^{(L)}$ allows ART-EMAP to choose the ART_b category K, the sequence $\mathbf{a}^{(1)}, \ldots, \mathbf{a}^{(L)}$ is re-presented, or rehearsed. Weights in an adaptive filter u_{jk}^{ab} from F_2^a to F_E^{ab} are then adjusted, shifting category decision boundaries so that each input $\mathbf{a}^{(l)}$ in the sequence becomes more likely, on its own, to predict category K.

Stage 4 Simulation. Unsupervised rehearsal learning improves single-view test set performance only marginally on the 3-D object simulations. Stage 4 rehearsal learning was conducted on the 51 noise-free test set views. Temporal evidence accumulation drew from an enlarged test set that included 72 additional views. Accessing exemplars from this larger test set allows stable fine-tuning by decreasing the percentage of ambiguous test views. After this fine-tuning, performance on individual views from the original 51 test set inputs was 73 percent, compared to 70.6 percent at stage 1 (Fig. 1.17*b*).

Spatial and temporal evidence accumulation by ART-EMAP has been shown to improve Fuzzy ARTMAP performance on both the ARPA benchmark circle-in-the-square problem (Carpenter and Ross, 1993, 1995; Wilensky, 1990) and the 3-D object recognition problem described here. Unsupervised rehearsal learning illustrates how self-training can fine-tune system performance. ART-EMAP is a general-purpose algorithm for pattern class prediction based on the temporal integration of predictive evidence resulting from distributed recognition across a small set of trained categories. The system promises to be useful in a variety of applications, including spatiotemporal image analysis and prediction as well as recognition of 3-D objects from ambiguous 2-D views.

1.12 CONCLUDING REMARKS

ARTMAP systems illustrate how neural networks can incorporate properties of fuzzy logic and expert production systems into a unified computational framework. Such algorithms are helping to overcome previously arbitrary boundaries between these disciplines. The algorithms exhibit combinations of properties that have not been attainable by more traditional approaches, which helps to explain the rapidly growing number of diverse applications in which they are being successfully used.

APPENDIX 1A   FUZZY ART AND FUZZY ARTMAP ALGORITHMS

Fuzzy ART Activity Vectors

Each ART system includes a field F_0 of nodes that represent a current input vector and a field F_1 that receives both bottom-up input from F_0 and top-down input from a field F_2 that represents the active code, or category. The F_0 activity vector is denoted $\mathbf{I} = (I_1, \ldots, I_M)$, with each component I_i in the interval [0, 1], $i = 1, \ldots, M$. The F_1 activity vector is denoted by $\mathbf{x} = (x_1, \ldots, x_M)$, and the F_2 activity vector is denoted by $\mathbf{y} = (y_1, \ldots, y_N)$. The number of nodes in each field is arbitrary.

Weight Vector

Associated with each F_2 category node j $(j = 1, \ldots, N)$ is a vector $\mathbf{w}_j \equiv (w_{j1}, \ldots, w_{jM})$ of adaptive weights, or LTM traces. Initially

$$w_{j1}(0) = \cdots = w_{jM}(0) = 1 \qquad (1.15)$$

Then each category is said to be *uncommitted*. After a category is selected for coding, it becomes *committed*. As shown below, each LTM trace w_{ji} is monotonic nonincreasing through time and hence converges to a limit. The Fuzzy ART weight vector $\mathbf{w}_j$ subsumes both the bottom-up and top-down weight vectors of ART 1.

Parameters

Fuzzy ART dynamics are determined by a choice parameter $\alpha > 0$, a learning rate parameter $\beta \in [0, 1]$, and a vigilance parameter $\rho \in [0, 1]$.

Category Choice

For each input $\mathbf{I}$ and F_2 node j, the *choice function* T_j is defined by

$$T_j(\mathbf{I}) = \frac{|\mathbf{I} \wedge \mathbf{w}_j|}{\alpha + |\mathbf{w}_j|} \tag{1.16}$$

where the fuzzy AND (Zadeh, 1965) operator $\wedge$ is defined by

$$(\mathbf{p} \wedge \mathbf{q})_i \equiv \min(p_i, q_i) \tag{1.17}$$

and where the norm $|\cdot|$ is defined by

$$|\mathbf{p}| \equiv \sum_{i=1}^{M} |p_i| \tag{1.18}$$

for any M-dimensional vectors $\mathbf{p}$ and $\mathbf{q}$. For notational simplicity, $T_j(\mathbf{I})$ in Eq. (1.16) is often written as T_j when input $\mathbf{I}$ is fixed.

The system is said to make a *category choice* when at most one F_2 node can become active at a given time. The category choice is indexed by J, where

$$T_J = \max \{T_j : j = 1, \ldots, N\} \tag{1.19}$$

If more than one T_j is maximal, the category j with the smallest index is chosen. In particular, nodes become committed in order $j = 1, 2, 3, \ldots$. When the Jth category is chosen, $y_J = 1$; and $y_j = 0$ for $j \neq J$. In a choice system, the F_1 activity vector $\mathbf{x}$ obeys the equation

$$\mathbf{x} = \begin{cases} \mathbf{I} & \text{if } F_2 \text{ is inactive} \\ \mathbf{I} \wedge \mathbf{w}_J & \text{if the } J\text{th } F_2 \text{ node is chosen} \end{cases} \tag{1.20}$$

Resonance or Reset

Resonance occurs if the *match function* $|\mathbf{I} \wedge \mathbf{w}_J|/|\mathbf{I}|$ of the chosen category meets the vigilance criterion

$$\frac{|\mathbf{I} \wedge \mathbf{w}_J|}{|\mathbf{I}|} \geq \rho \tag{1.21}$$

i.e., by Eq. (1.20) when the Jth category is chosen, resonance occurs if

$$|\mathbf{x}| = |\mathbf{I} \wedge \mathbf{w}_J| \geq \rho|\mathbf{I}| \tag{1.22}$$

Learning then ensues, as defined below. *Mismatch reset* occurs if

$$\frac{|\mathbf{I} \wedge \mathbf{w}_J|}{|\mathbf{I}|} < \rho \tag{1.23}$$

i.e., if

$$|\mathbf{x}| = |\mathbf{I} \wedge \mathbf{w}_J| < \rho|\mathbf{I}| \tag{1.24}$$

Then the value of the choice function T_J is set to zero for the duration of the input presentation to prevent the persistent selection of the same category during search. A new index J is then chosen, by Eq. (1.19). The search process continues until the chosen J satisfies Eq. (1.21).

Learning

Once the search ends, the weight vector $\mathbf{w}_J$ is updated according to the equation

$$\mathbf{w}_J^{\text{new}} = \beta(\mathbf{I} \wedge \mathbf{w}_J^{\text{old}}) + (1 - \beta)\mathbf{w}_J^{\text{old}} \tag{1.25}$$

Fast learning corresponds to setting $\beta = 1$.

Fast-Commit Slow-Recode Option

For efficient coding of noisy input sets, it is useful to set $\beta = 1$ when J is an uncommitted node and then to take $\beta < 1$ after the category is committed. Then $\mathbf{w}_J^{\text{new}} = \mathbf{I}$ the first time category J becomes active. Moore (1989) introduced the learning law, Eq. (1.25), with fast commitment and slow recoding, to investigate a variety of generalized ART 1 models. Some of these models are similar to Fuzzy ART, but none includes the complement coding option. Moore described a category proliferation problem that can occur in some analog ART systems when a large number of inputs erode the norm of weight vectors. Complement coding solves this problem.

Input Normalization and Complement Coding Option

Proliferation of categories is avoided in Fuzzy ART if inputs are normalized. *Complement coding* is a normalization rule that preserves amplitude information. Complement coding represents both the on response and the off response to an input vector $\mathbf{a}$ (Fig. 1.8). To define this operation in its simplest form, let $\mathbf{a}$ itself represent the on response. The complement of $\mathbf{a}$, denoted by $\mathbf{a}^c$, represents the off response, where

$$a_i^c \equiv 1 - a_i \tag{1.26}$$

The complement-coded input $\mathbf{I}$ to field F_1 is the $2M$-dimensional vector

$$\mathbf{I} = (\mathbf{a}, \mathbf{a}^c) \equiv (a_1, \dots, a_M, a_1^c, \dots, a_M^c) \tag{1.27}$$

Note that

$$|\mathbf{I}| = |(\mathbf{a}, \mathbf{a}^c)|$$

$$= \sum_{i=1}^{M} a_i + M - \sum_{i=1}^{M} a_i \qquad (1.28)$$

$$= M$$

so inputs preprocessed into complement coding form are automatically normalized. Where complement coding is used, the initial condition (1.15) is replaced by

$$w_{j1}(0) = \cdots = w_{j,2M}(0) = 1 \qquad (1.29)$$

Fuzzy ARTMAP Algorithm

The Fuzzy ARTMAP system incorporates two Fuzzy ART modules ART_a and ART_b that are linked together via an inter-ART module F^{ab} called a *map field* (Fig. 1.10). The map field is used to form predictive associations between categories and to realize the *match-tracking rule* whereby the vigilance parameter of ART_a increases in response to a predictive mismatch at ART_b. The interactions mediated by map field F^{ab} may be operationally characterized as follows.

ART_a and ART_b. Inputs to ART_a and ART_b are in the complement code form: For ART_a, $\mathbf{I} = \mathbf{A} = (\mathbf{a}, \mathbf{a}^c)$; for ART_b, $\mathbf{I} = \mathbf{B} = (\mathbf{b}, \mathbf{b}^c)$. Variables in ART_a and ART_b are designated by subscripts or superscripts a and b, respectively. For ART_a, let $\mathbf{x}^a \equiv (x_1^a, \ldots, x_{2M_a}^a)$ denote the F_1^a output vector; let $\mathbf{y}^a \equiv (y_1^a, \ldots, y_{N_a}^a)$ denote the F_2^a output vector; and let $\mathbf{w}_j^a \equiv (w_{j1}^a, w_{j2}^a, \ldots, w_{j2M_a}^a)$ denote the jth ART_a weight vector. For ART_b, let $\mathbf{x}^b \equiv (x_1^b, \ldots, x_{2M_b}^b)$ denote the F_1^b output vector; let $\mathbf{y}^b \equiv (y_1^b, \ldots, y_{N_b}^b)$ denote the F_2^b output vector; and let $\mathbf{w}_k^b \equiv (w_{k1}^b, w_{k2}^b, \ldots, w_{k2M_b}^b)$ denote the kth ART_b weight vector. For the map field, let $\mathbf{x}^{ab} \equiv (x_1^{ab}, \ldots, x_{N_b}^{ab})$ denote the F^{ab} output vector, and let $\mathbf{w}_j^{ab} \equiv (w_{j1}^{ab} \ldots, w_{jN_b}^{ab})$ denote the weight vector from the jth F_2^a node to F^{ab}. Vectors $\mathbf{x}^a$, $\mathbf{y}^a$, $\mathbf{x}^b$, $\mathbf{y}^b$, and $\mathbf{x}^{ab}$ are set to $\mathbf{0}$ between input presentations.

Map Field Activation. The map field F^{ab} is activated whenever one of the ART_a or ART_b categories is active. If node J of F_2^a is chosen, then its weights $\mathbf{w}_j^{ab}$ activate F^{ab}. If node K in F_2^b is active, then node K in F^{ab} is activated by one-to-one pathways between F_2^b and F^{ab}. If both ART_a and ART_b are active, then F^{ab} becomes active only if ART_a predicts the same category as ART_b via weights $\mathbf{w}_j^{ab}$. The F^{ab} output vector $\mathbf{x}^{ab}$ obeys

$$\mathbf{x}^{ab} = \begin{cases} \mathbf{y}^b \wedge \mathbf{w}_J^{ab} & \text{if } J\text{th } F_2^a \text{ node is active and } F_2^b \text{ is active} \\ \mathbf{w}_J^{ab} & \text{if } J\text{th } F_2^a \text{ node is active and } F_2^b \text{ is inactive} \\ \mathbf{y}^b & \text{if } F_2^a \text{ is inactive and } F_2^b \text{ is active} \\ \mathbf{0} & \text{if } F_2^a \text{ is inactive and } F_2^b \text{ is inactive} \end{cases} \qquad (1.30)$$

By Eq. (1.30), $\mathbf{x}^{ab} = \mathbf{0}$ if the prediction $\mathbf{w}_J^{ab}$ is disconfirmed by $\mathbf{y}^b$. Such a mismatch event triggers an ART_a search for a better category, as follows.

Match Tracking. At the start of each input presentation, the ART_a vigilance parameter ρ_a equals a baseline vigilance $\bar{\rho}_a$. The map field vigilance parameter is ρ_{ab}. If

$$|\mathbf{x}^{ab}| < \rho_{ab}|\mathbf{y}^b| \qquad (1.31)$$

then ρ_a is increased until it is slightly larger than $|\mathbf{A} \wedge \mathbf{w}_J^a| \|\mathbf{A}|^{-1}$, where $\mathbf{A}$ is the input to F_1^a, in complement coding form. Then

$$|\mathbf{x}^a| = |\mathbf{A} \wedge \mathbf{w}_J^a| < \rho_a|\mathbf{A}| \tag{1.32}$$

where J is the index of the active F_2^a node, as in Eq. (1.24). When this occurs, ART_a search leads to either activation of another F_2^a node J with

$$|\mathbf{x}^a| = |\mathbf{A} \wedge \mathbf{w}_J^a| \geq \rho_a|\mathbf{A}| \tag{1.33}$$

and

$$|\mathbf{x}^{ab}| = |\mathbf{y}^b \wedge \mathbf{w}_J^{ab}| \geq \rho_{ab}|\mathbf{y}^b| \tag{1.34}$$

or, if no such node exists, the shutdown of F_2^a for the remainder of the input presentation.

Map Field Learning.   Learning rules determine how the map field weights w_{jk}^{ab} change through time, as follows. Weights w_{jk}^{ab} in $F_2{}^a \to F^{ab}$ paths initially satisfy

$$w_{jk}^{ab}(0) = 1 \tag{1.35}$$

During resonance with the ART_a category J active, $\mathbf{w}_J{}^{ab}$ approaches the map field vector $\mathbf{x}^{ab}$. With fast learning, once J learns to predict the ART_b category K, that association is permanent; that is, $w_{JK}^{ab} = 1$ for all time.

REFERENCES

Amari, S. -I., and Takeuchi, A. (1978): "Mathematical theory on formation of category detecting nerve cells." *Biological Cybernetics,* **29:** 127–136.

Asfour, Y. R., Carpenter, G. A., Grossberg, S., and Lesher, G. W. (1993): "Fusion ARTMAP: A neural network architecture for multi-channel data fusion and classification." In *Proceedings of the World Congress on Neural Networks* (WCNN-93). Hillsdale, NJ: Lawrence Erlbaum, vol. 2, pp. 210–215. Technical Report CAS/CNS-TR-93-006, Boston: Boston University.

Bachelder, I. A., Waxman, A. M., and Seibert, M. (1993): "A neural system for mobile robot visual place learning and recognition." In *Proceedings of the World Congress on Neural Networks* (WCNN-93). Hillsdale, NJ: Lawrence Erlbaum, vol. 1, pp. 512–517.

Baloch, A. A., and Waxman, A. M. (1991): "Visual learning, adaptive expectations, and behavioral conditioning of the mobile robot MAVIN." *Neural Networks,* **4:** 271–302.

Bienenstock, E. L., Cooper, L. N., and Munro, P. W. (1982): "Theory for the development of neuron selectivity: Orientation specificity and binocular interaction in visual cortex." *Journal of Neuroscience,* **2:** 32–48.

Bradski, G., and Grossberg, S. (1994): "Recognition of 3-D objects from multiple 2-D views by a self-organizing neural architecture." In V. Cherkassky, J. H. Friedman, and H. Wechsler (eds.), *From Statistics to Neural Networks: Theory and Pattern Recognition.* New York: Springer-Verlag.

Carpenter, G. A., and Grossberg, S. (1987a): "A massively parallel architecture for a self-organizing neural pattern recognition machine." *Computer Vision, Graphics, and Image Processing,* **37:** 54–115.

Carpenter, G. A., and Grossberg, S. (1987b): "ART 2: Stable self-organization of pattern recognition codes for analog input patterns." *Applied Optics,* **26:** 4919–4930.

Carpenter, G. A., and Grossberg, S. (1987c): "Neural dynamics of category learning and recognition: Attention, memory consolidation, and amnesia." In S. Grossberg (ed.), *The Adaptive Brain, I: Cognition, Learning, Reinforcement, and Rhythm.* Amsterdam: Elsevier/North Holland, pp. 238–286.

Carpenter, G. A., and Grossberg, S. (1990): "ART 3: Hierarchical search using chemical transmitters in self-organizing pattern recognition architectures." *Neural Networks,* **3:** 129–152.

Carpenter, G. A., and Grossberg, S. (eds.) (1991): *Pattern Recognition by Self-Organizing Neural Networks.* Cambridge, MA: MIT Press.

Carpenter, G. A., and Grossberg, S. (1992): "Fuzzy ARTMAP: Supervised learning, recognition, and prediction by a self-organizing neural network." *IEEE Communications Magazine,* **30:** 38–49.

Carpenter, G. A., and Grossberg, S. (1993): "Normal and amnesic learning, recognition, and memory by a neural model or cortico-hippocampal interactions." *Trends in Neurosciences,* **16:** 131–137.

Carpenter, G. A., and Grossberg, S. (1994): "Fuzzy ARTMAP: A synthesis of neural networks and fuzzy logic for supervised categorization and nonstationary prediction." In R. R. Yager and L. A. Zadeh (eds.), *Fuzzy Sets, Neural Networks, and Soft Computing.* New York: Van Nostrand Reinhold, pp. 126–165.

Carpenter, G. A., Grossberg, S., and Iizuka, K. (1992a): "Comparative performance measures of Fuzzy ARTMAP, learned vector quantization, and back propagation for handwritten character recognition." In *Proceedings of the International Joint Conference on Neural Networks* (WCNN-93). Piscataway, NJ: IEEE Service Center, vol. 1, pp. 794–799.

Carpenter, G. A., Grossberg, S., Markuzon, N., Reynolds, J. H., and Rosen, D. B. (1992b): "Fuzzy ARTMAP: A neural network architecture for incremental supervised learning of analog multidimensional maps." *IEEE Transactions on Neural Networks,* **3:** 698–713.

Carpenter, G. A., Grossberg, S., and Mehanian, C. (1989): "Invariant recognition of cluttered scenes by a self-organizing ART architecture: CORT-X boundary segmentation." *Neural Networks,* **2:** 169–181.

Carpenter, G. A., Grossberg, S., and Reynolds, J. H. (1991a): "ARTMAP: Supervised real-time learning and classification of nonstationary data by a self-organizing neural network." *Neural Networks,* **4:** 565–588.

Carpenter, G. A., Grossberg, S., and Reynolds, J. H. (1993): "Fuzzy ARTMAP, slow learning, and probability estimation." In *Proceedings of the World Congress on Neural Networks* (WCNN-93). Hillsdale, NJ: Lawrence Erlbaum, vol. 2, pp. 26–30.

Carpenter, G. A., Grossberg, S., and Reynolds, J. H. (1995): "A fuzzy ARTMAP nonparametric probability estimator for nonstationary pattern recognition problems." *IEEE Transactions on Neural Networks,* in press. Technical Report CAS/CNS-TR-93-047. Boston: Boston University.

Carpenter, G. A., Grossberg, S., and Rosen, D. B. (1991b): "ART 2-A: An adaptive resonance algorithm for rapid category learning and recognition." *Neural Networks,* **4:** 493–504.

Carpenter, G. A., Grossberg, S., and Rosen, D. B. (1991c): "Fuzzy ART: Fast stable learning and categorization of analog patterns by an adaptive resonance system." *Neural Networks,* **4:** 759–771.

Carpenter, G. A., and Ross, W. D. (1993): "ART-EMAP: A neural network architecture for learning and prediction by evidence accumulation." *Proceedings of the World Congress on Neural Networks* (WCNN-93). Hillsdale, NJ: Lawrence Erlbaum, vol. 3, pp. 649–656.

Carpenter, G. A., and Ross, W. D. (1994): "3-D object recognition by the ART-EMAP evidence accumulation network." In *Proceedings of the World Congress on Neural Networks* (WCNN-94). Hillsdale, NJ: Lawrence Erlbaum, vol. 1, pp. 749–758.

Carpenter, G. A., and Ross, W. D. (1995): "ART-EMAP: A neural network architecture for object recognition by evidence accumulation." *IEEE Transactions on Neural Networks,* **6:**805–818. Technical Report CAS/CNS-TR-93-035. Boston: Boston University.

Carpenter, G. A., and Tan, A.-H. (1995): "Rule extraction: From neural architecture to symbolic representation." *Connection Science,* **7:**3–27. Technical Report CAS/CNS-TR-94-005. Boston: Boston University.

Caudell, T., Smith, S., Johnson, C., Wunsch, D., and Escobedo, R. (1991): "An industrial application of neural networks to reusable design." *Adaptive Neural Systems.* Technical Report BCS-CS-ACS-91-001. Seattle, WA: Boeing Company, pp. 185–190.

Cohen, M., and Grossberg, S. (1987): "Masking fields: A massively parallel architecture for learning, recognizing, and predicting multiple groupings of patterned data." *Applied Optics,* **26:** 1866–1891.

Daugman, J. G. (1988): "Complete discrete 2-D Gabor transforms by neural networks for image analysis and compression." *IEEE Transactions on Acoustics, Speech, and Signal Processing,* **36:** 1169–1179.

Desimone, R. (1992): "Neural circuits for visual attention in the primate brain." In G. A. Carpenter and S. Grossberg (eds.), *Neural Networks for Vision and Image Processing.* Cambridge, MA: MIT Press, pp. 343–364.

Dubrawski, A., and Crowley, J. L. (1994a): "Learning locomotion reflexes: A self-supervised neural system for a mobile robot." *Robotics and Autonomous Systems,* **12:** 133–142.

Dubrawski, A., and Crowley, J. L. (1994b): "Self-supervised neural system for reactive navigation." In *Proceedings of the IEEE International Conference on Robotics and Automation.* Los Alamitos, CA: IEEE Computer Society Press, pp. 2076–2081.

Escobedo, R., Smith, S. D. G., and Caudell, T. P. (1993): "The ART of design retrieval." *Adaptive Neural Systems.* Technical Report BCS-CS/ACS-93-008. Seattle, WA: Boeing Company, pp. 149–160.

Feng, C., Sutherland, A., King, S., Muggleton, S., and Henery, R. (1993): "Comparison of machine learning classifiers to statistics and neural networks." *Proceedings of the Fourth International Workshop on Artificial Intelligence and Statistics,* pp. 363–368.

Gabor, D. (1946): "A theory of communication." *Journal of the Institute of Electrical Engineers,* **93:** 429–457.

Gan, K. W., and Lua, K. T. (1992): "Chinese character classification using an adaptive resonance network." *Pattern Recognition,* **25:** 877–882.

Gopal, S., Sklarew, D. M., and Lambin, E. (1993): "Fuzzy neural networks in multi-temporal classification of landcover change in the Sahel." *Proceedings of the DOSES Workshop on New Tools for Spatial Analysis.* Lisbon, Portugal.

Grossberg, S. (1964): "The theory of embedding fields with applications to psychology and neurophysiology," New York: Rockefeller Institute for Medical Research.

Grossberg, S. (1969): "On learning and energy-entropy dependence in recurrent and nonrecurrent signed networks." *Journal of Statistical Physics,* **1:** 319–350.

Grossberg, S. (1972): "Neural expectation: Cerebellar and retinal analogs of cells fired by learnable or unlearned pattern classes." *Kybernetik,* **10:** 49–57.

Grossberg, S. (1973): "Contour enhancement, short term memory, and constancies in reverberating neural networks." *Studies in Applied Mathematics,* **52:** 213–257.

Grossberg, S. (1976a): "Adaptive pattern classification and universal recoding, I: Parallel development and coding of neural feature detectors." *Biological Cybernetics,* **23:** 121–134.

Grossberg, S. (1976b): "Adaptive pattern classification and universal recoding, II: Feedback, expectation, olfaction, and illusions." *Biological Cybernetics,* **23:** 187–202.

Grossberg, S. (1978): "A theory of human memory: Self-organization and performance of sensory-motor codes, maps, and plans." In R. Rosen and F. Snell (eds.), *Progress in Theoretical Biology,* vol. 5. New York: Academic Press, pp. 233–374. [Reprinted in S. Grossberg, *Studies of Mind and Brain: Neural Principles of Learning, Perception, Development, Cognition, and Motor Control.* Boston: Reidel Press, 1982.]

Grossberg, S. (1980): "How does a brain build a cognitive code?" *Psychological Review,* **1:** 1–51.

Grossberg, S. (1982). *Studies of Mind and Brain: Neural Principles of Learning, Perception, Development, Cognition, and Motor Control.* Boston: Reidel Press.

Grossberg, S. (ed.) (1987a): *The Adaptive Brain: Cognition, Learning, Reinforcement, and Rhythm,* vol. 1. Amsterdam: Elsevier/North Holland.

Grossberg, S. (ed.) (1987b): *The Adaptive Brain: Vision, Speech, Language, and Motor Control,* vol. 2. Amsterdam: Elsevier/North-Holland.

Grossberg, S. (ed.) (1988): *Neural Networks and Natural Intelligence.* Cambridge, MA: MIT Press.

Grossberg, S. (1994): "3-D vision and figure-ground separation." *Perception and Psychophysics,* **55:** 48–120.

Grossberg, S., and Kuperstein, M. (1986/1989): *Neural Dynamics of Adaptive Sensory-Motor Control: Expanded Edition.* Elmsford, NY: Pergamon Press.

Grossberg, S., and Merrill, J. W. L. (1992): "A neural network model of adaptively timed reinforcement learning and hippocampal dynamics." *Cognitive Brain Research,* **1:** 3–38.

Grossberg, S., and Mingolla, E. (1985): "Neural dynamics of form perception: Boundary completion, illusory figures, and neon color spreading." *Psychological Review,* **92:** 173–211.

Grossberg, S., Mingolla, E., and Ross, W. D. (1994): "A neural theory of attentive visual search: Interactions of visual, spatial, and object representations." *Psychological Review,* **101:** 470–789.

Grossberg, S., Mingolla, E., and Todorović, D. (1989): "A neural network architecture for preattentive vision." *IEEE Transactions on Biomedical Engineering,* **36:** 65–84.

Grossberg, S., and Stone, G. O. (1986): "Neural dynamics of word recognition and recall: Attentional priming, learning, and resonance." *Psychological Review,* **93:** 46–74.

Grossberg, S., and Wyse, L. (1991): "Invariant recognition of cluttered scenes by a self-organizing ART architecture: Figure-ground separation." *Neural Networks,* **4:** 723–742.

Grossberg, S., and Wyse, L. (1992): "Figure-ground separation of connected scenic figures: Boundaries, filling-in, and opponent processing." In G. A. Carpenter and S. Grossberg (eds.), *Neural Networks for Vision and Image Processing.* Cambridge, MA: MIT Press, pp. 161–194.

Ham, F. M., and Han, S. W. (1993): "Quantitative study of the QRS complex using fuzzy ARTMAP and the MIT/BIH arrhythmia database." In *Proceedings of the World Congress on Neural Networks* (WCNN-93). Hillsdale, NJ: Lawrence Erlbaum, vol. 1, pp. 207–211.

Harvey, R. M. (1993): "Nursing diagnosis by computers: An application of neural networks." *Nursing Diagnosis,* **4:** 26–34.

Johnson, C. (1993): "Agent learns user's behavior." *Electrical Engineering Times,* June 28, pp. 43, 46.

Kasperkiewicz, J., Racz, J., and Dubrawski, A. (1994): "HPC strength prediction using an artificial neural network." *ASCE Journal of Computing in Civil Engineering,* submitted.

Keyvan, S., Durg, A., and Rabelo, L. C. (1993): "Application of artificial neural networks for development of diagnostic monitoring system in nuclear plants." *American Nuclear Society Conference Proceedings,* April 18–21.

Koenderink, J. J., and van Doorn, A. J. (1979): "The internal representation of solid shape with respect to vision." *Biological Cybernetics,* **32:** 211–216.

Kohonen, T. (1984/1989): *Self-Organization and Associative Memory,* 3d ed. New York: Springer-Verlag.

Kosko, B. (1986): "Fuzzy entropy and conditioning." *Information Sciences,* **40:** 165–174.

Kumara, S. R. T., Merchawi, N. S., Karmarthi, S. V., and Thazhutaveetil, M. (1995): *Neural Networks in Design and Manufacturing.* London: Chapman and Hall Publishers.

Laird, J. E., Newell, A., and Rosenbloom, P. S. (1987): "SOAR: An architecture for general intelligence." *Artificial Intelligence,* **33:** 1–64.

Levy, W. B. (1985): "Associative changes at the synapse: LTP in the hippocampus." In W. B. Levy, J. Anderson, and S. Lehmkuhle (eds.), *Synaptic Modification, Neuron Selectivity, and Nervous System Organization.* Hillsdale, NJ: Lawrence Erlbaum, pp. 5–33.

Levy, W. B., and Desmond, N. L. (1985): "The rules of elemental synaptic plasticity." In W. B. Levy, J. Anderson, and S. Lehmkuhle (eds.), *Synaptic Modification, Neuron Selectivity, and Nervous System Organization.* Hillsdale, NJ: Lawrence Erlbaum, pp. 105–121.

Linsker, R. (1986): "From basic network principles to neural architecture: Emergence of spatial-opponent cells." *Proceedings of the National Academy of Sciences,* **83:** 8779–8783.

Malsburg, C. von der (1973): "Self-organization of orientation sensitive cells in the striate cortex." *Kybernetik,* **14:** 85–100.

Mehta, B. V., Vij, L., and Rabelo, L. C. (1993): "Prediction of secondary structures of proteins using fuzzy ARTMAP." In *Proceedings of the World Congress on Neural Networks* (WCNN-93). Hillsdale, NJ: Lawrence Erlbaum, vol. 1, pp. 228–232.

Moore, B. (1989): "ART 1 and pattern clustering." In D. Touretzky, G. Hinton, and T. Sejnowski (eds.), *Proceedings of the 1988 Connectionist Models Summer School.* San Mateo, CA: Morgan Kaufmann, pp. 174–185.

Moya, M. M., Koch, M. W., and Hostetler, L. D. (1993): "One-class classifier networks for target recognition applications." In *Proceedings of the World Congress on Neural Networks* (WCNN-93). Hillsdale, NJ: Lawrence Erlbaum, vol. 3, pp. 797–801.

Parker, D. B. (1982): "Learning-logic." Invention Report 581-64, File 1, Office of Technology Licensing, Stanford University, October.

Rauschecker, J. P., and Singer, W. (1979): "Changes in the circuitry of the kitten's visual cortex are gated by postsynaptic activity." *Nature,* **280:** 58–60.

Repp, B. H. (1991): "Perceptual restoration of a 'missing' speech sound: Auditory induction or illusion?" *Haskins Laboratories Status Report on Speech Research,* SR-107/108, pp. 147–170.

Rumelhart, D. E., Hinton, G., and Williams, R. (1986): "Learning internal representations by error propagation." In D. E. Rumelhart and J. L. McClelland (eds.), *Parallel Distributed Processing.* Cambridge, MA: MIT Press, pp. 318–362.

Rumelhart, D. E., and Zipser, D. (1985): "Feature discovery by competitive learning." *Cognitive Science,* **9:** 75–112.

Samuel, A. G. (1981a): "Phonemic restoration: Insights from a new methodology." *Journal of Experimental Psychology: General,* **110:** 474–494.

Samuel, A. G. (1981b): "The rule of bottom-up confirmation in the phonemic restoration illusion." *Journal of Experimental Psychology: Human Perception and Performance,* **7:** 1124–1131.

Schvaneveldt, R. W., and MacDonald, J. E. (1981): "Semantic context and the encoding of words: Evidence for two modes of stimulus analysis." *Journal of Experimental Psychology: Human Perception and Performance,* **7:** 673–687.

Schwartz, E. (1977): "Spatial mapping in primate sensory projection: Analytic structure and relevance to perception." *Biological Cybernetics,* **25:** 181–194.

Seibert, M., and Waxman, A. (1990a): "Learning aspect graph representations of 3-D objects in a neural network." In *Proceedings of the International Joint Conference on Neural Networks* (IJCNN-90). Washington: IEEE, vol. 2, pp. 233–236.

Seibert, M., and Waxman, A. (1990b): "Learning aspect graph representations from view sequences." In D. Touretzky (ed.), *Advances in Neural Information Processing Systems,* vol. 2. San Mateo, CA: Morgan Kaufmann, pp. 258–265.

Seibert, M., and Waxman, A. M. (1991): "Learning and recognizing 3D objects from multiple views in a neural system." In H. Wechsler (ed.), *Neural Networks for Perception,* vol. 1. New York: Academic Press.

Seibert, M., and Waxman, A. (1992): "Adaptive 3-D object recognition from multiple views." *IEEE Transactions on Pattern Analysis and Machine Intelligence,* **11:** 107–124.

Singer, W. (1983): "Neuronal activity as a shaping factor in the self-organization of neuron assemblies." In E. Basar, H. Flohr, H. Haken, and A. J. Mandell (eds.), *Synergetics of the Brain.* New York: Springer-Verlag, pp. 89–101.

Smith, E. E. (1990): In D. O. Osherson and E. E. Smith (eds.), *An Invitation to Cognitive Science.* Cambridge, MA: MIT Press.

Smith, J. W., Everhart, J. E., Dickson, W. C., Knowler, W. C., and Johannes, R. S. (1988): "Using the ADAP learning algorithm to forecast the onset of diabetes mellitus." In *Proceedings of the Symposium on Computer Applications and Medical Care.* Piscataway, NJ: IEEE Computer Society Press, pp. 261–265.

Suzuki, Y., Abe, Y., and Ono, K. (1993): "Self-organizing QRS wave recognition system in ECG using ART 2." In *Proceedings of the World Congress on Neural Networks* (WCNN-93). Hillsdale, NJ: Lawrence Erlbaum, vol. 4, pp. 39–42.

Warren, R. M. (1984): "Perceptual restoration of obliterated sounds." *Psychological Bulletin,* **96:** 371–383.

Warren, R. M., and Sherman, G. L. (1974): "Phonemic restorations based on subsequent context." *Perception and Psychophysics,* **16:** 150–156.

Werbos, P. (1974): "Beyond regression: New tools for prediction and analysis in the behavioral sciences." Ph.D. thesis, Harvard University, Cambridge, MA.

Wienke, D. (1993): "ART pattern recognition software for chemists." User documentation, University of Nijmegen, The Netherlands.

Wienke, D. (1994): "Neural resonance and adaptation—Towards nature's principles in artificial pattern recognition." In L. Buydens and W. Melssen (eds.), *Chemometrics: Exploring and Exploiting Chemical Information.* Nijmegen, The Netherlands: University Press.

Wienke, D., and Kateman, G. (1994): "Adaptive resonance theory based artificial neural networks for treatment of open-category problems in chemical pattern recognition—Application to UV-Vis and IR spectroscopy." *Chemometrics and Intelligent Laboratory Systems.*

Wienke, D., Xie, Y., and Hopke, P. K. (1994): "An adaptive resonance theory based artificial neural network (ART 2-A) for rapid identification of airborne particle shapes from their scanning electron microscopy images." *Chemometrics and Intelligent Laboratory Systems.*

Wilensky, G. (1990): "Analysis of neural network issues: Scaling, enhanced nodal processing, comparison with standard classification." *DARPA Neural Network Program Review,* October 29–30.

Willshaw, D. J., and Malsburg, C. von der (1976): "How patterned neural connections can be set up by self-organization." *Proceedings of the Royal Society of London (B),* **194:** 431–445.

Zadeh, L. (1965): "Fuzzy sets." *Information Control,* **8:** 338–353.

CHAPTER 2
A REVIEW OF PROBABILISTIC, FUZZY, AND NEURAL MODELS FOR PATTERN RECOGNITION†

James C. Bezdek
Department of Computer Science
University of West Florida,
Pensacola, Florida

Fuzzy sets were introduced by Zadeh[1] in 1965 to represent and manipulate data and information that possess nonstatistical uncertainty. Computational neural networks were first discussed by McCullough and Pitts in 1943 as a means of imitating the power of biologic systems for data and information processing. Probabilistic models for data analysis, are, of course, several hundred years old. This chapter discusses the basic ideas of and some synergisms between probabilistic, fuzzy, and computational neural networks models as they apply to pattern recognition. We also provide a brief discussion of the relationship of both approaches to statistical pattern recognition methodologies.

2.1 FUZZY MODELS

Fuzzy sets are a generalization of conventional set theory that was introduced as a new way to represent vagueness in everyday life. Fuzzy interpretations of data structures are a natural and intuitively plausible way to formulate and solve various problems in pattern recognition. The basic idea of fuzzy sets is simple. Suppose you are approaching a red light and must advise a driving student when to apply the brakes. Would you say, "Begin braking *74 feet* from the crosswalk?" Or would your advice be more like, "Apply the brakes pretty soon"? The latter, of course; the former instruction is too precise to be implemented. This illustrates that vagueness does not necessarily weaken utility; the latter phrase is more useful than the former. Natural language is one example of ways

†Reprinted with permission from *Journal of Intelligent and Fuzzy Systems,* vol. 1 (1), 1–25 (1993) © 1993 John Wiley & Sons, Inc. This research was supported by NSF Grant IRI-9003252.

vagueness arises, is used, and is propagated in everyday life. Imprecision in data and information gathered from and about our environment is either *statistical* (e.g., a coin toss)—the outcome is a matter of chance—or *nonstatistical* (e.g., "Apply the brakes pretty soon")—this latter type of uncertainty is called *fuzziness*.

Conventional (crisp) sets contain objects that satisfy *precise properties* required for membership. The set of numbers H from 6 to 8 is crisp; we write $H = \{r \in \mathcal{R} \mid 6 \leq r \leq 8\}$. Equivalently, H is described by its *membership* (or characteristic, or indicator) *function* $m_H: \mathcal{R} \mapsto \{0, 1\}$, defined as

$$m_H(r) = \begin{cases} 1 & 6 \leq r \leq 8 \\ 0 & \text{otherwise} \end{cases} \tag{2.1}$$

The crisp set H and the graph of m_H are shown in the left half of Fig. 2.1. Every real number r either is in H or is not. Because m_H maps all real numbers $r \in \mathcal{R}$ onto the two points $\{0, 1\}$, crisp sets correspond to two-valued logic—is or is not, on or off, black or white, 1 or 0. In logic, values of m_H are called *truth values* with reference to the question "Is r in H?" The answer is yes if and only if $m_H(r) = 1$, and no otherwise.

Next, consider the set F of real numbers that are close to 7. Because the property "close to 7" is fuzzy, there is *not a unique* membership function for F. Rather, the modeler must decide, based upon the potential application and properties desired for F, what m_F should be. Properties that seem plausible for this particular fuzzy set might include (1) normality $[m_F(7) = 1]$; (2) monotonicity [the closer r is to 7, the closer $m_F(r)$ is to 1, and conversely]; and (3) symmetry (numbers equally far left and right of 7 should have equal memberships). Given these intuitive constraints, either of the functions shown in the right half of Fig. 2.1 might be a useful representative of F. The function m_{F1} is discrete (the staircase graph), while m_{F2} is continuous but not smooth (the triangle graph). It is easy to construct a membership function for F so that *every* number has some positive membership in F, but we would not expect numbers "far from 7," for example, 20,000,987, to have much.

Readers new to the field often wonder what the "set" F *is*, physically. In conventional set theory, any set of real objects is completely equivalent to, and isomorphically described by, a crisp membership function such as m_H. However, there is no set-theoretic equivalent of "real objects" corresponding to m_F, the function-theoretic representation of F; that is, fuzzy sets are always (and only) *functions*, from some "universe of objects," say X, into [0, 1], the range of m_F. This is depicted graphically in Fig. 2.2.

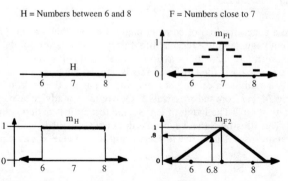

FIGURE 2.1 Membership functions for hard and fuzzy subsets of $\mathcal{R}$.

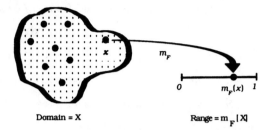

Domain = X   Range = $m_F[X]$

FIGURE 2.2   Fuzzy sets are membership functions.

So the membership function is the basic idea in fuzzy set theory; its values measure degrees to which objects satisfy imprecisely defined properties. To manipulate fuzzy sets, it is necessary to have operations that enable us to combine them. Zadeh defined *classical* operations for fuzzy sets in Ref. 1. Let $\mathcal{F}(X)$ = all fuzzy subsets of X [that is, $m \in \mathcal{F}(X) \Leftrightarrow m : X \mapsto [0, 1]$], and let fuzzy sets $m_A, m_B \in \mathcal{F}(X)$. We define ($\forall\ x \in X$: pointwise, function-theoretic operations)

$$(=) \qquad \text{Equality} \qquad A = B \Leftrightarrow m_A(x) = m_B(x) \qquad (2.2)$$

$$(\subset) \qquad \text{Containment} \qquad A \subset B \Leftrightarrow m_A(x) \le m_B(x) \qquad (2.3)$$

$$(\sim) \qquad \text{Complement} \qquad m_{\tilde{A}}(x) = 1 - m_A(x) \qquad (2.4)$$

$$(\cap) \qquad \text{Intersection} \qquad m_{A \cap B}(x) = \min\{m_A(x), m_B(x)\} \qquad (2.5)$$

$$(\cup) \qquad \text{Union} \qquad m_{A \cup B}(x) = \max\{m_A(x), m_B(x)\} \qquad (2.6)$$

Example 2.1.   Let $P = \{\text{people}\}$; $x = h(p)$ = height of $p \in P$; and let $X = h[P] = \{\text{heights of } p \in P\} = [0, 11]$. Shown in Fig. 2.3 are membership functions for two fuzzy sets, characterized as

$m_A \in \mathcal{F}(X) = \{(\text{heights}) \text{ close to 7 ft}\}\ (m_A \circ h) \in \mathcal{F}(P) \approx \{(\text{people}) \text{ close to 7 ft (tall)}\}$

$m_B \in \mathcal{F}(X) = \{(\text{heights}) \text{ close to 3 ft}\}\ (m_B \circ h) \in \mathcal{F}(P) \approx \{(\text{people}) \text{ close to 3 ft (tall)}\}$

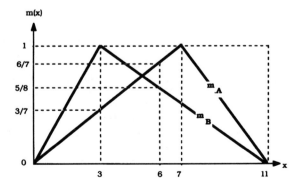

FIGURE 2.3   Membership functions for m_A and m_B.

$$m_A(3) = 3/7 \quad \text{extent to which a 3-ft } p \text{ is} \approx 7 \text{ ft tall}$$

$$m_{\bar{A}}(3) = 1 - 3/7 = 4/7 \quad \text{extent to which a 3-ft } p \text{ is } \textbf{NOT} \approx 7 \text{ ft tall}$$

$$m_A(6) = 6/7 \quad \text{extent to which a 6-ft } p \text{ is} \approx 7 \text{ ft tall}$$

$$m_B(6) = 5/8 \quad \text{extent to which a 6-ft } p \text{ is} \approx 3 \text{ ft tall}$$

$$m_{A \cap B}(6) = \min\{6/7, 5/8\} = 5/8 \quad \text{extent to which a 6-ft } p \text{ is} \approx (3 \textbf{ AND } 7 \text{ ft}) \text{ tall}$$

$$m_{A \cup B}(6) = \max\{6/7, 5/8\} = 6/7 \quad \text{extent to which a 6-ft } p \text{ is} \approx (3 \textbf{ OR } 7 \text{ ft}) \text{ tall}$$

Zadeh discussed these operations on fuzzy sets at length; many writers subsequently proposed other functions for these set operations. Indeed, there are at least 7 infinite families of fuzzy intersection and union operators, 2 infinite families of fuzzy complementation operators, and about 40 fuzzy implication operators in the literature.[2] Our purpose in reporting the original operations here is to familiarize readers with basic ideas about how to combine pairs of fuzzy sets. In fact, operations (2.2) to (2.6) seem nearly ubiquitous in real applications and in some sense thus remain more important than many of their subsequent generalizations. References 2 to 9 discuss many schemes that generalize both the operations above and, even more fundamentally, the notion of the fuzzy set itself.

Readers will have some questions about fuzzy sets at this point.

1. *Membership values—what are they?* The statement $m_{F2}(6.8) = 0.8$ (Fig. 2.1) tells us that a person 6.8 ft tall is "pretty close" to 7 ft tall. Thus, 0.8 is a measure of the *similarity* of this individual to other people who possess the imprecise property that m_{F2} represents. Note that we do *not* interpret this number as "the probability that a 6.8-ft tall person is 7 ft tall is 0.8."

2. *Membership functions—where do they come from?* It is important, when you ask this question, to remind yourself where probability density functions (PDFs) come from: *data and people.* Data, e.g., are used in parametric estimation of the means and covariances of the component densities in a mixture of normal distributions, just as data are used to find a fuzzy partition and prototypes by the fuzzy c-means clustering algorithm. But what of the normal density itself? Is it somehow different from, say, just "adopting" function m_{F2} because it seems to provide a reasonable and useful model of the process being described? Well, no. The normal distribution comes from Gauss, and we use it because it often fits the physical world. So we *do* get PDFs and membership functions (MFs) in the same ways.

3. *Isn't fuzziness just a clever disguise for probability?* No! To see why not, let $L =$ set of all liquids, and let fuzzy subset $\mathcal{L} = \{$all (potable) liquids$\}$. Suppose you had been in the desert for a week without a drink and you came upon two bottles A and B, marked with the following information: prob$(A \in L) = .91$ and memb$(B \in \mathcal{L}) = 0.91$. Confronted with these bottles, and given that you must drink from the one you choose, which would *you* choose to drink from first? Most readers see that while B could contain, say, swamp water, it would not (discounting the possibility of a machiavelian fuzzy modeler!) contain liquids such as hydrochloric acid; i.e., a membership of .91 means that the contents of B are "fairly similar" to perfectly potable liquids (pure water, perhaps). On the other hand, the probability that A is potable $= .91$ simply means that over a long run of experiments the contents of A are expected to be potable in about 91 percent of the trials, and in the other 9 percent the contents will be deadly—about 1 chance in 10. Thus, most readers will opt for the swamp water.

There is another facet to this example that concerns the idea of *observation*. Continuing, then, we examine the contents of A and B and discover that A is acid and B is beer. After observation, the membership value for B will not change, while the probability value must, dropping from .91 to 0. This example shows that these two models possess different kinds of information: fuzzy memberships, which represent *similarities* of objects to imprecisely defined properties; and probabilities, which convey information about *relative frequencies*. There are many amusing articles about the relationship between fuzzy sets and probability in the literature. Interested readers may consult, for example, Refs. 10 to 12.

4. *Where do fuzzy models fit in with other models?* Wherever they can provide either collateral or competitively better information about a physical process. No one will argue that the binomial distribution is an "optimal" model, in some philosophically intuitive sense, for the flip of a fair coin. One could model this process with a fuzzy technique, but the results would almost certainly be less satisfying in terms of a natural and verifiable representation of the process itself.

On the other hand, while we could certainly represent the idea of "pretty close to 7" with a statistical model, this is less satisfactory than the fuzzy models exhibited above because the notion of chance is absent from our naive description of the process. We should recognize and exploit the fact that different models provide us with auxiliary, and sometimes contradictory, information about various facts of the process rather than argue constantly about which approach is "better."

2.2 PATTERN RECOGNITION

What is *pattern recognition* (*PR*)? In 1973 Duda and Hart[13] characterized it as "a field concerned with machine recognition of meaningful regularities in noisy or complex environments." A workable definition is that PR is the *search* for *structure* in *data*.

We characterize numerical PR in terms of the four major areas shown in Fig. 2.4. The nodes in Fig. 2.4 are *not* independent. In practice, the successful PR system is developed by iteratively revisiting each of the four modules until the system satisfies (or is at least optimized for) a given set of performance requirements and economic constraints. Good treatments of many deterministic, statistical, and heuristic approaches to *numerical* PR may be found in Refs. 13 to 17. There is another approach to pattern recognition, i.e., the *structural* (syntactic) approach. This branch of PR is less well developed in terms of fuzzy and neural models and will not be discussed further in this chapter. The earliest reference to the use of fuzzy sets in pattern recognition was by Bellman et al.[18] Fuzzy pattern recognition techniques for many of the problems depicted in Fig. 2.4 are now fairly mature. Good general references include Refs. 19 to 22. Reference 23 is a recent offering of the IEEE Press that collects 51 articles about fuzzy and neural models for pattern recognition. Other surveys of fuzzy sets in pattern recognition include Refs. 24 and 25. Next, we discuss each element of Fig. 2.4.

2.2.1 Object Data

Generally speaking, two data structures are used in numerical *pattern recognition systems* (*PRSs*): *object data* vectors (feature vectors, pattern vectors) and (pairwise) *rela-*

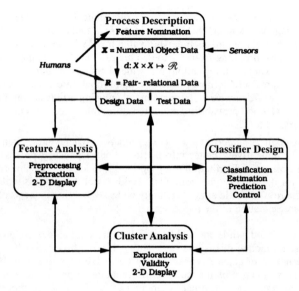

FIGURE 2.4   Elements of a typical numerical pattern recognition system.

tional data (similarities, proximities). Object data are represented in the sequel as $X = \{\mathbf{x}_1, \mathbf{x}_2, \ldots, \mathbf{x}_n\}$, a set of n feature vectors in feature space $\mathcal{R}^p$. The jth object observed in the process (some physical entity such as a person, airplane, seismic record, photograph, etc.) has vector $\mathbf{x}_j$ as its numerical representation; x_{jk} is the kth characteristic (or *feature*) associated with object j.

2.2.2 Relational Data

It may happen that, instead of an object data set X, we have access to a set of n^2 numerical *relationships*, say $\{r_{jk}\}$, between *pairs* of objects o_j and o_k; that is, r_{jk} represents the extent to which objects j and k are related in the sense of some binary relation ρ. It is convenient to array the relational values as an $n \times n$ relation matrix $R = [r_{jk}] = [\rho(o_j, o_k)]$. Many functions will convert $X \times X$ to relational data. For example, every metric d on $\mathcal{R}^p \times \mathcal{R}^p$ produces a (dis)-similarity relation matrix $R(X; d)$, as shown in Fig. 2.4, where we take $\rho = d$. If every r_{jk} is in $\{0, 1\}$, then R is a *hard* (or *crisp*) binary relation; if $0 < r_{jk} < 1$ for any j and k, we call R a *fuzzy relation*. Relational data are found in many applications, sometimes hiding in different semantic guises. For example, cognitive maps, influence diagrams, weighted digraphs, and repertory grids can all be put into this general form. Fuzzy models for pattern recognition associated with relational data are fairly well developed, but space will prevent us from saying much more about them here. An excellent general reference on (nonfuzzy) relational algorithms is Sneath and Sokal.[16] We comment briefly below on the use of relational data in fuzzy clustering and computational neural networks.

2.2.3 Feature Analysis

We refer to methods that are used to explore and improve "raw" data, i.e., the data that are nominated and collected during process description. With few exceptions, this problem area assumes object data. *Preprocessing* includes operations such as scaling, normalization, smoothing, and various other cleanup techniques. Fuzzy models are sometimes used for these purposes, especially in, e.g., fields such as image processing, where problems such as blurring, noise, low contrast, and occlusion can all be dealt with in a variety of ways. The utility of data for more complex downstream processing tasks such as clustering and classifier design is clearly affected by preprocessing operations, so this step in the design of a PRS is always important and should be given careful attention.

2.2.4 Feature Extraction

Techniques for object data can be cast in a single framework as follows. Any function f_E: $\Re^p \to \Re^q$ where $p \geq q$ is a *feature extractor* when applied to X. The new features are the image of X under f_E, say, $Y = f_E[X]$. Feature *selection*—choosing subsets of the original measured features—is done by taking f_E to be a projection onto some coordinate subspace of $\Re^p$. The basic idea is that feature space may be compressed by eliminating via selection or transformation redundant (dependent) and unimportant (for the problem at hand) features. If $p \gg q$, the time and space complexity of algorithms that use the transformed data is obviously reduced in the process. Representative papers on fuzzy feature analysis include Ref. 26, which applies the fuzzy c-means clustering algorithm to select an optimum feature subset from a set of 11 binary features representing six stomach diseases. In Ref. 27, indices of fuzziness such as fuzzy entropy are used to define an index for feature evaluation in terms of interset and intraset ambiguities (analogous to the concepts of interset and intraset distances, respectively, in classic pattern recognition). Possibility theory has also been considered for feature selection; cf. Ref. 28.

2.2.5 2-D Displays

The visual representation of p-dimensional data enables exploration of possible structure in the measured data. What can one learn from a 2-D display of multidimensional data? According to Tukey,[29] displays of this type are useful because "It is important to learn what you *can do* before you learn to measure how *well* you seem to have *done* it." Put simply, 2-D displays and diagrams afford a means for "looking" at data to see what they *seem* to say as opposed to *confirming* from and with them what we hold to be true about the process under study. This branch of data analysis seems a bit removed from the mainstream of pattern recognition. However, 2-D displays of multidimensional data enable us to cast hypotheses, postulate models, reject theories—in short, to *get ideas* about the data; how they seem to be structured, what cannot be true, etc. For example, Kohonen feature maps, discussed in the section on computational neural networks, are used for this purpose. Reference 30 is a typical application of the use of fuzzy models in the context of visualization of multidimensional data.

2.2.6 Label Vectors

To characterize solution spaces for clustering and classifier design, we define three label vector sets in $\Re^c$. Let c denote the number of clusters, $1 < c < n$, and set

$$N_{fcu} = \{y \in \mathscr{R}^c \mid y_k \in [0, 1] \; \forall k\} = \text{(unconstrained) labels} \qquad (2.7a)$$

$$N_{fc} = \{y \in N_{fcu} \mid \Sigma y_k = 1\} = \text{(constrained) labels} \qquad (2.7b)$$

$$N_c = \{y \in N_{fc} \mid y_k \in \{0, 1\} \; \forall k\} = \text{hard labels for c classes} \qquad (2.7c)$$

Here N_c is the canonical (unit vector) basis of euclidean c-space; N_{fc}, a piece of a hyperplane, is its convex hull; and N_{fcu} is the unit hypercube in $\mathscr{R}^c$. Figure 2.5 depicts these sets for $c = 3$. For example, the vector $\mathbf{y} = (0.1, 0.6, 0.3)^T$ is a typical constrained label vector; its entries lie between 0 and 1 and sum to 1. The interpretation of $\mathbf{y}$ depends upon its origin; e.g., if $\mathbf{y}$ is generated by, say, the fuzzy c-means clustering method, then we call $\mathbf{y}$ a fuzzy label. On the other hand, if $\mathbf{y}$ came from a method such as maximum likelihood estimation in mixture decomposition, then $\mathbf{y}$ would be a probabilistic label. The cube $N_{fcu} = [0, 1]^3$ is called *unconstrained* label vector space; vectors such as $\mathbf{z} = (0.7, 0.2, 0.7)^T$ have each entry between 0 and 1 but are otherwise unrestricted. Again, the interpretation of the values in $\mathbf{z}$ depends upon its origin; the values can be either probabilistic or fuzzy.

Although many readers will be unfamiliar with the concept of labeled (training) data themselves being probabilistic or fuzzy, it is clear that one might possess such data. A topic of great current interest in research at the interface of fuzzy models and computational neural networks is the use of fuzzily labeled training data for classifier nets. We return to this notion in the section on computational neural networks.

2.2.7 Cluster Analysis

Given any finite set of unlabeled data, the problem of *clustering* in X is to assign to the objects (hard *or* fuzzy *or* probabilistic) labels that identify "natural subgroups" in X. This problem is sometimes called *unsupervised learning* (or *self-organization*), the word *learning* here referring to learning the correct labels for "good" subgroups. Good introductions to many clustering algorithms are found in Refs. 31 and 32.

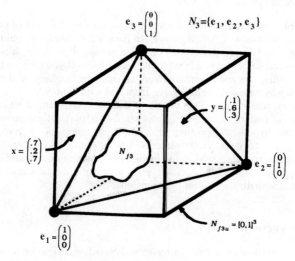

FIGURE 2.5 Hard, fuzzy, and probabilistic label vectors (for $c = 3$ classes)

Let c be an integer, $1 < c < n$, and let $X = \{\mathbf{x}_1, \mathbf{x}_2, \ldots, \mathbf{x}_n\}$ denote a set of n *unlabeled* feature vectors in $\mathfrak{R}^p$. Label vectors assigned to each object in a set of data can be conveniently arrayed as $c \times n$, *c-partitions* of X, characterized as sets of cn values $\{u_{ik}\}$ satisfying some of or all the following conditions:

$$0 \le u_{ik} \le 1 \qquad \forall i, k \tag{2.8a}$$

$$0 < \Sigma u_{ik} < n \qquad \forall i \tag{2.8b}$$

$$\Sigma u_{ik} = 1 \qquad \forall k \tag{2.8c}$$

Using Eqs. (2.8) with the values $\{u_{ik}\}$ arrayed as a $c \times n$ matrix $U = [u_{ik}]$, we define

$$M_{fcnu} = \{U \in \mathfrak{R}^{cn} \mid u_{ik} \text{ satisfies } (2.8a) \text{ and } (2.8b) \ \forall i, k\} \tag{2.9a}$$

$$M_{fcn} = \{U \in M_{fcnu} \mid u_{ik} \text{ satisfies } (2.8c) \ \forall i \text{ and } k\} \tag{2.9b}$$

$$M_{cn} = \{U \in M_{fcn} \mid u_{ik} = 0 \text{ or } 1, \ \forall i \text{ and } k\} \tag{2.9c}$$

Equations (2.9a), (2.9b), and (2.9c) define, respectively, the sets of unconstrained fuzzy, constrained fuzzy[33] or probabilistic, and crisp *c-partitions of X*. We represent clustering algorithms as $\mathcal{A} : X \to M_{fcnu}$. Each column of U in M_{fcnu} (M_{fcn}, M_{cn}) is a label vector from N_{fcu} (N_{fc}, N_c). The reason these matrices are called *partitions* follows from the interpretation of u_{ik} as the *membership* of $\mathbf{x}_k$ in the ith partitioning subset (cluster) of X. Models M_{fcnu} and M_{fcn} can be more realistic physical models than M_{cn}, for it is common experience that the boundaries between many classes of real objects (e.g., tissue types in magnetic resonance images) are in fact badly delineated (i.e., really fuzzy), so M_{fcn} provides a richer means of representing and manipulating data that have such structures. We give an example to illustrate hard and fuzzy *c-partitions* of X. Let $X = \{\mathbf{x}_1, \mathbf{x}_2, \mathbf{x}_3\} = \{\text{peach, plum, nectarine}\}$, and let $c = 2$. Typical 2-partitions of these three objects are shown in Table 2.1.

The nectarine, $\mathbf{x}_3$, is shown as the rightmost column of each partition, and in the hard case it must be (erroneously) given full membership in one of the two crisp subsets partitioning these data; in U_1, $\mathbf{x}_3$ is labeled *plum*. Fuzzy partitions enable algorithms to (sometimes!) avoid such mistakes. The final column of the first fuzzy partition in Table 2.1 allocates most (0.6) of the membership of $\mathbf{x}_3$ to the plum class but also assigns a lesser membership of 0.4 to $\mathbf{x}_3$ as a peach. The last partition in Table 2.1 illustrates an unconstrained set of membership assignments for the objects in each class. Columns like the one for the nectarine in the two fuzzy partitions serve a useful purpose—weak memberships in several classes are a signal to take a second look. Hard partitions of data cannot suggest this. In the present case, the nectarine is a *hybrid* of peaches and plums, and the memberships shown for it in the rightmost column of either fuzzy partition seem more plausible *physically* than crisp assignment of $\mathbf{x}_3$ to an incorrect class. It is appropriate to note that statistical clustering algorithms, e.g., unsupervised learning with maximum likelihood, also produce solutions in M_{fcn}. Algorithms that yield clusters in unconstrained label space M_{fcnu} are fairly new; see Ref. 34 for a recent study.

TABLE 2.1 Typical 2-Partitions of $X = \{\mathbf{x}_1, \mathbf{x}_2, \mathbf{x}_3\} = \{\text{Peach, Plum, Nectarine}\}$

Object	Hard $U_1 \in M_{23}$			Fuzzy $U_2 \in M_{f23}$			Fuzzy $U_3 \in M_{f23u}$			
	$\mathbf{x}_1$	$\mathbf{x}_2$	$\mathbf{x}_3$	$\mathbf{x}_1$	$\mathbf{x}_2$	$\mathbf{x}_3$	$\mathbf{x}_1$	$\mathbf{x}_2$	$\mathbf{x}_3$	
Peaches	1	0	0	0.9	0.2	0.4	0.9	0.5	0.5	(2.10)
Plums	0	1	1	0.1	0.8	0.6	0.6	0.8	0.7	

2.2.8 Cluster Validity

Let $\mathcal{A} : X \to M_{fcnu}$ be any hard or fuzzy clustering algorithm, and let $\mathcal{P} = \{ U_i \mid 1 \le i \le N \}$ denote N different "optimal" partitions of a fixed data set X. We regard $\mathcal{P}$ as a set of candidate partitions of X that may arise as a result of:

1. Applying different algorithms $\{ \mathcal{A}_j \}$ with fixed parameters to X
2. Clustering X with one algorithm $\mathcal{A}_j$ at various values of its parameters
3. Clustering X over different algorithmic parameters of various $\mathcal{A}_j$'s.

It should be clear that different U_is in $\mathcal{P}$ may in fact be optimal with respect to different *questions* about the structure in X. Here, we focus on candidates in $\mathcal{P}$ generated by different measures of *mathematical* optimality. Thus, cluster validity is the study (selection or rejection) of which $U_i \in \mathcal{P}$ best "explains" the (unknown) structure in X for a fixed question. If $U_i \in M_{cn}$ is *hard*, it defines *real* subsets in X, and various validity criteria such as cluster volume and separability can be measured in an attempt to rank U_i. Statistical hypotheses concerning population densities can be advanced and tested.[15] We call measures of validity on M_{cn} *direct* validity measures because they assess clusters by examining real subsets of the data. If $U_i \in M_{fcnu}$ is fuzzy (or probabilistic), there are two approaches to validity assessment. First, direct measures can be applied to any *defuzzification or deprobabilization* of U_i. For example, we can use the maximum membership (MM) conversion of fuzzy partitions to hard ones:

$$u_{MM_{ik}} = \left\{ \begin{array}{ll} 1 & u_{ik} \ge u_{sk}, \; 1 \le s \le c, \, s \ne i \\ 0 & \text{otherwise} \end{array} \right\} \tag{2.11}$$

As we shall see later, the same computation produces crisp labels from probabilistic clusters as well. And U_{MM} is always in M_{cn} (is hard), so direct validation approaches such as those in Ref. 32 can be used.

Another scheme is to attempt validation by computing some "measure of uncertainty" of each $U_i \in M_{fcnu}$. In this category, e.g., are measures such as partition entropy, partition norm, and the uniform data functional.[35] Because such schemes assess data substructures indirectly, they are *indirect* validity methods. Yet a third way to assess validity is by assigning each $U_i \in \mathcal{P}$ some common performance task (e.g., using its labels as the basis of a classifier design, so that empirical error rates on labeled data can be used to compare the efficacy of each U_i at the same well-defined task). This is called *performance-based validity* and is applicable to $U_i \in \mathcal{P}$ that is hard OR fuzzy/OR probabilistic, with or without defuzzification.[36]

So far, we have assumed that the set $\mathcal{P}$ is generated by different runs of various algorithms. Applying direct, indirect, or performance-based validity criteria to each partition in $\mathcal{P}$ is called *static* cluster validity. With the recent trend toward completely unsupervised ("adaptive") algorithms, several investigators have proposed the integration of validity assessment criteria into the clustering scheme itself so that $\mathcal{P}$ is not generated at all—rather, the algorithm generates U_i, assesses it, and then adjusts (or simply tries other) parameters in an attempt to find a "most valid" U for X. This approach is called *dynamic* cluster validity. References 37 to 41 provide entry points into the literature of fuzzy cluster validity.

Many algorithms find *hard clusters* in unlabeled data. The c-means algorithms and ISODATA clustering methods are probably the most widely used. The c-means algorithms assume that c is known, whereas c is unknown in the case of ISODATA algorithms. Hard c-means algorithm is based upon minimization of the sum-of-squared-errors function, which many authors refer to as J_1:

$$J_1(U, \mathbf{v}: X) = \sum_{k=1}^{n} \sum_{i=1}^{c} u_{ik} \| \mathbf{x}_k - \mathbf{v}_i \|^2 \tag{2.12}$$

where $\mathbf{v} = (\mathbf{v}_1, \mathbf{v}_2, \ldots, \mathbf{v}_c)$ is a vector of (unknown) cluster centers (weights or proto-types), $\mathbf{v}_i \in \mathcal{R}^p$ for $1 \le i \le c$, $U \in M_{cn}$ is a hard or conventional c-partition of X, and $\| * \|$ is the Euclidean norm on $\mathcal{R}^p$. Optimal partitions U^* of X are taken from pairs $(U^*, \mathbf{v}^*)$ that are *local minimizers* of J_1, which was popularized as part of the ISODATA algorithm by Ball and Hall.[42] Generalizations of J_1 have been introduced by many authors, beginning with Dunn.[43] Most of these can be written in the form

$$J_m(U, \mathbf{v}: X) = \sum_{k=1}^{n} \sum_{i=1}^{c} (u_{ik})^m D_{ikA} \tag{2.13}$$

where

$$m \in [1, \infty) = \text{weight exponent on each fuzzy membership} \tag{2.14a}$$

$$U \in M_{fcn} = \text{constrained fuzzy } c\text{-partition of } X \tag{2.14b}$$

$$\mathbf{v} = (\mathbf{v}_1, \mathbf{v}_2, \ldots, \mathbf{v}_c) = c \text{ vector prototypes in } \mathcal{R}^P \tag{2.14c}$$

$$A = \text{any positive definite } (s \times s) \text{ matrix} \tag{2.14d}$$

$$D_{ikA} = \| \mathbf{x}_k - \mathbf{v}_i \|_A = \sqrt{(\mathbf{x}_k - \mathbf{v}_i)^T A (\mathbf{x}_k - \mathbf{v}_i)} \tag{2.14e}$$

Equation (2.13) reduces to (2.12) when $m = 1$ and/or $U \in M_{cn}$ with $A = I$, the $p \times p$ identity. For point prototypes, two families of measures for D_{ik} are well known: the inner product norms in (2.14e) and the Minkowski norms.[44] Necessary conditions for minimization of J_m with point prototypes $(\mathbf{v}_1, \mathbf{v}_2, \ldots, \mathbf{v}_c)$ and inner product norms are well known for $m \ge 1$; they provide a basis for the hard/fuzzy c-means (HCM/FCM) algorithms.

Hard/Fuzzy c-Means (HCM/FCM) Theorems.[19] Let X have at least $c < n$ distinct points, $\mathbf{I} = \{1, 2, \ldots, c\}$; and for $k = 1$ to n, let $\mathbf{I}_k = \{i \in \mathbf{I} \mid D_{ik} = 0, 1 \le i \le c\}$. Then $(U, \mathbf{v}) \in M_{fcn} \times \mathcal{R}^{cp}$ may be a critical point for J_m only if

$$m > 1: \quad \mathbf{I}_j = \phi \Rightarrow u_{ik} = \left[\sum_{j=1}^{c} \left(\frac{\| \mathbf{x}_k - \mathbf{v}_i \|_A}{\| \mathbf{x}_k - \mathbf{v}_j \|_A} \right)^{2/m-1} \right]^{-1} \quad 1 \le i \le c; 1 \le k < n \tag{2.15a.1}$$

or if

$$m > 1: \quad \mathbf{I}_j \ne \phi \Rightarrow u_{ik} = 0 \quad \forall i \in (\mathbf{I} - \mathbf{I}_j) \quad \text{and arbitrarily}, \sum_{s \in \mathbf{I}_j} u_{sk} = 1 \tag{2.15a.2}$$

$$m = 1: \quad u_{ik} = \begin{cases} 1 & \| \mathbf{x}_k - \mathbf{v}_i \|_A < \| \mathbf{x}_k - \mathbf{v}_j \|_A, \quad j = 1, \ldots, c; j \ne i \\ 0 & \text{otherwise} \end{cases} \quad 1 \le i \le c; 1 \le k < n \tag{2.15b}$$

$$m \ge 1: \quad \mathbf{v}_i = \frac{\displaystyle\sum_{k=1}^{n} u_{ik}^m \mathbf{x}_k}{\displaystyle\sum_{k=1}^{n} u_{ik}^m} \quad \text{for } i = 1, 2, \ldots, c \tag{2.16}$$

Note especially that (2.15b) assigns crisp memberships to the points in each cluster, using the nearest prototype or winner-take-all rule. This is important in relating c-means to learning vector quantization. Looping through (2.15) and (2.16) is the basis of iterative optimization of J_m. Briefly, we specify the FCM/HCM algorithms.[19]

1. Given unlabeled data set $X = \{\mathbf{x}_1, \mathbf{x}_2, \ldots, \mathbf{x}_n\}$, fix c, T, $\|\|\|_A$, and $\varepsilon > 0$.
2. Initialize $U_0 \in M_{fcn}$. Choose $m \geq 1$. Compute weight vectors $\{\mathbf{v}_{i,t}\}$, using (2.16).
3. For $t = 1, 2, \ldots, T$:
   a. Compute all cn memberships $\{u_{ik,t}\}$: (2.15b) for HCM or (2.15a) for FCM.
   b. Update all c weight vectors $\{\mathbf{v}_{i,t}\} \to \{\mathbf{v}_{i,t+1}\}$ with (2.16).
4. Compute $E_t = \|\mathbf{v}_{t+1} - \mathbf{v}_t\| = \Sigma_{i=1}^c \|\mathbf{v}_{i,t+1} - \mathbf{v}_{i,t}\|$.
5. If $E_t \leq \varepsilon$, stop; else, next t.

This procedure converges q-linearly from any initialization to a local minimum or saddle point (local maxima are impossible) of J_m.[45,46] Gustafson and Kessel made one of the most important advances in FCM techniques by introducing variable-weight matrices.[47] This effort has continued to the present, culminating in recent work by Krisnapuram et al.[48] and Dave,[49] who developed a number of algorithms that use *hyperquadric shells* for the fitting prototypes. These schemes find and represent clusters in data (e.g., concentric and intersecting rings in the plane) that have confounded conventional approaches for many years. Fuzzy clustering is well represented in the literature; Refs. 50 to 74 provide a nice cross section of papers on theory and rather diverse application areas.

Numerical relational data can also be the basis for cluster analysis. This branch of pattern recognition finds many adherents, e.g., in fields such as numerical taxonomy (cf. Ref. 16). In this case, clustering of objects is accomplished implicitly by clustering groups of indices in the relational data matrix. Clustering numerical relational data with fuzzy models is less well studied than clustering of object data, perhaps because of the fact that sensors produce object data, and most fielded systems are at least partially dependent upon inputs from sensors. The solution space for relational clustering is still M_{fcnu}, and our remarks above about fuzzy partitions of the data are equally applicable in this case. Methods in this class are in general decompositional or constructive, and most stem from Zadeh's original work on fuzzy similarity relations,[75] which led other authors into studies of notions such as fuzzy transitivity and families of T and co-T norms for generalized unions and intersections of fuzzy sets. Representative articles for fuzzy relational clustering include Refs. 50, 51, and 76 to 81.

2.2.9 Classifier Design

A more ambitious, difficult, and potentially useful computational problem than clustering, *classifier design* refers to finding a (hard or fuzzy or probabilistic) partition of $\mathfrak{R}^p$ itself. The difference between clustering and classification is that clustering algorithms label given data sets $X \in \mathfrak{R}^p$, whereas a classifier is capable, once it is defined, of labeling *every* data point in the entire space $\mathfrak{R}^p$. Classifiers are usually (but not always!) designed with labeled data, in which case we sometimes refer to this problem as *supervised learning*. In this context, we are "learning" (the parameters of) a classifier function $\mathbf{D}$. In either case, the partitioning decision functions may be computationally *explicit* (e.g., discriminant functions, nearest prototype rules) or *implicit* (e.g., multilayered Perceptrons, k-nearest neighbor rules). Both kinds of methods will be reviewed in sections to follow.

We define a *classifier* on $\mathfrak{R}^p$ as any function $\mathbf{D}$ imaged in N_{fcu}; that is, classifiers are a special kind of vector field, which we shall denote as $\mathbf{D} : \mathfrak{R}^p \mapsto N_{fcu}$. Thus, the value of $\mathbf{D}$ at any $\mathbf{z} \in \mathfrak{R}^p$, $y = \mathbf{D}(\mathbf{z})$ is a label vector for $\mathbf{z}$ in N_{fcu}. And $\mathbf{D}$ is a *crisp* (or hard, or conventional) *classifier* if and only if the image of $\mathfrak{R}^p$ under $\mathbf{D}$ is N_c [that is, $\mathbf{D}(\mathbf{z}) = \mathbf{e}_i$

for some crisp vertex of N_{fc}]; otherwise, the classifier is fuzzy (or, in a different context, probabilistic).

In supervised classifier design, a labeled data set X is usually partitioned into a training or *design set* X_d with a hard (or fuzzy) *label matrix* U_d whose kth column exhibits, via the values $\{u_{d,ik}\}$, the memberships of $\mathbf{x}_k \in X_d$ in each of the c classes, for $k = 1$ to n_d, and a *test set* X_t, this latter set being the original set X with X_d removed. Each column of the label matrix is a label vector in N_{fcu}. Most methods covered in this chapter use crisp label matrices (every column of U_d is a vertex $\mathbf{e}_i$, as in Fig. 2.5); however, many of these methods can be adapted to use fuzzy label vectors for training, and methods based upon this more general technique are being investigated by many researchers at this time. *Testing* a classifier $\mathbf{D}$ designed or trained with X_d means to submit X_t to $\mathbf{D}$ and count mistakes (assuming hard labels for the points in X_t). This yields the apparent error rate $E_{\mathbf{D}}$ for $\mathbf{D}$; usually $E_{\mathbf{D}}$ is the performance index by which $\mathbf{D}$ is judged. Good practice includes at least *cross training*, i.e., training with X_d followed by testing with X_t, and then reversing the roles of X_d and X_t (this assumes that the cardinalities of X_d and X_t make this sensible).

Readers should distinguish carefully between input data having fuzzy labels, outputs of classifiers and clustering algorithms being fuzzy labels, and fuzzy or probabilistic models that produce hard output labels. For example, we can use fuzzy c-means to produce a set of c prototype vectors $V = \{\mathbf{v}_k\}$ from an unlabeled (or labeled) input data set X in $\mathfrak{R}^p$. Once the prototypes are found, we can use them to define a hard nearest prototype $1 - NP$ classifier in the usual way; i.e., we use the prototypes $\{\mathbf{v}_k\}$ to define $\mathbf{D}_{NP,V}$ as follows.

Crisp Nearest Prototype 1 – NP Classifier. Given prototypes $V = \{\mathbf{v}_k \mid 1 \le k \le c\}$ and $\mathbf{z} \in \mathfrak{R}^p$:

$$\text{Decide} \qquad \mathbf{z} \in i \Leftrightarrow D_{NP,V}(\mathbf{z}) = \mathbf{e}_i \Leftrightarrow \| \mathbf{z} - \mathbf{v}_i \| \le \| \mathbf{z} - \mathbf{v}_j \| \qquad 1 \le j \le c \quad (2.17)$$

Note that (2.17) operationalizes (2.15*b*) as a *classifier:* The crisp label assignment strategy necessary to find local extrema for J_1 for n unlabeled points is generalized, with any set of prototypes, to apply to all $\mathfrak{R}^p$. Equation (2.17) defines a hard classifier, even though its parameters may come from a fuzzy algorithm. It would be careless to call $\mathbf{D}_{NP,V}$ a fuzzy classifier if $\{\mathbf{v}_k\}$ came from FCM because (2.17) is a crisp classifier that can be implemented, and has the same geometric structure, using prototypes $\{\mathbf{v}_k\}$ from *any* algorithm that produces them. For example, $\{\mathbf{v}_k\}$ can be the weight vectors attached to the nodes in the competitive layer of a Kohonen clustering network (cf. the section on computational neural networks); or they may be estimates of c assumed mean vectors $\{\mu_k\}$ obtained by applying, e.g., unsupervised maximum likelihood estimation from statistical mixture theory to unlabeled data; or they may be centroids of crisply labeled data, and so on. While there is a certain amount of semantic hair-splitting in drawing attention to this fact, we feel it is worth pointing out because fielded pattern recognition systems inevitably require hard labels for objects being classified. So one must, at some point in any design that uses the idea of fuzzy sets or probability, reconcile this need with the model being used. Most fuzzy classifiers eventually 'defuzzify" fuzzy label vectors (if this is what the classifier produces), perhaps—but not necessarily—using the strategy in (2.11). Thus, "fuzzy classifier design" almost always means arriving at a hard classifier such as (2.17) but using the idea of fuzziness somewhere upstream. Readers may wonder, given the ultimate necessity for hard labels, whether there is any advantage to using fuzzy techniques at all. References 50 to 74 and 82 to 89 show, through computational examples, that incorporation of fuzzy ideas into the model leading to a hard classifier design does, indeed (sometimes!), yield better hard classifiers than simply looking for a hard design to begin with. This can again be attributed to the idea of embedding; we find a better solution to a crisp problem by looking in a larger space at first, which has different (usually fewer) constraints and therefore allows the algorithm more freedom to avoid errors forced by restriction to hard answers.

2.3 STATISTICAL PATTERN RECOGNITION: THE MIXTURE MODEL

Several widely known classifiers are based upon the mixture model (or, as we shall see, are related to it asymptotically). A comprehensive introduction to this area of classifier design can be found in Ref. 17. More generally Refs. 13 to 15 contain good introductions to many statistical pattern recognition schemes. Statistical pattern recognition is based upon the following assumptions: X is assumed to be drawn from a mixed population of c p-variate statistical distributions, say, with random vector variables $\{\mathbf{X}_i\}$, which have *prior probabilities* $\{\pi_i\}$ and class-conditional PDFs $\{g(\mathbf{x} \mid i)\}$. The convex combination

$$f(\mathbf{x}) = \sum_{i=1}^{c} \pi_i g(\mathbf{x} \mid i) \qquad (2.18)$$

is itself a PDF whose distribution is called a *mixture* of the components $\{\pi_i g(\mathbf{x} \mid i)\}$. Let the *posteriori probability* that, given $\mathbf{x}$, $\mathbf{x}$ came from class i be denoted by $\pi(i \mid x)$. Bayes' rule relates the elements of (2.18) to the probabilities $\{\pi(i \mid \mathbf{x})\}$ as follows:

$$\pi(i \mid \mathbf{x}) = \frac{\pi_i g(\mathbf{x} \mid i)}{f(\mathbf{x})} \qquad (2.19)$$

For a finite sample $X = \{\mathbf{x}_1, \mathbf{x}_2, \ldots, \mathbf{x}_n\}$ drawn i.i.d. from mixture f, the $c \times n$ matrix $P = [p(i \mid \mathbf{x}_k)] = [p_{ik}]$ of sample posterior probabilities satisfies constraints (2.9b); thus, $P \in M_{fcn}$, the space of fuzzy c-partitions of X. In the present context, π_{ik} is indeed a probability and plays much the same role in statistical PR that the fuzzy membership value u_{ik} plays in fuzzy PR. If the elements of the right side of (2.19) are known, we may compute, at any $\mathbf{z} \in \mathcal{R}^p$, the posterior probability vector $\pi(* \mid \mathbf{z}) = (\pi(1 \mid \mathbf{z}), \pi(2 \mid \mathbf{z}), \ldots, \pi(c \mid \mathbf{z}))^T$. This vector lies in the set N_{fc} shown in Fig. 2.5; it is a *probabilistic* label vector. Using the left side of (2.19), we define the statistical Bayes classifier $\mathbf{D}_{pb} : \mathcal{R}^p \mapsto N_{fc}$ as follows:

$$\mathbf{D}_{pb}(\mathbf{z}) = \pi(* \mid \mathbf{z}) \qquad (2.20)$$

where $\mathbf{D}_{pb}$ is a *probabilistic* classifier. For example, the vector $\mathbf{y} = \mathbf{D}_{pb}(\mathbf{z}) = (0.1, 0.6, 0.3)^T$ in Fig. 2.5 might be such a vector derived from (2.20) for some $\mathbf{z} \in \mathcal{R}^p$. Just as fuzzy labels are usually "defuzzified" (reduced to a crisp label, one of the vertices $\mathbf{e}_i$ displayed in Fig. 2.5) to render a crisp or hard decision about $\mathbf{z}$, probabilistic labels need to be converted to hard labels. Bayes' decision rule (BDR) is used to convert the probabilistic classifier at (2.20) into a crisp one, using the simple and intuitively plausible rationale that, given $\mathbf{z}$, we should assign $\mathbf{z}$ to the class of *maximum posterior probability*. In the form of a crisp classifier function, we write $\mathbf{D}_b : \mathcal{R}^p \mapsto N_c$ as follows:

$$\mathbf{D}_b(\mathbf{z}) = \mathbf{e}_i \Leftrightarrow \pi(i \mid \mathbf{z}) = \max_j \{\pi(j \mid \mathbf{z})\} \qquad (2.21)$$

where $\mathbf{D}_b$ is a *crisp* classifier. More directly, we can state BDR as follows:

BDR: Decide $\mathbf{z} \in$ class $i \Leftrightarrow \pi(i \mid \mathbf{z}) \geq \pi(j \mid \mathbf{z})$ for $j \neq i$ $\qquad (2.22)$

For example, if $\mathbf{y} = \mathbf{D}_{pb}(\mathbf{z}) = (0.4, 0.35, 0.25)$ is a posterior probability vector, we find by using (2.21) or (2.22) that the crisp label assigned to $\mathbf{z}$ is class 1 because the maximum (0.4) occurs in the first component of $\mathbf{y}$ [note this is *exactly* the same strategy as (2.11) and (2.17), used here for a different reason]. This rule minimizes the expected total misclassification error (or *error rate*) of *any* classifier $\mathbf{D} : \mathfrak{R}^p \mapsto N_{fc}$ under the assumptions implicit in (2.18) to (2.22) about mixtures, provided the cost of misclassification is equal for all wrong decisions and there is no cost for correct decisions (the 0-1 loss matrix assumption). In this case, $\mathbf{D}_b$ is often called the *optimal Bayes classifier.* Figure 2.6 may help readers understand the assumptions and geometry of the mixture model. Shown is a mixture of $c = 2$ univariate ($p = 1$) normal distributions with prior probabilities $\{\pi_i\}$ and class conditional densities $g(x \mid i) = n\,(\mu_i, \sigma_i) = \exp - [(x - \mu_i)/\sigma_i)]^2/(\sigma_i \sqrt{2\pi})$. The optimal Bayes classifier is defined by the point x^*; BDR is decide $z \in$ class 1 if and only if $z \le x^*$ and otherwise decide $z \in$ class 2. Regions D_{b1} and D_{b2} are called the *Bayes decision regions* of this classifier, and the (minimum) Bayes error rate E_b is the sum of the two areas shown in Fig. 2.6 (integrations to $\pm\infty$): $E_b = A_1 + A_2$. To see this, note that moving the decision boundary from x^* to, say, x, as in Fig. 2.6, results in a positive increase in the probability of error by the amount δA.

When we report that some classifier $\mathbf{D}$ has achieved an apparent error rate E_D on a set X_t of labeled test data, we often use E_b as a point of (psychological) reference for the statement—even if the mixture assumptions are not explicit in the construction of $\mathbf{D}$—because E_b is minimal with respect to the integrations that define it over the set of *all* classifier functions $\mathbf{D} : \mathfrak{R}^p \to N_{fc}$.

Parametric bayesian design begins by assuming functional forms for the densities $\{g(\mathbf{x} \mid i)\}$ in the mixture model and leads to the problem of parametric estimation of the Bayes classifier. We indicate this by attaching an unknown parameter vector θ_i to each PDF in the mixture, writing

$$f(\mathbf{x}: \theta) = \sum_{i=1}^{c} \pi_i g(\mathbf{x} \mid i; \theta_i) \tag{2.23}$$

The mixture density now depends upon a *parameter vector* $\theta = (\theta_1, \theta_2, \ldots, \theta_c)$. There are many schemes available for estimation of the $\{\theta_i\}$ using either labeled or unlabeled data. One of the most popular ways to do this is with the *maximum likelihood estimation*

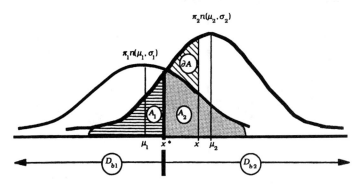

FIGURE 2.6   The mixture $f(x) = \pi_1 n(\mu_1, \sigma_1) + \pi_2 n(\mu_2, \sigma_2)$: Bayes' error $= E_B = A_1 + A_2$.

(MLE). Given a data set X, we form the likelihood function of the samples and try to maximize it. If the $\{g(\mathbf{z} \mid i)\}$ are sufficiently smooth, this can be attempted with constrained optimization methods.[17] In particular, if each of the component densities is p-variate *normal*, $g(\mathbf{x} \mid i) = n(\mu_i, \Sigma_i)$, where μ_i is the mean vector and Σ_i is the covariance matrix for class i, then the parameter vector for each class is $\theta_i = (\pi_i, \mu_i, \Sigma_i)$. In this special case, necessary conditions for the MLE of the parameter vectors in (2.23) can be derived and lead to two cases, depending upon whether the data are labeled or not.

If the data are *labeled*, the sample posterior probability matrix $P = [p_{ik}] = [p(i \mid \mathbf{x}_k)]$ $= U_d$, so the equations for MLE of each $\theta_i = (\pi_i, \mu_i, \Sigma_i)$ are uncoupled across classes and parameters and hence are explicit (noniterative). In this case, we simply take the training data X_{di} for each class, substitute them into the necessary equations, compute MLEs $(p_i, \mathbf{m}_i, S_i)$ of the parameters (π_i, μ_i, Σ_i) of each density, and use the resulting functions as estimators of the right side of (2.19). This yields a parametric estimate of the posterior probability vector (in the parlance of neural network terminology, we have at this point "trained" the classifier $\mathbf{D}_{bS}$ by finding its parameters, where bS stands here for the Bayes supervised data case). We shall refer to this design as the *supervised ML (SML)* classifier.

SML is called a *parametric* method because we assume some knowledge of the components of the mixture and then use labeled data and a principle of statistical inference such as ML to estimate the parameters of the functions in (2.19). Another widely used supervised technique is the k-nearest neighbor (k-NN) rule. This is called a *nonparametric* method because the k-NN rule does not require any knowledge of or assumptions about statistical properties of the data.[13] The k-NN rule essentially relies on having a large number of (presumably) correctly labeled samples from each class. Figure 2.7 displays the geometry of this scheme, which can be easily described without recourse to formulas. Basically, all that is needed is to choose k, the *number* of nearest neighbors to find in the neighborhood of any unlabeled vector $\mathbf{z}$, and some measure of distance between pairs of vectors in $\Re^p$, usually Euclidean distance $d(\mathbf{z}, \mathbf{x}_i) = \|\mathbf{z} - \mathbf{x}_i\| = \sqrt{(\mathbf{z} - \mathbf{x}_i)^T(\mathbf{z} - \mathbf{x}_i)}$. One must also choose a voting scheme, which is often to accept a simple majority of the votes for any class represented by points in the k-NN neighborhood. In Fig. 2.7, with $k = 6$ nearest neighbors having $c = 3$ class labels, the point $\mathbf{z}$ will be labeled class 2 because 3 of its nearest 6 neighbors have this crisp label.

To understand the relationship between this approach to classification and the SML design, we formalize the (hard or fuzzy) k-NN rule as follows for a simple majority voting case.[90]

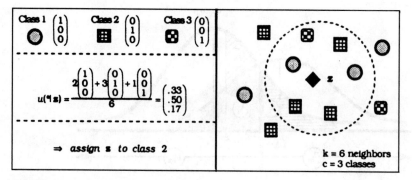

FIGURE 2.7 Geometric idea of the crisp k-NN rule classifier.

1. Store training data X_d with their hard or fuzzy c-partition U_d.
2. Choose k = number of neighbors to find.
3. Choose d: $\Re^p \times \Re^p \mapsto \Re^+$ any metric (distance measure) on $\Re^p$.
4. For any vector $\mathbf{z} \notin X_d$, using $X_d = \{\mathbf{x}_i\}$, compute and rank-order the distances $d(\mathbf{z}, \mathbf{x}_i)$ as $\{d_1 \leq d_2 \leq \cdots d_k \leq d_{k+1} \leq \cdots d_{n_d}\}$. Find the columns in U_D corresponding to the k-nearest neighbor indices $\{1, 2, \ldots, k\}$. Calculate the vector $\mathbf{u}(* \mid \mathbf{z}) = (u(1 \mid \mathbf{z}), u(2 \mid \mathbf{z}), \ldots, u(c \mid \mathbf{z}))^T$ with the NN labels:

$$u(i \mid \mathbf{z}) = \sum_{j=1}^{k} \frac{u_{d,ij}}{k} \qquad \text{for } i = 1, 2, \ldots, c \qquad (2.24)$$

Calculate

$$\mathbf{D}_{NN,k}(\mathbf{z}) = \mathbf{e}_i \Leftrightarrow u(i \mid \mathbf{z}) = \max_j \{u(j \mid z)\} \qquad (2.25)$$

Continue.

We emphasize the difference between $\mathbf{D}_{NN,k}$ and $\mathbf{D}_{NP}$: Nearest *neighbors* are points *in* the training data X_d; nearest *prototypes* are points in $\Re^p$ derived *from* X_d. Note that this procedure is *not* iterative; each unlabeled vector is processed once with this method. The vector $\mathbf{u}(* \mid \mathbf{z})$ is again a crisp or fuzzy label vector (of $\mathbf{z}$) in N_{fc}; Eq. (2.25) defuzzifies this label vector exactly as in Eqs. (2.11), (2.17), (2.21), but again for a different rationale—to yield a crisp assignment for any $\mathbf{z}$ in $\Re^p$. To compare this method to the SML (and subsequently feedforward schemes as well), we let $E_{NN,k}$ denote the expected error rate of the classifier $\mathbf{D}_{NN,k}$. Note that $\mathbf{u}(* \mid \mathbf{z})$ is similar to the posterior probability vector $\pi(* \mid \mathbf{z}) = (\pi(1 \mid \mathbf{z}), \pi(2 \mid \mathbf{z}), \ldots, \pi(c \mid \mathbf{z}))^T$ in that it lies in N_{fc} and thus has exactly the same formal properties as $\pi(* \mid \mathbf{z})$. A famous and remarkable (because the k-NN rule has *no* statistical assumptions whatsoever!) theorem due to Cover and Hart[91] shows that, under suitable restrictions on k and n_d, for crisply labeled training data $E_{NN,k} \mapsto E_b$ and $\|\mathbf{u}(* \mid \mathbf{z}) - \pi(* \mid \mathbf{z})\| \mapsto 0$ as $k, n_d \mapsto \infty$. Thus, the k-NN rule is asymptotically equivalent to Bayes' rule. We shall see below that feedforward neural networks possesses this same property. Although this result is psychologically reassuring, it is unfair to expect the k-NN rule to produce the Bayes error rate on small samples (all real samples are a *lot* smaller than ∞!). On the other hand, the mixture assumptions upon which the Bayes error rate is based may not be valid for the data being processed, so the k-NN rule may in fact produce much better results than SML, for example, on finite data sets of any size.

There are usually three algorithmic parameters associated with the k-NN rule: (1) k itself, (2) the measure of distance, and (3) the method of counting votes. To these, we added another: (4) the types of labels stored. The label vectors used for voting in our example in Fig. 2.7 were crisp. However, (2.24) is valid for fuzzy labels, and the "vote" for each label in this case will, in general, be noninteger. Equation (2.25) accounts for both cases automatically. Jozwik introduced the fuzzy k-NN rule in Ref. 92; see Ref. 93 for further discussion. Reference 94 is an excellent compilation of 51 milestone articles on the k-NN rule and its derivatives.

If the data are *unlabeled,* parametric estimation as described above can still be used as a basis for statistical classifier design. In this case, we have, e.g., *unsupervised ML* (*UML*), and the sample posterior probability matrix $P = [p_{ik}] = [p(i \mid \mathbf{x}_k)]$ is unknown. The equations for the MLE of each θ_i are now coupled across classes and parameters. Applying the technique of Lagrange multipliers to find necessary conditions for maxima of the likelihood function of the samples results in—even for the case of p-variate normal distributions—a large coupled set of nonlinear equations in the unknowns (P, θ). So we must resort to a numerical scheme such as gradient descent or grouped coordinate minimization (cf. Ref. 17) to find approximate solutions to the necessary conditions, using iterative optimization. This method suffers from all the usual problems of iterative schemes (local traps, initialization, numerical convergence, etc.) but usually enables us to compute MLEs of the parameters of each density and again use the resulting functions as estimators in the right side of (2.19). Parametric estimates from UML will be different from the ones obtained with SML and will yield a different classifier $\mathbf{D}_{bU}$ that can be used for labeling any $\mathbf{z} \in \mathcal{R}^p$. Moreover, at the end of the estimation phase, the left-hand side (LHS) of (2.19) yields a (direct) estimate of the posterior probability matrix P, which is a *probabilistic clustering* of the unlabeled data. There have been many studies relating various fuzzy algorithms to mixtures and mixture decompositions; interested readers may consult Refs. 95 to 100 for further details.

2.4 COMPUTATIONAL NEURAL NETWORKS AND FUZZY LOGIC IN PATTERN RECOGNITION

There are two distinct areas of integration between fuzzy pattern recognition and *computational neurallike networks* (CNNs). First, we often use the CNN as a tool for a variety of computational tasks within the larger framework of a preexisting fuzzy model. In this category, e.g., are attempts to build (membership) function representations with CNNs; implementation of fuzzy logic operations such as union (max nets), intersection (min nets), and the extension principle; and derivation of optimal rule sets for fuzzy controllers.

On the other hand, many writers are currently investigating ways and means of building "fuzzy CNNs" by incorporating the notion of fuzziness *into* a CNN framework (as opposed to using the CNN within a fuzzy framework). For example, the target outputs of a classifier net during training can be fuzzy label vectors (points in the interior of the triangle N_{fc}, shown in Fig. 2.5).

In this case, the CNN functions as a fuzzy classifier and is conceptually identical to any other fuzzy classifier function $\mathbf{D}$ imaged in N_{fc}. Operationally, of course, $\mathbf{D}$ is *implicitly* represented by the CNN. Another way to incorporate fuzziness into the standard CNN is by arranging the integrator/transfer functions at each node to perform some sort of fuzzy aggregation (fuzzy union, weighted mean, or intersection) on the numerical information arriving at each node. There are many suggestions in the current literature about making individual neurons fuzzy. Another way to introduce fuzziness into the CNN framework is through the input data themselves, which may be fuzzified in one of several ways.

On the third hand, any authors are engaged in comparisons to and integration of CNN techniques with well-established pattern recognition models. For example, integration of the fuzzy c-means algorithms with Kohonen's learning vector quantization is well underway. Some of these ideas are reviewed in this section. References 101 to 104 are good general texts on CNNs; Refs. 105 to 107 are introductions to CNN models with specific reference to numerical PR; and Refs. 108 and 109 are texts that consider fuzzy models in the context of various pattern recognition problems.

The *biological neural network* (*BNN*) is one of the systems that enables organisms (in particular, humans) to perform pattern recognition tasks; and, in turn, biologic pattern recognition is but one aspect of biologic intelligence. The simplest ideas we have about the components and configuration of a BNN are that it is a network of neurons, each of which has an axon (transmission line), soma (pulse emitter), dendrites (pulse receptors), and synapses (connectors) that offer variable resistance (synaptic weights $\mathbf{w}$) to the conduction of packets of data (electrochemical pulses $\mathbf{x}$) through the network. Our

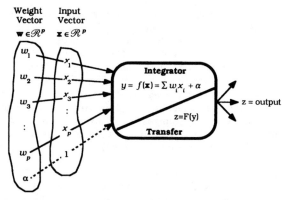

FIGURE 2.8   Mathematical (McCullogh-Pitts) neuron.

assumption is that each neuron does some (numerical) *computing*—this gives rise to the hope that computers can be used to imitate this structure and its performance.

Figure 2.8 reflects current thinking by many about the processing that should be performed at each node in a CNN. Two mathematical functions are usually active. An *integrator function f* first integrates the (synaptic) weights $\mathbf{w} = \{w_j\}$ with the pulse inputs $\mathbf{x} = \{x_j\}$ to the node. The last entry in each column vector in Fig. 2.8 is shown with a dotted line to indicate that the bias α does not mimic a "synaptic weight" in the BNN sense. However, if f is an inner product (typically, the euclidean dot product, as shown in Fig. 2.8), say, $y = f(\mathbf{x}) = \langle \mathbf{w}, \mathbf{x} \rangle = \Sigma\, w_i x_i + \alpha$, then α is an unknown parameter for each node that must be predefined or learned during training. This bias term represents the offset from the origin of $\mathcal{R}^p$ to the hyperplane normal to $\mathbf{w}$ defined by this f. This arrangement is called a *first-order neuron* because f is an affine (linear when $\alpha = 0$) function of its input vector $\mathbf{x}$. "Higher-order" neurons arise when the inner product f is replaced by a more complicated function; e.g., a second-order neuron is realized by replacing f with a quadratic form, say, $\mathbf{x}^t\mathbf{W}\mathbf{x}$, in $\mathbf{x}$. When using a linear integrator function as shown in Fig. 2.8, we can without loss regard the augmented vectors $\mathbf{x} = (x_1, x_2, \dots, x_p, 1)^T$ and $\mathbf{w} = (w_1, w_2, \dots, w_p, \alpha)^T$ as input and weight vectors, respectively, in $\mathcal{R}^{p+1}$. In subsequent figures concerned with nodes in CNNs, we assume the structure of Fig. 2.8 for each node and regard each node as having $p + 1$ unknowns but only p inputs.

The action of f is followed internally by applying a *transfer (or activation) function* F to the value of the integrator function on its inputs. Function F is used to decide if the node should "fire" and, if so, how much "charge," and of what sign, should be broadcast to the network by this node in response to its inputs. The most common choice for F is the logistic or *sigmoidal* function $z = F(y) = 1/(1 + e^{-y})$. The first discussion of the extension of the classical McCulloch-Pitts neuron model to allow fuzzy activity, i.e., a fuzzy neuron, seems to have been the article of Lee and Lee,[110] who showed that, under suitable circumstances, any n-state fuzzy automata can be realized by a network of m fuzzy neurons. Although some of the results given in that article have been subsumed by more recent research, it remains a true landmark in the evolution of the relationships between fuzzy models, pattern recognition, and computational neural networks. For additional reading on fuzzy neurons, readers may consult Refs. 111 and 112.

A third important mathematical operator for the CNN is the *update function U* that converts the current set of weights at every node to a new or updated set. The action of the update (or learning) rule can be written symbolically as $\mathbf{W}_{t+1} = U(\mathbf{W}_t)$, where $\mathbf{W}_t = (\mathbf{w}_{1,t}, \dots, \mathbf{w}_{M,t})$ is the *network weight vector* (the collection of all the individual weight vectors at the *M* nodes in the network) at any time (iteration) *t*. Updating is done during training, whenever the CNN system output(s) does (do) not correspond well enough to the desired target outputs. For pattern recognition, this usually means that the CNN is operating as a classifier, and in this context the CNN is simply a "box," or algorithmic representation of a classifier function, say $\mathbf{D}_{NN}$, imaged in N_{fcu} as described above. Many principles guide the choice of a learning strategy. Different update or learning rules are chosen to match a specific network architecture (layout of nodes and their interconnections); most attempt to optimize some function of the error(s) between the desired and observed outputs of the network. Learning in the context of CNNs is fairly well defined. However, a number of authors have used this term in connection with fuzzy pattern recognition methods that exhibit various forms of *adaptivity;* inquisitive readers may consult Refs. 113 to 117.

The classic one-node Perceptron is based upon the structure of Fig. 2.8.[106] Various schemes such as Widrow's LMS algorithm have been used to identify an "optimal" hyperplane [i.e., the parameters $(\mathbf{w}, \alpha)$] that provides the best fit to the data in some well-specified sense.[13] In pattern recognition, this usually means finding a set of weights that gives the closest reproduction of the correct label vectors for points in the training data X_d; we attempt to "learn" the weights that best replicate the target labels. Keller and Hunt's 1985 article[118] was the first attempt to incorporate the idea of fuzzy membership functions into the classic Perceptron algorithm. First, they combine membership functions of fuzzy clusters in the data into the usual Perceptron criterion function and prove that this fuzzy generalization of the crisp version also converges if the training data are separable. Second, Keller and Hunt described a method for fuzzifying the labeled target data used for training (i.e., they convert the hard label in N_c of each training data vector to a fuzzy label in N_{fc}). This was one of the first articles to suggest incorporation of basic ideas from fuzzy pattern recognition into the domain of classifier design with Perceptrons.

By far the most popular and pervasive CNN is the *feedforward neural network* (*FFNN*) classifier net;[105] Fig. 2.9 illustrates the major components of this architecture. Each feature vector is fed to the input layer, which fans out the values to nodes in one or more hidden layers. Finally, an output layer of nodes produces *c* numbers, shown as $\mathbf{u} \in \mathcal{R}^c$ in Fig. 2.9. Thus, the FFNN is a mapping of $\mathcal{R}^p$ to $\mathcal{R}^c$, that is, NN: $\mathcal{R}^p \mapsto \mathcal{R}^c$.

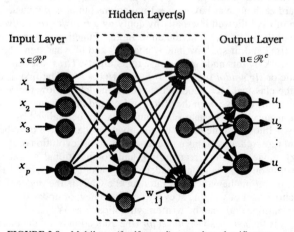

FIGURE 2.9   Multilayer (feedforward) network: a classifier net.

Because of this, representation of fuzzy membership functions $m : \Re^p \mapsto [0, 1]$ is one of the more obvious uses of the CNN in fuzzy models.[119]

An FFNN is a *classifier net* if NN: $\Re^p \mapsto N_{fcu}$. Of course, NN is an *implicit* function—we never have a closed-form expression for the mapping. Each node in the hidden and output layers may be configured much as in Fig. 2.8. Typically, the learning scheme used during training to adjust the weights is some form of *back propagation* of squared errors between the observed and target outputs. Several writers have made connections between classifier nets and statistical pattern recognition.[120,121] None have been as strong or as remarkable as the result of Ruck et al.,[122] who showed that *every* fully connected feedforward CNN driven by the performance goal of minimizing classifier errors on hard, labeled data from c classes (i.e., trained as a crisp classifier with crisp labeled data) is asymptotically equivalent to $\mathbf{D}_b$! This relationship was unknown when Lippman noted that CNNs of this kind were akin to k-NN rule designs.[105] More specifically, let E_{FF} denote the expected error rate of FF classifier $\mathbf{D}_{FF}$ that uses *any* updating scheme whatsoever, and let $\mathbf{D}_{FF}(* \mid \mathbf{z})$ be the crisp label assigned to any $\mathbf{z}$ once the FFNN is trained. Ruck et al. showed that for crisply labeled training data $E_{FF} \mapsto E_b$ and $\|\mathbf{D}_{FF}(* \mid \mathbf{z}) - \mathbf{D}_b(\mathbf{z})\| \mapsto 0$ as $n_d \mapsto \infty$. Thus, the FFNN is asymptotically equivalent to Bayes' rule, just like the k-NN rule. Classifiers $\mathbf{D}_{FF}$ and $\mathbf{D}_{NN,k}$ each have their advantages and limitations. The matter of convergence *rate* is open, and because these approaches are, in the final analysis, data-dependent, this result does *not* say that the (much easier to implement and interpret) k-NN rule is superior to multilayer perceptrons (MLPs). What it does say is that, in the limit, FFNNs will approximate the Bayes posteriors arbitrarily well, just as the k-NN rule does.

The importance of Ruck et al.'s result is threefold. First, it explains why so many published articles on FFNNs report little, if any, difference in error rates between FF designs and the k-NN rule. Second, that article illustrates that CNN architectures often turn out to be different (perhaps better, or more useful, perhaps not) implementations of well-known conventional designs. Third, that article opens the way for extending similar relationships to fuzzy CNNs. It may (undoubtedly *will*) turn out that there is a strong, or at least identifiable, link between statistical pattern recognition and this more general class of fuzzy CNNs. Results of this kind always strengthen our understanding of algorithms and, hence, subsequently improve their utility in fielded systems.

In summary, then, we have three different models to approximate the Bayes classifier $\mathbf{D}_b$:

1. Direct parametric estimates (for example, SML and UML): $\mathbf{D}_{bSML}$ and $\mathbf{D}_{bUML} \approx \mathbf{D}_b$.
2. Indirect, nonparametric k-NN rules: $\mathbf{D}_{NN,k} \approx \mathbf{D}_b$.
3. Implicit estimates via NNs: $\mathbf{D}_{FF} \approx \mathbf{D}_b$.

The point of collecting these methods here is that there are fuzzy generalizations of each of these classifiers. For example, FCM is often used to find initializations or even to replace the ML schemes; there are fuzzy k-NN rules; and there are many fuzzy variations on the FFNN architecture. For example, given the fuzzy Perceptron of Keller and Hunt,[118] it is an easy conceptual step to utilize the same ideas in a full-scale multilayered Perceptron; many authors have attempted to do so. In particular, there now exist fuzzy back propagation schemes, training with fuzzy labels, fuzzification of inputs to the FFNN, and so on. References 123 to 127 are a small but representative sample of different schemes that attempt to fuzzify one or more components of FFNN architectures.

Another major network structure is Kohonen's *learning vector quantization* (LVQ) scheme. The salient features of this model are contained in Fig. 2.10.[103]

LVQ algorithms do *not* produce or maintain a partition of X and hence are not, properly speaking, clustering algorithms. On the other hand, LVQ typically processes unla-

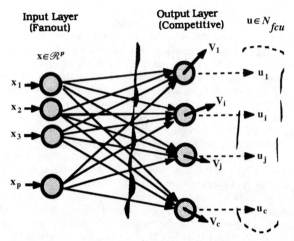

FIGURE 2.10   Kohonen's learning vector quantization: a clustering net.

beled data and is thus more akin to clustering algorithms than to classifier designs. Each node in the output layer has a weight vector attached to it, and the prototypes $\mathbf{v} = (\mathbf{v}_1, \mathbf{v}_2, \ldots, \mathbf{v}_c)$ are essentially a network vector of (unknown) cluster centers, $\mathbf{v}_i \in \mathcal{R}^p$ for $1 \leq i \leq c$. When an input vector $\mathbf{x}$ is submitted to this net, distances are computed between each $\mathbf{v}_i$ and $\mathbf{x}$. The output nodes compete, a (minimum distance) "winner" is found, and it, and perhaps some of its neighbors, is updated by using one of several update rules. To understand the connection between this type of model and, e.g., clustering algorithms such as FCM, we give a brief specification of the LVQ algorithm.[103]

1. Given unlabeled data set $X = \{\mathbf{x}_1, \mathbf{x}_2, \ldots, \mathbf{x}_n\}$, fix c, T, and $\varepsilon > 0$.
2. Initialize $\mathbf{v}_0 = (\mathbf{v}_{1,0}, \ldots, \mathbf{v}_{c,0}) \in \mathcal{R}^{cp}$ and learning rate $\alpha_0 \in (1, 0)$.
3. For $t = 1, 2, \ldots, T$; for $k = 1, 2, \ldots, n$:
   a. Find $\|\mathbf{x}_k - \mathbf{v}_{i,t-1}\| = \min_j\{\|\mathbf{x}_k - \mathbf{v}_{j,t-1}\|\}$.
   b. Update the winner:
$$\mathbf{v}_{i,t} = \mathbf{v}_{i,t-1} + \alpha_{ik,t}(\mathbf{x}_k - \mathbf{v}_{i,t-1}) \tag{2.26}$$
   c. Next k.
   d. Apply the $1 - NP$ rule to the data (noniteratively), using
$$u_{LVQ_{ik}} = \begin{cases} 1 & \|\mathbf{x}_k - \mathbf{v}_i\| \leq \|\mathbf{x}_k - \mathbf{v}_j\|, 1 \leq j \leq c, j \neq i \\ 0 & \text{otherwise} \end{cases} \quad 1 \leq i \leq c \text{ and } 1 \leq k \leq n$$
4. Compute $E_t = \|\mathbf{v}_t - \mathbf{v}_{t-1}\| = \Sigma_{i=1}^c \|\mathbf{v}_{i,t} - \mathbf{v}_{i,t-1}\|$. $\tag{2.27}$
5. If $E_t \leq \varepsilon$, stop; else, adjust learning rate α_t. Next t.

The geometry of the update scheme in Eq. (2.26) is depicted graphically in Fig. 2.11. As specified, LVQ uses only the euclidean distance in step 3*a*. This corresponds roughly to the update rule shown in Eq. (2.26) because $\nabla f(\mathbf{v}) = \|\mathbf{x} - \mathbf{v}\|_I^2 = -2I(\mathbf{x} - \mathbf{v}) = -2(\mathbf{x} - \mathbf{v})$. The winning prototype $\mathbf{v}_{i,t-1}$ is simply rotated toward the current data point by moving toward it along the vector $(\mathbf{x}_k - \mathbf{v}_{i,t-1})$, which connects it to $\mathbf{x}_k$. The amount of shift depends upon the value of the learning rate parameter $\alpha_{ik,t}$, which varies from 0 to 1. As seen in Fig. 2.11, there is no update if $\alpha_{ik,t} = 0$; and when $\alpha_{ik,t} = 1$, then $\mathbf{v}_{i,t}$ becomes $\mathbf{x}_k$ ($\mathbf{v}_{i,t}$ is just a convex combination of $\mathbf{x}_k$ and $\mathbf{v}_{i,t-1}$). Note that (2.27) is *required* as part of the iterative strategy in HCM at (2.15b). Computation of the hard $1 - NP$ c-partition of X at the end of each pass through the data in (2.27) is *not* part of the LVQ algorithm;

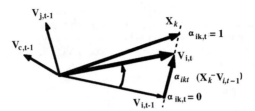

FIGURE 2.11   Updating the winning LVQ prototype.

i.e., the LVQ iteration sequence does not depend upon cycling through U's. Ordinarily, this computation is done once, noniteratively, outside and after termination of LVQ; we included this step in the algorithmic specification to enable readers to see the close similarity and relationship between these two approaches.

The extant theory for this scheme is contained in Kohonen's convergence theorem, which states that LVQ converges in the sense that the prototypes $v_t = (v_{1,t}, v_{2,t}, \ldots, v_{c,t})$ generated by the LVQ iteration sequence converge, that is, $\{v_t\} \overset{t \to \infty}{\to} \hat{v}$, provided two conditions are met by the sequence $\{\alpha_t\}$ of learning rates (indices i and k suppressed for convenience) used in (2.26). In particular, this sequence must satisfy $\Sigma_{t=0}^{\infty} \alpha_t = \infty$ *and* $\Sigma_{t=0}^{\infty} \alpha_t^2 < \infty$. The usual choice for a sequence of learning rates that satisfy these conditions is the harmonic sequence, that is, $a_t = 1/t$ for $t \geq 1$, $\alpha_0 \in (0, 1)$.

2.4.1   Comments on LVQ

1. *Limit point property.* Because LVQ does not model any well-defined property of clusters (in fact, LVQ does not maintain a partition of the data at all), the fact that $\{v_t\} \overset{t \to \infty}{\to} \hat{v}$ does not ensure that the limit vector $\hat{v}$ is a good set of prototypes in the sense of representation of clusters or clustering tendencies. All the theorem guarantees is that the sequence *has* a limit point. Thus, "good clusters" in X will result by applying the $1 - NP$ rule to the final LVQ prototypes only if, by chance, these prototypes are good class representatives. In other words, the LVQ model is not *driven* by a well-specified clustering goal.

2. *Learning rate α.* Different strategies for α_t may produce disparate results. LVQ seldom terminates unless $\alpha_t \to 0$ (that is, it is usually stopped by the predefined control limit for T).

3. *Sequential data feed.* When LVQ is implemented sequentially, different feeding sequences often alter the final results dramatically.

4. *Termination.* LVQ often passes the optimal solution in terms of minimal apparent label error rate when its prototypes are the basis for a $1 - NP$ classifier design. This is called the *overtraining phenomenon* in the neural network literature.

Lippman suggested in Ref. 105 that hard (sequential) c-means was in some sense similar to LVQ models, and our exposition has strengthened this supposition. The first article that explicitly linked fuzzy c-means to LVQ was by Huntsberger and Ajjimarangsee,[128] who suggested fuzzification of Kohonen's scheme by replacing the learning rates $\{\alpha_{ik,t}\}$ with fuzzy membership values $\{u_{ik,t}\}$ computed with FCM formula (2.15a.1). The numerical results reported in Ref. 128 showed that in many cases standard LVQ and this type of "fuzzy LVQ" produced similar answers. However, choice of a neighborhood was made in Ref. 128 by using ideas borrowed from Kohonen's self-organizing feature map method, which is not a clustering algorithm and which has a completely different purpose (2-D display of p-dimensional data). Moreover, termination was forced on this scheme by ultimately shrinking the update neighborhood to the empty set. Consequently, while the scheme in Ref. 128 was a partial integration of LVQ and FCM, it fell short of realizing a *model* for fuzzy LVQ clustering, and no properties regarding termination or convergence were established.

Integration of FCM and LVQ can be more fully realized by defining the learning rate for Kohonen updating as

$$\alpha_{ik,t} = (u_{ik,t})^{m_t} = \left(\sum_{j=1}^{c} \frac{D_{ikA,t}}{D_{jkA,t}} \right)^{-2m_t/(m_t - 1)} \tag{2.28a}$$

where

$$m_t = m_0 + t\,\frac{m_f - m_0}{T} = m_0 + t\Delta m \qquad m_f, m_0 \geq 1; t = 1, 2, \ldots, T \tag{2.28b}$$

and m_t replaces the (fixed) parameter m in (2.15). This results in three families of *fuzzy LVQ* or *FLVQ* algorithms, the cases arising by different treatments of parameter m_t. In particular, for $t \in \{1, 2, \ldots, T\}$ we have three cases depending upon the choice of the initial (m_0) and final (m_f) values of m:

$$m_0 > m_f \Rightarrow \{m_t\} \downarrow m_f \text{ descending FLVQ} \tag{2.29a}$$

$$m_0 > \mu_\phi \Rightarrow \{m_t\} \uparrow m_f \text{ ascending FLVQ} \tag{2.29b}$$

$$m_0 = m_f \Rightarrow m_f \equiv m_0 \equiv m \qquad \text{FLVQ} \equiv \text{FCM} \tag{2.29c}$$

Equation (2.29c) asserts that when $m_0 = m_f$, FLVQ reverts to FCM; this results from defining the learning rates as in (2.28a) and using them as defined in (2.30). FLVQ is not a direct generalization of LVQ because it does not revert to LVQ in case the $u_{ik,t}$ are either 0 or 1 (the crisp case). Instead, if $m_0 = m_f = 1$, then FCM reverts to HCM, but the HCM update formula (2.16) for the prototypes, which *is* driven by finding unique winners (2.15b) as in LVQ, is different from (2.26); so FLVQ is perhaps the closest possible link between LVQ and c-means type of algorithms. We provide a formal description of FLVQ.[29]

1. Given unlabeled data set $X = \{\mathbf{x}_1, \mathbf{x}_2, \ldots, \mathbf{x}_n\}$, fix $c, T, \|\ \|_A$, and $\varepsilon > 0$.
2. Initialize $(\mathbf{v}_0 = \mathbf{v}_{1,0}, \ldots, \mathbf{v}_{c,0}) \in \mathcal{R}^{cp}$. Choose $m_0, m_f \geq 1$.
3. For $t = 1, 2, \ldots, T$:
   a. Compute all cn learning rates $\{\alpha_{ik,t}\}$ with (2.28a).
   b. Update weight vectors $\{\mathbf{v}_{i,t}\}$ with

$$\mathbf{v}_{i,t} = \mathbf{v}_{i,t-1} + \sum_{k=1}^{n} \alpha_{ik,t}(\mathbf{x}_k - \mathbf{v}_{i,t-1}) / \sum_{s=1}^{n} \alpha_{is,t} \tag{2.30}$$

4. Compute $E_t = \|\mathbf{v}_t - \mathbf{v}_{t-1}\| = \Sigma_{i=1}^{c} \|\mathbf{v}_{i,t} - \mathbf{v}_{i,t-1}\|$.
5. If $E_t \leq \varepsilon_{\text{stop}}$, then stop, else, next t.

The learning rates $\alpha_{ik,t} = (u_{ik,t})^{m_t}$ at (2.28a) satisfy the following:

1. $\lim_{m_t \to \infty} \{\alpha_{ik,t}\} = 0 \ \forall i,k$ because $\lim_{m_t \to \infty} \{u_{ik,t}\} = 1/c \ \forall i,k$.

2. $\lim_{m_t \to 1} \{\alpha_{ik,t}\} = 1 \text{ or } 0 \ \forall i,k$ because $\lim_{m_t \to \infty}^{+} \{u_{ik,t}\} = 1 \text{ or } 0 \ \forall i,k$.

3. For fixed c, $\{\mathbf{v}_{i,t}\}$, and m_t, $\alpha_{ik,t}$ has the following form for each $\mathbf{x}_k$:

$$\alpha_{ik,t} = (u_{ik,t})^{m_t} = \left(\frac{\kappa}{D_{ikA,t}} \right)^{2m_t/(m_t - 1)} \tag{2.31}$$

where κ is a positive constant. Apparently, the contribution of $\mathbf{x}_k$ to the next update of the node weights is inversely proportional to their distances from it. The "winner" in (2.31) is the $\mathbf{v}_{i,t-1}$ closest to $\mathbf{x}_k$, and it will be moved farther along the line connecting $\mathbf{v}_{i,t-1}$ to $\mathbf{x}_k$ than any of the other weight vectors. Because $\Sigma\, u_{ik,t} = 1 \Rightarrow \Sigma\, \alpha_{ik,t} \le 1$, this amounts to distributing partial updates across all c nodes for each $\mathbf{x}_k \in X$. This update strategy, illustrated in Fig. 2.12, is in sharp contrast to LVQ, where only the winner is updated for each data point; note that in FLVQ *every* node is (potentially) updated at every iteration.

In *descending* FLVQ, for large values of m_t (near m_0), all c nodes are updated with lower individual learning rates; and as $m_t \to 1$, more and more of the update is given to the winner node. In other words, the lateral distribution of learning rates is a function of t, which in the descending case "sharpens" at the winner node (for each $\mathbf{x}_k$) as $m_t \overset{+}{\to} 1$. Finally, we note again that for fixed m_t, FLVQ updates the $\{\mathbf{v}_{i,t}\}$, using the conditions necessary for FCM; each step of FLVQ is one iteration of FCM.

2.4.2 Comments on FLVQ

1. There is no need to choose an update neighborhood.
2. Reduction of the learning coefficient with distance (either topological or in $\Re^p$) from the winner node is not required. Instead, reduction is done automatically and adaptively by the learning rule.
3. The greater the mismatch to the winner (i.e., the higher the quantization error), the *smaller* the impact to the weight vectors associated with other nodes.
4. The learning process attempts to minimize a well-defined objective function (stepwise).
5. The termination strategy is based upon small successive changes in the cluster centers. This method of algorithmic control offers the best chance for finding a set of centroids that compactly represent (quantize) each cluster.
6. This procedure depends upon generation of a fuzzy c-partition of the data, so it is an iterative clustering model.

A nonfuzzy version of LVQ called *generalized LVQ* (GLVQ) is reported in Ref. 130. Another class of CNN clustering algorithms is based on Grossberg's *adaptive resonance theory (ART)*. Many articles have been written on ART; fuzzy versions of ART are in their infancy. Several attempts to link ART to fuzzy models and conversely are given in Refs. 131 to 133. Pedrycz introduces fuzzy relations into the CNN framework in Ref. 134. One of the main ideas in Pedrycz' article is to connect the notions of fuzzy inter-

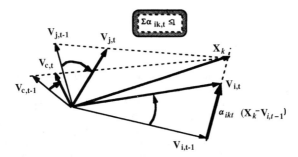

FIGURE 2.12 Updating feature space prototypes in FLVQ clustering nets.

section and union operators with learning in neural networks. The use of relational data is a much less well-developed idea in CNNs than is the use of feature vectors. Moreover, the use of *fuzzy* relations in this context is even more novel. Although this idea is new, research in this area will likely yield fruitful results.

While this chapter is expressly devoted to pattern recognition, a large portion of the current research on synergistic connections between fuzzy models and CNNs is in the realm of *control applications,* which are unequivocally linked to pattern recognition. For example, the control of automatic targeting devices requires a large, active, and reliable pattern recognition component. Thus, methods for constructing, handling, refining, and using, e.g., linguistic control rule bases with CNN methods are important in the context of pattern recognition; conversely, developments in pattern recognition technologies almost always impact control structures. We have not developed the general ideas needed to understand the fine points of this topic. Indeed, so much has happened in the area of fuzzy control in the last 5 years that a decent presentation of this younger relative of fuzzy pattern recognition would require its own volume. We circumvent our academic responsibilities in this regard by referring readers to the excellent survey by Lee,[135] who offers some 150 references on the topical area of fuzzy control. Suffice it to say here that commercial applications of fuzzy control technology developed in Japan have made this an exciting and interesting area for both scientific research and fielded applications.

In Ref. 136, Takagi and Hayashi discuss the use of CNNs to represent membership functions based upon numerical input data, and they propose a scheme for partitioning a set of fuzzy control rules based upon the use of CNNs. It is hard to make an accurate estimate of the number of variations on this scheme currently being investigated. In Ref. 137, Keller and Tahani explore the representation and computation of aggregation operators (fuzzy unions and intersections) as used in fuzzy logic inferencing schemes. This is a central problem in the design of fuzzy controllers and is also of great utility in vision systems that rely upon high-level reasoning methods to guide interpretation of image data using fuzzy models. Additional discussions about reasoning with CNNs and fuzzy logic in control applications may be found in Refs. 138 to 140.

Last, we should mention the field of *image processing.* This is a well-developed application area that utilizes pattern recognition, fuzzy models, and CNN structures to solve diverse problems. It would take ten more pages to give a satisfactory account of, e.g., fuzzy edge detection, enhancement, feature extraction, and so on, and perhaps another ten pages for CNN methods that use fuzzy ideas in image analysis. Because this chapter is already longer than it should be (!), this topic will have to wait for another reviewer. In the meantime, we provide (without comment) Refs. 141 to 159 for readers who want to explore the use of fuzzy and neural models in this area. The titles of most of these articles are more or less self-explanatory.

2.5 CONCLUSIONS

We considered the role of and interaction between statistical, fuzzy, and neurallike models for certain problems associated with the three main areas of pattern recognition system design. At present, publishers are bringing many volumes and special issues to press that address the wisdom and timeliness of the marriage of these three structures for solving pattern recognition problems.[160] Ultimately, a useful system is one that satisfies its performance requirements and design constraints. It is impossible to overemphasize the importance of iteration and feedback in the evaluation of specific model choices. Like most research, many of the articles reviewed here address a specific problem; i.e., they do not consider how the algorithm being studied will fit into a larger picture. We urge readers interested in systemic applications to approach the literature with this larger context in mind, for although this chapter is (*mostly!*) about fuzzy and neural approaches to pattern recognition, we are well aware of the fact that no graver error can be made than to commit to a particular model ahead of time. Indeed, it is our expectation and contention that synthesis between the statistical, fuzzy, and neural approaches to problems in this domain will continue to grow—perhaps this integration will be the single most important horizon for our research in the next decade or two.

REFERENCES

1. L. A. Zadeh, *Info. Control,* **8,** 338–352 (1965).
2. G. Klir, and T. Folger, *Fuzzy Sets, Uncertainty and Information,* Prentice-Hall, Englewood Cliffs, NJ, 1988.
3. D. Dubois and H. Prade, *Fuzzy Sets and Systems: Theory and Applications,* Academic Press, New York, 1980.
4. H. Zimmermann, *Fuzzy Set Theory and Its Applications,* 2d ed., Kluwer, Boston, 1990.
5. A. Kaufmann and M. Gupta, *Introduction to Fuzzy Arithmetic: Theory and Applications,* Van Nostrand Reinhold, New York, 1985.
6. K. Schmucker, *Fuzzy Sets, Natural Language and Computation,* Computer Science Press, Rockville, MD, 1984.
7. V. Novak, *Fuzzy Sets and Their Applications,* Adam Hilger, Bristol, UK, 1986.
8. M. Smithson, *Fuzzy Sets Analysis for Behavioural and Social Sciences,* Springer-Verlag, New York, 1986.
9. A. Kandel, *Fuzzy Mathematical Techniques with Applications,* Addison-Wesley, Reading, MA, 1986.
10. B. Y. Lindley, "Scoring rules and the inevitability of probability." *Int. Stat. Rev.* **50,** 1–26 (1982); with seven commentaries/replies.
11. P. Cheeseman, "An inquiry into computer understanding." *Comp. Intell.,* **4,** 57–142 (1988); with 22 commentaries/replies.
12. B. Kosko, "Fuzziness versus probability." *Int. J. Gen. Syst.* **17**(2/3), 211–240 (1990).
13. R. Duda and P. Hart, *Pattern Classification and Scene Analysis,* Wiley Interscience, New York, 1973.
14. J. T. Tou and R. C. Gonzalez, *Pattern Recognition Principles,* Addison-Wesley, Reading, MA, 1974.
15. P. Devijver and J. Kittler, *Pattern Recognition: A Statistical Approach,* Prentice-Hall, Englewood Cliffs, NJ, 1982.
16. P. Sneath and R. Sokal, *Numerical Taxonomy,* Freeman, San Francisco, 1973.
17. D. Titterington, A. Smith, and U. Makov, *Statistical Analysis of Finite Mixture Distributions,* Wiley, New York, 1985.
18. R. E. Bellman, R. Kalaba, and L. A. Zadeh, "Abstraction and pattern classification." *J. Math. Anal. Appl.* **13,** 1–7 (1966).
19. J. C. Bezdek, *Pattern Recognition with Fuzzy Objective Function Algorithms,* Plenum, New York, 1981.
20. A. Kandel, *Fuzzy Techniques in Pattern Recognition,* Wiley Interscience, New York, 1982.
21. R. Di Mori, *Computerized Models of Speech Using Fuzzy Algorithms,* Plenum Press, New York, 1983.
22. S. K. Pal and D. K. Dutta Majumder, *Fuzzy Mathematical Approach to Pattern Recognition,* Wiley, New York, 1986.

23. J. C. Bezdek and S. K. Pal, *Fuzzy Models for Pattern Recognition,* IEEE Press, Piscataway, NJ, 1992.

24. J. Keller and H. Qiu, "Fuzzy sets methods in pattern recognition." In *Pattern Recognition, Lecture Notes in Computer Science,* 301, J. Kittler, Ed., Springer-Verlag, New York, 1988, pp. 173–182.

25. W. Pedrycz, "Fuzzy sets in pattern recognition: Methodology and methods." *Patt. Recog.* **23**(1/2), 121–146 (1990).

26. J. C. Bezdek and P. F. Castelaz, "Prototype classification and feature selection with fuzzy sets." *IEEE Trans. Syst. Man Cybernetics,* **SMC7,** 87–92 (1977).

27. S. K. Pal and B. Chakraborty, "Fuzzy set theoretic measures for automatic feature evaluation." *Syst. Man Cybernetics,* **SMC16**(5), 754–760 (1986).

28. V. Di Gesu and M. C. Maccarone, "Feature selection and possibility theory." *Patt. Recog.* **9,** 63–72 (1986).

29. J. Tukey, *Exploratory Data Analysis,* Addison-Wesley, Reading, MA, 1977.

30. J. Bezdek and E. W. Chiou, "Core zone scatter-plots: A new approach to feature extraction for visual displays." *CVGIP,* **41,** 186–209 (1988).

31. J. Hartigan, *Clustering Algorithms,* Wiley, New York, 1975.

32. A. K. Jain and R. C. Dubes, *Algorithms for Clustering Data,* Prentice-Hall, Englewood Cliffs, NJ, 1988.

33. E. H. Ruspini, "A new approach to clustering." *Inf. Control,* **15,** 22–32 (1969).

34. R. Krishnapuram and J. Keller, "A possibilistic approach to clustering." *IEEE Trans. Fuzzy Syst.,* **1**(2), 98–110 (1993).

35. M. P. Windham, "Cluster validity for the fuzzy c-means clustering algorithm." *IEEE Trans. Patt. Anal. Mach. Intell.,* **PAMI4**(4) 357–362 (1982).

36. E. Backer and A. K. Jain, "A clustering performance measure based on fuzzy set decomposition." *IEEE Trans. Patt. Anal. Mach. Intell.,* **PAMI3,** 66–75 (1981).

37. J. Bezdek, M. Windham, and R. Ehrlich, "Statistical parameters of fuzzy cluster validity functionals." *Int. J. Comp. Info. Sci.,* **9**(4), 232–236 (1980).

38. X. L. Xie and G. Beni, A validity measure for fuzzy clustering." *IEEE Trans. Patt. Anal. Mach. Intell.,* **PAMI3**(8), 841–846 (1991).

39. M. Windham, "Cluster validity for fuzzy clustering algorithms." *Fuzzy Sets Syst.* **5,** 177–185 (1981).

40. M. Roubens, "Fuzzy clustering algorithms and their cluster validity." *Eur. J. Op. Res.,* **10,** 294–301 (1982).

41. E. Trauwert, "On the meaning of Dunn's partition coefficient for fuzzy clusters." *Fuzzy Sets Syst.,* **25,** 217–242 (1988).

42. G. Ball and D. Hall, "A clustering technique for summarizing multivariate data." *Behav. Sci.,* **12,** 153–155 (1967).

43. J. Dunn, "A fuzzy relative of the ISODATA process and its use in detecting compact, well-separated clusters." *J. Cybernetics,* **3**(3), 32–57 (1974).

44. L. Bobrowski and J. Bezdek, "c-Means clustering with the L_1 and L_∞ norms." *IEEE Trans. Syst. Man Cybernetics,* **21**(3), 545–554 (1991).

45. J. C. Bezdek, "A convergence theorem for the fuzzy ISODATA clustering algorithms." *IEEE Trans. Patt. Anal. Mach. Intell.,* **PAMI2**(1), 1–8 (1980).

46. J. C. Bezdek, R. J. Hathaway, M. J. Sabin, and W. T. Tucker, "Convergence theory for fuzzy means: Counterexamples and repairs." *IEEE Trans. Syst. Man Cybernetics,* **SMC17**(5), 873–877 (1987).

47. E. E. Gustafson and W. C. Kessel, "Fuzzy clustering with a fuzzy covariance matrix." In *Proceedings of the IEEE CDC,* San Diego, CA, 1979, pp. 761–766.

48. R. Krishnapuram, H. Frigui, and O. Nasraoui, "New fuzzy shell clustering algorithms for boundary detection and pattern recognition." In *Proceedings of the SPIE Conference on Intelligent Robotics and Computer Vision X*, 191, pp. 458–465.

49. R. Dave, "Fuzzy shell clustering and applications to circle detection in digital images." *Int. J. Gen. Syst.*, **16** 343–345 (1990).

50. J. C. Bezdek and J. D. Harris, "Fuzzy relations and partitions. An axiomatic basis for clustering." *Fuzzy Sets Syst.*, **1**, 111–127 (1978).

51. J. C. Bezdek and J. D. Harris, "Convex decompositions of fuzzy partitions." *J. Math. Anal. Appl.*, **67**(2), 490–512 (1979).

52. J. Bezdek, M. Trivedi, R. Ehrlich, and W. Full, "Fuzzy clustering: A new approach for geostatistical analysis." *Int. J. Syst. Meas. Decision*, **12**, 13–24 (1981).

53. J. C. Bezdek, C. Coray, R. Gunderson, and J. Watson, "Detection and characterization of cluster substructure: I. Linear structure: Fuzzy C-lines." *SIAM J. Appl. Math.* **40**(2) 339–357 (1981).

54. J. C. Bezdek, C. Coray, R. Gunderson, and J. Watson, "Detection and characterization of cluster substructure: II. Fuzzy C-varieties and convex combinations thereof." *SIAM J. Appl. Math.* **40**(2), 358–372 (1981).

55. W. Full, R. Ehrlich, and J. C. Bezdek, "Fuzzy QMODEL: A new approach for linear unmixing." *J. Math. Geo*, **14**(3), 259–270 (1982).

56. M. P. Windham, "Geometrical fuzzy clustering algorithms." *Fuzzy Sets Syst.* **3**, 271–280 (1983).

57. T. Jacobsen and R. Gunderson, "Trace element distribution in yeast and wort samples: An application of the FCV clustering algorithms." *Int. J. Man-Mach. Stud.*, **10**(1), 5–16 (1983).

58. R. W. Gunderson, "An adaptive FCV clustering algorithm." *Int. J. Man-Mach. Stud.*, **19**(1) 97–104 (1983).

59. G. Granath, "Application of fuzzy clustering and fuzzy classification to evaluate provenance of glacial till." *J. Math Geol.*, **16**(3), 283–301 (1984).

60. S. A. Selim and M. A. Ismail, "K-means type algorithms: A generalized convergence theorem and characterization of local optimality." *IEEE Trans. Patt. Anal. Mach. Intell.*, **PAMI6**(1), 81–87 (1984).

61. A. B. McBratney and A. W. Moore, "Application of fuzzy sets to climatic classification." *Agric. Forest Meteor*, **35**, 165–185 (1985).

62. K. Lesczynski, P. Penczek, and W. Grochulski, "Sugeno fuzzy measures and fuzzy clustering." *Fuzzy Sets Syst*, **15**, 147–158 (1985).

63. W. Pedrycz, "Algorithms of fuzzy clustering with partial supervision." *Patt. Recog. Lett.*, **3**, 13–20 (1985).

64. C. Windham, M. P. Windham, B. Wyse, and G. Hansen, "Cluster analysis to improve food classification within commodity groups." *J. Amer. Diet. Assoc.*, **85**(10), 1306–1314 (1985).

65. R. Cannon, J. Dave, and J. C. Bezdek, "Efficient implementation of the fuzzy C-means clustering algorithms." *Patt. Anal. Mach. Intell.*, **PAMI8**(2), 248–255 (1986).

66. K. Hirota and W. Pedrycz, "Subjective entropy of probabilistic sets and fuzzy cluster analysis." *IEEE Trans. Syst. Man Cybernetics*, **SMC16**, 173–179 (1986).

67. S. K. Pal and P. K. Pramanik, "Fuzzy measures in determining seed points in clustering." *Patt. Recog. Lett.* **4**(2), 159–164 (1986).

68. R. Hathaway and J. Bezdek, "Local convergence of the fuzzy c-means algorithms." *Patt. Recog.*, **19**(6), 477–480 (1986).

69. M. A. Ismail and S. A. Selim, "On the local optimality of the fuzzy ISODATA clustering algorithm." *IEEE Trans. Patt. Anal. Mach. Intell.*, **PAMI8**(2), 284–288 (1986).

70. M. J. Sabin, "Convergence and consistency of fuzzy C-means/ISODATA algorithms." *IEEE Trans. Patt. Anal. Mach. Intell.*, **PAMI9**, 661–668 (1987).

71. R. Hathaway and J. Bezdek, "Recent convergence results for the fuzzy c-means clustering algorithms." *J. Classification,* **5**(2), 237–247 (1988).

72. T. Kim, J. Bezdek, and R. Hathaway, "Optimality tests for fixed points of the fuzzy c-means algorithm." *Patt. Recog.,* **21**(6), 651–663 (1988).

73. I. Gath and A. B. Geva, "Unsupervised optimal fuzzy clustering." *IEEE Trans. Patt. Anal. Mach. Intell.,* **PAMI11,** 773–781 (1989).

74. S. K. Pal and S. Mitra, "Fuzzy dynamic clustering algorithm." *Patt. Recog. Lett.,* **11**(8), 525–535 (1990).

75. L. A. Zadeh, "Similarity relations and fuzzy orderings." *Info. Sci.,* **3,** 117–200 (1971).

76. S. Tamura, S. Higuchi, and K. Tanaka, "Pattern classification based on fuzzy relations." *IEEE Trans. Syst. Man Cybernetics,* **SMC1,** 61–66 (1971).

77. J. Dunn, "A graph theoretic analysis of pattern classification via Tamura's fuzzy relation." *IEEE Trans. Syst. Man Cybernetics,* **SMC4,** 310–313 (1974).

78. A. Kandel and L. Yelowitz, "Fuzzy chains." *IEEE Trans. Syst. Man Cybernetics,* **SMC4,** 472–475 (1974).

79. M. P. Windham, "Numerical classification of proximity data with assignment measures." *J. Classification,* **2,** 157–172 (1985).

80. J. Bezdek and R. Hathaway, "Relational duals of the c-means clustering algorithms." *Patt. Recog.,* **22**(2), 205–212 (1989).

81. J. Bezdek, R. Hathaway, and W. Windham, "Numerical comparison of the RFCM and AP algorithms for clustering relational data." *Patt. Recog.,* **24**(8), 783–791 (1991).

82. S. K. Pal and D. Dutta Majumder, "Fuzzy sets and decision making approaches in vowel and speaker recognition." *IEEE Trans. Syst. Man Cybernetics,* **SMC7,** 625–629 (1977).

83. R. L. P. Chang and T. Pavlidis, "Fuzzy decision tree algorithms." *IEEE Trans. Syst. Man Cybernetics,* **SMC7,** 28–35 (1977).

84. R. De Mori and P. Laface, "Use of fuzzy algorithms for phonetic and phonemic labeling of continuous speech." *IEEE Trans. Patt. Anal. Mach. Intell.,* **PAMI2,** 136–148 (1980).

85. L. Saitta and P. Torasso, "Fuzzy characteristics of coronary disease." *Fuzzy Sets Syst.,* **5,** 245–258 (1981).

86. A. K. Nath and T. T. Lee, "On the design of classifier with linguistic variables as input." *Fuzzy Sets Syst.,* **11,** 265–286 (1983).

87. A. Meisels, A. Kandel, and G. Gecht, "Entropy, and the recognition of fuzzy letters." *Fuzzy Sets Syst.,* **31,** 297–309 (1989).

88. J. R. Key, J. A. Maslanik, and R. G. Barry, "Cloud classification from satellite data using a fuzzy-sets algorithm—a polar example." *Int. J. Remote Sens,* **10,** 1823–1842 (1989).

89. A. M. Bensaid, J. C. Bezdek, L. O. Hall, R. P. Velthuizen, and L. P. Clarke, "A partially supervised fuzzy c-means algorithm for segmentation of MR images." In *Proceedings of the SPIE Conference on the Science of Neural Networks,* Orlando, FL, 1992.

90. J. Bezdek, S. Chuah, and D. Leep, "Generalized k-nearest neighbor rules." *Fuzzy Sets Syst.,* **18**(3), 237–256 (1986).

91. T. Cover and P. Hart, "Nearest neighbor pattern classification." *IEEE Trans. Inf. Theory,* **13,** 21–27 (1967).

92. A. Jozwik, "A learning scheme for a fuzzy k-NN rule." *Patt. Recog. Lett.* **1,** 287–289 (1983).

93. J. Keller, M. Gray, and J. Givens, "A fuzzy k-nearest neighbor algorithm." *IEEE Trans. Syst. Man Cybernetics,* **SMC15,** 580–585 (1985).

94. B. V. Dasarathy, *Nearest Neighbor (NN) Norms: NN Pattern Classification Techniques,* IEEE Computer Society Press, Los Alamitos, CA, 1990.

95. J. C. Bezdek and J. C. Dunn, "Optimal fuzzy partitions: A heuristic for estimating the parameters in a mixture of normal distributions." *IEEE Trans. Comp.,* **24**(8), 835–838 (1975).

96. J. C. Bezdek, R. J. Hathaway, and V. J. Huggins, "Parametric estimation for normal mixtures." *Patt. Recog. Lett.,* **3,** 79–84 (1985).

97. R. Hathaway and J. C. Bezdek, "On the asymptotic properties of fuzzy *C*-means cluster prototypes as estimators of mixture subpopulations." *Comm. Stat.* **5**(2), 505–513 (1986).

98. R. Redner, R. Hathaway, and J. Bezdek, "Estimating the parameters of mixture models with modal estimators." *Comm. Stat. (A),* **16**(9), 2639–2660 (1987).

99. J. Davenport, J. Bezdek, and R. Hathaway, "Parameter estimation for finite mixture distributions." *Int. J. Comp. Math. Appl.,* **15**(10), 819–828 (1988).

100. J. Bezdek and R. Hathaway, "Generalized regression and clustering." In *Proceedings of the International Conference on Fuzzy Logic and Neural Networks,* T. Yamakawa, Ed., Kyushu Institute of Technology, Iizuka, Japan, 1990, pp. 575–578.

101. M. Arbib, *Brains, Machines and Mathematics,* 2d ed., Springer-Verlag, Berlin, 1987.

102. *DARPA Neural Network Study,* AFCEA Press, Fairfax, VA, 1988.

103. T. Kohonen, *Self-Organization and Associative Memory,* 3d ed., Springer-Verlag, Berlin, 1989.

104. J. Hertz, A. Krogh, and R. G. Palmer, *An Introduction to the Theory of Neural Computing,* Addison-Wesley, Reading, MA, 1991.

105. R. Lippman, "An introduction to neural computing." *IEEE ASSP Mag.,* April, 4–22 (1987).

106. G. Carpenter, "Neural network models for pattern recognition and associative memory." *Neural Networks,* **2,** 243–257 (1989).

107. J. Bezdek, "On the relationship between neural networks, pattern recognition and intelligence." *Int. J. Approx. Reason.,* **6**(2), 85–107 (1992).

108. Y. H. Pao, *Adaptive Pattern Recognition and Neural Networks,* Addison-Wesley, Reading, MA, 1989.

109. B. Kosko, *Neural Networks and Fuzzy Systems: A Dynamical Approach to Machine Intelligence,* Prentice-Hall, Englewood Cliffs, NJ, 1991.

110. S. C. Lee and E. T. Lee, "Fuzzy neural networks." *Biosc.,* **23,** 151–177 (1975).

111. T. Yamakawa and S. Tomoda, "A fuzzy neuron and its application to pattern recognition." In *Proceedings of the 3d IFSA Congress,* J. Bezdek, Ed., Seattle, WA, pp. 30–38.

112. T. Watanabe, "A layered neural model using logic neurons." In *Proceedings of the International Conference on Fuzzy Logic and Neural Networks,* T. Yamakawa, Ed., Iizuka, Japan, 1990, pp. 675–679.

113. S. K. Pal, A. K. Datta, and D. Dutta Majumder, "Adaptive learning algorithm in classification of fuzzy patterns: An application to vowels in CNC context." *Int. J. Syst. Sci.,* **9**(8), 887–897 (1978).

114. B. B. Devi and V. V. S. Sarma, "A fuzzy approximation scheme for sequential learning in pattern recognition." *IEEE Trans. Syst. Man Cybernetics,* **SMC16,** 668–679 (1986).

115. A. Pathak-Pal and S. K. Pal, "Learning with mislabelled training samples using stochastic approximation." *IEEE Trans. Syst. Man Cybernetics,* **SMC17**(16), 1072–1077 (1987).

116. A. Pal(Pathak) and S. K. Pal, "Generalised guard zone algorithm (GGA) for learning: Automatic selection threshold." *Patt. Recog.,* **23** (3/4), 325–335 (1990).

117. A. Pal(Pathak) and S. K. Pal, "Effect of wrong samples on the convergence of learning processes—II: A remedy." *Inf. Sci.,* **60**(1/2), 77–105 (1992).

118. J. M. Keller and D. J. Hunt, "Incorporating fuzzy membership functions into the perceptron algorithms." *IEEE Trans. Patt. Anal. Mach. Intell.,* **PAMI1,** 693–699 (1985).

119. H. Ishibuchi and H. Tanaka, "Identification of real-valued and interval-valued membership functions by neural networks." In *Proceedings of the International Conference on Fuzzy Logic and Neural Networks,* T. Yamakawa, Ed., Iizuka, Japan, 1990, pp. 179–183.

120. P. Gallinari, S. Thiria, F. Badran, and F. Fogelman-Soulie, "On the relations between discriminant analysis and multilayer perceptrons." *Neural Networks,* **4,** 349–360 (1991).

121. H. Traven, "A neural network approach to statistical pattern classification by semiparametric estimation of probability density functions." *IEEE Trans. Neural Networks,* **NN2,** 366–377 (1991).

122. D. Ruck, S. Rogers, M. Kabrisky, M. Oxley, and B. Suter, "The multi-layer perceptron as an approximation to a Bayes optimal discriminant function." *IEEE Trans. Neural Networks,* **NN1**(4), 296–298 (1990).

123. S. Mitra and S. K. Pal, "Layered neural net as a fuzzy classifier." In *Proceedings of the Fourth International Conference on Industrial and Engineering Applications of Artificial Intelligence and Expert Systems,* Kauai, HI, June 2–5, 1991, pp. 128–137.

124. D. Kuncicky and A. Kandel, "A fuzzy interpretation of neural networks." In *Proceedings of the 3d IFSA Congress,* J. Bezdek, Ed., Seattle, WA, 1989, pp. 113–116.

125. L. O. Hall, "Learning on fuzzy data with a backpropagation scheme." In *Proceedings of the NAFIPS '91,* J. Keller and R. Krishnapuram, Eds., Columbia, MO, 1991, pp. 329–332.

126. L. Hall, A. Bensaid, L. Clarke, R. Velthuizen, M. Silbiger, et al., "A comparison of neural network and fuzzy clustering techniques in segmenting magnetic resonance images of the brain." *IEEE Trans. Neural Networks,* to appear.

127. S. K. Pal and S. Mitra, "Multilayer perceptrons, fuzzy sets and classification." *IEEE Trans. Neural Networks,* **3**(5), 683–697 (1992).

128. T. Huntsberger and P. Ajjimarangsee, "Parallel self-organizing feature maps for unsupervised pattern recognition." *Int. J. Gen. Syst.,* **16,** 357–372 (1990).

129. J. Bezdek, E. C. K. Tsao, and N. Pal, "Fuzzy Kohonen clustering networks." In *Proceedings of the First IEEE Conference on Fuzzy Systems,* IEEE Press, Piscataway, NJ, 1992, pp. 1035–1043.

130. N. Pal, J. Bezdek, and E. Tsao, "Generalized clustering networks and Kohonen's self-organizing scheme." *IEEE Trans. Neural Networks,* in press.

131. G. A. Carpenter, S. Grossberg, and D. B. Rosen, "Fuzzy ART: Fast stable learning and categorization of analog patterns by an adaptive resonance system." *Neural Networks,* **4,** 759–772 (1991).

132. S. Mitra, S. Pemmaraju, and S. C. Newton, "Adaptive fuzzy leader clustering of complex data sets pattern recognition." *IEEE Trans. Neural networks,* **3**(5), 794–801 (1992).

133. P. Simpson, "Fuzzy min-max neural networks. I: Classification." *IEEE Trans. Neural Networks,* **3**(5), 776–787, 1992.

134. W. Pedrycz, "Neurocomputations in relational systems." *IEEE Trans. Patt. Anal. Mach. Intell.,* **PAMI13,** 289–296 (1991).

135. C. C. Lee, "Fuzzy logic in control systems: Fuzzy logic controller, parts I and II." *IEEE Trans. Syst. Man Cybernetics,* **SMC20**(2), 404–435 (1990).

136. H. Takagi and I. Hayashi, "Artificial neural network driven fuzzy reasoning." *Int. J. Approx. Reason.,* **5,** 191–212 (1991).

137. J. Keller and H. Tahani, "Implementation of conjunctive and disjunctive fuzzy logic rules with neural networks." *Int. J. Approx. Reason.,* **6**(2), 221–240 (1992).

138. C. C. Lee, "A self-learning rule-based controller employing approximate reasoning and neural net concepts." *Int. J. Intell. Syst.,* **6,** 71–93 (1991).

139. P. Werbos, "Neurocontrol and fuzzy logic—connections and designs." *Int. J. Approx. Reason.,* **6**(2), 185–220 (1992).

140. J. Yen, "Using fuzzy logic to integrate neural networks and knowledge-based systems." In *Proceedings of the 2d NASA Workshop on Neural Networks and Fuzzy Logic,* R. Lea and J. Villereal, Eds., NASA JSC, 1990.

141. Y. Nakagowa and A. Rosenfeld, "A note on the use of local max and min operations in digital picture processing." *IEEE Trans. Syst. Man Cybernetics,* **SMC8,** 632–685 (1978).

142. V. Goetcherian, "From binary to gray tone image processing using fuzzy logic concepts." *Patt. Recog.,* **12,** 7–15 (1980).

143. S. K. Pal and R. A. Kin, "Image enhancement using smoothing with fuzzy set." *IEEE Trans. Syst. Man Cybernetics,* **SMC11**(7), 494–501 (1981).

144. S. Peleg and A. Rosenfeld, "A min-max medial axis transformation." *IEEE Trans. Patt. Anal. Mach. Intell.,* **PAMI3,** 208–210 (1981).

145. S. K. Pal and R. A. King, "On edge detection of x-ray images using fuzzy set." *IEEE Trans. Patt. Anal. Mach. Intell.* **PAMI5**(1), 69–77 (1983).

146. I. Anderson and J. C. Bezdek, "Curvature and tangential deflection of discrete arcs: A theory based on the commutator of scatter matrix pairs and its application to vertex detection in planar shape data." *IEEE Trans. Patt. Anal. Mach. Intell.* **PAMI6**(1), 27–40 (1984).

147. J. C. Bezdek and I. M. Anderson, "An application of the c-varieties clustering algorithms to polygonal curve fitting." *IEEE Trans. Syst. Man Cybernetics,* **SMC15**(5), 637–641 (1985).

148. T. L. Huntsberger, C. L. Jacobs, and R. L. Cannon, "Iterative fuzzy image segmentation." *Patt. Recog.,* **18,** 131–138 (1985).

149. T. L. Huntsberger, C. Rangarajan, and S. N. Jayaramamurthy, "Representation of uncertainty in computer vision using fuzzy sets." *IEEE Trans. Comp.,* **C35,** 145–156 (1986).

150. R. Cannon, J. Dave, J. C. Bezdek, and M. Trivedi, "Segmentation of a thematic mapper image using the fuzzy c-means clustering algorithm." *IEEE Trans. Geol. Remote Sens.,* **24**(3), 400–408 (1986).

151. M. Trivedi and J. C. Bezdek, "Low level segmentation of serial images with fuzzy clustering." *IEEE Trans. Syst. Man Cybernetics,* **SMC16**(4), 580–598 (1986).

152. J. Keller, G. Hobson, J. Wootton, A. Nafarieh, and K. Luetkemeyer, "Fuzzy confidence measures in midlevel vision." *IEEE Trans. Syst. Man Cybernetics,* **SMC17**(4), 676–683 (1987).

153. S. K. Pal and A. Rosenfeld, "Image enhancement and thresholding by optimization of fuzzy compactness." *Patt. Recog. Lett.,* **7**(2), 77–86 (1988).

154. H. Li and H. S. Yang, "Fast and reliable image enhancement using fuzzy relaxation technique." *IEEE Trans. Syst. Man Cybernetics,* **SMC19,** 1276–1281 (1989).

155. Y. W. Lim and S. U. Lee, "On the color image segmentation algorithm based on the thresholding and fuzzy c-means techniques." *Patt. Recog.,* **23**(9), 935–952 (1990).

156. H. Tahani and J. Keller, "Information fusion in computer vision using the fuzzy integral." *IEEE Trans. Syst. Man Cybernetics,* **SMC20**(3) 733–741 (1990).

157. W. X. Xie, "An information measure for a color space." *Fuzzy Sets Syst.,* **36,** 157–165 (1990).

158. S. K. Pal, "Fuzzy tools for the management of uncertainty in pattern recognition. image analysis, vision and expert system." *Int. J. Syst. Sci.,* **22**(3) 511–549 (1991).

159. L. O. Hall, A. M. Bensaid, L. P. Clarke, R. P. Velthuizen, M. L. Silbiger, et al., "A comparison of neural networks and fuzzy clustering techniques in segmenting magnetic resonance images of the brain." *IEEE Trans. Neural Networks,* **3**(5), 672–683 (1992).

160. Special issue on fuzzy logic and neural networks, *IEEE Trans. Neural Networks,* **3**(5) (1992).

CHAPTER 3

PROBABILISTIC NEURAL NETWORKS AND GENERAL REGRESSION NEURAL NETWORKS

Donald F. Specht
Lockheed Martin Missiles & Space
Palo Alto Research Laboratories
Palo Alto, California

Both *probabilistic neural networks* (PNNs) [1, 2] and *general regression neural networks* (GRNNs) [3] are feedforward neural networks; they respond to an input pattern by processing the input data from one layer to the next with no feedback paths. Feedback may or may not be used in the training of the networks.

Feedforward networks learn pattern statistics from a training set. The training may be in terms of global- or local-basis functions. The well-known *back propagation* (BP) of errors method [4] is a training method applied to global-basis functions, which are defined as nonlinear (usually sigmoidal) functions of the distance of the pattern vector from a hyperplane. The function to be approximated is defined to be a combination of these sigmoidal functions. Since the sigmoidal functions have nonnegligible values throughout all measurement space, many iterations are required to find a combination that has acceptable error in all parts of the measurement space for which training data are available.

The two main types of localized basis function networks are based on (1) estimation of probability density functions and (2) iterative function approximation. Both PNNs, for classification, and GRNNs, for estimation of the values of continuous variables, are based on the first type—estimation of probability density functions.

The second type, based on iterative function approximation, are usually referred to as *radial basis function* (RBF) networks. These networks use functions that have a maximum at some center location and fall off to zero as a function of distance from that center. The function to be approximated is approximated as a linear combination of these basis functions. An obvious advantage of these networks is that training a network to have the proper response in one part of the measurement space does not disturb the trained response in other, distant parts of the measurement space.

It is possible to train a network of local-basis functions in one pass through the data by straightforwardly applying the principles of statistics. The PNN is the classifier version, obtained when the Bayes strategy for decision making is combined with a nonparametric estimator for probability density functions. The GRNN is the function approximator version, which is useful for estimating the values of continuous variables such as future position, future values, and multivariable interpolation.

This chapter covers both the basic and the adaptive forms of PNN and GRNN. The basic forms are characterized by one-pass learning and the use of the same width for the basis function for all dimensions of the measurement space. Adaptive PNN and Adaptive GRNN are characterized by adapting separate widths for the basis function for each dimension. Because this adaptation is iterative, it sacrifices the one-pass learning of the basic forms, but it achieves better generalization accuracy than the basic forms and back propagation do.

Clustering is often used to reduce the number of nodes in the network from one per sample to one per cluster center. Both hard and soft clustering algorithms are described. Hard clustering requires that each training sample be assigned to one and only one cluster; soft (or fuzzy) clustering does not. A particular soft clustering technique, maximum likelihood training of a mixture of gaussians, is described.

Finally, RBF training techniques based on iterative function approximation are described. These techniques can often provide more-compact networks that can be evaluated with less computation or hardware; however, they are not easily understood in terms of probability theory.

3.1 PROBABILISTIC NEURAL NETWORKS

To understand the basis of the PNN paradigm, it is useful to begin with a discussion of the Bayes decision strategy and nonparametric estimators of probability density functions. It will then be shown how this statistical technique maps into a feedforward neural network structure typified by many simple processors ("neurons") that can all function in parallel.

There are four variations for implementation of the pattern units in the PNN network. In one variation, the topology of the PNN is similar in structure to back propagation, differing primarily in that the sigmoidal activation function is replaced by an exponential activation function. However, unlike BP, the PNN can be shown to asymptotically approach implementation of the Bayes optimal decision surface without the danger of getting trapped in local minima. It is also orders of magnitude faster to train and has only one free parameter to be assigned by the user. The main disadvantage of basic PNN is that the computational load is transferred from the training phase to the evaluation of new patterns.

Basic PNN is therefore ideal for exploration of new databases and preprocessing techniques, because this use of the neural network typically requires frequent retraining and evaluation, with relatively short test sets. Variations on the basic PNN that minimize run time computation are presented later in this chapter.

The remaining three implementations of the pattern units are optimized for implementation on multiply/accumulate digital signal processors or on special-purpose integer arithmetic processors.

3.1.1 Bayes' Strategy for Pattern Classification

An accepted norm for decision rules or strategies used to classify patterns is that they do so in a way that minimizes the *expected risk*. Such strategies are called *Bayes' strategies* [5] and can be applied to problems containing any number of categories.

Consider the two-category situation in which the state of nature θ is known to be either θ_A or θ_B. If it is desired to decide whether $\theta = \theta_A$ or $\theta = \theta_B$ based on a set of measurements represented by p-dimensional vector $\mathbf{X}^t = [X_1 \ldots X_j \ldots X_p]$, the Bayes decision rule becomes

$$d(\mathbf{X}) = \begin{cases} \theta_A & \text{if } h_A \ell_A f_A(\mathbf{X}) > h_B \ell_B f_B(\mathbf{X}) \\ \\ \theta_B & \text{if } h_A \ell_A f_A(\mathbf{X}) < h_B \ell_B f_B(\mathbf{X}) \end{cases} \qquad (3.1)$$

where $f_A(\mathbf{X})$ and $f_B(\mathbf{X})$ are the probability density functions for categories A and B, respectively; ℓ_A is the loss associated with the decision $d(\mathbf{X}) = \theta_B$ when $\theta = \theta_A$; ℓ_B is the loss associated with the decision $d(\mathbf{X}) = \theta_A$ when $\theta = \theta_B$ (the losses associated with correct decisions are taken to equal zero); h_A is the a priori probability of occurrence of patterns from category A; and $h_B = 1 - h_A$ is the a priori probability that $\theta = \theta_B$.

Thus, the boundary between the region in which the Bayes decision $d(\mathbf{X}) = \theta_A$ and the region in which $d(\mathbf{X}) = \theta_B$ is given by the equation

$$f_A(\mathbf{X}) = K f_B(\mathbf{X}) \qquad (3.2)$$

where

$$K = \frac{h_B \ell_B}{h_A \ell_A} \qquad (3.3)$$

In general, the two-category decision surface defined by Eq. (3.2) can be arbitrarily complex, since there is no restriction on the densities except for the conditions that all probability density functions (PDFs) must satisfy, namely, that they are everywhere nonnegative, they are integrable, and their integrals over all space equal unity. A similar decision rule can be stated for the many-category problem [6]

$$d(\mathbf{X}) = \theta_k \qquad \text{if } h_k \ell_k f_k(\mathbf{X}) > h_q \ell_q f_q(\mathbf{X}) \qquad \text{for all } k \neq q \qquad (3.4)$$

where ℓ_k is the loss associated with the decision $d(\mathbf{X}) \neq \theta_k$ when $\theta = \theta_k$. For complete generality, ℓ should be defined as a matrix with different losses assigned for misclassification of a pattern to each of the incorrect categories. In my experience, this is not usually necessary, with one exception. If it is desired to classify uncertain patterns as "unknown" rather than risk the wrong classification, the loss associated with the classification "unknown" is less than that for a hard decision to classify $\mathbf{X}$ into the wrong category [7]. This subject is treated in Sec. 3.6.3.

The key to using Eq. (3.1) or Eq. (3.4) is the ability to estimate PDFs based on training patterns. Often the a priori probabilities are known or can be estimated accurately, and the loss functions require subjective evaluation. However, if the probability densities of the patterns in the categories to be separated are unknown, and all that is given is a set of training patterns (training samples), then it is these samples that provide the only clue to the unknown underlying probability densities.

In his classic paper, Parzen [8] showed that a class of PDF estimators asymptotically approaches the underlying parent density, provided only that it is continuous.

3.1.2 Consistency of the Density Estimates

The accuracy of the decision boundaries depends on the accuracy with which the underlying PDFs are estimated. Parzen showed how one may construct a family of estimates of $f(X)$

$$f_n(X) = \frac{1}{n\lambda} \sum_{i=1}^{n} \omega\left(\frac{X - X_{ki}}{\lambda}\right) \qquad (3.5)$$

which is consistent at all points X at which the PDF is continuous.

Parzen proved that the estimate $f_n(X)$ is consistent in quadratic mean in the sense that

$$E|f_n(X) - f(X)|^2 \to 0 \qquad \text{as } n \to \infty \qquad (3.6)$$

Cacoullos [9] extended Parzen's results to cover the multivariate case. In his Theorem 4.1 Cacoullos indicates how the Parzen results can be extended to estimates in the special case where the multivariate kernel is a product of univariate kernels. In the particular case of the gaussian kernel, the multivariate estimates can be expressed as

$$f_k(\mathbf{X}) = \frac{1}{(2\pi)^{p/2}\,\sigma^p} \frac{1}{m} \sum_{i=1}^{m} \exp\left[-\frac{(\mathbf{X} - \mathbf{X}_{ki})^t(\mathbf{X} - \mathbf{X}_{ki})}{2\sigma^2}\right] \qquad (3.7)$$

where k = category
i = pattern number
m = total number of training patterns
$\mathbf{X}_{ki}$ = ith training pattern from category k
σ = smoothing parameter
p = dimensionality of measurement space

Note that $f_k(\mathbf{X})$ is simply the sum of small multivariate gaussian distributions centered at each training sample. However, the sum is not limited to being gaussian. It can, in fact, approximate any smooth density function.

Figure 3.1 illustrates the effect of different values for the smoothing parameter σ on $f_k(\mathbf{X})$ for the case in which the independent variable $\mathbf{X}$ is two-dimensional. The density

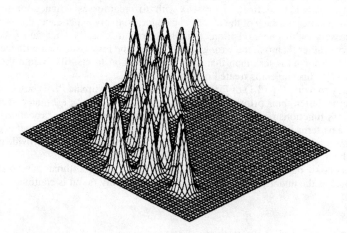

(a) A small value of σ

FIGURE 3.1   The smoothing effect of different values of σ on a PDF estimated from samples. [*From Computer-Oriented Approaches to Pattern Recognition (pp. 100–101) by W. S. Meisel, 1972, Orlando, FL: Academic Press. Copyright 1972 by Academic Press. Reprinted by permission.*]

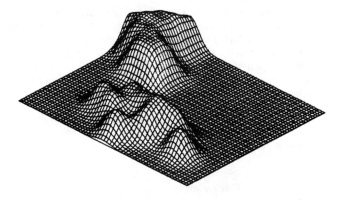

(b) A larger value of σ

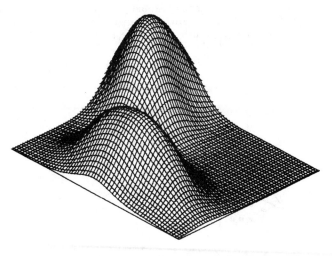

(c) An even larger value of σ

FIGURE 3.1   (Cont.)

is plotted from Eq. (3.7) for three values of σ with the same training samples in each case. A small value of σ causes the estimated parent density function to have distinct modes corresponding to the locations of the training samples. A larger value of σ produces a greater degree of interpolation between points, as indicated in Fig. 3.1b. Here, values of **X** that are close to the training samples are estimated to have about the same probability of occurrence as the given samples. An even larger value of σ produces a greater degree of interpolation, as indicated in Fig. 3.1c. A very large value of σ would cause the estimated density to be gaussian regardless of the true underlying distribution. Selection of the proper amount of smoothing is discussed in Sec. 3.1.5.

Equation (3.7) can be used directly with the decision rule expressed in Eq. (3.1). However, two limitations are inherent in the use of Eq. (3.7). First, the entire training set must be stored and used during testing; second, the amount of computation necessary to classify an unknown point is proportional to the size of the training set. When this approach was first proposed for pattern recognition [6, 10], both considerations severely limited the direct use of Eq. (3.7) in real-time or dedicated applications. Approximations had to be used instead. Computer memory has since become dense enough that storing the training set is no longer an impediment, but computation time with a serial computer is still a constraint. With large-scale neural networks with massively parallel computing capability on the horizon, the second impediment to the direct use of Eq. (3.7) is now being lifted.

3.1.3   Probabilistic Neural Network

There is a striking similarity between parallel analog networks that classify patterns using nonparametric estimators of a PDF and feedforward neural networks used with other training algorithms [1]. Figure 3.2 shows a neural network organization for classification of input patterns **X** into two categories.

In Fig. 3.2, the input units are merely distribution units that supply the same input values to all the pattern units. Each pattern unit (shown in more detail in Fig. 3.3) forms a dot product of the pattern vector **X** with a weight vector $\mathbf{W}_i$, $Z_i = \mathbf{X} \cdot \mathbf{W}_i$, and then performs a nonlinear operation on Z_i before outputting its activation level to the summation unit. Instead of the sigmoidal activation function commonly used for back propagation,

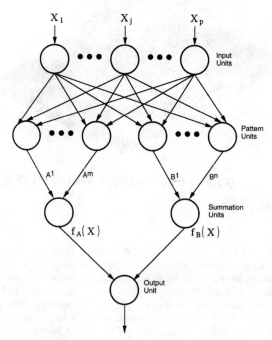

FIGURE 3.2   Organization for classification of patterns into categories.

the nonlinear operation used here is $\exp[(Z_i - 1)/\sigma^2]$. Assuming that both $\mathbf{X}$ and $\mathbf{W}_i$ are normalized to unit length, this is equivalent to using

$$\exp[-(\mathbf{W}_i - \mathbf{X})^t(\mathbf{W}_i - \mathbf{X})/2\sigma^2]$$

which is the same form as Eq. (3.7). Thus, the dot product, which is accomplished naturally in neural interconnections, is followed by the neuron activation function (the exponentiation).

The summation units simply sum the inputs for the pattern units that correspond to the category from which the training patterns were selected.

The output, or decision, units are two-input neurons, as shown in Fig. 3.4. These units produce binary outputs. They have only a single variable weight C

$$C = -\frac{h_B \ell_B}{h_A \ell_A} \cdot \frac{n_A}{n_B} \tag{3.8}$$

where n_A = number of training patterns from category A and n_B = number of training patterns from category B.

Note that C is the ratio of a priori probabilities divided by the ratio of samples and multiplied by the ratio of losses. In any problem in which the numbers of training samples from categories A and B are obtained in proportion to their a priori probabilities, $C = -\ell_B/\ell_A$. This final ratio can be determined not from the statistics of the training samples, but from the significance of the decision. If there is no particular reason for biasing the decision, C may simplify to -1 (an inverter).

The network is trained by setting the $\mathbf{W}_i$ weight vector in one of the pattern units equal to each of the $\mathbf{X}$ patterns in the training set and then connecting the pattern unit's output to the appropriate summation unit. A separate neuron (pattern unit) is required for every training pattern.

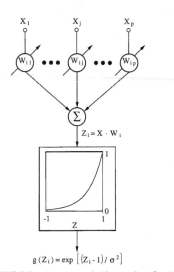

$$g(Z_i) = \exp\left[(Z_i - 1)/\sigma^2\right]$$

FIGURE 3.3 A pattern unit (dot product form).

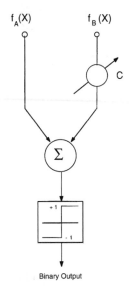

Binary Output

FIGURE 3.4 An output unit.

For a multiple category problem, the outputs of the summation units need to be multiplied by $h_k \ell_k / n_k$ and then the output unit is replaced by a maximum detector.

3.1.4   Alternative Pattern Units

Three alternative pattern units are shown in Figs. 3.5, 3.6, and 3.7. The pattern unit in Fig. 3.2 requires normalization of the input and exemplar vectors to unit length, but the pattern units of Figs. 3.5, 3.6, and 3.7 do not. The pattern unit of Fig. 3.2 can be made independent of the requirement of unit normalization by adding the lengths of both vectors as inputs to the pattern unit, as shown in Fig. 3.5. Figure 3.2 is a simplification of this, which shows congruence of the topology for PNN to that of BP.

The pattern unit of Fig. 3.6 subtracts a stored exemplar vector from the input vector and sums the squares of the differences to find the euclidean distance (squared). This distance is input to an exponential activation function, which provides the response of one neuron to the summation unit. This version of the pattern unit is the most direct implementation of Eq. (3.7) and is often used.

For basic PNN, the weights A^j and B^j shown in Fig. 3.2 all equal 1 and have no effect. It becomes necessary to have weights other than 1 when clustering is incorporated. The pattern unit of Fig. 3.7 performs the same function as that of Fig. 3.6, except that the "city block" distance metric is used instead of euclidean distance. We have noted in several practice problems that the two metrics work almost equally well. The city block metric is, of course, simpler to implement in parallel hardware, and was chosen for implementation in the DARPA/Nestor/Intel chip available from the Nestor Corporation [11].

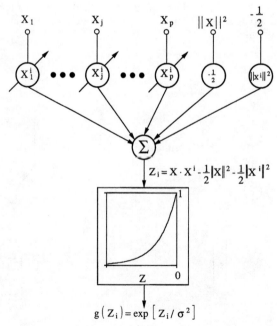

FIGURE 3.5   A pattern unit. Dot product form is expanded to accommodate vectors of any length.

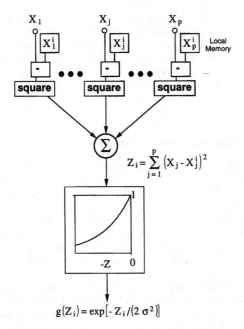

FIGURE 3.6 A pattern unit (euclidean distance form).

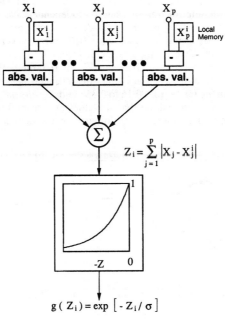

FIGURE 3.7 A pattern unit ("city block" distance form).

The best pattern unit to use for a particular application will depend on hardware availability. Implementation technologies that lend themselves to vector subtraction will be best used with the distance-measuring forms, and those that lend themselves to vector multiplication [such as those using digital signal processing (DSP) chips, and optical computers] will be best used with the dot-product form. Fixed-point computation is well suited for the distance-measuring forms, whereas floating-point computation can be used equally well with either form.

3.1.5   Limiting Conditions as $\sigma \to 0$ and as $\sigma \to \infty$

It has been shown [6] that the decision boundary defined by Eq. (3.2) varies continuously from a hyperplane when $\sigma \to \infty$ to a very nonlinear boundary representing the nearest-neighbor classifier when $\sigma \to 0$. The nearest-neighbor decision rule has been investigated in detail [12].

In general, neither limiting case provides optimal separation of the two distributions. A degree of averaging of nearest neighbors, dictated by the density of training samples, provides better generalization than basing the decision on a single nearest neighbor. The network proposed is similar in effect to the K-nearest neighbor classifier.

Specht [13] contains an involved discussion of how one should choose a value of the smoothing parameter σ as a function of the dimension of the problem p and the number of training patterns n. However, it has been found that in practical problems it is not difficult to find a good value of σ, because the misclassification rate does not change dramatically with small changes in σ.

An experiment [10] in which electrocardiograms were classified as normal or abnormal according to the two-category classification of Eqs. (3.1) and (3.7) yielded accuracy curves that are typical for practical problems we have examined. In that experiment 249 patterns were available for training, and 63 independent cases were available for testing. Each pattern was described by a 46-dimensional pattern vector. Figure 3.8 shows the percentage of testing samples classified correctly versus the value of the smoothing parameter σ. Several important conclusions are obvious. Peak diagnostic accuracy can be obtained with any σ between 0.2 and 0.3; the peak of the curve is sufficiently broad that finding a good value of σ experimentally is not difficult. Furthermore, any σ in the range from 0.15 to 0.35 yields results only slightly poorer than those for the best value. It turned out that all values of σ from 0 to ∞ gave results that were significantly better than those of cardiologists on the same testing set.

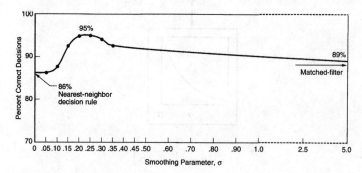

FIGURE 3.8   Percentage of testing samples classified correctly versus smoothing parameter σ.

The only parameter to be adjusted in basic PNN is the smoothing parameter σ, which is the same for every pattern unit and every dimension.

In order for each input variable to have equal influence on the decisions of the network, it is necessary to prescale the input variables to have roughly the same range or standard deviation. Standard deviations for each dimension should be computed by subtracting the category mean from each pattern vector and then pooling the data from all categories.

3.1.6 Associative Memory

In the human thinking process, knowledge accumulated for one purpose is often used in different ways for different purposes. Similarly, in this situation, if the decision category were known but not all the input variables were known, then the known input variables could be impressed on the network for the correct category and the unknown input variable could be varied to maximize the output of the network. These values represent those most likely to be associated with the known inputs. If only one parameter were unknown, then the most probable value of that parameter could be found by ramping through all possible values of the parameter and choosing the one that maximized the PDF. If several parameters are unknown, this method may be impractical. In this case, one might be satisfied with finding the closest mode of the PDF. This goal could be achieved by using the method of steepest ascent. A more general approach to forming an associative memory is to avoid distinguishing between inputs and outputs. By concatenating the $\mathbf{X}$ vector and the output vector into one longer measurement vector $\mathbf{X}'$, a single probabilistic network can be used to find $f(\mathbf{X}')$, the global PDF. This PDF may have many modes clustered at various locations in the measurement space. To use this network as an associative memory, one impresses on the inputs of the network those parameters that are known, and one allows the other parameters to relax to whatever combination maximizes $f(\mathbf{X}')$, which occurs at the nearest mode.

3.1.7 Speed Advantage Relative to Back Propagation

A principal advantage of the PNN paradigm is that it is very much faster in training than the well-known BP paradigm. In the first practical problem in which the two paradigms were tried on the same database (ship radar classification [14]), the time required for PNN was 0.7 s, compared to over-the-weekend computation for BP. This result, a 200,000-to-1 improvement in speed, is typical when the hold-one-out method of validation is used for both PNN and BP. When the available sample patterns are divided into separate training and test sets, the speedup ratio ranges from 1 to 6 orders of magnitude [15], with sample sizes of up to 10,000 training patterns. The only exception to the expectation of large speed improvements seems to be for overly defined problems, with huge redundant training sets.

3.1.8 Estimating a Posteriori Probabilities

The outputs $f_k(\mathbf{X})$ can also be used to estimate a posteriori probabilities or for other purposes beyond the binary decision of the output units. The most important use we have found is to estimate the a posteriori probability that $\mathbf{X}$ belongs to category k, $P[k|\mathbf{X}]$. If pattern $\mathbf{X}$ belongs to one and only one of c categories, then we have, from Bayes' theorem,

$$P[k|\mathbf{X}] = \frac{h_k f_k(\mathbf{X})}{\displaystyle\sum_{j=1}^{c} h_j f_j(\mathbf{X})} \tag{3.9}$$

3.1.9 Probabilistic Neural Networks Using Alternative Estimators of f(X)

The earlier discussion dealt only with multivariate estimators that reduced to a dot product form. Further application of Cacoullos [9], theorem 4.1, to other univariate kernels
suggested by Parzen [8] yields the following multivariate estimators (which are products of univariate kernels):

$$f_k(\mathbf{X}) = \frac{1}{n(2\lambda)^p} \sum_{i=1}^{n} 1 \qquad \text{when all } |X_j - X_{kij}| \leq \lambda \tag{3.10}$$

$$f_k(\mathbf{X}) = \frac{1}{n\lambda^p} \sum_{i=1}^{n} \prod_{j=1}^{p} \left(1 - \frac{|X_j - X_{kij}|}{\lambda} \right) \qquad \text{when all } |X_j - X_{kij}| \leq \lambda \tag{3.11}$$

$$f_k(\mathbf{X}) = \frac{1}{n(2\pi)^{p/2}\lambda^p} \sum_{i=1}^{n} \prod_{j=1}^{p} e^{-1/2 \frac{(X_j - X_{kij})^2}{\lambda^2}}$$

$$= \frac{1}{n(2\pi)^{p/2}\lambda^p} \sum_{i=1}^{n} \exp\left[\frac{-\displaystyle\sum_{j=1}^{p}(X_j - X_{kij})^2}{2\lambda^2} \right] \tag{3.12}$$

$$f_k(\mathbf{X}) = \frac{1}{n(2\lambda)^p} \sum_{i=1}^{n} \prod_{j=1}^{p} e^{-|X_j - X_{kij}|/\lambda} = \frac{1}{n(2\lambda)^p} \sum_{i=1}^{n} \exp\left(-\frac{1}{\lambda} \sum_{j=1}^{p} |X_j - X_{kij}| \right) \tag{3.13}$$

$$f_k(\mathbf{X}) = \frac{1}{n(\pi\lambda)^p} \sum_{i=1}^{n} \prod_{j=1}^{p} \left[1 + \frac{(X_j - X_{kij})^2}{\lambda^2} \right]^{-1} \tag{3.14}$$

$$f_k(\mathbf{X}) = \frac{1}{n(2\pi\lambda)^p} \sum_{i=1}^{n} \prod_{j=1}^{p} \left[\frac{\sin \dfrac{X_j - X_{kij}}{2\lambda}}{\dfrac{X_j - X_{kij}}{2\lambda}} \right]^2 \tag{3.15}$$

Equation (3.12) is simply an alternative form of the dot product estimator of Eq.
(3.7). The forms that do not reduce to a dot product would require an alternative network
structure; however, they can all be implemented computationally as is.

It has not been proved that any of these estimators is the best and should always be
used. Since all the estimators converge to the correct underlying distribution, the choice
can be made on the basis of computational simplicity or similarity to computational
models of biological neural networks. Of these, Eq. (3.13), in conjunction with Eqs.
(3.1) through (3.4), is particularly attractive from the point of view of computational

simplicity. This form has already been described in connection with the pattern unit of Fig. 3.7.

When the measurement vector **X** is restricted to binary measurements, Eq. (3.13) reduces to finding the Hamming distance between the input vector and a stored vector, followed by use of the exponential activation function.

3.1.10 Summary of Basic PNN

Operationally, the most important advantage of the PNN is that training is easy and instantaneous. PNN can be used in real time because as soon as one pattern representing each category has been observed, the network can begin to generalize to new patterns. As additional patterns are observed and stored in the network, the generalization will improve and the decision boundary can become more complex.

Other advantages of PNN include the following:

1. The shape of the decision surfaces can be made as complex as necessary or as simple as desired, by choosing the appropriate value of the smoothing parameter σ.

2. The decision surfaces can approach the bayesian optimal.

3. Erroneous samples are tolerated.

4. Sparse samples are adequate for network performance.

5. Parameter σ can be made smaller as n gets larger, without retraining.

6. For time-varying statistics, old patterns can be overwritten with new patterns.

Another practical advantage of the PNN is that, unlike many networks, it operates completely in parallel, without a need for feedback from the individual neurons to the inputs. For systems involving thousands of neurons (too many to fit into a single semiconductor chip), such feedback paths would quickly exceed the number of pins available on a chip. With the PNN, any number of chips could be connected in parallel to the same inputs if only partial sums from the summation units are run off-chip. There would be only two such partial sums per output bit. At this writing, one such chip is already available.

The PNN can, with variations, be used for mapping, classification, associative memory, or direct estimation of a posteriori probabilities.

The major disadvantage of PNN stems from the fact that it requires one node or neuron for each training pattern. For large databases, this presents a computational problem that can be overcome by using one of various types of clustering algorithms. All result in each PNN node representing a cluster center rather than individual patterns. The use of clustering in conjunction with basic PNN is covered in Sec. 3.5.

3.2 ADAPTIVE PNN

Up to this point, our description of PNN has been limited to discussion of a single smoothing parameter which is applied in the same way to all measurement variables; i.e., the PDF estimation kernel has been radially symmetric. The only special treatment for individual measurements is the scaling of input measurements to be all in the same range (usually by dividing by the standard deviation of each measurement).

An important improvement to PNN, called *Adaptive PNN,* is obtained by adapting separate smoothing parameters for each measurement dimension. This often greatly improves the generalization accuracy. The dimensionality of the problem and the complexity of the network can usually be simultaneously reduced. Adaptive PNN can be used for automatic feature selection. The price paid for these improvements is increased training time.

The accuracy of Adaptive PNN is compared with that of basic PNN in Sec. 3.2.2 and with back propagation in Sec. 3.2.3.

3.2.1   Adaptation of Kernel Shapes

Equation (3.7) is used to estimate a PDF as the sum of gaussian kernels which all have the simple covariance matrix $\sigma^2 I$, where I is the identity matrix. PDFs can also be estimated as the sums of gaussian kernels with a full covariance matrix. This will be explored in Sec. 3.5.2. However, the complexity of a full covariance matrix may not be justified for many problems. Also, the use of a full covariance matrix does not lend itself to automatic feature selection as does the method to be described.

We have found that the simpler technique of *adapting* separate σ's for each dimension greatly improves generalization accuracy. Two adaptation methods have been used. The first, described in Ref. 16, uses gradient descent with two optimization criteria. The controlling criterion was classification accuracy, using the holdout method for validation. Whenever the change to the σ vector was too small to cause a change in classification accuracy, the sum of probabilities, which renders a continuous criterion, was computed. The sum of probabilities is defined as the sum over all patterns of the probability that the pattern is correctly classified (using Bayes' theorem, as in Sec. 3.1.8).

In the second technique [17], adaptation is accomplished by perturbing each σ a small amount to find the derivative of the optimization criterion with respect to each sigma. Then conjugate gradient descent [18] (ascent) was used to find iteratively the set of σ's that maximize the optimization criterion. Brent's method [18, chap. 10], used for finding a maximum along a gradient line, was modified to constrain the σ's to positive values.

The second optimization criterion emphasizes improvements in category separation only between categories where misclassifications occurred. When patterns from category k are misclassified as members of category q, the likelihood ratios $\text{LR} = f_k(\mathbf{X})/f_q(\mathbf{X})$ are calculated for all category k patterns, using the hold-one-out validation method. The hold-one-out validation method consists of computing $f_k(\mathbf{X})$ by using Eq. (3.7) except that the training pattern $\mathbf{X} = \mathbf{X}_{ki}$ is not used in the summation when pattern i is evaluated. The mean log likelihood ratios of misclassified and correctly classified patterns are calculated separately, and their ratio is taken. This ratio is summed over all cross categories where misclassifications have occurred. The following criterion was then maximized:

$$\sum_k \sum_{q \neq k} \frac{\text{Mean log LR for misclassified patterns } (\text{CAT}_k/\text{CAT}_q)}{\text{Mean log LR for correctly classified patterns}(\text{CAT}_k/\text{CAT}_q)}$$

This criterion also provides a continuous measurement of classification accuracy so that improvements smaller than integer classification counts can be detected.

This adaptation, with a criterion of separating classes rather than simply estimating PDFs, not only finds a separate smoothing parameter σ for each variable, but also detects variables that are poorly correlated with the desired output. Note that variables with a large σ have a relatively small effect on the estimation of PDFs. After adaptation, as described above, has progressed for several passes, resulting in some variables being almost irrelevant to the classification decisions, these variables are removed one at a time and are left out if the resulting classification accuracy is improved or is the same. Thus, adaptation of σ's can also be used for feature selection and dimensionality reduction.

Although Adaptive PNN uses gradient descent with its attendant problems of selecting a starting position and a step size, it is easier to search σ space for a solution than the weight space of BP networks because of the typical broad accuracy peaks as indicated in Fig. 3.8, and the fact that there are only p σ's to evaluate rather than the much larger number of free parameters in BP networks.

3.2.2 Results Using Adaptive PNN

Nine databases had been tested with the original version of Adaptive PNN. Six additional databases were tested with the new version. The results are shown in Table 3.1. All the databases represent real problems with overlapping distributions and measurements contaminated with noise. Databases A through E and J through O came from sensor measurements with naturally occurring noises; simulated noise was used for F through I.

Adapting just the p smoothing parameters (one for each measurement) does not increase the complexity of the trained network, because the usual preprocessing needed for PNN requires division of each variable by its standard deviation or range to ensure that the numerical ranges of all input variables are comparable. Since the smoothing parameters are used subsequently but in the same way, they can be combined with the preprocessing divisors.

The Adaptive PNN described here, while often finding a reduced feature set and greatly increased accuracy, is iterative and trains much more slowly than basic PNN. The advantages of Adaptive PNN depend on the underlying distributions in the database. For database E, for example, no dimensionality reduction was possible, and the adapted σ's were almost equal; in this one case, the advantage of Adaptive PNN was insignificant.

TABLE 3.1 Comparative Accuracy: Adapted Smoothing Parameters per Feature versus Standard PNN Accuracy

	Database	Number of patterns	Original number of features	Basic PNN accuracy (%)	Adapted number of features	Accuracy with adapted σ's (%)
A	Drawings of 3-D parts	73	21	74	5	93
B	Aircraft health monitoring	90	16	78	6	95
C	Automatic targeting	270	9	93	4	97
D	Automatic targeting	792	9	94	5	98
E	97 categories	4187	3	72	3	74
F	17 categories active sonar	1530	9	95	7	95
G	Missile track discrimination	498	10	92	3	95
H	Missile track discrimination	1684	10	97	2	100
I	Missile track discrimination	3570	10	97	4	99.4
J	Multispectral imagery	756	12	98.68	6	100
K	Voice grade	3037	10	97.05	8	99.44
L	Thematic mapper sensor	628	12	92.25	6	96.26
M	Hyperspectral imagery	648	209	94.33	122	100
N	Engine misfire prediction	2520	4	77.54	3	87.40
O	Propellant pressure	68	51	97.3	21	100

3.2.3 Comparisons with Back Propagation

As shown previously, the generalization accuracy of basic PNN is approximately the same as that of the back propagation network. In Ref. 19, our group demonstrated this for a number of artificial databases. Sometimes PNN was better, and sometimes BP was better, depending on the database.

Since then, the National Institute of Standards and Technology (NIST) performed studies with basic PNN on two real databases: hand-printed character recognition [20] and fingerprint classification [21]. Both of these reports, and the published journal article [22], conclude that PNN had the highest generalization accuracy of any techniques they tried. Its error rate was about half that of BP for hand-printed character recognition, but was only marginally better for the fingerprints. Given the demonstrated improvements of Adaptive PNN over basic PNN, we infer that Adaptive PNN would, in turn, be superior to BP.

3.2.4 Summary of Adaptive PNN

Adaptive PNN usually greatly outperforms basic PNN in terms of generalization accuracy. Adaptive PNN differs from basic PNN in that a separate smoothing parameter is adapted for each input feature, and it has a continuous measure for separating classes.

PNN is usually orders of magnitude faster in training than BP. Since Adaptive PNN incorporates the incremental adaptation characteristic of BP, the learning speed advantage has been sacrificed in favor of an accuracy advantage. The user thus has a choice between fast learning with basic PNN or superior accuracy with Adaptive PNN. However, once Adaptive PNN has been used to select features and set σ's, the resulting network has the real-time learning ability of basic PNN for additonal training patterns.

Adaptive PNN also provides for automatic feature selection. Because large values of the smoothing parameter imply that the corresponding input feature has little influence on the classification, the algorithm tests for deletion of features. The reduction of the dimensionality of feature space actually leads to increased generalization accuracy with finite training sets.

Gradient descent is not the only technique which could be used for discovering separate smoothing parameters for each dimension. Genetic algorithms have been used very effectively for this same purpose [23]. When genetic algorithms are used, there is no need to take derivatives of the optimization criterion. Therefore the criterion to be minimized could be simply

$$\sum_k \text{(Number of category } k \text{ patterns misclassified) } h_k \ell_k / n_k$$

3.3 GENERAL REGRESSION NEURAL NETWORKS

A general regression neural network (GRNN) provides estimates of continuous variables and converges smoothly to the underlying (linear or nonlinear) regression surface. Like PNN, the GRNN features instant learning and a highly parallel structure. Even with sparse data in a multidimensional measurement space, the GRNN provides smooth transitions from one observed value to another. The mathematical form can be used for any regression problem in which an assumption of linearity is not justified. The parallel network form should find use in high-speed applications such as learning the dynamics of a plant (modeling) for prediction or control.

3.3.1 Background

Regression is the least-mean-squares estimation of the value of a variable based on examples. The term *general regression* implies that the regression surface is not restricted by being linear. If the variables to be estimated are future values, the GRNN is a predictor. If they are dependent variables related to input variables in a process, plant, or system, the GRNN can be used to model the process, plant, or system. Once the system is modeled, a control surface can be defined in terms of samples of control variables that, given a state vector of the system, improve the output of the system. If a GRNN is taught these samples, it can estimate the entire control surface, and it becomes a controller. A GRNN can be used to map from one set of sample points to another. If the target space is the same dimension as the input space, and if the mapping is one-to-one, an inverse mapping can easily be formed using the same examples. When the variable to be estimated is for intermediate values between given points, then the GRNN can be used as an interpolator.

In all cases, the GRNN instantly adapts to new data points. This could be a particular advantage for training robots to emulate a teacher or for any situation in which models have to be changed frequently. Several techniques for reducing the amount of computation required will be discussed.

3.3.2 General Regression

Assume that $f(\mathbf{x}, y)$ represents the known joint continuous probability density function of a vector random variable $\mathbf{x}$ and a scalar random variable y. Let $\mathbf{X}$ be a particular measured value of the random variable $\mathbf{x}$. The conditional mean of y given $\mathbf{X}$ (also called the *regression of y on* $\mathbf{X}$) is given by

$$E[y|\mathbf{X}] = \frac{\displaystyle\int_{-\infty}^{\infty} yf(\mathbf{X},y)\, dy}{\displaystyle\int_{-\infty}^{\infty} f(\mathbf{X},y)\, dy} \tag{3.16}$$

When the density $f(\mathbf{x}, y)$ is not known, usually it must be estimated from a sample of observations of $\mathbf{x}$ and y. For a nonparametric estimate of $f(\mathbf{x}, y)$, we will again use the class of consistent estimators proposed by Parzen. These estimators are a good choice for estimating the probability density function f, if it can be assumed that the underlying density is continuous and that the first partial derivatives of the function evaluated at any $\mathbf{x}$ are small. The probability estimator $\hat{f}(\mathbf{X}, Y)$ is based on sample values $\mathbf{X}^i$ and Y^i of the random values $\mathbf{x}$ and y, where n is the number of sample observations and p is the dimension of the vector variable $\mathbf{x}$:

$$\hat{f}(\mathbf{X}, Y) = \frac{1}{(2\pi)^{(p+1)/2}\sigma^{p+1}} \cdot \frac{1}{n}\sum_{i=1}^{n}\exp\left[-\frac{(\mathbf{X}-\mathbf{X}^i)^t(\mathbf{X}-\mathbf{X}^i)}{2\sigma^2}\right]\cdot\exp\left[-\frac{(Y-Y^i)^2}{2\sigma^2}\right]\tag{3.17}$$

A physical interpretation of the probability estimate $\hat{f}(\mathbf{X}, Y)$ is that it assigns a sample probability of width σ for each sample of $\mathbf{X}^i$ and Y^i, and the probability estimate is the sum of those sample probabilities. Substituting the joint probability estimate $\hat{f}$ in Eq.

(3.17) into the conditional mean in Eq. (3.16) gives the desired conditional mean of y given $\mathbf{X}$. In particular, combining (3.16) and (3.17) and interchanging the order of integration and summation yield the desired conditional mean:

$$\hat{Y}(\mathbf{X}) = \frac{\displaystyle\sum_{i=1}^{n} \exp\left[-\frac{(\mathbf{X}-\mathbf{X}^i)^t(\mathbf{X}-\mathbf{X}^i)}{2\sigma^2}\right]\int_{-\infty}^{\infty} y \exp\left[-\frac{(y-Y^i)^2}{2\sigma^2}\right]dy}{\displaystyle\sum_{i=1}^{n} \exp\left[-\frac{(\mathbf{X}-\mathbf{X}^i)^t(\mathbf{X}-\mathbf{X}^i)}{2\sigma^2}\right]\int_{-\infty}^{\infty} \exp\left[-\frac{(y-Y^i)^2}{2\sigma^2}\right]dy} \tag{3.18}$$

Defining the scalar function D_i^2 as

$$D_i^2 = (\mathbf{X}-\mathbf{X}^i)^t(\mathbf{X}-\mathbf{X}^i) \tag{3.19}$$

and performing the indicated integrations yields:

$$\hat{Y}(\mathbf{X}) = \frac{\displaystyle\sum_{i=1}^{n} Y^i \exp\left[-\frac{D_i^2}{(2\sigma^2)}\right]}{\displaystyle\sum_{i=1}^{n} \exp\left[-\frac{D_i^2}{(2\sigma^2)}\right]} \tag{3.20}$$

Because the particular estimator, Eq. (3.18), is readily decomposed into x and y factors, the integrations were accomplished analytically. The resulting regression, Eq. (3.20), which involves summations over the observations, is directly applicable to problems involving numerical data.

The estimate $\hat{Y}(\mathbf{X})$ can be visualized as a weighted average of all the observed values Y^i, where each observed value is weighted according to its euclidean distance from $\mathbf{X}$. When the smoothing parameter σ is made large, the estimated density is forced to be smooth and in the limit becomes a multivariate gaussian shape with covariance $\sigma^2 I$. On the other hand, a smaller value of σ allows the estimated density to assume nongaussian shapes, but with the hazard that wild points may have too large an effect on the estimate. As σ becomes very large, $\hat{Y}(\mathbf{X})$ assumes the value of the sample mean of the observed Y^i, and as σ goes to 0, $\hat{Y}(\mathbf{X})$ assumes the value of the Y^i associated with the observation closest to $\mathbf{X}$. For intermediate values of σ, all values of Y^i are taken into account, but those corresponding to points closer to $\mathbf{X}$ are given heavier weight.

When the underlying parent distribution is not known, it is not possible to compute an optimum σ for a given number of observations n. It is therefore necessary to find σ on an empirical basis. This can be done easily when the density estimate is being used in a regression equation, because there is a natural criterion that can be used for evaluating each value of σ, namely, the mean squared error between Y^j and the estimate $\hat{Y}(\mathbf{X}^j)$. For this purpose, the estimate in (3.20) must be modified so that the jth element in the summation is eliminated. Thus each $\hat{Y}(\mathbf{X}^j)$ is based on inference from all the observations except the actual observed value at $\mathbf{X}^j$. This procedure is used to avoid an artificial minimum error as $\sigma \to 0$ that results when the estimated density is allowed to fit the observed data points. Overfitting of the data is present in the least-squares estimation of linear regression surfaces, but it is not as severe there because the linear regression equation has only $p + 1$ degrees of freedom. If $n \gg p$, the phenomenon of overfitting is commonly ignored.

Both Y and $\hat{Y}$ can be vector variables instead of scalars. In this case, each component of vector **Y** would be estimated in the same way and from the same observations $(\mathbf{X}, \mathbf{Y})$, except that Y is now augmented by observations of each component. Note, from Eq. (3.20), that the denominator of the estimator and all the exponential terms remain unchanged for vector estimation.

3.3.3 Normalization of Input and Selection of Smoothing Parameter Value

As a preprocessing step, it is usually necessary to scale all input variables such that they have approximately the same ranges or variances. The need for this stems from the fact that the underlying probability density function is to be estimated with a kernel that has the same width in each dimension. This step is not necessary in the limit as $n \rightarrow \infty$ and $\sigma \rightarrow 0$, but it is very helpful for finite data sets. Exact scaling is not necessary, so the scaling variables need not be changed every time new data are added to the data set.

After rough scaling, the width of the estimating kernel σ must be selected. A useful method for selecting σ is the holdout method. For a particular value of σ, this method consists of removing one sample at a time and constructing a network based on all the other samples. The network is then used to estimate Y for the removed sample. By repeating this process for each sample and storing each estimate, the mean-squared error can be measured between the actual sample values Y^i and the estimates. The value of σ giving the smallest error should be used in the final network. Typically, the curve of mean-squared error versus σ exhibits a wide range of values near the minimum, so it is not difficult to pick a good value for σ without a large number of trials.

Finally, the gaussian kernel used in Eq. (3.17) could be replaced by any of the Parzen windows. Again, the kernel of Eq. (3.13) is attractive from the point of view of computational simplicity. Using this kernel results in the estimator

$$\hat{Y}(\mathbf{X}) = \frac{\sum_{i=1}^{n} Y^i \exp\left(-\dfrac{C_i}{\sigma}\right)}{\sum_{i=1}^{n} \exp\left(-\dfrac{C_i}{\sigma}\right)} \tag{3.21}$$

where

$$C_i = \sum_{j=1}^{p} |X_j - X_j^i| \tag{3.22}$$

3.3.4 Clustering and Adaptation to Nonstationary Statistics

For some problems, the number of observations $(\mathbf{X}, Y)$ may be small enough that all the data obtainable can be used directly in the estimator of (3.20) or (3.21). In other problems, the number of observations obtained may be large enough that it is no longer practical to assign a separate node (or neuron) to each sample. Various clustering techniques can be used to group samples so that the group can be represented by only one node, which measures the distance of input vectors from the cluster center. Burrascano [24] has suggested using learning vector quantization to find representative samples to use for PNN to reduce the size of the training set. This same technique can be used for the current procedure. Also K-means averaging [25], adaptive K-means [26], one-pass K-means clustering [27], or the clustering technique used by Reilly et al. [28] for the *restricted Coulomb energy* (RCE) network could be used. However the cluster centers are determined, let us assign a new variable N_i to indicate the number of samples that are represented by the ith cluster center. Equation (3.20) can then be rewritten as

$$\hat{Y}(\mathbf{X}) = \frac{\sum_{i=1}^{m} A^i \exp\left[-\frac{D_i^2}{(2\sigma^2)}\right]}{\sum_{i=1}^{m} B^i \exp\left[-\frac{D_i^2}{(2\sigma^2)}\right]} \tag{3.23}$$

$$A^i(k) = A^i(k-1) + Y^j \qquad B^i(k) = B^i(k-1) + 1 \tag{3.24}$$

incremented each time a training observation Y^i for cluster i is encountered; $m < n$ is the number of clusters.

The method of clustering can be as simple as establishing a single radius of influence r. Starting with the first sample point $(\mathbf{X}, Y)$, establish a cluster center $\mathbf{X}^i$ at $\mathbf{X}$. All future samples for which the distance $|\mathbf{X} - \mathbf{X}^i|$ is less than the distance to any other cluster center and is also less than or equal to r would update Eqs. (3.24) for this cluster. A sample for which the distance to the nearest clusters is greater than r would become the center for a new cluster. The numerator and denominator coefficients are completely determined in one pass through the data; no iteration is required to improve the coefficients.

Since the A and B coefficients can be determined by using recursion equations, it is easy to add a forgetting function. This is desirable if the network is being used to model a system with changing characteristics. If Eqs. (3.24) are written in the form

$$\begin{cases} A^i(k) = \dfrac{\tau-1}{\tau} A^i(k-1) + \dfrac{1}{\tau} Y^j \\[2mm] B^i(k) = \dfrac{\tau-1}{\tau} B^i(k-1) + \dfrac{1}{\tau} \end{cases} \quad \text{new sample assigned to cluster i}$$

$$\begin{cases} A^i(k) = \dfrac{\tau-1}{\tau} A^i(k-1) \\[2mm] B^i(k) = \dfrac{\tau-1}{\tau} B^i(k-1) \end{cases} \quad \text{new sample assigned to a cluster} \neq i \tag{3.25}$$

then τ can be considered the time constant of an exponential decay function (where τ is measured in update samples rather than in units of time). If all the coefficients were attenuated by the factor $(\tau-1)/\tau$, the regression Eq. (3.23) would be unchanged; however, the new sample information will have an influence in the local area around its assigned cluster center.

For practical considerations, there should be a lower threshold established for B^i, so that when sufficient time has elapsed without update for a particular cluster, that cluster (and its associated A^i and B^i coefficients) would be eliminated. In the case of dedicated neural network hardware, these elements could be reassigned to a new cluster.

When the regression function of Eq. (3.23) is used to represent a system that has many modes of operation, it is undesirable to forget data associated with modes other than the current one. To be selective about forgetting, one might assign a second radius $\rho \gg r$. In this case, Eqs. (3.25) would be applied only to cluster centers within a distance ρ of the new training sample.

Higher moments can also be estimated with y^q substituted for y in Eq. (3.16). Therefore the variance of the estimate and the standard deviation can also be estimated directly from the training examples.

3.3.5 Comparison with Other Techniques

Conventional nonlinear regression techniques involve either a priori specification of the form of the regression equation, with subsequent statistical determination of some undetermined constants, or statistical determination of the constants in a general regression equation, usually of polynomial form. The first technique requires that the form of the regression equation be known a priori or guessed. The advantages of that approach are that (1) it usually reduces the problem to an estimation of a small number of undetermined constants and (2) the values of these constants, when found, may provide some insight to the investigator. The disadvantage is that the regression is constrained to yield a "best fit" for the specified form of equation. If the specified form is a poor guess and not appropriate to the database to which it is applied, this constraint can be serious. Classical polynomial regression is usually limited to polynomials in one independent variable or low order, because high-order polynomials involving multiple variates often have too many free constants to be determined by using a fixed number n of observations ($\mathbf{X}^i$, $\mathbf{Y}^i$). A classical polynomial regression surface may fit the n observed points very closely, but unless n is much larger than the number of coefficients in the polynomial, there is no assurance that the error for a new point taken randomly from the distribution $f(x, y)$ will be small.

With the regression defined by Eq. (3.20) or (3.21), however, it is possible to let σ be small, which allows high-order curves if they are necessary to fit the data. Even in the limit as σ approaches 0, Eq. (3.20) is well behaved. It estimates $\hat{Y}(\mathbf{X})$ as being the same as the Y^i associated with the $\mathbf{X}^i$ that is closest in euclidean distance to $\mathbf{X}$ (nearest-neighbor estimator). For any $\sigma > 0$, there is a smooth interpolation between the observed points (as distinct from the discontinuous change of Y from one value to another at points equidistant from the observed points when $\sigma = 0$). Other methods used for estimating general regression surfaces include the back propagation (BP) of errors neural network, radial-basis functions (RBFs) [29], the method of Moody and Darken [26], CMAC [30], and the polynomial ratio approximation to Eq. (3.20) [31].

The principal advantages of GRNN are fast learning and convergence to the optimal regression surface as the number of samples becomes very large. GRNN is particularly advantageous with sparse data in a real-time environment because the regression surface is instantly defined everywhere, even with just one sample. The one-sample estimate is that $\hat{Y}$ will be the same as the one observed value regardless of the input vector $\mathbf{X}$. A second sample will divide hyperspace into high and low halves, with a smooth transition between them. The surface becomes gradually more complex with the addition of each new sample point.

The principal disadvantage of the technique of Eq. (3.20) is the amount of computation required of the trained system to estimate a new output vector. The version of Eqs. (3.23) to (3.25) using clustering overcomes this problem to a large degree. Soon the development of neural network semiconductor chips capable of performing all the indicated operations in parallel will greatly speed performance. Almost all the neurons are pattern units and are identical. The step-and-repeat microlithographic techniques of semiconductor manufacturing are ideally suited to replicating large numbers of identical cells.

Finally, GRNN can be combined with linear techniques.[†] When linear regression explains most of the data in a database, a linear equation can be used for first-order estimation, leaving GRNN to model only the deviations from linear.

[†]This idea was pointed out by Dr. Herbert Rauch, of Lockheed's Palo Alto Research Laboratory. Fisher and Rauch [32] have subsequently used the GRNN combination with extended Kalman filters for nonlinear control problems.

3.3.6   Neural Network Implementation of GRNN

Figure 3.9 is the overall block diagram of neural network topology implementing GRNN in its adaptive form, represented by Eq. (3.23). The input units are merely distribution units, which provide all the (scaled) measurement variables X to all the neurons on the second layer, the pattern units. It turns out that the first two layers, the input and pattern units, are identical to those for PNN. The pattern unit outputs are passed on to the summation units.

The summation units perform a dot product between a weight vector and a vector composed of the activations from the pattern units. The summation unit that generates an estimate of $f(\mathbf{X})K$ sums the outputs of the pattern units weighted by the number of observations each cluster center represents. When Eq. (3.25) is used, this number is also weighted by the age of the observations. And K is a constant determined by the Parzen window used, but is not data-dependent and does not need to be computed. The summation unit that estimates $\hat{Y}f(\mathbf{X})K$ multiplies each value from a pattern unit by the sum of the samples Y^j associated with cluster center $\mathbf{X}^i$. The output unit merely divides $\hat{Y}f(\mathbf{X})K$ by $f(\mathbf{X})K$ to yield the desired estimate of Y.

To estimate a vector $\mathbf{Y}$, each component is estimated by using one extra summation unit, which uses as its multipliers sums of samples of that component of vector $\mathbf{Y}$ associated with each cluster center $\mathbf{X}^i$. There may be many pattern units (one for each exemplar or cluster center); however, the addition of one element in the output vector requires only one summation neuron and one output neuron.

What is shown in Fig. 3.9 is a feedforward network that can be used to estimate vector $\mathbf{Y}$ from measurement vector $\mathbf{X}$. Because they are not interactive, all the neurons can operate in parallel. Not shown in Fig. 3.9 is a microprocessor that assigns training patterns to cluster centers and updates coefficients A^i and B^i.

3.3.7   GRNN Examples

Estimators of the type described have many potential uses as models, inverse models, and controllers. Two examples are presented here. The first is a contrived example to illustrate the behavior of the estimated regression line. The second is an identification problem in controls first posed by Narendra and Parthasarathy [33].

A One-Dimensional Example.   A simple problem with one independent variable will illustrate some of the differences between the techniques that have been discussed. Suppose that a regression technique is needed to model a "plant," which happens to be an amplifier that saturates in both polarities and has an unknown offset. Its input-output (I/O) characteristic is shown in Fig. 3.10. With enough sample points, many techniques would model the plant well. However, in a large measurement space, any practical data set appears to be sparse. The following illustration shows how the methods work on this example with sparse data, namely, five samples at $X = -2, -1, 0, 1$, and 2. When polynomial regression using polynomials of first, second, and fourth order was tried, the results were predictable. The polynomial curves are poor approximations to the plant except at the sample points. In contrast, Fig. 3.11 shows the input-output characteristic of this same plant as estimated by GRNN. Since GRNN always estimates using a (nonlinearly) weighted average of the given samples, the estimate is always within the observed range of the dependent variable. In the range from $x = -4$ to $x = 4$, the estimator takes on a family of curves depending on σ. Any curve in the family is a reasonable approximation to the plant of Fig. 3.10. The curve corresponding to $\sigma = 0.5$ is the best approximation. Larger values of σ provide more smoothing, and lower values provide a

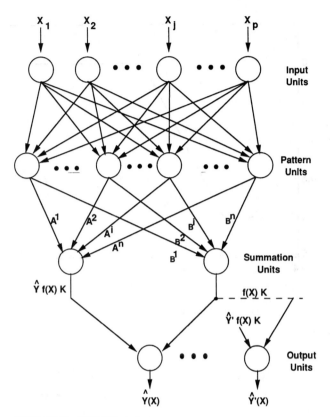

FIGURE 3.9   GRNN block diagram.

close approximation to the sample values plus a "dwell" region at each sample point. When the holdout method was used, $\sigma = 0.3$ was selected (based on only four sample points at a time).

The curve that would result from back propagation depends on a number of choices having to do with the configuration of hidden units, initial conditions, and other parameters. The main difference between Fig. 3.11 and the curve resulting from radial-basis functions is that the RBF ordinate would decrease to zero for large values of $|X|$.

Adaptive Control System.   The fields of nonlinear control systems and robotics are particularly good application areas that can use the potential speed of neural networks implemented in parallel hardware, the adaptability of instant learning, and the flexibility of a completely nonlinear formulation. A straightforward technique can be used. First, model the plant as in Fig. 3.12. The GRNN learns the relationships between the input vector (the input state of the system and the control variables) and the simulated or actual output of the system. Control inputs can be supplied by a nominal controller (with random variations added to explore inputs not allowed by the nominal controller) or by a human operator. After the model is trained, it can be used to determine control inputs by an automated "what if" strategy or by finding an inverse model. Modeling involves discovering the association between inputs and outputs; so an inverse model

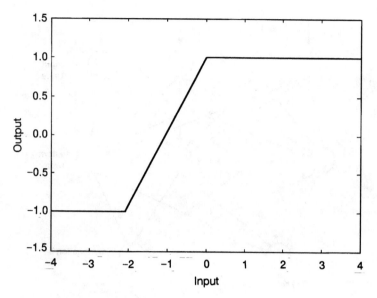

FIGURE 3.10   Input-output characteristics of simple "plant."

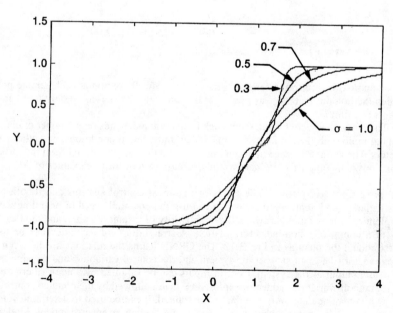

FIGURE 3.11   Input-output characteristics of plant of Fig. 3.10 as estimated by GRNN based on sample points at $X = -2, -1, 0, 1,$ and 2.

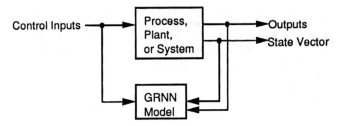

FIGURE 3.12   Modeling the system.

can be determined from the same database as the forward model by assigning the input variable(s) to the function of the desired output **Y** in Fig. 3.9, and the state vector and other measurements are considered components of the **X** vector in Fig. 3.9. One way the neural network could be used to control a plant is illustrated in Fig. 3.13.

Adaptive inverse neural networks can be used for control purposes in either the feedforward path or the feedback path. Atkeson and Reinkensmeyer [34] used an adaptive inverse in the feedforward path with positional and velocity feedback to correct for residual error in the model. They noted that the feedback had less effect as the inverse model improved from experience. They also used a content-addressable memory as the inverse model and reported good results. Interestingly, the success reported was based on using only single-nearest neighbors as estimators. Their paper mentions the possibility of extending the work to local averaging.

Farrell et al. [35] used both sigmoidal and gaussian processing units as neural network controllers in a model reference adaptive control system. They note that the gaussian processing units have an advantage in control systems, because the localized influence of each gaussian node allows the learning system to refine its control function in one region of measurement space without degrading its approximation in distant regions. The same advantage would hold true if Eq. (3.23) were used as an adaptive inverse.

Narendra and Parthasarathy [33] separate the problem of control of nonlinear dynamic systems into an identification of system (modeling) section and a model reference adaptive control (MRAC) section. Four different representations of the plant are described. Output of the plant is (1) a linear combination of delayed outputs plus a nonlinear combination of delayed inputs; (2) a nonlinear combination of delayed outputs plus a linear combination of delayed inputs; (3) a nonlinear combination of outputs plus a nonlinear combination of inputs; and (4) a nonlinear function of delayed outputs and delayed inputs. GRNN, together with tapped delay lines for the outputs and inputs, could directly implement the identification task for the most general of these models (which subsumes the others). This is true both for single-input, single-output (SISO) plants and for multi-input, multi-output (MIMO) plants. Once the plant has been identified (modeled), all the methods of Ref. 33, which are based on the back propagation network [4], can be used for adapting a controller to minimize the difference between

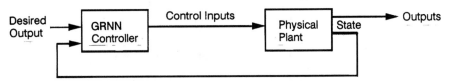

FIGURE 3.13   A GRNN controller.

the output of the reference model and the output of the identification model of the plant. This combination of technologies yields a controller with the simpler structure of BP but still uses the instant learning capability of GRNN for the plant modeling function.

One of the more difficult examples given in Ref. 33 is example 4, for which the authors identified the plant using the type 4 model above. In this example, the plant is assumed to be of the form

$$y_p(k + 1) = f[y_p(k), y_p(k - 1), y_p(k - 2), u(k), u(k - 1)] \tag{3.26}$$

where $y_p(k + 1)$ is the next time sample of the output of the plant, $y_p(k)$ is the current output, $y_p(k - 1)$ and $y_p(k - 2)$ are delayed time samples of the output, $u(k)$ is the current input, $u(k - 1)$ is the previous input, and the unknown function f has the form

$$f[x_1, x_2, x_3, x_4, x_5] = \frac{x_1 x_2 x_3 x_5(x_3 - 1) + x_4}{1 + x_2^2 + x_3^2} \tag{3.27}$$

In the identification model, a GRNN network was used to approximate the function f. Figure 3.14 shows the outputs of the plant and the model when the identification procedure was carried out for 1000 time steps using a random input signal uniformly distributed in the interval $[-1, 1]$ and $\sigma = 0.315$. In Fig. 3.14, the input to the plant and identified model is given by

$$u(k) = \begin{cases} \sin \dfrac{2\pi k}{250} & \text{for } k < 500 \\[3mm] 0.8 \sin \dfrac{2\pi k}{250} + 0.2 \sin \dfrac{2\pi k}{25} & \text{for } k > 500 \end{cases}$$

Figure 3.14 shows approximately the same amount of error between the model and the plant as does Ref. 33 (fig. 16); however, the GRNN model required only 1000 time steps

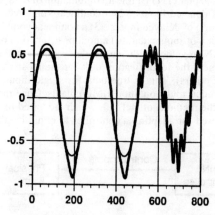

FIGURE 3.14   Outputs of plant (dark line) and of the GRNN model (lighter line) after training with 1000 random patterns.

to achieve this degree of accuracy, compared with 100,000 time steps required for the back propagation model used in Ref. 33. In other words, only 1 percent of the training was required to achieve comparable accuracies. The identification was accomplished with 1000 nodes in a five-dimensional space. No attempt was made to reduce the number of nodes through clustering.

For back propagation, it may be that for the 100,000 presentations of training points, the same 1000 patterns could have been repeated 100 times to achieve the same results. In this case, it could be said that GRNN learned in one pass through the data instead of 100 passes.

An experiment was performed to determine the extent to which performance degrades with fewer training data. The training set was reduced first to 100 patterns, then to 10 patterns. Figure 3.15 shows the output of the plant and the model when the identification procedure was carried out for only the first 10 random patterns of the 1000 (instead of the 100,000 used for BP). The model predicted the plant output with approximately twice the error of the fully trained BP network, but using only 0.01 percent of the training data. Although it is not to be expected that equivalent performance would result from training with any 10 random patterns, this performance was achieved on the first trial of only 10 patterns.

3.3.8 Summary of Basic GRNN

The general regression neural network (GRNN) is similar in form to the probabilistic neural network (PNN). Whereas PNN finds decision boundaries between categories of patterns, GRNN estimates values for continuous dependent variables. Both do so through the use of nonparametric estimators of probability density functions.

The advantages of GRNN relative to other nonlinear regression techniques are as follows:

1. The network "learns" in one pass through the data and can generalize from examples as soon as they are stored.

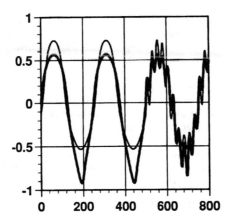

FIGURE 3.15 Outputs of plant (dark line) and of the GRNN model (lighter line) after training with only 10 random patterns.

2. The estimate converges to the conditional mean regression surfaces as more and more examples are observed; yet, as indicated in the examples, it forms very reasonable regression surfaces based on only a few samples.

3. The estimate is bounded by the minimum and maximum of the observations.

4. The estimate cannot converge to poor solutions corresponding to local minima of the error criterion (as sometimes happens with iterative techniques).

5. A software simulation is easy to write and use.

6. The network can provide a mapping from one set of sample points to another. If the mapping is one-to-one, an inverse mapping can easily be generated from the same sample points.

7. The clustering version of GRNN, Eq. (3.23), limits the numbers of nodes and (optionally) provides a mechanism for forgetting old data.

The main disadvantage of GRNN (without clustering) relative to other techniques is that it requires substantial computation to evaluate new points. There are several ways to overcome this disadvantage. One is to use the clustering versions of GRNN. Another is to take advantage of the inherent parallel structure of this network and design semiconductor chips to do the computation. The two approaches in combination provide high throughput and rapid adaptation.

3.4 ADAPTIVE GRNN

Just as adapting a separate smoothing parameter for each measurement dimension leads to greatly improved generalization accuracy for PNN, the same technique can be applied to the PDF estimation kernel for GRNN to greatly improve its accuracy. This change results in Adaptive GRNN. Like Adaptive PNN, Adaptive GRNN can be used for automatic feature selection. Again, the price paid for these benefits is the increased training time.

3.4.1 Adaptation of Kernel Shapes

Adapting separate σ's for separate dimensions is a bit simpler for Adaptive GRNN than for Adaptive PNN (Sec. 3.2.1) because the primary criterion to be minimized is inherently continuous. This criterion is the mean-squared error between the GRNN estimate (measured by the holdout method) and the desired response.

Adaptation is accomplished by perturbing each σ a small amount to find the derivative of the optimization criterion. Then conjugate gradient descent is used to find iteratively the set of σ's that minimize the criterion. Brent's method, modified to constrain the σ's to positive values, is used to find the minimum along each gradient line.

After adaptation has progressed for several passes, some σ's will usually become so large that their corresponding inputs are almost irrelevant to the estimation of the dependent variables. These inputs are tentatively removed one at a time. If the resulting regression accuracy is improved or left the same, the input is left out.

3.4.2 Results Using Adaptive GRNN

Although basic GRNN has been found to be very valuable for interpolation and extrapolation of multivalued functions, the accuracy obtained with Adaptive GRNN is usually better and often greatly improved. Table 3.2 shows comparative results for 13 databases of five distinct types. The *pressure predictor* is the prediction of pressure profiles in a rocket motor. *Phase diversity* refers to an optical wavefront sensor based on image data at two focal planes. The estimated wavefront can be used to correct for optical aberrations by controlling a deformable mirror. GRNN has been used to estimate the piston positions needed to bring the object into focus [36]. For the active sonar databases, GRNN was used to infer aspect angles of six different bodies.

The accuracy criterion in Table 3.2 is the *mean-squared error (MSE)* normalized by the variance of the predicted variable. Adaptive GRNN achieved significant reduction in the error rate in all cases. In addition, the numbers of features and of prototypes required were almost always reduced. Clustering, which was not used here, could further reduce the number of prototypes. Prototype pruning was not attempted on the pressure predictor database. An equivalent criterion, the multiple coefficient of determination R^2, can be obtained by dividing the MSE shown by 10,000 and subtracting the result from 1.0. The improvement ratio, which is the ratio of the error rate for GRNN to that of Adaptive GRNN, varies from a minimum of 1.4:1 to better than 10:1 for these databases.

3.4.3 Summary of Adaptive GRNN

This section has shown that Adaptive GRNN usually greatly outperforms basic GRNN in terms of estimation accuracy. Adaptive GRNN differs from basic GRNN in that a separate smoothing parameter is adapted for each input feature.

Adaptive GRNN also provides for automatic feature selection. Because large values of the smoothing parameter imply that the corresponding input feature has little influence on the output estimates, the algorithm tests for deletion of features. The reduction of the dimensionality of feature space leads to increased generalization accuracy with finite training sets.

In the experimental work reported here, adaptation of the σ vector was accomplished by using conjugate gradient descent. Other techniques for discovering the best combination of σ's are possible. Ward Systems Group has recently used genetic algorithms for this purpose [23].

3.5 HIGH-SPEED CLASSIFICATION

The major disadvantage of PNN stems from the fact that it requires one node or neuron for each training pattern. Although training is extremely fast, classification of large numbers of new patterns can be slow because the amount of computation required to classify a new pattern is proportional to the number of neurons in the network.

Special-purpose parallel hardware has been developed to speed up classification. One example is the DARPA/Nestor/Intel Ni1000 chip, which has 512 parallel processors that perform kernel computations common to PNN, GRNN, RCE, P-RCE, and RBF paradigms. Another is the Adaptive Solutions, Inc., CNAPS chip, which has a more general, single-instruction multiple-data architecture.

An approach to speeding up classification in a dedicated application is to simplify the network. Several researchers have suggested various types of clustering techniques to overcome the limitation. These techniques yield a smaller number of cluster centers, so that each node represents a group of training patterns.

TABLE 3.2 Comparative Accuracy; MSE for Basic GRNN and Adaptive GRNN

Database	Original number of patterns	Original number of features	Basic GRNN error rate (MSE × 10,000)	Adapted number of patterns	Adapted number of features	Adaptive error rate (MSE × 10,000)	Improvement ratio
Pressure predictor	17,450	17	3	17,450	8	2	1.5
Stock forecast	372	9	9,334	98	6	6,936	1.4
Sales forecast	64	17	4,186	37	8	1,117	3.8
Sales forecast	416	9	5,381	236	9	1,410	3.8
Phase diversity 1	543	245	1,498	265	39	349	4.3
Phase diversity 2	543	245	1,118	293	43	225	5.0
Phase diversity 3	543	245	147	280	50	56	2.6
Simulated active sonar 1	910	10	79	418	8	14	5.6
Simulated active sonar 2	910	10	1,047	344	8	277	3.8
Simulated active sonar 3	910	10	467	401	9	119	3.9
Simulated active sonar 4	910	10	274	370	8	72	3.8
Simulated active sonar 5	910	10	126	343	5	12	10.5
Simulated active sonar 6	910	10	531	369	10	64	8.3

3.5.1   Reducing Network Size by Using Clustering Techniques

Burrascano [24] has advocated using Kohonen's learning vector quantization (LVQ) technique to find representative exemplars to be used for PNN. Any standard clustering technique, such as K-means clustering, can also be used for this purpose.

Tseng [27] has proposed using K-means clustering in conjunction with PNN in its dot product form. After expanding the dot product form (as in Fig. 3.5) to avoid the problem of unit normalization, he then used the K-means clustering algorithm with a look-ahead feature to assign training patterns to particular clusters and to adapt the weights of the pattern units. In his formulation, patterns are assigned to the cluster which would be closest to the next pattern if the new pattern had been added to the cluster. Thus, pattern X^k is assigned to cluster j which minimizes the quantity

$$\frac{(A^j)^2 \, \| X^k - X^j \|^2}{(A^j + 1)^2}$$

where A^j is the number of patterns represented by cluster j.

As emphasized by Tseng [27], this technique provides a "conscience" which tends to add new patterns to clusters which have the smallest number of patterns. In his experiments, this look-ahead feature worked so well that a single pass through the data produced a condensed set which generalized nearly as well in classification of new points as basic PNN without clustering. For complex databases, multiple passes could be used to find the condensed set of exemplars. The difference between the accuracy of basic PNN and clustered PNN could be used to determine when an additional pass is needed.

To accommodate clustering, only the weighting function A^j, indicating the number of patterns represented by cluster j, needs to be added to standard PNN (Fig. 3.2). The weighting function modifies the output of the associated pattern unit before it is added to the summation unit. The stored coefficients for cluster j are updated by the recursion equations

$$X^j(\text{new}) = \frac{A^j X^j + X^k}{A^j + 1}$$

$$A^j(\text{new}) = A^j + 1$$

The cluster centers are then used instead of individual training patterns in standard PNN.

The same method of assigning patterns can be used with the distance-measuring pattern units of Figs. 3.6 and 3.7.

Bezdek and Castelaz [37] have shown that fuzzy K-means clustering is often, but not always, better than hard K-means clustering. In fuzzy K-means clustering, each new pattern is assigned partially to all the clusters in proportion to its degree of membership to each cluster, as determined by a membership function. The membership function is a decreasing function of distance from the cluster center.

The clustering technique of the *restricted Coulomb energy* (RCE) paradigm [28] can also be used to find cluster centers and associated weights corresponding to the number of samples represented by each cluster. These can then be used with standard PNN as above. Nestor Corporation refers to this combination as *probabilistic RCE* [11].

3.5.2   Reducing Network Size by Using a Mixture of Gaussian Techniques

Traven [38] and Streit [39, 40] independently took approaches that use the concept of estimating probability density functions as mixtures of gaussian densities as part of the overall problem of classification or estimation. Traven estimates the PDF as a mixture of gaussian densities with varying covariance matrices, whereas Streit restricts the covariance matrices to being identical (homoscedastic) to further simplify the network and to use pooling of data to estimate the single covariance. Traven estimates a single PDF for all categories and estimates continuous variables instead of category classification. Both techniques can use far fewer gaussian nodes than training patterns.

The following description is adapted from Streit and Luginbuhl [40]:

Let p denote the dimension of input vector $\mathbf{X}$, and let M denote the number of different class labels in the training set τ of size T. For $j = 1, \ldots, M$, let $G_j \geq 1$ denote the total number of different components in the jth class mixture PDF. Let $p_{ij}(\mathbf{X})$ denote the multivariate PDF of the ith component in the mixture for class j, and let π_{ij} denote the proportion of component i in class j. The "within-class" mixing proportions π_{ij} are nonnegative and satisfy the equations

$$\sum_{i=1}^{G_j} \pi_{ij} = 1 \qquad j = 1, \ldots, M \tag{3.28}$$

The PDF of class j, denoted by $f_j(\mathbf{X})$, is approximated by a general mixture PDF, denoted by $g_j(\mathbf{X})$, that is,

$$f_j(\mathbf{X}) \approx g_j(\mathbf{X}) = \sum_{i=1}^{G_j} \pi_{ij} p_{ij}(\mathbf{X}) \qquad j = 1, \ldots, M \tag{3.29}$$

In Ref. 40, only multivariate homoscedastic gaussian mixtures are considered, hence $p_{ij}(\mathbf{X})$ has the form

$$p_{ij}(\mathbf{X}) = (2\pi)^{-p/2} |\Sigma|^{-1/2} \exp\left[-\frac{1}{2}(\mathbf{X} - \mu_{ij})^t \Sigma^{-1}(\mathbf{X} - \mu_{ij})\right] \tag{3.30}$$

where μ_{ij} is the mean vector, Σ is the positive definite covariance matrix of $p_{ij}(\mathbf{X})$, and superscript t denotes transpose. The covariance matrix Σ is chosen independent of the class index j and the component index i. And $|\Sigma|$ denotes the determinant of matrix Σ.

Let h_l denote the a priori probability of class l. Let ℓ_{jl} denote the loss associated with classifying an input vector $\mathbf{X}$ into class j when the correct decision should have been class l. The risk $\rho_j(\mathbf{X})$ of classifying the input $\mathbf{X}$ into class j is the expected loss, so that

$$\rho_j(\mathbf{X}) \approx \sum_{l=1}^{M} \ell_{jl} h_l f_l(\mathbf{X}) \tag{3.31}$$

The decision risk $\rho_j(\mathbf{X})$ is thus approximated by a mixture of gaussian PDFs, as is seen by substituting Eq. (3.29) into Eq. (3.31). The minimum-risk decision rule is to classify $\mathbf{X}$ into that class j having minimum risk, that is, $j = \arg \min \{\rho_j(\mathbf{X})\}$. The decision j is the optimum bayesian classification decision if $g_j(\mathbf{X}) \equiv f_j(\mathbf{X})$ for all j, that is, provided approximation (3.29) is an equality.

The PDFs are estimated by a maximum likelihood method called the *expectation-maximization (EM)* method, which is described in Ref. 41. A brief description of the training algorithm for finding the mixtures of gaussian PDFs to be implemented in the nodes of PNN is given here. The mathematical justification is given by Streit and Luginbuhl [40].

The first step of the estimation process is somewhat arbitrary. It is necessary to specify in advance how many gaussian nodes will be assigned to each category and to give them starting centers and a common starting covariance matrix. The PDF of each category is estimated as the weighted sum of each of the gaussian densities (with the restriction that the sum of the weights must equal 1, so that the integral of the sum over all measurement space is unity). Once the conditional PDFs are estimated, classification proceeds as in basic PNN.

Unlike hard clustering, each training sample for category j is considered to belong partially to every cluster node which comprises the estimate of the PDF for category j. Assignment of a sample $\mathbf{X}$ to each cluster i of category j is made in proportion to the likelihood $p_{ij}(\mathbf{X})$ and is designated $\omega_{ij}(\mathbf{X})$.

The sum of the proportions of sample $\mathbf{X}$ assigned to each component in its class must equal unity so that each training sample is assigned 100 percent to its category, although less than (or at most equal to) 100 percent to each component.

Once this is done, the component means must be recomputed. The component mean μ_{ij} is the weighted average of all the training vectors in category j (weighted by $\omega_{ij}(\mathbf{X})$, the proportion of each sample in that component). The weight of the component in the estimation of the conditional PDF for category j is:

$$\pi_{ij}^{(n+1)} = \frac{1}{T_j} \sum_{k=1}^{T_j} \omega_{ij}^{(n)}(\mathbf{X}_{kj})$$

where T_j is the number of samples with class label j.

Next, the covariance is recomputed by using all the training samples from all the categories, but μ_{ij} of the appropriate category j and component i is subtracted from each training vector before being used in the computation:

$$\Sigma^{n+1} = T^{-1} \sum_{j=1}^{M} \sum_{i=1}^{G_j} \sum_{k=1}^{T_j} \omega_{ij}^{(n)}(\mathbf{X}_{kj})(\mathbf{X}_{kj} - \mu_{ij}^{(n+1)})(\mathbf{X}_{kj} - \mu_{ij}^{(n+1)})^t$$

The summation is over all training vectors $\mathbf{X}_{kj}$, each multiplied by the computed proportions to be assigned to each category j and component i. T is the total number of training samples for all categories.

The computations indicated in the last two paragraphs are repeated for n iterations until a stopping criterion is satisfied.

A typical stopping criterion is to stop when the likelihood function $\mathfrak{S}$ as a function of iteration number stops increasing at a sufficient rate. The likelihood function is the sum of the log likelihoods for all patterns in the training sets,

$$\mathfrak{S}(\tau) = \sum_{k} \log \sum_{l=1}^{m} h_l g_l(\mathbf{X}_k)$$

Since Σ is positive definite, matrix L^{-1} can be chosen such that $\Sigma^{-1} = (L^{-1})^t L^{-1}$. If L^{-1} is chosen to be the Cholesky factor of Σ^{-1}, then L^{-1} is lower triangular. The Cholesky factor (sometimes referred to as the "square root" of the matrix) can be computed easily by using the algorithm in Ref. 42, section 2.9. Substituting into Eq. (3.30) yields

$$p_{ij}(\mathbf{X}) = (2\pi)^{-p/2} |\Sigma|^{-1/2} \exp\left[-\frac{1}{2}(\mathbf{X} - \mu_{ij})^t (L^{-1})^t L^{-1}(\mathbf{X} - \mu_{ij}) \right]$$

$$= (2\pi)^{-p/2} |\Sigma|^{-1/2} \exp\left(-\frac{1}{2} \|L^{-1}\mathbf{X} - L^{-1}\mu_{ij}\|^2 \right) \qquad (3.32)$$

where $\|\cdot\|$ is the usual euclidean norm on R^N.

Alternatively, matrix L can be chosen so that it characterizes the discrete Karhunen-Loeve transformation corresponding to Σ, that is, $L^{-1} = \Lambda^{-1/2} U^t$, where $\Sigma = U \Lambda U^t$. However, the Cholesky decomposition requires less computation to determine L^{-1} and less computation in the evaluation of Eq. (3.31), since L^{-1} is then lower triangular.

A neural network topology for implementation of classification using the mixture-of-gaussians technique is shown in Fig. 3.16. It is similar to, but more general than, the PNN topology of Fig. 3.2. Between the input units and the pattern units are now placed $p\,L^{-1}$ transform units, which perform the function of rotating the measurement space to

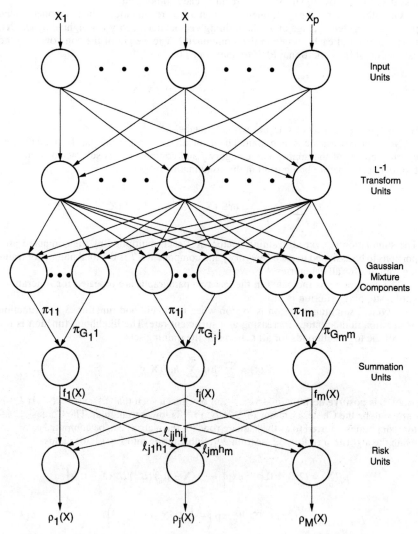

FIGURE 3.16 Probabilistic neural network using mixture of gaussian densities (after Streit and Luginbuhl).

a new set of axes. The gaussian mixture components are identical to the pattern units, except for the method used for training and the π coefficients, which give the components weight in proportion to the number of training samples represented.

The summation units are unchanged. The risk units implement the minimum risk strategy for decision making for multiple categories, and are equally appropriate for basic PNN with multiple categories.

As pointed out to me by Dr. Roy Streit [43], estimation of PDFs by a mixture of gaussian densities can proceed iteratively in the same way with or without constraints on covariance matrices. If the covariance matrices for all nodes are constrained to be the same and diagonal, the procedure will simultaneously find a set of prototype vectors and the set of variances. When this is done, the L^{-1} transform units of Fig. 3.16 can be eliminated if the input units perform a simple division of the raw input by the square root of the corresponding variance term.

From this diagram, it is clear that the benefit of restricting mixtures to homoscedastic kernels is that only one L^{-1} transform has to be performed on each input (pattern) vector. After that, the pattern units, of which there may be large numbers, can be as simple as those described in Fig. 3.6.

Since the pattern units of Fig. 3.5 are mathematically equivalent to those of Fig. 3.6, the entire network, with the exception of the exponential activation, can be implemented by using multiply/accumulate chips common for digital signal processing.

Note that the Adaptive PNN of Sec. 3.2 can be used very effectively to reduce the dimensionality p of the patterns before any of the clustering techniques are applied.

3.6 ONE CATEGORY AND PROVISION FOR UNKNOWN CATEGORIES

3.6.1 Detection

When it is necessary to classify a pattern as the category of interest versus everything else, it may be impractical to get a sufficient number of training samples for "everything else." In this case, it is important to train a PDF on just one category and then establish a threshold on that PDF.

In most of the classification problems discussed, the kernel parameters were determined based on classification accuracy. The PDFs for one category by itself can be estimated by using maximum likelihood to establish the values of the smoothing parameters to be used. Referring back to Eq. (3.7), which is the likelihood of pattern **X** belonging to category k, we see that the *likelihood* (*LH*) that all patterns $\mathbf{X}_{ki}$ belong to category k is the sum of the logs of $f_k(\mathbf{X})$ evaluated at each pattern (using the holdout method to avoid an artificial maximum at $\sigma = 0$).

$$\text{Log LH} = \sum_{i=1}^{m} \log \sum_{\substack{j=1 \\ j \neq i}}^{m} \frac{1}{(2\pi)^{p/2}\sigma^p} \exp\left(-\frac{\left|\mathbf{X}_{ki} - \mathbf{X}_{kj}\right|^2}{2\sigma^2}\right)$$

The best σ for the one-category case can be found as the value that maximizes the log likelihood.

The log likelihood can also be maximized with more than one free parameter such as a separate smoothing parameter for each dimension or the mixture-of-gaussians procedure of the previous section.

In any of these cases, the threshold on the estimated PDF will have to be determined on the basis of the number of false-positive detections or misses one is able to tolerate.

3.6.2 Different Kernels for Different Categories

In many problems, it is clear that the underlying probability distributions are quite different for different categories. Again, the maximum-likelihood technique can be used separately for each category (with or without the mixture-of-gaussians technique of Sec. 3.5). It is also possible to optimize classification accuracy by adapting separate σ's for each category.

The choice between selection of σ based on classification accuracy or selection based on maximum likelihood depends on the problem to be solved. Selection based on classification accuracy optimizes the value of σ at the decision boundary, with little concern for estimating the shape of the PDF in other regions. On the other hand, estimation based on maximum likelihood is better when categories have widely differing variances, and therefore one size-estimating kernel is not appropriate for all categories.

3.6.3 Unknown Categories

Most neural network classifiers are based on the assumption that all patterns belong to one of a fixed set of possible categories. When examples of a new category, for which there have been no training examples, first appear, it is important not to classify them into one of the known categories. Instead, the classifier should recognize novelty in the new patterns and establish a new category.

This can be accomplished within the framework of PNN by simply postulating an unknown category θ_u and then assigning lower values of loss to misclassification of a pattern from a known category as unknown than the loss associated with misclassifying the pattern into the wrong known category. To simplify the following analysis, ℓ_i is defined as the loss associated with misclassification of a category i pattern as belonging to any other known category. In addition to supplying values for the ℓ_i's, the user must supply rough approximations for the following values:

- ℓ_{uk}, the loss associated with misclassification of a pattern from an unknown category into a known category
- ℓ_{ku}, the loss associated with misclassification of a pattern from any of the N known categories as an unknown
- h_i, the a priori probability of observing a pattern from category i
- h_u, the a priori probability of observing a pattern from a new category (unknown)
- $f_u(\mathbf{X})$, the PDF for unknowns and assumed uniform over the range of measurement variables

The loss values ℓ_i are always larger than ℓ_{ku}. ℓ_{ku} may or may not be equal to ℓ_{uk}.

The risk associated with classifying a pattern $\mathbf{X}$ into one of the N known categories θ_j is then

$$\text{Risk } (\theta = \theta_j) = \ell_{uk} h_u f_u(\mathbf{X}) + \sum_{\substack{i=1 \\ i \neq j}}^{N} \ell_i h_i f_i(\mathbf{X})$$

The risk associated with classifying a pattern $\mathbf{X}$ into the unknown category is

$$\text{Risk } (\theta = \theta_u) = \ell_{ku} \sum_{i=1}^{N} h_i f_i(\mathbf{X})$$

The decision to classify the pattern $\mathbf{X}$ into one of the N known categories is

$$d(\theta = \theta_j) \qquad \text{if } \ell_j h_j f_j(\mathbf{X}) > \ell_i h_i f_i(\mathbf{X}) \qquad \text{for all } i \neq j$$

and

$$\ell_{uk} h_u f_u(\mathbf{X}) + \sum_{\substack{i=1 \\ i \neq j}}^{N} \ell_i h_i f_i(\mathbf{X}) < \ell_{ku} \sum_{i=1}^{N} h_i f_i(\mathbf{X})$$

The decision to classify the pattern $\mathbf{X}$ as an unknown is made if the second condition is not true.

These decision rules replace the original PNN decision rule of Eq. (3.4).

An example of this approach, using multispectral imagery, involved the classification of clouds against a background of ice and snow. Meteorologists and photo interpreters have traditionally done poorly with this problem, since everything looks white.

A 12-channel imager produced the image in the California Sierras near the town of Bridgeport shown in Fig. 3.17. Thirty-seven pixel samples each were collected of clouds, snow, water, bare soil, and runoff. These were used as training examples for their respective categories. The classified image (Fig. 3.18) shows the results with clouds labeled white, snow, water, bare soil, and runoff labeled by various shades of gray as shown, and unknown labeled black. In this case, unknown tends to indicate only transition pixels on the border between one category and the next. What seemed to impress the meteorologists the most was the correct classification of snow and water in shadow regions produced by the clouds.

The PNN used only the pixel vectors for classification with no other contextual information.

This same neural network was given a new image to classify, taken over Mono Lake. The known categories all appear to be correct, and three significant regions of unknown pixels are obvious in the classified image (Fig. 3.19). These regions are a region of lava,

FIGURE 3.17   Natural color image.

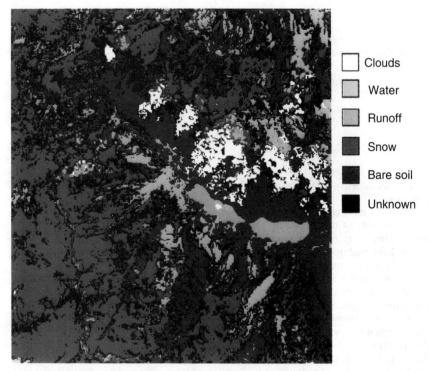

FIGURE 3.18   PNN classification of the multispectral image.

an island covered with seagull droppings, and Highway 395 (asphalt). These were correctly identified as unknown because no examples of these regions were provided in the
training. We now have the option of adding the pixels from the lava, island, and highway to the PNN as new categories or as additional samples of the old categories (for
instance, lava may be chosen to be another example of bare soil).

3.7   RADIAL-BASIS FUNCTIONS

Neural networks based on localized basis functions and iterative function approximation are usually referred to as *radial-basis function* (RBF) *networks*. RBF networks have
a long history, dating back to the Russian school of Bashkirov et al. [44] and Aizerman
et al. [45], at which time the networks were referred to as the *method of potential functions*. They were introduced with the more descriptive name by Broomhead and Lowe
[29], Moody and Darken [26], and Poggio and Girosi [46].

   Classification of new patterns is done in much the same way with RBFs as with
PNNs. In both cases, localized basis functions respond strongly when the input vector
presented is similar to the center of the basis function. The response of the localized
basis function falls off rapidly as the distance between the center of the basis function
and the input vector gets large. In the simplest case, the output of the network is a linear combination of all the basis function responses (see Fig. 3.20). Again, the pattern

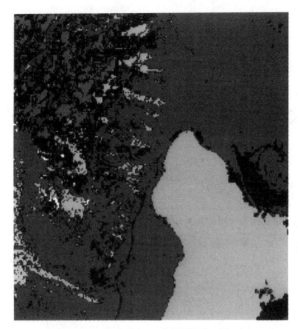

FIGURE 3.19   Mono Lake image with PNN classifications.

units can be represented by Fig. 3.6, 3.7, or 3.5. The output unit multiplies each pattern unit activation by a weight, sums them, and adds a bias.

The most significant difference between RBF and PNN is the method of training. Training the RBF consists of iteratively adapting the parameters of the network until the output approaches the desired output over the whole range of training patterns. The RBF network is inherently a regression network and so estimates the value of a continuous variable. When it is desired to use the RBF as a two-category classifier, the desired output is usually set to +1 for one category and –1 for the other. The parameters of the network which can be adjusted are not only the output weights W but also the centers of the basis functions and any or all of their shape parameters.

There are as many variations and nuances to RBFs as there are to PNN and GRNN networks. Although space does not permit going into all of them here, I will make some general comparisons.

1. RBFs always cluster whereas PNNs are defined with one node per training point and have to have clustering added.

2. An RBF network can be assigned a fixed number of nodes. The complexity of the network does not grow as new training samples become available.

3. The fixed number of nodes can be small, leading to efficient classification or estimation from new patterns.

4. It is easy to mix nodes of different widths and other parameters.

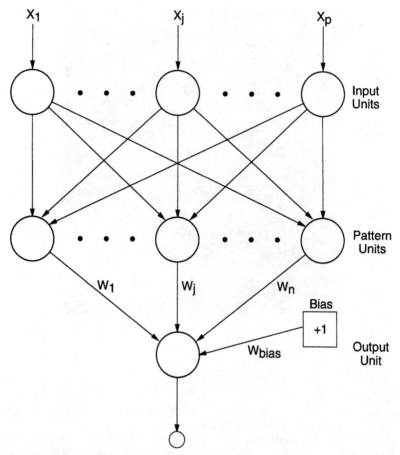

FIGURE 3.20   A radial-basis function network.

On the other hand, PNN and GRNN have certain advantages based on their roots in probability theory:

1. PNN can begin to classify after having just one training pattern from each category; GRNN can begin to estimate after having just one training pattern.
2. In addition to classifying patterns, PNN is able to estimate the probability that a pattern belongs to a certain class.
3. Novelty detection is possible, and the method for classification into the "unknown" category is easily justified.
4. The principal of maximum likelihood can be used to estimate the parameters of the kernel.
5. For small training sets, PNN and GRNN train instantaneously and can begin classification in real time. When the training sets are large enough that clustering is required, this advantage disappears.

6. Detection is possible by estimating only a single PDF and thresholding.

7. It is easier for the human to understand how the network works, or to understand why it is not working when it is not.

One variant of RBF which has interesting qualities is the resource allocation network of Platt [47]. It does not start out with a fixed number of nodes; it allocates just enough nodes of varying widths to obtain the desired accuracy on the training set. This results in a very fast network for production estimation problems. In our laboratory we have also modified it to be a classifier by adjusting the targets to be +1 or −1. In training, there is no error correction if the network produces a value > +1 for a desired +1, or for a value < −1 for a desired −1.

3.8 SUMMARY

This chapter has described probabilistic neural networks (PNNs), which have broad applicability to classification problems based on learning from labeled samples, and general regression neural networks (GRNNs), which estimate values of continuous variables such as future position, future values, or multivariate interpolation.

Basic PNN is based on Parzen window estimation of probability density functions and the Bayes strategy for decision making. Further developments which are also described are Adaptive PNN, clustering to reduce the number of nodes, mixture-of-gaussians clustering, discovery of unknown categories by using PNN, and detection of a single category. Adaptive PNN is a technique which can be used to simultaneously reduce dimensionality and improve generalization accuracy.

Basic GRNN is followed by descriptions of versions that use clustering and can follow nonstationary statistics. Adaptive GRNN is a technique that can be used to simultaneously reduce dimensionality and improve generalization accuracy (similarly to Adaptive PNN).

Radial-basis function networks are discussed briefly in the context that they also use localized receptive fields, but differ in training techniques.

The use of special-purpose parallel hardware to speed classification and estimation is described.

In all, many different variations of PNN and GRNN have been discussed. The basic forms have the important advantage of instant learning. These are ideal for exploring new databases and preprocessing algorithms because frequent retraining is often required in these circumstances. The adaptive versions, being iterative, require long training times but offer (usually) much-improved generalization accuracy relative to the basic forms and also relative to back propagation networks. The clustering versions, particularly the mixture-of-gaussians form, and RBFs provide compact networks that are the fastest for evaluating new patterns after training is complete.

ACKNOWLEDGMENTS

This work was supported by Lockheed Missiles & Space Company, Inc., independent research project RDD360 (neural network technology). The author wishes to thank Dr. R. C. Smithson, Dr. W. A. Fisher, T. P. Washburne, Bob Drake, Dr. E. Reyna, Dr. L. Senbetu, and Harlan Romsdahl for many helpful discussions and for programming and testing the techniques discussed.

REFERENCES

1. D. F. Specht, "Probabilistic Neural Networks for Classification, Mapping or Associative Memory," *Proc. IEEE International Conference on Neural Networks,* vol. 1, pp. 525–532, 1988.

2. D. F. Specht, "Probabilistic Neural Networks," *Neural Networks,* vol. 3, pp. 109–118, 1990.

3. D. F. Specht, "A General Regression Neural Network," *IEEE Transactions on Neural Networks,* vol. 2, pp. 568–576, November 1991.

4. D. E. Rumelhart, G. E. Hinton, and R. J. Williams, "Learning Internal Representation by Error Propagation," *Parallel Distributed Processing: Explorations in the Microstructure of Cognition,* vols. 1 and 2, MIT Press, Cambridge, MA, 1986.

5. A. M. Mood and F. A. Graybill, *Introduction to the Theory of Statistics,* Macmillan, New York, 1962.

6. D. F. Specht, "Generation of Polynomial Discriminant Functions for Pattern Recognition," *IEEE Trans. on Electronic Computers,* vol. EC-16, pp. 308–319, 1967.

7. T. P. Washburne, D. F. Specht, and R. M. Drake, "Identification of Unknown Categories with Probabilistic Neural Networks," *Proc. IEEE International Conference on Neural Networks,* vol. 1, pp. 434–427, San Francisco, March 28–April 1, 1993.

8. E. Parzen, "On Estimation of a Probability Density Function and Mode," *Annals of Mathematical Statistics,* vol. 33, pp. 1065–1076, 1962.

9. T. Cacoullos, "Estimation of a Multivariate Density," *Annals of Institute of Statistical Mathematics (Tokyo),* vol. 18, no. 2, pp. 179–189, 1966.

10. D. F. Specht, "Vectorcardiographic Diagnosis Using the Polynomial Discriminant Method of Pattern Recognition," *IEEE Transactions on Biomedical Engineering,* vol. BME-14, pp. 90–95, 1967.

11. C. L. Scofield and D. L. Reilly, "Into Silicon: Real Time Learning in a High Density RBF Neural Network," *Proceedings of the International Joint Conference on Neural Networks,* vol. 1, pp. 551–556, Seattle, WA, July 1991.

12. T. M. Cover and P. E. Hart, "Nearest Neighbor Pattern Classification," *IEEE Trans. Inf. Theory,* vol. IT-13, pp. 21–27, 1967.

13. D. F. Specht, "Generation of Polynomial Discriminant Functions for Pattern Recognition," Ph.D. dissertation, Stanford University. Also available as report SU-SEL-66-029, Stanford Electronic Laboratories, 1966.

14. P. S. Maloney, *An Application of Probabilistic Neural Networks to a Hull-to-Emitter Correlation Problem.* Paper presented at the 6th Annual Intelligence Community AI Symposium, Washington, DC, October 1988.

15. D. F. Specht and P. D. Shapiro, "Training Speed Comparison of Probabilistic Neural Networks with Back-Propagation Networks," *Proceedings of the International Neural Network Conference,* vol. 1, pp. 440–443, Paris, France, July 9–13, 1990.

16. D. F. Specht, "Enhancements to Probabilistic Neural Networks," *Proceedings of the IEEE International Joint Conference on Neural Networks,* Baltimore, MD, June 7–11, 1992.

17. D. F. Specht and H. Romsdahl, "Experience with Adaptive PNN and Adaptive GRNN," *Proceedings of the IEEE International Conference on Neural Networks,* vol. 2, pp. 1203–1208, Orlando, FL, June 28–July 2, 1994.

18. W. H. Press, B. P. Flannery, S. A. Teukolsky, and W. T. Vetterling, *Numerical Recipes in C: The Art of Scientific Computing,* Cambridge University Press, Cambridge, England, 1988.

19. D. F. Specht and P. D. Shapiro, "Generalization Accuracy of Probabilistic Neural Networks Compared with Back-Propagation Networks," *Proceedings of the International Joint Conference on Neural Networks,* vol. 1, pp. 887–892, Seattle, WA, July 1991.

20. P. J. Grother and G. T. Candela, "Comparison of Handprinted Digit Classifiers," National Institute of Standards and Technology Report NISTIR 5209, June 1993.

21. G. T. Candela and R. Chellappa, "Comparative Performance of Classification Methods for Fingerprints," National Institute of Standards and Technology Report NISTIR 5163, April 1993.

22. J. L. Blue, G. T. Candela, P. J. Grother, R. Chellappa, and C. L. Wilson, "Evaluation of Pattern Classifiers for Fingerprint and OCR Applications," *Pattern Recognition,* vol. 27, no. 4, pp. 485–501, 1994.

23. "NeuroShell 2" software package, Ward Systems Group, Frederick, MD.

24. P. Burrascano, "Learning Vector Quantization for the Probabilistic Neural Network," *IEEE Trans. on Neural Networks,* vol. 2, pp. 458–461, July 1991.

25. J. T. Tou and R. C. Gonzales, *Pattern Recognition Principles,* Addison-Wesley, Reading, MA, 1974.

26. J. Moody and C. Darken, "Fast Learning in Networks of Locally Tuned Processing Units," *Neural Computation,* vol. 1, pp. 281–294, 1989.

27. Ming-Lei Tseng, "Integrating Neural Networks with Influence Diagrams for Multiple Sensor Diagnostic Systems," Ph.D. dissertation, University of California at Berkeley, August 1991.

28. D. L. Reilly, L. N. Cooper, and C. Elbaum, "A Neural Model for Category Learning," *Biological Cybernetics,* vol. 45, pp. 35–41, 1982.

29. D. S. Broomhead and D. Lowe, "Multivariable Functional Interpolation and Adaptive Networks," *Complex Systems,* vol. 2, pp. 321–355, 1988.

30. W. T. Miller, III, F. H. Glanz, and L. G. Kraft, III, "CMAC: An Associative Neural Network Alternative to Backpropagation," *Proc. IEEE,* vol. 78, pp. 1561–1567, October 1990.

31. D. F. Specht, "A Practical Technique for Estimating General Regression Surfaces," LMSC-6-79-68-6, Lockheed Missiles & Space Co., Inc., Palo Alto, CA, June 1968; also available as Defense Technical Information Center no. AD-672505 or NASA no. N68-29513.

32. W. A. Fisher and H. E. Rauch, "Augmentation of an Extended Kalman Filter with a Neural Network," *Proc. IEEE International Conference on Neural Networks,* vol. 2, pp. 1191–1196, Orlando, FL, June 1994.

33. K. S. Narendra and K. Parthasarathy, "Identification and Control of Dynamical Systems Using Neural Networks," *IEEE Trans. Neural Networks,* vol. 1, pp. 4–27, March 1990.

34. C. G. Atkeson and D. J. Reinkensmeyer, "Using Associative Content-Addressable Memories to Control Robots", pp. 255–285 in *Neural Networks for Control,* edited by W. T. Miller , R. S. Sutton, and P. J. Werbos, MIT Press, Cambridge, MA, 1990, Chap.11, pp. 255–285.

35. J. Farrell, W. Goldenthal, and K. Govindarajan, "Connectionist Learning Control Systems: Submarine Depth Control," in *Proc. 29th IEEE Conf. on Decision and Control,* December 1990.

36. R. L. Kendrick, D. S. Acton, and A. L. Duncan, "Phase-Diversity Wave-Front Sensor for Imaging Systems," *Applied Optics,* vol. 33, pp. 6533–6546, September 1994.

37. J. C. Bezdek and P. F. Castelaz, "Prototype Classification and Feature Selection with Fuzzy Sets," *IEEE Trans. SMC,* SMC-7, pp. 87–92, 1977.

38. H. G. C. Traven, "A Neural Network Approach to Statistical Pattern Classification by 'Semiparametric' Estimation of Probability Density Functions," *IEEE Trans. on Neural Networks,* vol. 2, pp. 366–377, May 1991.

39. R. L. Streit, "A Neural Network for Optimum Neyman-Pearson Classification," *Proc. Int. Joint Conf. on Neural Networks,* vol. 1, pp. 685–690, June 1990.

40. R. L. Streit and Tod E. Luginbuhl, "Maximum Likelihood Training of Probabilistic Neural Networks," *IEEE Trans. on Neural Networks,* vol. 5, pp. 764–783, 1994.

41. A. P. Dempster, N. M. Laird, and D. B. Rubin, "Maximum Likelihood from Incomplete Data via the EM Algorithm," *J. Royal Statistical Society,* series B, vol. 39, pp. 1–38, 1977.

42. W. H. Press, B. P. Flannery, S. A. Teukolsky, and W. T. Vetterling, *Numerical Recipes in Fortran: The Art of Scientific Computing,* 2d ed., Cambridge University Press, New York, 1992.

43. Roy Streit, Personal communication at Naval Underwater Systems Center, Newport, RI, August 7–11, 1990.

44. O. A. Bashkirov, E. M. Braverman, and I. B. Muchnik, "Potential Function Algorithms for Pattern Recognition Learning Machines," *Automation and Remote Control,* vol. 25, pp. 692–695, 1964.

45. M. A. Aizerman, E. M. Braverman, and L. I. Rozonoer, "Theoretical Foundations of Potential Function Method in Pattern Recognition," *Automation and Remote Control* , vol. 25, pp. 917–936, 1964.

46. T. Poggio and F. Girosi, "A Theory of Networks for Approximation and Learning," A.I. Memo 1140, Artificial Intelligence Laboratory, Massachusetts Institute of Technology, Cambridge, MA, July 1989.

47. J. Platt, "A Resource-Allocating Network for Function Interpolation," *Neural Computation,* vol. 3, pp. 213–225, 1991.

CHAPTER 4
RECURRENT NEURAL NETWORKS FOR OPTIMIZATION

Jun Wang

Department of Industrial Technology
University of North Dakota, Grand Forks
and
Department of Mechanical and Automation Engineering
The Chinese University of Hong Kong, Shatin, Hong Kong

The ability to solve large-scale optimization problems in real time is essential in many design, planning, control, and information processing applications. In the past few years, the role of neural networks in optimization has been widely recognized by researchers in many disciplines such as engineering and operations research. This chapter provides an overview of neural network models and their role in real-time optimization. Following a general discussion of neural networks, this chapter describes various recurrent neural networks for solving optimization problems. In particular, a recurrent neural network for convex programming, called the deterministic annealing neural network, is discussed in detail.

4.1 INTRODUCTION

Most design and planning tasks in engineering and business applications can be formulated as optimization problems. An optimization problem maximizes or minimizes a single or multiple objective functions subject to a set of constraints to determine a set of optimal solutions. In many practical optimization problems such as the planning of power systems and telecommunication systems, the numbers of decision variables and constraints are usually very large. It is even more challenging when a large-scale optimization procedure has to be performed in real time to optimize the performance of a dynamic system. For such applications, classical optimization techniques may not be competent due to the problem of dimensionality and stringent requirements on computational time.

Neural networks are composed of many massively connected neurons. With their structures resembling more or less their biological counterparts, artificial neural networks are representational and computational models composed of interconnected simple processing elements called *artificial neurons*. In processing information, the processing elements in an artificial neural network operate concurrently and collectively in a parallel and distributed fashion. It has been postulated that such models with the structures similar to biological neural networks could possess some degree of intelligent characteristics. Based on this bottom-up postulate and supported by the results of numerous studies, artificial neural networks have been perceived as potentially powerful tools for solving a variety of problems.

Neural networks have very close ties with optimization, and the ties are manifested mainly in two aspects. On one hand, many learning algorithms have been developed based on optimization techniques to train neural networks (typically feedforward neural networks) to perform numerous modeling tasks. The popular back propagation algorithm, for example, is essentially based on the gradient descent method. On the other hand, neural networks (typically recurrent neural networks) have been developed for solving various optimization problems. As dynamic systems, recurrent neural networks can serve as parallel computational models suitable for solving computationally intensive optimization problems. Because of the inherent nature of parallel and distributed information processing in neural networks, neural networks are promising computational models for solving large-scale optimization problems in real time.

Organized in two parts, this chapter discusses the role of neural networks in optimization. Following a brief historic account of well-known existing neural network models, the first part of this chapter provides a taxonomy of neural network models, a discussion of the use of recurrent neural networks for optimization, and an overview of various recurrent neural network models developed for optimization purposes. The second part of this chapter focuses on a specific recurrent neural network for solving convex programming problems, called the *deterministic annealing neural network*. Dynamics and characteristics of the deterministic annealing neural network are described in detail.

4.2   OVERVIEW OF NEURAL NETWORK MODELS

4.2.1   Early Neural Network Models

Neural network research stemmed from McCulloch and Pitts' pioneering work a half-century ago. Since then, numerous neural network models have been developed. One of the well-known classic neural network models is the Perceptron developed by Rosenblatt. The Perceptron is a single-layer adaptive feedforward network of threshold logic units, which possess some learning capability. Another important early neural network model is the Adaline, which is a one-layer linear network using the delta learning rule. The Perceptron and Adaline were designed primarily for the purpose of pattern classification. Given a set of input-output training patterns, the Perceptron and Adaline could learn from the exemplar patterns and adapt their parametric representations accordingly to match the patterns. The limitation of the Perceptron and Adaline is that they could only classify linearly separable patterns because, among others, they lacked an internal representation of stimuli.

In the last decade, there was an exciting resurgence in the studies of artificial neural networks due to the introduction of new net topologies, new activation functions, and new learning algorithms as well as progress in neuroscience and cognitive science. Advances in theory and methodology have overcome many obstacles that hindered neural network research a few decades ago, and neural networks have been proposed for numerous applications. The well-known existing neural networks include *adaptive resonance theory (ART), self-organizing map (SOM)*, Hopfield networks, the Boltzmann machine, and multilayer Perceptron. Grossberg and Carpenter developed the ART models as unsupervised learning systems for clustering. Kohonen developed a neuronlike system which could reconstruct the ordering of input patterns in output space. A stochastic neural network model called the *Boltzmann machine* developed by Hinton et al. is a parallel realization of the simulated annealing procedure. Neural network models of binary and continuous variables were proposed by Hopfield [23, 24] as associative memories and by Hopfield and Tank [25, 56] to solve optimization problems such as the traveling salesperson problem. A multilayer Perceptron with an error back propagation learning algorithm proposed by Rumelhart et al. [47] is one of the most popular artificial neural network models. Rather than using threshold logic units or linear functions for activation, the multilayer Perceptron uses a differentiable sigmoidal activation function to facilitate learning. Therefore, the multilayer Perceptron possesses a better learning capability than the Perceptron or Adaline for linearly inseparable patterns.

4.2.2   Neural Network Architecture

Neural Network Components.   Despite the diversity of the existing neural network models, there are many common features in the architecture of neural network models. A neural network model is composed of a number of inputs, a number of outputs, and a number of artificial neurons (also called *nodes, processing units,* or *computational elements*). The neurons are represented by a set of state variables. The state variables are usually functions of the weighted sum of input variables and other state variables, and the output variables are usually a subset of the state variables of output neurons. Each neuron performs a simple transformation concurrently in a parallel distributed manner. The input-output relationship of the transformation (i.e., the function of the weighted sum) in a neuron is usually characterized by a real-valued continuous function and usually is called the *activation function.* Two typical examples of real-valued activation functions are the threshold function and sigmoidal function. The strength of interaction among the neurons is reflected by the weights on connections which determine the functional behavior of the neural network. The combination of inputs, outputs, neurons, and connection links constitutes the architecture of a neural network.

Neural networks can be classified in different ways. According to the nature of activation, neural networks can be categorized as deterministic neural networks and stochastic neural networks. According to the nature of connectivity, neural networks can be categorized as feedforward neural networks and recurrent neural networks. According to the nature of state integration, neural networks can be categorized as semilinear neural networks and higher-order neural networks.

Deterministic and Stochastic Neural Networks.   Deterministic neural networks are those whose activation functions are deterministic, usually real-valued and monotonic increasing. Typical examples of activation functions in deterministic neural networks are the threshold logic unit as used in the Perceptron and the binary Hopfield network [23], the linear function as used in the Adaline, and the sigmoidal (logistic) function as used in the multilayer Perceptron [47] and the continuous Hopfield network [24]. Most of the existing neural network models are deterministic.

Stochastic neural networks activate their states according to a probability distribution. The probability distribution functions for activation are usually monotonic increasing. A typical example of stochastic neural networks is the Boltzmann machine. The introduction of randomness in activation provides stochastic neural networks with hill-climbing capability and enables state transition to avoid local optima in use for optimization. The tradeoff is usually a long transition period needed for convergence.

Feedforward and Recurrent Neural Networks.   In a feedforward neural network, all the connections are unidirectional in a feedforward way. A typical example of feedforward neural networks is the popular multilayer Perceptron. A multilayer Perceptron consists of an input layer of input variables, an output layer of output variables, and at least one hidden layer of hidden neurons. Unidirectional connections exist from the input layer to the hidden layer and from the hidden layer to the output layer. There is no connection between any neurons in the same layer. The output variables are real-valued functions of input variables and weights. The input-output mapping can be changed by adjusting the weights. It has been proved that multilayer feedforward neural networks are universal approximators [26]. It has also been demonstrated that neural networks trained based on a limited number of training samples possess a good generalizing capability. Feedforward neural networks, such as the popular multilayer Perceptron, are usually used as representational models trained using a learning rule based on a set of input-output sample data. A popular learning rule is the widely used back propagation algorithm (also known as the *generalized delta rule*). Large-scale systems that contain a large number of variables and complex systems where little analytical knowledge is available are typical examples of potential applications of feedforward neural networks.

In the architecture of a recurrent neural network, feedback connections exist among neurons. Because of the existence of state feedback, a recurrent neural network exhibits dynamic behavior. That is, given the initial state, the state of a recurrent neural network evolves as time elapses. If the recurrent neural network is stable, a state equilibrium can eventually be reached. Recurrent neural networks, exemplified by the Hopfield networks [23, 24], are usually used as computational models for storing information as associative memories and solving computationally intensive problems. Typical examples of neural network applications are solving NP-complete combinatorial optimization problems and large-scale or real-time computation problems. Neural networks are advantageous over traditional approaches for such problems because neural information processing is inherently parallel and distributed.

Semilinear and Higher-Order Neural Networks.   Semilinear neural networks are the neural networks using weighted sums of states and input variables as arguments of activation functions. Semilinear neural networks are simplified models of biological neural networks. They are relatively easy for analysis, design, and hardware implementation. The majority of the existing neural networks are semilinear networks due to their simplicity.

Higher-order neural networks are those using nonlinear functions of states, such as a quadratic function or a trigonometric function, for activation. The introduction of the higher-order effect usually improves the learning convergence rate and generalization results. A typical example of the higher-order neural network is the functional link network [42] which is a single-layer nonlinear network.

4.3   NEURAL NETWORKS FOR OPTIMIZATION

4.3.1   Design

Much of the impetus for the neural network approaches to optimization was initialized by Hopfield and Tank. In their seminal work, Hopfield and Tank used the continuous Hopfield networks [24] for solving combinatorial optimization problems (e.g., the traveling salesperson problem) [25] and linear programming problems [56].

The rationale behind optimization using recurrent neural networks is that a recurrent neural network can act as a goal-seeking dynamic system, and the equilibrium state of the neural network can minimize an abstract energy function. The crux for the success of optimization using a neural network lies in the formulation of an energy function, based on the objective function and constraints of a given optimization problem, and the derivation of a dynamic equation of the neural network, based on the formulated energy function.

The procedure of a neural network approach to optimization usually begins with the formulation of an energy function based on the objective function and constraints of the optimization problem under study. Ideally, the minimum of a formulated energy function corresponds to the optimal solution (minimum or maximum whatever applicable) of the original optimization problem. Clearly, a convex energy function should be used to eliminate local minima. In nontrivial constrained optimization problems, the minimum of the energy function has to satisfy a set of prespecified constraints. The majority of, if not all, the existing neural network approaches to optimization formulate an energy function by incorporating an objective function and constraints through functional transformation and numerical weighting. Functional transformation is usually used to convert constraints to a penalty function to penalize the violation of constraints. Numerical weighting is often used to balance constraint satisfaction and objective minimization (or maximization). The way the energy function is formulated plays an important role in the optimization problem-solving procedure based on neural networks.

The second step in designing a neural network for optimization usually involves the derivation of a dynamic equation (also known as the *state equation* or *motion equation*) of the neural network based on a formulated energy function. The dynamic equation of a neural network prescribes the motion of the activation states of the neural network. The derivation of a dynamic equation is crucial to the success of the neural network approach to optimization. A properly derived dynamic equation can ensure that the state of the neural network reaches an equilibrium, and the equilibrium state of the neural network satisfies the constraints and optimizes the objective function of the optimization problems under study. Presently, the dynamic equations of most neural networks for optimization are derived by letting the time derivative of a state vector be directly proportional to the negative gradient of an energy function.

The next step is to determine the architecture of the neural network in terms of the neurons and connections based on the derived dynamic equation. An activation function models important characteristics of a neuron. The range of an activation function usually prescribes the domain of state variables (the state space of the neural network). In the use of neural networks for optimization, the activation function depends on the feasible region of decision variables delimited by the constraints of the optimization problem under study. Specifically, it is necessary for the state space to include the feasible region. Any explicit bound on decision variables can be realized by properly selecting the range of activation functions. The activation function is also related to the energy function. If the gradient-based method is adopted in deriving the dynamic equation, then the convex energy function requires an increasing activation function. Precisely, if the steepest-descent method is used, the activation function should be equal to the derivative of the energy function. Figure 4.1 illustrates four examples of energy functions and corresponding activation functions, where the linear activation function can be used for unbounded variables.

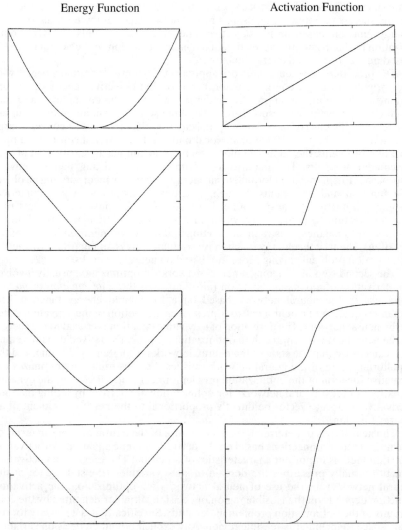

Energy Function   Activation Function

FIGURE 4.1 Examples of convex energy functions and corresponding increasing activation function.

The last step in developing neural networks for optimization is usually devoted to simulation to test the performance of the neural network. Simulations can be performed numerically by using commercial software packages or self-programmed simulators. Simulation can also be implemented physically in hardware (e.g., by using off-the-shelf electronic components).

One of the main advantages of the neural network approach to optimization is that the nature of the dynamic solution procedure is inherently parallel and distributed. Therefore, the convergence rate of the solution process is not decreasing as the size of the problem increases from a statistical point of view. Furthermore, unlike other parallel algorithms, neural networks can be implemented physically in designated hardware such as application-specific integrated circuits where optimization is carried out in a truly parallel and distributed manner. This feature is particularly desirable for real-time optimization in decentralized decision-making situations.

4.3.2 Neural Networks for Combinatorial Optimization

The seminal works of Hopfield and Tank [25, 26] on optimization using the Hopfield networks have opened a new dimension for solving optimization problems. Inspired by Hopfield and Tank's attempts, many researchers have been investigating recurrent neural networks for solving combinatorial optimization problems; see Ref. 35 for a recent survey.

Unfortunately, the Hopfield-Tank neural network paradigm did not provide a panacea for optimization. Insufficiency of the Hopfield networks for combinatorial optimization was soon reported. For example, Wilson and Pawley [71] reported the inability of the Hopfield-Tank neural network paradigm [25] to solve the *traveling salesperson problem* (*TSP*). To overcome the limitations of the Hopfield network for optimization, numerous remedies have been proposed and some improvements have been made for solving combinatorial optimization problems, especially the TSP. To name a few, Brandt et al. [5] used a different energy function for the Hopfield network to solve the TSP; Cuykendall and Reese [18] used a scaling technique, and Van den Bout and Miller [59] used normalization and annealing techniques to improve the performance of the Hopfield network for solving the TSP; Xu and Tsai [73] used the Hopfield network and an improved Hopfield network based on the adaptive subtour elimination technique for solving the TSP; Abe et al. [2] used eigenvalue analysis to characterize the stability of the Hopfield networks for combinatorial optimization with inequality constraints. Wacholder et al. [61] developed a neural network for solving the multiple TSP.

In view of the difficulties in using the Hopfield networks for solving the TSP, many alternative neural networks have been proposed. Angeniol et al. [3], Favata and Walker [22], and Burke [8] discussed neural network approaches to the TSP using SOM. Aarts and Korst [1] proposed solving the TSP by using the Boltzmann machines. Durbin et al. [19] and Simmen [48] used elastic nets to solve the TSP. Peterson [43] summarized the results of several TSP benchmarks using neural network, elastic net, genetic algorithm, and simulated annealing. Peterson and Soderberg [44] proposed a new method for mapping optimization problems onto neural networks. Burke and Damany [6] proposed an adaptive neural network called the *guilty net* for solving the TSP. Javadeva and Bhaumik [27] proposed a neural network based on sequential unconstrained minimization techniques. Wang [67] proposed a recurrent neural network with time-varying connections and thresholds for solving the TSP. Sun and Fu [50] proposed a hybrid neural network which contains a constraint subnetwork and a goal subnetwork for solving the TSP.

Meanwhile, numerous neural networks have also been proposed for solving other combinatorial optimization problems [17, 54, 55]. For example, deterministic and stochastic neural networks have been developed for solving the *linear assignment problem* (*LAP*) [10, 20, 32, 49, 57, 64, 72], *quadratic assignment problem* (*QAP*) [9, 40, 67], *generalized assignment problem* (*GAP*) [21], the knapsack problem [41], and the job-shop scheduling problem [60]. Many neural networks have been developed for solving combinatorial optimization problems [7, 12, 13, 51–54], some of them directly related to graph theory.

Although neural networks have shown great potential for solving combinatorial optimization problems, many theoretical problems are unsolved. Except for special classes of combinatorial optimization problems (e.g., linear integer programming with total unimodular constraint matrix), none of the existing recurrent neural networks can be guaranteed to generate optimal solutions to general combinatorial optimization problems in polynomial time. The majority of proposed procedures for constructing neural networks are heuristic in nature and lack rigorous justifications. Although stochastic neural networks such as the Boltzmann machine are able to generate optimal solutions with probability 1, the computational time required to generate an optimal solution is usually formidable for real-time applications. Therefore, they cannot be guaranteed to obtain optimal solutions to combinatorial optimization problems in polynomial time. The discrete nature of integer programming has eluded the researchers. Because of the insufficient theoretical underpinning, some early excitement on neural network research has faded slightly. In view of the facts that the existing neural network model insofar cannot be guaranteed to obtain optimal solutions and solution optimality is always desirable, further investigations on neural networks for combinatorial optimization are deemed absolutely necessary and rewarding.

4.3.3 Neural Networks for Linear and Nonlinear Programming

While the mainstream of neural network research for optimization has concentrated on NP-complete combinatorial optimization problems, many neural networks have been developed for solving linear and nonlinear programming problems [for example, 4, 11, 14–17, 28–31, 33, 34, 36–39, 45, 46, 56, 58, 62–70, 74–76].

In 1986, Tank and Hopfield [56] showed by means of an illustrative example that the Hopfield network can be used to solve linear programming problems. Although the approach was not rigorously proved, it inspired much enthusiastic research on linear and nonlinear programming using neural networks. Earlier research following Tank and Hopfield's work was mainly pursued by electrical engineering professionals. Kennedy and Chua [30, 31] analyzed the Tank-Hopfield linear programming circuit and the Chua-Lin nonlinear programming circuit from a circuit-theoretic viewpoint and reconciled a modified canonical nonlinear programming circuit. In fact, Chua and Lin [14, 15] developed some approaches to nonlinear programming using electric circuits prior to Tank and Hopfield's effort. Rodriguez-Vázquez et al. [45, 46] and Cichocki and Unbehauen [16] developed switched-capacitor neural networks for linear and nonlinear programming. Kalaba et al. [28, 29] and Moore et al. [39] used feedforward and recurrent neural networks for obtaining good initial solutions to linear programs. Wang [62] and Wang and Chankong [63] proposed recurrent neural networks with monotonically increasing penalty parameters for linear and nonlinear programming. Chen et al. [11] proposed improved neural networks for linear and nonlinear programming based on a combination penalty function. Maa and Shanblatt [36, 37] analyzed and justified the neural network presented by

Kennedy and Chua [30] and proposed a two-phase neural network for linear and nonlinear programming. Zhang and Constantinides [74] and Zhu et al. [76] proposed Lagrange programming neural networks. Zhang et al. [75] proposed second-order neural networks for nonlinear programming. Bouzerdoum and Pattison [4] proposed a neural network for solving quadratic programming problems subject to bound constraints. Milic and Lucic [38] presented quantitative analysis on a Tank-Hopfield-like electronic neural network for linear programming. Wang [68] and Wang and Li [69] developed recurrent neural networks for solving the quadratic programming problem with equality constraints.

4.4 A NEURAL NETWORK PARADIGM FOR CONVEX PROGRAMMING

4.4.1 Problem Statement and Reformulation

Problem Statement. Convex programming deals with the problem of minimizing a convex function over a convex set of variables. Convex programming problems represent a class of widespread optimization problems arising in diverse design and planning contexts. Many large-scale and real-time applications, such as traffic routing and image restoration, require solution of large-scale convex programming problems in real time. In such applications, because of the large number of variables and stringent time requirements, existing algorithmic solution methods are usually not efficient.

While the results of the investigations have demonstrated great potential, most of the existing neural network models, however, are not guaranteed to yield optimal solutions. Although the capability of the recurrent neural networks for solving convex programming problems [62, 63] is substantiated theoretically, the neural network models are not very easy to implement in hardware. Recently, a recurrent neural network, called a *deterministic annealing neural network* [65, 66], was developed for solving convex programming problems. The deterministic annealing neural network has been shown to be capable of generating optimal solutions to convex programming problems. The conditions for asymptotic stability, solution feasibility, and solution optimality have been derived. In this section, the deterministic annealing neural network is detailed. The design methodology for determining design parameters and hardware realization is discussed. Three detailed illustrative examples are also presented to demonstrate the functional and operational characteristics of the deterministic annealing neural network in solving linear and quadratic programs.

Consider a general constrained convex programming problem described as follows:

$$\text{Minimize} \quad f(v) \tag{4.1}$$

$$\text{Subject to} \quad g(v) \leq 0 \tag{4.2}$$

$$h(v) = 0 \tag{4.3}$$

where $v \in \Re^N$ is a column vector of decision variables, $f: \Re^N \to \Re$ is a convex objective function to be minimized, $g: \Re^N \to \Re^m$ is an m-tuple convex function used to define m inequality constraints, and $h: \Re^N \to \Re^n$ is an n-tuple linear function used to define n equality constraints. The inequality constraints (4.2) and equality constraints (4.3) characterize a convex feasible region in N-dimensional euclidean space. Let $\hat{\mathbf{V}}$ denote the convex feasible region, and let $v^* = [v_1^*, v_2^*, \ldots, v_N^*]^T$ denote an optimal solution that minimizes $f(v)$ over $\hat{\mathbf{V}}$, where the superscript T denotes the transpose operator, that is, $\hat{\mathbf{V}} = \{v \in \mathfrak{R}^N | g(v) \leq 0, h(v) = 0\}$ and $v^* = \arg\min_{v \in \hat{\mathbf{V}}} f(v)$. For an obvious reason, we assume that the feasible region $\hat{\mathbf{V}}$ is nonempty and that the objective function value $f(v)$ is bounded from below over $\hat{\mathbf{V}}$. Furthermore, for operational reasons, we assume that $f(v), g(v)$, and $h(v)$ are differentiable with respect to v over $\mathfrak{R}^N$.

Two classes of important convex programming problems are the linear program (LP) and the quadratic program (QP). In the standard form of a linear program, $f(v) = c^T v$ and $g(v) = -v$, $h(v) = Av - b$, where c is an N-dimensional column vector, A is an $n \times N$ matrix, and b is an n-dimensional column vector. In a quadratic program, $f(v) = v^T Q v/2 + c^T v$, and $g(v) = -v$, $h(v) = Av - b$, where Q is an $N \times N$ matrix and A, b, and c are the same as those defined in an LP.

Problem Reformulation.   For a constrained optimization problem to be solved through neural computing, it is usually necessary to characterize the feasible set $\hat{\mathbf{V}}$ by using a penalty function $p(v)$ to penalize a constraint violation. A penalty function characterizes the feasible region of an optimization problem with a functional equality. The basic requirement for the penalty function is nonnegativity, precisely

$$p(v) \begin{cases} = 0 & \text{if } v \in \hat{\mathbf{V}} \\ > 0 & \text{otherwise} \end{cases} \tag{4.4}$$

Additional requirements for the penalty function $p(v)$ are convexity and differentiability. If $p(v)$ is convex and differentiable, then $\min_v p(v) = 0$ and $\forall v \in \hat{\mathbf{V}}$, $\nabla p(v) = 0$.

There are basically two ways to construct the penalty function based on the functional constraints: functional transformation and state augmentation.

Functional Transformation.   Functional transformation involves a mapping of an inequality constraint or an equality constraint to an equality. Specifically,

$$p_g(v) \begin{cases} = 0 & g(v) \leq 0 \\ > 0 & g(v) > 0 \end{cases} \tag{4.5}$$

$$p_h(v) \begin{cases} = 0 & h(v) = 0 \\ > 0 & h(v) \neq 0 \end{cases} \tag{4.6}$$

There are several logical choices of $p_g(v)$ and $p_h(v)$. For example, for $g(v) \leq 0$, the integral of the Heaviside function can be used; for $h(v) = 0$, $\|h(v)\|_2^2$ can be used, where $\|\cdot\|_2$ is the Euclidean norm. Namely,

$$p_g(v) = \sum_{i=1}^{m} \int_{-\infty}^{g_i(v)} H(x)\, dx \tag{4.7}$$

and

$$p_h(v) = \frac{1}{2} \sum_{j=1}^{n} h_j(v)^2 \tag{4.8}$$

where $H(\cdot)$ is the *Heaviside function* defined as follows:

$$H(x) = \begin{cases} 0 & x \leq 0 \\ x & x > 0 \end{cases} \tag{4.9}$$

Since both $g(v)$ and $h(v)$ are differentiable, $p_g(v)$ and $p_h(v)$ are differentiable with respect to v. Based on the convexity of $g(v)$ and $h(v)$, the convexity of $p_g(v)$ and $p_h(v)$ can be proved (see Ref. 66 for the proof).

State Augmentation. State augmentation is an approach that converts the inequality constraints to equality constraints by adding slack or surplus variables. First, the inequality constraint $g(v) \leq 0$ can be converted to equality by adding m slack variables, e.g.,

$$g(v) + v^+ = 0 \tag{4.10}$$

where $v^+ \in \Re^m$ and $v^+ \geq 0$. For example, in an LP problem, if we let $g(v) = Av - b$, then $g(v) + v^+ = Av + v^+ - b = 0$. If $g(v) = r(v) - s$, where $r(v) \geq 0$ and $s \in \Re^m$, then a surplus variable vector $v^- \in \Re^m$ can also be applied as follows:

$$r(v) - s \circ v^- = 0 \tag{4.11}$$

where $0 \leq v_i^- \leq 1$ $(i = 1, 2, \ldots, m)$ and $\circ$ denotes the operator for array multiplication (Schur product). Once all the inequality constraints are converted to equality constraints, a penalty function can be constructed similarly to Eq. (4.8), i.e.,

$$p_g^{(1)}(v) = \frac{1}{2} [g(v) + v^+]^T [g(v) + v^+] \tag{4.12}$$

$$p_g^{(2)}(v) = \frac{1}{2} [r(v) - s \circ v^-]^T [r(v) - s \circ v^-] \tag{4.13}$$

$$p_h(v) = \frac{1}{2} h(v)^T h(v) \tag{4.14}$$

Obviously, $p_g(v)$ and $p_h(v)$ are also differentiable and convex with respect to v.

The penalty function can be constructed based on $p_g(v)$ and $p_h(v)$, for example,

$$p(v) = p_g(v) + p_h(v) \tag{4.15}$$

Since $p_g(v)$ and $p_h(v)$ are convex and differentiable, $p(v)$ is also convex and differentiable. The convex programming problem described in Eqs. (4.1), (4.2), and (4.3) thus can be reformulated as the following equivalent convex programming problem:

$$\text{Minimize} \quad f(v) \tag{4.16}$$

$$\text{Subject to} \quad p(v) = 0 \tag{4.17}$$

4.4.2 Network Dynamics and Architectures

The dynamic equations of the deterministic annealing neural network can be described as follows:

$$\frac{du(t)}{dt} = -T(t) \, \nabla f[v(t)] - \nabla p[v(t)] \tag{4.18}$$

$$v(t) = F[u(t)] \tag{4.19}$$

where $u(t) \in \Re^N$ is a column vector of instantaneous net inputs to neurons, $v(t) \in \mathbf{V} \subset \Re^N$ is a column vector of activation states corresponding to the decision variables, $\mathbf{V}$ is the activation state space, $u(0)$ and $v(0)$ are unspecified, $T(t)$ is a time-varying temperature parameter, $F : u \mapsto v$ is an N-tuple activation function, and ∇ is the gradient operator.

Because the temperature parameter is a function of time, the deterministic annealing neural network is virtually a time-varying dynamic system. Equation (4.18) defines the neural network dynamics, in which the first term of the right-hand side enforces the minimization of the objective function and the second term enforces penalization of violation of constraint (4.17). Equation (4.19) is the activation function that defines the sensitivity and range of the activation state $v(t)$.

The major difference between the existing recurrent neural networks for optimization and the deterministic annealing neural network lies in essentially the treatment of their penalization procedures for violation of constraints. In the Hopfield network for optimization, the penalization is realized by constant penalty parameters (Hopfield and Tank [25] and Tagliarini et al. [51]). As evidenced by many empirical studies, the steady state of the Hopfield network may not represent a feasible solution or an optimal solution to the optimization problem. In the recurrent neural networks developed earlier (Wang [62]; Wang and Chankong [63]), the penalization is realized by a monotonically increasing penalty parameter. Since the penalty parameter is supposed to be unbounded above, it is not easy to implement physically. In the deterministic annealing neural network, the penalization is realized by using a time-varying temperature parameter. The role of the time-varying temperature parameter will be more apparent in Sec. 4.5.

To solve an optimization problem via neural computation, the key is to cast the problem into the architecture of a recurrent neural network whose stable state represents the solution to the optimization problem. As shown in Eq. (4.18), the architecture of the deterministic annealing neural network depends on specific forms of $f(v)$ and $p(v)$ [that is, $f(v)$, $g(v)$, $h(v)$, and the method for constructing $p(v)$].

If the functional transformation method [e.g., Eqs. (4.7) and (4.8)] is used to construct a penalty function, then

$$\nabla p_g(v) = \sum_{i=1}^{m} H[g_i(v)] \nabla g_i(v) \tag{4.20}$$

$$\nabla p_h(v) = \sum_{j=1}^{n} h_j(v) \, \nabla \, h_j(v) \tag{4.21}$$

Obviously, $\forall v \in \hat{\mathbf{V}}, \nabla p_g(v) = \nabla p_h(v) = 0$. Furthermore, since $H(x)$ is continuous, $\nabla p_g(v)$ is also continuous.

If the state augmentation method is used to construct a penalty function based on $g(v)$, then the dimension of the activation state vector increases from N to $N + m$; so does the size of the neural network architecture. According to Eqs. (4.12) and (4.13),

$$\nabla p_g^{(1)}(v^+) = g(v) + v^+ \tag{4.22}$$

$$\nabla p_g^{(2)}(v^-) = -s \circ r(v) + s \circ s \circ v^- \tag{4.23}$$

In view of the fact that $f(v)$ has nothing to do with the augmented state variables, Eqs. (4.22) and (4.23) imply that there is no connection between the neurons corresponding to the augmented state variables $v^+(t)$ or $v^-(t)$ in a neural network architecture.

In the standard form of LP, for example, $f(v) = c^T v$, $g(v) = -v$, and $h(v) = Av - b$. Since the nonnegativity constraint $v \geq 0$ can be realized by using a nonnegative activation function $F[u(t)] \geq 0$, only $h(v)$ needs to be used in the penalty function. Let

$p(v) = p_h(v) = h(v)^T h(v)/2 = (Av - b)^T (Av - b)/2$; thus $\nabla p(v) = \nabla p_h(v) = A^T Av - A^T b$. Equation (4.18) becomes

$$\frac{du(t)}{dt} = -A^T Av(t) + A^T b - T(t)c \qquad (4.24)$$

In the standard form of quadratic program (QP), $f(v) = v^T Qv/2 + c^T v$, $g(v) = -v$, and $h(v) = Av - b$. If we let Q be symmetric and positive semidefinite, similar to the case of LP, Eq. (4.18) becomes

$$\frac{du(t)}{dt} = -[A^T A + T(t)Q]v(t) + A^T b - T(t)c \qquad (4.25)$$

There are two ways to map the dynamic equations, Eqs. (4.24) and (4.25), to a neural network architecture. The first method results in a single-layer recurrent neural network. The single-layer architecture of the deterministic annealing neural network for convex programming consists of N laterally connected neurons, as shown in Fig. 4.2. Each neuron represents one decision variable. The lateral connection weight matrix is defined as $-A^T A$ for an LP and $-A^T A - T(t)Q$ for a QP. The biasing threshold vector of the neurons is defined as $A^T b - T(t)c$ for both the LP and QP. In other words, the connection weight w_{ij} from neuron j to neuron i is defined as $-\Sigma_{k=1}^{n} a_{ki}a_{kj}$ for an LP and $-\Sigma_{k=1}^{n} a_{ki}a_{kj} - T(t)q_{ij}$ for a QP, the biasing threshold θ_i of neuron i is defined as $\Sigma_{k=1}^{n} a_{ki}b_k - T(t)c_i$, where a_{ij} and q_{ij} are the elements in the ith row and the jth column of A and Q, respectively, and b_i and c_i are the ith elements of b and c, respectively. Since Q is symmetric, the connection weight matrices are symmetric for both LP and QP (that is, $\forall i, j, w_{ij} = w_{ji}$). If Q is positive semidefinite and $T(t) \geq 0$, then the eigenvalues of the weight matrices are always real and nonpositive for both the LP and QP.

By letting $e(t) = Av(t) - b$, Eqs. (4.24) and (4.25) can be decomposed, respectively, as

$$\frac{du(t)}{dt} = -A^T e(t) - T(t)c \qquad (4.26)$$

$$\frac{du(t)}{dt} = -A^T e(t) - T(t)Qv(t) - T(t)c \qquad (4.27)$$

The second approach for mapping the dynamic equations to a neural network architecture results in a two-layer architecture composed of an output layer and an input layer, as shown in Fig. 4.2. The output layer consists of N neurons, and the input layer consists of n neurons. The state vectors of the input and output layers are denoted by $e(t)$ and $v(t)$, respectively. The output state vector $v(t)$ represents the decision variable vector v, and the input state vector $e(t)$ represents the error vector that measures the solution feasibility of the output state vector. The connection weight matrix from the input layer to output layer is defined as $-A^T$, and the weight matrix from output layer to input layer is A. In the LP case, there is no lateral connection among input and output neurons. In the QP case, there is no lateral connection among input neurons, and the connection weight matrix among output neurons is $-T(t)Q$. The bias vectors are $-b$ in the input layer and $-T(t)c$ in the output layer, respectively, for both the LP and QP neural networks. The advantage of the second configuration is that the connection weight matrices and bias vectors can be determined directly from the coefficient matrices and vectors without involving matrix multiplication.

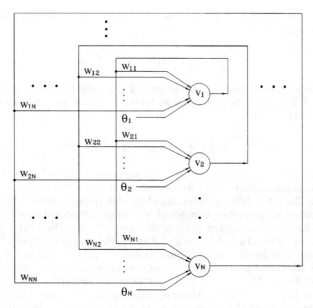

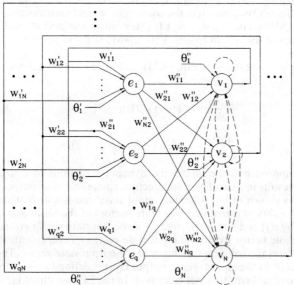

FIGURE 4.2 Single-layer and two-layer architectures of the deterministic annealing neural network.

4.4.3 Stability and Convergence Analyses

Asymptotic Stability

  Theorem 4.1. Assume that the jacobian matrix of $F[u(t)]$ exists and is positive semidefinite. If the temperature parameter $T(t)$ is nonnegative, strictly monotonic decreasing for $t \geq 0$ and approaches zero as time approaches infinity, then the deterministic annealing neural network is asymptotically stable in the large; that is, $\forall t \geq 0$, $J\{F[u(t)]\}$ is positive semidefinite, $T(t) \geq 0$, $dT(t)/dt < 0$, and $\lim_{t \to \infty} T(t) = 0$ imply $\forall v(0) \in \mathbf{V}, \exists \bar{v} \in \mathbf{V}$ such that $\lim_{t \to \infty} v(t) = \bar{v}$, where $J\{F[u(t)]\}$ is the jacobian of $F[u(t)]$ and $\bar{v}$ is a steady state of $v(t)$.

  PROOF. Since $f(v)$ is bounded from below, there exists M such that $-\infty < M < \inf_{v \in \mathbf{V}} f(v)$. Let

$$E[v(t),T(t)] = T(t)\{f[v(t)] - M\} + p[v(t)] \tag{4.28}$$

Since $\forall t \geq 0$, $T(t) \geq 0$, $f[v(t)] - M > 0$, and $p[v(t)] \geq 0$, $\forall v \in V$, $E[v(t),T(t)] \geq 0$. Furthermore, since $\lim_{t \to \infty} T(t) = 0$ and $\min_v p(v) = 0$, $\min_{v,T} E[v,T] = 0$. To facilitate the stability analysis, let's consider $T(t)$ as a dummy state variable for the time being; i.e., we let $\bar{v}(t)^T = [v(t)^T, T(t)]$ be the augmented state vector. In view of the fact that $f(v)$ and $p(v)$ are convex and $T(t) \in [0, \infty)$, $E \to \infty$ as $\|\bar{v}\| \to \infty$; that is, E is radially unbounded. Since $-du(t)/dt = T(t) \nabla f[v(t)] + \nabla p[v(t)]$ and $v(t) = F[u(t)]$ according to Eqs. (4.18) and (4.19), $dv(t)/dt = J\{F[u(t)]\}\ du(t)/dt$ and

$$\frac{dE[v(t),T(t)]}{dt} = \{f[v(t)] - M\}\frac{dT(t)}{dt} + T(t)\frac{df[v(t)]}{dt} + \frac{dp[v(t)]}{dt}$$

$$= \{f[v(t)] - M\}\frac{dT(t)}{dt} + \{T(t)\nabla f[v(t)] + \nabla p[v(t)]\}^T \frac{dv(t)}{dt}$$

$$= \{f[v(t)] - M\}\frac{dT(t)}{dt} - \frac{du(t)^T}{dt}\frac{dv(t)}{dt}$$

$$= \{f[v(t)] - M\}\frac{dT(t)}{dt} - \frac{du(t)^T}{dt} J\{F[u(t)]\}\frac{du(t)}{dt}$$

Since $J\{F[u(t)]\}$ is positive semidefinite, $du(t)^T/dt\ J\{F[u(t)]\}\ du(t)/dt \geq 0$. Furthermore, since $f[v(t)] - M > 0$ and $dT(t)/dt < 0$, $dE[v(t), T(t)]/dt < 0$. Therefore, $E[v(t), T(t)]$ is positive definite and radially unbounded, $dE[v(t), T(t)]/dt$ is negative definite. According to Lyapunov's theorem, the deterministic annealing neural network is asymptotically stable in the large.

Solution Feasibility. For the deterministic annealing neural network to realize a solution procedure for a convex programming problem, its steady state must represent, at least, a feasible solution to the problem. Toward this end, the following theorem is derived.

  Theorem 4.2. Assume that $J\{F[u(t)]\}$ exists and is positive semidefinite. If $T(t) \geq 0$, $dT(t)/dt < 0$, and $\lim_{t \to \infty} T(t) = 0$, then the steady state of the deterministic annealing neural network represents a feasible solution to the convex programming problem described in Eqs. (4.16) and (4.17); that is, $\bar{v} \in \hat{\mathbf{V}}$.

  PROOF. The proof of Theorem 4.1 shows that the energy function $E[v(t), T(t)]$ is positive definite and strictly monotonic decreasing with respect to time t, which implies $\lim_{t \to \infty} E[v(t), T(t)] = 0$. Since $\lim_{t \to \infty} T(t) = 0$, $\lim_{t \to \infty} E[v(t), T(t)] = \lim_{t \to \infty} T(t)\{f[v(t)] - M\} + p[v(t)] = \lim_{t \to \infty} p[v(t)]$. Therefore, $\lim_{t \to \infty} E[v(t), T(t)] = \lim_{t \to \infty} p[v(t)] = 0$. Since $p(v)$ is continuous, $\lim_{t \to \infty} p[v(t)] = p[\lim_{t \to \infty} v(t)] = p(\bar{v}) = 0$.

REMARK. Theorems 4.1 and 4.2 show that the asymptotic stability of the deterministic annealing neural network implies the solution feasibility of the steady state.

Solution Optimality. Theorems 4.1 and 4.2 ensure the asymptotic stability and solution feasibility. The optimality of the steady-state solutions, however, is not guaranteed and deserves further exploration.

There are two possibilities for the locality of the optimal solution v^*: an interior point or a boundary point of the feasible region $\hat{\mathbf{V}}$. If v^* is an interior point of $\hat{\mathbf{V}}$, then v^* is the same as the global minimum of the objective function $f(v)$, hence $\nabla f(v^*) = \nabla p(v^*) = 0$, since both $f(v)$ and $p(v)$ are convex and differentiable. In this case, according to Eq. (4.18), a steady state of the deterministic annealing neural network is an optimal solution if the temperature parameter $T(t)$ sustains sufficiently long. The solution process for this case is trivial. In most convex programming problems, such as linear programs, v^* is a boundary point of $\hat{\mathbf{V}}$. In this case, $\forall v \in \hat{\mathbf{V}}, \nabla f(v) \neq 0$. Theorem 4.3 provides a sufficient condition for the deterministic annealing neural network to solve convex programming problems in which the optimal solutions are boundary points.

Theorem 4.3. Assume that $\forall t \geq 0, J\{F[u(t)]\} \neq 0$ and is positive semidefinite, and $\nabla f[v(t)] \neq 0$. If $dT(t)/dt < 0$, $\lim_{t \to \infty} T(t) = 0$, and

$$T(t) \geq \max \left\{ 0, \frac{\nabla p[v(t)]^T J\{F[u(t)]\}\nabla p[v(t)] - \nabla f[v(t)]^T J\{F[u(t)]\} \nabla p[v(t)]}{\nabla f[v(t)]^T J\{F[u(t)]\} \nabla f[v(t)] - \nabla p[v(t)]^T J\{F[u(t)]\} \nabla f[v(t)]} \right\} \quad (4.29)$$

then the steady state of the deterministic annealing neural network represents an optimal solution to the convex programming problem described in (4.16) and (4.17), that is, $\bar{v} = \arg \min_{v \in \hat{\mathbf{V}}} f(v)$.

PROOF. According to Theorems 4.1 and 4.2, the steady state of the deterministic annealing neural network represents a feasible solution to the convex programming problem; that is, $\lim_{t \to \infty} v(t) = \bar{v} \in \hat{\mathbf{V}}$ and $p(\bar{v}) = 0$. Since $E[v(t), T(t)] = T(t)\{f[v(t)] - M\} + p[v(t)]$ and $\nabla E[v(t), T(t)] = T(t) \nabla f[v(t)] + \nabla p[v(t)]$, $du(t)/dt = -\nabla E[v(t), T(t)]$, where $\nabla E[v(t), T(t)] = \{\partial E[v(t), T(t)]/\partial v_1, \partial E[v(t), T(t)]/\partial v_2, \dots, \partial E[v(t), T(t)]/\partial v_N\}^T$ is the gradient of $E[v(t), T(t)]$ with respect to v. Moreover, since $v(t) = F[u(t)]$ and $du(t)/dt = -\nabla E[v(t),T(t)]$, $dv(t)/dt = J\{F[u(t)]\} du(t)/dt = -J\{F[u(t)]\} \nabla E[v(t),T(t)]$. In view of the fact that $J\{F[u(t)]\} \neq 0$ and is positive semidefinite, the state $v(t)$ of the deterministic annealing neural network approaches a local minimum of the energy function in a gradient-descent manner. Furthermore, since $T(t) \geq 0$ and both $f(v)$ and $p(v)$ are convex, $E[v(t), T(t)]$ is also convex. The convexity property of $E[v(t),T(t)]$ guarantees that a local minimum of E is always a global one. Because of the presence of $T(t)$ in $E[v(t),T(t)]$, the global minimum is time-varying, Equation (4.29) implies

$$T(t)\{\nabla f[v(t)]^T J\{F[u(t)]\}\nabla f[v(t)] - \nabla p[v(t)]^T J\{F[u(t)]\} \nabla f[v(t)]\} \geq$$
$$\nabla p[v(t)]^T J\{F[u(t)]\} \nabla p[v(t)] - \nabla f[v(t)]^T J\{F[u(t)]\} \nabla p[v(t)]$$

Rearranging the above inequality, we have

$$T(t) \nabla f[v(t)]^T J\{F[u(t)]\} \nabla f[v(t)] + \nabla f[v(t)]^T J\{F[u(t)]\} \nabla p[v(t)] -$$
$$\{T(t) \nabla p[v(t)]^T J\{F[u(t)]\} \nabla f[v(t)] + \nabla p[v(t)]^T J\{F[u(t)]\} \nabla p[v(t)]\} \geq 0;$$

that is,

$$\nabla f[v(t)]^T J\{F[u(t)]\}\{T(t) \nabla f[v(t)] + \nabla p[v(t)]\} -$$
$$\nabla p[v(t)]^T J\{F[u(t)]\}\{T(t) \nabla f[v(t)] + \nabla p[v(t)]\} \geq 0$$

Substituting Eq. (4.18) and $dv(t)/dt = J\{F[u(t)]\}\, du(t)/dt$ into the above inequality, we have

$$\nabla f[v(t)]^T J\{F[u(t)]\}\, \frac{du(t)}{dt} - \nabla p[v(t)]^T J\{F[u(t)]\}\, \frac{du(t)}{dt} =$$

$$\nabla f[v(t)]^T \frac{dv(t)}{dt} - \nabla p[v(t)]^T \frac{dv(t)}{dt} \leq 0$$

Note that since $\nabla f[v(t)]^T dv(t)/dt = df[v(t)]/dt$ and $\nabla p[v(t)]^T dv(t)/dt = dp[v(t)]/dt$, Eq. (4.29) implies that $df[v(t)]/dt \leq dp[v(t)]/dt$. Furthermore, $df[v(t)]/dt \leq dp[v(t)]/dt$ implies that $f[v(t'')] - f[v(t')] \leq p[v(t'')] - p[v(t')]$ for any $t' \leq t''$. Let t^* be the time associated with an optimal solution v^*. We have $f[v(\infty)] - f[v(t^*)] \leq p[v(\infty)] - p[v(t^*)]$; that is, $f(\bar{v}) - f(v^*) \leq p(\bar{v}) - p(v^*)$. Since $p(\bar{v}) = p(v^*) = 0, f(\bar{v}) \leq f(v^*)$. Also since $\bar{v} \in \hat{\mathbf{V}}$ and $v^* = \arg \min_{v \in \hat{\mathbf{V}}} f(v), f(\bar{v}) \geq f(v^*)$ by definition of v^*. Consequently, $f(\bar{v}) = f(v^*) = \min_{v \in \hat{\mathbf{V}}} f(v)$.

REMARK.   Theorem 4.3 gives a lower bound on the temperature parameter $T(t)$. Note that $T(t) \geq 0, dT(t)/dt < 0$, and $\lim_{t \to \infty} T(t) = 0$ imply that $T(t) \neq 0$. Since $\lim_{t \to \infty} p[v(t)] = p(\bar{v}) = \min_v p(v) = 0, p(v)$ is convex and $\nabla p[v(t)]$ is continuous, $\nabla p(\bar{v}) = \lim_{t \to \infty} \nabla p[v(t)] = 0$. Hence

$$\lim_{t \to \infty} \frac{\nabla p[v(t)]^T J\{F[u(t)]\}\, \nabla p[v(t)] - \nabla f[v(t)]^T J\{F[u(t)]\}\, \nabla p[v(t)]}{\nabla f[v(t)]^T J\{F[u(t)]\}\, \nabla f[v(t)] - \nabla p[v(t)]^T J\{F[u(t)]\}\, \nabla f[v(t)]} = 0 \qquad (4.30)$$

In addition, Theorem 4.3 relaxes the infeasibility requirement for initial states of the recurrent neural networks proposed earlier (Wang [62]; Wang and Chankong [63]).

4.4.4 Design Methodology and Hardware Realization

The convergence analysis in the preceding section reveals the desirable properties of the deterministic annealing neural network for convex programming. In this section, design principles are discussed, based on the results of convergence analysis discussed above, for determining the activation function and temperature parameter of the deterministic annealing neural network.

Activation Function.   In light of Theorems 4.1, 4.2, and 4.3, the activation function F should be differentiable, and its jacobian should be nonzero and positive semidefinite at any time. The existing activation functions are all uncoupled; that is, $v_i(t) = F_i[u_i(t)]$ for all i. In this case, $J\{F[u(t)]\} = \text{diag}\{dF_i[u_i(t)]/du_i | i = 1, 2, \dots, N\}$, and the nonzero and positive semidefinite requirements on $J\{F[u(t)]\}$ can be replaced by strictly monotonic increasing F_i for all i. In the typical sigmoidal activation function, $F_i[u_i(t)] = v_{max}/\{1 + \exp[-\xi u_i(t)]\}$, where $v_{max} > 0$. To ensure increasing monotonicity, parameter ξ must be positive. Moreover, parameter ξ can be used to control the slope of the sigmoidal activation functions, as shown in Fig. 4.3a. Since the activation sensitivity increases as ξ increases, a large value of parameter ξ is usually selected to expedite the convergence of the deterministic annealing neural network. The range of the sigmoidal activation function is defined as $[0, v_{max}]$, since the infimum and supremum of the activation state are 0 and v_{max}, respectively. The state space of the deterministic annealing neural network is then defined as a hypercube $\mathbf{V} = [0, v_{max}]^N$, where v_{max} depends on the feasible region of decision variables. Furthermore, v_{max} is a factor for the sensitivity of the sigmoidal activation function, as illustrated in Fig. 4.3b. Since the slope of the sigmoidal activation function $F_i[u_i(t)]$ increases as v_{max} increases, the upper bound v_{max} need not be tight unless an explicit upper bound on v exists. A large

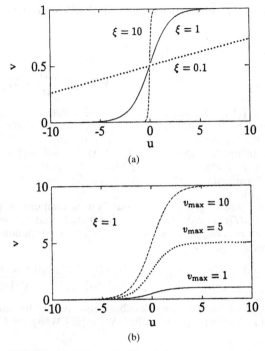

FIGURE 4.3 Effects of different ξ and v_{max} on the sigmoidal activation function. (*Reprinted from J. Wang., "A Deterministic Annealing Neural Network for Convex Programming," Copyright 1994, pages 629–641, Neural Networks, with kind permission from Elsevier Sciences Ltd., The Boulevard, Langford Lane, Kidlington, 0X5 1GB, UK.*)

upper bound could increase the sensitivity of activation and hence increase the convergence rate as long as the hypercube state space contains the feasible region. Therefore, the rule for determining v_{max} is to set it to maximum such that $\hat{\mathbf{V}} \subseteq \mathbf{V}$. If there is no explicit bound on decision variable vector v, then a linear activation function $F[u(t)] = \xi u(t)$ can be used where $\xi > 0$ is also a scaling constant. In this case, $\mathbf{V} = \Re^N$.

Temperature Parameter. Because $T(t)$ represents the "annealing" effect, the determination of the cooling temperature parameter $T(t)$ is very important for solution optimality. Theorems 4.1 and 4.2 provide the necessary conditions for selecting the temperature parameter by requiring the nonnegativity and decreasing monotonicity of $T(t)$ with respect to time. The following polynomial, exponential, and logarithmic functions of t are three simple examples of open-loop $T(t)$.

$$T(t) = \beta(1 + t)^{-\eta} \tag{4.31}$$

$$T(t) = \beta \alpha^{-\eta t} \tag{4.32}$$

$$T(t) = \beta[\log_\alpha(t + \alpha)]^{-\eta} \tag{4.33}$$

where $\alpha > 1, \beta > 0$, and $\eta > 0$ are constant parameters. Parameters β and η can be used to scale the temperature parameter.

Theorem 4.3 provides a sufficient condition for determining $T(t)$. If $J\{F[u(t)]\}$ is a symmetric matrix such as the aforementioned diagonal matrix, then $\nabla f[v(t)]^T J\{F[u(t)]\} \nabla p[v(t)] = \nabla p[v(t)]^T J\{F[u(t)]\} \nabla f[v(t)]$, hence Eq. (4.29) becomes

$$T(t) \geq \max \left\{ 0, \frac{\nabla p[v(t)]^T J\{F[u(t)]\} \nabla p[v(t)] - \nabla f[v(t)]^T J\{F[u(t)]\} \nabla p[v(t)]}{\nabla f[v(t)]^T J\{F[u(t)]\} \nabla f[v(t)] - \nabla f[v(t)]^T J\{F[u(t)]\} \nabla p[v(t)]} \right\} \quad (4.34)$$

Since $J\{F[u(t)]\}$ is positive semidefinite, $\nabla p[v(t)]^T J\{F[u(t)]\} \nabla p[v(t)] \geq 0$ and $\nabla f[v(t)]^T J\{F[u(t)]\} \nabla f[v(t)] \geq 0$. In the cases of the LP and QP, if $v(0) = 0$ and $J\{F[u(t)]\}$ is symmetric as in most of neural network models, then Eq. (4.29) implies

$$\max_{t \geq 0} T(t) = T(0) \geq \max \left\{ 0, \frac{b^T A J\{F[u(t)]\}(c + A^T b)}{c^T \{F[u(t)]\}(c + A^T b)} \right\} \quad (4.35)$$

In addition, if $F(u) = [F_1(u_1), F_2(u_2), \dots, F_N(u_N)]$ and $F_1 = F_2 = \dots = F_N$, then Eq. (4.35) becomes

$$\max_{t \geq 0} T(t) = T(0) \geq \max \left\{ 0, \frac{b^T A(c + A^T b)}{c^T(c + A^T b)} \right\} \quad (4.36)$$

As discussed in Sec. 4.3, the terms $-T(t) \nabla f[v(t)]$ and $-\nabla p[v(t)]$ on the right-hand side of the dynamic Eq. (4.18) represent, respectively, the objective minimization effect and the constraint satisfaction effect. Since a feasible solution is not necessarily an optimal one, it is essential for the first term not to vanish until $v(t)$ reaches an optimal solution. Theorem 4.3 suggests essentially that $T(t)$ sustains sufficiently long to obtain an optimal solution. In other words, similar to the temperature parameter in the stochastic counterpart, the value of the temperature parameter in the deterministic annealing neural network should decrease slowly. A simple way to implement this requirement is to select a sufficiently small value of η in Eq. (4.31), (4.32), or (4.33). Since Eq. (4.29) is not a necessary condition, violation of this condition could still result in an optimal solution. As will be shown in the illustrative examples in the ensuing section, optimal solutions can still be obtained when $df[v(t)]/dt \not\leq dp[v(t)]/dt$.

An exponential function $\beta \exp(-\eta t)$ is used implicitly as the temperature parameter in the recurrent neural networks for solving the assignment problem and linear programming problems (Wang [63–65]); that is, $a = e$ in Eq. (4.32) where $e = 2.71838\cdots$. In this case, if the first term of the right-hand side of dynamic Eq. (4.18) is dominant as time elapses, then the convergence rate of the recurrent neural network is exclusively dictated by η and the deterministic annealing neural network needs approximately $5/\eta$ units of time to converge, since η is the time constant of the temperature parameter. This feature enables one to control or determine the convergence rate of the deterministic annealing neural network.

Since $\beta = T(0)$ in Eqs. (4.31) to (4.33), parameter β defines the maximal and initial values of temperature parameter $T(t)$. According to Eq. (4.34),

$$\beta \geq \max \left\{ 0, \frac{\nabla p[v(0)]^T J\{F[u(0)]\} \nabla p[v(0)] - \nabla f[v(0)]^T J\{F[u(0)]\} \nabla p[v(0)]}{\nabla f[v(0)]^T J\{F[u(0)]\} \nabla f[v(0)] - \nabla p[v(0)]^T J\{F[u(0)]\} \nabla f[v(0)]} \right\} \quad (4.37)$$

In addition, β is a design parameter related to convergence rate of the deterministic annealing neural network and can be used to balance the penalization effect on constraint violation and the minimization effect on the objective function. In general, a small β results in an underpenalization, and a large β results in an overpenalization of constraint violations. The convergence is slow in either case. An excessively small β could even result in convergence to a suboptimal solution, as will be shown in Example 4.2. In other words, a properly selected parameter β can make the deterministic annealing neural network converge rapidly. If $p_g(v), p_h(v)$, and $f(v)$ are normalized in the same scale, then a design rule is to set $\beta \approx 1$.

Hardware Realization.   The essence of the neural network approach to optimization lies in its potential for electronic implementation where the optimization procedure is truly parallel and distributed. This section discusses an analog circuit that realizes the deterministic annealing neural network. For simplicity, only the case of linear programming is discussed.

Equation (4.24) indicates that a deterministic annealing neural network for linear programming is easy to realize in an analog circuit. The analog neural network consists of N artificial neurons (processing elements). A circuit schematic of an op-amp based analog circuit is shown in Fig. 4.4, where g denotes the activation function and both v_i

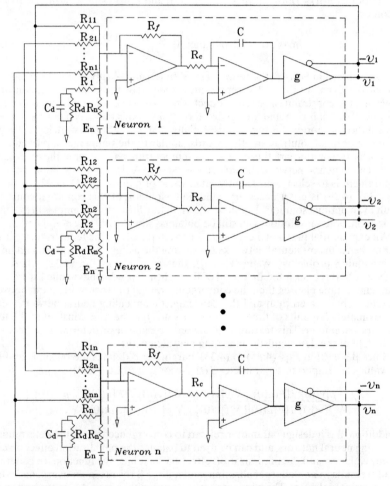

FIGURE 4.4 Circuit schematic of an analog implementation of the deterministic annealing neural network. (*Reprinted with permission from Wang [65]. © 1993 IEEE.*)

and $-v_i$ terminals are given for neuron i $(i = 1,2,\ldots,n)$. The symmetric connection weight w_{ij} from neuron i to neuron j can be implemented by a feedback resistor R_f and a connection resistor with ohmic value R_{ij} such that $|w_{ij}| = R_f/R_{ij}$; that is, $R_{ij} = R_f/|w_{ij}| = R_f/|\Sigma_{k=1}^m a_{ki}a_{kj}|$, where a_{pq} is the element in the pth row and qth column in matrix A. If $w_{ij} > 0$, then the v_i terminal of the analog neuron is to be used; if $w_{ij} < 0$, then the $-v_i$ terminal is to be used, instead of realizing a negative resistor; and if $w_{ij} = 0$, then no link is to be established. The constant term $\alpha\Sigma_{k=1}^m a_{ki}b_k$ in the biasing threshold θ_i of neuron i can be realized by a voltage source E_i and a series resistor R_i such that $R_f E_i/R_i = \theta_i$ or by a current source I_i such that $R_f I_i = \theta_i$. An exponentially decaying temperature parameter $T(0)\exp(-\eta t)$ can be realized by a discharging loop. Initially, C_d in neuron i is charged $-T(0)c_i$ volts for $i = 1,2,\ldots,n$. The parallel resistor R_d is to provide a discharging path for realizing the decaying temperature parameter. If $R_d \ll R_f$, then the decaying time constant is approximately $R_d C_d$; that is, $\eta \approx 1/(R_d C_d)$.

4.4.5 Illustrative Examples

Simulations have been performed by using a simulator for a number of sample problems. The following illustrative examples demonstrate the operating characteristics of the deterministic annealing neural network in solving linear and quadratic programs. Specifically, Example 4.1 shows the performance of the deterministic annealing neural network with different initial states; Example 4.2 shows the effects of the design parameters β, η, and ξ on the performance of the deterministic annealing neural network; and Example 4.3 shows the performance of the neural network in solving a quadratic program.

Example 4.1. Consider the following linear program with two decision variables and three functional constraints.

$$\text{Minimize} \quad -2v_1 - 3.5v_2$$
$$\text{subject to} \quad -v_1 + 4v_2 \le 1$$
$$2v_1 + 3v_2 \le 3.5$$
$$2v_1 + v_2 \le 3$$
$$v_1 \ge 0 \qquad v_2 \ge 0$$

The optimal solution of this problem is $v^* = [1.0, 0.5]^T$, the minimal objective value is $c^T v^* = -3.75$, and the minimum nonzero eigenvalue of $A^T A$ is $\lambda_{\min} = 1$.

Based on $f(v) = 2/\{1 + \exp[-10^5 u(t)]\}$ and $T(t) = \exp(-10^3 t)$, the simulation results show that the steady state of the recurrent neural network always accurately represents the optimal solution starting from four different corners of a 2×2 square in the state space; that is, $\bar{v} = [1.000000, 0.500000]^T$ and $c^T\bar{v} = -3.750000$. Figures 4.5 and 4.6 illustrate, respectively, the convergent state trajectories on the $v_1 v_2$ plane and the convergent states versus the number of time intervals (iterations). Figures 4.5 and 4.6 indicate that state v_1 initially remains unchanged for all four starting points. It is interesting to note that the four trajectories merge in their final stages. This phenomenon indicates a deep valley of the energy function in the vicinities of the trajectories. Figure 4.7 illustrates the convergence patterns of the values of the objective function, penalty function, and energy function versus the number of time intervals. Using *PSpice*, the steady-state vector of an analog neural network based on LT1028 op-amps was $\bar{v} = [1.001, 0.500]^T$, where $R_f = 1\ M\Omega$, $R_i = 10\ k\Omega$, $R_c = 10\ k\Omega$,

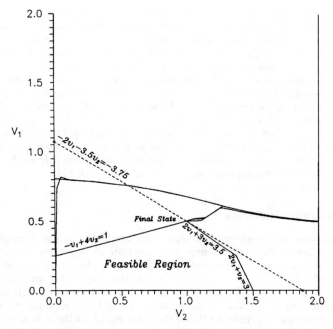

FIGURE 4.5 Feasible region and state trajectories of the deterministic annealing neural network in Example 4.1. (*Reprinted with permission from Wang [65]. © 1993 IEEE.*)

$C = 100 \ \mu\text{F}$, $R_d = 1 \ \Omega$, and $C_d = 100 \ \mu\text{F}$. Figures 4.8 and 4.9 illustrate, respectively, the transient behavior and convergent state trajectory of the op-amp based analog neural network in solving the linear programming problem.

Example 4.2. Consider the following linear program with five variables and three constraints.

Minimize $2.4v_1 + 1.6v_2 + 4.2v_3 + 5.2v_4 + 2.4v_5$

subject to $-4.3v_1 + 5.3v_2 + 1.6v_3 + 0.5v_4 - 2.1v_5 = 12.5$

$7.2v_1 - 2.6v_2 + 2.4v_3 + 1.6v_4 + 2.9v_5 = 7.2$

$1.3v_1 - 1.2v_2 + 2.5v_3 + 4.1v_4 - 2.7v_5 = 6.3$

$v_1 \geq 0 \qquad v_2 \geq 0 \qquad v_3 \geq 0 \qquad v_4 \geq 0 \qquad v_5 \geq 0$

The optimal solution of this problem is $v^* = [0.671138, 1.963131, 3.113311, 0, 0]^T$, and the corresponding value of objective function is $f(v^*) = 17.827650$. Simulation via the simulator shows that the steady state of the deterministic annealing neural network $\bar{v} = [0.671138, 1.963132, 3.113310, 0.000001, 0.000000]^T$ and $f(\bar{v}) = 17.827648$, where $v(0) = [2.5, 2.5, 2.5, 2.5, 2.5]^T$, $v_i(t) = v_{max}/\{1 + \exp[-\xi u_i(t)]\}$, $T(t) = \beta \exp(-\eta t)$, $v_{max} = 5$, $\xi = 10^4$, $\beta = 1$, $\eta = 10^3$, and $\Delta t = 10^{-6}$ unless otherwise indicated. Figure 4.10 illustrates the transient behavior of the activation states of the deterministic annealing neural network. Since $\eta = 10^3$ and $\Delta t = 10^{-6}$, $5/\eta = 0.005$ and $5/(\eta \ \Delta t) = 5000$. Figure

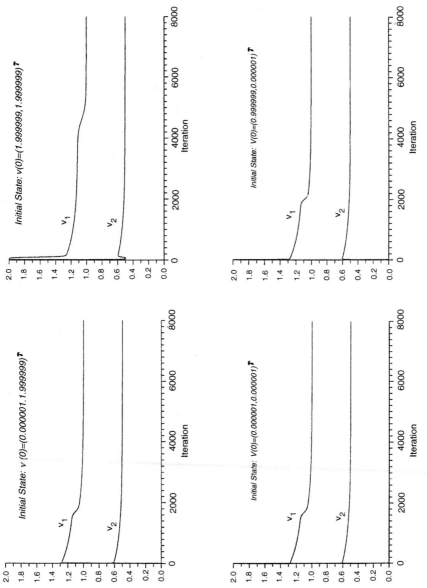

FIGURE 4.6 Timing diagram of the transient states of the deterministic annealing neural network in Example 4.1. (*Reprinted with permission from Wang [65]. © 1993 IEEE.*)

4.23

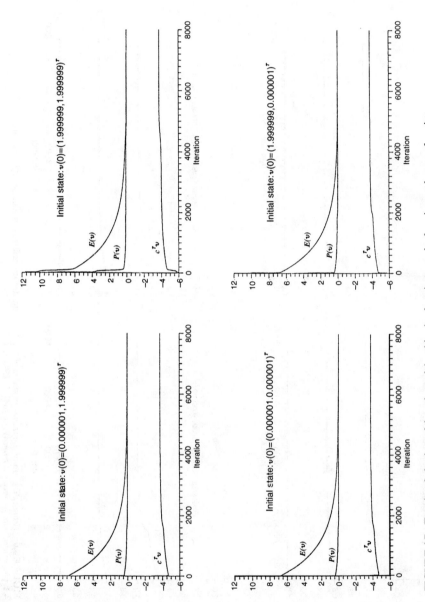

FIGURE 4.7 Transient behaviors of the values of the objective function, penalty function, and energy function in Example 4.1. *(Reprinted with permission from Wang [65]. © 1993 IEEE.)*

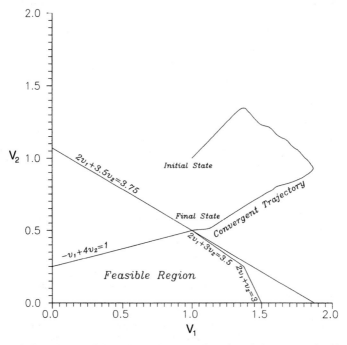

FIGURE 4.8 Feasible region and state trajectories of the op-amp based deterministic annealing neural network in Example 4.1. (*Reprinted with permission from Wang [65]. © 1993 IEEE.*)

4.10 clearly shows that the deterministic annealing neural network can converge in approximately 5000 time intervals or 0.005 time unit. Figures 4.11, 4.12, and 4.13 illustrate the transient behaviors of the values of the temperature parameter, objective function, penalty function, and energy function based on different values of design parameters β, η, and ξ, respectively.

Example 4.3. Consider the following convex quadratic program with four variables and three constraints.

$$\text{Minimize} \quad 1.5v_1^2 - v_1v_2 + v_1v_3 - 2v_1v_4 + 2v_2^2 + 2v_2v_3 + 2.5v_3^2 + v_3v_4 + 3v_4^2$$
$$- 6v_1 + 15v_2 + 9v_3 + 4v_4$$

$$\text{subject to} \quad v_1 + 2v_2 + 4v_3 + 5v_4 = 12$$

$$3v_1 - 2v_2 - v_3 + 2v_4 = 8$$

$$2v_1 - 3v_2 + v_3 - 4v_4 = 6$$

$$v_1 \geq 0 \quad v_2 \geq 0 \quad v_3 \geq 0 \quad v_4 \geq 0$$

The optimal solution to this problem is $v^* = [2.967033, 0.000000, 1.736264, 0.417582]^T$, and the corresponding value of objective function is $f(v^*) = 24.157710$. Simulation via the simulator shows that the steady state of the deterministic anneal-

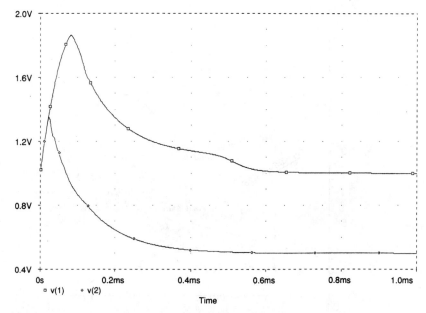

FIGURE 4.9 Timing diagram of the transient states of the op-amp based deterministic anneal-ing neural network in Example 4.1. (*Reprinted with permission from Wang [65]. © 1993 IEEE.*)

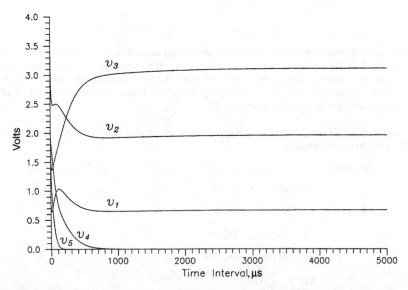

FIGURE 4.10 Transient states of the deterministic annealing neural network in Example 4.2. (*Reprinted from J. Wang, "A Deterministic Annealing Neural Network for Convex Programming," Copyright 1994, pages 629–641, Neural Networks, with kind permission from Elsevier Sciences Ltd., The Boulevard, Langford Lane, Kidlington, 0X5 1GB, UK.*)

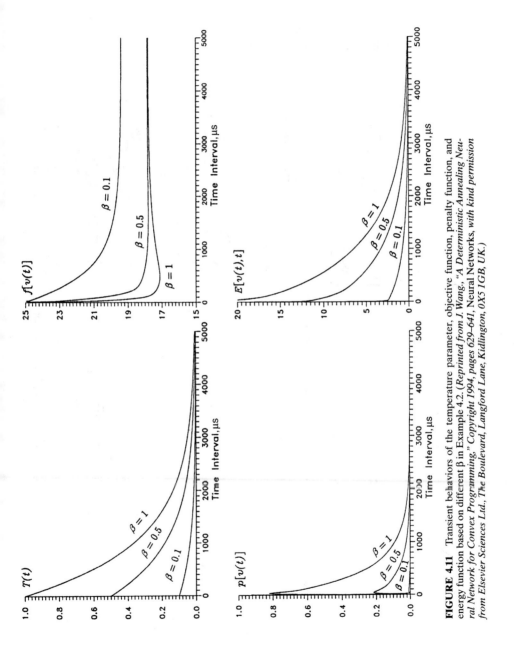

FIGURE 4.11 Transient behaviors of the temperature parameter, objective function, penalty function, and energy function based on different β in Example 4.2. (Reprinted from J. Wang, "A Deterministic Annealing Neural Network for Convex Programming," Copyright 1994, pages 629–641, Neural Networks, with kind permission from Elsevier Sciences Ltd., The Boulevard, Langford Lane, Kidlington, 0X5 1GB, UK.)

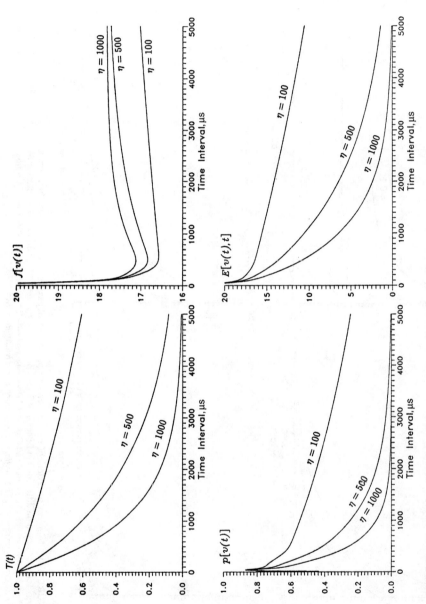

FIGURE 4.12 Transient behaviors of the temperature parameter, objective function, penalty function, and energy function based on different η in Example 4.2. (*Reprinted from J. Wang, "A Deterministic Annealing Neural Network for Convex Programming," Copyright 1994, pages 629–641, Neural Networks, with kind permission from Elsevier Sciences Ltd., The Boulevard, Langford Lane, Kidlington, OX5 1GB, UK.*)

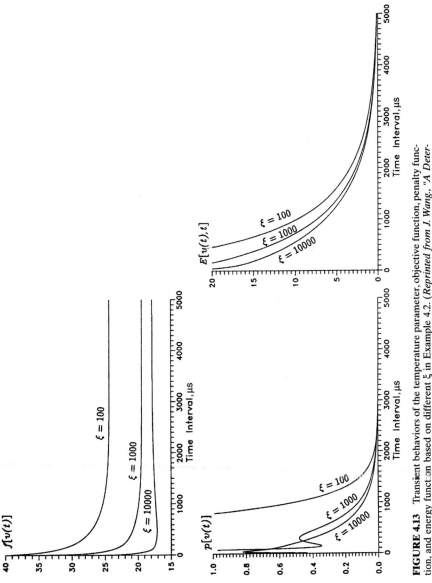

FIGURE 4.13 Transient behaviors of the temperature parameter, objective function, penalty function, and energy function based on different ξ in Example 4.2. (*Reprinted from J. Wang, "A Deterministic Annealing Neural Network for Convex Programming," Copyright 1994, pages 629–641, Neural Networks, with kind permission from Elsevier Sciences Ltd., The Boulevard, Langford Lane, Kidlington, OX5 1GB, UK.*)

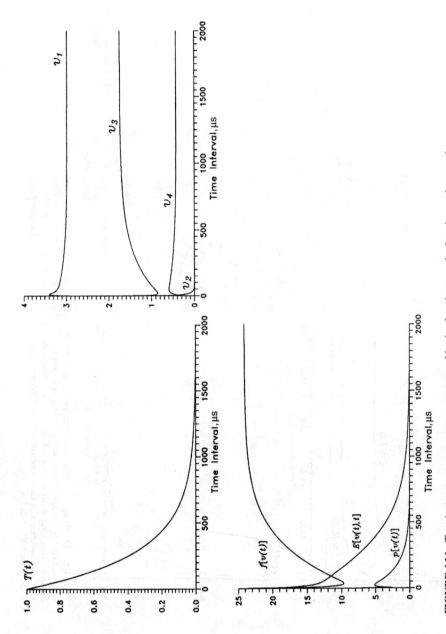

FIGURE 4.14 Transient states, temperature parameter, objective function, penalty function, and energy function in Example 4.3. (*Reprinted from J. Wang, "A Deterministic Annealing Neural Network for Convex Programming," Copyright 1994, pages 629–641, Neural Networks, with kind permission from Elsevier Sciences Ltd., The Boulevard, Langford Lane, Kidlington, OX5 1GB, UK.*)

ing neural network $\bar{v} = [2.967033, 0.000000, 1.736263, 0.417583]^T$ and $f(\bar{v}) = 24.157701$, where the initial state is $v(0) = [2.5, 2.5, 2.5, 2.5]^T$, $v_i(t) = v_{max}/\{1 + \exp[-\xi u_i(t)]\}$, $T(t) = \beta[\ln(t+e)]^{-\eta}$, $v_{max} = 5$, $\xi = 10^4$, $\beta = 1$, $\eta = 10^4$, and $\Delta t = 10^{-6}$. Figure 4.14 illustrates the transient behavior of the activation states, temperature parameter, objective function, penalty function, and energy function in Example 4.3.

4.5 CONCLUDING REMARKS

Neural network research has opened a new horizon for solving computationally intensive optimization problems. Neural networks have been proposed for optimization in a variety of application areas such as the design and layout of very large-scale integrated (VLSI) circuits and cellular manufacturing systems. The nature of parallel and distributed information processing makes recurrent neural networks viable for solving complex optimization problems in real time. One of the salient features of neural networks is their suitability for hardware implementation, in which the convergence rate is not increasing statistically as the size of the problem increases. The rapid development of electronic and optical neural networks enables us to develop intelligent systems using neural networks for decentralized decision making.

Although great progress has been made in using neural networks for optimization, many theoretical and practical problems remain unsolved. Many avenues are open for future work. For example, the existing neural networks have not yet been shown to be capable of solving nonconvex optimization problems. Nor could the existing neural networks guarantee to obtain the optimal solutions to NP-hard combinatorial optimization problems. Further investigations should aim at the in-depth analysis of the dynamics of recurrent neural networks for solving nonconvex and discrete optimization problems, the wide applications of recurrent neural networks to practical problems for real-time design and planning, and the hardware prototyping of recurrent neural networks for optimization.

REFERENCES

1. Aarts, E. H., and J. H. Korst, "Boltzmann Machines for Traveling Salesman Problems," *European Journal of Operational Research,* 39(1): 79–95 (1989).

2. Abe, S., J. Kawakami, and K. Hirasawa, "Solving Inequality Constrained Combinatorial Optimization Problems by the Hopfield Neural Networks," *Neural Networks,* 5(4): 663–670 (1992).

3. Angeniol, B., G. De La Groix Vaubois, and J.-Y. Le Texier, "Self-Organizing Feature Maps and the Traveling Salesman Problem," *Neural Networks,* 1: 289–293 (1988).

4. Bouzerdoum, A., and T. R. Pattison, "Neural Network for Quadratic Optimization with Bound Constraints," *IEEE Transactions on Neural Networks,* 4(2): 293–304 (1993).

5. Brandt, R. D., Y. Wang, A. J. Laub, and S. K. Mitra, "Alternative Networks for Solving the Traveling Salesman Problem and the List-Matching Problem," *Proceedings of International Conference on Neural Networks,* 2: 330–340 (1988).

6. Burke, L. I., and P. Damany, "The Guilty Net for the Traveling Salesman Problem," *Computers and Operations Research,* 19(3/4): 255–266 (1992).

7. Burke, L. I., "A Neural Design for Solution of the Maximal Independent Set Problem," *European Journal of Operational Research,* 62: 186–193 (1992).

8. Burke, L. I., "Neural Networks for the Traveling Salesman Problem: Insights from Operations Research," *Neural Networks,* 7(4): 681–690 (1992).

9. Chakrapani, J., and J. Skorin-Kapov, "Connectionist Approaches to the Quadratic Assignment Problem," *Computers and Operations Research,* 19(3/4): 287–295 (1992).

10. Urahama, K., "Analog Circuit for Solving Assignment Problems," *IEEE Transactions on Circuits and Systems, I: Fundamental Theory and Applications,* 41(5): 426–429 (1994).

11. Chen, J., M. A. Shanlatt, and C.-Y. Maa, "Improved Neural Networks for Linear and Nonlinear Programming," *International Journal of Neural Systems,* 2(4): 331–339, 1992.

12. Chiu, C., C.-Y. Maa, and M. A. Shanblatt, "Energy Function Analysis of Dynamic Programming Neural Networks," *IEEE Transactions on Neural Networks,* 2(4): 418–426, 1991.

13. Chiu, C., C.-Y. Maa, and M. A. Shanblatt, "An Artificial Neural Network Algorithm for Dynamic Programming," *International Journal of Neural Systems,* 1(3): 211–220 (1990).

14. Chua, L. O., and G.-N. Lin, "Nonlinear Optimization with Constraints," *International Journal of Circuit Theory and Applications,* 11: 141–159 (1983).

15. Chua, L. O., and G.-N. Lin, "Nonlinear Programming without Computation," *IEEE Transactions on Circuits and Systems,* 31: 182–188 (1984).

16. Cichocki, A., and R. Unbehauen, "Switched-Capacitor Neural Networks for Differential Optimization," *International Journal of Circuit Theory and Applications,* 19: 161–187 (1991).

17. Cichocki, A., and R. Unbehauen, *Neural Networks for Optimization and Signal Processing,* Wiley, New York, 1993.

18. Cuykendall, R., and R. Reese, "Scaling the Neural TSP Algorithm," *Biological Cybernetics,* 60: 365–371 (1989).

19. Durbin, R., R. Szeliski, and A. Yuille, "An Analysis of the Elastic Net Approach to the Traveling Salesman Problem," *Neural Computation,* 1(3): 348–358 (1989).

20. Eberhardt, S. P., T. Duad, D. A. Kerns, T. X. Brown, and A. P. Thakoor, "Competitive Neural Architecture for Hardware Solution to the Assignment Problem," *Neural Networks,* 4(4): 431–442 (1991).

21. Fang, L., and T. Li, "Design of Competition-Based Neural Networks for Combinatorial Optimization," *International Journal of Neural Systems,* 1(3): 221–235 (1990).

22. Favata, F., and R. Walker, "A Study of the Application of Kohonen-Type Neural Networks to the Traveling Salesman Problem," *Biological Cybernetics,* 63: 463–468 (1991).

23. Hopfield, J. J., "Neural Networks and Physical Systems with Emergent Collective Computational Ability," *Proceedings of National Academy of Sciences, USA, Biophysics,* 79: 2554–2558 (1982).

24. Hopfield, J. J., "Neurons with Graded Response Have Collective Computational Properties Like Those of Two-State Neurons," *Proceedings National of Academy of Sciences, USA, Biophysics,* 81: 3088–3092 (1984).

25. Hopfield, J. J., and D. W. Tank, " 'Neural' Computation of Decisions in Optimization Problems," *Biological Cybernetics,* 52(3): 141–152 (1985).

26. Hornik, K., M. Stinchcombe, and H. White, "Multilayer Feedforward Networks Are Universal Approximators," *Neural Networks,* 2: 359–366, 1989.

27. Javadeva, and B. Bhaumik, "Optimization with Neural Networks: A Recipe for Improving Convergence and Solution Quality," *Biological Cybernetics,* 67: 445–449 (1992).

28. Kalaba, R., M. Kim, and J. E. Moore, II, "Linear Programming and Associative Memories," *Applied Mathematics and Computation,* 40: 203–214 (1990).

29. Kalaba, R., M. Kim, and J. E. Moore, "Linear Programming and Recurrent Associative Memories," *International Journal of General Systems,* 20: 177–194 (1992).

30. Kennedy, M. P., and L. O. Chua, "Unifying the Tank and Hopfield Linear Programming Circuit and the Canonical Nonlinear Programming Circuit of Chua and Lin," *IEEE Transactions on Circuits and Systems,* 34(2): 210–214 (1987).

31. Kennedy, M. P., and L. O. Chua, "Neural Networks for Nonlinear Programming," *IEEE Transactions on Circuits and Systems,* 35(5): 554–562 (1988).

32. Kosowsky, J. J., and A. L. Yuille, "The Invisible Hand Algorithm: Solving the Assignment Problem with Statistical Physics," *Neural Networks,* 7(3): 477–490 (1994).

33. Lillo, W. E., M. H. Loh, and S. Hui, "On Solving Constrained Optimization Problems with Neural Networks: A Penalty Method Approach," *IEEE Transactions on Neural Networks,* 4(6): 931–940 (1993).

34. Lillo, W. E., S. Hui, and S. H. Zak, "Neural Networks for Constrained Optimization Problems," *International Journal of Circuits Theory and Applications,* 21(4): 385–400 (1993).

35. Looi, C.-K., "Neural Network Methods in Combinatorial Optimization," *Computers & Operations Research,* 19(3/4): 191–208 (1992).

36. Maa, C. Y., and M. A. Shanblatt, "Linear and Quadratic Programming Neural Network Analysis," *IEEE Transactions on Neural Networks,* 3: 580–594 (1992).

37. Maa, C. Y., and M. A. Shanblatt, "A Two-Phase Optimization Neural Network," *IEEE Transactions on Neural Networks,* 3(6): 1003–1009 (1992).

38. Milic, M., and V. Lucic, "Qualitative Analysis of Electronic Linear Programming Neural Networks," *International Journal of Electronics,* 53(3): 441–450 (1993).

39. Moore, J. E., M. Kim, J. G. Seo, Y. Wu, and R. Kalaba, "Linear Programming, Recurrent Associative Memories, and Feedforward Neural Networks," *Computers and Mathematics with Applications,* 22(11): 71–90 (1991).

40. Nissen, V., "Solving the Quadratic Assignment Problem with Clues from Nature," *IEEE Transactions on Neural Networks,* 5(1): 66–72 (1994).

41. Ohlasson, T., P. Peterson, and B. Soderberg, "Neural Networks for Optimization Problems with Inequality Constraints: The Knapsack Problem," *Neural Computation,* 5(2): 331–339 (1993).

42. Pao, Y. H., *Adaptive Pattern Recognition and Neural Networks,* Addison-Wesley, Reading, MA, 1989.

43. Peterson, C., "Parallel Distributed Approaches to Combinatorial Optimization: Benchmark Studies on Traveling Salesman Problem," *Neural Computation,* 2(3): 261–269 (1990).

44. Peterson, C., and B. Soderberg, "A New Method for Mapping Optimization Problems onto Neural Networks," *International Journal of Neural Systems,* 1(1): 3–22 (1989).

45. Rodriguez-Vázquez, A., A. Ruede, J. L. Huertas, and R. Dominguez-Castro, "Switched-Capacitor 'Neural' Networks for Linear Programming," *Electronics Letters,* 24: 496–498 (1988).

46. Rodriguez-Vázquez, A., R. Dominguez-Castro, A. Ruede, J. L. Huertas, and E. Sanchez-Sinencio, "Nonlinear Switched-Capacitor 'Neural' Networks for Optimization Problems," *IEEE Transactions on Circuits and Systems,* 37(3): 384–398 (1990).

47. Rumelhart, D. E., G. E. Hinton, and R. J. Williams, "Learning Internal Representations by Error Propagation," in *Parallel Distributed Processing—Explorations in the Microstructures of Cognition,* vol. 1: *Foundations,* D. E. Rumelhart, J. L. McClelland, the PDP Research Group (eds.), MIT Press, Cambridge, MA, 1986, pp. 318–362.

48. Simmen, M. W., "Parameter Sensitivity of the Elastic Net Approach to the Traveling Salesman Problem," *Neural Computation,* 3(3): 363–374 (1991).

49. Sriram, K. B., and L. M. Patnaik, "Neural Network Approach for the Two-Dimensional Assignment Problem," *Electronics Letters,* 26(12): 809–810 (1990).

50. Sun, K. T., and H. C. Fu, "A Hybrid Neural Network for Solving Optimization Problems," *IEEE Transactions on Computers,* 42(2): 218–227 (1993).

51. Tagliarini, G. A., J. F. Christ, and E. W. Page, "Optimization Using Neural Networks," *IEEE Transactions on Computers,* 40(12): 1347–1358 (1991).

52. Takefuji, Y., and K. C. Lee, "A Near-Optimum Parallel Planarization Algorithm," *Science,* 245: 1221–1223 (1989).

53. Takefuji, Y., L. L. Chen, K. C. Lee, and J. Huffman, "Parallel Algorithms for Finding a Near-Maximum Independent Set of a Circle Graph," *IEEE Transactions on Neural Networks,* 1(3): 263–267 (1990).

54. Takefuji, Y., *Neural Network Parallel Computing,* Kluwer, Boston, 1992.

55. Takefuji, Y., and J. Wang (eds.), *Neural Computing for Optimization and Combinatorics,* World Scientific, Singapore, 1995.

56. Tank, D. W., and J. J. Hopfield, "Simple 'Neural' Optimization Networks: An A/D Converter, Signal Decision Circuit, and a Linear Programming Circuit," *IEEE Transactions on Circuits and Systems,* 33(5): 533–541 (1986).

57. Ting, P. Y., and P. A. Iltis, "Diffusion Network Architectures for Implementation of Gibbs Samplers with Applications to Assignment Problems," *IEEE Transactions on Neural Networks,* 5(4): 622–638 (1994).

58. Tsirukis, A. G., G. V. Reklaitis, and M. F. Tenorio, "Nonlinear Optimization Using Generalized Hopfield Networks," *Neural Computation,* 1(4): 511–521 (1989).

59. Van den Bout, D. E., and T. K. Miller, "Improving the Performance of the Hopfield-Tank Neural Network through Normalization and Annealing," *Biological Cybernetics,* 62: 129–139 (1989).

60. Van Hulle, M. M., "A Goal Programming Network for Mixed Integer Linear Programming: A Case Study for the Job-Shop Scheduling Problem," *International Journal of Neural Systems,* 2(3): 201–210, 1991.

61. Wacholder, E., J. Han, and R. C. Hann, "A Neural Network Algorithm for the Multiple Traveling Salesman Problem," *Biological Cybernetics,* 61(1): 11–20 (1989).

62. Wang, J., "On the Asymptotic Properties of Recurrent Neural Networks for Optimization," *International Journal of Pattern Recognition and Artificial Intelligence,* 5(4): 581–601 (1991).

63. Wang, J., and V. Chankong, "Recurrent Neural Networks for Linear Programming: Analysis and Design Principles," *Computers & Operations Research,* 19(3/4): 297–311 (1992).

64. Wang, J., "Analog Neural Network for Solving the Assignment Problem," *Electronics Letters,* 28(11): 1047–1050 (1992).

65. Wang, J., "Analysis and Design of a Recurrent Neural Network for Linear Programming," *IEEE Transactions on Circuits and Systems, I: Fundamental Theory and Applications,* 40(9): 613–618 (1993).

66. Wang, J., "A Deterministic Annealing Neural Network for Convex Programming," *Neural Networks,* 7(4): 629–641 (1994).

67. Wang, J., "Deterministic Neural Networks for Combinatorial Optimization," chap. 11 in O. M. Omidvar (ed.), *Progress in Neural Networks,* vol. 3, Ablex, Norwood, NJ, 1994, pp. 319–340.

68. Wang, J., "Recurrent Neural Network for Solving Quadratic Programming Problems with Equality Constraints," *Electronics Letters,* 28(14): 1345–1347 (1992).

69. Wang, J., and H. Li, "Solving Simultaneous Linear Equations Using Recurrent Neural Networks," *Information Sciences,* 76(3/4): 255–277 (1993).

70. Wells, D. M., "Solving Degenerate Optimization Problems Using Networks of Neural Oscillators," *Neural Networks,* 5(6): 949–960 (1992).

71. Wilson, G. V., and G. S. Pawley, "On the Stability of the Traveling Salesman Problem Algorithm of Hopfield and Tank," *Biological Cybernetics,* 58: 63–70, 1988.

72. Wolfe, W. J., J. M. MacMillan, G. Brady, R. Mathews, J. A. Rothman, et al., "Inhibitory Grids and the Assignment Problem," *IEEE Transactions on Neural Networks,* 4(2): 319–331 (1993).

73. Xu, X., and W. T. Tsai, "Effective Neural Algorithms for the Traveling Salesman Problem," *Neural Networks,* 4(2): 193–205 (1991).

74. Zhang, S., and A. G. Constantinides, "Lagrange Programming Neural Networks," *IEEE Transactions on Circuits and Systems, II: Analog and Digital Signal Processing,* 39(7): 441–452 (1992).

75. Zhang, S., X. Zhu, and L.-H. Zou, "Second-Order Neural Networks for Constrained Optimization," *IEEE Transactions on Neural Networks,* 3(6): 1021–1024 (1992).

76. Zhu, X., S. Zhang, and A. G. Constantinides, "Lagrange Neural Networks for Linear Programming," *Journal of Parallel and Distributed Computing,* 14: 354–360 (1992).

CHAPTER 5
THE SEMANTICS OF APPROXIMATE REASONING

Enrique H. Ruspini[†]
Artificial Intelligence Center,
SRI International, Menlo Park, California

In this chapter we examine basic issues related to the meaning of imprecise, uncertain, and vague knowledge, its manipulation, and its utilization. The informational deficiencies that characterize this type of knowledge are described in terms of the impossibility to determine, without ambiguity, the truth value of certain hypotheses—i.e., statements of interest to those seeking to understand the state and behavior of a real-world system.

Using a "possible worlds" perspective, this inability may also be characterized by the presence of conceivable (i.e., consistent with evidence) circumstances where the proposition is true, and of equally admissible circumstances where it is false. From such a viewpoint, approximate reasoning techniques are presented as producers of correct descriptions of properties of the class of possible worlds that are consistent with observed evidence, rather than as the results of some relaxation of the notion of "truth-value."

Two major classes of approximate reasoning systems are identified—probabilistic and possibilistic—and their major conceptual differences are described. The theoretical underpinnings of each methodological approach are described, and the current level of understanding of their major functional structures and concepts is discussed.

The discussion of probabilistic approaches encompasses both subjectivist and objectivist perspectives, and also includes nonclassical approaches (such as the Dempster/Shafer calculus of evidence) that are related to the notion of interval probabilities. The discussion of possibilistic approaches, on the other hand, stresses the relations between the concepts of possibility and similarity that have been recently studied by the author.

[†]This chapter is a slightly modified and enhanced version of the paper "The Semantics of Vague Knowledge," which originally appeared in *Revue Internationale de Systémique,* vol. 3, pp. 387–420, 1989.

Finally, nonmonotonic logic concepts are briefly examined from the perspective of possible-world semantics.

5.1 INTRODUCTION

In this work we examine basic issues relevant to the purpose of approximate reasoning methodologies with emphasis on the meaning of their basic structures and concepts. Approximate reasoning systems may be briefly characterized as automated agents (e.g., computer programs and systems) that seek to identify the state of a real-world system on the basis of knowledge that it is *imprecise* (i.e., available information does not possess the desired degree of detail) and *uncertain* (i.e., we are not absolutely certain about the correctness of such information).

Under these conditions it is possible, usually easily so, to conceive of situations where, given available information, some statement about the real world is true. Under other conceivable circumstances—equally admissible, given the available knowledge—that statement is false. In a majority of weather-forecasting applications, e.g., the information collected by a variety of sensors is often insufficient to determine if rain will fall at a given location at a given future time. Depending on the evolution and interaction of different components and subsystems of the atmosphere, rain may actually fall or may not fall.

The importance and ubiquity of problems characterized by information that is imprecise and uncertain make the development of *approximate reasoning* systems one of the most important technological requirements to be met by artificial intelligence procedures which, going beyond the foundations of classical deductive techniques, must cope with the undesirable features of the underlying knowledge. The current lack of understanding of the principles that underlie these methodologies combined with their present state of technological development—often exemplified by the use of questionable "ad hoc" methods—has led to considerable controversy among practitioners who have, in the recent past, debated the relative advantages and disadvantages.

The absence of a formal unified framework for the description of the underlying concepts and structures of various applicable technologies has complicated their understanding and comparison, making it nearly impossible to develop even a partial consensus about the relative applicability of each methodology. Given the lack of formal structures to guide, in a rigorous fashion, the use of terms such as *probability* and *possibility*, each capable of being interpreted in a variety of ways, it is nearly impossible to evaluate arguments advanced for or against particular positions. Furthermore, problems such as the determination of the validity of the output of approximate reasoning systems, or of their usefulness in specific circumstances (or even establishing the meaning of such notions), have remained largely unaddressed.

In this chapter we present results of research toward the development of firm foundations for the unified description of approximate reasoning methods, with emphasis on the interpretation of their underlying concepts and structures. The formal framework derived in this research is based on the notion of *possible worlds* as introduced in modal logics [18]. Our attention will be mainly focused on various types of probabilistic reasoning methods, discussed in Sec. 5.2, and possibilistic reasoning methods, presented in Sec. 5.3. Included is a discussion of relations with nonmonotonic reasoning methods, which are also concerned with problems associated with imprecise and uncertain information. Before we present such issues, it is important to consider the general nature of the approximate reasoning problem.

5.1.1　The Nature of Approximate Reasoning

The goal of any system that relies on inference techniques is to assign a *truth value,* which may be either **true** or **false,** to statements, called *hypotheses,* about the state or behavior of a real-world system. Due to its very nature, however, the approximate reasoning problem is unsolvable, because of either fundamental or practical limitations.

Available information is often insufficient to determine, by means of conventional inference procedures, if a hypothesis is true or false. In some problems, the impossibility is of a more practical nature: there are not enough resources (e.g., memory, computer time) to determine if the hypothesis is true.

Whether the impossibility is fundamental or practical, the important fact is that as posed, an approximate reasoning problem is not solvable. Information *constrains* the possible truth values of hypotheses but rarely restricts them to unique values. In general, those constraints determine a set of possible solutions. Each such solution is an assignment of truth values that is logically consistent with observed facts and system knowledge (typically expressing laws of system behavior). For example, an observation made several days earlier about the location of an automobile on a highway, augmented by knowledge about the capability of such a vehicle to proceed at certain speeds through some roads, may be sufficient to determine a set of its possible current locations, but it will usually be unable to pinpoint any one of them as the only possible place where the vehicle could be at present.

The solution of an approximate reasoning problem is therefore a *set of possibilities*[†] that are logically consistent with available information. In this chapter we use the term *possible worlds,* which is borrowed from logic, to denote each such possibility [5].

In most approximate reasoning problems, it is not practically possible to describe a set of possible worlds to an acceptable level of detail. Different methodologies have been developed, however, to describe some properties of the set of possible solutions or, more generally, certain constraints on values that measure such properties. For example, probabilistic methods seek to identify the probability distribution of some of the variables used to characterize each possible world. As we will see, often even this level of detail may not be attained, and the best we can do is to indicate that certain probability distribution values are possible while others are not (e.g., the probability of rain will be between 60 and 80 percent).

5.1.2　Possible Worlds

Possible worlds, as informally described above, are the solutions of an approximate reasoning problem that are consistent with existing information and knowledge. In many problems, each of these solutions corresponds to the state of a real-world system at a given instant. In other examples, each possible world may also include descriptions of past, present, and future (predicted) states of the real world. In some planning and control problems (e.g., autonomous robot path and activity planning), each possible world may correspond to a description of the characteristics of a plan formulated by *rational agents* seeking to control certain aspects of system behavior together with its resulting effects on the planned system and its environment.

The characteristics and complexity of each possible solution are, therefore, highly dependent on the particular real-world system being studied and the analytical

---

[†]Note that this use of the term *possibility* is different from its use below in connection with possibilistic reasoning.

requirements of the users of the approximate reasoning system. Although, as we have just seen, this diversity of needs leads to widely different types of possible worlds, there exists a high-level, logical characterization of the concept of possible world in terms of the possible truth of statements (propositions) about the real-world system being studied. This characterization was derived by Carnap [6], who also proposed a conceptual procedure for the generation of descriptions of all possible states of affairs.

While Carnap considered first-order-logic systems in his characterization of the concept, we shall confine ourselves to a simpler, proposition-based description that captures the essence of his construction procedure. Before we proceed to its discussion, it is very important to remark, however, that the Carnap procedure is a *conceptual process* intended primarily to formalize the notion of possible world while providing clear foundations for the discussion of other concepts (e.g., *possible truth*). The combinatorial explosion associated with Carnap's process makes unfeasible the actual enumeration and representation of possible-world spaces in real-life problems.

The procedure of Carnap starts with consideration of a finite number of *ground* propositions

$$p_1, p_2, \ldots, p_m$$

that describe characteristics of a real-world system. For example, in a weather-forecasting application, these propositions may include such declarative knowledge statements as "the total rainfall will be less than 1 cm." These statements are intended to capture those aspects of the behavior of the world that are important to analysts and to identify that behavior to the necessary degree of precision.

After these propositions have been identified, the process considers all the conjunctions of the type[†]

$$p_1 \wedge p_2 \wedge \neg p_3 \wedge \cdots \wedge p_m$$

where each of the ground propositions appears once either as given or negated. If m ground propositions have been identified, this process leads to 2^m conjunctions. We eliminate from this set the conjunctions that represent logical impossibilities, e.g., "the total rainfall will be less than 1 cm **and** the total rainfall will be more than 3 cm."

The remaining members of this propositional set, or *carnapian universe*, are called *possible worlds*. Each possible world is a description (to the maximum level of detail allowed by the original set of ground propositions) of a possible, although typically unknown, state of the system under study. Each such description is consistent both with the laws of logic and with the axioms that constrain system behavior, and the description may be thought of as a function (called a *valuation*) that assigns to each relevant proposition a truth value that is either "true" or "false." Similarly, possible worlds may be thought of as sets of propositions that contain all propositions which are true and the negation of those which are false, as illustrated in Fig. 5.1, where each possible world is revealed, through the help of a hypothetical "logical" microscope, as a collection of true propositions. Furthermore, each possible world differs from any other in that at least one proposition that is true in one world is false in the other world.

From this logical perspective, which is particularly useful in artificial intelligence applications, the observations in a body of evidence, which correspond to the truth

---

[†]Throughout this chapter we use the conjunction symbol $\wedge$ to mean *and,* the disjunction symbol $\vee$ to mean *or,* and the negation symbol $\neg$ to mean *not.*

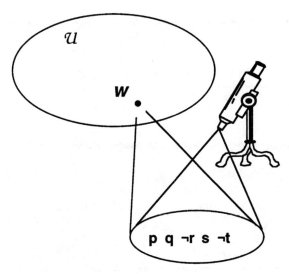

FIGURE 5.1   The carnapian universe.

of certain propositions, may be thought of as constraints on the subsets of possible worlds where the state of the real-world system actually lies. Possible worlds that are logically consistent with those propositions (said to be *compatible* with the evidence) are, generally, a proper subset of the carnapian universe of possibilities.

It is generally agreed that "stronger" or "better" evidence results in subsets of possible worlds that are smaller, in some sense, than "weak" evidence. The quality of evidence, however, should be judged from a variety of standards. Among those, domain-dependent criteria are usually the most important in assessing the quality of informational bodies. In general, it is desirable that the evidence be such as to allow unambiguous answers to certain questions of importance (i.e., hypotheses). To rephrase this statement with the help of the carnapian characterization, it is desirable that the evidence be such that propositions of importance are true (or false) for every possible world compatible with the evidence, rather than true for some worlds and false for others.

As we have stressed before, however, an approximate reasoning problem is such that the evidence is incapable of determining whether a hypothesis is true or false, as illustrated in Fig. 5.2. Approximate reasoning systems are concerned with the description of certain properties of the set $\mathscr{E}$ of possible worlds that are consistent with the evidence, seeking primarily to characterize the subsets $\mathscr{H} \cap \mathscr{E}$ and $\overline{\mathscr{H}} \cap \mathscr{E}$ of worlds compatible with the evidence where a hypothesis is either true or false, respectively. The descriptions that they provide, however, are of a substantially different nature for different approaches—not being all based or explained, as often erroneously claimed, by probabilistic notions.

5.1.3   Probabilistic and Possibilistic Reasoning

We will be concerned primarily with the two major types of approximate reasoning methodologies that are being actively used to treat practical situation assessment

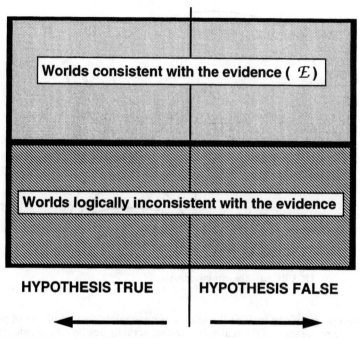

FIGURE 5.2   The approximate reasoning problem.

and planning/decision problems. These methodologies are commonly said to be *probabilistic* or *possibilistic,* respectively.

Probabilistic methods seek to describe the structure of a set of possible worlds by means of certain conditional probability distributions (the condition being the actual evidence at hand). If these distributions are considered to represent, on one hand, the *tendency* or *propensity* of the world to act in a repetitive fashion that may be described by a *frequency of occurrence,* they are said to have an *objectivist* interpretation; if they represent, on the other hand, the degrees of belief (or of commitment to certain courses of action) of certain rational agents, then they are said to have a *subjectivist* interpretation.

Irrespective of the particular interpretation used, probabilistic reasoning methods are concerned with the *likelihood* (either measured by previous experience or believed by an agent) that a particular hypothesis will be true in a given situation. Save for exceptional cases (i.e., probabilities equal to 0 or 1), no firm assurances are given to the user of any probabilistic methodology about the actual state of the world or its behavior. The probabilistic assessment is one of *tendency* and is primarily useful in the "long run," i.e., when evaluated by criteria that take into account the aggregate performance of the approximate reasoner over many situation assessment and decision aid examples.

Probabilistic results are particularly useful in organizations such as insurance companies or gambling houses, where success is evaluated in terms of a population of examples rather than on a case-by-case basis (i.e., all insurance policies or all gambling customers). By this statement we do not mean that probabilistic information is useless for single cases or "short runs." Our point is that, for all we know, the hypothesis may be true or may be false (that is the nature of the approximate reasoning problem). Under such circumstances, decisions applicable to a specific case that could possibly lead to an undesirable state of affairs may deserve to be analyzed from other viewpoints.

Possibilistic reasoning, however, seeks to describe possible worlds in terms of their similarity to other sets of possible worlds by placing emphasis on assessments that may be assured to be valid in each particular case and situation. Rather than describing relative proportions (of occurrence) of possible worlds where a given hypothesis of interest is true or false, as done by probabilistic methods, possibilistic reasoning seeks to describe all possible worlds that are compatible with evidence, in terms of their resemblance to members of certain sets of "exemplary" or "typical" worlds.

For example, a probabilistic method may determine that a corporation has a probability of 80 percent of exceeding its profit goal for the year. This assessment is not an assurance that such a goal will be attained. It does provide, however, some basis for subsequent management policy. While there is a chance that profits will fall short of the goal, if management policy is consistently applied in every fiscal period, then, in the long run, proper rational decisions will have been made and the company could be expected to prosper (despite possible occasional setbacks). A possibilistic method, however, may assert that profits will amount to *at least* 70 percent of the goal figure. On some previously agreed similarity scale, such a statement may be translated to the possibilistic statement "the possibility of achieving the profit goal is .7." Note that the emphasis is on certainty and *comparison* between statements rather than on *likelihood* and *chance*.

In general, possibilistic methods, which are strongly rooted in *fuzzy set theory* [48], provide assessments such as "the profit will be adequate," indicating that the predicted value of the profit will have a similarity greater than zero (sometimes possibilistic techniques produce specific lower bounds) to a value that is a good example of "adequate gain." Often it is also said that these vague statements describe the degree of ease by which the concept "adequate" matches the situation at hand. The ability to represent vague concepts by possibility distributions—attained by indicating that a value of a variable matches the vague concept to a degree—is central to fuzzy set theory, which was conceived as a basis for the formal treatment of linguistic utterances as they are commonly found in everyday discourse.

In summary, we may say that the approach to the analysis of imprecise and uncertain information that is used by any approximate reasoning methodology is based on the solution of a problem that is related to, but different from, the unsolvable problem of determining, without ambiguity, the truth of a hypothesis. In the probabilistic case, the answers provided consist of estimates of the frequency of truth of the hypothesis in similar cases as determined by prior observation (objectivist interpretation) or degree of commitment in a gamble based on the actual truth of the hypothesis (subjectivist interpretation). In the possibilistic case, in contrast, the answers provided assert that a related similar hypothesis is true.

5.2 PROBABILISTIC REASONING

Probabilistic reasoning methods focus on the description of the relative proportions of occurrence of truth or falsehood of certain hypotheses under certain evidential constraints. These evidential constraints, representing available evidence $\mathscr{E}$, condition the probabilities $P(X = x|\mathscr{E})$ describing the frequency of occurrence of the value x of state variable X when $\mathscr{E}$ is true. Using again the carnapian characterization, we may describe these techniques as being concerned with the determination of the probability of some subsets of the carnapian universe on the basis of the probability of related subsets.

If possible worlds in the carnapian universe correspond to individual combinations of values of n state variables $X_1, X_2, \ldots, X_n$, that is,

$$p_\alpha \equiv (X_1 = x_1) \wedge (X_2 = x_2) \wedge \cdots \wedge (X_n = x_n)$$

then, in general, probabilistic reasoning problems require the determination of either the joint probability distribution

$$P(X_1 = x_1, X_2 = x_2, \ldots, X_n = x_n | \mathscr{E})$$

or, alternatively, one of its marginal distributions on the basis of information consisting of related marginal and conditional probability distributions.

5.2.1 Conventional Probabilistic Reasoning

Classical probabilistic techniques rely on a calculus that is directly derived from the axioms of probability theory and that, in addition, assumes that all required numerical probability values are available, as the result of either prior empirical observation (i.e., frequencies of occurrence) or elicitation of personal commitment to gambling outcomes ("degrees of belief").

The rules used for this derivation include the additivity axiom of probability

$$P(A) + P(B) = P(A \cap B) + P(A \cup B)$$

and the celebrated identity of Bayes and Laplace

$$P(B|A) = \frac{P(A|B)P(B)}{P(A)}$$

which is a direct consequence of the definition of conditional probability.

The bane of all methods relying on the use of classical probability procedures is the lack of sufficient information about the required values of conditional and marginal (a priori) probabilities. Even when assumptions of independence between variable values, i.e.,

$$P((X = x) \wedge (Y - y)) = P(X = x) \, P(Y = y)$$

and conditional independence between variable values, i.e.,

$$P(X = x | Y = y, Z = z) = P(X = x | Y = y)$$

are used to simplify the required computations [30], the number of variables involved in a typical approximate reasoning problem leads to the need to estimate a large number (usually exponentially related to the number of variables) of marginal and conditional probability distributions.

The difficulties inherent in such estimation required early efforts, such as the development of PROSPECTOR [12], to use a combination of probabilistic procedures and ad hoc or heuristic techniques to overcome problems associated with lack of probabilistic information and to resolve some inconsistencies that occurred whenever estimated information overconstrained some probability distributions.

Some of these methodological problems can also be traced to the desire to generalize the network-based, goal-oriented procedures of classical expert systems to situations where the traditional truth values of classical logic (i.e., **true** and **false**) were generalized to a continuous scale by equating truth value with probability. The difficulties involved in such a generalization were soon apparent, as, e.g., the transitivity of implication valid in conventional inference, i.e.,

If X implies Y and if Y implies Z, then X implies Z

fails to hold for probabilities; that is, $P(Y|X)$ may be high, $P(Z|Y)$ may be high, but $P(Z|X)$ may be zero. Current methodologies based on the use of classical probability theory to compute the values of a joint probability distribution [25, 28] have solved these methodological problems; but in spite of the deft exploitation of independence assumptions in *probabilistic networks* [30], they still face the combinatorial explosion difficulties typical of multivariable problems.

5.2.2   Estimation of Probability Distributions

If, on one hand, a purely objectivist viewpoint is taken, it is clear that the probability distributions required to determine the probability of a hypothesis given available evidence may not be available. In this view, which we hold, probability can only be the result of experience accumulated through previous observation, and while, theoretically, absent values may be derivable by empirical means, often the required experiments are unfeasible or impractical. This is particularly true in problems involving systems that are not easy to manipulate or observe (e.g., evaluation of building damage due to earthquakes) or when the required information is actively denied or obscured by adversaries (e.g., in military situation assessment problems).

The orthodox subjectivist view of probability claims, on the other hand, that it is impossible to ignore the values of probability distributions, since they are always statements of the degree of belief that certain agents have about the truth of hypotheses. The rationale supporting the representation of such beliefs by numerical functions having the properties of a probability function is based on the famous "Dutch book" argument [7]. If an agent is to engage in a gamble involving the truth or falsehood of a certain hypothesis, it will be irrational for her or him to choose a combination of bets that will be sure to lose (a Dutch book) regardless of the outcome of the gamble. Under such conditions, it can be shown that the agent's personal beliefs (assumed to be numbers) on the truth and falsehood of hypotheses must satisfy the axioms of probability.

Other personalistic axiomatic systems have been proposed to support the contention that personal beliefs on hypothetical truth can always be estimated by using a single numerical value [39]. These axiomatic systems have, however, been subject to considerable criticism on the basis of both their naturality or rationality [43, 24] and the actual behavior of rational agents under controlled circumstances [2, 13].

Perhaps more controversial is the "pragmatic necessity" argument proposed by some decision scientists to justify their choice of probability values in the absence of relevant knowledge. The essential point of this argument emphasizes the decision-oriented nature of most approximate reasoning problems. It is said that if a decision must be made, when all empirical information has been considered, then any missing probability values (consistent with such knowledge) may be chosen because something, after all, must be done. While it is not claimed that this procedure replaces objectively determined probability values, it is said that ignorance of such quantities is inconsequential.[†] Such light dismissal of required probability values may have, of course, significant undesirable consequences.

Metaphysical principles, such as the *principle of insufficient reason* or the *maximum entropy principle,* that seek to formalize the choice of single distributions on purportedly "rational" bases other than empirical knowledge, are vulnerable to the same criticism. Regardless of claims that some may make invoking pragmatic needs or metaphysics to develop AI tools to assess complex situations, scientific practice— fundamentally interested in understanding the world and interacting with it— eschews these practices, relying instead on experiment-based, hypothesis-testing paradigms.

When it is accepted, at least, that sometimes probability values may not be either observable or capable of being elicited, it is clear that probabilistic reasoning techniques must proceed beyond classical probability calculus and develop alternative computation schemes that do not assume such informational availability. This generalization does not require, as claimed by some, to abandon either the axioms of probability or Bayes' rule as essential elements of the underlying calculus. Instead, we are simply extending our computational—rather than our conceptual—schemes to determine the effects of our ignorance on the results of probabilistic analyses.

5.3   GENERALIZED PROBABILISTIC REASONING

Current approaches that generalize the calculus of probabilities are, as stated above, based on generalization of computational rather than conceptual schemes. As such, the qualifier *nonbayesian,* which is sometimes associated with them, is basically incorrect; its validity is limited to the current skepticism, among orthodox subjectivists (often called bayesians), about their necessity. All these schemes are based on variations of the same idea: the determination of intervals [42] where unknown probability values must lie.

5.3.1   Interval-Valued Probabilities

General formalisms for the representation and manipulation of interval probability bounds have been investigated by Kyburg [23], who also studied issues germane to the relations between this general formulation and the calculus of evidence of Dempster-Shafer [22]. The central notion in his treatment of probabilistic knowledge is *convex probabilities,* used to describe the set of probability values in multidimensional space where possible values of the underlying distributions lie.

Although general interval-valued probability is preferable to other schemes, which are limited by their theoretical representation capabilities, the corresponding calculus of intervals is hampered by the difficulties associated with the storage and processing of a large number of probability bounds. If m ground propositions are identified as the initial generators of a carnapian universe, it may be necessary to store and manipulate 2^{2^m} bounds corresponding to all subsets of this universe. These difficulties have effectively limited the application of interval-based approaches in practice.

[†]It is important to point out, however, that many decision scientists rely, under these circumstances, on analyses of the sensitivity of the results to such convenient assumptions.

Practical schemes that are amenable to computer-based implementation, however, do not have the same generality. In general, these approaches rely on manipulation of intervals that have been generated by knowledge of probability values for *some* subsets which are then used to determine interval bounds for the probabilities of subsets of interest (i.e., inner or lower probabilities). Among such schemes relying on the use of lower probabilities, the calculus of evidence of Dempster-Shafer has found the largest acceptance in the approximate reasoning community.

5.3.2 Evidential Reasoning

Evidential reasoning is the name of the methodology based on the Dempster-Shafer calculus of evidence.[†] The basic structures of the calculus of evidence were introduced in 1966 by Dempster [8]. Shafer [40] proposed in 1976 the use of those constructs to represent and manipulate evidence. The methodology was first applied to the solution of approximate reasoning problems in artificial intelligence [16, 26]. Although the calculus of evidence is often regarded as being nonbayesian (meaning primarily nonprobabilistic), its original derivation by Dempster is fully consistent with conventional probability theory [33, 34].

Evidential reasoning is based on the representation of probabilistic evidence by means of *mass functions* or *basic probability assignments*. Mass functions assign a nonnegative mass value to every subset in a space of possible solutions (or possible worlds). The sum of all these mass assignments over the set of all such subsets (called the *power set*) is always 1.

Evidential reasoning is advantageous in that it allows representation of the degree of support provided by evidence toward the truth of a hypothesis without requiring that such support be split among more specific propositions implying that hypothesis. For example, in a criminal investigation case, evidence may indicate that the perpetrator is blonde without actually identifying his or her identity. In such a case, a mass function that assigns a mass of 1 to the set of all blonde suspects and 0 to all other subsets is used to represent the evidential weight. Note that in this case the sum of the masses for all sets consisting of a single blonde suspect (0) is different from the mass assigned to the set of all blonde suspects (1). Had masses corresponded to actual probabilities of guilt, those two quantities would have been the same.

Closely associated with the notion of mass are the *belief* and *plausibility* functions, defined by

$$\text{Bel}(A) = \sum_{B \subseteq A} m(B)$$

and

$$\text{Pl}(A) = \sum_{B \cap A \neq \emptyset} m(A)$$

respectively. The belief function is a measure of the total support provided by evidence toward the truth of a particular proposition, while the plausibility function measures the degree by which the evidence fails to refute it.

[†]The reader must be warned about a tendency in the literature to use the expression *evidential reasoning* as a synonym of *approximate reasoning*.

Logical Bases for Evidential Reasoning.   Our possible-worlds approach to the description of probabilistic reasoning may be extended to develop a formal foundation for the basic functions and structures of evidential reasoning. This extension is based on the use of a form of modal logic, called *epistemic logic,* introduced to deal with issues relevant to the states of knowledge of rational agents. The insight provided by this characterization has helped to clarify a number of fundamental issues in evidential reasoning, notably in the areas of semantic characterization of the notion of evidential independence and the derivation of schemes for the combination of dependent and conditional evidence.

Epistemic logic is, like conventional boolean logic, a two-valued logic where each proposition is assigned one and only one of the classical truth values, i.e., **true** or **false.** In epistemic logic, however, propositions not only may be true or false, but also may be *known* to be true or false; alternatively, they may not be known to be either true or false. Rather than introduce new scales of truth, as is done in multivalued logic [32], epistemic logic resorts to a representation scheme where knowledge of a proposition is represented by means of another related proposition.

A rational agent's state of knowledge about the truth of a proposition is represented by a special operator **K,** used as a prefix to symbols describing other propositions. For example, knowledge of the truth of proposition p is denoted $\mathbf{K}p$, while $\neg\mathbf{K}p$ symbolizes lack of such knowledge.[†] The discussion of epistemic systems also requires differentiation between propositions that describe certain properties of the real world (*objective* propositions) and propositions that include one or more epistemic operators (*epistemic* propositions).

In our investigation, we have employed a particular form of epistemic logic proposed by Moore [27] to deal with problems of reasoning and planning in artificial intelligence applications. The axiom schemata for such a modal system is as follows:

1. Axioms of the ordinary propositional calculus.

2. $\mathbf{K}p \to p$ (If a proposition is known to be true, then it is true.)

3. $\mathbf{K}p \to \mathbf{K}\mathbf{K}p$ (*Positive introspection:* If a proposition is known to be true, then it is known that it is known to be true.)

4. $\mathbf{K}(p \to q) \to (\mathbf{K}p \to \mathbf{K}q)$ (*Consequential omniscience:* If it is known that p implies q, then knowledge of the truth of p implies knowledge of the truth of q.)

5. If p is an axiom, then $\mathbf{K}p$ is true.

6. $\neg\mathbf{K}p \to \mathbf{K}\neg\mathbf{K}p$ (*Negative introspection:* If the truth value of a proposition is unknown, then such a state of ignorance is known.)

The set of all possible truth assignments to the sentences of a modal propositional system that satisfy these axioms is called an *epistemic universe* (Fig. 5.3), a concept that generalizes the carnapian universe. Each member of this universe is a *possible world* that represents both a particular state of the world and the state of knowledge that certain rational agents have about it. In this universe two classes of subsets are of special importance.

The first class consists of subsets of possible worlds where some objective proposition p is true. These subsets are called *truth sets.* The truth set for a proposition p is denoted $\mathbf{t}(p)$.

[†]The meaning of the notation $\neg\mathbf{K}p$ should not be confused with ignorance about the truth of p represented by $\neg\mathbf{K}p \wedge \neg\mathbf{K}(\neg p)$; that is, neither p nor its negation is known to be true.

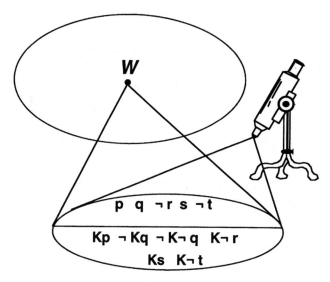

FIGURE 5.3   The epistemic universe.

The second class consists of subsets having as members possible worlds where some objective proposition p is *known* to be true. These subsets are called *support sets*, with $\mathbf{k}(p)$ denoting the support set for objective proposition p.

Closely related to support sets are the *epistemic sets*, which partition the epistemic universe into subsets characterized by the same knowledge pattern. Each such epistemic set may be associated with a proposition p that represents the *best* or *most specific* knowledge available in each possible world within that epistemic set (this proposition is the conjunction of all known propositions in each world). Epistemic subsets are identical to the elements of the quotient space of the epistemic universe by the *accessibility relation*. The accessibility relation captures the informal notion that, for all we know in a possible world w, we might just as well be in an *accessible* or *conceivable* world w'. The epistemic set corresponding to an objective proposition p is denoted $\mathbf{e}(p)$.

Several important set-theoretic relations, illustrated in Fig. 5.4, exist between members of these classes:

- The support set for a proposition p is the union of the (disjoint) epistemic sets corresponding to propositions q that imply p, that is,

$$\mathbf{k}(p) = \bigcup_{q \to p} \mathbf{e}(q)$$

In plain words, if p is known to be true, it is either because that is the "best available knowledge" or because such "most specific knowledge" is that another proposition q, which implies p, is true.

- The support set $\mathbf{k}(p)$ is the largest support set (in fact, it is the largest arbitrary union of epistemic sets) included in the truth set $\mathbf{t}(p)$.

Because epistemic and support sets are always uniquely associated with an objective proposition, their probabilities may be thought of also as measures that assign a unique nonnegative value to each such objective proposition.

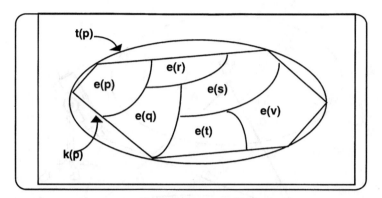

FIGURE 5.4   Relations between special sets in the epistemic universe.

If **P** is such a probability, the functions

$$m(p) = \mathbf{P}(\mathbf{e}(p))$$

$$\mathrm{Bcl}(p) = \mathbf{P}\,(\mathbf{k}(p))$$

are related by the basic identity

$$\mathrm{Bel}(q) = \sum_{p \Rightarrow q} m(p)$$

which is central to the calculus of evidence [40].

Probabilities over the epistemic algebra (and their associated functions) represent the effect of uncertain evidence on a rational agent's state of knowledge. The corresponding probabilities defined on the *truth algebra* of the truth set $\mathbf{t}(p)$ can be interpreted as the degrees of likelihood (usually unknown) of objective propositions.

Because the largest member of the epistemic algebra that is contained in the truth set $\mathbf{t}(p)$ is the support set $\mathbf{k}(p)$, it follows (from standard results on lower- and upper-probability functions) that any extension of a probability **P**, defined over the epistemic algebra, to a probability $\hat{\mathbf{P}}$ defined over the truth algebra must satisfy the inequality

$$\mathrm{Bel}(p) \le \hat{\mathbf{P}}(\mathbf{t}(p)) \le \mathrm{Pl}(p)$$

where $\mathrm{Pl}(p)$ is the *plausibility function* of the Dempster-Shafer calculus of evidence. Furthermore, these bounds are the best possible and cannot be improved. In other words, knowledge of actual probability values over some subsets provides bounds, which may not be improved except by incorporation of additional evidence—on the probability values of other sets.

Issues related to the combination of evidence are readily modeled by considering another, more complex, set of possible worlds called the *product epistemic universe*. The members of this set are, as was the case in previous epistemic universes, possible worlds, i.e., functions that assign conventional binary truth values (i.e., **true** or **false**) to certain propositions of interest. The difference in this case consists in the use of multiple epistemic operators $\mathbf{K}_1, \mathbf{K}_2, \ldots$ representing the knowledge possessed by several rational agents about the truth of objective propositions or of other epistemic propositions.

If we constrain ourselves momentarily to situations involving two different rational agents A_1 and A_2, each ignorant of the knowledge of the other, their *common* (or integrated) knowledge may be modeled by introduction of a third, nonindexed, epistemic operator **K**. It is assumed that the knowledge available to this third agent is the sole and exclusive result of the combination of knowledge available to A_1 and A_2 without any other additional sources of information. This assumption is formally modeled by means of the following *knowledge combination (KC) axiom:*

KC $\mathbf{K}p$ is true if and only if there exist sentences p_1 and p_2 such that $\mathbf{K}_1 p_1$ and $\mathbf{K}_2 p_2$ are true, and, in addition, such that $p_1 \wedge p_2 \Rightarrow p$.

If the epistemic sets corresponding to operators $\mathbf{K}$, $\mathbf{K}_1$, and $\mathbf{K}_2$ are denoted by $\mathbf{e}(p)$, $\mathbf{e}_1(p)$, and $\mathbf{e}_2(p)$, respectively, the following important set equation, relating all types of epistemic sets, is the basis for the derivation of a variety of combination formulas:

$$\mathbf{e}(p) = \bigcup_{p_1 \wedge p_2 = p} (\mathbf{e}_1(p_1) \cap \mathbf{e}_2(p_2))$$

from which, under certain assumptions of probabilistic independence, the Dempster combination formula

$$m(p) = \lambda \sum_{p_1 \wedge p_2 = p} m_1(p_1) m_2(p_2)$$

is readily derived.

Semantic Issues of Evidential Reasoning. Using an objectivist interpretation of the concept of probability, the author has formulated a Kripke-type model [20] that explicates basic probability assignments as the principal output estimated by a *generalized statistical experiment*. This model-theoretic formalism also sheds light on the general character and nature of probabilistic knowledge and on the mechanisms used to capture it. Rather than provide a formal characterization of the kripkean formulation, we will informally describe a general model of a statistical experiment that provides insight into the nature of the theoretical structures discussed further below.

The informal model that serves as our point of departure is illustrated in Fig. 5.5, which presents the typical steps involved in the collection of statistics about the behavior of a real-world system. A *statistical experiment,* as illustrated, commences with a mechanism for the generation of samples (i.e., sequences of possible worlds that reflect the relative frequency of occurrence of such states of affairs in actual experience).

Each such sample is then examined for compliance with some experimental criteria used to determine if the corresponding possible world satisfies the criteria used for generation of the desired statistical distribution. In other words, we are interested in estimating a conditional probability, and this test determines whether the condition is met. Future use of the generated statistical values is valid *solely* if available evidence (i.e., a true proposition about the world) corresponds exactly to the condition used in the generation of the statistics.

Note that the nature of the device (sensor) used to make this determination is very important in determining whether the generated statistics correspond to an

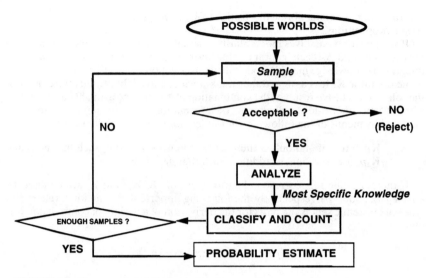

FIGURE 5.5   The general statistical experiment.

epistemic probability over the truth set $\mathbf{t}(p)$ (for example, if the sensor is capable of reliable binary discrimination between samples where p is true and samples where p is false), or over a support set $\mathbf{k}(p)$ corresponding to a rational agent that may or may not be that involved in the next analysis step (e.g., some sensor, not necessarily that used to further analyze the sample, is used to determine if p is valid; its failures, however, do not mean that p is false).

If the sample satisfies the conditions defining the statistical distribution being estimated, then the next step consists in the determination of properties (i.e., propositions that are true) in this particular possible world. The conjunctions of these propositions are the "most specific knowledge" available for that sample. In classical statistical setups, the analyzing devices that perform such a determination are designed so as to determine if the sample falls into one of several exclusive categories. For example, in clinical trials, the result of each trial is typically classified on the basis of its success into several disjoint sets (e.g., "success" or "failure"). In more general experiments, however, the ability to determine most specific knowledge may be severely limited, and the sample will be placed into one of several classes that may be overlapping. For example, if the samples correspond to medical patients having certain types of afflictions (e.g., the "condition" is that they have a renal or a hepatic disorder), available knowledge may indicate that a particular patient has a disorder within a certain class (e.g., kidney disease), while failing to determine a specific disease.

If each sample is so classified and the results of successive analysis are tabulated as frequencies, the resulting distribution is a mass distribution in the sense of Shafer rather than a conventional probability distribution. When the differences between probability distributions and their sample-based estimates (which are often the source of second-order probability distributions) are ignored, the computed frequencies may be considered to be the same as a nonconventional distribution that corresponds to an epistemic probability. The rational agent in this distribution is the *statistical experimenter* who has a "most specific knowledge" for each possible world (actually for a relevant sample of such worlds).[†]

The knowledge of the approximate reasoner, on the other hand, is limited to knowledge of (aggregated) results of the statistical experiment coupled with knowledge of the condition validating the use of the statistical (epistemic) distribution (i.e., the condition used to determine if the samples were acceptable). Note that this distribution generally induces bounds on the probability of truth sets. The latter, however, are needed to solve typical decision-making problems.

In closing our description of the calculus of evidence, it is important to point out that, in addition to our objectivist model, subjectivist interpretations of belief and mass functions have been proposed by Smets [41] and Jaffray [19]. The formulation of Jaffray is particularly attractive in that it provides a simple, direct generalization of the basic results of DeFinetti [7] on the probabilistic nature of degrees of belief.

5.4 POSSIBILISTIC REASONING

Possibilistic approaches produce, as is the case with their probabilistic counterparts, solutions to problems that are a modified formulation of the impossible (or, at least, very difficult) task of determining hypothesis validity. The emphasis, however, is not on determination of the frequency of instances where, under similar conditions, the hypothesis will be true or false. Possibilistic methods seek to produce unequivocal answers to *other* questions that are *similar* in some sense to those of interest to the system analyst.

For example, in a medical diagnosis problem, a probabilistic method may answer the question "Does the patient have disease *D*?" by means of a probability value that fails to indicate whether the disease exists but that allows evaluation of the chances of successful treatment. A possibilistic method, on the other hand, may answer the same question by responding unequivocally (i.e., true or false) to the modified query "Does the patient have a disease of type *D**?" where *D** stands for a class of diseases that are similar, in some sense, to disease *D*.

Similarity between propositions (sometimes regarded as the *degree of ease* by which a proposition describes a particular state of affairs) may be used as the basis for explaining the basic concepts and structures of fuzzy set theory and its logic-oriented extensions.

A fuzzy set f [48] is defined by its *membership function,* mapping elements from a universe $\mathcal{U}$ to the [0, 1] interval of the real line

$$\mu_f : \mathcal{U} \mapsto [0,1]$$

The concept of membership function generalizes the notion of characteristic function of a conventional set. For a particular element x of $\mathcal{U}$, the value $\mu_f(x)$ represents the degree of membership of x to fuzzy set f. Unlike conventional sets where elements either belong or do not belong to a set, fuzzy sets—representing vague concepts—admit partial membership ranging from 0 (nonmembership) to 1 (full membership).

[†]Note that in classical experimental setups, where the conditions of the experiment may be closely controlled, the most specific knowledge corresponds to the determination of the actual possible world where the sample lies. In those cases, the sample frequencies estimate probability values for an actual probability distribution.

Fuzzy sets may also be described by means of their α *cuts,* consisting of all members with a degree of membership greater than or equal to a value α:

$$f(\alpha) = \{x \mid \mu_f(x) \ge \alpha\}$$

By using this important concept, fuzzy sets may also be regarded, from a logical viewpoint, as a set of related indexed propositions representing different levels of conceptual applicability to a particular state of affairs.

The set-theoretic operations (union, intersection, complementation), originally proposed by Zadeh [48], generalize the corresponding operations for conventional sets:

$$\mu_{f \cap g}(x) = \min[\mu_f(x), \mu_g(x)]$$

$$\mu_{f \cup g}(x) = \max[\mu_f(x), \mu_g(x)]$$

$$\mu_{\bar{f}}(x) = 1 - \mu_f(x)$$

where x is a member of the universe $\mathcal{U}$.

An important concept in fuzzy set theory is the *fuzzy relation,* which generalizes the conventional set-theoretic notion of relation. If $\mathcal{U}$ and $\mathcal{V}$ are universes, then a fuzzy relation between $\mathcal{U}$ and $\mathcal{V}$ is a fuzzy set in the set of all pairs (u, v) (or *cartesian product*), where u is an element of $\mathcal{U}$ and where v is an element of $\mathcal{V}$. One of the main reasons for the importance of fuzzy relations is their role in the representation of vague relationships between variables, e.g.,

If u is high, then v is small.

Approximate reasoning systems used in possibilistic systems use fuzzy relations to represent inferential rules in their knowledge bases.

5.4.1 Possibility Theory

Possibility theory is based on the representation of vague information as *elastic* constraints on the possible values that may be attained by a variable. For example, if information is available indicating that "James is rich," a possibilistic approach represents this fact as a *possibility distribution* on the values of a variable describing James's wealth (called here *James-net-worth*) in the form

$$\Pi_{James\text{-}net\text{-}worth} = rich$$

where *rich* is a fuzzy set defined over the real numbers intended to describe for each possible value of *James-net-worth* the degree of ease by which the concept *rich* agrees with that particular net worth.

In general, if a variable X takes values over a universe $\mathcal{U}$, then a linguistic expression of the form "X is F" will be formally translated by a possibilistic assignment $\Pi_X = F$, such translation being denoted as

$$X \text{ is } F \rightarrow \Pi_X = F$$

meaning that the values that may be attained by X are constrained as specified by the fuzzy set F. Because vague statements in natural language are translated, in possibility theory, to formal statements that assign a fuzzy value to a variable (as opposed to assigning a precise value, as for a *precise* statement), such a variable is called a *linguistic variable.*

Other translation rules are used to derive representations for more complicated linguistic statements, such as "*X* is *F* and *Y* is *G*" or "*Q X*'s are *F*" (where *Q* is a generalized quantifier such as *most*), are the basis of an uncertainty calculus that is complemented by certain inferential rules which allow the derivation of possibilistic constraints for certain variables as a function of constraints on related variables. Among these rules, the most important is the *generalized modus ponens* which produces an approximate conclusion

$$\Pi_Y = G'$$

meaning "*Y* is *G'*," from knowledge that

$$\Pi_X = F'$$

meaning that "*X* is *F'*" and that

$$\Pi_{Y/X} = F \to G$$

that is, "if *X* is *F*, then *Y* is *G*."

The qualifier *generalized* is used to indicate the important fact that, unlike classical modus ponens, this inference rule allows a rule to be used even when available facts *F'* do not match *precisely* the antecedent of the rule (that is, *F*). The conclusion *G'* in such a case differs also, in general, from the consequent of the rule, being a *more general* or *less specific* constraint than *G*.

5.4.2 Similarity Relations and Possible Worlds

A *similarity relation* in a set *X* is a function that assigns a real value between 0 and 1 to every pair of objects from *X*. Similarity relations play an important role, investigated in detail by the author [36], in the interpretation of the basic concepts and structures of possibility theory. The results of this research show that the notion of possibility may be explained in terms of a similarity function defined over a universe of possible worlds. This similarity defines a metric that quantifies the extent of resemblance between pairs of states (as evaluated from the viewpoint of the particular problem being considered). For example, in a planning problem, the planner may use such measures to describe the extent to which the plan's effects resemble some planning goal or objective.

The value $S(w, w')$ that a similarity relation assigns to a pair of worlds (w, w') in a universe $\mathcal{U}$ is a numerical[†] measure of the extent to which propositions that are true at *w* may be expected to hold true at *w'*. A similarity value of 1 for $S(w, w')$ (the highest possible value) indicates that, from the point of view of the propositions used to construct our universe, both worlds are *indiscernible*, i.e., that the same propositions are true in *w* and in *w'*. A value of 0, in contrast, tells us that knowledge of propositional truth in *w* does not have any predictive value over truth values in *w'* (and vice versa).

[†]The requirement that similarities be numerical may be relaxed considerably. We shall confine our exposition, however, to [0,1]-valued similarities for the sake of clarity.

Unlike probability values that represent the behavior of a system and, as such, are a property of the system (the same may be said, under a subjectivist interpretation, of degrees of belief as a property of a rational agent), similarity functions are arbitrarily defined (but not necessarily subjective) scales that facilitate the description of the degree to which an object has some property. Thus, similarities are as useful (and arbitrary) as any other metric scale; their utility is essentially a function of the degree to which the scale distinguishes between different states of a system and the degree to which similarity scales that are associated with different properties (e.g., the pressure and volume of a perfect gas) are related to each other by means of actual physical laws (or facilitate the expression of such laws).

Simply stated, similarities provide the measurement sticks that must be employed to characterize, in an approximate fashion, the state of the real world. Correspondingly, approximate inference rules describe how similarity from some respect (e.g., resemblance of the actual state, pressure = 80 kg/m^2, to some prototypical situation, pressure > 100 kg/m^2) relates to similarity from another viewpoint (e.g., temperature > 200°C), by means of a fuzzy relation (e.g., "if the pressure is high, then the temperature is high").

Properties of Similarities: Triangular Norms.   A *similarity function S* defined on a possible-world universe $\mathcal{U}$ may be regarded as a generalization of the modal-logic notion of *accessibility* or *conceivability* [18], by introduction of multiple binary relations R_α between possible worlds (one for each value of α between 0 and 1), defined by

$$R_\alpha(w, w') \quad \text{if and only if} \quad S(w, w') \geq \alpha$$

Using these relations, we may say that conditions in w are *possible* to some degree in w' on the basis of the value of $S(w, w')$ (generalizing the classical definition of the modal operator for possible truth).

To ensure that the function S has the properties of a similarity function, a number of properties must be required to ensure that S is truly a measure of a resemblance between objects. Among these, the requirements that $S(w, w) = 1$ (i.e., the similarity between any world and itself is as high as possible) and that $S(w, w') = S(w', w)$ (that is, w resembles w' as much as w' resembles w) are rather natural.

Less obvious than those properties is a form of transitivity that may be understood by noting that if S assigned values of similarity to the pairs (w, w') and (w', w'') that make both w and w' highly similar and w' and w'' also highly similar, then it would be surprising if w and w'' did not resemble each other at all. Any function claiming to measure resemblance must be such, therefore, that the similarity value $S(w, w'')$ is bounded from below by a function of $S(w, w')$ and $S(w', w'')$, expressed by means of a binary operation $\otimes$ in the form

$$S(w, w'') \geq S(w, w') \otimes S(w', w'')$$

which is graphically illustrated in Fig. 5.6.

In terms of accessibility relations, this condition is a generalization of the classical expression for the transitivity of R, that is,

$$R \subseteq R \circ R$$

to the form

$$R_{\alpha \otimes \beta} \subseteq R_\alpha \circ R_\beta \quad \text{for all } 0 \leq \alpha, \beta \leq 1$$

involving multiple relations R_α.

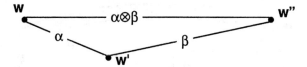

FIGURE 5.6   Transitivity of the similarity relation.

Imposition of reasonable requirements upon the operation ⊗ immediately shows it to be a *triangular norm,* introduced here by means of arguments related to metrics and similarity, but of extreme importance, otherwise, in multivalued logic [44]. Important examples of this operation include these functions

$$a \otimes b = \min(a,b) \qquad a \otimes b = \max(a + b - 1, 0) \qquad a \otimes b = ab$$

called the *Zadeh, Lukasïewicz,* and *product* triangular norms, respectively.

If a function δ is defined, between pairs of possible worlds, by the relation

$$\delta = 1 - S$$

then it may be seen that when ⊗ is the triangular norm of Lukasïewicz, δ is an ordinary metric or distance, satisfying the well-known triangular inequality

$$\delta(w, w'') \leq \delta(w, w') + \delta(w', w'')$$

When ⊗ is the Zadeh triangular norm, however, the transitivity property is equivalent to the more stringent condition

$$\delta(w, w'') \leq \max(\delta(w, w'), \delta(w', w''))$$

stating that δ is an *ultrametric* distance.

Logic and Metrics: Generalized Modus Ponens.   Metric structures, introduced via similarity relations, provide a mechanism for the characterization of logic relations by means of structures that stress proximity rather than subset-membership relations between possible worlds.

If a typical "conditional" proposition in boolean logic, i.e., "if q, then p," is thought of as a statement that every world where q is true is one where also p is true, then it is clear that implications are equivalent, as is well known, to a relationship of inclusion between possible worlds: the subset of q worlds is a subset of the set of p worlds.

However, statements of inclusion between subsets of possible worlds may also be characterized in metric terms by stating that every q world has a p world (i.e., itself) that is as similar as possible to it. Logic structures, however, allow us only to say that q implies p, or that q implies its negation $\neg p$, or that neither is true. Similarity relations, by contrast, permit the measurement of the amount by which a set must be "stretched" (as illustrated in Fig. 5.7) in order for an inclusion relation to hold.

One such measure of inclusion is provided by function **I** (called the *degree of implication*), defined for pairs of propositions p and q by the expression

$$\mathbf{I}(p|q) = \inf_{w' \vdash q} \ \sup_{w \vdash p} S(w, w')$$

which is related to the well-known Hausdorff distance, introduced in metric space theory to measure distance between subsets as a function of the distance between their elements.

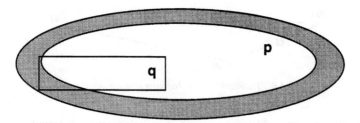

FIGURE 5.7   Extended set inclusion.

Note, in particular, if $\mathbf{I}(p|q) = 1$, then every q world is similar to a p world that is logically *indistinguishable* from it (i.e., implication), whereas if both $\mathbf{I}(p|q)$ and $\mathbf{I}(q|p)$ are equal to 1, then p and q are logically equivalent.

From this perspective, if inferential rules, such as the *modus ponens,* are thought of as the tools of an "implicational" calculus (i.e., if q is a subset of p and r is a subset of q, then r is a subset of pr"), then possibility theory generalizes such a calculus by deriving relations between neighborhoods of certain subsets of possible worlds (actually between their sizes).

The *generalized modus ponens* of Zadeh [46] is a direct consequence of the transitivity property

$$\mathbf{I}(p|r) \geq \mathbf{I}(p|q) \otimes \mathbf{I}(q|r)$$

of the degree-of-implication function, which is illustrated in Fig. 5.8.

Derivation of the actual form of the generalized modus ponens from similarity-based structures, which involve possibility distributions, is outside the scope of this chapter. It will suffice to say here that (1) possibility distributions measure the similarity, from the restricted viewpoint (called *marginal similarity*) of one or more *variables,* between certain subsets of possible worlds and (2) fuzzy inference rules provide metric knowledge about inclusion relations between such subsets.

In closing, it is important to stress that similarity relations justify the use of possibilistic logic as a form of *logical extrapolation,* exploiting similarities between possible worlds. The topological and metric structures that are introduced to enhance our basic carnapian universe are of a substantially different nature from the set measures exploited by probability theory which typically measure the "sizes" of the complementary subsets of possible worlds where a proposition is true or false, respectively.

Possibility and Necessity Distributions.   The concept of degree of inclusion and its related *degree of consistency,* defined by

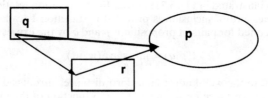

FIGURE 5.8   Generalized modus ponens.

$$C(p|q) = \sup_{w' \vdash q} \sup_{w \vdash p} S(w, w')$$

as the *possible* level of similarity between p and q worlds permits the expression of possibility and necessity functions in terms of similarity-based constructs.

To understand these relationships, we define first the *unconditioned necessity and possibility measures* of proposition p with respect to the evidential set $\mathscr{E}$ as the functions $I(p|\mathscr{E})$ and $C(p|\mathscr{E})$, respectively.

An *unconditioned necessity distribution* $\mathbf{Nec}_{\mathscr{E}}(\cdot)$ with respect to the evidential set $\mathscr{E}$ is then simply defined as a lower bound of the unconditioned necessity measure $I(\cdot|\mathscr{E})$, that is, as any real function defined over propositions satisfying

$$\mathbf{Nec}_{\mathscr{E}}(p) \le I(p|\mathscr{E})$$

for any proposition p. Informally, $\mathbf{Nec}_{\mathscr{E}}(p)$ is an estimate of $I(p|\mathscr{E})$ that bounds from below the necessary degree of similarity between any $\mathscr{E}$ world and its closest p world.

The dual of this notion is given by *unconditioned possibility distributions*, defined as upper bounds of degrees of consistency, i.e., as any real function defined over propositions satisfying

$$\mathbf{Poss}_{\mathscr{E}}(p) \ge C(p|\mathscr{E})$$

for any proposition p. $\mathbf{Poss}_{\mathscr{E}}(p)$ is an estimate of how close some $\mathscr{E}$ world may be to some p world.

The notions of unconditioned necessity and possibility measures may be extended to define conditional functions that measure the similarity of p and q worlds from the perspective of an evidential body $\mathscr{E}$. The *conditional necessity and possibility* measures with respect to a distribution $\mathscr{E}$ are defined by the expressions

$$I_{\mathscr{E}}(p|q) = \sup_{\mathscr{E}} [I(p|w) \oslash I(q|w)]$$
$$C_{\mathscr{E}}(p|q) = \inf_{\mathscr{E}} [I(p|w) \oslash I(q|w)]$$

respectively.

The function $\oslash$, called the *quasi-inverse* of the t norm $\otimes$, is defined by the expression

$$x \oslash y = \sup\{c \mid c \otimes x \le y, 0 \le c \le 1\}$$

for any $x, y \in [0, 1]$. This *residuation* operation has been used to characterize generalized implication operators in fuzzy logic [44]. The residuation value $a \oslash b$ may also be informally characterized as a measure of the extent to which a is larger than b, gauged by the scale provided by a chosen t norm t. When $a \ge b$, then $a \oslash b = 1$; otherwise, $a \oslash b$ has a value that decreases, for fixed b, as a decreases.

The following result [15], extending original results of Ruspini [36], validates the *generalized modus ponens* of Zadeh as commonly applied to the inferential propagation of possibility distributions:

Theorem 5.1: Generalized Modus Ponens for Possibility Functions.   Let $\mathscr{E}$ and $\mathscr{F}$ be two evidential bodies such that the intersection $\mathscr{E} \cap \mathscr{F}$ is nonempty. Furthermore, let $\{p_i \mid i \text{ in } I\}$ be a partition of the universe of discourse, that is, $\cup_I p_i = \mathfrak{U}$. Then

$$\sup_I [C_{\mathscr{F}}(q|p_i) \otimes C(p_i|\mathscr{E})] \ge C(p|\mathscr{E} \cap \mathscr{F})$$

A similar result holds for necessity distributions.

Note that these results produce an estimate of the similarities between the q world and the $\mathcal{E} \cap \mathcal{F}$ world on the basis of unconditioned measures on $\mathcal{E}$ and conditional measures on $\mathcal{F}$. In practice, the former measures correspond to the *a priori* evidence—approximated (from above) by a possibility distribution—while the latter are generally approximated by a set of fuzzy if-then rules [36, 15].

Utility and Preference Logics.   No treatment of the semantics of fuzzy logic can be complete without a discussion of interpretations based on the notions of preference and utility. Since the author discusses in some detail these characterizations in Chap. 24 of this collection [37], we will limit this examination to a very brief discussion of major concepts and developments.

Bellman and Zadeh [3] first proposed a utility-oriented fuzzy logic where both system goals and restrictions are expressed by means of fuzzy sets as *elastic constraints*. This initial characterization has been the source of almost all novel treatments of optimization problems within the framework of fuzzy logic.

Dubois, Prade, and their collaborators have pursued this interpretation from a formal logic viewpoint [10, 11], which has led to the development of a particular form of *possibilistic logics*.

Ruspini [35] also explored the relationship between similarity and preference logics both from the perspective of the multivalued logics of preference—stressing the representation of truth of a proposition as a numerical assessment of the degree by which such state of affairs is a "good thing"—and from considerations arising from the mathematical relations between generalized preorders and similarity relations [45]. Recently, Esteva et al. [14] have further established strong relationships between preference-based interpretations and those rooted in similarity notions, having also examined their connections with fuzzy truth-valued logic models.

5.5 NONMONOTONIC LOGIC AND COMMONSENSE REASONING

Nonmonotonic logic and commonsense reasoning are also concerned with the problems caused by a lack of information that is required to deduce the truth value of certain hypotheses. As is the case with approximate reasoning methodologies, these concerns go beyond considerations about the theoretical ability to produce the required knowledge, encompassing also the practical issues involved in such production. To use a most famous example, to deduce that a particular bird flies requires knowledge that such bird is not a penguin or an ostrich (at least, a nonflying ostrich), that the bird is not sick, dead, and so forth. The production and storage of this information impose heavy burdens on both users and systems.

Faced with the impossibility of collecting such information, nonmonotonic logic systems [31, 17, 9] are also forced to deal with a subset of possible solutions. Rather than rely on descriptions of *extensive* properties of such a set, as done by approximate reasoning methods, nonmonotonic procedures choose one of its members. If subsequent information eliminates that choice as a possible choice, then one or more of the "defeasible" assumptions are retracted. Use of the term *nonmonotonic* to characterize this type of reasoning is intended to reflect both the nature of the variation of truth values and the corresponding changes in the set of true statements as the consequence of the assimilation of new information (classical logic methods always *add* new truths to the set of existing theorems, thus leading to "smaller" sets of possible worlds).

The majority of nonmonotonic logic techniques rely on minimality arguments to choose possible worlds among a set of potential solutions. The general idea of these methods consists in the identification of a "least exceptional" world, i.e., a world where the only objects that satisfy certain predicates are precisely those that are known to do so. Recent work [4] has extended these ideas to the approximate reasoning domain by consideration of numerical degrees of exceptionality.

Similar commonsense reasoning techniques [31], notably *default reasoning,* are also related to probabilistic reasoning. Default assumptions (such as the hypothesis that, by default, birds fly) can be thought of as stating that the assumption, given our current state of knowledge, has a high probability of being true. Known characteristics of default reasoning, notably the lack of transitivity of modus ponens, have equivalent counterparts in probabilistic reasoning.

Studies of problems where knowledge is expressed by high-probability statements [29, 1] and developments in possibilistic reasoning techniques concerned with the manipulation of certain generalized quantifiers (e.g., *most*) [47] and with linguistic statements of probability (e.g., *usually*) [50] have also shown substantial similarities between default and probabilistic reasoning.

5.6 CONCLUSIONS

Possible-world semantics provides a perspective into approximate reasoning problems and methods that helps clarify many fundamental issues surrounding the nature and usefulness of different methodologies.

Through use of constructs based in possible-world formalisms, it is easy to see that all existing techniques produce correct and sound descriptions of the properties of the subset of possible worlds that are consistent with observed evidence rather than, as sometimes thought, ad hoc characterizations of an ambiguously relaxed notion of truth.

Furthermore, these formalizations underscore the basic relations between probabilistic techniques, showing that the Dempster-Shafer calculus of evidence is fully consistent with the theory of probability. By contrast, these models also reveal basic, substantial differences between probabilistic and possibilistic methods—the former related to set measures that characterize the frequency of occurrence of some event and the latter linked to notions of similarity between possible situations. From this viewpoint, it is evident that possibilistic and probabilistic techniques should not be regarded as competing tools but, rather, as complementary techniques seeking to describe different properties of sets of possible worlds.

Finally, it is important to point out that possible-world semantics also helps to clarify the characteristics and purposes of nonmonotonic and commonsense approaches to deductive inference.

ACKNOWLEDGMENTS

The development of the unified view of approximate reasoning methods discussed in this chapter was helped immeasurably by numerous conversations and discussions with Nadal Battle, Hamid Berenji, Piero Bonissone, Bernadette Bouchon-Meunier, Miguel Delgado, Didier Dubois, Francesc Esteva, Oscar Firschein, Pere García, Tom Garvey, Luis Godo, Joseph Goguen, Andrew Hanson, David Israel,

Henry Kyburg, Kurt Konolige, John Lowrance, Ramón López de Mántaras, Jose Miró, Robert Moore, Ray Perrault, Henri Prade, Elie Sanchez, Philippe Smets, Tom Strat, Enric Trillas, Llorenç Valverde, Len Wesley, and Lotfi Zadeh.

This work was supported by the Air Force Office of Scientific Research under contract no. F49620-89-K-0001 and by the National Science Foundation under grant DCR-85-13139.

The views and conclusions contained in this work are those of the author and should not be interpreted as representative of the official policies, either express or implied, of the Air Force Office of Scientific Research or the U.S. government.

REFERENCES

1. E. W. Adams. *The Logic of Conditionals.* Reidel, Dordrecht, 1975.

2. M. Allais. "Le comportement de l'homme rationnel devant le risque: critique des postulats et axiomes de l'école Américaine." *Econometrica,* 21:503–546, 1953. (*Behavior of a Rational Man under Risk: Critique of the Postulates and Axioms of the American School*).

3. R. E. Bellman and L. A. Zadeh. "Decision-making in a fuzzy environment." *Management Science,* 17:B141–B164, 1980.

4. P. P. Bonissone, D. A. Cyrluk, J. A. Goodwin, and J. Stillman. *Uncertainty and Incompleteness: Breaking the Symmetry of Defeasible Reasoning.* Internal Report, General Electric Co. Corporate Research and Development Center, Schenectady, NY, 1989.

5. R. Bradley and N. Swartz. *Possible Worlds: An Introduction to Logic and Its Philosophy.* Hackett, Indianapolis, IN, 1979.

6. R. Carnap. *Meaning and Necessity,* 2d ed. The University of Chicago Press, Chicago, 1957.

7. B. DeFinetti. "La prévision: ses lois logiques, ses sources subjectives." *Annales de l'Institut H. Poincaré,* 7:1–68, 1937.

8. A. P. Dempster. "Upper and lower probabilities induced by a multivalued mapping." *Annals of Mathematical Statistics,* 38:325–339, 1967.

9. J. Doyle. "A truth-maintenance system." *Artificial Intelligence,* 12:231–272, 1979.

10. D. Dubois and H. Prade. "Criteria aggregation and ranking of alternatives in the framework of fuzzy set theory." In H. J. Zimmermann, L. A. Zadeh, and B. R. Gaines, eds., *Fuzzy Sets and Decision Analysis,* North-Holland, Amsterdam, 1984, pp. 209–240.

11. D. Dubois and H. Prade. "An introduction to possibility theory and fuzzy logic." In P. Smets, ed., *Non-standard Logics for Automated Reasoning,* Academic Press, New York, 1988.

12. R. O. Duda, P. E. Hart, and N. J. Nilsson. "Subjective bayesian methods for rule-based inference systems." In *Proc. AFIPS 45,* AFIPS Press, New York, 1976, pp. 1075–1082.

13. D. Ellsberg. "Risk, ambiguity, and the Savage axioms." *The Quarterly Journal of Economics,* 75(4):643–669, 1961.

14. F. Esteva, P. García-Calvés, and L. Godó. "Relating and extending semantical approaches to possibilistic reasoning." *International Journal of Approximate Reasoning,* 10: , 1994.

15. F. Esteva, P. García, L. Godó, E. H. Ruspini, and L. Valverde. "On similarity logic and the generalized modus ponens." In *Proceedings of the 1994 IEEE International Conference on Fuzzy Systems,* Orlando, FL, June 1994, pp. 1423–1427.

16. T. D. Garvey, J. D. Lowrance, and M. A. Fischler. "An inference technique for integrating knowledge from disparate sources." In *Proceedings Seventh International Joint Conference on Artificial Intelligence,* Vancouver, British Columbia, Canada, 1981.

17. M. L. Ginsberg, ed. *Readings in Nonmonotonic Reasoning.* Morgan Kaufmann, Los Altos, CA, 1987.

18. G. E. Hughes and M. J. Creswell. *An Introduction to Modal Logic.* Methuen, London, 1968.

19. J.-Y. Jaffray. *Coherent Bets under Partially Resolving Uncertainty and Belief Functions.* Internal Report, University Pierre et Marie Curie, Paris, 1987.

20. S. A. Kripke. "Semantical analysis of modal logic I: Normal propositional calculi." *Zeitschrift für mathematische Logik und Grundlagen der Mathematik,* 67–96, 1963.

21. B. Kuipers. "Qualitative simulation." *Artificial Intelligence,* 29:289–338, 1986.

22. H. E. Kyburg. "Bayesian and non-Bayesian evidential updating." *Artificial Intelligence,* 31:271–293, 1987.

23. H. E. Kyburg. *Logical Foundations of Statistical Inference.* Reidel, Dordrecht, 1974.

24. H. E. Kyburg. "Subjective probability: Criticisms, reflections, and problems." *Journal of Philosophical Logic,* 7: 157–180, 1978.

25. S. L. Lauritzen and D. Spiegelhalter. "Local computations with probabilities on graphical structures and their application to expert systems." *Journal Royal Statistical Society* B50, 1988.

26. J. D. Lowrance, T. D. Garvey, and T. M. Strat. "A framework for evidential-reasoning systems." In *Proceedings National Conference on Artificial Intelligence,* American Association for Artificial Intelligence, Menlo Park, CA, 1986, pp. 896–903.

27. R. Moore. *Reasoning about Knowledge and Action.* Technical Note 408, SRI International, Menlo Park, CA, 1980.

28. J. Pearl. "Fusion, propagation, and structuring in belief networks." *Artificial Intelligence,* 29: 241–288, 1986.

29. J. Pearl. "On logic and probability." *Computational Intelligence,* 4: 99–103, 1988.

30. J. Pearl. *Probabilistic Reasoning in Intelligent Systems: Networks of Plausible Inference.* Morgan Kaufmann, San Mateo, CA, 1988.

31. R. Reiter. "A logic for default reasoning." *Artificial Intelligence,* 13:81–132, 1980.

32. N. Rescher. *Many-Valued Logic.* McGraw-Hill, New York, 1969.

33. E. H. Ruspini. "Epistemic logic, probability, and the calculus of evidence." In *Proceedings Tenth International Joint Conference on Artificial Intelligence,* Milan, Italy, 1987.

34. E. H. Ruspini. *The Logical Foundations of Evidential Reasoning.* Technical Note 408, Artificial Intelligence Center, SRI International, Menlo Park, California, 1987.

35. E. H. Ruspini. "On truth and utility." In R. Kruse and P. Siegel, eds., *Symbolic and Quantitative Approaches to Uncertainty,* Springer, New York, 1991.

36. E. H. Ruspini. "On the semantics of fuzzy logic." *International Journal Approximate Reasoning,* 5:45–88, 1991.

37. E. H. Ruspini. "Reactive control using fuzzy logic." In C. H. Chen, ed., *Fuzzy Logic and Neural Network Handbook,* McGraw-Hill, New York, forthcoming, 1995.

38. A. Saffiotti, K. Konolige, and E. H. Ruspini. "A multivalued logic approach to integrating planning and control." *Artificial Intelligence,* forthcoming, 1995.

39. L. J. Savage. *The Foundations of Statistics,* 2d ed. Dover, New York, 1972.

40. G. Shafer. *A Mathematical Theory of Evidence.* Princeton University Press, Princeton, NJ, 1976.

41. P. Smets. "Belief functions." In P. Smets, A. Mamdani, D. Dubois, and H. Prade, eds., *Non-Standard Logics for Automated Reasoning.* Academic Press, New York, 1988.

42. C.A.B. Smith. Consistency in statistical inference and decision. *J. Roy. Stat. Soc. Ser. B,* 23:1–37, 1961.

43. P. Suppes. "The measurement of belief." *J. Roy. Stat. Soc.* B36:160–175, 1974.

44. E. Trillas and L. Valverde. "On mode and implication in approximate reasoning." In M. M. Gupta, A. Kandel, W. Bandler, and J. B. Kiszka, ed., *Approximate Reasoning and Expert Systems.* North Holland, Amsterdam, 1985, pp. 157–166.

45. L. Valverde. "On the structure of F-indistinguishability operators." *Fuzzy Sets and Systems,* 17:313–328, 1985.

46. L. A. Zadeh. "A theory of approximate reasoning." In D. Michie and L. I. Mikulich, eds., *Machine Intelligence,* vol. 9, Halstead Press, New York, 1979, pp. 149–194.

47. L. A. Zadeh. "A computational approach to fuzzy quantifiers in natural language." *Computers and Mathematics,* 9:149–184, 1983.

48. L. A. Zadeh. "Fuzzy sets." *Information and Control,* 8:338–353, 1965.

49. L. A. Zadeh. "Outline of a new approach to the analysis of complex systems and decision processes" *IEEE Trans. Systems, Man and Cybernetics,* SMC-3: 28–44, 1973.

50. L. A. Zadeh. "Syllogistic reasoning in fuzzy logic and its application to usuality and reasoning with dispositions." *IEEE Trans. Systems, Man and Cybernetics,* SMC-15: 754–765, 1985.

CHAPTER 6
CONSTRAINED DEFUZZIFICATION IN DATA-DRIVEN ADAPTIVE FUZZY LOGIC CONTROLLERS

J. DeWitte, Jr.
The George Washington University
Washington, D.C.

H. Szu
Naval Surface Warfare Center
Silver Spring, Maryland

A noncentroidal defuzzification methodology is presented based on constraining the relationship between the output variable of a fuzzy logic controller (FLC) and its fuzzy membership functions (FMFs). It is shown that centroidal defuzzifiers are a subset of this alternative formulation. A simple example of the fuzzy exclusive OR (XOR) is presented to illustrate supervised adaptation of the FMFs in the defuzzifier. This procedure can be enhanced by allowing adaptation of input fuzzification and inference processes in an FLC. A comparison is made between a parallel implementation of the fuzzy XOR FLC and corresponding artificial neural network (ANN) solutions. The comparison indicates that it may be possible to build more efficient FLC structures by changing the mechanism used in FLCs for fuzzy partitioning of the input space.

6.1 INTRODUCTION

One of the topics of high interest to researchers in the fuzzy logic (FL) field is the development of automatic data-driven adaptive controllers. Static fuzzy logic controllers (FLCs) have already been widely used in engineering applications [1, 2, 3]. Their ability to "exploit the tolerance of imprecision" ([1(74)]: Zadeh) has allowed the development of robust low-cost controllers in complex stationary environments.

The engineering solutions possible with FLC techniques, where there exists a lack of precise mathematical models required by traditional proportional integral derivative (PID) methods, has made the fuzzy logic industry worth at least hundreds of millions of dollars [4]. While static FLCs have been very useful in many situations, adaptive controllers are important for good performance in nonstationary environments. As the environment changes, the controller must modify its internal structure to provide the proper input-to-output mapping in the new situation.

FL has been used in other areas besides control problems [2, 3]. In particular, it is also being used successfully in pattern recognition problems [5, 6, 7, 8]. The emphasis in such problems is to approximate multiple pattern classes in a joint input-output space. In contrast, the controller problem, which is the focus of this chapter, is concerned with approximating a single curve in input-output space. As this optimal control curve changes with the environment, the FLC must adapt to follow the changes.

There have been many approaches to adaptivity in fuzzy logic controllers. Werbos describes a method for providing weights to rules stored in the inference engine section of an FLC [9]. This is done by means of an exponentiated product fuzzy intersection operator [10]. In environments where the fuzzy membership functions provided by the human expert can be treated as initial conditions and allowed to vary, a variety of methods exist for modifying the membership functions of the input or output variables [11, 12, 13, 14].

This chapter focuses on a general noncentroidal form of defuzzification that can be used in data-driven adaptive fuzzy logic controllers. We provide a new visualization method, utilizing *constraint paths* and *walk functions* in the multidimensional fuzzy membership space, to modify membership functions. A type of inversion defuzzifier results, but the membership functions are not required to be monotonic as in Ref. 15.

The possibility of modifying both the size and the entries in the fuzzy associative memory matrix may confer additional advantages to an adaptive FLC. This is a multiresolution problem, which may potentially be solved with techniques taken from wavelets and chaotic artificial neural network (ANN) theory, which produces the identical attributes of fuzzy logic—namely, an open set of bounded but unpredictable possibilities [16, 17].

The chapter is composed of three major discussion sections in addition to this one. Section 6.2 introduces the principle of complementarity (TPC), which constrains the sum of the fuzzy membership functions for a single variable. Normalization of this sum to unity is often done in practical engineering applications, though other constraint surfaces are allowed in fuzzy logic. The TPC concepts of *constraint paths* and *walk functions* are introduced, from which constrained membership functions can be created. Two examples are presented in which a variable is fuzzified into three fuzzy sets. These three-dimensional examples are piecewise linear (trapezoidal) memberships and continuously differentiable memberships.

By imposing the principle of complementarity on the output variable of a fuzzy logic controller, an alternative noncentroidal method of defuzzification is developed in Sec. 6.3. To illustrate this methodology, a supervised adaptive constrained defuzzifier is taught to create a fuzzy XOR function. This defuzzifier is compared with the traditional centroidal defuzzifier, and it is shown that the centroidal rule is a special case of the constrained defuzzifier.

Section 6.4 is concerned with the relationship between fuzzy logic controllers and artificial neural networks. For the simple case of the exclusive OR function, it is shown that FLC and ANN implementations are functionally equivalent. The point is made that the rectangular fuzzy partitioning of the input space by FLCs can be generalized with a multilayer ANN. This holds the potential for creating more efficient FLC structures—ones with fewer processing elements.

6.2 THE PRINCIPLE OF COMPLEMENTARITY

The purpose of this section is to present the principle of complementarity, which states that the degrees of membership (DOMs) for a fuzzified variable must add up to a constant. This constant is usually chosen to be unity for convenience in engineering applications. The TPC concept is central to understanding of constrained defuzzification and the fuzzy membership function (FMF) adaptation examples presented in the section following this one.

While the principle of complementarity is not strictly required in formal fuzzy logic, practical controllers can be built that satisfy this constraint. There is precedent for utilizing a constraint of this type, although it is found more often in pattern recognition problems than in controller applications [18 (543)]. At the end of this section, a short discussion of non-TPC membership function generation is given.

A variable v can simultaneously be a member of multiple fuzzy sets as shown in Fig. 6.1. When v takes on a specific value on the unit interval, membership values for each of the fuzzy sets are generated. In this way the scalar v is transformed into the vector $\mathbf{v}$. The sum of the fuzzy memberships can be unity, although it is not required

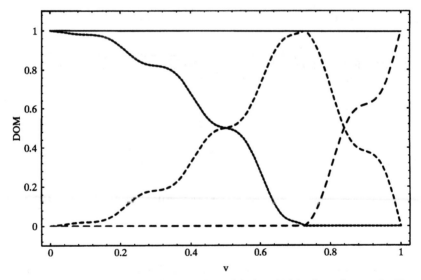

FIGURE 6.1 Fuzzy membership functions that satisfy the principle of complementarity. The upper line is the sum of the FMFs, which is identically 1 for all values of the independent variable v over its unit interval range. Indices for FMFs are normally ordered from left to right—from low to high values of the independent variable. The curve with the densest dashes and unity degree of membership at $v = 0$ is the v_1 FMF. The curve with the most widely spaced dashes, whose maximum is at $v = 1$, is the v_3 FMF. The v_2 FMF is the curve in the middle whose peak is near $v = 0.7$. These curves were generated with a walk function (see discussion in Sec. 6.2) of $s(v) = 2\sqrt{2}\,[v + \sin(\pi v)/(12\pi)]^2$ along a constraint path consisting of two edges of the 3-D constraint plane. This constraint path is the same one as shown in Fig. 6.2.

to be. For convenience in engineering applications, a constant sum of one is often used. For example, suppose that v represents temperature normalized to the unit interval. Suppose also that there are three fuzzy sets with the linguistic labels *cold*, *warm*, and *hot*. A specific value of v, such as 0.8, can be cold, warm, and hot *to some degree* all at the same time. For example, $v = 0.8$ means a zero degree of membership in the cold set, a 0.3 DOM in the warm set, and a 0.7 DOM in the hot set.

Fuzzy membership is not the same as a probability [2, 3, 19]. Probability implies the relative frequency of occurrence of one event from a multiplicity of possible outcomes. Fuzzy membership implies the *simultaneous* occurrence of all possible outcomes *to some degree*. Because of the overlap in the meaning of linguistic labels, there is no particular restriction on the sum of degrees of membership as there is in probability theory. A constant sum in fuzzy logic is simply one case of a multitude of allowed situations. The simple constant-sum constraint, however, makes the notion of defuzzification easier to visualize. After the development of the constant-sum constrained defuzzifier presented in the succeeding section, it will be apparent how to generalize to the non-constant-sum case.

The following equations reinterpret the unit sum of DOMs as vectors in N-dimensional space. The symbol $\mathbf{1}$ represents a vector with all of its components set to 1.

$$\sum_{i=1}^{N} v_i = 1 \qquad \mathbf{v} \cdot \mathbf{1} = 1 \qquad \mathbf{v} \cdot \mathbf{1} - 1 = 0$$

$$\mathbf{v} \cdot \mathbf{1} - \frac{1}{N} \cdot \mathbf{1} = 0 \qquad \left(\mathbf{v} - \frac{1}{N}\right) \cdot \mathbf{1} = 0 \qquad \left(\mathbf{v} - \frac{1}{N}\right) \cdot \frac{1}{N} = 0$$

The last line is the equation of a plane in N-dimensional space, the plane being defined by its normal vector $\mathbf{1}/N$. Now, consider the unit "axis" vectors, $\mathbf{u}_i$. These vectors have a 1 in the ith position and zeros everywhere else.

$$\left(\mathbf{u}_i - \frac{1}{N}\right) \cdot \frac{1}{N} = 1\left(1 - \frac{1}{N}\right)\frac{1}{N} + (N-1)\left(-\frac{1}{N}\right)\frac{1}{N}$$

$$= \left[\left(1 - \frac{1}{N}\right) - (N-1)\frac{1}{N}\right]\frac{1}{N}$$

$$= \left(1 - \frac{1}{N} - 1 + \frac{1}{N}\right)\frac{1}{N}$$

$$= 0$$

So, every axis vector lies in the constraint plane. These points can be used to draw the plane in two or three dimensions. In two dimensions, the axis vectors are $(v_1, v_2) = (1, 0)$ and $(v_1, v_2) = (0, 1)$. The constraint plane in this case is actually a line connecting these two points, with a normal vector $(1, 1)/2$. In three dimensions, the axis vectors in the (v_1, v_2, v_3) unit cube are $(1, 0, 0)$, $(0, 1, 0)$, and $(0, 0, 1)$. The constraint plane is a filled-in triangle whose vertices are the three corners closest to the origin of the unit cube. Also note that the minimum distance from the origin to the constraint plane is the length of the normal, or $1/\sqrt{N}$. In two dimensions, this is $1/\sqrt{2}$; in three dimensions, it is $1/\sqrt{3}$. As N gets very large, the plane gets very close to the origin.

The importance of the constraint plane generated by the principle of complementarity is that it allows valid fuzzy membership functions to be generated easily. Traversal of any path in the constraint plane will *automatically* generate membership functions that satisfy TPC. Path traversal is defined by a *walk function, s(v)*. This function determines where on the constraint path one should be for a given value of the prefuzzification variable. The endpoints of $s(v)$ are fixed: $s(0) = 0$ and $s(1) = L$, where L is the length of the constraint path. For example, a minimum-length piecewise linear path among the axis vectors in N dimensions has a length $L = (N-1)\sqrt{2}$. A linear walk function passes through an axis vector for every multiple of $\sqrt{2}$ in v. These axis vectors are points for which one of the membership functions passes through a value of 1; at multiples of $\sqrt{2}$, v is a member of *only one* of the fuzzy sets.

Consider two 3-D examples of constraint paths and the three FMFs they generate. In the first example, classical trapezoidal fuzzy membership functions are created. Figure 6.2 shows the constraint path in the unit cube and the walk function along that path. The path lies in the constraint plane defined by the normal vector **1**/3.

The walk function shown in Fig. 6.2 is piecewise linear with five constant-slope segments. If one imagines rastering the prefuzzification variable v linearly with time, the walk function prescribes how one would walk along the constraint path. For example, suppose that the entire unit range for v is rastered uniformly in one minute and that the size of the top drawing in Fig. 6.2 is such that the constraint path length is $2\sqrt{2}$ cm. The walk function $s(v)$ then specifies the following motion:

1. Remain stationary at $(v_1, v_2, v_3) = (1, 0, 0)$ for 12 s (0.2 min)
2. Walk to $(0, 1, 0)$ at a constant speed of $\sqrt{2}/12$ cm/s
3. Remain stationary at $(0, 1, 0)$ for 12 s
4. Walk to $(0, 0, 1)$ at a constant speed of $\sqrt{2}/12$ cm/s
5. Remain stationary at $(0, 0, 1)$ for 12 s

Of course, the variables s and v really do not have any units, but putting them in one-to-one correspondence with distance and time gives one a more intuitive grasp of the walk function concept.

Figure 6.3 shows the membership functions that are generated by the constraint path and walk function specified in Fig. 6.2. It is easy to see how the piecewise linear FMFs relate to the five walking motions described above. The flat region for the leftmost membership function $v_1(v)$ corresponds to the waiting period at $(1, 0, 0)$ in step 1 above. Values for v in this area are considered full members of the v_1 fuzzy set, with no membership in v_2 or v_3. The region between $v = 0.2$ and $v = 0.4$ corresponds to step 2 above. The crossover between full membership in v_1 to full membership in v_2 occurs during the constant-speed motion from $(1, 0, 0)$ to $(0, 1, 0)$. The flat regions for v_2 and v_3 as well as the crossover region between them can be understood in an analogous fashion.

In the second example of TPC-generated membership functions, a continuously differentiable walk function is used to generate smooth FMFs. The top drawing in Fig. 6.4 shows the constraint path, which is a portion of the circle that can be inscribed in the constraint plane. Recall that since each of the three FMFs can take on values only in the interval $[0, 1]$, the portion of the constraint plane that falls inside the unit cube is just a triangle with vertices at $(0, 0, 1), (0, 1, 0)$, and $(1, 0, 0)$. The base of this triangle is defined to be the line that runs between $(1, 0, 0)$ and $(0, 1, 0)$. The angle θ is measured in the constraint plane from the middle of the triangle counterclockwise from a line parallel to the base. The constraint path is defined to be the

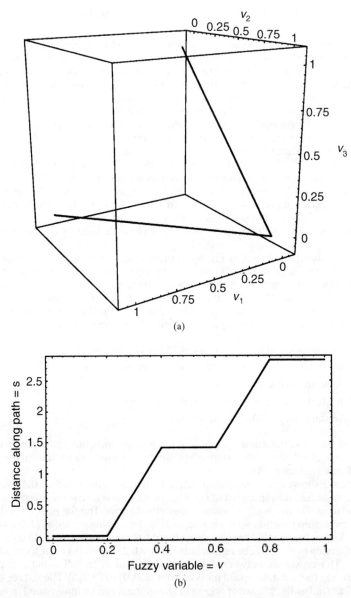

(a)

(b)

FIGURE 6.2 The 3-D constraint path and walk function for the generation of classical trapezoidal fuzzy membership functions. (*a*) The constraint path is simply the union of two of the three borders of the constraint plane inside the unit cube. (*b*) The piecewise linear walk function consists of three plateaus and two interspersed sloped areas. If one imagines putting *v* and *s* into one-to-one correspondence with time and distance, respectively, then the walk function prescribes the motion from one end point of the constraint path to the other. The first plateau indicates a pause at $(v_1, v_2, v_3) = (1, 0, 0)$. The first slope specifies constant-speed travel from $(1, 0, 0)$ to $(0, 1, 0)$. The second plateau is a pause at $(0, 1, 0)$, while the third is a pause at $(0, 0, 1)$. The slope between these two plateaus corresponds to constant-speed motion between $(0, 1, 0)$ and $(0, 0, 1)$. The FMFs generated by the constraint path and walk function depicted here are shown in Fig. 6.3.

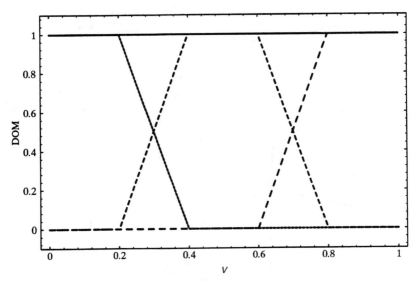

FIGURE 6.3 The fuzzy membership functions generated by the constraint path and walk function in Fig. 6.2. The sum line at DOM = 1 indicates that these FMFs satisfy the principle of complementarity. Note that the three exclusive full membership regions are due to the plateaus in the walk function and the fact that the vertices of the constraint triangle in Fig. 6.2 are included in the path. The crossovers between the full membership regions correspond to the sloped regions in the walk function.

line running from $-\theta = 5\pi/6$ to $\theta = +\pi/2$ at a radius of $1/\sqrt{6}$. This radius is equal to the minimum distance between the midpoint of the triangle and any point on its border. Thus, this constraint path is two-thirds of the circle that can be inscribed in the constraint triangle. The bottom drawing in Fig. 6.4 shows the walk function. It is linear corresponding to constant-speed travel around the constraint path.

The fuzzy membership functions generated by this constraint path and walk function are shown in Fig. 6.5. As before, the sum line shows that TPC is satisfied. Note that all membership functions are nonzero for all values of v. While each FMF has a dominant region, the other two still contribute. For example, v_2 dominates in the middle of the unit interval for v, but its DOM is still only 2/3. At $v = 0.5$, the DOMs for v_1 and v_3 are both 1/6. If the variable v represented the temperature of water between freezing (0°C) and boiling (100°C), then this set of membership functions would deem that a temperature of 50°C would be about 17 percent cold, 66 percent warm, and 17 percent hot *all at the same time.*

What these two examples point out is that by specifying a constraint path and a monotonic walk function, a wide variety of membership functions can easily be generated. This is important for adaptive controllers that must change their input-to-output mapping due to nonstationary conditions. In the next section, this adaptivity is illustrated by means of a single-parameter walk function in the defuzzifier. The adaptation is supervised, and the controller adjusts the single parameter to yield the best fit to the desired mapping.

As was pointed out early in this section, memberships that violate TPC are allowed in the definition of FL. In the context of the geometrical interpretation that has been used throughout this section, FMFs that violate TPC can be viewed as coming from a path on some nonplanar constraint surface. That is, more general FMF

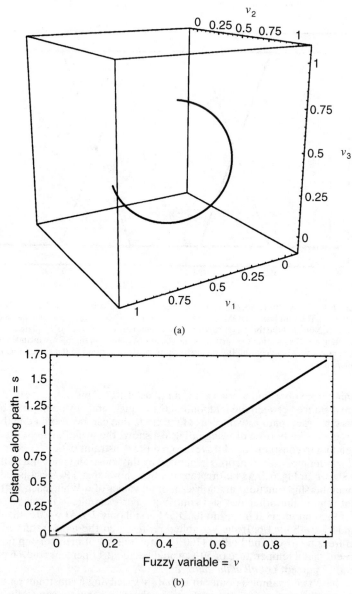

(a)

(b)

FIGURE 6.4 The 3-D constraint path and walk function for the generation of continuously differentiable fuzzy membership functions. (*a*) The constraint path is two-thirds of a circle inscribed in the constraint triangle. This triangle lies in the constraint plane and is formed by the vertices $(v_1, v_2, v_3) = (1, 0, 0), (0, 1, 0),$ and $(0, 0, 1)$. The inscribed circle has a radius of $1/\sqrt{6}$ and its angle runs from $-5\pi/6$ to $+\pi/2$. The circle angle is measured counterclockwise around the midpoint of the triangle from a line parallel to the triangle's base. The length of the constraint path is $1/\sqrt{6}$ $\times 4\pi/3 = \pi(2/3)^{3/2} \approx 1.71$. (*b*) The linear walk function, indicating constant-speed travel around the circular constraint path. The FMFs generated by the constraint path and walk function depicted here are shown in Fig. 6.5.

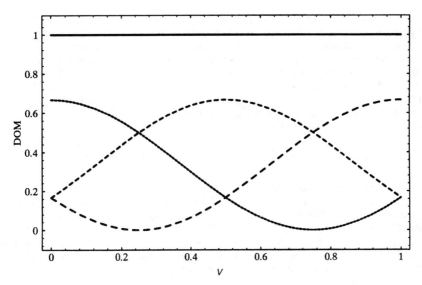

FIGURE 6.5   The fuzzy membership functions generated by the constraint path and walk function in Fig. 6.4. The sum line at DOM = 1 indicates that these FMFs satisfy the principle of complementarity. The maximum for each membership function is 2/3. When an FMF reaches its maximum, the other FMFs split the difference. At $v = 0.5$, for example, $v_2 = 2/3$, while $v_1 = v_3 = 1/6$.

combinations can be generated by using nonplanar constraint paths, while still retaining the monotonic walk function concept.

6.3   DATA-DRIVEN ADAPTIVE LEARNING IN FUZZY LOGIC CONTROLLERS USING CONSTRAINED DEFUZZIFICATION

In this section, the internal workings of the fuzzy logic controller are looked at in detail using the tools developed in the previous section. The principle of complementarity, constraint planes, constraint paths, and walk functions make it possible to understand the process of defuzzification in a new way. This alternative viewpoint makes it possible to both generalize and simplify the defuzzification process at the same time. A simple example of a data-driven adaptive defuzzifier is shown to illustrate how centroidal defuzzification is a special case of the generalized procedure utilizing walk functions.

The previous section makes clear what happens in the fuzzification process. In the first of the three processing sections in an FLC, each input variable is mapped to a vector that satisfies TPC. The number of elements in this vector, its dimensionality, is equal to the number of fuzzy membership functions defined for the variable.

The second part of an FLC, rule processing, consists of two distinct operations. First, all possible fuzzy intersections of input FMFs are formed. This process defines a set of fuzzy rectangular subregions in the input space. In general, all output FMFs are activated to some degree in each subregion, but the fuzzy associative memory matrix (FAMM) determines the dominant output degree of membership. The second rule processing operation is fuzzy union. Here, all of the subregions dominated by a particular output FMF are collected together into a single composite rule.

Figure 6.6 illustrates the results of rule processing for a 2-D problem. The number of dimensions is determined by the number of FMFs in the output variable. Each of the two plots was created by running several hundred random input vectors through the fuzzification and rule processing sections of an FLC, and the (z_1, z_2) DOM pairs that result are plotted against each other (the trapezoidal FMFs for the two input variables are shown in Fig. 6.7). The difference between the two plots is that they use different FAMMs:

$$\text{FAMM (top plot)} = \begin{bmatrix} 1 & 2 \\ 1 & 2 \end{bmatrix} \qquad \text{FAMM (bottom plot)} = \begin{bmatrix} 1 & 2 \\ 2 & 1 \end{bmatrix}$$

The entries in the FAMM indicate how the two output degrees of membership are created: the x DOMs are indexed along the columns of the FAMM, while the rows index the y DOMs. For the right-hand FAMM, the (row, column) = (1, 1) element in the FAMM corresponds to the computation $\text{Min}(y_1, x_1)$. Element (1, 2) represents $\text{Min}(y_1, x_2)$, and so forth. The right-hand FAMM above therefore directs that the diagonal elements be combined via fuzzy union to create the z_1 output DOM. The cross-diagonal elements are combined to create z_2:

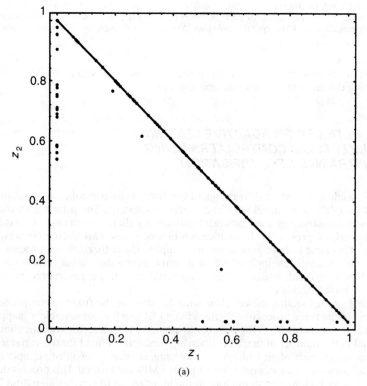

(a)

FIGURE 6.6 Two-dimensional vectors from rule processing plotted in relation to the constraint line. (*a*) For FAMM = {{1, 2}, {1, 2}}.

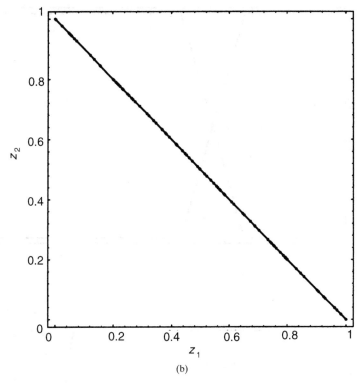

(b)

FIGURE 6.6 (*Continued*)   (*b*) For the special FAMM = {{1, 2}, {2, 1}}. All of the points for the special FAMM lie on the constraint line. The points for the other FAMM all lie below the constraint line, as is the case for all other 2-D FAMMs. Most of the points lie either on the constraint line or along the axes, although there are interior points. The data shown represent 400 random input vectors on the unit *xy* square.

$$z_1(x, y) = (y_1 \wedge x_1) \vee (y_2 \wedge x_2) = \text{Max} \left(\text{Min} \left(y_1, x_1 \right), \text{Min} \left(y_2, x_2 \right) \right)$$

$$z_2(x, y) = (y_1 \wedge x_2) \vee (y_2 \wedge x_1) = \text{Max} \left(\text{Min} \left(y_1, x_2 \right), \text{Min} \left(y_2, x_1 \right) \right)$$

The points in the top plot cluster along the constraint line and the axes, with just a few points in the interior. The bottom plot shows that all of the points fall on the constraint line. This is very special behavior. It is relatively easy to show that, of the 14 possible FAMMs for the 2-D case, only the two symmetrical FAMMs with identical diagonal elements cause output DOMs that follow the principle of complementarity. All other 12 cases generate points on or below the constraint line.

Figure 6.8 shows a 3-D rule processing example. Each of the two inputs has three FMFs (see Fig. 6.9), as does the output variable. The FAMM for this example is:

$$\text{FAMM} = \begin{bmatrix} 2 & 2 & 2 \\ 1 & 1 & 3 \\ 1 & 1 & 3 \end{bmatrix}$$

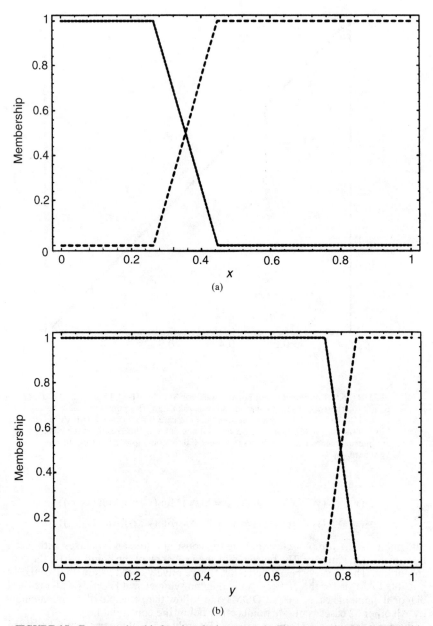

FIGURE 6.7   Fuzzy membership functions for inputs x and y. The two membership functions (a) for the x input and (b) for y. Both inputs have piecewise linear (trapezoidal) FMFs. The crossover points are $x_c = 0.355$ and $y_c = 0.798$. The crossover region for x is wider than for y: 0.184 vs. 0.088. These FMFs were used to compute the results in Fig. 6.6. Freeman's Mathematica code was used to create these trapezoidal FMFs [27].

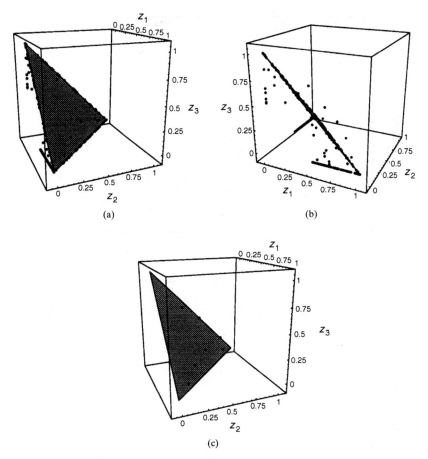

FIGURE 6.8 Three-dimensional vectors from rule processing plotted in relation to the constraint plane. The FAMM for this example is $\{\{2, 2, 2\}, \{1, 1, 3\}, \{1, 1, 3\}\}$. (*a*) A plot of all of the points, where most of them lie on the borders of the constraint plane or along the axes, although there are interior points. (*b*) An almost edge-on view of the constraint plane, showing points above, below, and on the constraint plane. (*c*) The eight points that lie above the constraint plane. The data shown represent 500 random input vectors on the unit *xy* square.

Figure 6.8 shows where several hundred random input points map to at the output of rule processing. Three different views are shown. The top left plot is a view from above and in front of the constraint plane. In the top right plot, the unit cube has been rotated, so that the constraint plane is viewed edge-on. It is clear from this edge-on view that most points are either on or below the constraint plane. As in the 2-D case, the points cluster along the edges of the constraint plane and the axes. There are a fair number in the interior of the unit cube below the constraint plane, and there are even a few *above* it as shown in the bottom figure. As was pointed out in the previous section, the distance from the origin to the constraint plane gets smaller and smaller as the number of dimensions increases. One would expect, therefore, that the number of points above the plane increases with dimensionality.

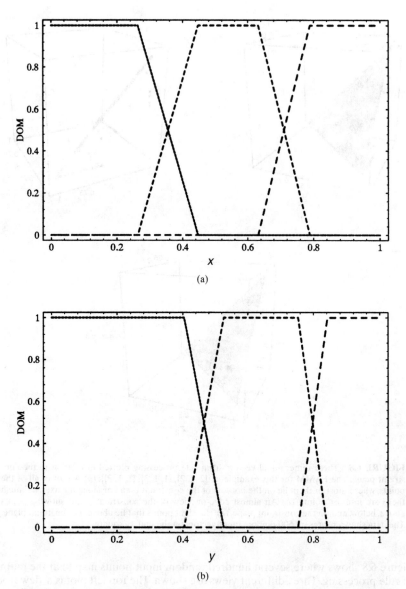

(a)

(b)

FIGURE 6.9 Fuzzy membership functions for inputs x and y. The three membership functions (*a*) for the x input and (*b*) for y. Both inputs have piecewise linear (trapezoidal) FMFs. The corners for the membership functions are at 0.263, 0.447, 0.632, and 0.789 for x. The corners for y are 0.404, 0.526, 0.754, and 0.842. The crossover points are $x_{c1} = 0.355$, $x_{c2} = 0.7105$, $y_{c1} = 0.465$, and $y_{c2} = 0.798$. These FMFs were used to compute the results in Fig. 6.8. Freeman's Mathematica code was used to create these trapezoidal FMFs [27].

The main point of the above discussion is that rule processing in a fuzzy logic controller nearly always results in DOMs that do not satisfy TPC. It is the job of the defuzzifier to pick the value of the output that generates TPC-compliant DOMs that most closely match the DOMs generated prior to defuzzification. Different types of defuzzifiers can be created, depending on the closeness metric that is used. For example, one procedure would be to take the outputs from rule processing and move the represented point to the closest point on the constraint path using a Euclidean metric. Alternatively, a two-step process could be used: move the errant point to the closest point in the constraint plane, and *then* move that point to the closest point on the constraint *path*. A third method would be to simply renormalize the non-TPC vector until it hits the constraint plane, and then find the closest point on the constraint path. The renormalization step simply changes the length of the vector, but not its direction as would happen in the first method.

The use of constraint paths and walk functions results in a more straightforward defuzzification technique than the traditional centroid-based forms. The ANN-like parallel implementation of the constrained defuzzifier is also straightforward. ANN implementations of the centroidal defuzzifier typically do not compute the true centroid. In order to keep the computation in the defuzzifier local, the membership overlap regions are counted more heavily than in a true centroid. In software simulations on general-purpose computers, the constrained defuzzifier also requires much less computation than the true centroidal method. This fact may not be particularly important, however, in analog hardware implementations that utilize approximate centroid calculations.

Since the rule processing in an FLC causes the violation of TPC, it is reasonable to ask whether an alternative formulation of rule processing can avoid errant points altogether. This issue is discussed in the next section. An alternative formulation *is* possible, and is discovered by comparing parallel FLC and ANN implementations.

In order to illustrate how to use the constrained defuzzification machinery in an *adaptive* fuzzy logic controller, consider the following example in which a single-parameter FLC is trained to mimic a fuzzy exclusive OR (XOR) function. This function is considered again in the following section where parallel implementations of FLCs are viewed in relation to parallel feedforward artificial neural networks.

The desired fuzzy XOR function, $z_d(x, y) = (x - y)^2$, which the FL is trained to mimic, is shown in Fig. 6.10. The two inputs are x and y, with one output z. One can imagine this to be the control surface for some physical device. The inputs are readings from sensors that monitor the state of the device, and the FLC must provide the correct output z to keep the device operating correctly. The training data consist of 25 random pairs of inputs $\{(x_i, y_i)\}$, with $z_d(x_i, y_i) = (x_i - y_i)^2$ used as the desired FLC output.

A detailed description of the internal structure of the adaptive FLC used in this example is now given. Consider first the fuzzification section. There are two membership functions assigned for each of the two input variables. In this case the constraint plane degenerates into a constraint line from $(1, 0)$ to $(0, 1)$. The constraint path and constraint plane become identical in this case. The length of the constraint path is $\sqrt{2}$. The walk functions used for these variables have the same form:

$$s(v) = \sqrt{2}\, v^{\ln (2)/\ln (1/v_c)}$$

where v is either x or y. The path variable s is measured along the constraint line from the $(1, 0)$ point. Notice that $s(0) = 0$ and $s(1) = \sqrt{2}$. Using the time and distance

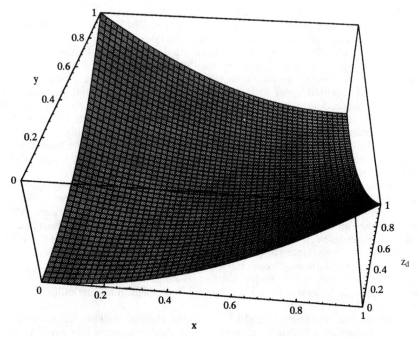

FIGURE 6.10 The fuzzy exclusive OR function $z_d(x, y) = (x - y)^2$, used for adapting the fuzzy logic controller. The corners of the fuzzy XOR agree with the binary logic XOR: $z_d(0, 0) = z_d(1, 1) = 0$ and $z_d(0, 1) = z_d(1, 0) = 1$.

analogy discussed in the previous section, the crossover point v_c can be interpreted as the "time" at which half the length of the constraint line has been traversed. Also note that, because of the simple geometry in the 2-D case, $v_2(v) = s(v)/\sqrt{2}$. It is now clear why v_c is called the crossover point: $v_1(v_c) = v_2(v_c) = 0.5$. For the example being presented, x_c and y_c were both set to 0.5. The walk functions become linear in this case:

$$x_1(x) = 1 - x \qquad x_2(x) = x$$
$$y_1(y) = 1 - y \qquad y_2(y) = y$$

A classical structure for the rule processing section of the FLC is used. The Min function is used for fuzzy intersection, and Max is used for fuzzy union. In order to simplify the example further, a symmetric fuzzy associative memory matrix with identical diagonal elements is used:

$$\text{FAMM} = \begin{bmatrix} 1 & 2 \\ 2 & 1 \end{bmatrix}$$

The choice of this FAMM is not arbitrary. The structure of the FAMM is closely related to the FLC input-to-output mapping. The FAMM indicates that the 2-D input space will be fuzzy-partitioned into four regions. The upper left corner of the FAMM applies to smaller values of both x and y, while the lower right pertains to larger values of both inputs. The upper right and lower left entries in the FAMM correspond to large values of one variable, but small values of the other.

Larger numbers for the entries in the FAMM correspond to output membership functions concentrated at larger values of the unit output interval. The off-diagonal 2 entries in the FAMM above will result in higher outputs in those regions than the diagonal 1 entries. The FAMM, therefore, gives a coarse sketch of the input-to-output mapping. One can visualize two short boxes coming out of the page covering up the diagonal elements of the FAMM above. Two tall boxes would cover up the off-diagonals. This is roughly the shape of the XOR function: 0 (short box) on two opposite corners; 1 (tall box) on the others. This was the rationale for choosing the FAMM for the XOR example. One of the other 14 nondegenerate FAMMs can be used, but much larger errors occur. The resulting input-to-output mapping does not fit the desired function very well.

Rule processing creates two degrees of membership, z_1 and z_2. The purpose of defuzzification is then to find the best match between these DOMs and the ones computed from the z variable's fuzzy membership functions. The z value at which the best match occurs is then the output of the controller. Since the FAMM has been chosen to guarantee TPC, the best match is an *exact* match.

The form of the walk function for z is chosen to be the same as that for the input variables. However, the parameter z_c is adapted rather than set to some fixed value. By varying this parameter, the FMFs for z change, and the adaptive FLC alters its input-to-output mapping to closely fit the desired XOR function of Fig. 6.10.

The adaptation of z_c is done in the traditional way. An energy function is constructed that measures how closely the FLC's input-to-output mapping matches $z_d(x, y) = (x - y)^2$. This energy function depends on the parameter z_c. Taking the derivative of the energy function E with respect to time yields

$$\frac{dE}{dt} = \frac{\partial E}{\partial p} \frac{dp}{dt}$$

where p is the parameter z_c. By setting $dp/dt = -\partial E/\partial p$, the energy is forced to be a decreasing function of time. The adaptation was simulated on a Sun Microsystems SparcStation 10 computer using the Mathematica program [20]. In discrete-time form, the parameter adaptation is given by

$$z_c(k + 1) = z_c(k) - \Delta\left(\frac{\partial E}{\partial z_c}\bigg|_k\right)$$

where Δ is the step size, which was set to 0.01.

The energy function used for this example is

$$E(z_c) = \frac{1}{25} \sum_{i=1}^{25} [z(x_i, y_i; z_c) - z_d(x_i, y_i)]^2$$

where $z_d(x, y) = (x - y)^2$ is the desired output mapping and $z(x, y; z_c)$ is the output of the FLC which depends on the adaptation parameter z_c. The derivative of the energy with respect to the parameter is easy to compute:

$$\frac{\partial E}{\partial z_c} = \frac{2}{N} \sum_{i=1}^{N} [z(x_i, y_i; z_c) - z_d(x_i, y_i)] \frac{\partial z(x_i, y_i; z_c)}{\partial z_c}$$

$$= \frac{2}{z_c N \ln 2} \sum_{i=1}^{N} [z_d(x_i, y_i) - (z_{2,i})^{-\ln z_c/\ln 2}](z_{2,i})^{-\ln z_c/\ln 2} \ln z_{2,i}$$

where $N = 25$ and $z_{2,i}$ means $z_2(x_i, y_i)$. The second line in the equation was derived by utilizing the *inverse* walk function $z(s) = (s/\sqrt{2})^{(-\ln z_c/\ln 2)}$ and the fact that $s/\sqrt{2} = z_2(x, y)$.

Figure 6.11 shows the adaptation behavior of the FLC. The initial value for z_c was set at 0.9. With a step size $\Delta = 0.01$, the system converges to the minimum energy at about $z_c = 0.1$ in about 20 iterations. The minimum energy, which is equivalent to the average squared error over the 25 sample points, is about 0.0042. The root-mean-

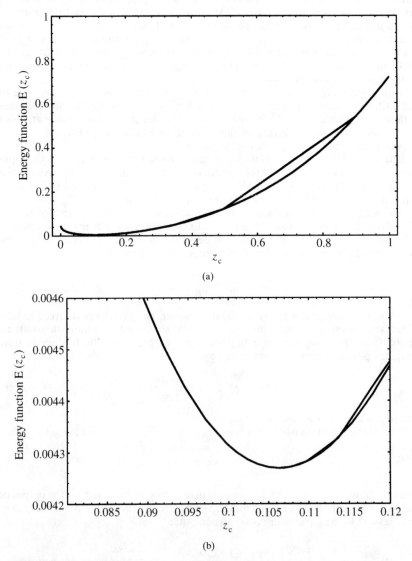

(a)

(b)

FIGURE 6.11 Adaptation history of the FLC. The optimal value for the crossover parameter is about $z_c = 0.106294$. The initial z_c was set to 0.9. The step size parameter for the adaptation experiment was 0.01. Accuracy of z_c to 6 decimal places was achieved in about twenty iterations. Minimum energy (average squared error) is about 0.00426936. (*a*) Energy function; (*b*) expanded view of energy function near minimum.

square error is, therefore, about 6 percent of the unit interval. The resulting input-to-output mapping for the FLC with the converged value of z_c is shown in Fig. 6.12. It is a relatively close approximation to the desired mapping, given that only a single parameter in the FLC was allowed to adapt. Allowing the crossover points of the input FMFs to adapt would yield a better approximation.

It is interesting to compare the structure of the FLC using the classical centroidal defuzzifier with the constrained one just examined. By doing this, it will be shown that the centroidal method is included in the constrained technique. That is, the centroidal defuzzifier has a walk function associated with it. To see this, first find the best z_c for centroidal defuzzification. An augmented version of the centroidal method is used. The membership function for z_1 is extended to negative values so that the augmented FMF is symmetric about $z = 0$. Similarly, the FMF for z_2 is extended so it is symmetric about $z = 1$.

Figure 6.13 shows the energy for both the constrained and centroidal defuzzifiers. Note that the optimal crossover point is very different for the two methods. The best z_c for constrained defuzzification is around 0.1, while the best centroidal defuzzifier needs z_c to be around 0.9. On the surface, it appears that the two methods are doing something very different. In fact, it will be seen that the walk functions for the two techniques are actually very similar.

Figure 6.14 shows the walk functions for both methods when z_c is around 0.1: the curve on the left is for constrained defuzzification; the curve on the right is for centroidal. The walk function curve for the centroidal method was generated by taking 100 random points in the input space and computing the z_1 and z_2 DOMs resulting from fuzzification and rule processing. Because of the simple geometry of this 2D

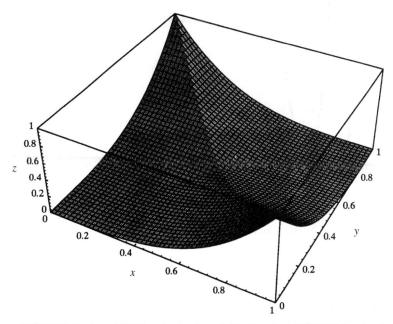

FIGURE 6.12 Fuzzy XOR function implemented by the adapted FLC. This function is described by $z(x,y) = [s(x,y)/\sqrt{2}]^{-\ln z_c/\ln 2}$ where $z_c = 0.106294$ and $s(x,y) = \sqrt{2} \max(\min(x, y), \min(1 - x, 1 - y))$. The root mean square (RMS) error between this surface and the one in Fig. 6.10 at the 25 random input sample points is $\sqrt{0.00426936} \approx 6.5$ percent.

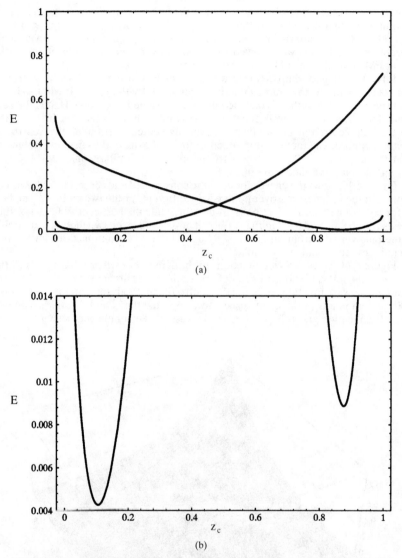

FIGURE 6.13   (*a*) Energy profiles for constrained (lower curve on left) and centroidal (lower curve on right) defuzzification methodologies; (*b*) magnified energy profiles.

problem, z_2 is multiplied by $\sqrt{2}$ to get s. The 100 (z_1, z_2) pairs are used in a centroidal defuzzifier to get 100 output z values. Then the 100 (s, z) pairs are plotted in the figure. This procedure is in contrast to the curve for the constrained defuzzifier for which there is an explicit function $s(z)$.

The curves in Fig. 6.14 are very different, but this is not the whole story. Recall that in this figure, the 0.1 value for z_c is optimal only for the constrained defuzzifica-

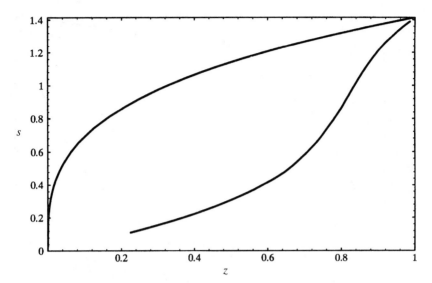

FIGURE 6.14 Walk functions implemented by constrained (upper curve) and centroidal (lower curve) defuzzification methodologies. The adaptation parameter is set to $z_c = 0.106294$, which yields minimum energy for the constrained technique.

tion method. The energy (error) for the centroidal method is terrible at this value of z_c. A comparison of the walk function for the *best* constrained defuzzifier and the *best* centroidal defuzzifier is needed.

Consider now Fig. 6.15, which shows the walk functions for the two defuzzification techniques at z_c around 0.9. In this case, the centroidal energy is minimized, but the error for the constrained method is high. The curve on the left is now the centroidal walk function, while the one on the right is for the constrained function. In both Figs. 6.14 and 6.15, the curve on the left results in the minimal error. By comparing the two left curves in these figures, it is now obvious that the two methods are not so different after all. The two left curves have roughly the same behavior: the steep rise in the walk function occurs for low values of z.

One final point should be made about the centroidal walk functions. Since the walk function is just a scaled version of the membership function for z_2, the centroidal method is effectively transforming the FMFs. That is, the centroidal method turns the left curve in Fig. 6.14 into the right one; in Fig. 6.15, it transforms the right curve into the left. Centroidal defuzzification can thus be accomplished with the constrained method, but by using the centroidal walk function. In this sense, the set of constrained defuzzifiers includes the set of centroidal defuzzifiers.

One criticism that could be levied at the previous statement is that the centroidal walk function is not available *a priori* in closed form as a function of the parameter z_c. Strictly speaking, this is true, but in practice it does not matter much. While Fig. 6.13 shows that constrained defuzzification is better than the centroidal technique, it is not *a lot* better. Any reasonable family of walk functions would work well in practice. For example, two other single-parameter walk functions have been used in the same sort of adaptation experiments, with very similar results. The first is based on the so-called Butterworth filters from electrical engineering [21]:

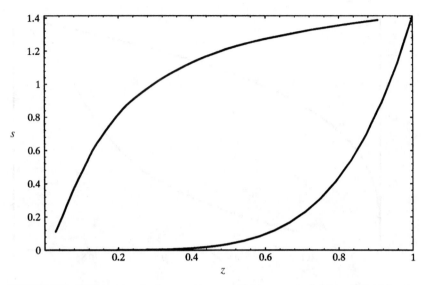

FIGURE 6.15 Walk functions implemented by centroidal (upper curve) and constrained (lower curve) defuzzification methodologies. The adaptation parameter is set to $z_c = 0.876667$, which yields minimum energy for the centroidal technique.

$$s(z) = \sqrt{2}\,\frac{(z/z_c)^\beta + z^\beta}{(z/z_c)^\beta + 1}$$

$$\beta = \alpha\,\csc(\pi z_c)$$

The other single-parameter walk function is based on the sigmoids found so often in neural network research:

$$s(z) = \sqrt{2}\left(\frac{1 - e^{-\beta z}}{1 + e^{-\beta}}\right)\left(\frac{1 + e^{-\beta(1 - z_c)}}{1 + e^{-\beta(z - z_c)}}\right)$$

$$\beta = \alpha\,\csc(\pi z_c)$$

Both of these walk functions have the advantage that the maximum slope (which is related to α) moves with z_c, unlike the example presented earlier in which the maximum slope is fixed at $z = 0$ or $z = 1$. In both cases, α controls the maximum slope which occurs near z_c. The formulas above were derived by taking the raw Butterworth or sigmoid function and transforming it so that the new function takes on the proper values at the end points of the unit interval. If the raw functions are denoted $r(z)$, then the transformation used is $s(z) = \sqrt{2}\,[r(z) - r(0)]/[r(1) - r(0)]$. This type of transformation has been known from the early days of the development of fuzzy logic [22(257)].

The lower energy minimum for the constrained method seen in Fig. 6.13 is not a consistent behavior. Which method turns out to be better depends on the input-to-output mapping that the FLC is trying to mimic. For example, the adaptation procedure was carried out for the alternative XOR functions:

$$z_d(x, y) = x + y - 3xy + x^2 y + xy^2 - x^2 y^2$$

$$z_d(x, y) = 2(x + y) - (x + y)^2$$

In both of these cases, the constrained defuzzification has a higher minimum than the centroidal method. Again, however, the difference is not great.

The above example of adapting the constrained defuzzifier is only a simple one. In practical applications, many more inputs and multiple outputs are typical. This implies multiple FAMMs, each of which is much larger than the 2×2 example presented. For more flexibility in input-to-output mappings, the walk functions for the inputs would also be adapted. The walk functions themselves might also take a more general form than the single-parameter one used in the example.

The principle of complementarity is not strictly required in FL. For the more general case, the path will be constrained to some nonplanar surface that includes the unit axis vectors. In three dimensions, such a surface might be an octant of a sphere, for example. A monotonic walk function along a constraint path will still generate a set of FMFs, but they will now obey a more general version of TPC.

As the FLC becomes more complicated, with more and more parameters to adapt, the energy function will rarely have the simple global minimum seen in the simple example presented above. Typically, the energy surface will have many *local* minima. Therefore, a global minimum search technique should be employed to find the best. One such technique that has proved very successful is simulated Cauchy annealing [23].

Nothing has been said yet about adapting the FAMM itself. So far, the internal *structure* of the FLC has remained fixed. Only adaptation of parameters of components in that structure has been covered. This is proper in cases where an expert's knowledge is available to set up the FAMM. In such cases, exponential weight parameters can be used to strengthen or weaken rules [9].

In situations where no expert is available, a *structurally adaptive* FLC is desired— one where the size and entries in the FAMM can be varied to discover an optimal solution. This feature would be needed in situations where nonstationarity can be found. For example, mechanical parts in the device being controlled can wear out, changing the control dynamics [11].

For such situations, the number of FMFs for the input and output variables can change. This is a multiresolution problem. Based on an internal assessment of the structure of the inputs, membership functions can be split or combined for each input. Both wavelet and chaos theory approaches to the automatic generation of FMFs at varying resolutions appear to hold promise [16, 17].

6.4 GENERALIZATION OF FLC FUZZIFICATION AND RULE PROCESSING SEGMENTS

Since both feedforward artificial neural networks and fuzzy logic controllers implement mappings between inputs and outputs, it is natural to wonder how the two approaches compare. In this section, it is shown that, under special conditions, the two architectures are equivalent. The special case examined is that of a fuzzy exclusive-OR function. What results is a method for generalizing the fuzzy partitioning portion of an FLC to make it more efficient. The generalization is to change the FLC rectangular partitioning that occurs because each input variable is fuzzified independently of the others. By fuzzifying nonrectangular regions in the input space, as is done in feedforward ANNs, fewer processing elements are needed. This property is of obvious interest to FLC chip designers.

ANN solutions to the XOR problem have been known for some time [24(64, 321, 331)]. Recall that the binary XOR function provides zero output when the two binary inputs, x and y, are the same; the output is one when x and y are different. Fig-

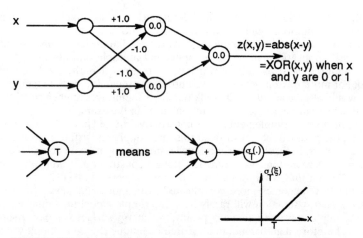

FIGURE 6.16 An ANN that implements an XOR function. The two leftmost neurons do no processing; they just pass the input signals through unaltered. The numbers along the arrows indicate the weights to multiply signals by; the signal at the tail of the arrow is multiplied by the weight and fed into the neuron at the head of the arrow. Each of the three processing neurons consists of two parts: an input summation and an output threshold operation. A soft threshold scheme is used: an input summation below threshold results in a zero output; an input summation above threshold is passed through unaltered. All thresholds are set to zero. The resulting input-to-output mapping $z(x, y)$ for this circuit is shown in Fig. 6.17.

ure 6.16 depicts the three-neuron ANN solution. Nonprocessing input buffer neurons are not included in the neuron count. Each processing neuron performs a summation and then a threshold operation. The thresholds for all three neurons are set to 0.

The three processing neurons are organized into two layers. There are two neurons in the first, so-called hidden, layer. There is one neuron in the output layer. Connections between neurons occur only between adjacent layers. There are four weights connecting the two nonprocessing neurons in the input (zeroth) layer and the hidden (first) layer. There are two weights between the two hidden-layer neurons and the output (second) layer.

It should be noted here that there exists a two-neuron solution to the XOR problem [24(321, 331)], where there is only one hidden-layer neuron, and direct connections between input and output neurons are allowed. This architecture is not considered in this exposition. The three-neuron solution provides a more direct linkage between ANN and FLC implementations.

Figure 6.17 shows the input-to-output mapping for the feedforward ANN architecture of Fig. 6.16. Linear soft thresholding is used for $\sigma(v)$, in which the neuronal output is zero below threshold and linear above. The use of the soft threshold fuzzifies the ANN mapping. That is, the net can provide outputs other than the extremes of the unit interval for inputs on the square unit interval. For example, if $x = 0.1$ and $y = 0.7$, then the output is $z = 0.6$. The use of a hard threshold, where $\sigma(v)$ is 0 for v below threshold and 1 above, causes a more degenerate input-to-output mapping. In this case the output z is 1 everywhere except for an infinitesimally small "ravine" of zeros along the $y = x$ line. These minimal ANN implementations have decidedly nonsmooth behavior. A recent article by Lenze utilizes so-called sigma-pi neurons to

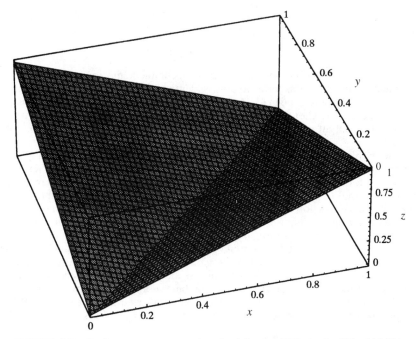

FIGURE 6.17 The input-to-output mapping $z(x, y)$ for the ANN circuit of Fig. 6.16. This implementation of the XOR function is $z(x, y) = |x - y|$. This causes the zero ravine along the line $y = x$. If one imagines sighting along the ravine from the upper right corner at $(x, y) = (1, 1)$ to the lower left at $(0, 0)$, the hill to the left is created by the upper hidden-layer neuron in Fig. 6.16. The right-hand hill is created by the lower hidden-layer neuron in Fig. 6.16. The summation-threshold operation of the output neuron is equivalent to the Max function applied to the inputs from the two hidden-layer neurons.

obtain a smooth input-output map [25]. The number of processing neurons in Lenze's network is equal to 1 plus the number of sample values. Since the fuzzy XOR function is constrained at the corners of the 2-D unit interval, Lenze's solution has four hidden units and one output neuron.

Imagine, in Fig. 6.17, sighting along the $y = x$ line from the origin to $(1, 1)$. The hill that rises linearly to the left of the zero ravine is created by the lower processing neuron of Fig. 6.16. The hill on the right side is created by the upper neuron. The input-to-output mapping can be written in the following equivalent forms:

$$z(x, y) = \sigma(\sigma(x - y) + \sigma(y - x)) = \text{Max}(\sigma(x - y), \sigma(y - x)) = |x - y|.$$

As will be seen momentarily, the second form, involving the Max function, provides the key to understanding the relationship between the ANN and FLC implementations of the XOR function.

To begin the discussion, consider the simplest classical FLC for a mapping between two input variables and one output. For each of the input variables, there are two membership functions. The fuzzy associative memory matrix in this case is 2×2. The output variable also has two membership functions. All three variables use simple triangular functions for the membership functions:

$$x_1(x) = 1 - x \qquad x_2(x) = x$$
$$y_1(y) = 1 - y \qquad y_2(y) = y$$
$$z_1(z) = 1 - z \qquad z_2(z) = z$$

Obviously, these functions obey the principle of complementarity, so that the sum of the membership functions for a variable is identically 1. Other choices for membership function shapes can be made. As long as TPC is obeyed, the following discussion is not affected. The choice of membership functions affects only the actual form of the input-to-output mapping at points on the square unit interval other than the corners.

The architecture for this classical FLC is shown in Fig. 6.18 and its input-to-output mapping is shown in Fig. 6.19. In addition to the input (zeroth) buffer layer, there are four additional layers: three hidden layers and an output layer. This requires a total of 11 processing neurons. The first hidden layer accomplishes the fuzzification conversion of the input variables into degrees of membership. The second hidden layer accomplishes the fuzzy intersection operations which "partition" the input space into four subregions. The word *partition* is in quotes to denote that this is a fuzzy partitioning. For example, $\text{Min}(x_1(x), y_1(y))$ takes on values larger than $1/2$ in the $[0, 1/2]$ by $[1/2, 1]$ square subregion, but it also takes on nonzero values in the subregions dominated by the other intersections. The third hidden layer accomplishes the fuzzy union operations which combine subregions into two output membership regions. For example $z_1(x, y) = \text{Max}(\text{Min}(x_1(x), y_1(y)), \text{Min}(x_2(x), y_2(y)))$. The output layer accomplishes defuzzification, which maps (z_1, z_2) pairs back to a specific z value.

The neurons in the parallel FLC implementation are not the sum-and-threshold type used in the ANN implementation of Fig. 6.16. The four neurons in the first FLC hidden layer are single-input single-output transformations to compute degrees of membership of each input variable in fuzzy membership functions. The two neurons connected to the x input have transfer functions of $x_1(x) = 1 - x$ and $x_2(x) = x$. Similarly, the two y-input FMF neurons have transfer functions $y_1(y) = 1 - y$ and $y_2(y) = y$. The four neurons in the second hidden layer are all identical dual-input single-output transformations. The output is simply the minimum (Min) of the two inputs. The third hidden layer performs the fuzzy union operations. Each of the two neurons in this layer are identical dual-input single-output nonlinear transformations: the maximum (Max) function. While choices for fuzzy intersection and union operators other than the Min and Max functions are possible [9, 10, 24(423–443)], the equivalence of FLC and ANN implementations is more readily apparent using Zadeh's classical operators [26].

With the insight into defuzzification gained from the previous section, it is easy to see that this process can be accomplished with a single dual-input single-output neuron. The transfer function in this case is $s^{-1}(2^{1/2} z_2/(z_1 + z_2)) = z_2/(z_1 + z_2)$, which combines the operations of moving (z_1, z_2) pairs to the constraint line, computing the walk distance, and calculating the appropriate z value via the inverse of the walk function. Moving points to the constraint line is accomplished simply by dividing the vector by the sum of its elements. The walk distance is simply the length along the constraint line from $(1, 0)$. Since the membership functions for the output variable are constant-slope functions that cross at $z = 0.5$, the walk function is simply $s(z) = 2^{1/2} z = 2^{1/2} z_2(z)$.

It is easy to show that the special case of a symmetric 2-D FAMM with identical diagonal elements creates only (z_1, z_2) pairs that satisfy TPC. That is, $z_2 = 1 - z_1$. Thus, the defuzzification does not require the step of moving non-TPC points to the con-

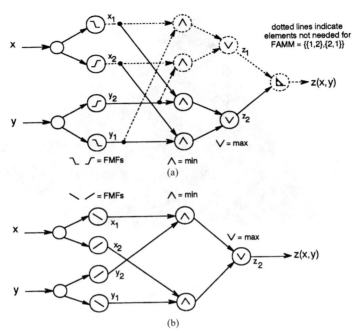

FIGURE 6.18 An FLC that implements an XOR function. As in Fig. 6.16, the two left-most neurons are just input buffers. They accomplish no processing. The first hidden layer computes the degrees of membership in each input variable's fuzzy membership function. The next two hidden layers accomplish the rule-based processing in an FLC: first fuzzy intersection operations using Min($\cdot$), then fuzzy union using Max($\cdot$). The output layer performs defuzzification. (a) The fully general 11-neuron FLC; (b) a simplified version, taking advantage of the fact that a 2-D symmetric FAMM with identical diagonal elements creates outputs that satisfy the principle of complementarity. Thus, $z_1(x, y)$ + $z_2(x, y) = 1$, and $z_2(x, y)$ is used directly as the output: $z(x, y) = z_2(x, y)$. The resulting input-to-output mapping $z(x, y)$ for this circuit is shown in Fig. 6.19.

straint line. The degrees of membership for the output fuzzy membership functions generated by FLC rule processing are already on the constraint line $z_2 = 1 - z_1$. The determination of the best z value to provide as an output of defuzzification is trivial in this case: $z = z_2$. With this observation, two simplifications can be made to the top-most architecture shown in Fig. 6.18. All neurons and signal paths that go solely to creating the z_1 value can be discarded, and the defuzzification layer can be replaced by a straight-through path joining z_2 and z. This reduces the total processing neuron count to seven, as shown in the lower architecture in Fig. 6.18.

At this point, it is natural to ask the question: can the seven-neuron FLC be simplified any further, and if so, how can it be accomplished? It is not immediately obvious that the seven-neuron architecture in Fig. 6.18 can be pared any further, as all of the required elements of the classical FLC are shown there in minimal form. However, by observing what the three-neuron ANN does to the input space compared with the FLC, a more efficient FLC architecture can be developed.

In particular, note that the two hidden-layer neurons of the ANN partition the input xy space along the $y = x$ line. One neuron handles the region above this line; the other neuron is active for inputs below the line. The classical FLC, on the other

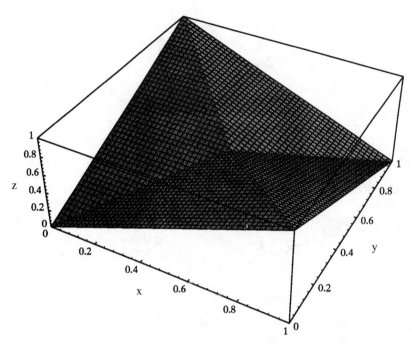

FIGURE 6.19 The input-to-output mapping $z(x, y)$ for the FLC circuit of Fig. 6.18. Notice that this is not exactly the same mapping as in Fig. 6.17. While the corner values are identical, the values along the border of the unit square and inside it are not the same as the function in Fig. 6.17. This is because the classical FLC and feedforward ANN implement their input-to-output mappings in different ways. In order to further reduce the neuron count in the parallel FLC implementation to that of the three-neuron ANN architecture, the rectangular fuzzy partitioning accomplished by the fuzzy intersection layer would need to be replaced by the more general linearly separable partitioning that ANNs use.

hand, has no ability to partition the input space in this diagonal fashion. Since fuzzy membership functions are created for each input variable separately, the fuzzy partitions are rectangular. If more general regions could be described in an FLC, more efficient architectures might be possible.

If the rectangular fuzzy partitioning of the FLC input space is to be relaxed, two-dimensional FMFs must be constructed. The seven neurons in three layers of processing neurons in the classical FLC implementation of Fig. 6.18 (lower drawing) are replaced by three neurons in two layers that partition the input space in the same diagonal way that the ANN does. The first replacement layer consists of two dual-input single-output neurons which have the same transfer functions as those in the ANN: $\sigma(x - y)$ for one neuron and $\sigma(y - x)$ for the other. These neurons perform the functions of fuzzification and rule processing. The output neuron in the second replacement layer performs the defuzzification function. It can be implemented as a sum-and-threshold or as a Max operation. In this fashion, a three-neuron FLC implementation that provides the same input-to-output mapping as the ANN can be constructed. This means that the three-neuron ANN implementation of the XOR function shown in Fig. 6.16 can be interpreted as a minimized FLC where the first hidden layer does multidimensional fuzzification and rule processing and the second layer performs defuzzification.

The rule processing in an FLC carries out fuzzy membership intersection and union operations according to rules of the type IF $(((x \in x_1)$ and $(y \in y_1))$ or $((x \in x_2)$ and $(y \in y_2)))$ THEN $(z \in z_1)$. The generalization to multidimensional FMFs means that rules now take on the form IF $((x,y) \in R_1)$ THEN $(z \in z_1)$. R_i is the ith fuzzy subregion in the input space and is typically not rectangular. In the case of the XOR example, the subregions are triangles. Once again, these subregions are *fuzzy* subregions. Unlike closed sets in conventional set theory, the fuzzy subregions are open sets. The "shape" of the subregion is really just an artifice constructed from a contour level of the fuzzy membership functions. Such contours, however, do yield useful information about which fuzzy output region is dominant in any particular area in the input space.

The additional advantage of using multidimensional input FMFs, with their non-rectangular contours, is that the principle of complementarity is guaranteed. In the classical FLC, where each variable is treated independently, with its own membership functions, the output degrees of membership coming from rule processing do not necessarily sum to 1. An exception, of course, is the 2-D symmetric FAMM with identical diagonal elements. This is a special case, however, as the principle of complementarity is almost always violated for the output degrees of membership computed by rule processing. This is why traditional defuzzification, in the form of such algorithms as the centroidal technique, has been somewhat complicated. These traditional techniques are really accomplishing two things at once: finding the closest point, in some sense, that satisfies TPC, and then computing the appropriate output value corresponding to that closest point. With multidimensional input FMFs, TPC is always satisfied. So the first implicit step, moving points to the constraint path, is not required. Defuzzification reduces to a simple lookup operation using the inverse of the output variable's walk function.

6.5 CONCLUSIONS

There are four major points the reader should take from the preceding discussion: the principle of complementarity, the geometrical interpretation of constrained defuzzification, generalized data-driven adaptation of membership functions, and generalized fuzzification and rule processing in fuzzy logic controllers. The principle of complementarity simply states that the vector created by the fuzzification process has a simple property: the sum of the elements of the vector, which represent the degrees of membership in the set of fuzzy membership functions, sum to a constant. That constant is typically chosen to be one for convenience. While formal fuzzy logic tenets do not require this constraint, it allows simpler defuzzification procedures to be used.

The geometrical interpretation of defuzzification allows this final process in a fuzzy logic controller to be understood in a new way. The fuzzification and rule processing segments of a classical FLC create points in the output variable's fuzzy vector space which do not satisfy the principle of complementarity. That is, the degrees of membership for the output variable do not sum to 1. These fuzzy vectors do not lie on the path in the constraint plane that describes the membership functions for the output variable. Therefore, defuzzification can be interpreted geometrically as the process of moving these errant fuzzy vectors to the closest point, in some sense, *on* the path in the constraint plane. All defuzzification schemes, including the commonly used centroidal method, accomplish this operation. A generalized method, using so-called walk functions, for defuzzification has been developed. This defuzzification procedure is based on inversion of the monotonic walk function along the constraint path, rather than on membership functions themselves [13]. Thus, inversion can be done in cases where the output variable includes nonmonotonic membership functions.

Finally, the last section discusses the equivalence of parallel implementations of ANNs and FLCs for the simple example of the fuzzy XOR function. The ANN implementations of XOR are more compact than the direct FLC architecture. That is, the ANN requires fewer processing neurons than the FLC. In order to reduce the complexity of an FLC to that of an ANN, the FLC's rectangular fuzzy partitioning of the input space by the Min function must be generalized. Instead of membership functions being created for each input variable individually, multidimensional FMFs are required.

LIST OF ABBREVIATIONS

$$
\begin{aligned}
\text{2-D} &= \text{two-dimensional} \\
\text{3-D} &= \text{three-dimensional} \\
N\text{-D} &= N\text{-dimensional} \\
\text{ANN} &= \text{artificial neural network} \\
\text{DOM} &= \text{degree of membership} \\
\text{FAM} &= \text{fuzzy associative memory} \\
\text{FAMM} &= \text{FAM matrix} \\
\text{FL} &= \text{fuzzy logic} \\
\text{FLC} &= \text{fuzzy logic controller} \\
\text{FMF} &= \text{fuzzy membership function} \\
\text{PID} &= \text{proportional integral derivative} \\
\text{RMS} &= \text{root mean square} \\
\text{TPC} &= \text{the principle of complementarity} \\
\text{XOR} &= \text{exclusive OR}
\end{aligned}
$$

REFERENCES

Throughout the preceding text, the work of other authors is cited in one of two ways. One or more numbers, separated by commas, within square brackets, are each indices to the books or articles listed below. When references to general discussions within these books or articles are intended, this is the format used. When a specific formula or point is referenced, the book or article index will be followed by a page or list of pages in parentheses: [6(88, 143), 8(22), 12(18–19)].

1. T. Williams, "New tools make fuzzy/neural more than an academic amusement," *Computer Design,* July 1994, pp. 69–84.

2. B. Kosko, *Neural Networks and Fuzzy Systems: A Dynamical Systems Approach to Machine Intelligence,* Prentice-Hall International Editions, 1992.

3. B. Kosko, *Fuzzy Thinking: The New Science of Fuzzy Logic,* Hyperion, New York, 1993.
4. D. Schwartz and G. Klir, "Fuzzy logic flowers in Japan," *IEEE Spectrum,* July 1992, pp. 32–35.
5. E. Ruspini, "Numerical Methods for Fuzzy Clustering," *Information Science,* vol. 2, 1970, pp. 319–350.
6. J. Bezdek, "A Convergence Theorem for the Fuzzy ISODATA Clustering Algorithms," *IEEE Transactions on Pattern Analysis and Machine Intelligence,* vol. 2, no. 1, pp. 1–8.
7. G. Carpenter, S. Grossberg, N. Markuzon, H. Reynolds, and D. Rosen, "Fuzzy ARTMAP: A Neural Network Architecture for Incremental Supervised Learning of Analog Multidimensional Maps," *IEEE Transactions on Neural Networks,* vol. 3, no. 5, September 1992, pp. 698–713.
8. P. Simpson, "Fuzzy Min-Max Neural Networks—Part 2: Clustering," *IEEE Transactions on Fuzzy Systems,* vol. 1, no. 1, February 1993, pp. 32–45.
9. P. Werbos, "Elastic Fuzzy Logic: A Better Way to Combine Neural and Fuzzy Capabilities," *World Conference on Neural Networks '93,* Portland, Oregon, July 1993, vol. II, pp. 623–626.
10. R. Yager, "Toward a Unified Approach to Aggregation in Fuzzy and Neural Systems," *World Conference on Neural Networks '93,* vol. II, pp. 619–622.
11. E. Cox, "Adaptive Fuzzy Systems," *IEEE Spectrum,* February 1993, pp. 27–31.
12. R. Yager and D. Filev, "SLIDE: A Simple Adaptive Defuzzification Method," *IEEE Transactions on Fuzzy Systems,* Volume 1, Number 1, February 1993, pages 69–78.
13. D. Nauck, F. Klawonn, and R. Kruse, "Combining Neural Networks and Fuzzy Controllers", *Fuzzy Logic and Artificial Intelligence Conference (FLAI) '93,* Linz, Austria.
14. H. Berenji and P. Khedkar, "Learning and Tuning Fuzzy Logic Controllers Through Reinforcements," *IEEE Transactions on Neural Networks,* Volume 3, Number 5, September 1992, pages 724–740.
15. C. Lee, "Fuzzy Logic in Control Systems: Fuzzy Logic Controller," *IEEE Transactions on Systems, Man, and Cybernetics,* vol. 20, 1990, pp. 404–435.
16. H. Szu, J. Garcia, L. Zadeh, C. Hsu, J. DeWitte, and M. Zaghloul, "Multi-Resolution Analyses of Fuzzy Membership Functions by means of Chaotic Neural Networks," *World Conference on Neural Networks '94,* San Diego, California, June 5–9, 1994, Volume IV, pages 675–683.
17. C. Hsu, M. Zaghloul, and H. Szu, "CMOS Circuit Implementation to Control a Chaotic Neuron," *World Conference on Neural Networks '94,* San Diego, California, June 5–9, 1994, Volume IV, pages 684–689.
18. F. Chung and T. Lee, "Fuzzy Competitive Learning," *Neural Networks,* vol. 7, no. 3, pp. 539–551.
19. J. Bezdek, "Editorial: Fuzzy Models—What Are They, and Why?", *IEEE Transactions on Fuzzy Systems,* vol. 1, no. 1, February 1993, pp. 1–6.
20. S. Wolfram, *Mathematica: A System for Doing Mathematics by Computer,* 2d ed., Addison-Wesley, Redwood City, Calif., 1991.
21. G. Temes and J. LaPatra, *Introduction to Circuit Synthesis and Design,* McGraw-Hill, New York, 1977.
22. L. Zadeh, "A Fuzzy-Algorithmic Approach to the Definition of Complex or Imprecise Concepts," *International Journal of Man-Machine Studies,* vol. 8, 1976, pp. 249–291.
23. H. Szu and R. Hartley, "Nonconvex Optimization by Fast Simulated Annealing," *Proceedings of the IEEE,* vol. 75, no. 11, November 1987, pp. 1538–1540.
24. D. Rumelhart, J. McClelland, and the PDP Research Group, *Parallel Distributed Processing: Explorations in the Microstructure of Cognition,* vol. 1: *Foundations,* MIT Press, Cambridge, Mass., ninth printing, 1989.

25. B. Lenze, "How to Make Sigma-Pi Neural Networks Perform Perfectly on Regular Training Sets," *Neural Networks,* vol. 7, no. 8, 1994, pp. 1285–1293.

26. L. Zadeh, "Fuzzy Sets," *Information and Control,* vol. 8, Academic Press, New York; 1965, pp. 338–353.

27. J. Freeman, "Fuzzy Systems for Control Applications: The Truck Backer-Upper," *The Mathematica Journal,* vol. 4, issue 1, pp. 64–69.

CHAPTER 7
EFFICIENT METHODS FOR FUZZY RULE EXTRACTION FROM NUMERICAL DATA

Shigeo Abe
Chief Researcher
Hitachi Research Laboratory, Hitachi, Ltd.

Ming-Shong Lan
Member of Technical Staff
Science Center, Rockwell International Corporation

In this chapter, we discuss two methods for extracting fuzzy rules from numerical data. The first method extracts fuzzy rules directly from numerical data, while the second method extracts fuzzy rules from a neural network that is trained by using the data. We first describe each method for generating fuzzy rules for pattern classification, and then describe their extension for creating fuzzy systems that approximate complex functions. The performance of the fuzzy system created by these methods for pattern classification are evaluated by using a vehicle license plate recognition system, a blood cell classification system, and widely used iris data. Meanwhile, the performance of the fuzzy system for function approximation is evaluated using a system for water purification plant operation.

7.1 FUZZY RULE EXTRACTION FROM DATA FOR PATTERN CLASSIFICATION: DIRECT METHOD

The direct method extracts fuzzy rules for pattern classification directly from numerical data by recursively defining activation hyperboxes which define the existence regions of a class and, if necessary, an inhibition hyperbox which inhibits the existence of data in the associated activation hyperbox. Since an activation hyperbox is determined by calculating, for each input variable, the minimum and maximum values of the data belonging to a class, the rule extraction process is extremely fast compared to the learning process of neural networks, while the performance is comparable to that of neural networks.

7.1.1 Extraction Process and Definitions of Activation and Inhibition Hyperboxes

To illustrate the fuzzy rule extraction process, let us assume that we are going to classify numerals 3 and 4 using only two input features: the depth from the left-hand side of the edge and the curvature at a selected location as shown in Fig. 7.1. First we define the activation hyperboxes of level 1 for numerals 3 and 4, $A_{33}(1)$ and $A_{44}(1)$, respectively. Since these two activation hyperboxes overlap, we further define the overlapping region as an inhibition hyperbox, i.e., $I_{34}(1)$. Thus the fuzzy rule of level 1 for numeral 3 is

If the values of the input features of a given datum are in $A_{33}(1)$ but not in $I_{34}(1)$, then the datum is classified as numeral 3.

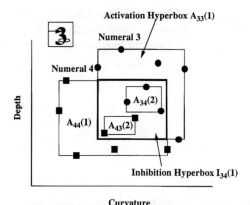

FIGURE 7.1   Recursive definition of activation and inhibition hyperboxes.

Similarly, we can define fuzzy rules for numeral 4. Since some data of numerals 3 and 4 reside in the inhibition hyperbox $I_{34}(1)$, as shown in Fig. 7.1, we further define activation hyperboxes $A_{34}(2)$ and $A_{43}(2)$. But $A_{34}(2)$ and $A_{43}(2)$ do not overlap, hence the rule extraction process ends. The fuzzy rule of level 2 for numeral 3 is

If the values of the input features of a given datum are in $A_{34}(2)$, then the datum is classified as numeral 3.

In the following, we generalize the extraction process for generating fuzzy rules for classifying data with an m-dimensional input vector $\mathbf{x}$ into one of n classes. First assume we have a training data set of input data X_i for class i, where $i = 1, \ldots, n$. Using X_i, an activation hyperbox of level 1, denoted as $A_{ii}(1)$, is defined, which is the maximum region of class i data:

$$A_{ii}(1) = \{\mathbf{x} \mid v_{iik}(1) \le x_k \le V_{iik}(1), k = 1, \ldots, m\} \qquad (7.1)$$

where $x_k = k$th element of input vector $\mathbf{x}$
$v_{iik}(1)$ = minimum value of x_k of $\mathbf{x} \in X_i$
$V_{iik}(1)$ = maximum value of x_k of $\mathbf{x} \in X_i$

If the activation hyperboxes A_{ii} (1) and A_{jj} (1) ($j \neq i, j = 1, \ldots, n$) do not overlap, we obtain a fuzzy rule of level 1 for class i as follows:

If $\mathbf{x}$ is A_{ii} (1) then $\mathbf{x}$ is class i. $\hspace{4cm}$ (7.2)

If the activation hyperboxes $A_{ii}(1)$ and $A_{jj}(1)$ overlap, we resolve the overlap recursively, defining the overlapping region as the inhibition hyperbox of level 1 denoted as $I_{ij}(1)$:

$$I_{ij}(1) = \{\mathbf{x} | w_{ijk} (1) \leq x_k \leq W_{ijk}(1), k = 1, \ldots, m\} \hspace{2cm} (7.3)$$

where $v_{iik}(1) \leq w_{ijk}(1) \leq W_{ijk}(1) \leq V_{iik}(1)$. The minimum and maximum values of inhibition hyperbox $I_{ij}(1)$ are given by (see Fig. 7.2)

1. For $v_{jjk}(1) \leq v_{iik}(1) \leq V_{jjk}(1) < V_{iik}(1)$

$$w_{ijk}(1) = v_{iik}(1), W_{ijk}(1) = V_{jjk}(1) \hspace{3cm} (7.4)$$

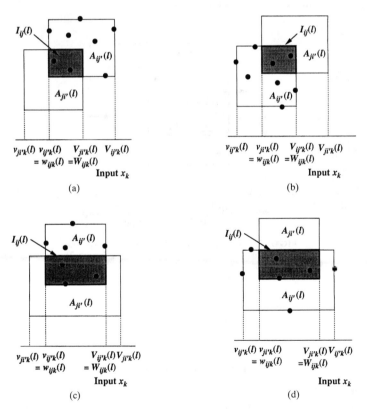

FIGURE 7.2 Definition of activation and inhibition hyperboxes ($j' = i$ and $i' = j$ for $l = 1, j' = j$, and $i' = i$ for $l \geq 2$). (*Reprinted with permission from Abe and Lan [2]. Copyright © IEEE.*)

2. For $v_{iik}(1) < v_{jjk}(1) \leq V_{iik}(1) \leq V_{jjk}(1)$

$$w_{ijk}(1) = v_{jjk}(1), W_{ijk}(1) = V_{iik}(1) \tag{7.5}$$

3. For $v_{jjk}(1) \leq v_{iik}(1) \leq V_{iik}(1) \leq V_{jjk}(1)$

$$w_{ijk}(1) = v_{iik}(1), W_{ijk}(1) = V_{iik}(1) \tag{7.6}$$

4. For $v_{iik}(1) < v_{jjk}(1) \leq V_{jjk}(1) < V_{iik}(1)$

$$w_{ijk}(1) = v_{jjk}(1), W_{ijk}(1) = V_{jjk}(1) \tag{7.7}$$

However, the inhibition hyperbox defined in this way has a drawback, that is, data that exist on the surface of the inhibition hyperbox may not be classified as either of the two classes, as discussed in Ref. 1. To overcome this problem, we expand the originally defined inhibition hyperbox $I_{ij}(1)$, associated with $A_{ii}(1)$ and $A_{jj}(1)$, in the way shown in Fig. 7.3. We denote the expanded inhibition hyperbox as $J_{ij}(1) = \{\mathbf{x}|u_{ijk}(1) \leq x_k < U_{ijk}(1), k = 1, \ldots, m\}$. The expanded inhibition hyperboxes for $A_{ij}(1)$ and $A_{ji}(1)$ are $J_{ij}(1)$ and $J_{ji}(1)$, respectively, which are different. The expanded inhibition hyperbox $J_{ij}(1)$ is defined as follows (see Fig. 7.2).

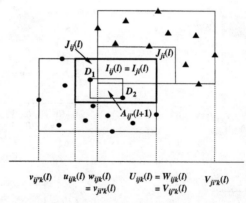

FIGURE 7.3 Expansion of the inhibition hyperbox ($j' = i$ and $i' = j$ for $l = 1$, $j' = j$ and $i' = i$ for $l \geq 2$). (*Reprinted with permission from Abe and Lan [2]. Copyright © IEEE.*)

1. For $v_{jjk}(1) \leq v_{iik}(1) \leq V_{jjk}(1) < V_{iik}(1)$

$$u_{ijk}(1) = v_{iik}(1)$$

$$U_{ijk}(1) = V_{jjk}(1) + \alpha(V_{iik}(1) - V_{jjk}(1)) \tag{7.8}$$

where $\alpha \, (> 0)$ is an expansion parameter.

2. For $v_{iik}(1) < v_{jjk}(1) \leq V_{iik}(1) \leq V_{jjk}(1)$

$$u_{ijk}(1) = v_{jjk}(1) - \alpha(v_{jjk}(1) - v_{iik}(1)), U_{ijk}(1) = V_{iik}(1) \tag{7.9}$$

3. For $v_{jjk}(1) \leq v_{iik} \leq V_{iik}(1) \leq V_{jjk}(1)$. In this case we do not expand the inhibition hyperbox for class i since we need not calculate the degree of membership for the x_k axis. Namely,

$$u_{ijk}(1) = v_{iik}(1)$$
$$U_{ijk}(1) = V_{iik}(1) \tag{7.10}$$

4. For $v_{iik}(1) < v_{jjk}(1) \leq V_{jjk}(1) < V_{iik}(1)$

$$u_{ijk}(1) = v_{jjk}(1) - \alpha(v_{jjk}(1) - v_{iik}(1))$$
$$U_{ijk}(1) = V_{jjk}(1) + \alpha(V_{iik}(1) - V_{jjk}(1)) \tag{7.11}$$

Then we define a fuzzy rule of level 1 with inhibition by

If **x** is $A_{ii}(1)$ and **x** is not $J_{ij}(1)$ then **x** is class i. $\tag{7.12}$

If $A_{ii}(1)$ is included in $A_{jj}(1)$, i.e., (7.6) holds for all k, $k = 1, \ldots, m$, $A_{ii}(1)$ coincides with $I_{ij}(1)$. In this case (7.12) is a void rule (i.e., it is not created), since no **x** can satisfy (7.12).

If some data belonging to X_i exist in $J_{ij}(1)$, we define the activation hyperbox of level 2 denoted as $A_{ij}(2)$ within the expanded inhibition hyperbox $J_{ij}(1)$ by calculating the minimum and maximum values of x_k based on the data in $J_{ij}(1)$:

$$A_{ij}(2) = \{\mathbf{x} \mid v_{ijk}(2) \leq x_k \leq V_{ijk}(2), k = 1, \ldots, m\} \tag{7.13}$$

where $\mathbf{x} \in X_i$, **x** is in $J_{ij}(1)$, and

$$v_{ijk}(2) = \text{minimum value of } x_k \text{ where } \mathbf{x} \in X_i \text{ and } \mathbf{x} \text{ is in } J_{ij}(1)$$
$$V_{ijk}(2) = \text{maximum value of } x_k \text{ where } \mathbf{x} \in X_i \text{ and } \mathbf{x} \text{ is in } J_{ij}(1)$$
$$u_{ijk}(1) \leq v_{ijk}(2) \leq x_k \leq V_{ijk}(2) \leq U_{ijk}(1) \tag{7.14}$$

If there is only one activation hyperbox of level 2 or there are two activation hyperboxes but they do not overlap, we define a fuzzy rule of level 2 for class i by

If **x** is $A_{ij}(2)$ then **x** is class i. $\tag{7.15}$

If $A_{ij}(2)$ and $A_{ji}(2)$ overlap, the overlapping region of level 2 is denoted as $I_{ij}(2)$:

$$I_{ij}(2) = \{\mathbf{x} \mid w_{ijk}(2) \leq x_k \leq W_{ijk}(2), k = 1, \ldots, m\} \tag{7.16}$$

where $v_{ijk}(2) \leq w_{ijk}(2) \leq W_{ijk}(2) \leq V_{ijk}(2)$.

Similar to what has been described for level 1, we define the expanded inhibition hyperbox $J_{ij}(2)$:

$$J_{ij}(2) = \{\mathbf{x} \mid u_{ijk}(2) \leq x_k \leq U_{ijk}(2), k = 1, \ldots, m\} \tag{7.17}$$

where $u_{ijk}(2) \leq w_{ijk}(2) \leq W_{ijk}(2) \leq U_{ijk}(2)$.

Then we define a fuzzy rule of level 2 with inhibition:

If **x** is $A_{ij}(2)$ and **x** is not $J_{ij}(2)$ then **x** is class i. $\tag{7.18}$

Fuzzy rules of levels higher than 2 can be defined in a similar manner if an overlap can be defined. In a general form, the fuzzy rule $r_{ij}(l)$ of level l (≥ 1) without inhibition can be expressed as follows:

If **x** is $A_{ij}(l)$ then **x** is class i $\tag{7.19}$

where $j' = i$ for $l = 1$ and $j' = j$ for $l \geq 2$. Likewise, the fuzzy rule $r_{ij'}(l)$ of level l with inhibition can be expressed as follows:

$$\text{If } \mathbf{x} \text{ is } A_{ij'}(l) \text{ and } \mathbf{x} \text{ is not } J_{ij}(l) \text{ then } \mathbf{x} \text{ is class } i. \tag{7.20}$$

The recursion process for defining fuzzy rules terminates when $A_{ij}(l)$ and $A_{ji}(l)$ do not overlap or $A_{ij}(l) = A_{ji}(l) = I_{ij}(l - 1)$ holds. In the latter case, since the overlap cannot be resolved by the recursive process, instead of defining $A_{ij}(l)$ and $A_{ji}(l)$, for each datum of class i and/or j in $I_{ij}(l - 1)$ we define an activation hyperbox which includes only that datum. And we do not further define inhibition and activation hyperboxes of levels higher than l, because as long as no identical data exist in both classes i and j, no overlap exists between the activation hyperboxes of level l.

7.1.2 Inference Procedure

Membership Function for Activation Hyperboxes. For pattern classification, it is reasonable to assume that the degree of membership of $\mathbf{x}$ for a fuzzy rule given by Eq. (7.19) is 1 if $\mathbf{x}$ is in the activation hyperbox $A_{ij}(l)$, and that the degree of membership decreases as $\mathbf{x}$ moves away from the activation hyperbox. Namely, if all the input variables are normalized to the same scale, e.g., between 0 and 1, the contour surface, on which every location has the same degree of membership, is parallel to, and lies at an equal distance from, the surface of the activation hyperbox as illustrated in Fig. 7.4. To realize a membership function with this characteristic we use the following function, which is similar to that proposed in Ref. 2:

$$m_{A_{ij}(l)}(\mathbf{x}) = \min_{k = 1,\ldots,m} m_{A_{ij}(l)}(\mathbf{x}, k), \tag{7.21}$$

$$m_{A_{ij}(l)}(\mathbf{x}, k) = [1 - \max(0, \min(1, \gamma_k(v_{ijk}(l) - x_k)))] \times$$
$$[1 - \max(0, \min(1, \gamma_k(x_k - V_{ijk}(l))))] \tag{7.22}$$

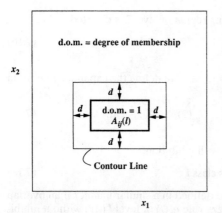

d.o.m. = degree of membership

x_2

d

d d.o.m. = 1 d
$A_{ij}(l)$

d

Contour Line

x_1

FIGURE 7.4 The contour line of membership function for the activation hyperbox (two-dimensional case). (*Reprinted with permission from Abe and Lan [2]. Copyright © IEEE.*)

where γ_k is the sensitivity parameter for the kth input variable x_k. Figure 7.5 is the one-dimensional membership function given by Eq. (7.22). Although the value of sensitivity parameter γ_k can be different for different k, in the following we assume that x_k's are normalized and $\gamma_k = \gamma$, where $k = 1, \ldots, m$, for easy discussion. The parameter γ serves to control the generalization region.

Thus, the degree of membership of $\mathbf{x}$ for a fuzzy rule $r_{ij}(l)$ given by Eq. (7.19) is

$$d_{r_{ij}(l)}(\mathbf{x}) = m_{A_{ij}(l)}(\mathbf{x}) \tag{7.23}$$

Membership Function for Inhibition Hyperboxes. The degree of membership of $\mathbf{x}$ for a fuzzy rule given by Eq. (7.20) is 1 when $\mathbf{x}$ is in the activation

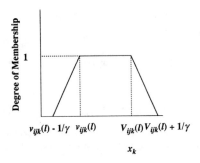

FIGURE 7.5 One-dimensional membership function of the activation hyperbox $A_{ij}(l)$. (*Reprinted with permission from Abe and Lan [2]. Copyright © IEEE.*)

hyperbox but not within the expanded inhibition hyperbox, i.e., $\mathbf{x}$ is in $\overline{A_{ij}(l)} - \overline{J_{ij}(l)}$, where $\overline{S}$ denotes the closure of set S and $j' = i$ for $l = 1$ and $j' = j$ for $l \geq 2$. If $\mathbf{x}$ moves away from this region the degree of membership decreases. Namely, in this case it is also favorable that the contour surface is parallel to, and lies at an equal distance from, the surface of $\overline{A_{ij}(l)} - \overline{J_{ij}(l)}$ as shown in Fig. 7.6. (If $A_{ij}(l) = I_{ij}(l)$, i.e., if the rule is void, we do not calculate the degree of membership for this rule.) To realize this membership function we first define a region $H_{ij}(l)$ associated with $A_{ij}(l)$ and $I_{ij}(l)$ as follows (see Fig. 7.2):

$$H_{ij}(l) = \{\mathbf{x} \mid x_k \leq U_{ijk}(l) \qquad \text{for } v_{ji'k}(l) \leq v_{ij'k}(l) \leq V_{ji'k}(l) < V_{ij'k}(l)$$

$$x_k \geq u_{ijk}(l) \qquad \text{for } v_{ij'k}(l) < v_{ji'k}(l) \leq V_{ij'k}(l) \leq V_{ji'k}(l)$$

$$-\infty < x_k < \infty \qquad \text{for } v_{ji'k}(l) \leq v_{ij'k}(l) \leq V_{ij'k}(l) \leq V_{ji'k}(l) \tag{7.24}$$

$$u_{ijk}(l) \leq x_k \leq U_{ijk}(l) \qquad \text{for } v_{ij'k}(l) < v_{ji'k}(l) \leq V_{ji'k}(l) < V_{ij'k}(l), k = 1, \ldots, m\}$$

where $j' = i$ and $i' = j$ for $l = 1$, $j' = j$ and $i' = i$ for $l \geq 2$, and $H_{ij}(l)$ and $H_{ji}(l)$ are in general different. According to the definition

$$H_{ij}(l) \supset J_{ij}(l) \tag{7.25}$$

The region $H_{ij}(l)$ defines an input region where the expanded inhibition hyperbox affects the degree of membership of the rule given by (7.20). If $\mathbf{x} \notin H_{ij}(l)$, the degree of membership for a fuzzy rule $r_{ij}(l)$ given by Eq. (7.20) is the same as Eq. (7.23). Thus, for $\mathbf{x} \in J_{ij}(l)$ the degree of membership $m_{J_{ij}(l)}(\mathbf{x})$ is given by

$$m_{J_{ij}(l)}(\mathbf{x}) = \max_{k = 1, \ldots, m} m_{J_{ij}(l)}(\mathbf{x}, k) \tag{7.26}$$

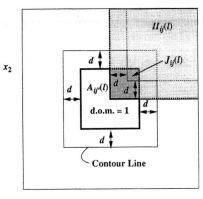

FIGURE 7.6 The contour line of membership function for the activation and inhibition hyperboxes (two-dimensional case). (*Reprinted with permission from Abe and Lan [2]. Copyright © IEEE.*)

where $m_{J_{ij}(l)}(\mathbf{x}, k)$ is the degree of membership of x_k and is calculated by:

1. For $v_{ji\varkappa}(l) \le v_{ij\varkappa}(l) \le V_{ij\varkappa}(l) < V_{ij\varkappa}(l)$ (see Fig. 7.2a)

$$m_{I_{ij}(l)}(\mathbf{x}, k) = 1 - \max\,(0, \min\,(1, \gamma(U_{ijk}(l) - x_k)))$$ (7.27)

2. For $v_{ij\varkappa}(l) < v_{ji\varkappa}(l) \le V_{ij\varkappa}(l) \le V_{ji\varkappa}(l)$ (see Fig. 7.2b)

$$m_{J_{ij}(l)}(\mathbf{x}, k) = 1 - \max\,(0, \min\,(1, \gamma(x_k - u_{ijk}(l))))$$ (7.28)

3. For $v_{ji\varkappa}(l) \le v_{ij\varkappa}(l) \le V_{ij\varkappa}(l) \le V_{ji\varkappa}(l)$. Since $x_k = v_{ij\varkappa}(l)$ and $x_k = V_{ij\varkappa}(l)$ do not constitute the surface of $\overline{A_{ij'}(l) - J_{ij}(l)}$, it is not necessary to define a membership func-
tion in the x_k axis. Thus we set

$$m_{J_{ij}(l)}(\mathbf{x}, k) = 0$$ (7.29)

Equation (7.29) holds for all k, where $k = 1, \ldots, m$, only when $A_{ij'}(l) \supset A_{ij'}(l) = I_{ij}(l)$, in other words, when the rule is a void rule. Thus, the x_k axis is ignored when
calculating the degree of membership using Eqs. (7.29) and (7.26).

4. For $v_{ij'k}(l) < v_{ji'k}(l) \le V_{ji'k}(l) < V_{ij'k}(l)$ (see Fig. 7.2d)

$$m_{J_{ij}(l)}(\mathbf{x}, k) =$$

$$\begin{cases} 1 - \max\,(0, \min\,(1, \gamma(U_{ijk}(l) - x_k))) & \text{for } (u_{ijk}(l) + U_{ijk}(l))/2 \le x_k \le U_{ijk}(l) \\ 1 - \max\,(0, \min\,(1, \gamma(x_k - u_{ijk}(l)))) & \text{for } u_{ijk}(l) \le x_k \le (u_{ijk}(l) + U_{ijk}(l))/2 \end{cases}$$ (7.30)

Then the degree of membership for $\mathbf{x} \in H_{ij}(l)$ and $\mathbf{x} \notin J_{ij}(l)$ is obtained by cal-
culating both $m_{A_{ij}(l)}(\mathbf{x})$ and $m_{J_{ij}(l)}(\mathbf{x})$, and taking the minimum, i.e., $\min(m_{A_{ij}(l)}(\mathbf{x}), m_{J_{ij}(l)}(\mathbf{x}))$.
Thus $d_{r_{ij}(l)}(\mathbf{x})$ for Eq. (7.20) is given by

$$d_{r_{ij}(l)}(\mathbf{x}) = \begin{cases} m_{A_{ij}(l)}(\mathbf{x}) & \text{for } \mathbf{x} \notin H_{ij}(l) \\ m_{J_{ij}(l)}(\mathbf{x}) & \text{for } \mathbf{x} \in J_{ij}(l) \\ \min\,(m_{A_{ij}(l)}(\mathbf{x}), m_{J_{ij}(l)}(\mathbf{x})) & \text{for } \mathbf{x} \in H_{ij}(l) \text{ and } \mathbf{x} \notin J_{ij}(l) \end{cases}$$ (7.31)

Since $m_{A_{ij}(l)}(\mathbf{x}) = 1$ for $\mathbf{x} \in J_{ij}(l)$, Eq. (7.31) can be rewritten as follows:

$$d_{r_{ij}(l)}(\mathbf{x}) = \begin{cases} m_{A_{ij}(l)}(\mathbf{x}) & \text{for } \mathbf{x} \notin H_{ij}(l) \\ \min\,(m_{A_{ij}(l)}(\mathbf{x}), m_{J_{ij}(l)}(\mathbf{x})) & \text{for } \mathbf{x} \in H_{ij}(l) \end{cases}$$ (7.32)

Rule Inference.   The final degree of membership of $\mathbf{x}$ for a set of fuzzy rules $\{r_{ij}(l) \mid l = 1, \ldots\}$ denoted as $d_{r_{ij}}(\mathbf{x})$ is given by

$$d_{r_{ij}}(\mathbf{x}) = \min_{l = 1, \ldots}\,(d_{r_{ij}(l)}(\mathbf{x}))$$ (7.33)

We take the maximum because the activation hyperbox $A_{ij}(l + 1)$, if it exists, is
included in the expanded inhibition hyperbox $J_{ij}(l)$, and thus all fuzzy rules in $\{r_{ij}(l) \mid l = 1, \ldots\}$ are exclusive of one another.
Now the degree of membership of $\mathbf{x}$ for class i denoted as $d_i(\mathbf{x})$ is given by

$$d_i(\mathbf{x}) = \min_{\substack{j \ne i, j = 1, \ldots, n, \\ A_{ii}(1) \cap A_{ij}(1) \ne \varnothing}}\,(d_{r_{ij}}(\mathbf{x}))$$ (7.34)

When the activation hyperbox of class i overlaps with those of classes j and k, we resolve the conflict, independently, first between classes i and j, then between classes i and k. This process is reflected by taking the minimum in Eq. (7.34). For example, if $d_{r_{ij}}(\mathbf{x}) = 1$ and $d_{r_{ik}}(\mathbf{x}) = 0$, this means that $\mathbf{x}$ is in the region inhibited by the inhibition hyperbox between classes i and k and thus $\mathbf{x}$ should not be classified as class i.

The input $\mathbf{x}$ is finally classified as class i if $d_i(\mathbf{x})$ is the maximum among $d_j(\mathbf{x})$, where $j = 1, \ldots, n$.

The fuzzy inference procedure described above can be represented by a neural network-like architecture as shown in Fig. 7.7 in which only the portion for class i is shown for simplicity. Different classes have different numbers of units for the second to fourth layers of the network and there is no connection among units of different classes. The second-layer units consist of fuzzy rules and they calculate the degrees of membership based on the input vector $\mathbf{x}$. The third-layer units take the maximum values of inputs from the second layer [see Eq. (7.26)], which are the degrees of membership generated by resolving overlaps between two classes. The number of third-layer units for class i is determined by the number of classes that overlap with class i. Therefore, if there is no overlap between class i and any other classes, the network for class i reduces to two layers. The fourth-layer unit for class i takes the minimum value among the maximum values [see Eq. (7.34)]; each of them is associated with a two-class overlap. Therefore, if class i overlaps with only one class, the network for class i reduces to the three layers; in other words, the min node in the fourth layer is not required. Calculation of a minimum in the fourth layer resolves overlaps among more than two classes. Thus, in the process of creating hyperboxes, we need to resolve the overlap of two classes each time.

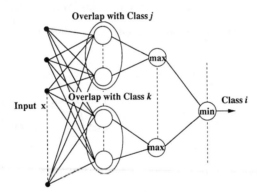

FIGURE 7.7 Architecture of a fuzzy classification system (only the network for class i is shown). (*Reprinted with permission from Abe and Lan [2]. Copyright © IEEE.*)

7.1.3 Selection of Input Variables

For a given set of training data, as long as different classes do not contain identical data, the fuzzy classifier can correctly classify all the training data. In regard to the generalization ability of a classifier, the smaller the number of fuzzy rules it contains the better. Therefore, if the number of rules obtained for one class is larger than that for another, the former class is considered more difficult to classify than the latter. (The expansion parameter α affects the number of rules generated. Since α is introduced only to prevent any of the training data residing on the surface of the inhibition hyper-box from being incorrectly classified, in practice it is preferable to set α small enough to avoid creating extra rules.) In the following, we discuss a method for selecting optimum input variables using the number of fuzzy rules as a selection criterion.

Let M be a set of input variables and $r_i(M)$ be the number of fuzzy rules obtained for class i with input variables M and a training data set. We set the maximum number of rules r_s which ensures enough generalization ability. If for some i

$$r_i(M) \le r_s \qquad (7.35)$$

does not hold, that implies the fuzzy system based on the set M is insufficient to provide enough generalization ability.

If Eq. (7.35) holds for all i, the procedure described below can be performed to eliminate the input variables which are redundant for having the same generalization ability. Let M' be a set in which one input variable is deleted from M. Then acquire new fuzzy rules using the training data set with M'. If

$$r_i(M) = r_i(M') \qquad (7.36)$$

holds for all i, delete the variable deleted from M' also from M. Repeat the above procedure until testing is done for all the input variables initially included in the set M.

7.1.4 Performance Evaluation Using the Iris Data and a Vehicle License Plate Recognition System.

To evaluate the performance of the fuzzy classifiers created by the method described above, we used Fisher iris data [3], which have been widely used for comparing various pattern classification methods, and a vehicle license plate recognition system.

Iris Data.   Using the iris data, we compared the performance of the fuzzy classification system with that of the fuzzy min-max neural networks [2]. The iris data consisted of 150 data for three classes (each class had 50 data) and each datum had four input features. We used the same training and test data sets as those used in Ref. 2. The first 25 data of each class in the iris data set were used for training while the remaining 25 data of each class were used for testing. As reported in Ref. 2, two test data were misclassified by the fuzzy min-max neural network with 48 hyperboxes (fuzzy rules).

The number of rules generated and the number of misclassified test data for various α and $\gamma = 1$ using our method are listed below.

α	No. of rules	No. of wrongs
0.001	5	6
0.1–0.3	7	5
0.4–0.6	9	4
0.7, 0.8	11	3
0.9	17	2

There were no misclassifications for the training data and also for class 1 of the test data. As α increased, the number of misclassified data decreased, and when α was equal to or greater than 0.9, the number of misclassified test data was the same as that obtained by using the fuzzy min-max neural network. Although the number of rules increased as α increased, the number of rules generated for our fuzzy classification system was still less than that in the fuzzy min-max neural network. Since the number of rules for class 1 was always 1, that clearly indicated that no overlap existed between classes 1 and 2, and between classes 1 and 3.

A Vehicle License Plate Recognition System. Here, we used the data which were used to develop a vehicle license plate recognition system [4, 5] using a decision tree algorithm to recognize 10 numbers based on 12 input features extracted from the images of running cars taken by a TV camera (see Fig. 7.8). The features used are the number of holes, the depth from the left-hand side, the curvature of some point, etc. [5]. The numeral images were distorted and covered with dirt. In our study a total of 1630 data were divided into two combinations of training and test data sets: (1) 200 training data and 1430 test data and (2) 810 training data and 820 test data. We compared the classification performance with that of a three-layered neural network which had six hidden units. The number of hidden units was determined using the statistical method discussed in Ref. 6. Since the performance of the network varies with the initial values of connection weights, we trained the network for 100 different initial conditions with initial values randomly assigned between −0.1 and 0.1, and calculated the average recognition rate based on 100 different trained networks.

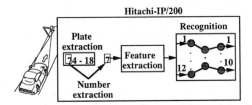

FIGURE 7.8   License plate recognition system.

1. *Effect of sensitivity parameters.* Using a 16-MIPS (million instructions per second) workstation, fuzzy rules based on 200 or 810 training data were generated in less than 1 second. When using the 810 training data, one rule was extracted for each class except class 7; two rules were generated for class 7. And when using the same set of data for testing, the recognition rate was 100 percent irrespective of the values of the sensitivity parameter γ and the positive expansion parameter α. We further evaluated the recognition rates for different values of the sensitivity parameters using the 1430 and 820 test data sets with $\alpha = 0.001$; the results are listed below.

	Recognition rate, %	
γ	1430 data	820 data
100	42.80	94.13
10	84.90	99.63
8	90.70	99.63
6	92.87	99.63
4	95.66	99.63
2, 1	97.06	99.63

As the sensitivity parameter becomes larger, the generalization region for each class becomes smaller. Thus, when $\gamma = 100$, the rules are considered to be crisp. In this case, since the recognition rate was only 42.80 percent for the 1430 test data, that indicates that the training data and test data sets were very different from each other, while for the 820 test data, the 94.13 percent recognition rate indicates that the training and test data sets were very similar. As the value of the sensitivity parameter decreased, the recognition rate improved and reached a plateau of 97.06 percent at $\gamma = 2$ for the 1430 test data or of 99.63 percent at $\gamma = 10$ for the 820 test data. Therefore, the following discussions are based on $\gamma = 2$ for both the 1430 and 820 test data. When the value of expansion parameter α was varied, the recognition rate for the 1430 test data remained constant and that for the 820 test data did not change much; this was attributed to the fact that the class regions did not overlap. When the class regions overlapped due to the deletion of some input variables, we varied the value of expansion parameter α and checked how the recognition rate changed.

Training a six-hidden-unit neural network using the 200 training data took an average of 11.7 seconds on a 31-MIPS mainframe computer. The average recognition rate for 1430 test data was 96.54 percent based on 100 trained networks and the maximum and minimum rates were 98.25 percent and 95.17 percent, respectively. Thus, fuzzy rule acquisition is more than 20 times faster than training a neural network. Also, the recognition rate of the fuzzy classification system is higher than the average recognition rate of the neural networks.

Training the six-hidden-unit neural network using the 810 training data took an average 2.63 minutes on the 31-MIPS computer. The average recognition rate for the 820 test data was 99.41 percent and the maximum and minimum rates were 99.76 percent and 98.90 percent, respectively. Thus, fuzzy rule acquisition is more than 300 times faster than training a neural network. Meanwhile, the recognition rate of the fuzzy classification system is better than the average recognition rate of the neural networks.

2. *Selection of input features.* We selected input features according to the method discussed in Sec. 7.1.3, in which the input features were deleted from the first to the twelfth features. Figure 7.9 shows the recognition rate of the fuzzy classification system and the average recognition rate of the neural networks when using the 200 training data set and one or more than one input feature is deleted from the total of 12 input features. As seen in Fig. 7.9, when the first feature was deleted, two rules were generated for classes 5 and 9, instead of one rule. Therefore, the deleted feature

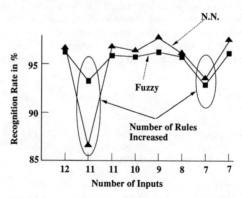

FIGURE 7.9   Effect of input variable selection (200 training data, 1430 test data).

was restored in the original set of input features used in the fuzzy rules. Since when the second feature was deleted the number of rules for each class was 1, we deleted this feature. By this procedure, eventually five features were deleted and the recognition rate for the test data was slightly lower than that of using all 12 input features.

Figure 7.10 shows the recognition rate of the fuzzy classification system and the average recognition rate of the neural networks when the 810 training data set was used and one or more than one input feature was deleted from the total of 12 input features. When one and up to three features were deleted, the recognition rate of the fuzzy classification system was always better than the average recognition rate of the neural network for both the training and test data sets.

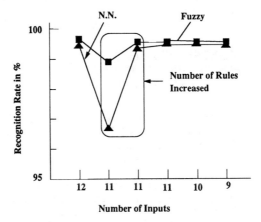

FIGURE 7.10   Effect of input variable selection (810 training data, 820 test data).

3. *Training time comparison.* In our study, we also compared the time required for fuzzy rules extraction using the method described in this chapter with that for training a neural network under severe convergence conditions. Namely, we chose the input features so that the recognition rate of the fuzzy classification system for the training data set was 100 percent but if any of the input features was deleted the recognition rate was no longer 100 percent.

In this study, for the 200 training data set, we used the features from the ninth to twelfth as input features. Two rules were extracted for classes 4 and 8; three rules were extracted for class 9; four rules were extracted for class 5; and one rule was extracted for each of the remaining classes. The recognition rate for the 200 training data was 100 percent. For the 1430 test data, the recognition rate was 72.10 percent when $\alpha = 0.001$. The maximum recognition rate of 75.52 percent was obtained when $\alpha = 0.6$. It took less than 1 second to extract fuzzy rules using a 16-MIPS computer. When training the neural network with different initial conditions, it converged only four times out of 100 trials with the maximum number of epochs of 10,000. The average training time was 4.49 minutes on a 31-MIPS computer. Thus fuzzy rule extraction was at least 500 times faster than training the neural network (the average recognition rate for the 200 training data was 98.55 percent), and the average recognition rate for the 1430 test data was 74.50 percent. (The maximum and minimum recognition rates were 77.76 percent and 71.33 percent, respectively.)

For the 810 training data, we used the first and the eighth to twelfth features as input features. Two rules were extracted for classes 2, 4, 5 and 7; three rules were extracted for class 10; and one rule was extracted for each of the remaining classes. The recognition rate for the 810 training data was 100 percent. For the 820 test data, the recognition rate was 98.05 percent when $\alpha = 0.001$. The maximum recognition rate of 98.17 percent was obtained when $\alpha = 0.2$. The training time was less than 1 second on the 16-MIPS computer. The average recognition rate of the neural network for the 810 training data was 99.88 percent. The network converged 22 times out of 100 trials with the maximum number of epochs of 10,000. The average training time was 13.90 minutes on the 31-MIPS computer. Thus, extracting fuzzy rules was at least 1500 times faster than training the neural network. The average recognition rate for the 820 test data was 97.78 percent. (The maximum and minimum recognition rates were 98.66 percent and 96.83 percent, respectively).

7.2 FUZZY RULE EXTRACTION FROM DATA FOR PATTERN CLASSIFICATION: NEURAL NETWORK BASED METHOD

In Sec. 7.2, we discuss another method for fuzzy rule extraction. This method extracts fuzzy rules from a trained neural network [7] and the derived fuzzy classifier has a better performance than neural networks. In the method, separation hyperplanes between classes are first extracted from a trained neural network, then convex existence regions in the input space for each class are approximated by shifting these hyperplanes in parallel using the training data of each respective class. With the obtained fuzzy rules, input data can be directly classified without the use of the neural network. We apply this method to the vehicle license plate recognition system used in Sec. 7.1.4 as well as to a blood cell classification system. The classification performance of the fuzzy classifier derived by this method is compared with that of neural networks.

7.2.1 Neural Network Structure for Pattern Classification

Definition of a Neural Network.   Consider a typical multilayered feedforward neural network in which biased terms, represented by neurons with no input and a fixed output of 1, are added to the input and the hidden layers, respectively. For each layer, without considering the bias neuron, the number of neurons is $N(i)$, where $i = 1, \ldots, L$ and L is the number of layers. The neurons of the hidden layer and the output layer process incoming signals by a nonlinear sigmoid function with saturation, which can be expressed by $f(y) = 1 / (1 + e^{-y/T_c})$, where y is the input of the neuron and T_c is a constant. The neurons of the input layer are linear and are used to distribute input signals to the neurons of the first hidden layer. The neurons of two consecutive layers are fully connected by synapses represented by the weight matrix between these two layers.

Thus, the output vector $\mathbf{z}^{i+1}$ of the $(i+1)$st layer is given by

$$\mathbf{z}^{i+1} = \mathbf{f}(\mathbf{y}^{i+1})$$
$$\mathbf{y}^{i+1} = \mathbf{W}^i \mathbf{x}^i \qquad \text{for } i = 1, \ldots, L-1 \qquad (7.37)$$
$$\mathbf{x}^{i+1} = \mathbf{z}^i \qquad \text{for } i = 2, \ldots, L-1$$

where $\mathbf{x}^i = [x_1^i, \ldots, x_{N(i)}^i, 1]^T$, $\mathbf{y}^{i+1} = [y_1^{i+1}, \ldots, y_{N(i+1)}^{i+1}]^T$
$\mathbf{z}^{i+1} = [z_1^{i+1}, \ldots, z_{N(i+1)}^{i+1}]^T$, $\mathbf{f}(\mathbf{y}^{i+1}) = [f(y_1^{i+1}), \ldots, f(y_{N(i+1)}^{i+1})]^T$
$\mathbf{x}^i = i$th layer input vector and

$$\mathbf{W}^i = \begin{bmatrix} w_{11}^i & \cdots & w_{1N(i)+1}^i \\ \vdots & w_{pq}^i & \vdots \\ w_{N(i+1)1}^i & \cdots & w_{N(i+1)N(i)+1}^i \end{bmatrix} \tag{7.38}$$

is the weight matrix between the ith and the $(i+1)$st layer, w_{pq}^i is the weight between the pth neuron of the $(i+1)$st layer and the qth neuron of the ith layer. Weights w_{pq}^i are determined by the backpropagation algorithm (BP) [8] using a training data set composed of M pairs of $N(1)$-dimensional inputs and their respective $N(L)$-dimensional target outputs as follows:

$$\{(x_i^m, t_j^m)\} \qquad \text{for } i = 1, \ldots, N(1), j = 1, \ldots, N(L), \text{ and } m = 1, \ldots, M \tag{7.39}$$

When a neural network is applied to pattern classification, the number of output neurons is the same as the number of classes and the jth neuron corresponds to the jth class. The target vectors $\mathbf{t}^m = [t_1^m, \ldots, t_{N(L)}^m]^T$ are formed so that for any class, say class c, the value t_c^m is 1 and all other t_j^m, with $c \neq j$, are 0. Thus, an input vector which produces the highest value at the cth output neuron of the neural network is classified as class c. Figure 7.11 shows a three-layered network architecture used in this study.

Interpreting Weight Matrices as Hyperplanes.   The rows of the weight matrix of a neural network can be interpreted as the coefficients of hyperplanes [9–11]. Assuming $y_j^{i+1} = 0$ in Eq. (7.37),

$$\mathbf{w}_j^i \mathbf{x}^i = 0 \tag{7.40}$$

where $\mathbf{w}_j^i$ is the jth row vector of $\mathbf{W}^i$, represents a hyperplane in the $N(i)$-dimensional space. When $x_{N(i)+1}^i = 1$, a change of weight $w_{jN(i)+1}^i$ causes a parallel displacement of the jth hyperplane. From Eq. (7.37), the value of z_j^{i+1} which corresponds to y_j^{i+1} satisfying Eq. (7.40), i.e., a point on the hyperplane, is ½. We say that the $N(i)$-dimensional point is on the positive side of the hyperplane if

$$y_j^{i+1} \geq 0 \qquad \text{or} \qquad z_j^{i+1} \geq \tfrac{1}{2} \tag{7.41}$$

and on the negative side if

$$y_j^{i+1} < 0 \qquad \text{or} \qquad z_j^{i+1} < \tfrac{1}{2} \tag{7.42}$$

In this sense, we can interpret the weight matrix between the ith and the $(i+1)$st layers of the neural network as a set of $N(i+1)$ hyperplanes, which partition the universe of discourse of the $N(i)$-dimensional space. Therefore, we call these hyperplanes separation hyperplanes.

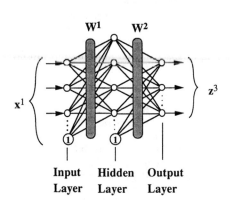

W¹   **W²**

$\mathbf{z}^3$

$\mathbf{x}^1$

Input   Hidden   Output
Layer   Layer   Layer

FIGURE 7.11   Architecture of a three-layered pattern classification neural network. (*Reprinted with permission from Uebele et al. [7]. Copyright © 1995 IEEE.*)

7.2.2 Class Existence Regions in the Input Space

In this section we show how existence regions of classes in the input space can be defined by extracted hyperplanes of the weight matrix between the input and hidden layers.

Class Existence Regions Defined by Extracted Separation Hyperplanes.   Since the $N(1)$-dimensional input space of the neural network is divided by $N(2)$ hyperplanes, we can define a maximum $2^{N(2)}$ disjoint regions $\mathbf{R}^k$ by

$$\mathbf{R}^1 = \{ \mathbf{x} \mid \mathbf{w}_1\mathbf{x} < 0 \cap \mathbf{w}_2\mathbf{x} < 0 \cap \cdots \cap \mathbf{w}_{N(2)}\mathbf{x} < 0 \}$$

$$\mathbf{R}^2 = \{ \mathbf{x} \mid \mathbf{w}_1\mathbf{x} \geq 0 \cap \mathbf{w}_2\mathbf{x} < 0 \cap \cdots \cap \mathbf{w}_{N(2)}\mathbf{x} < 0 \}$$

$$\vdots$$

$$\mathbf{R}^{2^{N(2)}} = \{ \mathbf{x} \mid \mathbf{w}_1\mathbf{x} \geq 0 \cap \mathbf{w}_2\mathbf{x} \geq 0 \cap \cdots \cap \mathbf{w}_{N(2)}\mathbf{x} \geq 0 \} \tag{7.43}$$

where some regions may be empty, i.e., $\mathbf{R}^k = \varnothing$. The conjunction of all regions $\{\mathbf{R}^1 \cup \mathbf{R}^2 \cup \cdots \cup \mathbf{R}^{2^{N(2)}}\}$ constitutes the entire input space and any $N(i)$-dimensional vector $\mathbf{x}$ is included in one region $\mathbf{R}^k$.

The region $\mathbf{R}^k$ can be specified by the set of separation hyperplanes and the information about which side of the hyperplanes it resides on. Thus, using a given set of hyperplanes, we can define a region $\mathbf{R}^k$ with a vector $\mathbf{p}^k = [p_1^k, \dots, p_{N(2)}^k]^T$, whose jth element indicates on which side of the jth hyperplane the region resides. To designate a datum $\mathbf{x}$ is on the negative side of the hyperplane $\mathbf{w}_j\mathbf{x} = 0$, with $j = 1, \dots, N(2)$, the corresponding value p_j^k in $\mathbf{p}^k$ is set to 0, while to designate that it is on the positive side of the hyperplane, p_j^k is set to 1. The vector $\mathbf{p}^k$ is considered the signature of region $\mathbf{R}^k$. All signatures $\mathbf{p}^k$ are disjoint.

For simple illustration, let us consider classifying four classes in a two-dimensional input space using a three-layered neural network with three hidden neurons, as shown in Fig. 7.12. We assume that a set of suitable separation hyperplanes has been obtained by successfully training the network. The arrows attached to the three hyperplanes P1, P2, and P3 indicate the positive side of the hyperplanes, and each symbol in the figure denotes a datum belonging to the tagged class in the input space. As an input datum can lay on either side of the hyperplanes, the existence regions of the classes in the input space can be expressed in terms of the regions $\mathbf{R}^1, \dots, \mathbf{R}^8$, formed by the separation hyperplanes P1, P2, and P3. Note that in the example of Fig. 7.12 $\mathbf{R}^7$ is empty. Thus, each class has at least one existence region and one signature.

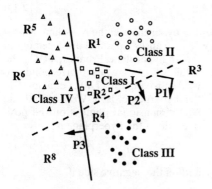

FIGURE 7.12   Regions and separation hyperplanes in a two-dimensional input space. (*Reprinted with permission from Uebele et al. [7]. Copyright © 1995 IEEE.*)

To obtain the existence regions of classes in terms of regions $\mathbf{R}^k$, we check the output of the neurons of the first hidden layer for all M training input vectors $\mathbf{x}^m$, if either (7.41) or (7.42) holds, to decide on which side of the hyperplanes $\mathbf{x}^m$ is found. Then we generate an associated signature vector $\mathbf{p}^m$ in the same way as described above. We call this procedure digitization, and the resulting vector $\mathbf{p}^m$ is the digitized output or the signature of the datum $\mathbf{x}^m$, and the value p_j^m is the jth digit of signature $\mathbf{p}^m$. All different signatures of all classes are stored, so that after digitizing all M training data, we can obtain a set of signatures $\mathbf{P}_c$ for each class c as follows:

$$\mathbf{P}_c = \{\mathbf{p}^m \mid m = 1, \ldots, M, \mathbf{x}^m \in \text{class } c\} \qquad (7.44)$$

Thus all the signatures in $\mathbf{P}_c$ form the existence region

$$\bigcup_{m \text{ for } \mathbf{p}^m \in \mathbf{P}_c} \mathbf{R}^m \qquad (7.45)$$

of class c. We call this region an unclustered existence region in contrast to the clustered regions which will be defined in the following subsection.

If all regions $\mathbf{R}^m$ belonging to one class are different from those of other classes, in other words, no data of one class exist in a region of another class, we consider these two classes independent; otherwise, they are dependent. If two classes are dependent, they share the same signature $\mathbf{p}^m$. As an example, Fig. 7.13 shows two dependent classes in a two-dimensional input space.

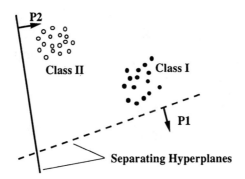

FIGURE 7.13 Existence of two dependent classes in a two-dimensional input space. (*Reprinted with permission from Uebele et al. [7]. Copyright © 1995 IEEE.*)

If the data of one class, for example, Class IV in Fig. 7.12, exist on both sides of a hyperplane $\mathbf{w}_j\mathbf{x} = 0$, i.e., P1, we can combine the two original regions on both sides of that hyperplane into one hyper region. In this case, we allow the digitized value p_j^m to be indefinite and denote it as *dc*. As discussed in the following, hyper existence regions can be obtained by clustering connected regions of one class using *dc*s.

Clustering Class Existence Regions. Two methods for clustering existence regions, that reduce the number of signatures of a class, are presented here. The first method defines a single region for each class where most of the class data exist, while the second method combines neighboring regions of each class.

Heuristic Approximation of Class Regions by a Single Signature. A heuristic method for clustering was proposed in Ref. 9. This method assumes that a class is singly separable, namely, each class region is approximated by only one connected region in the input space, that can be separated by the $N(2)$ hyperplanes of the input-to-hidden weights [12]. Namely, for each class a single signature can be created. First, all digits p_j^k of all signatures $\mathbf{p}^k$ of a class are checked successively. If the values of the jth digit of p_j^k for all the signatures of that class are identical, the digit of the clustered signature then has the same value. Otherwise, the digit of the clustered signature is set to dc. In the second step, some digits with values of dcs of the clustered signatures are changed to either 0 or 1 until each signature has at least one different digit for all clustered signatures of the remaining classes that is not dc. Digits are considered different if their values are different, e.g., dc and 1 are different. In this case, the digit of the class with the highest number of occurrences of the same value, either 0 or 1, is changed. Thus, this method generates regions which include most of the training data of classes. The resulting regions are called *heuristically clustered regions*.

Neighboring Region Clustering. The premise of the second method for clustering signatures is that only neighboring regions containing the data of one class can be combined into a hyper region. An advantage of this method over the heuristic method is that all regions of classes, obtained by digitizing the training data set, are considered. Thus, regions clustered by this method have the ability to approximate the complex shapes of class existence regions and hence allow plurally separable classes. To generate combined signatures, the following algorithm is applied to each class:

1. For class c check all the combinations of signatures $\mathbf{p}^i \in \mathbf{P}_c$ successively. If two signatures $\mathbf{p}^j$ and $\mathbf{p}^k$ of $\mathbf{P}_c$ differ in only one digit, namely $p_l^j \neq p_l^k$, for $l \in 1, \ldots, N(2)$ and $p_i^j = p_i^k$, for $i = 1, \ldots, N(2)$, $i \neq l$, create a new signature $\mathbf{p}^r$ whose value for p_l^j is dc and the values for all other p_i^j are the same as those of the signatures $\mathbf{p}^j$ and $\mathbf{p}^k$. The region of the new associated signature then is $\mathbf{C}_c^r = \mathbf{R}^j \cup \mathbf{R}^k$. After all combinations are checked, step 2 is followed.

2. Check all combinations of signatures in $\mathbf{P}_c$, including the newly created signatures $\mathbf{p}^r$. If two signatures $\mathbf{p}^j$ and $\mathbf{p}^k$ differ in one digit 1 only, with $p_l^j \neq p_l^k$, and either $p_l^j = dc$ or $p_l^k = dc$, delete the signature which has the smaller number of dcs. After all combinations are checked, return to step 1 until no two signatures of this class can be clustered further.

The resulting signatures $\mathbf{p}^u$ and regions $\mathbf{C}_c^u$, where $u = 1, \ldots, U$ and $c \in \{1, \ldots, N(L)\}$, incorporate all the signatures of the classes, which are obtained by digitizing the training data set, where U is the number of resulting signatures of all classes after combination. If overlaps among different classes exist before clustering, these overlaps remain after clustering. However, they may be resolved by shifting the separation hyperplanes as described next.

Class Representation with Shifted Hyperplanes. From our knowledge of the existence regions of all classes in the input space, we can construct a decision-tree-like classifier like the one described in Ref. 9 without using the neural network. The existence regions are expressed in terms of regions $\mathbf{C}_c^u$, whose boundaries are the separation hyperplanes extracted from the input-to-hidden weights of the neural network. Classification is performed by digitizing a test datum $\mathbf{x}$ using the extracted separation hyperplanes and by comparing the digits of the resulting signature one at a time through the decision tree with the stored signature set of the classes. However, the performance of this classifier will be poor, if training and test data sets are very different, because test data may produce signatures that are not stored in the decision tree and thus cannot be classified.

If the signatures of two classes are dependent, another problem arises, namely two different classes exist in the same region, i.e., for $u \neq \tilde{u}$ and $c \neq \tilde{c}$, $C_c^u = C_{\tilde{c}}^{\tilde{u}}$. In this case, a test datum can belong to either of the dependent classes and hence no data in this region can be correctly classified.

Since class boundaries are expressed in terms of the artificial limits of separation hyperplanes, they are merely rough estimates of the regions a class occupies. When using the existence regions C_c^u, we lose valuable information about in which part of region C_c^u the data of a class reside. To improve the performance and to reduce or resolve the overlapping regions between classes, the existence regions need to be defined more precisely.

To adjust the boundaries of existence regions, the $N(2)$ separation hyperplanes obtained from a trained network are shifted in parallel to the limits of the training data set, as illustrated in Fig. 7.14a to c. Figure 7.14a shows the training data of two classes in a two-dimensional input space and two extracted separation hyperplanes. If we shift a separation hyperplane to the datum of the considered region in the training data set which is closest to the extracted hyperplane, this type of shifting, as shown in Fig. 7.14b, is called *single-sided shifting*. This approach requires knowing on which side of a hyperplane a region resides. If data of the region exist on either side of the considered hyperplane, namely the corresponding signature value is *dc*, we do not shift the hyperplane of this region.

Furthermore, we can shift the hyperplanes in two directions to the closest and the farthest data points of the training data set of the considered existence region, as shown in Fig. 7.14c. This type of shifting is called *double-sided shifting*. If class data reside on either side of the considered hyperplane, namely the corresponding signature value is *dc*, we shift the hyperplane to the points of the training data set for that

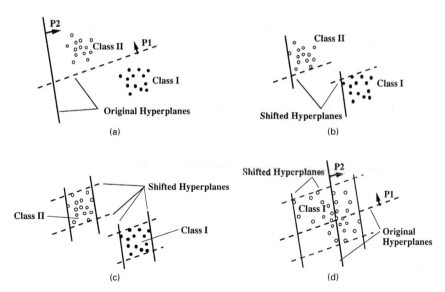

FIGURE 7.14 (*a*) Class regions in a two-dimensional input space. (*b*) Single-sided shifting of separation hyperplanes in a two-dimensional input space. (*c*) Double-sided shifting of separation hyperplanes in a two-dimensional input space ($p_j^u = 0, 1$). (*d*) Double-sided shifting of separation hyperplanes in a two-dimensional input space ($p_j^u = dc$). (*Reprinted with permission from Uebele et al. [7]. Copyright © 1995 IEEE.*)

existence region with the longest distance in the positive and the negative direction of the hyperplane vector **w**, as illustrated in Fig. 7.14d. Double-sided shifting limits the regions in two directions and thus reduces overlapping.

To apply shifting, we vary the weights $w^1_{j\,N(1)\,+\,1}, j = 1, \ldots, N(2)$, which correspond to the bias terms in the input-to-hidden matrix $\mathbf{W}^1$. The resulting column weight vectors are $\tilde{\mathbf{w}}^u_{N(1)\,+\,1} = [\tilde{w}^u_{1N(1)\,+\,1}, \ldots, \tilde{w}^u_{N(2)N(1)\,+\,1}]^T$ for $u = 1, \ldots, U$ and U is the number of class regions. Thus, we obtain a set of U class existence regions $\tilde{C}^u_c$, whose boundaries, parallel to the original separation hyperplanes, define the limits of the training data set within the specified class regions C^u_c.

According to the discussion in the section "Interpreting Weight Matrices as Hyperplanes," above, the new weights $\tilde{w}^u_{jN(1)\,+\,1}$ of the existence regions $\tilde{C}^u_c$ can be expressed by

$$\tilde{w}^u_{j\,N(1)\,+\,1} = w^1_{j\,N(1)\,+\,1} - s^u_j \qquad \text{for } u = 1, \ldots, U \text{ and } j = 1, \ldots, N(2) \qquad (7.46)$$

where s^u_j is a shifting factor. In the following, we describe the algorithms for single-sided shifting and for double-sided shifting.

Single-Sided Shifting. Check all the signatures $\mathbf{p}^u$ of all classes c successively. For each signature $\mathbf{p}^u$, check the values p^u_j, for $j = 1, \ldots, N(2)$. If p^u_j is not dc, the shifting factor is determined by

$$s^u_j = \begin{cases} \displaystyle\max_{\mathbf{x}^m \text{ in } C^u_c, m\,=\,1,\ldots,M} (\mathbf{w}^1_j \mathbf{x}^m) & \text{for } p^u_j = 0 \\[2mm] \displaystyle\min_{\mathbf{x}^m \text{ in } C^u_c, m\,=\,1,\ldots,M} (\mathbf{w}^1_j \mathbf{x}^m) & \text{for } p^u_j = 1 \end{cases} \qquad (7.47)$$

where $\mathbf{w}^1_j \mathbf{x}^m$ is a scalar product between the jth row of the weight matrix $\mathbf{W}^1$ and a training datum vector $\mathbf{x}^m$ belonging to the region C^u_c. Thus, we obtain a shifting vector $\mathbf{s}^u = [s^u_1, \ldots, s^u_{N(2)}]^T$ for each signature $\mathbf{p}^u$. The new weights $\tilde{w}^u_{jN(1)\,+\,1}$ of the shifted hyperplanes are calculated using Eq. (7.46). After single-sided shifting, the class regions are approximated more precisely by a set of shifted hyperplanes.

Double-Sided Shifting. Check all the signatures of all classes successively. For each signature $\mathbf{p}^u$ calculate two shifting vectors $\mathbf{s}^u_{\min} = [s^u_{1,\min}, \ldots, s^u_{N(2),\min}]^T$ and $\mathbf{s}^u_{\max} = [s^u_{1,\max}, \ldots, s^u_{N(2),\max}]^T$ with the following shifting factors

$$s^u_{j,\min} = \min_{\mathbf{x}^m \text{ in } C^u_c,\ m\,=\,1,\ldots,M} (\mathbf{w}^1_j \mathbf{x}^m) \qquad (7.48)$$

and

$$s^u_{j,\max} = \max_{\mathbf{x}^m \text{ in } C^u_c,\ m\,=\,1,\ldots,M} (\mathbf{w}^1_j \mathbf{x}^m) \qquad (7.49)$$

where $\mathbf{w}^1_j \mathbf{x}^m$ is a scalar product between the jth row of the weight matrix $\mathbf{W}^1$ and a training datum vector $\mathbf{x}^m$ belonging to region C^u_c. Thus, for each class region $\mathbf{p}^u$, we obtain two shifting vectors and two sets of shifted hyperplanes. Each class region is limited by a set of $N(2)$ hyperplanes in both directions of these hyperplanes. Using Eqs. (7.46), (7.48), and (7.49) the weights $\tilde{w}^u_{j,\min}$ and $\tilde{w}^u_{j,\max}$, which correspond to $s^u_{j,\min}$ and $s^u_{j,\max}$, respectively, are calculated.

Because the generated regions are limited on both sides, double-sided shifting reduces overlapping. In general, resolving existing overlaps between different classes is difficult, because we do not have enough knowledge about the shifted hyperplanes and regions $\tilde{C}^u_c$.

7.2.3 Rule Generation Process and Inference Method

The existence region $\tilde{C}_c^u$ for class c is defined as

$$\tilde{C}_c^u = \{\mathbf{x} \mid \tilde{\mathbf{w}}_j^u \mathbf{x} \geq 0 \text{ if } p_j^u = 1, \text{ and } \tilde{\mathbf{w}}_j^u \mathbf{x} \leq 0 \text{ if } p_j^u = 0, \text{ for } j = 1, \ldots, N(2) \text{ and } p_j^u \neq dc\}$$

(7.50)

for single-sided shifting and

$$\tilde{C}_c^u = \{\mathbf{x} \mid \tilde{\mathbf{w}}_{j,\min}^u \mathbf{x} \geq 0 \cap \tilde{\mathbf{w}}_{j,\max}^u \mathbf{x} \leq 0 \text{ for } j = 1, \ldots, N(2)\}$$

(7.51)

for double-sided shifting, and $\tilde{\mathbf{w}}_j^u$ represents the jth shifted hyperplane. Then we can define fuzzy rules FR_c^u as follows:

$$FR_c^u: \text{If } \mathbf{x} \text{ is in } \tilde{C}_c^u \text{ then } \mathbf{x} \text{ belongs to class } c$$

(7.52)

where $u = 1, \ldots, U$.

Using membership functions, we can create more generalized regions in the input space by replacing the crisp boundaries of existence regions with fuzzy boundaries. Thus for every existence region $\tilde{C}_c^u$, we define a set of membership functions in the direction of the hyperplane vectors. Membership functions for single- and for double-sided shifting are different. For fuzzy inference, we calculate the degree of membership of the test datum for each rule and the datum is classified as the class whose degree of membership is the highest.

Definitions of Membership Functions and Fuzzy Regions. An intuitive assumption is that data, which reside within the crisp boundaries of the existence region $\tilde{C}_c^u$, should belong to the same class c with the degree of membership 1. As the datum location becomes farther away from the boundaries of the original class region, the degree of membership decreases and eventually reaches the minimum value of 0, where the distance between the test datum and the considered class region becomes so large that the datum is unlikely to belong to that class. Hence we can define membership functions $\mu(\mathbf{x}, p_j^u)$ of a region $\tilde{C}_c^u$ with the corresponding signature $\mathbf{p}^u$ in the direction of the hyperplane vectors $\mathbf{w}_j$ by

$$\mu(\mathbf{x}, p_j^u) = \begin{cases} \min(1, \max(0, 1 - \gamma_j^u \tilde{\mathbf{w}}_j^u \mathbf{x})) & \text{for } p_j^u = 0 \\ \min(1, \max(0, 1 + \gamma_j^u \tilde{\mathbf{w}}_j^u \mathbf{x})) & \text{for } p_j^u = 1 \\ 1 & \text{for } p_j^u = dc \end{cases}$$

(7.53)

for single-sided shifting, and

$$\mu(\mathbf{x}, p_j^u) = \min(1, \max(0, 1 + \gamma_{j,\min}^u \tilde{\mathbf{w}}_{j,\min}^u \mathbf{x})) \times \min(1, \max(0, 1 - \gamma_{j,\max}^u \tilde{\mathbf{w}}_{j,\max}^u \mathbf{x}))$$

(7.54)

for double-sided shifting, where γ_j^u, $\gamma_{j,\min}^u$ and $\gamma_{j,\max}^u$ are sensitivity parameters as discussed before. Figure 7.15a and b shows membership functions for single- and for double-sided shifting in the direction of the considered hyperplane vector $\mathbf{w}_j$, respectively.

Fuzzy Inference Operators. To calculate the degree of membership for a fuzzy rule, we propose to use a minimum operator and a summation operator defined in the following. The final step in classifying a given datum $\mathbf{x}$ is carried out by using the maximum operator, which selects a class whose degree of membership is the highest

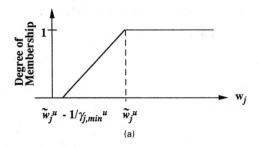

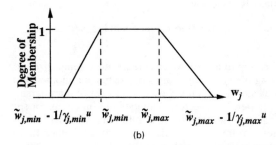

FIGURE 7.15 (*a*) Membership function in the direction of the hyperplane vector $\mathbf{w}_j$ for single-sided shifting ($p_j^u = 1$). (*b*) Membership function in the direction of the hyperplane vector $\mathbf{w}_j$ for double-sided shifting. (*Reprinted with permission from Uebele et al. [7]. Copyright © 1995 IEEE.*)

among all rules. We denote the combination of the minimum and maximum operators for fuzzy inference as min-max inference and the combination of the summation and maximum operators as sum-max inference.

   Minimum Operator. The minimum operator [13], which takes the minimum value of all one-dimensional membership functions for the fuzzy rule FR_c^u, is given by

$$\mu(\mathbf{x}, \mathbf{p}^u) = \min_{j = 1, \ldots, N(2)} \mu(\mathbf{x}, p_j^u) \qquad (7.55)$$

The minimum value is taken to ensure the degree of membership within the class boundaries of the training data set is 1. The minimum operator selects the smallest degree of membership, that is, the largest distance of the test datum from any of the boundaries of the considered region $\tilde{C}_c^u$. When selecting the minimum degree of membership, we lose information on the distance of the test datum from the other boundaries of the considered region.

   Summation Operator. As an alternative, a summation operator is proposed to calculate the degree of membership of a fuzzy rule, which calculates the summation of all one-dimensional degrees of membership. This operator imitates neural-network-based inference. Since a datum $\mathbf{x}$ more likely belongs to a fuzzy region $\tilde{C}_c^u$ if its average distance is closer to all shifted hyperplanes of $\tilde{C}_c^u$, we define the summation operator as

$$\mu(\mathbf{x}, \mathbf{p}^u) = \frac{1}{N(2)} \sum_{j=1}^{N(2)} \mu(\mathbf{x}, p_j^u) \qquad (7.56)$$

Maximum Operator. The maximum operator selects the fuzzy rule $FR_c^{U_{max}}$ whose degree of membership is the highest among all fuzzy rules for an input vector **x** according to

$$u_{max} = \arg \max_{u = 1, \ldots, U} \mu(\mathbf{x}, \mathbf{p}^u) \qquad (7.57)$$

where $\mu(\mathbf{x}, \mathbf{p}^u)$ represent the degrees of membership obtained by Eq. (7.55) or (7.56) and U is the number of fuzzy rules for all classes. Thus a datum **x** is classified as class c if the fuzzy rule $FR_c^{U_{max}}$ corresponds to that class. However, if two classes overlap and the test datum resides in the overlapping region, it is impossible to correctly classify this datum, since more than one class has the degree of membership 1. The same thing happens if two or more fuzzy rules have the highest degree of membership or if all the fuzzy rules have the degree of membership 0. When the degree of membership is 0, the generalization ability may be enhanced by reducing the values of sensitivity parameters and hence might lead to correctly classifying this datum.

7.2.4 Performance Evaluation Using a Vehicle License Plate Recognition System and a Blood Cell Classification System

For performance evaluation, in our study, we used two different classification systems. The first system was the vehicle license plate recognition system used in Sec. 7.1.4, which had very well-defined class regions, while the second system was a blood cell classification system, which had complicated class regions with severe overlapping. Since we found that the performance of the fuzzy classification systems based on double-sided shifting was superior to that based on single-sided shifting and better results were obtained when applying sum-max inference instead of min-max inference, in the following we show only the results which were based on double-sided shifting and sum-max inference.

Vehicle License Plate Recognition System. We used the same data sets as used in 7.1.4, i.e., the 200 training data and 1430 test data. For performance comparison, we used a three-layered neural network with 12 input neurons plus a bias neuron and 10 output neurons. Since the performance of neural networks varies with initial weights, we trained 100 networks using different sets of initial weights randomly assigned between −1 and 1. A learning parameter of 0.3 and a momentum term [11] of 0.5 were used for training neural networks. After training, separation hyperplanes were extracted from each trained network and fuzzy rules were created by applying single- and double-sided shifting to the unclustered existence regions and regions clustered by the heuristic method and by the neighboring region clustering method. The recognition rates for the training and test data were measured for the original network obtained by the BP and for the fuzzy systems. Since the minimum number of hyperplanes required for separating 10 classes was 4, we varied the number of hidden neurons from 4 to 10. All measures were obtained with a training convergence criterion ε between 0.01 and 0.3. For each network we started the training process with $\varepsilon = 0.3$. After training converged, the fuzzy rules were created and then the performance of the neural network and the fuzzy classifiers were evaluated. With the same network the process was reiterated successively while lowering ε from 0.3 to 0.01. The above-described procedure was carried out for 100 networks, each had 8 hidden neurons, with different initial connection weights using a 70-MIPS workstation. On average, training each network took about 4.8 minutes. Nevertheless, the time required for generating fuzzy rules was less than 1 second on average.

The sensitivity parameter γ that determines the slope steepness of the membership functions was set to 0.2. With this value the degree of membership for all data spread between 0.1 and 1. Similar results were obtained when smaller values for γ were used.

For all the cases where 6, 8, and 10 hidden neurons were used, on average training converged after 41, 105, 212, and 467 epochs for $\varepsilon = 0.3$, $\varepsilon = 0.15$, $\varepsilon = 0.05$ and $\varepsilon = 0.01$, respectively, while for the cases of using four hidden neurons, the network converged after 67, 213, 442, and 1021 training epochs. For all the cases that we tried, a 100 percent recognition rate was obtained for the neural networks and the fuzzy classifiers with double-sided shifting when the 200 training data set was used for testing.

Figure 7.16 shows the average recognition rates for the cases where different numbers of hidden neurons were used; the networks were trained with $\varepsilon = 0.01$ and the recognition rates were evaluated using the 1430 test data set. (In the next several figures, the term *u-reg* indicates unclustered regions; *m-reg* indicates neighbored region clustering; and *s-reg* indicates the use of a single hyper region for every class, generated by the heuristic clustering method.) The advantage of using a larger number of hidden neurons in the neural networks and using the fuzzy classifiers with regions clustered by the heuristic method can be seen in the figure. The performance of the fuzzy classifiers based on unclustered and neighboring regions reached a plateau when six and more hidden neurons were used. And the performance of the fuzzy classifiers, which were derived from the neural networks having a large number of hidden neurons, was inferior to the neural networks. The performance difference between the neural networks and the fuzzy classifiers reduced from 0.5 to 0.07 percent when more hidden neurons were used, although the number of fuzzy classifiers that performed better than the neural networks dropped only from a ratio of 60:40 to 57:43 for the cases where regions were clustered by the heuristic method. The total number of fuzzy rules generated for the neighboring regions clustering method increased steadily as more hidden neurons were used, e.g., from 10 to 24 rules as the number of hidden neurons increased from 4 to 10.

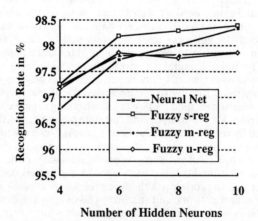

FIGURE 7.16 Average recognition rate for 1430 test data vs. the number of hidden neurons (convergence criterion $\varepsilon = 0.01$, sum-max inference, double-sided shifting). (*Reprinted with permission from Uebele et al. [7]. Copyright © 1995 IEEE.*)

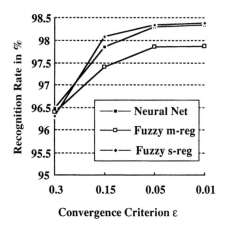

FIGURE 7.17 Average recognition rate for 1430 test data vs. the convergence criterion (10 hidden neurons, sum-max inference, double-sided shifting). (*Reprinted with permission from Uebele et al. [7]. Copyright © 1995 IEEE.*)

Figure 7.17 shows the influence of the convergence criteria on the performance based on 1430 test data and the networks with 10 hidden neurons. In all cases a smaller ε led to a better average performance. The trends for all the cases were very similar. The fuzzy classifiers derived for the heuristic clustering method outperformed the neural networks and the fuzzy classifiers derived for the neighboring regions clustering method. The number of fuzzy rules generated decreased as the convergence criterion ε decreased. For example, when ε varied from 0.3 to 0.01 for the cases where six hidden neurons were used, the number of rules varied from 30 to 23 for the cases where unclustered regions were considered, while it varied from 19 to 14 for the cases where the neighboring regions clustering method was applied.

Blood Cell Classification. The second application discussed here is a blood cell classification system [14] which was used to classify optically screened white blood cells into 12 categories of mature and immature cells based on 13 features such as area and perimeter of a kernel. For performance evaluation, we divided a set of 6197 input-target data into a training data set of 3097 input-target pairs and a test data set of 3100 input-target pairs. Meanwhile we used three-layered neural networks which had 13 input neurons, a bias neuron, 12 output neurons and different numbers of hidden neurons. The number of hidden neurons was varied from 5 to 15; each type of network was trained for 25 different initial conditions with initial weights randomly assigned between −1 and 1. The learning rate and the momentum term were initially set to 0.3 and 0.5, respectively, and the learning rate was lowered three times to reach 0.05. Training neural networks for blood cell classification turned out very difficult. For example, for ε = 0.3, even though the networks were trained for 50,000 epochs, they did not really converge although the summed square error decreased. Due to the difficulty in training the networks, the recognition rate for the training data set after training spread between 80.7 percent and 92.4 percent for all trials of the neural networks. Because of severe overlapping in the data, the performance of the fuzzy classifiers ranged between 86.2 percent and 95.7 percent. In these studies, the fuzzy classifiers used 0.1 for γ.

Figure 7.18 shows the average recognition rate based on 3100 test data for the networks which had different numbers of hidden neurons and were trained for 15,000 epochs. The average number of rules generated was between 122 and 302 for the cases where unclustered regions were considered and was between 53 and 152 for the cases where neighboring regions were clustered. The number of rules increased with the number of hidden neurons used in the network from which the rules were extracted and with the number of training epochs performed for training the network. In all cases we studied, the fuzzy classifiers outperformed the neural network by an average of 2 to 7.5 percent. The best neural network had a recognition rate of 90.46 percent, while the recognition rate of the best fuzzy classifier was 91.68 percent. Because of overlapping, the performance of the classifier based on

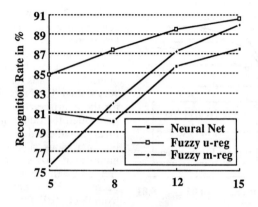

FIGURE 7.18 Average recognition rate for 3100 test data vs. the number of hidden neurons (15,000 epochs, sum-max inference). (*Reprinted with permission from Uebele et al. [7]. Copyright © 1995 IEEE.*)

clustered regions was worse than that based on unclustered regions. Class regions could be defined more precisely when the network was trained longer and more hidden neurons were used; this was clearly indicated by the increase of number of rules generated. That also made the performance of the fuzzy classifier based on clustered regions approach the performance of that based on unclustered regions. For example, for a network which had 15 hidden neurons and was trained for 15,000 training epochs, on average 302 rules were generated based on unclustered regions, while the number reduced to 179 when clustering was applied.

Figure 7.19 shows the influence of the number of training epochs on the performance of the classifiers for 3100 test data. In the figure, at epoch 5000, both fuzzy

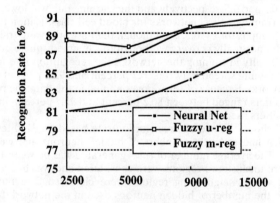

FIGURE 7.19 Average recognition rate for 3100 test data vs. number of training epochs (15 hidden neurons, sum-max inference). (*Reprinted with permission from Uebele et al. [7]. Copyright © 1995 IEEE.*)

classifiers achieved the performance of the neural network which was trained for 15,000 epochs. Thus we conclude that if classification is performed by using a fuzzy classifier, there is no need to train the network from which the fuzzy classifier is derived for a large number of epochs, as required for training a good neural network classifier.

For performance comparison, besides the overall recognition rate, two other measures were also used; they were the percentage of correctly classified mature cells against detected mature cells and the percentage of detected immature cells against total immature cells. For all the tests we did, we found that a three-layered neural network using 10 hidden neurons and trained for 6000 epochs performed best. The best performance by the neural network classifier and by the fuzzy classifier are listed below.

	Neural network	Fuzzy classifier
Overall recognition rate	89.99%	91.97%
Correct mature cell class	99.20%	99.49%
Correct immature cell class	95.47%	96.00%

7.3 FUZZY SYSTEM FOR FUNCTION APPROXIMATION: EXTENSION FROM PATTERN CLASSIFICATION

In this section, we discuss an extension of the fuzzy rule extraction methods discussed in Secs. 7.1 and 7.2 to development of fuzzy systems for function approximation [15]. To develop such fuzzy systems from numerical training data, we first divide the range of an output variable into multiple intervals, which are conceptually treated as classes. Using the input data belonging to each interval, we extract fuzzy rules using the same methods described in Secs. 7.1 and 7.2. A difference between performing pattern classification and function approximation using a fuzzy system is that the latter requires defuzzifying a fuzzy inference result to produce a crisp value.

7.3.1 System Architecture

Although in the following discussion we assume that the output space is only one-dimensional, extending the function approximation approach to multiple-output problems is straightforward. Let output y be one-dimensional and input vector $\mathbf{x}$ be m-dimensional. We divide the universe of discourse of y into n intervals as follows:

$$[y_0, y_1]: y_0 \le y \le y_1$$
$$(y_1, y_2]: y_1 < y \le y_2$$
$$\vdots$$
$$(y_{n-1}, y_n]: y_{n-1} < y \le y_n \tag{7.58}$$

The ith interval is called output interval i. Using the input data whose corresponding outputs are in output interval i, we can extract fuzzy rules directly from numerical data or from a trained neural network. Figure 7.20 shows a fuzzy system architecture which includes a fuzzy inference net generated by either of the above two methods

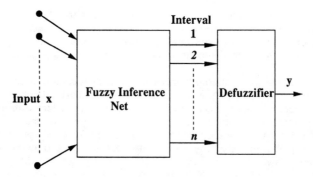

FIGURE 7.20 Architecture of a fuzzy system.

and a defuzzifier. For a given input vector **x**, the degrees of membership for all output intervals, from 1 to n, are calculated by the inference net and then the crisp output y is calculated by the defuzzifier using the degrees of membership as inputs.

7.3.2 Defuzzification and Tuning Methods

Although the method based on the center of gravity is often used for defuzzifying a fuzzy set into a nonfuzzy value, here we use the method discussed in Ref. 16, which uses a bell-shaped function as the membership function of the output variable, whose center of gravity is approximated by

$$\hat{y} = \frac{\sum_{i=1}^{n} m_i \sigma_i d_i(\mathbf{x})}{\sum_{i=1}^{n} \sigma_i d_i(\mathbf{x})} \tag{7.59}$$

where m_i and σ_i are the center (or mean) and the width (or variance) of a bell-shaped function of the input interval i, respectively. We choose this expression for convenience, in particular, when tuning m_i and σ_i becomes necessary in order to increase approximation accuracy. Good initial estimates of m_i and σ_i are

$$m_i = \frac{y_i + y_{i-1}}{2} \qquad \sigma_i = \frac{y_i - y_{i-1}}{2} \tag{7.60}$$

Tuning m_i and σ_i can be done by using the method described below [16]:

$$m_i^{(l+1)} = m_i^{(l)} + \eta \Delta m_i^{(l)}$$

$$\Delta m_i^{(l)} = [y(\mathbf{x}) - \hat{y}(\mathbf{x})] \frac{\sigma_i d_i(\mathbf{x})}{\sum_{i=1}^{n} \sigma_i d_i(\mathbf{x})}$$

$$\sigma_i^{(l+1)} = \sigma_i^{(l)} + \eta \Delta \sigma_i^{(l)}$$

$$\Delta\sigma_i^{(l)} = [y(\mathbf{x}) - \hat{y}(\mathbf{x})] \frac{m_i d_i(\mathbf{x})\left(\sum_{i=1}^{n} \sigma_i d_i(\mathbf{x})\right) - d_i(\mathbf{x})\left(\sum_{i=1}^{n} m_i \sigma_i d_i(\mathbf{x})\right)}{\left(\sum_{i=1}^{n} \sigma_i d_i(\mathbf{x})\right)^2} \qquad (7.61)$$

where l and η denote the number of epochs and a tuning parameter, respectively, and the latter controls the rate of change. $\Delta m_i^{(l)}$ and $\Delta\sigma_i^{(l)}$ are changes determined by the steepest descent method.

7.3.3 Performance Evaluation Using a System for Water Purification Plant Operation

We evaluated our approach to development of a fuzzy system for function approximation using a system for water purification where the amount of coagulant injection needed to be estimated [17]. The amount of coagulant injection was determined on the basis of ten measurement variables on water qualities such as turbidity, temperature of water, and on floc image properties, e.g., floc diameter. In our study, we divided 563 input-output data which were gathered over a 1-year period into 478 stationary data and 95 nonstationary data according to whether turbidity values were smaller or larger than a specified value. Then for each type of the data, we further divided them into two groups to form a training data set and a test data set; they were divided in such a way that both sets have a similar distribution in the output space. The data sets used in this study are: (1) 241 training data and 237 test data for stationary data and (2) 45 training data and 40 test data for nonstationary data.

Using each group of the data, we empirically studied the effects of the number of divisions of output variable, tuning of the mean value and variance of output membership functions, and the sensitivity parameter of input membership functions on approximation accuracy.

Performance Evaluation Using the 241 Training Data and 237 Test Data (Stationary Data).   First we investigated the average and maximum approximation errors of the fuzzy system based on 241 training data and 237 test data for different numbers of divisions of the universe of discourse for the output variable, which varies from 3 to 8. For one or two data in this test data set, the fuzzy system could not determine an output value because the inputs of these data were outside the ranges defined by the training data set. To overcome this problem, for these data we changed the sensitivity parameter γ from 4 to a smaller value by which the fuzzy region in the input space was enlarged. To check the effect of tuning the parameters m_i and σ_i on approximation errors, we set η in Eq. (7.61) to be 0.01 and tuned them for 100 epochs using the training data. Here the sensitivity parameter was set to 4. The approximation errors (in mg/L) are listed below.

No. of divisions	Training data		Test data	
	Av. error	Max. error	Av. error	Max. error
3	1.75	6.47	1.90	8.33
5	1.12	4.42	1.25	5.31
7	**1.07**	**4.75**	**1.18**	**5.57**

The case where the universe of discourse divided into seven regions gave the best performance. In some cases, tuning the parameters for 10 epochs was sufficient because good initial values of m_i and σ_i were used, and, in most cases, tuning the parameters for more than 100 epochs did not further improve the performance.

To compare the results with those generated by using neural networks as function approximators, we trained three-layer networks with 5, 10, and 15 hidden units, respectively; and for each of the three different networks, 100 trials were performed and each trial used different initial values for the connection weights. The results indicated that the performance of these three networks did not differ very much; therefore here we show only the approximation errors (in mg/L) of the network which used 10 hidden units:

No. of epochs	Training data		Test data	
	Av. error	Max. error	Av. error	Max. error
1000	0.95	5.20	1.03	7.08
2000	**0.84**	**4.75**	**0.99**	**6.95**
3000	0.83	4.61	1.00	6.95

When the network was trained for more than 2000 epochs, e.g., 3000 epochs, the average approximation error for the test data increased because the neural approximator overfitted the training data, resulting in the loss of generality. Thus in this case the best performance of the neural approximator was obtained when it was trained for about 2000 epochs. Meanwhile, the average approximation error of the neural approximator was slightly better than that of the fuzzy system, but the maximum error of the former was worse than that of the latter. Therefore the performance of these two types of approximators was considered comparable for the application presented here.

Training the neural network on a 31-MIPS mainframe computer took an average of 1 minute, while it only took less than 1 second on a 16-MIPS workstation to extract fuzzy rules. Although time was required to tune the parameters of the fuzzy system, it was still less than the time required for training the neural network.

Performance Evaluation Using the 45 Training Data and 40 Test Data (Nonstationary Data). The range of output variable was divided into five divisions when we evaluated the effect of the sensitivity parameter γ on the approximation error. The approximation errors (in mg/L) after tuning the parameters for 100 epochs with $\eta = 0.01$ are listed below.

γ	Training data		Test data	
	Av. error	Max. error	Av. error	Max. error
12	1.60	7.75	1.66	6.28
16	1.57	7.64	1.64	5.90
20	**1.56**	**7.20**	**1.46**	**4.97**

The best results were obtained when $\gamma = 20$. The associated average approximation errors (in mg/L) of the neural network with 10 hidden units and 100 trials are

No. of epochs	Training data		Test data	
	Av. error	Max. error	Av. error	Max. error
1000	**1.59**	**6.83**	**1.74**	**6.78**
2000	1.34	5.52	2.04	6.30
3000	1.11	3.41	2.15	8.49

The best performance was obtained when the network was trained for 1000 epochs. Comparing this result with the best result obtained by the fuzzy system shows that the average approximation errors for the training data were about the same, whereas the average approximation error of the fuzzy system for the test data was better than that of the neural network.

7.4 COMPARISONS WITH NEURAL NETWORKS AND CONVENTIONAL FUZZY SYSTEMS

In the following, we describe the advantages and disadvantages of the fuzzy classifiers obtained by the direct method and by the neural-network-based method, respectively, by comparing with neural network classifiers and conventional fuzzy systems, respectively.

7.4.1 Direct Method

The advantages of the fuzzy classifier obtained by the direct method described in Section 7.1 over neural network classifiers are as follows:

1. The network structure is automatically determined through the acquisition of fuzzy rules according to the overlap between classes. Namely, the network is two layers if there is no overlap between classes, three if each class overlaps with only one class at most, and four if one class overlaps with more than one class.
2. Knowledge acquisition or training is very fast. As long as there are no identical data presented in different classes, we can obtain a recognition rate of 100 percent for training data. Thus, retraining according to misclassification is not a problem.
3. Misclassification can be easily analyzed by fuzzy rules. Thus modification of rules is also possible.
4. Generalization ability can be directly controlled by modifying the sensitivity parameter γ. If a test datum is in the region where no activation hyperbox is in the neighborhood, the system can determine that the input is not classifiable.
5. Implementation is relatively easy since activation and inhibition hyperboxes can be determined recursively.

The disadvantages compared to neural networks are as follows:

1. Generalization ability may be lower than that of neural networks when only one rule per class is extracted and when the characteristics of training and test data are very different.
2. Since overlapping is resolved by considering two classes each time, the network shown in Fig. 7.7, created by using our method, may be larger than the conventional backpropagation networks for difficult classification problems.

There are two advantages of our fuzzy classification system over conventional fuzzy systems.

1. Fuzzy rules can be easily obtained from numerical data.
2. The classifier can be generated even for a large number of input variables.

7.4.2 Neural-Network-Based Method

The advantages of the fuzzy classifier obtained by the neural-network-based method described in Sec. 7.2 over the original neural network from which fuzzy rules are extracted can be summarized as follows:

1. The fuzzy classifier outperforms the original neural network.
2. The training time can be shortened while maintaining the same performance.
3. Misclassification can be analyzed by checking the degree of membership of the fuzzy rules.
4. The generalization ability can be easily controlled by modifying the sensitivity parameter γ. If a test datum is in a region not covered by class existence regions, the system can determine that this datum cannot be classified.
5. Class boundaries can easily be adjusted, without retraining the neural network.
6. Additional fuzzy rules can be added easily, without retraining.

A disadvantage of the fuzzy classifier over the neural network is the following:

1. For complicated-shaped class regions, a lot of fuzzy rules are generated, slowing down the inference speed.

The advantages over conventional fuzzy systems can be summarized as follows:

1. Fuzzy rules are generated automatically by the learning ability of neural networks.
2. Since the boundaries of the fuzzy regions need not be parallel to the input variables, separation of two classes can be defined more precisely, and that also requires fewer rules.

A disadvantage over conventional fuzzy systems is the following:

1. Analyzing and modifying the existence regions are difficult tasks, because the boundaries between the class regions are not parallel to the input variables.

Similar arguments also apply for our fuzzy system approach to function approximation.

REFERENCES

1. S. Abe and M.-S. Lan, "A Method for Fuzzy Rules Extraction Directly from Numerical Data and Its Application to Pattern Classification," *IEEE Trans. Fuzzy System,* vol. 3, no. 1, pp. 18–28, Feb. 1995.
2. P. K. Simpson, "Fuzzy Min-Max Neural Networks—Part 1: Classification," *IEEE Trans. Neural Networks,* vol. 3, no. 5, pp. 776–786, September 1992.

3. R. Fisher, "The Use of Multiple Measurements in Taxonomic Problems," *Annals of Eugenics*, vol. 7, part II, pp. 179–188, 1936.

4. M. Takatoo, M. Kanasaki, T. Mishima, T. Shibata, and H. Ota, "Gray Scale Image Processing Technology Applied to Vehicle License Number Recognition System," *Proc. International Workshop on Industrial Applications of Machine Vision and Machine Intelligence*, pp. 76–79, February 1987.

5. H. Takenaga et al., "Input Layer Optimization of Neural Networks by Sensitivity Analysis and Its Application to Recognition of Numerals," *T. IEE Japan* (in Japanese), vol. 111-D, no. 1, pp. 36–44, 1991. (Translated into English by Scripta Technica, Inc., *Electrical Engineering in Japan*, vol. 111, no. 4, pp. 130–138, 1991.)

6. M. Kayama, S. Abe, H. Takenaga, and Y. Morooka, "Constructing Optimal Neural Networks by Linear Regression Analysis," *Proc. Neuro-Nimes '90*, pp. 363–376, 1990.

7. F. Uebele, S. Abe, and M.-S. Lan, "A Neural-Network-Based Fuzzy Classifier," *IEEE Trans. Systems, Man, and Cybernetics*, vol. 25, no. 2, pp. 353–361, 1995.

8. D. E. Rumelhart et al., "Learning Internal Representations by Error Backpropagation," *Parallel Distributed Processing: Explorations in the Microstructures of Cognition*, vol. 1: *Foundations*, pp. 318–362, MIT Press, Cambridge, Mass., 1986.

9. S. Abe, M. Kayama, H. Takenaga and T. Kitamura, "Extracting Algorithms from Pattern Classification Neural Networks," *Neural Networks*, vol. 6, no. 5, pp. 729–735, 1993.

10. R. P. Lippmann, "An Introduction to Computing with Neural Nets," *IEEE ASSP Magazine*, vol. 4, pp. 4–22, 1987.

11. J. Hertz, A. Krogh, and R. Palmer, *Introduction to the Theory of Neural Computation*, Addison-Wesley, Reading, Mass.,1991.

12. S. Abe, M. Kayama, and H. Takenaga, "How Neural Networks for Pattern Recognition Can Be Synthesized," *Journal of Information Processing*, vol. 14, no. 3, pp. 344–350, 1991.

13. J. C. Bezdek and S. K. Pal, "Fuzzy Models for Pattern Recognition," IEEE Press, New York, 1992.

14. A. Hashizume, J. Motoika, and R. Yabe, "Fully Automated Blood Cell Differential System and Its Application," *Proceedings of the IUPAC Third International Congress on Automation and New Technology in the Clinical Laboratory*, pp. 297–302, September 1988.

15. S. Abe and M-S Lan, "Fuzzy Rules Extraction Directly from Numerical Data for Function Approximation," *IEEE Trans. SMC*, vol. 25, no. 11, pp.119–129, 1995.

16. C. T. Lin and C. S. G. Lee, "Neural Network-based Fuzzy Logic Control and Decision System," *IEEE Trans. Computers*, vol. 40, no. 12, pp. 1320–1336, 1991.

17. K. Baba, I. Enbutsu, and M. Yoda, "Explicit Representation of Knowledge Acquired from Plant Historical Data Using Neural Network," *Proc. IJCNN-90*, San Diego, vol. 3, pp. 155–160, June 17–21, 1990.

CHAPTER 8

FUZZY RELATIONAL EQUATION PROBLEM SOLVING: TOOLS FOR MODELING

E. Levrat
G. Dubois
L. Rondeau
M. Lamotte
J. Bremont

Center for Automation Research of
Henri Poincaré University, Nancy, France

As the dawn of the twenty-first century approaches, the modeling and control processes are becoming increasingly complex. The goals of automation are directed toward increasing quality, which corresponds, in terms of model error or control error, to a value as low as possible. It is desirable to have a model as close as possible to the real world or to use a control law, thus inducing less error. In the '70s, the situation of working with uncertain knowledge and imprecise data appeared. This situation has necessitated the development of approximate reasoning based on fuzzy logic [41, 42, 43]. This reasoning is constructed on a basis of linguistic facts and activated by proposals coming from system observation which is then used to generate conclusions. This use of fact-based or linguistic rule sets describes the link between fuzzy proposals. We present various methods, with some examples, for finding this rule construction for a structure identification.

8.1 THE FUZZY RULES

These are elementary or composed proposals. They result from a conjunction between elementary fuzzy proposals. A fuzzy rule is composed of a premise and a conclusion. The classical structure of a rule is the following:

if < premise > **then** < conclusion >

When the premise is an elementary fuzzy proposal, the rule is described as follows: **if** $< x$ is $A >$ **then** $<$ conclusion $>$. The x is a variable, generally real, defined on a referential called the *universe of discourse,* given as a capital letter here, X. A is a linguistic term, taken in a set of terms noted as T_x. A fuzzy characterization of x is a subset of the universe of discourse X. A membership function $f_A(x)$ is associated to this fuzzy subset. The triplet (x, X, T_x) defines a linguistic variable.

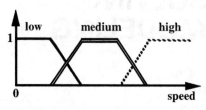

Example 8.1. x speed; $X = \mathbb{R}^+$; $T_x = \{$ low, medium, high $\}$ (Fig. 8.1).

FIGURE 8.1

The case of a composed premise does not change the general structure of a rule. Several elementary fuzzy proposals are simply conjugated via a conjunction operator: *AND*. In the case of the two fuzzy variables included in the premise, the rule takes the form:

if $< x$ is A *AND* y is $B >$ **then** $<$ conclusion $>$

The construction of a rule set is an important step to establish the model of a process or construct a fuzzy controller. If this set is known, the conclusion must now be evaluated when the premise is not exactly $< x$ is $A >$ but $< x$ is $A' >$. This is done by using an approximate reasoning model (the rule of generalized modus ponens extension of the classical modus ponens). The reasoning mechanism follows:

Rule: **if** $< x$ is $A >$ **then** $< y$ is $B >$
AND
observation: $< x$ is $A' >$
THEN
conclusion: $< y$ is $B' >$

The membership function $f_{B'}(y)$ is obtained by combining the rule with the observation. This combination is made by a *T*-norm operator. The evaluation of $f_{B'}(y)$ for all y of Y is obtained by the relation

$$f_{B'}(y) = \sup_{x \in X} \{T(f_{A'}(x), r(x, y))\}$$

When $f_{A'}(x)$ is reduced to a normalized fuzzy singleton, the previous relation becomes $f_{B'}(y) = r(x_0, y)$. In both expressions, $r(x, y)$ is a fuzzy relation translating the implication between the two fuzzy proposals, $< x$ is $A >$ and $< y$ is $B >$. This relation is defined by $r(x, y) = $ imp $(f_A(x), f_B(y))$ for an imp function from $[0,1] \times [0,1]$ into $[0,1]$.

Example 8.2.   Consider a case where the conjunction operator is the minimum and the implication function is also the minimum. We suppose that $f_{A'}(x)$ is reduced to a normalized fuzzy singleton. In this case, the evaluation of $f_{B'}(y)$ for all y of Y is obtained by

$$f_{B'}(y) = \min (f_A(x_0), f_B(y))$$

This principle corresponds to Mamdani's model. The evaluation of the membership function $f_{B'}$ results from a projection of the membership degree of the x_0 observation along the linguistic term A for all points y of Y.

8.2 FUZZY RELATIONAL EQUATIONS

8.2.1 General Definition

Let x and y represent two variables defined on the respective finite referentials X and Y. Let A and B represent two particular fuzzy sets, respectively defined on X and Y. The effect B, for known R and A, is calculated with the fuzzy relational equation: $R \circ A = B$. The composition law noted as $\circ$ includes two operators, OP1 and OP2, which have a sequential action. Dealing with the membership degrees, the fuzzy relational equation is expressed as follows:

$$f_B(y) = \text{OP1}[\underset{x}{\text{OP2}}[f_R(y,x), f_A(x)]]; \forall y \in Y$$

$$\text{OP1, OP2}: [0,1] \times [0,1] \rightarrow [0,1]$$

The equation $R \circ A = B$ expresses the deduction of B from the knowledge of A and R, in other terms, A induce B by R. We can generally assume that A is a set of causes acting on the system whose effects are represented by B.

8.2.2 The Nature of Causes and Effects

The nature of the sets A and B depends on the studied system. More precisely, it depends on the number of inputs. The effects set B is considered as the observation descriptor of the output variable. This is the concatenation of the characterization set of the variable for a given set of terms. When the system has multioutputs, the relations linking the set of causes to each output descriptor are identified separately. The assumption is that outputs have no direct links between them. On the contrary, two cases can be distinguished for inputs when the system is monovariable or multivariable. In the first case, the fuzzy set A is the descriptor of an observation of the input variable. In the second case, the fuzzy set A is a composed descriptor, which results from the conjunction of a fuzzy characterization (i.e., x_1 is A_1 AND x_2 is A_2).

   Example 8.3.   A system of one input x and one output y is considered. Both variables x and y are respectively defined along the universe of discourse X and Y. They are qualified by the sets of terms $T_x = \{t_1, \ldots, t_i, \ldots, t_n\}$ and $T_y = \{s_1, \ldots, s_j, \ldots, s_m\}$. For two observations (x_k, y_k), the descriptors $D(x_k)$ and $D(y_k)$ take the form:

$$D(x_k) = \{(x_k \mid f_{t1}(x_k)), \ldots, (x_k \mid f_{ti}(x_k)), \ldots, (x_k \mid f_{tn}(x_k))\}$$

$$D(y_k) = \{(y_k \mid f_{s1}(y_k)), \ldots, (y_k \mid f_{sj}(y_k)), \ldots, (y_k \mid f_{sm}(y_k))\}$$

Let $A = D(x_k)$, $B = D(y_k)$. For simplification, we note the following membership degrees: $a_{ik} = f_{ti}(x_k)$; $b_{jk} = f_{sj}(y_k)$; $r_{jik} = f_R(x_k, y_k)$.

   The existence of a link between the inputs and the outputs of the system can now be assumed. This link is formalized by a fuzzy relational equation including the input/output descriptors. This equation takes the following matrix form:

$$
\begin{pmatrix}
r_{11k} & \cdots & r_{1ik} & \cdots & r_{1nk} \\
 & & & & \\
r_{j1k} & \cdots & r_{jik} & \cdots & r_{jnk} \\
 & & & & \\
r_{m1k} & \cdots & r_{mik} & \cdots & r_{mnk}
\end{pmatrix}
\circ
\begin{pmatrix}
a_{1k} \\
\cdots \\
a_{ki} \\
\cdots \\
a_{nk}
\end{pmatrix}
=
\begin{pmatrix}
b_{1k} \\
\cdots \\
b_{jk} \\
\cdots \\
b_{mk}
\end{pmatrix}
$$

8.2.3 The Composition Law

The composition law includes two actions. The first is the numerical weight adjustment of membership degrees contained in A. The second is a combination of partial results to compute b_{jk}. Both operators OP1 and OP2, which form the composition law, are defined from $[0,1] \times [0,1]$ into $[0,1]$. The space, divided into unit length segments, contains an infinity of applications. The choice of a particular application is guided by the desired mathematical properties, such as associativity and commutativity. Associativity, for example, is required if the final result does not depend on the particular order of the calculations. Among the possible applications is an important group which concerns the triangular norms and conorms, respectively noted T norms and T conorms. If we replace the symbols OP1 and OP2 by, respectively, S and T, which are designated in the fuzzy relational equation by both applications T conorm and T norm, we obtain

$$b_{jk} = \underset{i}{S} \; (T(r_{jik}, a_{ik}))$$

8.2.4 Fuzzy Relational Equation Interpretation

Here we propose a semantic interpretation of a fuzzy relational equation, written with logical operators, in the case where fuzzy sets A and B are the descriptors of input/output observations of a system. In order to make this interpretation easier, a system with one input and one output is considered. Along the respective universe of discourse X and Y, these variables are qualified with the sets of terms T_x and T_y as $T_x = \{t_1, t_2\}$ and $T_y = \{s_1, s_2\}$. For an observation couple (x_k, y_k), the fuzzy relational equation takes the form

$$\begin{pmatrix} r_{11} & r_{12} \\ r_{21} & r_{22} \end{pmatrix} \circ \begin{pmatrix} a_1 \\ a_2 \end{pmatrix} = \begin{pmatrix} b_1 \\ b_2 \end{pmatrix}$$

Recalling that a T conorm is equivalent to a logical OR operator and that a T norm is equivalent to a logical AND operator, we can write the previous equation as

$$(r_{11} \; AND \; a_1) \; OR \; (r_{12} \; AND \; a_2) = b_1$$
$$(r_{21} \; AND \; a_1) \; OR \; (r_{22} \; AND \; a_2) = b_2$$

Each equation can be expressed in a logical manner, which suggests the general implication structure and the rule of the generalized modus ponens:

$$\{'x \text{ is } t_1' \to 'y \text{ is } s_1' \; AND \; a_1\} \; OR \; \{'x \text{ is } t_2' \to 'y \text{ is } s_1' \; AND \; a_2\} \text{ then } y \text{ is } s_1$$
$$\{'x \text{ is } t_1' \to 'y \text{ is } s_2' \; AND \; a_1\} \; OR \; \{'x \text{ is } t_2' \to 'y \text{ is } s_2' \; AND \; a_2\} \text{ then } y \text{ is } s_2$$

The r_{ij} coefficients of R are the true degrees of implications:

$$'x \text{ is } t_i' \to 'y \text{ is } s_j'$$

With this example, we can observe that R contains the fuzzy implication structure involved in the system. A fuzzy relation, as well as a fuzzy relational equation, is consequently a linguistic model of the observed system. This model may be used later for generating the control law. Other fields of research have used this linguistic model for expert systems, pattern recognition, etc.

8.3 VARIOUS TYPES OF COMPOSITION AND EQUATIONS

Four types of composition based on T conorms, T norms, and pseudo-complement operators (respectively noted as τ and σ) can be distinguished. Figure 8.2 illustrates the duality and adjunction relationships.

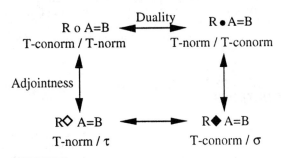

FIGURE 8.2

These pseudo-complement operators are used during the resolution of a fuzzy relational equation. τ is an operator associated to a T norm. It allows the computation of the maximal relation, if existing, in the case of a T-norm/max composition. It is defined as an application from $[0,1] \times [0,1]$ to $[0,1]$ with respect to a set of conditions [16, 23, 40]. By duality, σ is a minimization operator associated with a T conorm. It allows the computation of the minimal relation, if existing, in the case of min/T-conorm composition.

Studies [4, 8] show that τ is an implication operator between two fuzzy propositions. Let p and q be two propositions whose respective true values are a and b. $c = a \tau b$ represents the true value of the proposition $p \Rightarrow q$. Figure 8.3 presents the different true values of the implication $p \Rightarrow q$. The four corners of the square represent the truth table of a binary implication. By duality, σ corresponds to a non-inclusion operator. Figure 8.3 also illustrates the $a \sigma b$ operation corresponding to $p \nRightarrow q$.

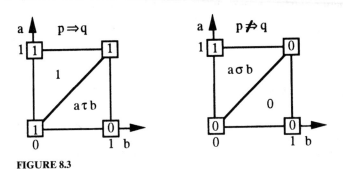

FIGURE 8.3

These different types of equations represent, in fact, different reasoning logics. In a very generalized control problem, R and A being known, the goal is to compute B. Considering an input characterization or a conjunction of characterizations associated with several inputs, we want to conclude the output characterization. In this case, the composition law is T-conorm/T-norm type corresponding to a modus ponens deduction model. When A and B are known by system observation, we want to determine the different implications involved in the system to obtain a fuzzy model corresponding to a modus ponens reasoning structure. This structure leads to use of the T-norm/τ composition law. The two other laws (T norm/T conorm and σ/T norm) are not used practically because of the inherent reasoning structure of these laws, which is the modus tollens structure corresponding to a negative logic.

8.4 DIFFERENT TYPES OF INVERTED INVERSE EQUATIONS

We now present the case of a fuzzy model whose composition law is of the T-conorm/T-norm type. This corresponds to control and modelization applications. We give the inverse equation, with respect to the direct equation $R \circ A = B$, the following structure: $R = B * A$. This allows the determination, assuming A and B are known, of the inherent implications of the system as well as their truth degree. The symbol $*$ is a solving operator. Two groups of inverse equations are examined. The first concerns the case where the composition law of the direct equation is of the max/T-norm type. The second includes the previous one, since it corresponds to the general T-conorm/T-norm case. Moreover, we shall consider two different problems: a unique equation to be solved and a system of equations to be solved. The general form of an inverse equation is the following:

$$
R_k = B_k * A_k{}^T \text{ with }
\begin{pmatrix}
r_{11k} & \cdots & r_{1ik} & \cdots & r_{1nk} \\
 & \cdot & \cdot & \cdot & \\
r_{jlk} & \cdots & r_{jik} & \cdots & r_{jnk} \\
 & \cdot & \cdot & \cdot & \\
r_{mlk} & \cdots & r_{mik} & \cdots & r_{mnk}
\end{pmatrix}
=
\begin{pmatrix}
b_{1k} \\
\cdots \\
b_{jk} \\
\cdots \\
b_{mk}
\end{pmatrix}
*
\begin{pmatrix}
a_{1k} \\
\cdots \\
a_{ik} \\
\cdots \\
a_{nk}
\end{pmatrix}^T
$$

In the particular case of the max/T-norm composition law, the solution space for only one equation, if it is not empty, is ordered. The $*$ operator will be τ or σ, depending on whether we are looking for the maximal or minimal relation. In the case of a system of equations where a common relation is generally searched, a method exists to determine the intersection of the different solution spaces.

8.5 SOLVING METHOD

As noted previously, when we face practical identification problems, the goal is to find the solution of an equation system of fuzzy relations. However, the study of the resolution of a single fuzzy equation provides some interesting tools for the system case.

8.5.1 One Equation

The classical methods, which have been thoroughly discussed in published literature, were mainly developed for the max/T-norm composition law [5, 6, 24, 25, 35]. This can be explained by the fact that the T-conorm max has interesting properties which transfer ordered structures, if existing, to the solution set. It offers the possibility of obtaining operators characteristic of this structure by computing particular solutions. However, this composition, excluding the max operator, is very rare in the literature. The major disadvantage is not providing an ordered structure, if it exists, to the solution set. The resolution method is, consequently, different.

Resolution in the Max/T-Norm Composition Case. Numerous papers have already dealt with this problem [15, 21, 26, 36, 38]. The problem exists in finding R when A and B are known. If a solution exists, it belongs to a solution set $E(\circ, A, B)$ such as $E(\circ, A, B) = (R \mid R \circ A = B)$. Before seeking the solution, it is important to know if this set is nonempty. In Ref. 4, the author assesses the following condition:

The set $E(\circ, A, B)$ is nonempty when: $\forall\, j \in [1, m], b_j \leq \max_{i \in [1,n]} (a_i)$.

This condition means that the exact deduction of B, from the knowledge of A by R, is possible if the set of causes is representative of the effects. Sanchez [35] demonstrated that this set is governed by an order relation, in particular, for the maximal relation $\check{R}$. If $R \in E(\circ, A, B)$, then the following relation can be verified:

$$\check{r}_{ji} \geq r_{ji} \ \forall\, i, \forall\, j$$

A second relation, noted as $\mathring{R}$, corresponds to a particular relation such as

$$\mathring{r}_{ji} \leq r_{ji} \leq \check{r}_{ji} \ \forall i, \forall j$$

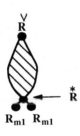

FIGURE 8.4

Finally, a set of minimal relation, noted as R_{ml}, is obtained from the particular relation. These minimal elements result from keeping a nonnull active element on each line of $\mathring{R}$ [6, 21]. Therefore, the solution set can be symbolically represented by Fig. 8.4.

In Refs. 4, 5, 8, and 35, the authors proposed two operators (noted as τ and α) which lead, respectively, to the $\check{R}$ and $\mathring{R}$ solutions. These maximalization and minimalization operators are directly linked with each T norm and have properties that can be found in Ref. 21.

Example 8.4. $\check{r}_{ji}$ and $\mathring{r}_{ji}$, solutions of a fuzzy relational equation with the max/product composition, are obtained by

$$\check{r}_{ji} = b_j \,\tau\, a_i = \begin{cases} 1 & \text{if } a_i \leq b_j \\[2mm] \dfrac{b_j}{a_i} & \text{if } a_i > b_j \end{cases}$$

and

$$\dot{r}_{ji} = b_j \, \alpha \, a_i = \begin{cases} 0 \text{ if } a_i > b_j \\ b_j \, \tau \, a_i \text{ if } a_i \leq b_j \end{cases}$$

As demonstrated, the resolution of a single fuzzy relational equation for a max/T-norm composition law is easy as a result of the resolution operators.

Resolution When the T Conorm Is Different from the Max Operator. Here, we are interested in a more general problem-solving method utilizing all possible T-conorm operators. This study is justified by some inherent constraints induced by the max. Indeed, a problem appears when we get two or more equal or nearly equal maxima. The max operator considers only one contribution, and not all partial results, which does not seem to be logical.

Condition of Existence for a Solution. Bour [8] has demonstrated the existence conditions of solutions, conditions that we shall review. If the following condition is verified:

$$\forall \, j, b_j \leq \underset{i \in [1,n]}{S} (a_i)$$

then the set $E(\circ, A, B)$ is nonempty. We know that if this set is nonempty, it has an ordered structure. But this property is specific to the max. Two relations, represented as R_1 and $R_2 \in E(\text{T conorm} \neq \text{max/T norm}, A, B)$, are not submitted to an order relation. The following figure presents the space solution of a particular system, such that $A = [0.5, 0.8]'$, $B = [0.4]$ with $S(a, b) = a + b - ab$ and $T(a, b) = ab$. If $R = [r_1, r_2]$ is a solution of the equation $R \circ A = B$, then:

$$r_2 = \frac{0.4 - r_1 0.5}{0.8 - r_1 0.4} \qquad \text{with } r_1, r_2 \in [0, 1]$$

The solution space is a hyperbolic arc. Figure 8.5 includes the solution sets obtained with max/min and max/product compositions. They are characterized for the max/min composition by $\check{R}_1 = \overset{*}{R}_1$ and R_{mm1}, R_{mm2}, for the max/product composition by $\check{R}_2 = \overset{*}{R}_2$ and R_{mp1}, R_{mp2}.

This figure illustrates the ordered structure of solution relations for max/min and max/product, as well as the nonordered structure of solution relations for the probabilistic sum/product composition.

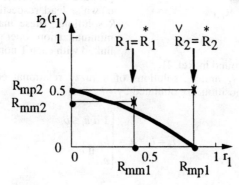

FIGURE 8.5

Specific Resolution. The following approach is based on the associativity property of a T conorm. To facilitate this development, we consider that B is a fuzzy singleton whose membership degree is b. This condition is justified by the fact that the rows of R are independent. We suppose that the necessary existence condition is verified. Thus, we obtain b by developing the fuzzy relational equation in the following form:

$$b = S[\dots S[\dots S[T(r_1, a_1), T(r_2, a_2)], \dots T(r_i, a_i)], \dots T(r_n, a_n)]$$

$$= \underset{i \in [1,n]}{S}[T(r_i, a_i)]$$

By considering the specific case of the probabilistic sum T conorm, we obtain the following result:

$$b = w_i + T(r_i, a_i) - w_i T(r_i, a_i) \qquad \text{with } w_i = \underset{j \in [1,n], j \neq i}{S}[T(r_j, a_j)]$$

This can be expressed as

$$T(r_i, a_i) = \frac{b - w_i}{1 - w_i} \tag{8.1}$$

In Ref. 21, the author defines an operator σ that allows the computation of the minimal solution of a fuzzy relational equation in the case of a T conorm/min composition, if it exists. For the probabilistic sum T conorm, the σ operator is defined by:

$$x \, \sigma \, y = \begin{cases} 0 & \text{if } x < y \\ \dfrac{x - y}{1 - y} & \text{if } x \geq y \end{cases}$$

Introducing the σ operator in Eq. (8.1), we arrive at

$$T(r_i, a_i) = b \, \sigma \, w_i \qquad \text{under the condition } b \geq w_i$$

The determination of the r_i coefficient is obtained by clearly stating the chosen T norm. Then we have

$$r_i = \frac{b - w_i}{a_i(1 - w_i)}$$

This expression includes the τ operator associated with the T-norm product. So, we can write

$$r_i = (b \, \sigma \, w_i) \, \tau \, a_i \qquad \text{under the two conditions } b \geq w_i \text{ and } (b \, \sigma \, w_i) \leq a_i$$

The generalization of all composition laws and the demonstrations are presented in Ref. 15. To summarize, if the following conditions exist—R is a relation solution of the fuzzy relational equation, $n - 1$ elements of R are known, and w_i is the contribution of these elements to the result of the composition of R with A—then the remaining element of index i is calculated by the previously expressed equation. This equation includes both implication and noninclusion operators. Thus, the logical interpretation of this expression is: the evaluation of the true degree of the ith rule is obtained by the direct contribution of the a_i cause to the b effect where partial causes are not taken into account.

Computation Algorithm. This algorithm is based on the fuzzy relational equation decomposition to subequations with a link via w_i values. Let us take $w_0 = b$ and compute the first r_i element of the relation, assuming that $\{r_2, r_3 \ldots, r_n\}$ are known. We then have $r_1 = (w_0 \sigma w_1) \tau a_1$ with $w_1 = [0, r_2, r_3, \ldots, r_n] \circ A_{-1}$ under the condition $w_0 \sigma w_1 \leq a_1$. A represents the input descriptor whose first element has been suppressed. We try to adjust this condition in order to express w_1 in relation with w_0 and a_1; and since $w_0 \geq w_1$, we get: $w_1 \geq w_0 \sigma a_1$. We choose a value for w_1, so that the inequality $w_0 \sigma a_1 \leq w_1 \leq w_0$ is verified. However, this inequality does not lead to the existence solution of the subproblem defined by $w_1 \leq \underset{i \in [2,n]}{S} [a_i] = w_{1m}$. Thus, the previous inequality becomes: $w_0 \sigma a_1 \leq w_1 \leq \min (w_0, w_{1m})$ Therefore, we are now able to compute the first coefficient r_i.

In a second step, we consider the fuzzy relational equation that generates w_1. Still, a subproblem equivalent to the previous one remains. Thus, we compute $r_2 = (w_1 \sigma w_2) \tau a_2$, with $w_2 = [0, r_3, \ldots, r_n] \circ A_{-2}$ under the condition $w_1 \sigma w_2 \leq a_2$. Then, we choose w_2 such that $w_1 \sigma a_2 \leq w_2 \leq \min (w_1, w_{2m})$.

To the ith step, we compute the ith element of the $(i-1)$th subproblem; that is, $r_i = (w_{i-1} \sigma w_i) \tau a_i$, with $w_i = [0, r_{i+1}, \ldots, r_n] \circ A_{-(i-1)}$ under the condition $w_{i-1} \sigma w_i \leq a_i$. Then, we choose a w_i element such that

$$w_{i-1} \sigma a_i \leq w_i \leq \min \left(w_{i-1}, \underset{j, j > i}{S} (a_j)\right)$$

Finally, the last step consists of the determination of the r_n element such as $r_n = (w_{n-1} \sigma w_n) \tau a_n$, with $w_n = [0] \circ A_{-(n-1)} = 0$; that is $r_n = w_{n-1} \tau a_n$. For this step, all elements of R are calculated, leaving no free choice.

8.5.2   An Example of Resolution

In order to illustrate this approach, we shall apply the algorithm to the following example. Let us take two fuzzy sets, $A = [0.8, 0.2, 0.1]^t$ and $B = [0.5]$, and the composition law of probabilistic sum/product. The existence condition of the solutions is satisfied. We take $w_0 = 0.5$, and k corresponds to the step index.

$k = 1$: $w_0 \sigma a_1 = 0.5 \sigma 0.8 = 0$
   $\underset{i=2,3}{S} (a_i) = 0.28$, then w_1 takes its values in $[0, 0.28]$.
   Let us take $w_1 = 0.2$. Then $r_1 = (w_0 \sigma w_1) \tau a_1 = 0.468$.

$k = 2$: $w_1 \sigma a_2 = 0.2 \sigma 0.2 = 0$
   $\underset{i=3}{S} (a_i) = 0.1$, then w_2 takes its values in $[0, 0.1]$.
   Let us take $w_2 = 0.1$. Then $r_2 = (w_1 \sigma w_2) \tau a_2 = 0.588$.

$k = 3$: $w_2 \sigma a_3 = 0$. Then $w_3 = 0$, and $r_3 = w_3 \tau a_3 = 0$.

A solution relation is consequently $R = [0.468, 0.588, 0]$. This solution is, of course, not unique since it depends on the arbitrary choice of each w_i. By sampling the solution space and knowing each definition domain of subproblems, we can obtain the solution space shown in Fig. 8.6

8.5.3   Conclusion

This chapter provides a series of tools for solving fuzzy relational equations. Two types of resolution have been distinguished, depending on the composition law that

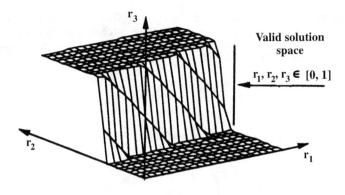

FIGURE 8.6

is chosen. The abundant literature mainly deals with the resolution for a max/ T-norm composition. Computation operators, such as a maximalization operator, allow particular solutions to be obtained which characterize the solution space, if it is nonempty.

In the general case of a T-conorm/T-norm composition, few works are available. However, when the objective is to identify the behavior of a complex system with fuzzy relational equations, the max operators appear not to be the best choices, since they retain only one partial cause to generate the effect. So, using a T conorm different from the max appears to be a necessity to avoid this disadvantage. In this case, the resolution is more difficult because of the lack of a particular structure of the solution set when it is nonempty.

We have demonstrated a general method of problem solving for all T conorms based on maximalization and minimalization operators. We have proposed an original algorithm for exact solution determination. As a result of this algorithm, we can generalize the resolution of a single fuzzy relational equation.

8.5.4 Resolution of a System of Fuzzy Relational Equations

Max/T-norm Composition.   We are looking for a relation or a set of relations which verify, for each descriptor couple (A_k and B_k), the general fuzzy relational equation $R \circ A_k = B_k$ for all the system observations $k \in [1, N]$.

This problem involves two different situations. On one hand, we are interested in a system of fuzzy relational equations whose solution space is nonempty. In this case, the resolution is exact. On the other hand, there is no exact solution. Therefore, we are looking for a relation which minimizes the error between the real and estimated descriptors of the output. We note A and B, both fuzzy sets respectively constituted by the concatenation in columns of each fuzzy set A_k and B_k.

Nonempty Solution Set, Exact Resolution.   The search for a solution R, common to each $R_k \circ A_k = B_k$ equation type, assumes that each equation answers the existence condition of solutions, in order to ensure that the set $E_k(\circ, A_k, B_k)$ of the solutions of the kth equation is nonempty. In Refs. 25, 35, and 38, several theorems and propositions offer some answers to this problem. If E represents the solution set of an equation system, then E is nonempty, if and only if, a relation $R = \bigcap_k \check{R}_k$ element of E

exists, such as $R \circ A = B$. R is the maximal relation. If $\check{R} \circ A \neq B$, then $E = \varnothing$. The intersection operator is justified by the fact that the researched solution must satisfy the entirety of equations. The researched maximal relation must be less than the smallest maximal relation of each equation.

Example 8.5. Let

$$A = \begin{pmatrix} 0.1 & 0.2 & 0.4 \\ 0 & 0.7 & 0.9 \\ 0.5 & 0.3 & 1 \end{pmatrix}$$

and

$$B = \begin{pmatrix} 0.5 & 0.6 & 0.6 \\ 0.1 & 0.5 & 0.5 \\ 0.5 & 0.6 & 0.9 \end{pmatrix}$$

be two matrices of descriptors and $\circ$ the max/min composition law. We determine the maximal relation $\check{R}_k$ for each equation. Then, we obtain the three following relations:

$$\check{R}_1 = \begin{pmatrix} 1 & 1 & 1 \\ 1 & 1 & 0.1 \\ 1 & 1 & 1 \end{pmatrix} \quad \check{R}_2 = \begin{pmatrix} 1 & 0.6 & 1 \\ 1 & 0.5 & 1 \\ 1 & 0.6 & 1 \end{pmatrix} \quad \check{R}_3 = \begin{pmatrix} 1 & 0.6 & 0.6 \\ 1 & 0.5 & 0.5 \\ 1 & 1 & 0.9 \end{pmatrix}$$

Computing the intersection between these three relations, using the min operator, we get the relation

$$R = \begin{pmatrix} 1 & 0.6 & 0.6 \\ 1 & 0.5 & 0.1 \\ 1 & 0.6 & 0.9 \end{pmatrix}$$

We can easily verify that the composition of this solution produces the B matrix. Thus, the solution set is nonempty and R is the maximal relation.

Example 8.6. Let

$$A = \begin{pmatrix} 0.8 & 0.7 \\ 0.3 & 0.4 \end{pmatrix}$$

and

$$B = \begin{pmatrix} 0.4 & 0.4 \\ 0.5 & 0.7 \end{pmatrix}$$

be two other matrices of descriptors. For each (A_k, B_k) couple, the solution space is nonempty. For the same composition law, we obtain

$$R = \begin{pmatrix} 0.4 & 1 \\ 0.5 & 1 \end{pmatrix}$$

We can verify that, in this case, the composition of this relation does not produce the B matrix. Thus, the solution set intersection is empty and $E = \varnothing$. For a single fuzzy relational equation, the solution set E has minimal relations if E is nonempty. Several propositions can be found in Ref. 21 and enable us to compute them. In the case of Example 8., we get

$$R_{m1} = \begin{pmatrix} 0 & 0.6 & 0.5 \\ 0.1 & 0.5 & 0 \\ 0 & 0.6 & 0.9 \end{pmatrix} \qquad R_{m2} = \begin{pmatrix} 0 & 0.6 & 0.5 \\ 0 & 0.5 & 0.1 \\ 0 & 0.6 & 0.9 \end{pmatrix}$$

Empty Solution Set, Approximate Relation. When $E = \varnothing$, it is always possible to define a relation, noted as R_{app}, such as $R_{app} \circ A = B'$. B' is a fuzzy descriptor close to B in the sense of a distance criterion $J(R)$.

Fuzzy Intersection of Partial Maximal Relations. As seen previously, the first method [10, 11, 24] consists in computing the fuzzy intersection of maximal relations for each solution space. Let us define two fuzzy descriptors taken from Ref. 30:

$$A = \begin{pmatrix} 1 & 0.3 & 0.9 & 0.4 & 0.8 \\ 0.6 & 1 & 0.4 & 1 & 0.2 \\ 0.5 & 0.4 & 0.1 & 0.7 & 0.1 \end{pmatrix} \qquad B = \begin{pmatrix} 0.7 & 0.3 & 0.3 & 0.6 & 0.5 \\ 0.4 & 1 & 0.5 & 0.4 & 0.7 \\ 0.7 & 0.2 & 0.8 & 0.2 & 0.7 \end{pmatrix}$$

The fuzzy intersection of maximal relations obtained by using the min operator is

$$R = \begin{pmatrix} 0.3 & 0.3 & 0.3 \\ 0.4 & 0.4 & 0.4 \\ 0.2 & 0.2 & 0.2 \end{pmatrix}.$$

Recomposing R with A, we obtain the B' descriptor. The mean of the Hamming distances between B and B' is $d = 0.233$.

Fuzzy Junction of Partial Minimal Relations. Just as it is possible to take the intersection of maximal relations, we can now define the junction of minimal relations as $R = \cup_k \check{R}_k$. The fuzzy junction of minimal relations is obtained with the max operator. Therefore, we get the following relation:

$$R = \begin{pmatrix} 0.7 & 0.6 & 0.6 \\ 0.7 & 1 & 0.4 \\ 0.8 & 0.2 & 0.2 \end{pmatrix}$$

with a Hamming distance $d = 0.167$.

Mean Relation. In Ref. 15, the author proposes the evaluation of the mean relation. This method consists of computing a matrix which has the same dimension as R and containing the number of activations of the r_{ij} coefficient when this coefficient acts on the elaboration of the b_{jk} degree. Next, we compute the mean value of active coefficients which appear in the maximal relations $\check{R}_k$. The mean value of active elements represents the general tendency of the system. The mean relation, denoted R_{moy}, obtained with this method is

$$R_{moy} = \begin{pmatrix} 0.625 & 0.4 & 0.45 \\ 0.3325 & 0.6 & 0.4 \\ 0.52 & 0.2 & 0.2 \end{pmatrix}$$

The Hamming distance for this relation is now equal to $d = 0.198$.

Pedrycz Method. In Ref. 28, Pedrycz presents a method based on the minimization of a square criterion. However, this method consists of searching for a solution to a fuzzy relation equation only when the existence condition of the solution is not verified. In the following elaboration, we consider only the jth line of R, noted as R_j, in order to lighten the notations. The distance criterion $J(R_j)$ is defined by

$$J(R_j) = \sum_{k=1}^{k=N} (b_k - b_k')^2 \quad \text{with } b_k' = \max_{i \in [1,n]} [T(r_i, a_{ik})]$$

The solution is obtained by deriving the criterion in relation to each r_i, then by assuming the derivative null, $\partial J(R_j)/\partial r_i = 0$. By using, for instance, the iterative Newton method, the solution at step t is written $R^{(t+1)} = R^{(t)} - [F'(R^{(t)})]^{-1} F(R^{(t)})$. $F(R^{(t)})$ represents the criterion gradient and $F'(R^{(t)})$ the criterion hessian. The vth term of $F(R^{(t)})$ is denoted by the following expression:

$$\frac{\partial J(R_j)}{\partial r_v} = \frac{\partial \left\{ \sum_{k=1}^{k=N} (b_k - \max_{i \in [1,n]} [T(r_i, a_{ik})])^2 \right\}}{\partial r_v}$$

$$= 2 \sum_{k=1}^{k=N} \left\{ (b_k - \max_{i \in [1,n]} [T(r_i, a_{ik})]) P_v \right\}$$

with

$$P_v = \frac{\partial \max_{i \in [1,n]} [T(r_i, a_{ik})]}{\partial r_v}$$

$$= \begin{cases} \dfrac{\partial T(r_v, a_{vk})}{\partial r_v} & \text{if } T(r_v, a_{vk}) \ge \max_{i \in [1,n], i \neq v} [T(r_i, a_{ik})] \\ 0 & \text{otherwise} \end{cases}$$

In the case of the min T norm, this derivative equals 1 under the condition $r_v \le a_v$. In order to avoid the calculation of the hessian, Pedrycz proposes an approximation by a scalar, denoted as α_t, whose expression is $\alpha_k = 1/(c + t^\kappa)$ with $c = 2$ and $\kappa \ge 0$. κ is a parameter allowing the convergency tuning.

Applying this algorithm to our example with $\kappa = 1.2$ yields the following R_{ped} relation:

$$R_{ped} = \begin{pmatrix} 0.4158 & 0.5044 & 0.8592 \\ 0.5984 & 0.6968 & 0.8147 \\ 0.6934 & 0.3721 & 0.3707 \end{pmatrix}$$

In this case, the Hamming distance is $d = 0.146$

For this example, the best solution is given by the Pedrycz method. With other data, the solution it is not as satisfactory. Thus, we cannot generalize about the choice of a particular method when facing a given problem. However, other numerous tests stress that the solution obtained with the intersection of maximal relation is rarely efficient.

T-Conorm Composition Different from the Max. The example below supports our following discussion. We shall consider four observations of a system, and build the input descriptor. A in addition to the output descriptor B as follows:

$$A = \begin{pmatrix} 0.7 & 0.3 & 0.5 & 0.8 \\ 0.5 & 0.7 & 0.8 & 0.3 \end{pmatrix} \qquad B = (0.5 \quad 0.6 \quad 0.4 \quad 0.3)$$

Solving each equation independently, we obtain the four following solutions:

$$R_{p1} = (0.535, 0.400) \qquad \text{for } w_1 = 0.2 \qquad w_1 \in [0, 0.5]$$

$$R_{p2} = (0.906, 0.641) \qquad \text{for } w_1 = 0.45 \qquad w_1 \in [0.428, 0.6]$$

$$R_{p3} = (0.666, 0.125) \qquad \text{for } w_1 = 0.1 \qquad w_1 \in [0, 0.4]$$

$$R_{p4} = (0.156, 0.666) \qquad \text{for } w_1 = 0.2 \qquad w_1 \in [0, 0.3]$$

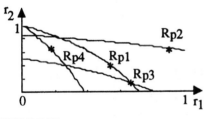

FIGURE 8.7

Figure 8.7 represents the solution spaces, which are hyperbolic arcs, and the previous solution points. Thus, the problem is to determine a common solution which minimizes the distance criterion, since it is evident that no exact solution exists.

Analytical Approach. The starting point is the same as the Pedrycz method, that is, the minimization of the error criterion between B and B'. We suppose, in the following elaboration, that the T conorms and T norms used in the composition law are continuously derivable on $[0, 1]$. The rows of R being independent, we consider that the descriptors of each observation are reduced to fuzzy singletons whose membership degrees are b_k. The criterion must be minimized in relation to R under the condition $r_i \in [0, 1]$. Then the criterion takes the following form:

$$J(r_i) = \frac{1}{2} \sum_{k=1}^{k=N} \{b_k - S(w_{ik}, T(r_i, a_{ik}))\}^2$$

Adjusting the T conorm S to the probabilistic sum and the T norm to the product, we get

$$J(r_i) = \frac{1}{2} \sum_{k=1}^{k=N} \{b_k - r_i a_{ik}(1 - w_{ik}) - w_{ik}\}^2$$

Assuming that w_{ik} is known, the goal is to minimize the criterion in relation to r_i. Here, the minimum is obtained for a null value of the criterion derivative. This leads to the following expression of r_i:

$$\frac{\partial J(r_i)}{\partial r_i} = 0 \Leftrightarrow r_i = \frac{\displaystyle\sum_{k=1}^{k=N} a_{ik}(1-w_{ik})(b_k - w_{ik})}{\displaystyle\sum_{k=1}^{k=N} a_{ik}^2(1-w_{ik})^2}$$

under the condition

$$w_{ik} \leq \min \left(b_k, \underset{j \in [1,n], j \neq i}{S} \; [T(r_j, a_{jk})]\right)$$

8.6 NUMERICAL EXAMPLES

8.6.1 Example from Page 8.15

We examine two cases. The first one consists of solving the system constituted by observations 1, 2 and by observations 3, 4. This yields an exact solution with respect to a given threshold of accuracy. The second case consists of solving the system constituted by the entirety of observations. Then, an approximate relation must be found since the solution set is empty. Figure 8.8 represents the results.

Relations	d	Iter.	B	B'
R_{app1} = [0.2584, 0.3891]	2.843×10^{-7}	8	[0.4, 0.3]	[0.4002, 0.2993]
R_{app2} = [0.2171, 0.8184]	7.6×10^{-7}	8	[0.5, 0.6]	[0.4990, 0.6007]

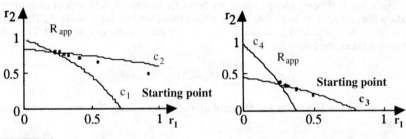

FIGURE 8.8

We observe that, for a given accuracy, the algorithm behaves very well. The resultant Hamming distance is very low. Then, it can be applied to the entirety of observations in order to determine a common solution (Fig. 8.9)

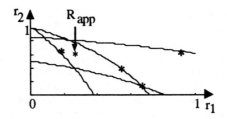

Relations	Performance
R_{opt}=[0.23, 0.62]	0.0118
R_{app}=[0.2631, 0.6]	0.0120

FIGURE 8.9

8.6.2 Example from Ref. 32

In Ref. 32, Pedrycz presents a numerical example as support for his method. The system of fuzzy relational equations with two inputs and one output is represented by the table below:

X_{1k}	X_{2k}	Y_k
0.60	0.20	0.45
0.10	0.18	0.81
0.20	0.35	0.45
0.56	0.12	0.31
0.05	0.67	0.27
0.10	0.43	0.56

We will analyze the character of the learning process by summarizing it in terms of speed of iteration. The first is the Pedrycz method, the second is the Dubois method, and the third is a genetic algorithm presented by Rondeau in Ref. 33. The next table represents the results:

Pedrycz	Dubois	Rondeau
R = [0.515, 0.841]	R = [0.544, 0.831]	R = [0.533, 0.831]
Iter = 100	Iter = 3	Iter = 10

For all three methods, the mean square error is similar.

8.7 *CONCLUSION*[†,‡]

Various methods of resolution were presented in this chapter. Two principle cases were studied, for one equation and a system of equations. In each case, we made the distinction between the composition law as max/T norm and T conorm/T norm.

The vast interest in this subject shown by many different teams of researchers proves the absolute necessity to better understand the tools of resolution. Other areas of interest, such as the neural network and the genetic algorithm, are in development and are not presented here.

By the twenty-first century, with continued perfection of our tools for modeling, we will be ready to further study these complex processes.

REFERENCES

1. A. N. Averkin and V. B. Tarasov, "The fuzzy modelling relation and its application in psychology and artificial intelligence." *FSS* **22** (1987) 3–24.

2. N. P. Baboshin and D. G. Naryshkin, "On identification of multidimensional fuzzy systems," *FSS* **35** (1990) 325–331.

3. W. Bandler and L. Kohout, "Fuzzy power sets and fuzzy implication operators," *FSS* **4** (1980) 13–30.

4. L. Bour, G. Hirsch, and M. Lamotte, "Détermination d'un opérateur de maximalisation pour la résolution d'équations de relations floues," *BUSEFAL* **25** (1986) 95–106.

5. L. Bour, G. Hirsch, and M. Lamotte, "Opérateur de minimisation pour la résolution d'équations de relation floue," *BUSEFAL* **28** (1986) 68–77.

6. L. Bour and M. Lamotte, "Solutions minimales d'équations de relations floues avec la composition max norme triangulaire," *BUSEFAL* **31** (1987) 24–31.

7. L. Bour and M. Lamotte, "Equations de relations floues avec la composition conorme-norme triangulaires," *BUSEFAL* **34** (1988) 86–94.

8. L. Bour and M. Lamotte, "Existence et propriétés d'un opérateur de maximalisation," *BUSEFAL* **37** (1988) 34–41.

9. J. Bremont, "Contribution à la reconnaissance automatique de la parole par les sous-ensembles flous," thesis, University of Nancy, 1975.

10. E. Czogala, J. Drewniak, and Witold Pedrycz, "Fuzzy relation equations on a finite set," *FSS* **7** (1982) 89–101.

11. A. Di Nola and S. Sessa, "On the set of solution of composite fuzzy relation equations," *FSS* **9** (1983) 275–285.

12. G. Dubois, E. Levrat, M. Lamotte, and J. Bremont, "Solving a system of fuzzy relation equations by using a hierarchical process," *FUZZ-IEEE '92,* 679–686, San Diego.

13. G. Dubois, E. Levrat, J. Bremont, and M. Lamotte, "Résolution approchée d'une équation de relation floue dans le cadre d'une composition générale," *Canadian Conference* on Industrial Automation, 32.17–32.20, Montréal.

14. G. Dubois and E. Levrat, "Résolution d'un système d'équations de relation floue, composition T conorme–T norme générale," Second National Meeting on Fuzzy Systems, 73–79, Nîmes.

[†]Acknowledgment: Thanks go to Pamela Dubois for her editing of our English. Without her, this chapter would not be the same.
[‡]Correspondence may be addressed to G. Dubois at dubois@cran.u-nancy.fr.

15. G. Dubois, "Résolution d'un système d'équations de relations floues Contribution à l'identification de systèmes complexes," thesis at the University of Nancy, 30 January 1992.

16. J. C. Fodor, "A remark on constructing t-norms," *FSS* **41** (1991) 195–199.

17. S. Gottwald, "On the existence of solutions of systems of fuzzy equations," *FSS* **12** (1984) 301–302.

18. S. Gottwald, "Generalized solvability criteria for fuzzy equation," *FSS* **17** (1985) 285–296.

19. M. Higashi and G. J. Klir, "Resolution of finite fuzzy relation equations," *FSS* **13** (1984) 65–82.

20. J. Hihi, A. Richard, G. Dubois, and E. Levrat, "Identification by fuzzy relational equations," MIM-S'93, *Proceedings of IMACS/IFAC,* Second International Symposium on Mathematical and Intelligent Models in System Simulation, vol. 2, Brussels.

21. G. Hirsch, "Equations de relation floue et mesure d'incertain en reconnaissance de formes," thesis Nancy, 27 April 1987.

22. E. Levrat, G. Dubois, V. Bombardier, and M. Lamotte, "Generalisation of the resolution of a fuzzy relational equation," *Second IEEE International Conference on Fuzzy Systems,* 1414–1418, San Francisco

23. G. Mayor and J. Torrens, "On a family of t-norms," *FSS* **41** (1991) 161–166.

24. M. Miyakoshi, M. Shimbo. Solutions of composite fuzzy relational equations with triangular norms. FSS 16 (1985) 53–63.

25. M. Miyakoshi and M. Shimbo, "Lower solutions of systems of fuzzy equations," *FSS* **19** (1986) 37–46.

26. C. P. Pappis and M. Sugeno, "Fuzzy relational equations and inverse problem," *FSS* **15** (1985) 79–90.

27. W. Pedrycz, "Fuzzy relational equations with generalized connectives and their applications," *FSS* **10** (1983) 185–201.

28. W. Pedrycz, "Numerical and applicational aspects of fuzzy relational equations," *FSS* **11** (1983) 1–18.

29. W. Pedrycz, "An identification algorithm in fuzzy relational systems," *FSS* **13** (1984) 153–167.

30. W. Pedrycz, "Fuzzy set framework for development of a perception perspective," *FSS* **37** (1990) 123–138.

31. W. Pedrycz, "Fuzzy sets in pattern recognition: Methodology and methods," *Pattern Recognition,* vol. 23, no. 1/2 (1990) 121–146.

32. W. Pedrycz, "s-t Fuzzy relational equations," *FSS* **59** (1993) 189–196.

33. L. Rondeau, G. Dubois, E. Levrat, M. Lamotte, and M. Fonteix, "Résolution d'un système d'équations de relation floue par les algorithmes génétiques," *Fifth International Conference IPMU '94,* vol. 2, pp. 1093–1098, Paris, 4–8 July 1994.

34. L. Rondeau, G. Dubois, and E. Levrat, "Le problème de la défuzzification en identification par le modèle flou de Mamdani," *NEURONIMES 1993,* Third National Meeting on Applications of Fuzzy Systems, Nîmes.

35. E. Sanchez, "Resolution of composite fuzzy relations equations," *Information and Control,* **30** (1976) 38–49.

36. E. Sanchez, "Solution of fuzzy equations with extended operations," *FSS* **12** (1984) 237–248.

37. D. Sauter, G. Dubois, E. Levrat, and J. Bremont, "Fault diagnosis in systems using fuzzy logic," EUFIT'93, First European Congress on Fuzzy and Intelligent Technologies, Aachen.

38. S. Sessa, "Some results in the setting of fuzzy relation equations theory," *FSS* **14** (1984) 281–297.

39. G. M. Trojan, J. B. Kiszka, and M. M. Gupta, "Solution of multivariable fuzzy equations," *FSS* **23** (1987) 271–279.

40. S. Weber, "A general concept of fuzzy connectives, negations and implications based on t-norms and t-conorms," *FSS* **11** (1983) 115–134.

41. L. A. Zadeh, "The concept of a linguistic variable and its application to approximate reasoning I," *Information Sciences*, **8** (1975) 199–249.

42. L. A. Zadeh, "The concept of a linguistic variable and its application to approximate reasoning II," *Information Sciences*, **8** (1975) 301–357.

43. L. A. Zadeh, "The concept of a linguistic variable and its application to approximate reasoning III," *Information Sciences*, **9** (1975) 43–80.

CHAPTER 9

ADDITIVE FUZZY SYSTEMS: FROM FUNCTION APPROXIMATION TO LEARNING

Bart Kosko

Signal and Image Processing Institute
Electrical Engineering Department
University of Southern California
Los Angeles, California

This chapter presents the theory of additive fuzzy systems. This family of functions is dense in the space of continuous functions. An additive fuzzy system with a finite number of rules can approximate any continuous function on a compact domain to any degree of accuracy. Each rule defines a patch or fuzzy subset of the input-output product space. The system approximates a function when it covers its graph with rule patches and adds or averages patches that overlap. Blind approximation leads to combinatorial rule explosion in the graph cover. The number of rules needed to cover a graph grows exponentially with the number of input and output variables. Lone optimal rule patches cover the extrema of the approximand and offer one way to deal with the rule explosion. Learning moves and shapes the rule patches. The best learning schemes quickly find and cover the extrema or bumps in the graph of the approximand and then move rule patches between the extrema as the rule budget allows. Fuzzy function representation allows a standard additive model (SAM) F to exactly represent continuous functions in the sense of $F = f$ if we have full knowledge of f. It reduces the exponential rule complexity to linear complexity. Additive systems F act as model-free conditional expectations and thus define a class of probabilistic systems. The SAM theorem shows that the global conditional mean is a convex sum of local conditional means. SAMs with constant volume then-part sets reduce to the popular but ad hoc family of "center of gravity" fuzzy systems. Unsupervised learning clusters data in the product space to form and tune rules in a SAM. Supervised gradient descent tunes SAM parameters when a teacher gives desired outputs to form error signals.

9.1   *THE STANDARD ADDITIVE MODEL:*
SUMMED AND SCALED THEN-PART SETS

An *additive* fuzzy system [13, 15–19] $F: R^n \to R^p$ stores m if-then rules of the word form "If $X = A_j$, then $Y = B_j$," or patch form $A_j \times B_j \subset R^n \times R^p$ and then *adds* or sums the "fired" then-parts $B'_j \subset R^p$:

$$B = \sum_{j=1}^{m} w_j B'_j \qquad (9.1)$$

for scalar rule weights $w_j \in R$. The rule weights can reflect the importance of a rule, the credibility of a knowledge source, or the frequency or what Zadeh [40] calls the "usuality" of a rule. In contrast, most *non*additive fuzzy systems of Mamdani [21, 22] and Sugeno [7, 32, 34] combine fired then-part sets with pairwise maxima:

$$B = \bigcup_{j=1}^{m} w_j B'_j \qquad (9.2)$$

The sum combiner in Eq. (9.1) lets each rule contribute to the output set B. The max combiner in Eq. (9.2) ignores all fired then-part set consensus or overlap $B'_j \cap B'_{j+1} \neq \varnothing$ and gives B as just the envelope of the fired sets. When many rules fire this envelope tends toward a rectangle or nonfuzzy set in the output space [12, 16]. The max combiner is part of the legacy of the "extension principle" [7, 11] of earlier abstract fuzzy theory [39, 40]. This chapter deals with only additive fuzzy systems.

The fuzzy system is a *standard additive model* or SAM if it computes the output value $F(x) \in R^p$ from B in Eq. (9.1) as the centroid of B and if the vector input $x \in R^n$ fires each rule through scaling or correlation-product inference [15, 26]:

$$F(x) = \text{centroid}\,(B) = \text{centroid}\left(\sum_{j=1}^{m} w_j a_j(x) B_j \right) \qquad (9.3)$$

The rule weights cancel out of Eq. (9.3) if they all equal the same value: $w_1 = \ldots = w_j$.

In Eq. (9.3) $a_j: R^n \to [0, 1]$ is the joint set function of the *multivalued* (or "vague" [1] or "fuzzy" [39]) if-part set $A_j \subset R^n$ and $b_j: R^p \to [0, 1]$ is the set function of the then-part set $B_j \subset R^p$. In practice we often work with scalar systems $F: R^n \to R$ with $b_j: R \to [0, 1]$ and with factored if-part sets $A_j = A_j^1 \times \ldots \times A_j^n$. The factored sets allow us to work with their n coordinate projections A_j^i as scalar fuzzy sets on n independent input axes. The SAM structure allows us to replace the then-part set B_j with just its area or volume V_j and its centroid c_j.

The input x belongs to A_j to the degree or *fit* (fuzzy unit) value $a_j(x)$. Then the input x_0 "fires" or "activates" a rule or its if-part set A_j when it convolves with the set as a precise delta pulse $\delta(x - x_0)$:

$$a_j(x_0) = \int_{R^n} a_j(x)\delta(x - x_0)dx$$

The value $a_j(x_0)$ then scales the then-part set B_j to give the fired then-part in the SAM system Eq. (9.3): $B'_j = a_j(x_0) B_j$.

Figure 9.1 shows the geometry of a scalar additive fuzzy system $F: R \to R$ with m rules. In general each rule defines the product-space patch [15] $A_j \times B_j \subset R^n \times R^p$. The additive fuzzy system approximates the function f by covering its graph with rule patches and adding with Eq. (9.1) or averaging patches that overlap. The patch cov-

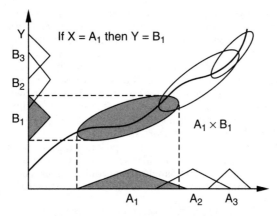

FIGURE 9.1 Rule-patch geometry of an additive fuzzy system. Each of the m rules of the form "If X is if-part fuzzy set A_j, then Y is then-part fuzzy set B_j" defines the cartesian-product rule patch $A_j \times B_j$ or fuzzy subset of the input-output product space $X \times Y$. The additive fuzzy system approximates the function f by covering its graph with rule patches and adding or averaging patches that overlap. The fuzzy graph cover suffers an exponential rule explosion when the dimension of the input space X or of the output space Y grows. Lone optimal rules cover the extrema of the approximand f. Learning tends to move rule patches to extrema and then fill in between them with extra tuned patches.

ering shows the fundamental weakness of fuzzy systems: they suffer an exponential rule explosion as the input dimension n grows or as output dimension p grows [17]. For blind approximation the fuzzy system $F: R^n \to R^p$ needs on the order of k^{n+p-1} rules [18] to approximate the vector map $f: R^n \to R^p$. Thus fuzzy systems do not scale up. This shows up in even small-scale scalar fuzzy systems $F: R^n \to R$ with overlapping factored if-part fuzzy sets A_j^i. Then each input x tends to belong to a nonzero degree to 2^n if-part fuzzy sets A_j^i and thus tends to fire 2^n of the $m \approx k^n$ rules.

Optimal rules can help deal with the rule explosion. How do we best allocate a fixed budget of rules? Lone optimal rules cover the extrema of the approximand [17] or *patch the bumps*. This reduces much of fuzzy function approximation to a search [20] for the zeroes $\hat{x}$ of the approximand's derivative map: $f'(\hat{x}) = 0$. Better learning schemes move rule patches to or near extrema and then fill in with extra rules between these bumps so as to minimize the residual error function [28] and thus to patch its bumps. This holds not only for mean-squared error but for all l^p with $p > 0$. Zadeh [39] observed that scalar rule patches can cover both functions and relations. But Zadeh failed to observe the resulting exponential rule explosion or the optimality of extrema-covering rules. He also did not show how to convert a set of abstract rules or rule patches into a well-defined function $F: R^n \to R^p$ with output $F(x)$ for each input x.

The *fuzzy approximation theorem* (FAT) [16] below shows that an additive fuzzy system can uniformly approximate any continuous (or bounded and measurable) function f on a compact set amid the rule explosion in the patch cover. Watkins [36, 37] has shown that an additive fuzzy system F can exactly represent f in the sense of

$f(x) = F(x)$ for all x if we have complete knowledge of f and if we pack the structure of f into the if-part sets A_j. Indeed an F with just *two* rules can represent a bounded $f: R \to R$ even if f is not continuous. This reduces the exponential rule complexity of blind fuzzy function approximation to linear rule complexity.

The SAM structure also allows us to combine any number of fuzzy systems of any type [19]. A pool of q experts can each define a fuzzy system $F_k: R^n \to R^p$ with their own set of if-then rules. We can then additively combine their own combined rule "firings" $B^1, \ldots, B^q$ to form a new weighted set B in Eq. (9.1) and then use Eq. (9.3) to define the new combined mapping. In this case the weights $w_1, \ldots, w_q$ measure each expert's credibility [33] or test-score status [12].

The SAM theorem in Sec. 9.2 allows us to pick any if-part set functions $a_j: R^n \to [0, 1]$. In practice we work with the n scalar set-function factors $a_j^1, a_j^2, \ldots, a_j^n$. These factors $a_j^i: R \to R$ are the familiar triangles, trapezoids, and bell curves of fuzzy engineering. The most common way to combine them is with pairwise minimum:

$$a_j(x) = a_j^1(x_1) \wedge a_j^2(x_2) \wedge \ldots \wedge a_j^n(x_n) \tag{9.4}$$

for input vector $x = (x_1, x_2, \ldots, x_n)$. Suppose the input temperature value is 80 percent warm and the input humidity is 60 percent high in a simple air conditioner. Then the factor 60% = min (80%, 60%) scales the then-part set B_j to give $0.6B_j$.

The min combiner is a conjunctive or AND combiner. Both factors must hold to high degree to "fire" the rule to a high degree. We assume that the if-part factors combine a_j^i with AND though the SAM model allows any logic scheme to arrive at $a_j: R^n \to [0, 1]$. So we could replace the min in Eq. (9.4) with max to model OR if-parts. This seldom occurs in practice. In this chapter we work with Eq. (9.4) as the default combiner.

Engineers increasingly use product in place of min to factor the if-part set function:

$$a_j(x) = \prod_{i=1}^{n} a_j^i(x_i) \tag{9.5}$$

This may arise in hardware devices that compute product more easily than minimum [23]. Optical devices compute products and sums with ease but have more trouble with mins, maxes, divisions, and differences. The if-part product [Eq. (9.5)] can also arise when working with a radial basis [9, 24, 31] or Gaussian [34] if-part set functions:

$$a_j^i(x_i) = s_i^j \exp\left[-\frac{1}{2}\left(\frac{x_i - \bar{x}_i^j}{\sigma_i^j} \right)^2 \right] \tag{9.6}$$

for scaling constant $0 < s_i^j \le 1$. Then the product in Eq. (9.5) gives the exponential of a sum. These radial basis nets center a gaussian ball at the mean vector $\bar{x}_j = (\bar{x}_1^j, \ldots, \bar{x}_n^j)$. Each scalar mean value $\bar{x}_i^j$ centers a bell curve with variance $(\sigma_i^j)^2$. These n variances make up the diagonal of some covariance matrix K [14] with zero entries off the diagonal. So Eq. (9.5) assumes that the n factors in Eq. (9.6) are independent gaussian random variables. The product factor remains sensitive to input changes while the min factor ignores data.

In theory any conjunctive combiner T can compute $a_j(x)$ from its n factors a_j^1, $a_j^2, \ldots, a_j^n$:

$$a_j(x) = T(a_j^1(x_1), \ldots, a_j^n(x_n)) \tag{9.7}$$

Here T can be a so-called *T norm* or *triangular norm* [11, 15] with dual disjunctive or OR T conorm S. T norms and T conorms obey $T(x,y) \le \min(x,y) \le \max(x,y) \le S(x,y)$

for x and y in $[0, 1]$. The product T-norm $T(x,y) = xy$ has De Morgan dual T conorm $S(x,y) = 1 - T(1 - x, 1 - y) = x + y - xy$. We can also use a T norm to form the fired or inferred set B'_j in (1): $B'_j = T(a_j(x), B_j)$. Few engineers use T norms in practice other than min or product. The min clip $B'_j = a_j(x) \wedge B_j$ or *correlation-minimum inference* [15] still occurs in practice but much less so than it once did. It both ignores all information in B'_j above the fit-value threshold $a_j(x)$ and does not lead to as simple a transfer function as the SAM equation (9.8). T norms are far more popular among theorists than engineers. They do capture the De Morgan duality of AND and OR among if-part factors. But their popularity in the older fuzzy literature is far more the result of the analytical platform they provide than of their proven value in real systems.

9.2 THE SAM THEOREM: SYSTEM OUTPUTS AS CONVEX SUMS OF THEN-PART CENTROIDS

The computational power of additive systems comes from the standard additive model theorem [15]. This gives the system output $F(x)$ as a simple convex sum of the m then-part set centroids c_j. The m convex coefficients $p_1(x), \ldots, p_m(x)$ change only with the if-part set values $a_j(x)$ and act as the m terms of a discrete probability density:

$$\sum_{j=1}^{m} p_j(x) = 1$$

for each input x. This lets us precompute the m then-part volumes V_j and centroids c_j in advance. Wang [35] has recently renamed the m convex coefficients $p_1(x), \ldots, p_m(x)$ as "fuzzy basis functions" in the gaussian SAM case with product if-part sets Eq. (9.5).

Theorem 9.1 (SAM Theorem). Suppose the fuzzy system $F: R^n \rightarrow R^p$ is a *standard additive model*: $F(x) = centroid\ (B) = centroid\ (\sum_{j=1}^{m} a_j(x)B_j)$. Then $F(x)$ is a convex sum of the m then-part set centroids:

$$F(x) = \frac{\sum_{j=1}^{m} a_j(x)V_j c_j}{\sum_{j=1}^{m} a_j(x)V_j} \tag{9.8}$$

$$= \sum_{j=1}^{m} p_j(x)c_j \tag{9.9}$$

The convex coefficients or discrete probability weights $p_1(x), \ldots, p_m(x)$ depend on the input x through

$$p_j(x) = \frac{a_j(x)V_j}{\sum_{k=1}^{m} a_k(x)V_k} \tag{9.10}$$

V_j is the finite positive volume (or area if $p = 1$) and c_j is the centroid of then-part set B_j:

$$V_j = \int_{R^p} b_j(y_1, \ldots, y_p)dy_1 \cdots dy_p > 0 \tag{9.11}$$

$$c_j = \frac{\int_{R^p} y b_j(y_1, \ldots, y_p) dy_1 \cdots dy_p}{\int_{R^p} b_j(y_1, \ldots, y_p) dy_1 \cdots dy_p} \tag{9.12}$$

Proof. There is no loss of generality to prove the theorem for the scalar-output case $p = 1$ when $F: R^n \to R$. This simplifies the notation. We need but replace the scalar integrals over R with the p-multiple or volume integrals over R^p in the proof to prove the general case. The scalar case $p = 1$ gives Eqs. (9.11) and (9.12) as

$$V_j = \int_{-\infty}^{\infty} b_j(y) dy \tag{9.13}$$

$$c_j = \frac{\int_{-\infty}^{\infty} y b_j(y) dy}{\int_{-\infty}^{\infty} b_j(y) dy} \tag{9.14}$$

Then the theorem follows if we expand the centroid of B and invoke the SAM assumption [Eq. (9.3)] to rearrange terms:

$$F(x) = \text{centroid}(B) \tag{9.15}$$

$$= \frac{\int_{-\infty}^{\infty} y b(y) dy}{\int_{-\infty}^{\infty} b(y) dy} \tag{9.16}$$

$$= \frac{\int_{-\infty}^{\infty} y \sum_{j=1}^{m} b_j'(y) dy}{\int_{-\infty}^{\infty} \sum_{j=1}^{m} b_j'(y) dy} \tag{9.17}$$

$$= \frac{\int_{-\infty}^{\infty} y \sum_{j=1}^{m} a_j(x) b_j(y) dy}{\int_{-\infty}^{\infty} \sum_{j=1}^{m} a_j(x) b_j(y) dy} \tag{9.18}$$

$$= \frac{\sum_{j=1}^{m} a_j(x) \int_{-\infty}^{\infty} y b_j(y) dy}{\sum_{j=1}^{m} a_j(y) \int_{-\infty}^{\infty} b_j(y) dy} \tag{9.19}$$

$$= \frac{\sum_{j=1}^{m} a_j(x) V_j \dfrac{\int_{-\infty}^{\infty} y b_j(y) dy}{V_j}}{\sum_{j=1}^{m} a_j(x) V_j} \tag{9.20}$$

$$= \frac{\sum_{j=1}^{m} a_j(x)V_j c_j}{\sum_{j=1}^{m} a_j(x)V_j} \tag{9.21}$$

as we set out to prove.

The SAM structure [Eq. (9.8)] lets us replace all then-part fuzzy sets B_j with rectangles or *nonfuzzy* sets R_j that have the same volume V_j and centroid c_j. Consider the hypercube R_j centered at c_j that has volume V_j and unit height. Then R_j has a binary set function $r_j : R^p \rightarrow \{0, 1\}$ and so defines a standard or nonfuzzy set. In the scalar case $F : R^n \rightarrow R$ the jth rectangle has the one-dimensional cube base $[c_j - V_j/2, c_j + V_j/2]$. In the vector case $F : R^n \rightarrow R^p$ the jth rectangle has a p-dimensional cube base with p sides of the form $[c_j^k - \sqrt[p]{V_j}/2, c_j^k + \sqrt[p]{V_j}/2]$. So we can dispense with half the fuzziness of a fuzzy system F. An exercise shows that we can find rectangles centered at the then-part centroids c_j that partition the p coordinates of the range space. These rectangles need not have unit height.

Sometimes we normalize the volumes to unity so the terms V_j do not appear in Eq. (9.8). Otherwise the volumes act as rule weights. The larger V_j the more it forces the global output $F(x)$ to act like the local rule output c_j:

$$\lim_{V_j \rightarrow \infty} F(x) = \lim_{V_j \rightarrow \infty} \frac{\sum_{k=1}^{m} a_k V_k c_k}{\sum_{k=1}^{m} a_k V_k} \tag{9.22}$$

$$= \lim_{V_j \rightarrow \infty} \frac{a_j V_j c_j + c}{a_j V_j + d} \tag{9.23}$$

$$= c_j \tag{9.24}$$

Some learning schemes may weight the jth rule with the inverse volume $1/V_j$ to give less weight to large or uncertain rules. This can arise when we grow ellipsoidal rules from error covariance matrices [4–6].

Learning schemes may also require that $F(x)$ be differentiable. This holds in the SAM case [Eq. (9.8)] just in case all the if-part sets $a_j(x)$ are differentiable. So the fuzzy system is only *piecewise* differentiable if the if-part sets are triangles, trapezoids, rectangles, or other curves with "corners." The gaussian bell curves in Eq. (9.6) give a differentiable SAM system.

The convex weights $p_1(x), \ldots, p_m(x)$ define a discrete probability density function $p(x)$ for each input x since the m terms are nonnegative and sum to one. So for each input x the fuzzy system F defines the expected value of the m output centroids c_j with respect to $p(x)$:

$$F(x) = \sum_{j=1}^{m} p_j(x)c_j = E_{p(x)}[C] \tag{9.25}$$

We show below that each such value $F(x)$ is just one realization of a random conditional mean vector $\mathbf{E}[Y \mid X = x]$. So we can view a SAM fuzzy system as a way to pick a good set of centroid weights for each input x.

Convexity also implies the key geometric constraint that $F(x)$ lies at or between the least and greatest centroid value for each of the p centroid components in the range space R^p. We can state this for the scalar case $F : R^n \rightarrow R$ as follows:

$$c_1 \leq F(x) \leq c_m \tag{9.26}$$

This holds for all densities $p(x)$ and for all centroidal additive systems. The proof below of the fuzzy approximation theorem depends on this fact.

The vector case $\bar{F}: R^n \to R^p$ shows that $F(x)$ lies in a p-dimensional hyperrectangle or centroid box of the form $[c_{\text{left}}^1, c_{\text{right}}^1] \times \cdots \times [c_{\text{left}}^p, c_{\text{right}}^p] \subset R^p$. The convex weight $p_j(x)$ scales the jth vector centroid $c_j = (c_j^1, \ldots, c_j^p)$ by scaling its p components: $p_j(x)c_j = (p_j(x)\, c_j^1, \ldots, p_j(x)\, c_j^p)$. Then

$$F(x) = (F_1(x), \ldots, F_p(x)) = \sum_{j=1}^{m} p_j(x)c_j \tag{9.27}$$

$$= \left(\sum_{j=1}^{m} p_j(x)c_j^1, \ldots, \sum_{j=1}^{m} p_j(x)c_j^p \right) \tag{9.28}$$

So each fuzzy output component $F_k(x)$ is a convex combination of the m scalars $c_1^k, \ldots, c_m^k$. So $c_{\text{left}}^k \leq F_k(x) \leq c_{\text{right}}^k$ holds for $c_{\text{left}}^k = \min (c_1^k, \ldots, c_m^k)$ and $c_{\text{right}}^k = \max (c_1^k, \ldots, c_m^k)$. So $F(x) \in [c_{\text{left}}^1, c_{\text{right}}^1] \times \cdots \times [c_{\text{left}}^p, c_{\text{right}}^p] \subset R^p$ as claimed. To match the centroid cube to the range of f is the first geometric step in fuzzy function approximation. Before we explore how SAMs can uniformly approximate functions we briefly look at the most popular special cases of SAMs.

9.3   THE CENTER OF GRAVITY METHOD AS A CONSTANT-VOLUME SAM

The SAM fuzzy system

$$F(x) = \frac{\displaystyle\sum_{j=1}^{m} a_j(x)V_j c_j}{\displaystyle\sum_{j=1}^{m} a_j(x)V_j} \tag{9.29}$$

reduces to the *center of gravity* (COG) fuzzy model

$$F(x) = \frac{\displaystyle\sum_{j=1}^{m} a_j(x)P_j}{\displaystyle\sum_{j=1}^{m} a_j(x)} \tag{9.30}$$

if the modes or "peaks" P_j of the then-part sets $B_j \subset R^p$ equal the then-part set centroids c_j and if the then-part sets B_j all have the same areas or volumes V_j: $P_j = c_j$ and $V_1 = \cdots = V_m > 0$. Sugeno [32] and other Japanese fuzzy engineers [34] have popularized the COG model as an *ad hoc* scheme to defuzzify a fuzzy system's set output B. In this way many fuzzy engineers have used the SAM model without knowing it.

Some engineers dispense with the fuzzy structure of B_j and replace it with a spike centered at c_j on the real line R or in theory at some point in R^p. Then the set function $b_j: R^p \to [0, 1]$ of then-part set B_j is just a delta pulse: $b_j(y) = \delta(y - c_j)$. Some use the unit-pulse convention that $b_j(c_j) = 1$ but this is not needed. Indeed formally a Dirac delta function [15] obeys $\delta(y - c_j) = \infty$ if $y = c_j$ and $\delta(y - c_j) = 0$ if $y \neq c_j$. In any case the pulse set B_j has unit volume and c_j as its centroid:

$$V_j = \int_{R^p} \delta(y - c_j)dy = 1 \tag{9.31}$$

$$\text{Centroid } (B_j) = \frac{\int_{R^p} y\, \delta(y - c_j)dy}{\int_{R^p} \delta(y - c_j)dy} = \int_{R^p} y\, \delta(y - c_j)dy = c_j \tag{9.32}$$

So the proof of the SAM theorem still holds. Again the SAM system [Eq. (9.29)] reduces to the COG model [Eq. (9.30)] with $P_j = c_j$ and $V_1 = \cdots = V_m > 0$.

Often engineers misuse the SAM/COG model because they vary the structure of the then-part sets B_j while they still assume that the set structure does not vary. They hand-tune the sets B_j or let a learning scheme move and reshape them. Then the peaks P_j may differ from the set centroids c_j. More often the then-part set widths or volumes differ. This practice seems to stem from a desire to keep each then-part set triangle, trapezoid, or bell curve of unit height and yet adjust its width or base to reflect the rule's importance to the system output $F(x)$. We tend to place narrow sets near equilibrium regions for more precise control and place wider sets further away for rougher control and to quickly bring the system closer to equilibrium. But then the COG model gives more weight to the less important rules since their then-parts B_j have more area or volume V_j. This can lead to needless bouts of tuning and to poor function approximation. The simple solution is either to use the full SAM system (29) with variable set volumes V_j or to not insist that the then-part "sets" B_j have unit height and normalize them to again use a proper SAM system.

The misuse of COG models runs so deep in fuzzy engineering because of the model's *ad hoc* nature. Engineers often use the COG model [Eq. (9.30)] to compute a quick $F(x)$ and then justify the model by pointing to its practical effects and by wrongly citing the nonadditive combiner [Eq. (9.2)] as the theoretical basis for the method. The warping effects of the COG models would improve somewhat or perhaps a great deal if a SAM processed the same data with the same rules.

A simple gaussian SAM gives both a COG model and the popular radial-basis-function (RBF) model of neural networks of Moody [9, 24] and Specht [31]. Wang and Mendel [35] have recently restated this RBF model in fuzzy notation as a simple scalar gaussian SAM $F: R^n \to R$:

$$F(x) = \frac{\sum_{j=1}^{m} \bar{z}^j \left(\prod_{i=1}^{n} \mu_{A_i^j}(x_i) \right)}{\sum_{j=1}^{m} \left(\prod_{i=1}^{n} \mu_{A_i^j}(x_i) \right)} \tag{9.33}$$

The SAM of Eq. (9.8) reduces to Eq. (9.33) for gaussian sets with product combination of if-part set values:

$$y = z \tag{9.34}$$

$$a_j(x) = \prod_{i=1}^{n} a_j^i(x_i) \tag{9.35}$$

$$= \prod_{i=1}^{n} \mu_{A_i^j}(x_i) \tag{9.36}$$

$$V_j = 1 \qquad (9.37)$$

$$c_j = \bar{z}^j \qquad (9.38)$$

The unity volume follows in Eq. (9.37) since Wang and Mendel integrate their m then-part gaussian sets over all of R and thus use the scaling constant in Eq. (9.6) in their if-part gaussian sets to account for the input truncation to a compact set. Equation (9.38) follows because the mode of a gaussian set equals its centroid and Wang and Mendel use the mode definition "$\bar{z}^j$ is the point in R at which $\mu_{B_j}(z)$ achieves its maximum value." Moody [24] arrived at Eq. (9.33) in his search for a neural network built from the m input-output pairs (x_j, y_j) with light computation. Specht [31] independently arrived at Eq. (9.33) from the theory of Parzen density estimators and the use of conditional expectations as mean-squared optimal estimators. They all center a vector gaussian set or ball at each input vector x_j and center a gaussian bell curve at each output value y_j.

9.4 FUZZY SYSTEMS AS CONDITIONAL MEANS: F(x) = E[Y | X = x]

The debate over whether fuzziness differs from randomness occurs at both the set level and the system level. The set-level debate turns on how we use binary or multivalued sets to model events. Then fuzziness deals with the degree that an event occurs [15]: "The rain today is light." All rain patterns are both light L and not-light L^c to some degree. In general this breaks the bivalent "laws" of noncontradiction and excluded middle: $L \cap L^c \neq \varnothing$ and $L \cup L^c \neq X$. Randomness deals with whether an event occurs: "There is a 20 percent chance that it will rain today." Here whether it rains is binary, or either-or. It will rain R or it will not rain R^c and not both or neither: prob $\{R \cap R^c \neq \varnothing\} = 0$ and prob $\{R \cup R^c = X\} = 1$. Standard probability measures [30] map only binary sets to real numbers. So noncontradiction and excluded middle always hold: $R \cap R^c = \varnothing$ and $R \cup R^c = X$.

These two modes of set or event uncertainty can apply to each other at a higher level if one mode describes the other. Fuzzy probability deals with the vagueness in a random description [40]: "The odds are slight it will rain today." Here the odds of the event are vague but the raining event itself is binary. The probability of fuzzy events deals with whether vague events occur: "There is a 20 percent chance of light rain today." Here the odds are exact but the event is not binary or either-or.

We can also view a fuzzy set A as a random set [25] or locus of two-point conditional probability densities. Then the set degree $a(x) = $ degree $\{x \in A\}$ becomes the local conditional probability prob $\{X = A | X = x\}$ and the complement fit value $1 - a(x) = $ degree $\{x \notin A\}$ becomes the dual probability prob $\{X \neq A \mid X = x\}$. Suppose A is the subset of cool air temperatures. On the global set view $a(x)$ is the degree to which air temperature value x is a cool value. On the local random-set view $a(x)$ is the probability that the temperature is cool given that the temperature value is x. So we can equally view A as a locus of multivalued set values or a locus of two-point conditional probabilities.

We can also view how much one set contains another as a measure of subsethood [15] or conditional probability and from this derive many of the key concepts of both fuzzy sets and probability theory. These views range from the mathematical to the aesthetic. They do not directly affect the nature of fuzzy systems even though they often arose when fuzzy engineers first put forth their systems and the press first tried to describe them.

The debate at the system level $F:R^n \to R^p$ is not a debate at all. A simple argument shows that *all* centroidal fuzzy systems are probabilistic systems. Indeed the result is stronger: A centroidal fuzzy system F computes conditional expectation $E[Y \mid X]$ and thus computes a mean-squared optimal nonlinear estimator [27]. The power of the fuzzy system lies both in this optimality result and in its *model-free* structure. Most popular conditional-mean systems use a math model of the plant. The linear Kalman filter uses a linear Gauss-Markov state model and assumes all variables are jointly gaussian. A fuzzy system does its mean-squared best to model a system or approximate a function with its rules or paired sets or densities. The sets themselves can be rectangles and thus nonfuzzy and still the rules may give a good graph cover and thus a good approximation to some sampled or learned approximand f.

The proof that centroidal fuzzy systems are conditional means follows from the ratio structure of the centroid and the nonnegativity of the set values ($b(x, y) \geq 0$) of the combined set B of fired then-part sets in Eqs. (9.1) or (9.2) or in any other combination scheme. Each input x gives its own $B(x)$ and thus its own output $F(x)$:

$$F(x) = \text{centroid } (B(x)) \tag{9.39}$$

$$= \frac{\int_{R^p} y b(x,y) dy}{\int_{R^p} b(x,y) dy} \tag{9.40}$$

$$= \int_{R^p} y p(y \mid x) dy \tag{9.41}$$

$$= E[Y \mid X = x] \tag{9.42}$$

for each $x \in R^n$. This holds because the joint/marginal ratio in Eq. (9.40) defines a proper conditional probability

$$p(y \mid x) = \frac{b(x,y)}{\int_{R^p} b(x,y) dy} \tag{9.43}$$

even though $b(x,y) > 0$ may hold.

The fuzzy system F in Eq. (9.39) need not be additive. The SAM theorem above shows what happens if F is additive and SAM in structure. Then $F(x)$ is a convex sum of centroids or local conditional (then-part set) means. We now show [19] that this convexity property holds for all additive systems and that the same convex weights decompose the conditional variance of the system. The conditional variance gives us a confidence measure for each output $F(x)$.

In practice we can compute the local conditional means or centroids in advance but not so with the local conditional variances. The result holds for general additive maps $F:R^n \to R^p$. For simplicity and to avoid the matrix notation we prove it for the scalar case where F maps to R. The result holds for standard additive models when $B_j'(x) = a_j(x) B_j$.

Theorem 9.2. Suppose $F:R^n \to R$ is an additive fuzzy system such that

$$F(x) = \text{centroid } (B) \quad \text{and} \quad B(x) = \sum_{j=1}^{m} B_j'(x)$$

Then
$$F(x) = E[Y \mid X = x] = \sum_{j=1}^{m} p_j(x) E_{B'_j}[Y \mid X = x] \tag{9.44}$$

$$V[Y \mid X = x] = \sum_{j=1}^{m} p_j(x) \, V[Y \mid X = x, B'_j] \tag{9.45}$$

The convex coefficients $p_j(x)$ are volume ratios of fired sets B'_j:

$$p_j(x) = \frac{V'_j}{\displaystyle\sum_{k=1}^{m} V'_k} \tag{9.46}$$

$$V'_j = \int b'_j(x,y)\,dy \tag{9.47}$$

Proof. We first repeat the chain of equalities to show that the additive fuzzy system F computes a realization of the conditional expectation for each input x. The same chain of equalities then shows that $F(x)$ is a convex sum of local conditional mean realizations or centroids:

$$F(x) = \text{centroid}\,(B(x)) \tag{9.48}$$

$$= \frac{\displaystyle\int_{-\infty}^{\infty} y\,b(x,y)\,dy}{\displaystyle\int_{-\infty}^{\infty} b(x,y)\,dy} \tag{9.49}$$

$$= \int_{-\infty}^{\infty} y\,p_B(y \mid x)\,dy \tag{9.50}$$

$$= E[Y \mid X = x] \tag{9.51}$$

$$= \frac{\displaystyle\sum_{j=1}^{m} \int_{-\infty}^{\infty} y\,b'_j(x,y)\,dy}{\displaystyle\sum_{j=1}^{m} \int_{-\infty}^{\infty} b'_j(x,y)\,dy} \tag{9.52}$$

$$= \frac{\displaystyle\sum_{j=1}^{m} \int_{-\infty}^{\infty} b'_j(x,y)\,dy\,\frac{\displaystyle\int_{-\infty}^{\infty} y\,b'_j(x,y)\,dy}{\displaystyle\int_{-\infty}^{\infty} b'_j(x,y)\,dy}}{\displaystyle\sum_{j=1}^{m} \int_{-\infty}^{\infty} b'_j(x,y)\,dy} \tag{9.53}$$

$$= \frac{\displaystyle\sum_{j=1}^{m} V'_j \int_{-\infty}^{\infty} y\,b'_j(y \mid x)\,dy}{\displaystyle\sum_{j=1}^{m} V'_j} \tag{9.54}$$

$$= \sum_{j=1}^{m} p_j(x) E_{B_j'}[Y \mid X = x] \tag{9.55}$$

$$= \sum_{j=1}^{m} p_j(x) c_j' \tag{9.56}$$

which proves Eq. (9.44). The proof of Eq. (9.45) follows in the same way:

$$V[Y \mid X = x] = \frac{\int_{-\infty}^{\infty} (y - E[Y \mid X = x])^2 \, b(x, y) dy}{\int_{-\infty}^{\infty} b(x, y) dy} \tag{9.57}$$

$$= \sum_{j=1}^{m} p_j(x) \int_{-\infty}^{\infty} (y - E[Y \mid X = x])^2 p_{B_j'}(y \mid x) dy \tag{9.58}$$

$$= \sum_{j=1}^{m} p_j(x) V[Y \mid X = x, B_j'] \tag{9.59}$$

Then the unconditional output variance $V_Y(Y)$ follows from Eqs. (9.44) and (9.45) and from the standard variance decomposition

$$V_Y(Y) = E_X(V[Y \mid X]) + V_X(E[Y \mid X]) \tag{9.60}$$

The variance term $V[Y \mid X = x, B_j']$ does not equal the local jth conditional variance $V_{B_j'}[Y \mid X = x]$ in general since it measures the dispersion about the global centroid $F(x)$ and not about the local centroid c_j' of the jth fired then-part set B_j':

$$V_{B_j'}[Y \mid X = x] = \int_{-\infty}^{\infty} (y - c_j')^2 p_{B_j'}(y \mid x) dy \tag{9.61}$$

The rare case of $F(x) = c_j'$ may arise if input x belongs more to if-part fuzzy set A_j than to the near neighbors A_{j-1} and A_{j+1}: $a_j(x) > \max(a_{j-1}(x), a_{j+1}(x))$. The extreme case of $a_j(x) = 1$ and $a_k(x) = 0$ for $k \neq j$ and Eq. (9.59) leads to $V[Y \mid X = x] = V_{B_j'}[Y \mid X = x]$ as well as to $F(x) = c_j'$. In the standard additive model $c_j' = c_j$ holds and we can compute the local then-part set centroids c_j in advance. Equation (9.45) confirms that we must compute the local variance-like terms for each input x. The variance term $V[Y \mid X = x, B_j']$ is large when $F(x)$ lies far from c_j'. But then a_j tends to be small and so too will be the variance weight V_j'.

9.5 FUNCTION APPROXIMATION AND REPRESENTATION WITH ADDITIVE FUZZY SYSTEMS

Additive fuzzy systems $F: R^n \to R^p$ can uniformly approximate any continuous function $f: U \subset R^n \to R^p$ on a compact (closed and bounded) domain U [16]. This result holds for fuzzy sets of all types and for additive systems other than SAMs. The proof below exploits the convex expansion of $F(x)$ in Eq. (9.26). The result holds for other methods [38] of defuzzifying B in Eq. (9.1) that trap $F(x)$ between the same bounds.

A finer and finer rule-patch cover is the thrust of the uniform fuzzy approximation theorem. We can always find a finite number of rule patches to cover the graph of f to keep the distance $|f(x) - F(x)|$ as small as we please for all x. In practice we must guess at the rules or use a neural or statistical scheme to learn them from data. We must also balance the fineness of the patch approximation with how much it costs to process and tune the rules.

The uniform approximation lets us pick the error level ε in advance. Then for all $\varepsilon > 0$ we have that $|f(x) - F(x)| < \varepsilon$ for all x in X. The domain X is a compact (closed and bounded) subset of R^n. X may be an interval $[u,v]$ where $u < v$ or a product of intervals $[u_1, v_1] \times \cdots \times [u_n, v_n]$. The uniform approximation of continuous functions allows us in theory to replace each continuous fuzzy set with a finite discretization or a point in a unit hypercube [13, 15] or fuzzy space of high dimension.

The fuzzy approximation would not be of much use if each input x had its own error level $\varepsilon(x)$. Thus we insist on a uniform approximation. Then once we pick the error level we can find a finite set of fuzzy rules that gives a fuzzy system F ε-close to f. These ε-rules "exist" just as in a chess game an optimal set of moves exists from any stage in the game even though no one has found these moves.

In practice we may never find the rules or we may find only some of them in some regions of the state space $X \times Y$. We can ask experts for the rules or watch experts or real processes to learn them or we can just guess at them. These first rules initialize the learning process. We can then tune them with gradient descent or random hill climbing or other search techniques. But the rules learned from a finite stream of data may not give an F ε-close to f.

The history of fuzzy function approximation starts in the early 1990s and tracks the history of neural function approximation that starts in the late 1980s. Fuzzy systems have a left-to-right feedforward structure that acts much as a feedforward multilayer neural network acts. Nodes combine inputs and pass those signals to the next layer of nodes.

In 1989 Hornik et al. [10] first used the Stone-Weierstrass theorem of functional analysis [30] to show uniform convergence of such neural networks. (The Stone-Weierstrass theorem states that $A = C(X)$ if $C(X)$ is the sup-norm space of continuous functions on a compact and Hausdorf space X and if the set of functions $A \subset C(X)$ is a closed algebra and if A is self-adjoint and separates points and contains the constant functions.) Cybenko [3] published a like result in the same year. These results do not show how to build or learn real neural systems. The neurons and synapses do not correspond to fuzzy rule patches and their patch geometry. Radial basis nets [24, 31] come close to additive fuzzy systems with gaussian fuzzy sets and some are the same thing. Hartman and Keeler [9] showed that radial basis nets are universal approximators and thus extended a wide literature on gaussian-sum approximators [24, 31].

Most neural approximation theorems use any number of "hidden" neurons between the input and output neurons. So far no one has shown how to choose or even interpret these neurons. In the end the user must guess at both the number of layers of hidden neurons in the network and the number of these neurons in each layer.

The first fuzzy approximation theorem appeared in 1991 [15]. It showed that additive fuzzy systems can define simple functions and so can uniformly approximate bounded measurable functions. Then even bivalent expert systems can act as universal approximators. The fuzzy approximation theorem (or FAT theorem) for additive fuzzy systems appeared the next year [16]. It was the first such theorem to hold for fuzzy sets of all shapes.

The FAT theorem used the simple geometry of shrinking rule patches and the simple scheme of sums and products of the additive model. The proof traps the fuzzy system's output $F(x)$ between the centroids of the scaled then-part fuzzy sets as Theorems 9.1 and 9.2 show. This geometry and ease of computation soon led to new learning algorithms [4, 5] and an array of low-cost software tool kits and digital VLSI chips. Wang and Mendel [35] used the Stone-Weierstrass theorem to prove the special case of the FAT theorem for continuous functions $f: R^n \to R$ on a compact domain when the additive system uses the gaussian set functions [Eq. (9.8)] in the constant-volume SAM [Eq. (9.33)]. But this is just the case where an additive fuzzy system coincides with the gaussian Parzen estimator of Specht's generalized regression neural network [31].

Watkins [36] extended the FAT theorem in the scalar case. He showed that an additive fuzzy system F with just two rules can *represent* any bounded function $f: R \to R$ in the sense that $F(x) = f(x)$ for all x in R. We present this clever result below. The scalar function f need not be continuous. Then Watkins showed that SAMs cannot represent all functions on compact spaces of higher dimension. They can, of course, approximate them. No finite set of fuzzy rules will give an additive F such that $F(x,y) = f(x,y)$ for all x and y if $f(x,y) = xy$ on some compact domain that contains the origin in R^2. Watkins [37] has since showed that whether a SAM system F can represent f often depends on whether a certain differential equation has a solution.

Other fuzzy approximation theorems have since appeared for nonadditive systems. Buckley [2] showed in 1993 that some abstract fuzzy control nets act as uniform approximators for continuous maps $f: R^2 \to R$ on compact domains if the approximator uses actual samples $(x, f(x))$ from the function. The result does not show how to build such a system. Dubois [8] used the abstract "extension principle" [7] to map if-part fuzzy sets to then-part sets in rules and then used sets of these rules to approximate *monotone* functions. These abstract proofs do not show how to build or learn real fuzzy systems. Indeed their complex operations can compound the high costs of computation that all fuzzy systems face when the number of rules grows. In contrast the following proof of the FAT theorem is constructive.

Theorem 9.3 (Fuzzy Approximation Theorem).   An additive fuzzy system $F: X \to Y$ uniformly approximates $f: X \to Y$ if X is compact and f is continuous.

Proof. Pick any small $\varepsilon > 0$. We must show that $|F(x) - f(x)| < \varepsilon$ for all $x \in X$. X is a compact subset of R^n. $F(x)$ is the centroidal output of B in the additive Eq. (9.1).

Continuity of f on compact X gives uniform continuity. So there is a fixed distance δ such that for all x and z in X we have $|f(x) - f(z)| < \varepsilon/4$ if $|x - z| < \delta$. We can construct open cubes $M_1, \ldots, M_m$ that cover X and that have ordered overlap in their n coordinates so that each cube corner lies at the midpoint c_j of its neighbors M_j. Pick then-part fuzzy sets B_j centered at $f(c_j)$. Thus the centroid of B_j is $f(c_j)$.

Pick $u \in X$. Then by construction u lies in at most 2^n overlapping open cubes M_j. Pick any w in the same set of cubes. Suppose $u \in M_j$ and $w \in M_k$. Then for all $v \in M_j \cap M_k$ we have $|u - v| < \delta$ and $|v - w| < \delta$. Uniform continuity implies $|f(u) - f(w)| \leq |f(u) - f(v)| + |f(v) - f(w)| < \varepsilon/2$. So for cube centers c_j and c_k we have $|f(c_j) - f(c_k)| < \varepsilon/2$.

Pick $x \in X$. Then x too lies in at most 2^n open cubes with centers c_j and with $|f(c_j) - f(x)| < \varepsilon/2$. Along the kth coordinate of the range space R^p the kth component of the additive system centroid $F(x)$ lies as in Theorem 9.2 on or between the kth components of the centroids of the then-part B_j sets. So $|F(x) - f(c_j)| < \varepsilon/2$ holds since $|f(c_j) - f(c_k)| < \varepsilon/2$ holds for all $f(c_j)$. Then

$$|F(x) - f(x)| \leq |F(x) - f(c_j)| + |f(c_j) - f(x)| < \frac{\varepsilon}{2} + \frac{\varepsilon}{2} = \varepsilon$$

which proves the theorem.

We next restate Watkins' theorem [36, 37] that a scalar SAM F needs just two rules to exactly represent a bounded $f: R \to R$. This extends the FAT theorem but at the expense of building the structure of f into the two then-part sets. In practice we may have little or no knowledge of f.

Theorem 9.4 (Scalar Representation).   A SAM $F: R \to R$ with just two rules of the form

   If $X = A$, then $Y = B_1$

   If $X = $ not-A, then $Y = B_2$

can represent a bounded nonconstant $f: R \to R$ in the sense that $F(x) = f(x)$ for all $x \in R$.

Proof. Boundedness lets us define $\alpha = \inf f$ and $\beta = \sup f$. Center then-part sets B_1 and B_2 of any shape at α and β with finite but constant volumes (areas): $0 < V_1 = V_2 < \infty$. So $c_1 = \alpha$ and $c_2 = \beta$. B_1 and B_2 might be rectangles or triangles of unit area. Define then-part set A_1 as the ratio

$$a_1(x) = \frac{\beta - f(x)}{\beta - \alpha} \tag{9.62}$$

Then $0 \le a_1(x) \le 1$ holds for all x and so A_1 is a fuzzy set. Define the second then-part set A_2 as the complement of A_1: $a_2(x) = 1 - a_1(x)$. Then Eq. (9.62) and the SAM theorem give the result:

$$F(x) = \frac{\displaystyle\sum_{j=1}^{m} a_j(x)V_j c_j}{\displaystyle\sum_{j=1}^{m} a_j(x)V_j} \tag{9.63}$$

$$= \frac{a_1(x)\alpha + (1 - a_1(x))\beta}{a_1(x) + 1 - a_1(x)} \tag{9.64}$$

$$= a_1(x)\alpha + (1 - a_1(x))\beta \tag{9.65}$$

$$= a_1(x)(\alpha - \beta) + \beta \tag{9.66}$$

$$= \left(\frac{\beta - f(x)}{\beta - \alpha} \right)(\alpha - \beta) + \beta \tag{9.67}$$

$$= \left(\frac{f(x) - \beta}{\alpha - \beta} \right)(\alpha - \beta) + \beta \tag{9.68}$$

$$= f(x) - \beta + \beta \tag{9.69}$$

$$= f(x) \tag{9.70}$$

which proves Theorem 9.4.

Consider the bounded function $f(x) = \sin x$. Pick the two then-part sets B_1 and B_2 as unit-area rectangles centered at -1 and 1: $c_1 = \alpha = -1$ and $c_2 = \beta = 1 = V_1 = V_2$. Then

$$a_1(x) = \frac{1 - \sin x}{1 - (-1)} = \frac{1 - \sin x}{2} \quad \text{and} \quad a_2(x) = \frac{1 + \sin x}{2}$$

Then the SAM theorem gives

$$F(x) = \frac{\left(\frac{1-\sin x}{2}\right)(-1) + \left(\frac{1+\sin x}{2}\right)(1)}{\frac{1-\sin x}{2} + \frac{1+\sin x}{2}} = \frac{\sin x - 1 + 1 + \sin x}{1 - \sin x + 1 + \sin x} = \frac{2\sin x}{2} = \sin x$$

Representations can fail in higher dimensions. Consider the product function $f(x,y) = xy$. Watkins [37] showed that $F = f$ leads to the unique separation of the form

$$F(x,y) = \frac{\alpha x + \beta y}{\beta/x + \alpha/y}$$

Then the product function separates away from the coordinate axes. Then no SAM can represent the product function on any domain that includes any part of the coordinate axes. Watkins has further shown that twice-differentiable functions have piecewise SAM representations if and only if a system of SAM partial differential equations has a solution. There are $n(n-1)/2$ such simultaneous equations for a function $f : R^n \to R$. These representations can require *bipolar* set functions $a : X \to [-1, 1]$.

Fuzzy representations reduce the exponential rule complexity of blind function approximation to linear (or quadratic) complexity but at the cost of a complete knowledge of f. Future research may find algorithms that reduce the SAM rule complexity from exponential to polynomial as the system learns more of the structure of f. Other research may show us more of the boundary between the set of functions that SAMs can and cannot represent.

9.6 LEARNING IN SAMS: UNSUPERVISED CLUSTERING AND SUPERVISED GRADIENT DESCENT

A fuzzy system learns if and only if its rule patches move or change shape in the input-output product space $X \times Y$. Learning might change the centers or widths of triangle or trapezoid sets. These changing sets then change the shape or position of the cartesian rule patches built out of them. The mean-value theorem and the calculus of variations show [18] that optimal lone rules cover the extrema or bumps of the approximand. Good learning schemes [4–6] tend to quickly move rule patches to these bumps and then move extra rule patches between them as the rule budget allows. Hybrid schemes use unsupervised clustering to learn the first set of fuzzy rule patches in position and number and to initialize the gradient descents of supervised learning.

Learning changes system parameters with data. Unsupervised learning amounts to blind clustering in the system product space $X \times Y$ to learn and tune fuzzy rules or the sets that compose them. Then k quantization vectors $q_j \in X \times Y$ can move in the product space to filter or approximate the distribution of incoming data pairs $(x(t), y(t))$ or the concatenated data points $z(t) = [x(t) \mid y(t)]^T$. The simplest form of such *product space clustering* [15] centers a rule patch at each data point and thus puts $k = m$ [35]. In general the data greatly outnumber the rules and so $k \gg m$.

A natural way to grow and tune rules is to identify a rule patch with the uncertainty ellipsoid [4, 5] that forms around each quantizing vector q_j from the inverse of its positive definite covariance matrix K_j. Then sparse or noisy data grow a large patch and thus less certain rules than do denser or less noisy data. Unsupervised competitive learning [15] can learn these ellipsoidal rules in three steps:

$$|z(t) - q_j(t)| = \min \left(|z(t) - q_1(t)|, \ldots, |z(t) - q_k(t)| \right) \tag{9.71}$$

$$q_i(t+1) = \begin{cases} q_j(t) + \mu_t \, [z(t) - q_j(t)] & \text{if } i = j \\ q_i(t) & \text{if } i \neq j \end{cases} \tag{9.72}$$

$$K_i(t+1) = \begin{cases} K_j(t) + v_t \, [(z(t) - q_j(t))^T(z(t) - q_j(t)) - K_j(t)] & \text{if } i = j \\ K_i(t) & \text{if } i \neq j \end{cases} \tag{9.73}$$

for the Euclidean norm $|z|^2 = z_1^2 + \cdots + z_{n+p}^2$.

The first step Eq. (9.71) is the competitive step. It picks the nearest quantizing vector q_j to the incoming data vector $z(t)$ and ignores the rest. This correlation matching approximates a great deal of the competitive dynamics of nonlinear neural networks. The second step updates the winning quantization or "synaptic" vector and drives it toward the centroid of the sampled data pattern class [14]. The third step updates the covariance matrix of the winning quantization vector. We initialize the quantization vector with sample data ($q_i(0) = z(i)$) to avoid skewed groupings and initialize the covariance matrix with small positive numbers on its diagonal to ensure that it is positive definite. Projection schemes [14, 15] can then convert the ellipsoids into coordinate fuzzy sets. Supervised learning can also tune the eigenvalue parameters of the rule ellipsoids.

The sequences of learning coefficients $\{\mu_t\}$ and $\{v_t\}$ should decrease slowly [15] in the sense of

$$\sum_{t=1}^{\infty} \mu_t = \infty$$

but not too slowly in the sense of

$$\sum_{t=1}^{\infty} \mu_t^2 < \infty$$

In practice $\mu_t \approx 1/t$. The covariance coefficients obey a like constraint as in the practical choice $v_t = 0.2[1 - t/1.2N]$ where N is the total number of data points. The supervised learning schemes below also use a like sequence $\{\mu_t\}$ of decreasing learning coefficients.

Supervised learning changes SAM parameters with error data. The error at each time t is the desired system output minus the actual SAM output: $\varepsilon_t = d_t - F(x_t)$. Unsupervised learning uses the blind data point $z(t)$ instead of the desired or labeled value d_t. The teacher or supervisor supervises the learning process by giving the desired value d_t at each training time t. Most supervised learning schemes perform stochastic gradient descent on the squared error and do so through iterated use of the chain rule of differential calculus.

Supervised gradient descent can learn or tune SAM systems [19] by changing the rule weights w_j in (1), the then-part volumes V_j, the then-part set centroids c_j, or parameters of the if-part set functions a_j. The rule weight w_j enters the ratio form of the general SAM system

$$F(x) = \frac{\sum\limits_{j=1}^{m} w_j a_j(x) V_j c_j}{\sum\limits_{j=1}^{m} w_j a_j(x) V_j} \tag{9.74}$$

in the same way as does the then-part volume V_j in Theorem 9.1 or the general volume V_j' in Theorem 9.2. So both have the same learning law if we replace the nonzero weight w_j with the nonzero volume V_j or V_j':

$$w_j(t+1) = w_j(t) - \mu_t \frac{\partial E}{\partial w_j} \tag{9.75}$$

$$= w_j(t) - \mu_t \frac{\partial E}{\partial F} \frac{\partial F}{\partial w_j} \tag{9.76}$$

$$= w_j(t) + \mu_t \varepsilon_t \frac{p_j(x_t)}{w_j(t)} [c_j - F(x_t)] \tag{9.77}$$

for instantaneous squared error $E_t = \frac{1}{2}(d_t - F(x_t))^2$ with desired-minus-actual error $\varepsilon_t = d_t - F(x_t)$. The volumes then change in the same way if they do not depend on the weights (which they may be in some ellipsoidal learning schemes):

$$V_j(t+1) = V_j(t) - \mu_t \frac{\partial E}{\partial V_j} \tag{9.78}$$

$$= V_j(t) + \mu_t \varepsilon_t \frac{p_j(x_t)}{V_j(t)} [c_j - F(x_t)] \tag{9.79}$$

The learning law (77) follows since $\partial E/\partial w_j = -\varepsilon$ and since

$$\frac{\partial F}{\partial w_j} = \frac{a_j(x) V_j c_j \sum\limits_{i=1}^{m} w_i a_i(x) V_i - a_j(x) V_j \sum\limits_{i=1}^{m} w_i a_i(x) V_i c_i}{\left(\sum\limits_{i=1}^{m} w_i a_i(x) V_i \right)^2} \tag{9.80}$$

$$= \frac{w_j a_j(x) V_j}{w_j \sum\limits_{i=1}^{m} w_i a_i(x) V_i} \left[\frac{c_j \sum\limits_{i=1}^{m} w_i a_i(x) V_i}{\sum\limits_{i=1}^{m} w_i a_i(x) V_i} - \frac{\sum\limits_{i=1}^{m} w_i a_i(x) V_i c_i}{\sum\limits_{i=1}^{m} w_i a_i(x) V_i} \right] \tag{9.81}$$

$$= \frac{p_j(x)}{w_j} [c_j - F(x)] \tag{9.82}$$

from the SAM theorem.

The centroid c_j in the SAM theorem or the conditional mean c_j' in Theorem 9.2 has the simplest learning law:

$$c_j(t+1) = c_j(t) - \mu_t \frac{\partial E}{\partial F} \frac{\partial F}{\partial c_j} \tag{9.83}$$

$$= c_j(t) + \mu_t \varepsilon_t p_j(x_t) \tag{9.84}$$

So the terms w_j, V_j, and c_j do not change when $p_j \approx 0$ and thus when the jth if-part set barely fires: $a_j(x_t) \approx 0$.

Tuning the if-part sets involves more computation since the update law contains an extra partial derivative. Suppose if-part set function a_j is a function of l parameters: $a_j = a_j(m_j^1, \ldots, m_j^l)$. Then we can update each parameter with

$$m_j^k(t+1) = m_j^k(t) - \mu_t \, \frac{\partial E}{\partial F} \, \frac{\partial F}{\partial a_j} \, \frac{\partial a_j}{\partial m_j^k} \tag{9.85}$$

$$= m_j^k(t) + \mu_t \varepsilon_t \, \frac{p_j(x_t)}{a_j(x_t)} [c_j - F(x_t)] \frac{\partial a_j}{\partial m_j^k} \tag{9.86}$$

Exponential if-part set functions can reduce the learning complexity. They have the form $a_j = e^{f_j(m_j^1, \ldots, m_j^l)}$ and obey

$$\frac{\partial a_j}{\partial m_j^k} = a_j \, \frac{\partial f_j(m_j^1, \ldots, m_j^l)}{\partial m_j^k}$$

Then the parameter update (86) simplifies to

$$m_j^k(t+1) = m_j^k(t) + \mu_t \varepsilon_t p_j(x_t)[c_j - F(x_t)] \, \frac{\partial f_j}{\partial m_j^k} \tag{9.87}$$

This can arise for independent exponential or gaussian set functions

$$a_j(x) = \prod_{i=1}^{n} e^{f_j^i(x_i)} = \exp \sum_{i=1}^{n} f_j^i(x_i) = e^{f_j(x)}$$

The exponential

$$a_j(x) = \exp \sum_{i=1}^{n} u_j^i(v_j^i - x_i)$$

has $\partial f_j / \partial u_j^k = v_j^k - x_k(t)$ and $\partial f_j / \partial v_j^k = u_j^k$.

The gaussian

$$a_j(x) = \exp -\frac{1}{2} \sum_{i=1}^{n} \left(\frac{x_i - m_j^i}{\sigma_j^i} \right)^2$$

has mean partial $\partial f_j / \partial m_j^k = x_k - m_j^k / (\sigma_j^k)^2$ and variance partial $\partial f_j / \partial \sigma_j^k = (x_k - m_j^k)^2 / (\sigma_j^k)^3$. Such gaussian set functions reduce the SAM model to Specht's [31] radial basis function network. We can use the smooth update law [Eq. (9.87)] to update triangles or trapezoids or other nondifferentiable sets by viewing their centers and widths as the gaussian means and variances.

REFERENCES

1. Black, M., "Vagueness: An Exercise in Logical Analysis," *Philosophy of Science,* vol. 4, 427–455, 1937.

2. Buckley, J. J., and Y. Hayashi, "Fuzzy I/O Controllers as Universal Approximators," *Proceedings of the World Congress on Neural Networks (INNS WCNN-93),* vol. 2, 92–96, July 1993.

3. Cybenko, G., "Approximation by Superpositions of a Sigmoidal Function," *Mathematics of Control, Signals, and Systems,* vol. 2, 303–314, 1989.

4. Dickerson, J. A., and B. Kosko, "Fuzzy Function Learning with Covariance Ellipsoids," *Proceedings of the IEEE International Conference on Neural Networks (IEEE ICNN-93),* 1162–1167, March 1993.

5. Dickerson, J. A., and B. Kosko, "Fuzzy Function Approximation with Supervised Ellipsoidal Learning," *Proceedings of the World Congress on Neural Networks (INNS WCNN-93),* vol. 2, 9–17, July 1993.

6. Dickerson, J. A., and B. Kosko, "Virtual Worlds as Fuzzy Cognitive Maps," *Presence,* vol. 3, no. 2, 173–189, Spring 1994.

7. Dubois, D., and H. Prade, *Fuzzy Sets and Systems: Theory and Applications,* Academic Press, Orlando, 1980.

8. Dubois, D., M. Grabisch, and H. Prade, "Synthesis of Real-valued Mappings Based on Gradual Rules and Interpolative Reasoning," *Proceedings of the 13th International Joint Conference on Artificial Intelligence (IJCAI-93) Workshop on Fuzzy Logic in AI,* 29–40, September 1993.

9. Hartman, E., J. D. Keeler, and J. Kowalski, "Layered Neural Networks with Gaussian Hidden Units as Universal Approximators," *Neural Computation,* vol. 2, 210–215, 1990.

10. Hornik, K., M. Stinchcombe, and H. White, "Multilayer Feedforward Networks are Universal Approximators," *Neural Networks,* vol. 2, 359–366, 1989.

11. Klir, G. J., and T. A. Folger, *Fuzzy Sets, Uncertainty, and Information,* Prentice Hall, Englewood Cliffs, N.J., 1988.

12. Kosko, B., "Fuzzy Knowledge Combination," *International Journal of Intelligent Systems,* vol. I, 293–320, 1986.

13. Kosko, B., *Foundations of Fuzzy Estimation Theory,* Ph.D. dissertation, Department of Electrical Engineering, University of California at Irvine, June 1987; order number 8801936, University Microfilms International, 300 N. Zeeb Road, Ann Arbor, MI 48106.

14. Kosko, B., "Stochastic Competitive Learning," *IEEE Transactions on Neural Networks,* vol. 2, no. 5, 522–529, September 1991.

15. Kosko, B., *Neural Networks and Fuzzy Systems: A Dynamical Systems Approach to Machine Intelligence,* Prentice Hall, 1991.

16. Kosko, B., "Fuzzy Systems as Universal Approximators," *IEEE Transactions on Computers,* vol. 43, no. 11, 1329–1333, November 1994; an earlier version appears in the *Proceedings of the First IEEE International Conference on Fuzzy Systems (IEEE FUZZ-92),* 1153–1162, March 1992.

17. Kosko, B., and S. Isaka, "Fuzzy Logic," *Scientific American,* vol. 269, no. 1, 76–81, July 1993.

18. Kosko, B., "Optimal Fuzzy Rules Cover Extrema," *International Journal of Intelligent Systems,* vol. 10, no. 2, 249–255, February 1995; an earlier version appears in the *Proceedings of the 1994 World Congress on Neural Networks (INNS WCNN-94).*

19. Kosko, B., "Combining Fuzzy Systems," *Proceedings of the IEEE FUZZ-95,* vol. IV, 1855–1863, March 1995.

20. Kreysig, E., *Advanced Engineering Mathematics,* 6th ed., John Wiley & Sons, New York, 1988.

21. Mamdani, E. H., and S. Assilian, "An Experiment in Linguistic Synthesis with a Fuzzy Logic Controller," *International Journal of Man-Machine Studies,* vol. 7, 1–13, 1977.

22. Mamdani, E. H., "Application of Fuzzy Logic to Approximate Reasoning Using Linguistic Synthesis," *IEEE Transactions on Computers,* vol. C-26, no. 12, 1182–1191, December 1977.

23. Mead, C., *Analog VLSI and Neural Systems,* Addison-Wesley, 1989.

24. Moody, J., and C. Darken, "Fast Learning in Networks of Locally Tuned Processing Units," *Neural Computation,* vol. 1, 281–294, 1989.

25. Nguyen, H. T., "On Random Sets and Belief Functions," *Journal of Mathematical Analysis and Applications,* vol. 65, 531–542, 1978.

26. Pacini, P. J., and B. Kosko, "Adaptive Fuzzy System for Target Tracking," *Intelligent Systems Engineering,* vol. 1, no. 1, 3–21, Fall 1992.

27. Papoulis, A., *Probability, Random Variables, and Stochastic Processes,* 2d ed., McGraw-Hill, New York, 1984.

28. Rice, J. R., *The Approximation of Functions,* Addison-Wesley, Reading, Mass., 1964.

29. Rudin, W., *Functional Analysis,* McGraw-Hill, New York, 1973.

30. Rudin, W., *Real and Complex Analysis,* 2d ed., McGraw-Hill, New York, 1974.

31. Specht, D. F., "A General Regression Neural Network," *IEEE Transactions on Neural Networks,* vol. 4, no. 4, 549–557, 1991.

32. Sugeno, M., "An Introductory Survey of Fuzzy Control," *Information Sciences,* vol. 36, 59–83, 1985.

33. Taber, W. R., "Knowledge Processing with Fuzzy Cognitive Maps," *Expert Systems with Applications,* vol. 2, no. 1, 82–87, February 1991.

34. Terano, T., K. Asai, and M. Sugeno, *Fuzzy Systems Theory and Its Applications,* Academic Press, Orlando, 1992.

35. Wang, L., and J. M. Mendel, "Fuzzy Basis Functions, Universal Approximation, and Orthogonal Least-Squares Learning," *IEEE Transactions on Neural Networks,* vol. 3, no. 5, 807–814, September 1992.

36. Watkins, F. A., "Fuzzy Engineering," Ph.D. dissertation, Department of Electrical Engineering, University of California at Irvine, 1994; University Microfilms International, 300 North Zeeb Road, Ann Arbor, MI 48106.

37. Watkins, F. A., "The Representation Problem for Additive Fuzzy Systems," *Proceedings of the IEEE FUZZ-95,* vol. I, 117–122, March 1995.

38. Yager, R. R., and D. P. Filev, "On the Issue of Defuzzification and Selection Based on a Fuzzy Set," *Fuzzy Sets and Systems,* vol. 55, 255–273, 1993.

39. Zadeh, L. A., "Fuzzy Sets," *Information and Control,* vol. 8, 338–353, 1965.

40. Zadeh, L. A., *Fuzzy Sets and Applications: Selected Papers by L. A. Zadeh,* R. R. Yager, S. Ovchinnikov, R. M. Tong, and H. T. Nguyen, eds., John Wiley and Sons, 1987.

CHAPTER 10

NEURAL NET PROCESS MONITORING AND OPTIMAL CONTROL

Yoh-Han Pao
Percy P. C. Yip
Electrical Engineering and Applied Physics
Case Western Reserve University and AI WARE, Inc.
Cleveland, Ohio

Neural-net computing is an adaptive computational paradigm which is well suited to the building of computational models of processes. These models can then serve as the basis for predictive monitoring of such processes and for the planning and implementation of optimal control. Basic conceptual elements are described in this chapter together with descriptions of preferred methods of implementation. Topics covered in this chapter include the learning of computational models, interpretation of parameters, evolutionary programming for optimal control, combined feedforward/feedback control, and issues of deterministic chaos and stability. Fuzzy control and the automatic discovery of fuzzy control rules are mentioned briefly, primarily for calibration and comparison purposes.

10.1 INTRODUCTION AND OVERVIEW OF CHAPTER

Neural net computing is a computational paradigm which is well-suited for use in the monitoring and control of complex dynamic processes. Such processes may be of various natures, including physical, chemical, socioeconomic, biological, environmental, and financial.

The neural net computing approach to process monitoring is founded on the idea that it is possible to "learn" a computational model of the process in question. This is achieved by observing the system in question to see how the process evolves with time or in response to additional external actions. The net then builds a functional relationship which mimics the actual process, describing accurately how the system would evolve from any specific initial state either on its own or in response to additional external actions, the so-called control actions. In principle and in practice, the net builds the computational model adaptively, modifying the model continually to obtain a good description of the process not only for the known cases but for all circumstances, known and unknown—even for circumstances hitherto not encountered, provided that they are within the assumed normal range of operation of the process.

This functionality of being able to learn a computational model of a process is generally referred to as the *supervised learning* capability of neural nets and in retrospect can be understood quite directly in terms of ordinary mathematical concepts and operations. However, the approach of neural net computing has brought with it new methodology and new insights. Initially, it was bold new optimism, inspired by biological analogs, which led the way, but now the neural net computing paradigm continues to suggest interesting ways of thinking about the underlying mathematical procedures.

This matter of learning a model is crucial to process monitoring and optimal control. The multilayered feedforward net architecture can be used with the backpropagation of error algorithm for problems of low complexity, but that combination becomes less effective for problems of higher dimensionality or where the process itself is of high complexity. To date, many methods have been proposed for augmenting and strengthening the standard backpropagation algorithm.

Model learning is discussed in Sec. 10.2 with the help and perspective of the functional-link approach. That approach was advocated by one of the present authors (Pao, 1989) as a measure for freeing neural net computing conceptually from the constraints imposed by exclusive use of linear links. In practice, functional-link nets are trained much more easily than the conventional linear link nets and the functionality of functional-link nets is more easily understood intuitively as well as mathematically.

Once an accurate computational model is available, predictive monitoring of the successive states of a system is, in principle, a straightforward matter. Given the present state of a system and a model of the process in question, it should be possible to predict all future states of the system, at least for a short while. Failure to do so can be attributed to one or more of the following causes:

- Inadequacy of the computational model
- Changes in the nature of the process
- Faulty sensor readings characterizing the system states
- Faulty sensor readings characterizing control actions

The point is that *patterns* in the failure to predict can provide indications of faults in the model, or in the process, or in the equipment. This is the basis for process monitoring and for diagnostic interpretation of process parameters. These matters are described schematically in Sec. 10.3.

Also, once an accurate computational model has been established, it is possible to look well into the future and visualize what would happen if various control actions were taken. It is possible, therefore, to plan and select courses of action which would bring the system to the desired states at specified junctures in preferred manners. This is how optimal control can be planned and executed with neural net computing, and these matters are described in Sec. 10.4. That mode of control would be of the nature of pure feedforward control if no account is taken of what is actually happening to the system.

In practice, it is prudent to constantly compare the predicted system states with the actual system state as reported by sensor readings. This is not only for process monitoring and diagnostic purposes but also because feedback is extremely important if control is to be robust and accurate, as well as optimal. The research and development groups with which the authors are associated have developed control methodology which incorporates important features of both the feedforward and feedback control paradigms. Those matters are also described in Sec. 10.4.

In the present scheme of things, optimality is attained with use of a mode of evolutionary programming consisting of guided evolutionary programming with simulated annealing (GESA). More generally, evolutionary programming is another one of a number of adaptive computational paradigms which are sometimes collectively referred to as the *technologies of computational intelligence*. These computational paradigms go beyond the practices of traditional artificial intelligence and of fuzzy sets in enabling the computer algorithm to adaptively adjust its own validity to suit the task at hand. GESA is in the tradition of developments along the lines of the genetic algorithm (Holland, 1975; Holland et al., 1986; Goldberg, 1989), Evolutionary Programming (Fogel et al., 1966) and stochastic search (Aarts, 1989). The GESA algorithm is described in App. 10.2.

It is appropriate to refer in passing to the practice of control known as *fuzzy control*. That methodology has its own realm of validity and can be very helpful when used appropriately. Like traditional artificial intelligence, it can be enhanced with the addition of adaptivity. For calibration and comparison purposes, some recent work on the automatic inference of fuzzy control rules is described in Sec. 10.5. In essence, current practice in fuzzy control depends on human experts prescribing the single variable membership functions and also how they combine. However, using a form of fuzzy logic which supports universal approximation (Wang, 1992) it is possible to automatically learn what those membership functions should be (Nyberg and Pao, 1995). Over the years, a large body of literature has been built up on the topic of fuzzy control. The remarks made in this report have to do with those efforts which are concerned with the automatic design or automatic fine tuning of such fuzzy systems.

The question of stability in the control of nonlinear processes remains an important and interesting topic awaiting further detailed study. There are the expected considerations of whether a system under the action of the process alone would remain in its state, undergo periodic motion, evolve toward some stable fixed point, or move infinitely far away from some fixed repelling point. But in addition to these considerations, there is the matter of *deterministic chaos* which impinges directly on the issues of process monitoring and control. Deterministic chaos manifests itself as wild, seemingly unpredictable, behavior. This can happen with perfectly deterministic, completely predictable systems. A characteristic of those systems is that a slight difference in the initial state results in vastly different trajectories in time in the evolution of the system. Such systems are sensitive to noise and inaccuracies in the reporting of system parameters. In practice, a slight error in the estimate of the system state can result in the system being driven into unstable trajectories. The quadratic map system is discussed briefly in Sec. 10.6 to illustrate some aspects of that type of unstable behavior.

Neural net computing, evolutionary programming, optimization, process monitoring, controls, fuzzy sets, and so on all have large volumes of published technical literature. It would be a major project to attempt to review even any one of those fields alone. It is impossible to attempt anything resembling that venture in the confines of this one short chapter. What is attempted instead is a concise and focused account of the related topics of process monitoring and optimal control as enabled principally by neural net computing, but with some help from evolutionary programming. The account is limited in the sense that reference to previous work is not as extensive as it might have been or should have been and in retrospect it seems that the choice of references has been greatly influenced by the perspectives and interests of the authors and their colleagues. This is primarily due to a desire to make the account a coherent one. The framework of the discussion is fashioned so that the discussion is compatible with the concepts and established practices of traditional systems theory and control methodology. Remarks of a bibliographic nature are collected together at the end of the chapter in Sec. 10.7.

There are two appendixes and a list of suggested readings. A version of the conjugate gradient algorithm is given in App. 10.1. A version of the GESA algorithm is described in App. 10.2, and sources for material for additional reading are listed in "Suggestions for Additional Reading" following the list of cited references.

10.2 LEARNING A COMPUTATIONAL MODEL OF A PROCESS

2.1 Concepts and Definitions

Without loss of generality, the present discussion is couched in terms of one-dimensional scalar systems monitored and controlled in time-indcx-labeled discrete manner. This is done purely in the interest of achieving simplicity in exhibiting mathematical relationships. The procedures are generally valid for realistic multidimensional systems. In a sense, the time index is equivalent to additional dimensions.

The evolution of a dynamic system with time can be illustrated as shown in Fig. 10.1. The state of the system is specified by the measurements $y(t), \ldots, y(t - n)$, $u(t), \ldots, u(t - n)$, where $y(t)$ is the value at time t of the system parameter being considered in this simple illustrative case, and $u(t)$ is the value of the control action being exercised at that same time t. In general, a process may have time delays and the consequences of the process may depend not only on the instantaneous value of the parameter but also on higher time derivatives of that variable. In the present context, it is useful to distinguish conceptually between the *system* and the *process*. As shown in Fig. 10.1, the state of the system is specified by the set of $\{y(k)\}$ and $\{u(t)\}$ measurements, and the process is a functional relationship which transforms the value of the variable $y(t)$ from its current value $y(t)$ to a new next step value $y(t + 1)$.

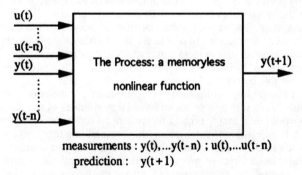

measurements : y(t),...y(t- n) ; u(t),...u(t- n)
prediction :   y(t + 1)

FIGURE 10.1 Depiction of a monitoring and control task, with emphasis on distinguishing between the system and the process.

For linear discrete-time systems, the generic nth order linear discrete-time process can be described by the difference equation

$$y(t+1) = \sum_{k=1}^{k=n} a_k y(t+1-k) + \sum_{m=0}^{m=n} b_m u(t-m) \tag{10.1}$$

This is the deterministic autoregressive moving average (DARMA) model in the language of Goodwin and Sin (1984).

Thus the $y(t)$ and $u(t)$ are the system parameters and the $a(k)$ and $b(m)$ coefficients are the process parameters for the linear system. However, as depicted in Fig. 10.1, in general a process can be thought of as a memoryless nonlinear function which might be expressed as

$$y(t+1) = f(y(t), y(t-1), \ldots, y(t-n); u(t), u(t-1), \ldots, u(t-n)) \tag{10.2}$$

The task in neural net process monitoring and control is to learn a computational model of the function $f(\ )$, given a sufficient number of instances of observed transformations of the system, for a range of system states. The neural net model depicted schematically in Fig. 10.2 should be a faithful replica of the nonlinear function depicted in Fig. 10.1, insofar as system transformations are concerned.

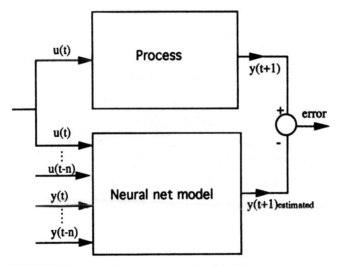

FIGURE 10.2 A neural net computational model of the process.

10.2.2 Training a Neural Net

It is known that the multilayer feedforward net with even but one hidden layer can serve as a universal approximator (Funahashi, 1989; Hornik, Stinchcombe, and White, 1989). Therefore it is assured that in principle a net of such architecture can serve as a computational model of any process which can be expressed as an analytic function of the process inputs, namely the $\{y(t); u(t)\}$ of Sec. 10.2.1. In practice, there are two types of difficulties: (1) lack of knowledge of how many hidden layer nodes are required and (2) lack of universally practicable means for training such nets. It is well-known that the backpropagation of error algorithm is effective for training nets with a moderate number of nodes and for problems with a moderate number of training patterns. The method is one of gradient search in network parameter space, and there is a strong tendency to become trapped in local minima. Such a net is depicted in Fig. 10.3*a*.

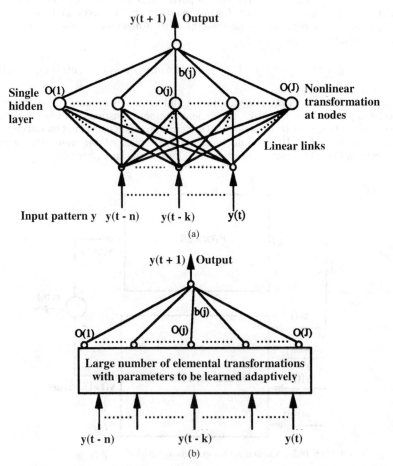

FIGURE 10.3   Illustration of the functional-link concept. (*a*) A feedforward neural net with one hidden layer of nodes; (*b*) the same net viewed as a linear expansion in terms of optimal functions.

However, that same architecture can be viewed with other different perspectives to open the way to significantly different ways of training the net. For example, if the details of constructing the hidden-layer nodes are ignored, then the task of learning a scalar function of a multivariable field is simply an exercise in the linear expansion

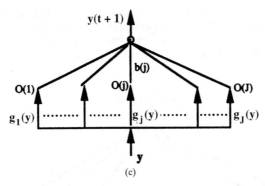

(c)

FIGURE 10.3 (*Continued*)   Illustration of the functional-link concept. (*c*) The functional-link net perspective.

of the (as yet unknown) function in terms of a set of other multivariable functions. The question is what multivariate functions are appropriate for serving as a set of basis functions. The complexity of the expansion task becomes astronomically large if these expansion functions are built up from products of well-behaved single-variable basis functions.

Perhaps it can be said that one major contribution of neural net computing consists of the contention (initially without justification) by Rosenblatt (1958, 1961) that such basis functions might be synthesized with linear links and a logistic function. Addition of a hidden layer is tantamount to the statement that the basis functions are indeed to be of that form. Namely, the form of the individual basis functions is fixed; all that remains is to determine the expansion coefficients of a linear expansion. The contribution of the backpropagation algorithm is to show how the optimum internal parameter values of the basis functions can be learned. Thus both the upper-level expansion coefficients and the expansion function parameters are learned at the same time. However it is this aspect of the (otherwise excellent) back-propagation algorithm that makes the training task so difficult.

The early work by Giles and his collaborators (Giles and Maxwell, 1987; Lee et al., 1986) suggested to Pao (1989) that if expansion were done in terms of suitable basis functions then there would be no need for learning at the lower layer. The lower-layer links would carry out functional transforms of fixed mathematical nature and only the upper-level linear expansion coefficients need to be learned. The task is then one of quadratic optimization, and convergence is fast and guaranteed.

The validity of the functional-link approach has been borne out over the years. It is important to note that it does not consist of expansion necessarily in terms of any particular set of basis functions such as radial basis functions. What is being said is that, if certain multivariate elemental functions are suspected of being suitable for description of the function $f(\ )$, then those known elemental functions should be volunteered as basis functions. The magnitudes of their expansion coefficients would indicate quite readily whether they are useful or not, but there are no internal parameters to be adjusted. It has been both proven theoretically (Igelnik and Pao, 1994) and demonstrated experimentally (Pao et al., 1994) that even randomly chosen sigmoidal functions can serve as a sufficiently good representation of functions, and training with use of the conjugate gradient procedure is very efficient (Park, et al., 1995). The architecture of a "random vector" functional-link net is depicted schematically in Fig. 10.4 and a statement of a conjugate gradient training procedure is provided in App. 10.1. Typically, for complex tasks, the time needed to train a functional-link net is orders of magnitude less than that of a conventional backpropagation net. This is illustrated schematically in Fig. 10.5.

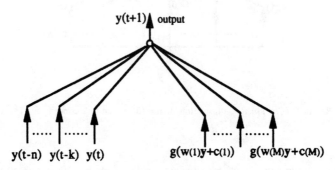

FIGURE 10.4   A random-vector functional-link net using randomly specified lower-level logistic functions.

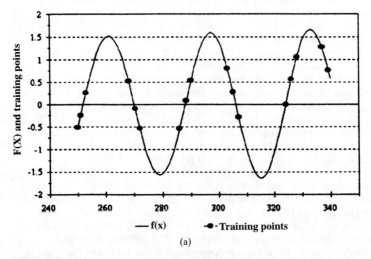

(a)

FIGURE 10.5   Comparison of typical backpropagation and functional-link training times. (*a*) Function to be learned and training set patterns.

10.2.3   Some Additional Fundamental Considerations

It should not be denied that function estimation has been a topic of profound and scholarly study for a long time (Lorentz, 1966). One question had been whether a scalar function of many variables can be expressed simply, perhaps as sums of products of some set of single-variable functions. That question was of fundamental interest to mathematicians. As is known, Kolmogorov (1957) proved that a solution of that form did indeed exist but the single-variable functions themselves were not

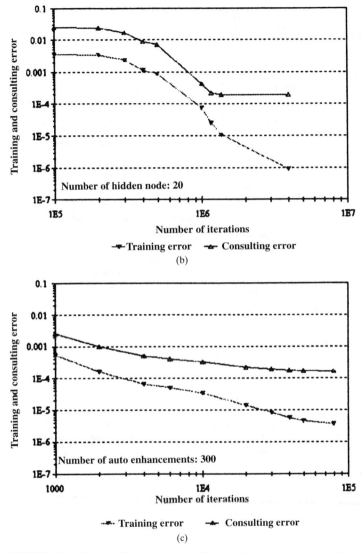

FIGURE 10.5 (*Continued*) Comparison of typical backpropagation and functional-link training times. (*b*) Backpropagation algorithm in about 1 million iterations; (*c*) functional-link net in about 10,000 iterations.

specified and remain unknown. Prior to the development of neural net computing, a conventional approach to function estimation was to carry out expansions in terms of polynomials such as splines. The question then was always to know when to stop, that is, at what order to terminate an expansion of rapidly increasing complexity.

A comparative overview of several approaches to this function estimation task is illustrated in Fig. 10.6. It is seen that the conventional backpropagation net would

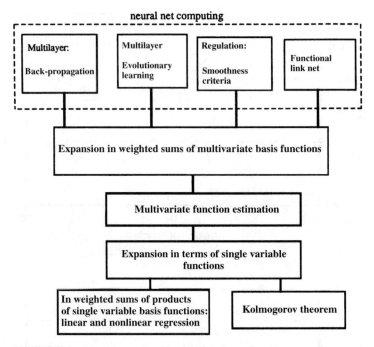

FIGURE 10.6   A taxonomy of multivariate function estimation approaches.

constitute an expansion in terms of a set of multivariate basis functions, the forms of which are fixed but with internal parameters which need to be learned. The functional-link net constitutes expansion in terms of "suitable" basis functions with the restriction that these basis functions have no adjustable parameters which need to be learned during training. The regularization theory approach constitutes expansion with the constraint that some aspect of the attempted representation have minimal curvature or so on. The radial basis function expansion is often given more credit than due. That expansion may or may not be suitable, depending on the symmetry of the function to be represented. In a sense, the Kolmogorov theorem approach is not dissimilar to the other approaches except that the explicit forms of the functions are not known. It is merely known that they do exist.

Despite the generally optimistic tone of the remarks of this section, it should be noted that the difficulty of learning a model of a process does not lie with the training phase alone. The test of validity of the model comes in predicting outputs for inputs which had not been previously encountered before. It is essential that the root-mean-square error for the validation set be comparable to that for the training set. Otherwise use of the model can lead to dangerously inadequate monitoring and control. For example, for the training procedures shown in Fig. 10.5, it is clear that the generalization error is always larger than the training set error, and furthermore at some point in the training procedure, the generalization error no longer decreases. In practice, it would be appropriate to stop training at that juncture.

It may seem that this section is more concerned with overly theoretical matters of net architecture and training, but the truth is that in the practice of neural net process monitoring and control, *modeling is of the essence.* The entire process is compromised if the model of the process is not accurate or cannot be updated accurately and rapidly.

10.3 PROCESS MONITORING

10.3.1 Concepts and Basic Considerations

The primary task of process monitoring is to confirm that the *process* is proceeding as intended. With use of an accurately trained neural net model of the process, it is possible to take a set of system-state sensor readings as input to the model and predict the next step value of the system state. Continued agreement between the actual values and the predicted values would indicate that the process is proceeding well.

In real-world systems, processes are not completely deterministic. The training set data contained noise, perhaps a great deal of noise in some instances. The extent of that is known from the values of the training set system error and the validation set system error. Therefore, as monitoring proceeds, a record is kept of the root-mean-square error evaluated over short spans of time. It is the characteristics of the actual individual errors and of the records of the averaged errors which indicate whether something has gone wrong.

Demarcation of the responsibilities of the process monitoring function is not precise, and there can be considerable overlap between diagnostics and simple process monitoring. Neural net process monitoring differs from the charting practices of conventional statistical quality control (SQC) in that an entirely new dimension is added. In SQC, reported parameter values are charted and the variation of these with time or the deviation of these from desired values is charted. All that is still possible with the use of neural nets, but what is additionally available are measures of the deviations of *estimated* values from *actual reported values.* That provides a new type of information for process monitoring. These matters are illustrated schematically in Fig. 10.7.

Charting, trend analysis and reporting of individual parameter values. Sometimes relative to desired set points.
(a)

Charting, trend analysis and reporting of multidimensional patterns of parameter values (no model and no prediction involved).
(b)

Predictive monitoring: Charting, trend analysis of multidimensional system state and deviations between reported and predicted values.
(c)

FIGURE 10.7 Neural net process monitoring employs checks on internal consistency of sets of reported parameter values, making use of multidimensional nature of reported data and on deviations between predicted and reported values. (*a*) Conventional statistical quality control (SQC) practices; (*b*) neural net computing trend analysis of parameters; (*c*) neural net computing interpretation of patterns of parameters.

10.3.2   Diagnostic Interpretation of Violations in the Internal Consistency of Reported Parameter Values

With optimization tools such as GESA, it is possible to attempt to identify the cause, or causes, for various types of deviations between predicted and reported parameter values, or for inconsistencies in the pattern of deviations. The computational methodology consists of combined use of neural net computing and guided evolutionary programming. The approach consists of a guided stochastic search for that set of input parameter values which would be consistent with the reported output values assuming the model is valid, or a search for that set of model parameter values which would make the input parameter values consistent with the reported output values. There are many variations on this theme of search for consistency. For example, it might be advisable to cross-check between parameter readings so that a faulty sensor does not affect both the input reading and the output reading in misleading ways. Such practices are not in wide use as yet, probably because this is still a new art and also because robust versions of neural net and evolutionary programming tools are not readily accessible.

10.4   OPTIMAL CONTROL AND COMBINED FEEDFORWARD/FEEDBACK CONTROL

10.4.1   Neural Net Control

In principle, the same set of data used to train a net for predictive monitoring can also be used to train a net for generating control actions. This is illustrated in Fig. 10.8. In the one case, $\{y(t), y(t-1), \ldots; u(t), u(t-1), \ldots\}$ are used as input and the required output is $y(t+1)$. In training, many such associated input/output groupings are used to fashion a net which, one hopes, can be generalized to be valid for all circumstances within reason. But the same body of information may be regrouped so that $\{y(t+1), y(t), y(t-1), \ldots; u(t-1), u(t-2), \ldots\}$ are used as input and $u(t)$ is the required net output. The interpretation in this latter case is that $y(t+1)$ is the desired next-step value, and the net is required to learn what the appropriate control action $u(t)$ should be at this time. These two circumstances are illustrated in Fig. 10.8a and b respectively.

This approach to neural net control is intuitively easy to understand, but is not advisable because it might not be possible to invert the first net reliably; in other words, it is not possible to be sure that only one set of inputs results in a specific value of $y(t+1)$. Perhaps several different sets of inputs with different values of $u(t)$ might all yield very nearly the same value of $y(t+1)$. Under such circumstances, specifying the desired value of $y(t+1)$ might not be sufficient to generate the appropriate $u(t)$. What would be returned might be a weighted average of a number of the possible $u(t)$ values.

In practice, the feedforward net used to model the process is also used to generate appropriate control actions. The input $u(t)$ is taken to be unknown and a backpropagation search is undertaken to determine that value of $u(t)$ which would generate the desired value of $y(t+1)$ as closely as possible (Nguyen and Widrow, 1990). This is illustrated in Fig. 10.9. However the appropriate control action can also be found with use of a guided stochastic search (Pao et al., 1992). That can be carried out not only for the next-step control action but indeed for an entire sequence of control actions, so that overall path objectives can be optimized. That approach opens the way for control path planning and for optimal control.

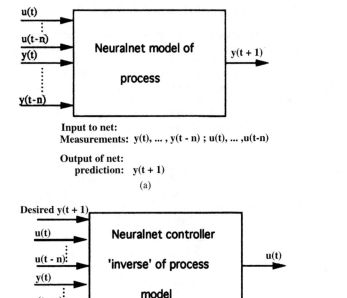

Input to net:
Measurements: y(t), ... , y(t - n) ; u(t), ... ,u(t-n)

Output of net:
    prediction: y(t + 1)

(a)

Input to net:
Measurements: y(t), ... ,y(t - n) ; u(t), ... ,u(t - n) ; desired y(t + 1)

Output of net:
Control action u(t)

(b)

FIGURE 10.8   Dual use of a set of system data: (*a*) for learning a model of
a process; (*b*) for training a control action generator.

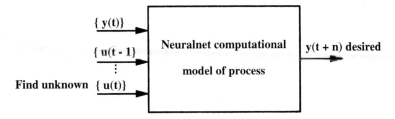

Given model, desired output and all inputs except u(t),
find u(t) either by stochastic search or by Backpropagation
through net.

FIGURE 10.9   Generation of control actions using the process model.

10.4.2 Control Path Planning and Optimal Control

The next-step neural net controller described in Sec. 10.4.1 is an optimal controller in the limited sense that, for a specified attainable new target state to be attained in the next step, that control action generator does indeed generate the control action which drives the system to the specified state. Things are different if only the ultimate desired state is known, to be reached after k steps rather than at the next step. For such circumstances, a sequence of control actions needs to be generated, to drive the system not only to the desired state but also along a certain optimal path, corresponding to the optimal value of some objective function. For example, it might be necessary that there be very little overshoot of the target value but yet the approach should be as rapid as possible.

Optimal path planning and optimal control can be attained with use of feedforward nets together with GESA, an evolutionary programming optimization procedure (Yip and Pao, 1994). A version of the GESA algorithm is outlined in App. 10.2.

The optimal control procedure is illustrated with the help of a simple system described in terms of a differential equation

$$\ddot{x} + \frac{3}{2}\dot{x} + 2x = u(t) \tag{10.3}$$

where x is the single system observable and u is the control action. The initial state is

$$x(0) = -1 \tag{10.4}$$

$$\dot{x}(0) = 0$$

and the desired final state

$$x(k) = 0 \tag{10.5}$$

$$\dot{x}(k) = 0$$

is to be attained after k steps, with k initially indeterminate.

If it is desired that x adjust as rapidly as possible to the desired final state, but without significant overshoot, then a suitable objective function might be

$$f(\mathbf{u}) = T + 5(\text{ov}) \tag{10.6}$$

where $\mathbf{u}$ is the sequence of control actions; T is the rise time (the time required to attain 90 percent of the required change); ov is the overshoot; and 5(ov) is the weighted overshoot. Using GESA, a stochastic search is carried out in control action sequence space to locate that $\mathbf{u}$ for which $f(\mathbf{u})$ attains a minimum, a sufficiently low minimum. The model is then driven over k steps to verify that the sequence $\mathbf{u}$ is indeed satisfactory. A solution obtained in this manner might be that exhibited in Fig. 10.10, which shows both the evolution path of the system and the sequence of control actions.

10.4.3 Combined Use of Feedforward and Feedback Control

A great deal is known about the theory and practice of feedback control, and in practice there is a large installed base of feedback control systems. Given these circumstances, it is clear that the advantages of both neural net feedforward control

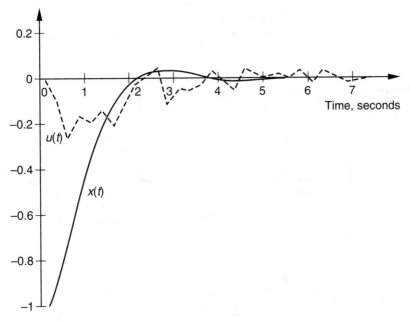

FIGURE 10.10   Optimal control actions and system response.

and feedback control can be attained if they are used in combination. One way of implementing this might be to keep on using proportional integral-differential (PID) controls but use neural-net computing to tune the PID gains. This approach is illustrated schematically in Fig. 10.11.

This combined approach has been investigated by the authors and straightforward use of the scheme is indeed feasible. This approach also opens the way to many other interesting and powerful variations on the theme, developing the scope of use of neural net computing, while still enjoying the robust characteristics of feedback control.

10.5   CONSIDERATIONS OF RELATIONSHIPS WITH RESPECT TO FUZZY CONTROL

10.5.1   Automatic Design and Tuning of Fuzzy Systems

Fuzzy systems have the advantage of being relatively easy to understand, but there are always design parameters that cannot be determined with expert knowledge or common sense. For example, it might be possible to have an expert determine most of the rules but some might be missed. Also, the approximate positions and shape of the membership functions can be determined by common sense but the *exact* (optimal) positions and shapes might be unknown. Therefore there is need for different degrees of automatic design or tuning of fuzzy systems, and there are continuing studies of how neural net computing and other computational intelligence method-

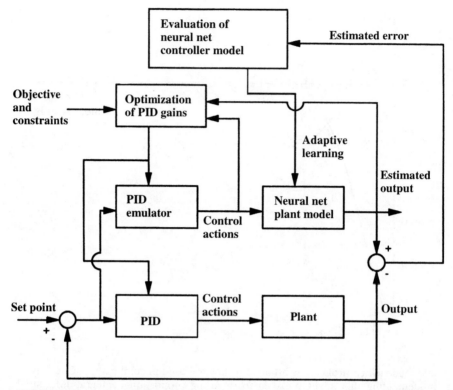

FIGURE 10.11 A schematic illustration of how neural net computing can be used to tune PID gains.

ologies might be used for such purposes. A challenging aspect of the situation is the promise that such automatically designed or tuned systems would be able to sort out important features from the unimportant ones and also discover relationships. Because fuzzy systems are easy to understand, the implications of the discovered knowledge can be readily incorporated into the larger scheme of things.

A summary of some representative previous investigations is presented in Fig. 10.12 in the form of an annotated listing of references. Most of these are in the nature of *tuning* rather than automatic *design,* although it is admittedly difficult to delineate a precise borderline between the two. The work of Nyberg and Pao (1995) is interesting in that it makes use of a fuzzy set formalism (Wang, 1992) which is known to be capable of universal approximation, and the fuzzy control rules are discovered through use of the GESA evolutionary programming procedure.

10.5.2 Automatic Design of a Fuzzy Controller

The inverted pendulum is a classical control problem that has become a benchmark problem for nonlinear control. Different control strategies can be and have been used. These include the state-variable model with linearization (Bryson and Leuenberger, 1970), neural networks (Widrow, 1987; Williams and Matsuoka, 1991) as well as fuzzy logic controllers (Kosko, 1991; Jang, 1992; Lee and Takagi, 1993; Jamshidi,

1. Self-organizing controller (SOC)   Efstathiou (1987)
            Procyk and Mamdani (1979)
    A technique for tuning consequents. Set an ideal trajectory, decrease deviations from ideal by changing rule or rules.
2. Neural net approaches   Jang (1992)
            Tsutomu (1993)
            Khan and Venkatapuram (1993)
    Use neural net methodology and continuous valued fuzzy system to tune parameters.
3. Input-output clustering   Kosko (1991)
    Cluster data and establish patterns of associations to form rules.
4. Evolution algorithms   Lee and Takagi (1993)
            Karr and Gentry (1993)
            Ishibuchi et al. (1993)
            Homaifar and McCormick (1992)
    Tuning of membership functions or rules.

FIGURE 10.12   An annotated list of some previous approaches to automated design of fuzzy control systems.

1991). The discussion in this section addresses the work of Nyberg and Pao (1995) aimed at automatic discovery of fuzzy control rules for the inverted pendulum task. Different versions of the inverted pendulum exist, but one of the most common is a pole hinged to a moving cart as shown in Fig. 10.13.

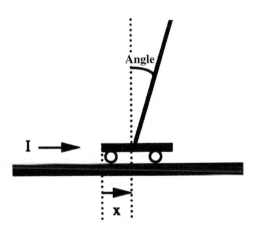

FIGURE 10.13   A schematic illustration of an inverted pendulum, hinged to a cart on a platform, and constrained to move within a plane.

The complexity of the task can be decreased by neglecting the effects of friction at the hinge and in cart motion. In addition, it can be taken that the mass of the cart is much larger than the mass of the pendulum.

For those circumstances, a mathematical simulation model of the pendulum system is provided by

$$\ddot{\theta} \approx \frac{g}{l} \sin \theta - \frac{F}{m_p} \cos \upsilon$$

$$\ddot{x} \approx \frac{F}{M_c + m_p}$$

If the second derivatives are further approximated by discrete forms with an integrating step size of h seconds and if instead of a force F, an impulse $I = Fh$ is used, it is possible to solve for the angle and cart position to obtain

$$\theta[k+1] = 2\theta[k] - \theta[k-1] + \frac{h^2 g}{l} \sin \theta[k] - \frac{Ih}{M_c l} \cos \theta[k]$$

$$x[k+1] = 2x[k] - x[k-1] + \frac{Ih}{M_c + m_p}$$

In the reference cited (Nyberg and Pao, 1995), some typical parameter values used in the computer simulation studies were

$$g = 9.81 \text{ m/s}^2 \qquad M_c = 1.0 \text{ kg} \qquad m_p = 0.1 \text{ kg} \qquad l = 1.0 \text{ m} \qquad h = 0.05 \text{ s}$$

The total length of the platform was chosen to be 4 m, which means that the range of x was from −2 to 2.

The inverted pendulum system had four state variables:

$$\theta = \text{angular position of the pole}$$
$$\dot{\theta} = \text{angular velocity of the pole}$$
$$x = \text{position of the cart on the platform}$$
$$\dot{x} = \text{velocity of the cart.}$$

Of these, only θ, $\dot{\theta}$ and x were used as inputs to the fuzzy controller system as depicted in Fig. 10.14. The reason for not using the linear velocity is to limit the complexity of the system. As shown in Fig. 10.14, the impulse I, which is applied every 0.1 s, is the output of the fuzzy logic controller. The control goal is to keep the pendulum balanced and the cart on the platform.

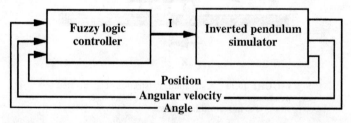

FIGURE 10.14   The simulated inverted pendulum controlled by the fuzzy controller.

The point of this present discussion is principally to report that it has been possible to use a special kind of fuzzy system (Wang, 1992), which has universal approximation properties, to format a fuzzy set controller for the inverted pendulum and then use the GESA algorithm to automatically discover fuzzy control rules. The shapes and positions of membership functions are also discovered in the rule discovery process.

Without going into details, it is still possible to give some idea of the procedure and results of the discovery process with the help of the illustrations of Fig. 10.15. The fuzzy sets for the angle are named $-, 0, +$. Similar practices are carried out for the angular velocity of the pole and for the position of the cart. In the Wang system, all the membership functions are gaussian in shape. The task of discovery is to determine the appropriate values for the widths and positions of the membership functions and also to determine what rules should link the input fuzzy sets to the outputs. The output is either an impulse from the right or from the left or zero.

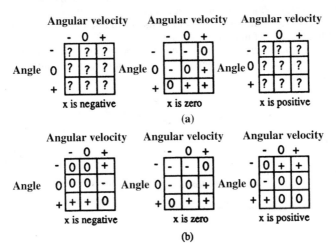

FIGURE 10.15 The three-dimensional rule matrix represented as three 2-dimensional matrices. The consequents of the rules in the middle matrix are predetermined and the other consequents are optimized by GESA. (a) Initial rules; (b) the rule base proposed by GESA.

The fuzzy controller can be described in terms of a three-dimensional rule matrix which, for convenience, can be represented as three 2-dimensional matrices. For example, the initial situation might be that shown in Fig. 10.15a. The consequents of the rules in the middle matrix are predetermined and the other consequents are found by GESA. One instance of the results is shown in Fig. 10.15b.

The inverted pendulum is controlled well by the rules discovered by GESA (Nyberg and Pao, 1995). There is some oscillation if the positions and shapes of membership functions are predetermined, but the performance is dramatically improved if the discovery system is allowed to learn optimal values of those parameters as well. However, the learning task was very lengthy even for a task of such relatively low complexity.

The point of this discussion is that it is very important that the formalism of a fuzzy set be capable of universal approximation. Given that, it is meaningful to think of process monitoring and optimal control. Nyberg and Pao (1995) also showed that it is possible to use GESA to learn an accurate fuzzy set model of a dynamical system. For example, in the case of the inverted pendulum it would mean that the model would describe well how an inverted pendulum would fall when uncontrolled, or how it would react when acted on by an impulse. In a sense, such a system would have the advantages of both neural net models and fuzzy set models. It would be possible to learn such a system and yet have the learned information expressible linguistically.

10.6 STABILITY AND CHAOS

10.6.1 Predictive Monitoring

The global issue of the stability of nonlinear dynamic systems under combined feed-forward/feedback control is certainly very interesting but it is also beyond the scope of this brief chapter. What is discussed here instead is the phenomenon of *deterministic chaos*, something which is not chaotic in its origin but can indeed lead to chaotic and unstable behavior of nonlinear systems.

The topic can be discussed from the perspective of predictive monitoring. To fix ideas, consider the question of whether it is possible to learn a neural net model of the process

$$x[n+1] = 4\lambda x[n](1 - x[n]) \qquad 0 \le x \le 1, 0 \le \lambda \le 1$$

as shown in Fig. 10.16.

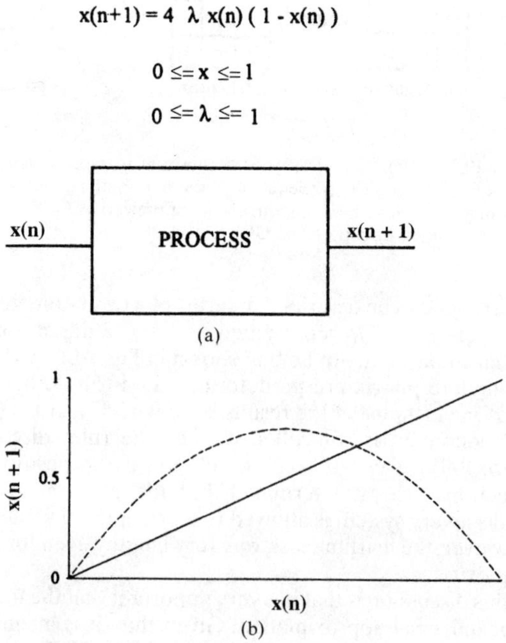

FIGURE 10.16 The quadratic map process: (*a*) the process; (*b*) the quadratic map.

This is the well-known quadratic map process (May, 1976; Feigenbaum, 1980), and the question of interest is whether it is possible to predict the value of $x[n + 1]$, given $x[n]$. The answer is quite surprising and has considerable bearing on what can be expected in practice in the predictive monitoring and control of nonlinear dynamic systems, in the realm of deterministic chaotic behavior.

A two-dimensional map is obtained when $x[n + 1]$ is plotted against $x[n]$, and it is known that there is a simple and interesting graphical procedure for generating the iterative values of $x[n + 1]$. Different sequences of $x[n]$ are generated depending on the value of λ and on the initial value of x. Some examples are shown in Fig. 10.17a and b. It is seen that for low values of λ, $x[n]$ converges to zero, or to some other fixed value, or oscillates with single or multiple frequencies. Finally, as λ approaches unity, the value of $x[n]$ varies drastically from step to step, seemingly *chaotically,* wildly, without rhyme or reason, manifestly in an unpredictable manner. The truth, of course, as is known, is that the process is still completely deterministic and, in principle, completely predictable.

It is important, however, to distinguish between the inherent predictability of the actual process and the issue of whether it is possible to *learn a neural net model* of the process which could be used to predict the values of $x[n + 1], x[n + 2], \ldots$, and so on, given the value of $x[n]$. Many investigators have found, as did Pao et al. (1990), that accurate open-loop prediction can be achieved quite readily for long sequences of values of $x[n]$ as long as the value of λ is not overly large. Otherwise there is extremely sensitive dependence on initial conditions. A small error in the reading of $x[n]$ would result in large deviations in the prediction of $x[n + 1]$. Under such conditions, use of a neural net which is only reasonably accurate would be quite inadequate and dangerous. Extremely accurate neural nets can be devised, but it is also necessary to avoid chaotic regions.

In summary, the most important point to be made in this section is that nonlinear systems can and do become deterministically chaotic, each in its own way, and such regimes are controlled not by exerting ever larger control actions but rather by adjusting the value of the critical parameter so that the system can become less sensitive to small inaccuracies.

There are many informative discussions and reviews of the quadratic map, including those by Lorenz (1963), May (1976), and Feigenbaum (1980). The topic is also addressed in many of the texts on nonlinear dynamics including the one on "an experimental approach" to nonlinear dynamics and chaos by Tufillaro, Abbott, and Reilly (1992).

10.7   COMMENTS AND REMARKS OF BIBLIOGRAPHIC NATURE

In current work, there is very little variation in the way system identification, or modeling, is carried out. All published accounts use some type of supervised learning to establish a network model of the plant, or process. However, as noted in the text, there are some differences in the approach to supervised learning. The most popular probably is still that of the standard multilayer network, with logistic activation functions and gradient search using the backpropagation algorithm. However, the issue of universal approximation is now much better understood and the practice of expansion in terms of multivariate basis functions is now being exercised with more theoretical guidance and with more confidence and success. Kol-

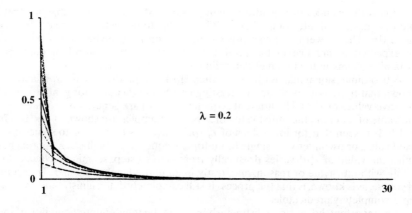

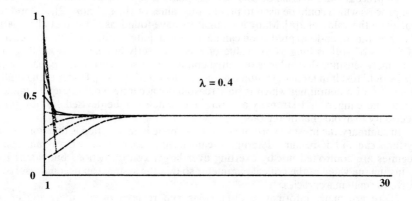

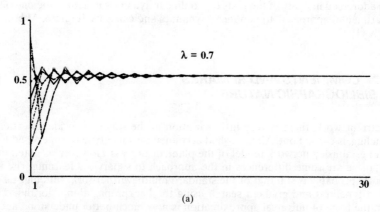

(a)

FIGURE 10.17 Evolution of the quadratic map system: (*a*) for low values of λ.

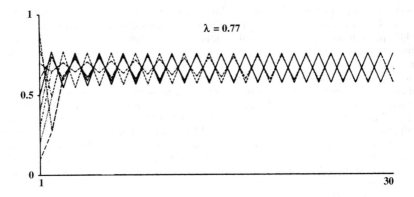

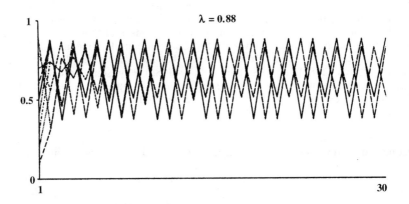

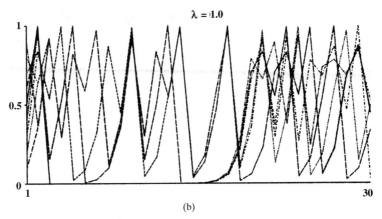

(b)

FIGURE 10.17 (*Continued*)   Evolution of the quadratic map system: (*b*) for high values of λ.

mogorov's superposition theorem (Kolmogorov, 1957) and neural net existence theorems based on mappings of that theorem (Hecht-Nielsen, 1987; Sprecher, 1965, 1993) provide assurance that suitable networks of simple architecture do exist for function approximation purposes, but of course the processing functions, or, equivalently, the basis functions are not only unknown but probably very complex. Along more practicable lines, it has been shown that universal approximation can be attained with logistic activation functions and a number of other simple activation functions (Hornik et al., 1989; Funahashi, 1989). In addition, in theory and in practice, it has been shown that there is basis for belief that an expansion in terms of a suitably large set of basis functions of fixed form can still provide an approximation of arbitrarily good accuracy; the latter is one instance of the functional-link approach (Pao et al., 1994; Igelnik and Pao, 1994). The nonlinear functional analog of the ARMA modeling scheme seems to be appropriate and adequate (Narendra and Parthasarthy, 1990; Pao et al., 1992).

There are differences in the ways in which neural net control actions are generated. Although several investigators refer to their own work as learning an "inverse" net or refer to others' approaches as using an inverse net, it is perhaps useful to distinguish between those instances where actual inverse nets were synthesized and used directly to generate control actions, and those other instances where the plant model was used with backpropagation or other means to infer what the control action should be. It would seem that the early work of Kawato et al. (1988), Psaltis (1988), and Chen and Pao (1988) represents true inverse net approaches while more recent work, such as that of Nguyen and Widrow (1990), Pao et al. (1992), and others uses the same net as that for modeling and either backpropagates to find the control action or determines that in some other manner, through optimization, for example.

Before the resurgence in neural net computing, there were, nevertheless, interesting and valid ways to approach the monitoring and control tasks in an essentially pattern recognition manner, related to the current neural net approaches. The CMAC approach of Albus (1975), the associative memory approach of Pao (1982), and the continuing accounts of Widrow and his collaborators over the years (Widrow and Smith, 1964; Widrow et al., 1973; Widrow, 1986) illustrate the continuing evolution of that line of thought.

As is well-known, control path planning, or, equivalently, the formation of control strategy, is a task that is quite separate from that of next-step control, and is of greater challenge. Accounts of investigations of control at that level are often reported in terms of reinforcement learning or reward and punishment learning. Accounts of such investigations may be found in articles by Widrow et al. (1973), Barto and Sutton (1981), Barto et al. (1983), Anderson (1989), Werbos (1990), and Williams (1988).

A list of suggestions for additional reading is provided after the list of cited references.

ACKNOWLEDGMENTS

The authors acknowledge with thanks the assistance of Sundar Amardar, Gwang-Hoon Park, C. Y. Shen, Boris Igelnik, and Donna Buggs in the preparation of this manuscript.

APPENDIX 10A   THE CONJUGATE GRADIENT ALGORITHM

Task.   Minimization of a multivariate function $F(y)$, where $y^T = (y_1, \ldots y_N)$.

General Description of the Algorithm.   The algorithm is designed for minimization of any smooth function but is especially good for minimization of quadratic functions.

Brief Description of Multivariate Quadratic Functions.   Quadratic functions are defined as follows

$$F(y) = y^T A y + b$$

where $A = \{a_{ij}\}$ is a positive definite matrix and b is a real number. In coordinate form quadratic function can be written as follows

$$F(y_1, \ldots y_N) = \sum_{i=1}^{N} \sum_{j=1}^{N} a_{ij} y_i y_j + b$$

For example, $F(y_1, y_2) = y_1^2 - 2y_1 y_2 + 3y_2^2$ is a quadratic function with matrix

$$A = \begin{bmatrix} 1 & -1 \\ -1 & 3 \end{bmatrix}$$

 In the case when F is a quadratic function, the conjugate gradient algorithm brings the function F to the point of minimum $y_* = (y_{*1}, \ldots y_{*N})$ *in not more than N iterations.* To define these iterations we need the following notations:

- For any constant $y_{k-1} = (y_{k-1,1}, \ldots, y_{k-1,N})$ and $d_k = (d_{k1}, \ldots, d_{kN})$, any variable λ, and any $k = 1, \ldots, N$ we define univariate function

$$\varphi_k(\lambda) = F(y_{k-1} + \lambda d_k)$$

That means that function $\varphi_k(\lambda)$ is defined at the points of the straight line passing the point y_{k-1} and having direction of the vector d_k.
- We denote $\lambda_k = \arg \min \varphi_k(\lambda)$, that is λ_k is a value of λ which brings function φ_k to the minimum.
- We denote $g_k = (g_{k1}, \ldots, g_{kN})$ the value of the gradient vector of the function F at the point $y_k = (y_{k1}, \ldots, y_{kN})$, $k = 0, \ldots, N$, that is,

$$g_{kn} = \frac{\partial F(y_{k1}, \ldots, y_{kn})}{\partial y_n} \qquad n = 1, \ldots, N$$

Then we can write the algorithm as the following sequence of iterations.

0th iteration
1. Choose y_0 arbitrarily.

2. Calculate d_1 by the formula

$$d_1 = -g_0$$

3. Solve the problem of univariate minimization of $\varphi_1(\lambda)$ and calculate λ_1. In the case of a quadratic function F we have following *explicit* formula

$$\lambda_1 = -\frac{\sum\limits_{i=1}^{N} \sum\limits_{j=1}^{N} a_{ij}(d_{i1}y_{j0} + d_{j1}y_{i0})}{2 \sum\limits_{i=1}^{N} \sum\limits_{j=1}^{N} a_{ij}d_i d_j}.$$

4. Calculate initial point for the next iteration by formula

$$y_1 = y_0 + \lambda_1 d_1$$

or in coordinate form

$$y_{1n} = y_{0n} + \lambda_1 d_{1n} \qquad n = 1, \dots, N$$

5. Calculate gradient g_1 at the initial point λ_1 of the next iteration.
6. Calculate norm $|g_1|$ of the vector g_1 by formula

$$|g_1| = \sqrt{\sum_{n=1}^{N} g_{1n}^2}$$

and check inequality

$$|g_1| < \varepsilon$$

where $\varepsilon > 0$ is a small positive number (for example, $\varepsilon = 10^{-5}$). If this inequality is true then stop, otherwise go to the next iteration.

***k*th iteration (1 ≤ k < N)**
2. Calculate d_{k+1} by the formula

$$d_{k+1} = -g_k + \frac{|g_k|}{|g_{k-1}|} d_k$$

3. Solve the problem of univariate minimization of $\varphi_{k+1}(\lambda)$ and calculate λ_{k+1}. In case of quadratic function F we have the following *explicit* formula

$$\lambda_{k+1} = -\frac{\sum\limits_{i=1}^{N} \sum\limits_{j=1}^{N} a_{ij}(d_{k+1,j}y_{kj} + d_{k+1,j}y_{ki})}{2 \sum\limits_{i=1}^{N} \sum\limits_{j=1}^{N} a_{ij}d_{ki}d_{kj}}$$

4. Calculate the initial point for the next iteration by the formula

$$y_{k+1} = y_k + \lambda_{k+1} d_{k+1}$$

or in coordinate form

$$y_{k+1,n} = y_{kn} + \lambda_{k+1} d_{k+1,n} \qquad n = 1, \ldots, N$$

5. Calculate gradient g_{k+1} at the initial point y_{k+1} of the next iteration.
6. Calculate norm $|g_{k+1}|$ of the vector g_{k+1} by formula

$$|g_{k+1}| = \sqrt{\sum_{n=1}^{N} g_{k+1,n}^2}$$

and check inequality

$$|g_{k+1}| < \varepsilon$$

If this inequality is true then stop, otherwise go to the next iteration.
Finally we will stop on the kth iteration, $K < N$, and an approximate solution is given by formula

$$y_* \approx y_K$$

APPENDIX 10B   GUIDED EVOLUTIONARY SIMULATED ANNEALING

Figures 10.18 to 10.20 describe a version of the GESA algorithm.

Step 1   Set initial temperature t.
Step 2   Randomly select N parents.
Step 3   Generate children from the parents (See Fig. 10.20).
Step 4   Find the best child for each parent (first level competition or local competition).
Step 5   Find the parents for the next generation (selection). For each family, we accept the best child as the parent for next generation if

$$y_1 < y_2 \text{ or } e^{-(y_1 - y_2)/t} > \rho$$

where y_1 = objective value of the best child
y_2 = objective value of its parent
t = temperature coefficient
ρ = random number uniformly distributed between 0 and 1

Step 6   Find the number of children that will be generated from the parents of the next generation (second level competition). The details of this step are given in Fig. 10.19.
Step 7   Decrease the temperature coefficient.
Step 8   Repeat steps 3 to 7 until an acceptable solution has been found or until a certain number of iterations have been reached.

FIGURE 10.18   A version of guided evolutionary simulated annealing algorithm.

Step 1   Repeat step 2 to 5 for each family; go to step 6.
Step 2   Count = 0.
Step 3   Repeat step 4 for each child; go to step 5.
Step 4   If the objective value of the child is lower than that of the lowest objective value, increase count by 1. If not, then we increase count by 1 if

$$e^{-(y_1 - y_2)/t} > \rho$$

where y_1 = objective value for the child
      y_2 = lowest objective value ever found
      t = temperature coefficient
      ρ = random number uniformly distributed between 0 and 1

Step 5   Acceptance number of the family is equal to count.
Step 6   Sum up the acceptance numbers of all the families.
Step 7   For each family, the number of children generated can be calculated according to the following formula:

$$M_i = \frac{T \times A_i}{S}$$

where M_i = number of children that will be generated for the ith family
      T = total number of points
      A_i = acceptance number for the ith family
      $S = \Sigma A_i$, the sum of the acceptance number.

FIGURE 10.19 Algorithm to find the number of children for the next generation.

Step 1   Set $x^c = x^p$, where x^c is the x value for the child and x^p is that for its parent.
Step 2   Randomly select one element in x, say the jth element, and compute

$$x_j^c = x_j^p + \Delta x$$

FIGURE 10.20 Algorithm to generate a child from its parent.

REFERENCES

Aarts, E., 1989. *Simulated Annealing and Boltzmann Machines: A Stochastic Approach to Combinatorial Optimization and Neural Computing,* Wiley, New York.

Albus, J. S., 1975. "A new approach to manipulator control: The cerebellor model articulation controller (CMAC)," *Transactions of the ASME,* Series G, *Journal of Dynamic Systems, Measurement and Control,* vol. 97, pp. 220–227.

Anderson, C. W., 1989. "Learning to control an inverted pendulum using neural networks," *IEEE Control Systems Magazine,* vol. 9, no. 3, pp. 31–27.

Barto, A. G., and R. S. Sutton, 1981. "Landmark learning: An illustration of associative search," *Biological Cybernetics,* vol. 42, pp. 1–8.

Barto, A. G., R. S. Sutton, and C. W. Anderson, 1983. "Neurolike adaptive elements that can solve difficult learning control problems," *IEEE Transactions on Systems, Man and Cybernetics,* vol. 13, pp. 834–846.

Bryson, A. E., and D. G. Leuenberger, 1970. "The synthesis of regulator logic using state-variable concepts," *Proceedings of the IEEE,* vol. 58, no. 11, pp. 1803–1811.

Efstathiou, J., 1987. "Rule-based process control using fuzzy logic," *Approximate Reasoning Intelligent Systems, Decisions and Control,* pp. 145–158, E. Sanchez and L. A. Zadeh (eds.), Pergamon Press, Oxford.

Feigenbaum, M. J., 1980. "Universal behavior in nonlinear systems," *Los Alamos Science,* vol. 1, pp. 4–27.

Fogel, L. J., A. J. Owens, and M. J. Walsh, 1966. *Artificial Intelligence Through Simulated Evolution,* Wiley, New York.

Funahashi, K., 1989. "On the approximate realization of continuous mappings by neural networks," *Neural Networks,* vol. 2, pp. 183–192.

Giles, C. L., and T. Maxwell, 1987. "Learning, invariance and generalization in higher-order neural networks," *Applied Optics,* vol. 26, pp. 4972–4978.

Goldberg, D., 1989. *Genetic Algorithms in Search, Optimization, and Machine Learning,* Addison-Wesley, Reading, Mass.

Goodwin, G. C. and K. S. Sin, 1984. *Adaptive Filtering Prediction and Control,* Prentice Hall, Englewood Cliffs, N.J.

Hecht-Nielsen, R., 1987. "Kolmogorov's mapping neural network existence theorem," *Proceedings of IEEE First International Conference on Neural Networks,* vol. 11, pp. 11–14, SOS Printing, San Diego.

Holland, J. H., 1975. *Adaption in Natural and Artificial Systems,* University of Michigan Press, Ann Arbor.

Holland, J. H., K. J. Hoyoak, R. E. Nisbett, and P. R. Thagard, 1986. *Induction: Processes of Inference, Learning, and Discovery,* MIT Press, Cambridge, Mass.

Homaifar, A. M., and E. McCormick, 1992. "Full design of fuzzy controllers using genetic algorithms," *Proceedings of SPIE,* vol. 1766, pp. 393–404, San Diego, July.

Hornik, K., M. Stinchcombe, and H. White, 1989. "Multilayer feedforward networks are universal approximators," *Neural Networks,* vol. 2, pp. 359–366.

Igelnik, B. and Y. H. Pao, 1994. "Random vector version of the Functional-Link net," *Proceedings of 28th Annual Conference on Information Science and Systems,* vol. 2, pp. 785–789, Princeton University, Princeton, New Jersey, March 16–19.

Ishibuchi, H., K. Nozaki, and N. Yamamoto, 1993. "Selecting fuzzy rules by genetic algorithm for classification problems," *IEEE International Conference on Fuzzy Systems,* pp. 1119–1124, San Francisco, March.

Jamshidi, M., 1991. "A comparison of an expert and an adaptive fuzzy control approach," *Proceedings of IEEE Conference on Decision and Control,* pp. 1907–1908, Brighton, England, December.

Jang, J. R., 1992. "Self-learning fuzzy controllers based on temporal back propagation," *IEEE Transaction on Neural Networks,* vol. 3, no. 5, pp. 714–723.

Karr, C. and E. J. Gentry, 1993. "Fuzzy control of pH using genetic algorithms," *IEEE Transactions on Fuzzy Systems,* vol. 1, no. 1, pp. 46–53.

Kawato, M., Y. Uno, M. Isobe, and R. Suzuki, 1988. "Hierarchical neural network model for voluntary movement with applications to robotics," *IEEE Control Systems Magazine,* vol. 8, pp. 8–16.

Kolmogorov, A. N., 1957. "On the representation of continuous functions of many variables by superposition of continuous functions of one variable and addition," *Doklady Akademii Nauk SSSR,* vol. 114, pp. 953–956, and *Translations American Mathematical Society,* 1963, vol. 2, no. 28, pp. 55–59.

Kosko, B., 1991. *Neural Networks and Fuzzy Systems: A Dynamical Systems Approach to Machine Intelligence,* Prentice-Hall, Englewood Cliffs, N.J.

Kurkova, V., 1992. Kolmogorov's theorem and multilayer neural networks, *Neural Networks,* vol. 5, pp. 501–506.

Lee, M. A., and H. Takagi, 1993. "Integrating design stages of fuzzy systems using genetic algorithms," *IEEE International Conference on Fuzzy Systems,* pp. 612–617, San Francisco, March.

Lee, Y. C., G. Doolen, H. H. Chen, G. Z. Sun, T. Maxwell, H. Y. Lee, and C. L. Giles, 1986. "Machine learning using higher order correlation network," *Physica* 22D, pp. 276–306, North-Holland, Amsterdam.

Lorentz, G. G., 1966. *Approximations of Functions,* Holt, Rinehart and Winston, New York.

Lorenz, E. N., 1963. "Deterministic nonperiodic flow," *Journal of Atmospheric Science,* vol. 20, pp. 130–141.

May, R. M., 1976. "Simple mathematical models with very complicated dynamics," *Nature,* vol. 261, pp. 459–467.

Narendra, K. S. and K. Parthasarathy, 1990. "Identification and control of dynamic systems using neural networks," *IEEE Transaction on Neural Networks,* vol. 1, pp. 4–27.

Nguyen, D. H., and B. Widrow, 1990 "Neural networks for self-learning control systems, *IEEE Control Systems Magazine,"* vol. 10, pp. 18–23, April.

Nguyen, D. H., and B. Widrow, 1990b. "Neural networks for self-learning control systems," *IEEE Controls Systems Magazine,* vol. 10, pp. 18–23.

Nyberg, M. and Y. H. Pao, 1995. "Automatic optimal design of fuzzy systems based on universal approximation and evolutionary programming," *Fuzzy Logic and Intelligent Systems,* H. L. Hua and M. Gupta (eds.), Kluwer Academic Publishers, Norwell, Mass.

Pao, Y. H., 1982. "Feasibility of using associative memories for static security assessment of power system overloads," Electric Power Research Institute Project 1047-2, final report, EPRI EL-2343, EPRI, Palo Alto, Calif.

Pao, Y. H., 1989. *Adaptive Pattern Recognition and Neural Networks,* Addison-Wesley, Reading, Mass.

Pao, Y. H., G. H. Park, and D. J. Sobajic, 1994. "Learning and generalization characteristics of the random vector Functional-Link net," *Neurocomputing,* vol. 6, no. 2, pp. 163–180, Elsevier Press, New York.

Pao, Y. H., G. M. Zwingelstein, and D. J. Sobajic, 1990. "Analysis of transients on basis of identification of signal generative structure: Even unto chaos," *IEEE Annual International Conference on Neural Networks,* San Diego, June 17–21.

Pao, Y. H., S. Phillips, and D. J. Sobajic, 1992. "Neural-net computing and the intelligent control of systems," *International Journal of Control,* vol. 56, pp. 263–290, Taylor and Francis, Ltd., London.

Park, G. H., Y. H. Pao, B. Igelnik, K. H. Eyink, and S. R. LeClair, 1995. "Neural-net computing for interpretation of semiconductor film optical ellipsometry parameters," *IEEE Transactions on Neural Networks,* in press.

Poggio, T., and F. Girosi, 1990. "Networks for approximation and learning," *Proceedings of the IEEE,* vol. 78, no. 9, pp. 1481–1496, September.

Procyk, T. J., and E. H. Mamdani, 1979. "A linguistic self-organizing process controller," *Automatica,* vol. 15, pp. 15–40.

Psaltis, D., A. Sideris, and A. A. Yamamura, 1988. "A multilayered neural network controller," *IEEE Controls Systems Magazine,* vol. 8, pp. 17–21.

Rosenblatt, F. 1981. *Principles of Neurodynamics: Perceptrons and the Theory of Brain Mechanisms,* Spartan Books, Washington, D.C., 1961.

Rosenblatt, F., 1958. *"The Perceptrons: a probabilistic model for information storage and organization in the brain",* Psychological Review, vol. 65, pp. 386–408.

Sprecher, D. A., 1965. "On the structure of continuous functions of several variables," *Transactions American Mathematical Society,* vol. 115, no. 3, pp. 340–355.

Sprecher, D. A., 1993. "A universal mapping for Kolmogorov's superposition theorem," *Neural Networks,* vol. 6, pp. 1089–1094.

Thrift, P., 1991. "Fuzzy logic synthesis with genetic algorithms," *Proceedings of the Fourth International Conference on Genetic Algorithms,* pp. 502–513, San Mateo, Calif.

Tsutomu, M., 1993. "Operator tuning in fuzzy production rules," *IEEE International Conference on Fuzzy Systems,* pp. 641–646, San Francisco, March.

Tufillaro, N. B., T. Abbott, and J. Reilly, 1992. *An Experimental Approach to Nonlinear Dynamics and Chaos,* Addison-Wesley, Reading, Mass.

Wang, L. X., 1992. "Fuzzy systems are universal approximators," *Proceedings of IEEE International Conference on Fuzzy Systems,* pp. 1163–1169, San Diego.

Werbos, P. J., 1990. "A menu of design for reinforcement learning over time," *Neural Networks for Control,* W. T. Miller, R. S. Sutton, and P. J. Werbos (eds.), MIT Press, Cambridge, Mass.

Widrow, B., and F. W. Smith, 1964. "Pattern-recognizing control systems," *1963 Computer and Information Services (COINS) Symposium Proceedings,* pp. 288–317, Washington, D.C., Spartan.

Widrow, B., N. K. Gupta, and S. Maitra, 1973. "Punish/reward: learning with a critic in adaptive threshold systems," *IEEE Transactions on Systems, Man and Cybernetics,* vol. 3, pp. 455–465.

Widrow, B., 1986. "Adaptive inverse control," *Adaptive Systems in Control and Signal Processing 1986* (International Federation of Automatic Control), pp. 1–15.

Widrow, B., 1987. "The original adaptive net broom-balancer," *IEEE International Symposium on Circuits and Systems,* pp. 351–357, May.

Williams, R. J., 1988. "On the use of backpropagation in associative reinforcement learning," *Proceedings IEEE International Conference on Neural Networks,* San Diego.

Williams, V., and K. Matsuoka, 1991. "Learning to balance the inverted pendulum using neural networks," *IEEE International Joint Conference on Neural Networks (IJCNN'91),* pp. 214–219, Singapore, November.

Yip, P. P. C., and Y. H. Pao, 1994. "A guided evolutionary simulated annealing approach to the quadratic assignment problem," *IEEE Transactions on Systems, Man and Cybernetics,* vol. 24, no. 9, pp. 1385–1388, September.

SUGGESTIONS FOR ADDITIONAL READING

Regarding Traditional Methods for Process Monitoring and Fault Diagnosis

Astrom, K. J., 1985. "Process control—past, present, and future," *IEEE Control System Magazine,* vol. 5, no. 3, pp. 3–10.

Frank, P. M., 1990. "Fault diagnosis in dynamic systems using analytical and knowledge-based redundancy—A survey and some new results," *Automatica,* vol. 26, no. 3, pp. 459–474.

Gertler, J. J., 1988. "Survey of model-based failure detection and isolation in complex plants," *IEEE Control System Magazine,* vol. 8, no. 6, pp. 3–11.

Isermann, R., 1985. "Process fault diagnosis with parameter estimation methods," *Proceedings of IFAC Conference on Digital Computer Applications to Process Control,* pp. 51–60.

Soeterboek, R. 1992. *Predictive Control,* Prentice Hall, Englewood Cliffs, N.J.

Wilsky, A. S., 1976. "A survey of design methods for failure detection in dynamic systems," *Automatica,* vol. 12, pp. 601–611.

Regarding Neural Network Methods for Process Monitoring, Fault Diagnosis, and Control

Bhat, P. Minderman, T. J. McAvoy, and N. S. Wang, 1990. "Modelling chemical process plants via neural computation," *IEEE Control Magazine,* vol. 10, no. 3, pp. 24–30.

Grossberg, S., 1989. *Neural Dynamics of Adaptive Sensory-Motor Control,* Elsevier North-Holland, Amsterdam.

Harris, C. J., 1994. *Advances in Intelligent Control,* Taylor and Francis Ltd., London.

Harris, C. J., C. G. Moore, and M. Brown (eds.), 1993. *Intelligent Control—Aspects of Fuzzy Logic and Neural Nets,* World Scientific, New Jersey.

IEEE Control Systems Magazine, April 1988, April 1989, April 1990, January 1991, special issues or sections.

Kosko, B., 1991. *Neural Networks and Fuzzy Systems: A Dynamical Systems Approach to Machine Intelligence,* Prentice Hall, Englewood Cliffs, N.J.

Mavrovouniotis, M. L. (ed.), 1990. *Artificial Intelligence in Process Engineering,* Academic Press, New York.

Miller III, W. T., R. S. Sutton, P. J. Werbos (eds.), 1990. *Neural Networks for Control,* MIT Press, Cambridge, Mass.

Moore, K. L., 1992. *Iterative Learning Control for Deterministic Systems,* Springer-Verlag, New York.

Narendra, K. S. and K. Parthasarathy, 1991. "Gradient methods for the optimization of dynamical systems using neural networks," *IEEE Transactions on Neural Networks,* vol. 2, pp. 252–262.

Report on the DARPA Sponsored Neural Network Study, October 1987–February 1988, Fairfax, Va., AFCEA International Press, November 1988.

Scott, G. M., and W. H. Ray, 1993. "Experience with model-based controllers based on neural network process models," *Journal of Process Control,* vol. 3, no. 3, pp. 179–196.

Sorsa, T., H. N. Koivo, and H. Koivisto, 1991. "Neural networks in process fault diagnosis," *IEEE Transaction on Systems, Man and Cybernetics,* vol. 21, no. 4, pp. 814–824.

Willis, M. J., C. Di Massimo, G. A. Montague, M. T. Tham, and A. J. Morris, 1991. "Artificial neural networks in process engineering," *IEEE Proceedings—D,* vol. 138, no. 3, pp. 256–266.

CHAPTER 11
NEURAL NETWORKS FOR

Casimir C. Klimasauskas
NeuralWare, Inc.
Pittsburgh, Pennsylvania

11.1 INTRODUCTION

This chapter discusses practical issues in applying neural networks to a variety of database applications. In the applications considered in this chapter, each record in the database is self-contained. The objective of building a model is to find a formula or program that facilitates predicting the value of one or more fields in the database from the other fields. Examples include predicting who will respond to a direct mail solicitation, determining which patients have a high risk of breast cancer, classifying rice, and picking stocks. This chapter highlights key techniques and issues that are often pivotal in the success or failure of these applications. It is not a cookbook. However, as a step toward making neural networks more of a science than an art, this chapter presents a basic structure that can be modified to suit your particular application.

11.2 NEURAL MODELS VERSUS STATISTICAL MODELS

A variety of approaches have been developed for applying neural networks to database problems. The most popular approach is to replace linear or logistic regression models with nonlinear feedforward neural net models. These are also known as *backpropagation* or *multilayer perceptrons*. This approach has many similarities to the development of statistical models. Figure 11.1 shows some of the key issues.

Neural as well as statistical models are based on nonparametric modeling techniques. As such, they are limited to interpolating within the domain of data used to develop the model. They interpolate. Extrapolation with these models is risky at best. Though it is perhaps an unfair stereotype, the most commonly used statistical modeling techniques are linear regression and logistic regression. Nonlinear feedforward neural networks are intrinsically nonlinear. (For purposes of this chapter,

Statistical models	Neural (nonlinear feedforward) models
Purpose is to interpolate	Purpose is to interpolate
Typically linear	Nonlinear
Data transformation improves model performance	Data transformation improves model performance
Variable selection is important for robust models	Variable selection is important for good generalization
Independent inputs are required	Correlated inputs are OK
Anyone can build a good model	Neural network expertise is required to build a good model

FIGURE 11.1   A comparison of nonlinear feedforward neural network and statistical models.

statistical models refers to models developed with linear or logistic regression. *Neural models* refers to nonlinear feedforward or backpropagation models.) Statistical as well as neural models benefit from data transformation. Variable selection, likewise, is important, even crucial, to building effective models. The most common procedures for building statistical models fail if the inputs are not independent. This is a failing of the numerical algorithms. Robust techniques, such as singular value decomposition, can handle highly correlated inputs. The numerical algorithms used to implement neural models usually deal well with correlated inputs. Though the tools for building linear models are easily accessible and anyone can use them, this does not mean that anyone can use them correctly. Building good linear models requires skill. The same is true for neural models. When building neural models, an easy trap is to believe that understanding how neural networks operate will result in good models. This is only part of the answer. Building good neural models requires a thorough understanding of the model building process as well as neural networks themselves.

The processes of building and applying statistical and neural models are very similar. Many of the issues discussed in the following sections apply equally to both.

Building a statistical or neural model is a multistep process. The essential steps are

1. Defining the system objective
2. Collecting data
3. Analyzing and transforming data
4. Selecting train, test, and validation sets
5. Variable selection
6. Model development
7. Model verification

The following sections describe these steps.

11.3   DEFINING THE SYSTEM OBJECTIVE

How much is this worth: a neural model that in 17 out of 20 days correctly predicts the direction of the next-day change in price of the 30-year U.S. Treasury bond? It may be worthless! It all depends on how it makes mistakes 15 percent of the time. The scatter plot in Fig. 11.2 shows the relationship between accuracy (the percentage of the time that the change in price is correctly predicted) and profit (based on a particular trading strategy) for several hundred neural networks developed for the deutsche mark. Notice that maximum profit is achieved at 65 percent accuracy. At 50 percent accuracy, some networks were profitable, and some lost money. It all depends on how you make mistakes (Klimasauskas, 1992).

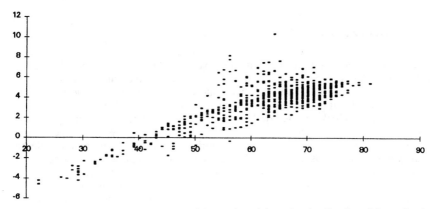

FIGURE 11.2   Accuracy as a percentage of the number of times that the direction of the market is correctly predicted (x axis) vs. profit for a particular trading strategy (y axis).

Another way of looking at this problem is to explore the relationship between profit and root-mean-square (rms) error. Figure 11.3 shows a scatter plot of this relationship. Notice that low rms error does not necessarily translate into profit. Some of the neural models with very low rms error actually *lost* money!

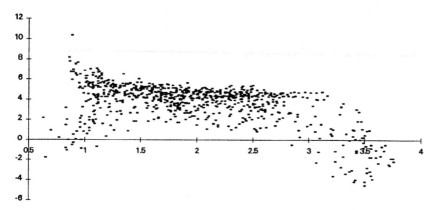

FIGURE 11.3   RMS error for forward price predictions (x axis) versus profit for a particular trading strategy (y axis).

The point of these illustrations is that technological measures such as rms error or accuracy may have little or no relationship to how a model will perform in a deployed environment. This applies equally well to both neural models and statistical models.

The first step in building a successful model is to understand the objectives of the total system in which it will be deployed. From there, it is possible to develop strategies and measures that optimize the performance of the total system. Many neural models fail because they maximize technological measures without regard for how the model works in the total system.

11.4   COLLECTING DATA

The process of collecting data also involves verifying it. There are several pitfalls in this process. Three in particular are data formats, field usage, and data availability.

America is enamored with data. We collect data even when we do not need it with the hope that it may someday provide us with a payback. Neural networks hold the promise of unlocking this storehouse of data and turning it into better decisions. Unfortunately, much of the data which is not essential to the day-to-day operation of a company are often poorly edited and poorly maintained. A common problem is that data formats on little-used fields may change over time without proper reformatting of the database, or may even have different formats in different programs. It is easy to check for proper formats, and it can save substantial time and effort.

It is 2:00 p.m., and the president has just sent word to the chief information officer (CIO) that he needs a new report on his desk tomorrow morning. The CIO passes the word down the ranks. The ranks respond that the new report will require adding new fields to the database and reorganizing it. This could take days. Under pressure from above, the programming staff comes up with a compromise. They use an existing field that does not show up in any of their normal programs, overwriting anything that might be there. The report is ready the following day. Two years later, an analyst using neural networks discovers a particular little-used field that has tremendous predictive power. Unfortunately, the predictive power is a by-product of a special report run occasionally for the president. Make sure that you really know the data you are working with.

In an insurance fraud application, one particular field had substantial discriminating power in predicting fraudulent claims. The field was a flag that helped an analyst decide whether to pay all or a portion of the claim. This information was not available in the deployed application.

A mail solicitation for a preapproved credit line was developed using a neural model. As the system moved into the deployment phase, it was discovered that the neural model relied heavily on credit-bureau supplied information. It was not economic to acquire this as part of the selection process. The project failed. Make sure the data you use are available in the deployed system.

Collecting data is a very important step in building a model. Take the time to make sure that you know what you have and that it looks as it should.

11.5   ANALYZING AND TRANSFORMING DATA

Converting data into a form suitable for building effective models is an iterative process that interacts with the model development process. This section addresses three crucial issues: structuring the problem, transforming enumerated data, and transforming continuous data.

11.5.1 Structuring the Problem

Suppose that it is important to predict how many times a person will visit the emergency room of a hospital over the next 5 years. In particular, it is important to know if they will visit it never, once, twice, three times, or four or more times. This problem has at least two possible encodings: linear and one-of-N.

Visits	Linear code	One-of-N code			
None	0.1	0	0	0	0
One	0.3	1	0	0	0
Two	0.5	0	1	0	0
Three	0.7	0	0	1	0
Four or more	0.9	0	0	0	1

Linear encoding provides a continuous output that estimates the number of visits. Building a model resulted in an accuracy of 60 percent. This did not provide the level of discrimination necessary in this application. The one-of-N code was used in an attempt to improve the ability to discriminate between each of these categories. A model built using the one-of-N code was accurate 11 percent of the time! What happened?

The one-of-N encoding actually made the problem much harder. The neural model was not able to solve this harder problem. An alternative encoding called a *thermometer code* was tested. The category with the largest change from one output to the next determined the class. A model built with the thermometer code had a 65 percent accuracy.

Visits	Thermometer code			
None	0	0	0	0
One	1	0	0	0
Two	1	1	0	0
Three	1	1	1	0
Four or more	1	1	1	1

This is an equivalent problem, but much more solvable by the neural model. It is possible to build a neural model which maps from the thermometer code to the one-of-N code without any hidden units. Though in theory it should not make a difference, in practice it does. This same phenomenon occurs in stock picking, stock market timing, and credit evaluation.

As you structure the problem, what you ask the model to produce can have a substantial impact on total model performance. The precise causes of this are not well-understood, but the empirical evidence is unequivocal. Take the time to explore alternative formulations of your problem.

11.5.2   Enumerated Data Transformations

Symbolic fields, such as title, are the most easily identified form of enumerated data. Even more common are integer data fields where each integer maps to a particular symbolic string through an external dictionary. A common example is a single digit used to represent marital status. Whether represented by a numeric value or the original string value, this is an enumerated field.

There are several methods for handling enumerated data. Three methods shown below are continuous encoding, binary encoding, and one-of-N coding. A linear or continuous encoding uses one model input, and simply scales the raw data into a target range 0.2 to 0.8. Binary encoding recognizes that the linear encoding has no meaning, and maps the various enumerated values into an arbitrary binary code using two network inputs. The one-of-N code assigns a separate model input to each enumeration. This requires as many inputs as categories in the enumerated field.

Marital status	Raw data	Linear	Binary		One-of-N			
Single	1	0.2	0	0	1	0	0	0
Married	2	0.4	0	1	0	1	0	0
Divorced	3	0.6	1	0	0	0	1	0
Other	4	0.8	1	1	0	0	0	1

When you are working with large data records, it is easy to assume that all numeric fields represent numbers, and to simply scale numeric enumerated fields into a range suitable for neural network input. This can have the effect of completely eliminating any predictive power a particular field may have. In a particular targeted marketing application, treating numeric enumerated fields as numbers provided an 87 percent correct classification with a logistic regression model. Translating the enumerated numeric fields into a one-of-N code increased this to 95 percent. Developing a neural model on the transformed data increased accuracy to 97 percent. Continuous or linear mappings of enumerated values should never be used.

Binary encodings, though marginally better than linear encodings, likewise keep data packed into a form that must be decoded by the model to be useful. They should not be used.

One-of-N codes are the most appropriate method for handling enumerated data. This is fine when there are few (less than 10 or 15) possible enumerated values. When a field may take on dozens, hundreds, or thousands of possible values, categorical codes are more appropriate. A categorical code maps an enumerated code into an appropriate set of component characteristics. For example, standard industry code (SIC) is found in a variety of databases. This is a five-digit code that uniquely identifies the industry a business belongs to. Creating a one-of-100,000 input code is not appropriate. Depending on the application, identify a set of characteristics that may be pertinent to the problem. Characteristics may be service, manufacturing, financial, high-tech, dangerous to life, etc. Each SIC is mapped into several dummy variables that identify the presence or absence of each characteristic for that SIC.

Another common enumerated field is the state in which a person resides. Consolidating the 50 states into 5 or 7 larger geographic areas reduces a 1-of-50 code to a 1-of-5 or 1-of-7 code. Do this carefully. In a credit approval application, the user divided the United States into five regions, one of which was the Northeast (Maine, Vermont, New Hampshire, Massachusetts, New York, Pennsylvania, New Jersey).

The model performed well on four of the five regions. It did not perform well for the Northeast. With further investigation, it became clear that the indicators for credit worthiness for New York City were very different from those for Rochester. Revising the grouping for the Northeast to separate the Northeastern seaboard resolved the performance problem.

These are the basic techniques for handling enumerated fields. Another important issue is scaling the data for input to a neural model. The appropriate scaling for each input is 0 or 1. Why? First, observe that for a 1-of-10 code, each input will be 1 about 10 percent of the time. The rest of the time, it will be 0. Second, the gradient or parameter update calculation for backpropagation typically uses cumulative weight updates, momentum, or both. These have the effect of smoothing the surface. Events that occur infrequently are averaged out of existence. Third, recall the basic parameter update rule for backpropagation:

$$\Delta W_{ij} = \alpha \delta_i X_j$$

The parameter change depends on the learning rate, the error on the input side of the hidden unit, and the current value of the input unit. When the input is zero, no parameter modification occurs. The parameters associated with the inputs change *only* when the input is active. If a logical input that is *on* 10 percent of the time is scaled into the range −1 to +1, the parameters associated with it learn that the input is always about −1, and tend to smooth the infrequent +1 events out of existence. Always scale logical and enumerated inputs into the range 0 to +1.

11.5.3 Continuous Numeric Transformations

The performance of a neural or statistical model is often improved by transforming the continuous numeric inputs. The primary purpose of these transformations is to modify the distribution of the input or explanatory variables so that they better match the distribution of the dependent variables.

$$Y = a_0 + a_1 X_1 + a_2 X_2 + \cdots + a_n X_n$$

In the linear model shown above, X_i is a good explanatory variable if the coefficient associated with it is large. When this happens, what can we say about the distributions of X_i and Y? They must be similar because they are linearly related. Figure 11.4 shows histograms (discrete distributions) of Y, X_i, X_j, and X_k. As you would expect,

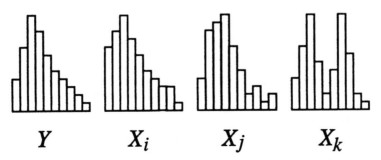

FIGURE 11.4 Distributions of dependent variable and various input variables.

the distribution of Y and X_i and X_j look very similar. We know that X_i is a good explanatory variable. What can we say about X_j? It is possible that it is a good explanatory variable. It is also possible that it was picked from a purely random distribution that has little relationship to Y. The distribution of X_k is quite different from Y. It is not possible for X_k to be a good explanatory variable of Y. However, if we can find a function that maps X_k to X_k' such that the transformed distribution of X_k' is similar to the distribution of Y, X_k' may be a good explanatory variable. This is the basic idea behind the transformation of continuous input data.

Test a variety of transformations. The transform which produces the most similar distribution to the output variable is the one selected. This does not guarantee that this input is useful to the model, but it makes it more likely that it will be useful. Two references in the statistics literature that deal with this in greater depth are *Exploratory Data Analysis* (Tukey, 1977), and *Regression Analysis by Example* (Chatterjee, 1991).

Continuous transforms of input variables are typically scaled into the range –1 to +1. The logic behind this is analogous to that for scaling of logical data. For most appropriately transformed inputs, the data are concentrated around the average or mean. Mapping the mean to zero and the balance of the range into the –1 to +1 interval provides maximum gradient adaptation as the input deviates from its average. When it is near the average, very little parameter modification occurs. Any offsets are handled by constant terms.

Quite a variety of other techniques for scaling continuous input variables have been developed and may be found in the statistics literature.

11.6 SELECTING TRAIN, TEST, AND VALIDATION SETS

Quite a bit of lore surrounds the selection of training, test, and validation sets. Much of it arises from misunderstanding the purpose of developing a neural or statistical model. To understand the appropriate processes, it is necessary first to make some definitions and understand the implications of the calculus of backpropagation.

The purpose of developing a neural model is to produce a formula that captures essential relationships in data. Once developed, this formula is used to interpolate from a new set of inputs to corresponding outputs. In neural networks, this is called *generalization*. The *training set* is the set of points that are used to fit the parameters of the model. The *test set* measures how well the model interpolates. It is used as part of the model building process to prevent overfitting. The *validation* set is used to estimate model performance in a deployed environment.

On the basis of this, select the training and test sets with an understanding of the mathematical algorithms used to estimate the model parameters in such a way as to maximize the performance of the deployed system.

Before a training or test set is selected from the data, it is essential to understand the purpose and use of the model. Figure 11.5 shows a scatter plot of data for a model with one input and one output. The straight line with the arrow is the result of using the linest ( ) function in Microsoft Excel to perform linear regression from the input to the output.

Is the linear regression line shown in Fig. 11.5 a good solution to this problem? The answer depends on how the model is used. The objective of linear regression is to minimize the sum squared error of the difference between the estimated and actual outputs. If that is what is required by the system objectives, this model does

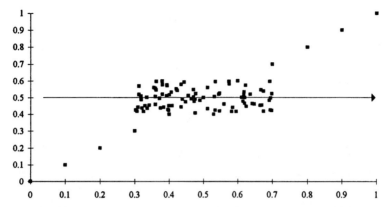

FIGURE 11.5 Scatter plot and linear regression line for data with a single input (x axis), and a single output (y axis). The linear regression line was produced using linest ( ) in Microsoft Excel.

that. However, if the purpose of this model is to interpolate well over the entire range of the input space, this model fails.

To interpolate well over all of the input space, select only three or four data points from the input region 0.3 to 0.7, and reestimate the regression line. Eliminate all the other data in this range. The result will be a model that interpolates well over the entire range of the input space, but does *not* have the lowest rms error given the raw data distribution.

The idea of discarding potentially substantial amounts of data is sometimes hard to accept. The empirical evidence is that it works. As an example, a model for predicting the 5-day trend in the Standard and Poor 500 index uses only 45 examples out of an initial data set of 375. Thirty of the 45 examples represent extreme moves in the market. Fifteen examples were randomly selected from the other 345. The results are a model that produces far more profit in the deployed system than those developed with all of the data. When you select training sets, less is more, small is beautiful (Plutowski, 1992).

Training set selection is based on the objectives of how the model will be used. Once the training set is selected, the test set is selected to determine how well the model estimated with the training set interpolates. The validation set uses a distribution similar to the native population to estimate performance in the deployed environment. It can also be used to convert neural model outputs to probabilities.

11.7 VARIABLE SELECTION

Picking the right input variables is critical to effective model development. A good subset of variables can substantially improve the performance of a model. The challenge is finding ways to pick good subsets of variables.

A variety of techniques have been suggested for variable selection. Most of them fail to produce the best possible results. One of the most common approaches to variable selection is stepwise linear regression. This approach, with similarities to other correlation-based techniques, can be fooled by masking variables. Figure 11.6

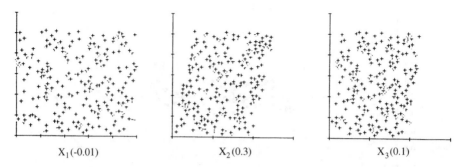

$X_1 (-0.01)$ $X_2 (0.3)$ $X_3 (0.1)$

FIGURE 11.6 Scatter plots of three candidate input variables (x axis) against the desired output (y axis).

shows scatter plots of three possible input variables (x axis) against an output variable (y axis). The linear correlation coefficient for each is shown under the scatter plot. Linear regression produces the following formula: $Y = 0.2 + (-0.2)X_2$. As expected, the linear correlation between the actual and estimated values of Y is -0.3. Using an exhaustive variable selection technique produces the following formula: $Y = -0.2X_1 + 0.2X_3$ with a linear correlation of 1.0! The relatively high correlation between X_2 and Y masks a more subtle and powerful relationship between X_1, X_3, and Y. Though this example was artificially constructed, it illustrates a relatively common phenomenon found in noisy data sets: seemingly highly predictive individual variables may mask more powerful linear and non-linear interactions between other variables.

One of the approaches used by NeuralWare's *Predict* product is to utilize a genetic algorithm to search for good sets of input variables. For each possible set, a network is developed and the performance of the network is used to rank the subset of inputs. This has proven itself quite effective across a range of problems.

Another novel approach uses tetrads (Spirtes, 1993). These techniques provide a mechanism for identifying subsets of variables with maximum mutual information. This has been used with moderate success on smaller problems.

Variable selection is an important step in the model development process. Effective variable selection can substantially improve model performance and generalization.

11.8 MODEL DEVELOPMENT

Quite a bit has been written on the topic of building backpropagation models. One area which has not received much attention is the selection of the output transform function.

When building predictive models with sigmoid or tanh outputs, models are often quite poor at predicting the extreme values. To overcome this problem, the target outputs are often scaled into the range 0.3 to 0.7 so that the output transform operates in the linear portion of its range. Another technique is to use a linear output. When using a linear output, it is essential to set the learning rates associated with the output weights to very small values. Failure to do so results in unstable parameter estimation. Linear output units often provide much better predictive capabilities than tanh or sigmoid.

Another variant useful for predictive models is to use sum of cubed or sum of fourth power errors rather than sum of squared error as the training objective. This has the effect of accentuating larger discrepancies between the actual and estimated outputs, while reducing the impact of smaller errors. This is particularly helpful for very noisy prediction or two-class discriminate problems. Hanson (1988) derives the mathematics behind this.

Classification problems present another problem. Particularly when there are multiple outputs, the network often learns that it can minimize the sum of squared errors by simply always predicting that the inputs belong to none of the classes. The more output classes, the more pronounced this effect. A different objective function is needed. An alternative that has been quite successfully used is the Softmax function. It maximizes the relative entropy $\Sigma d_i \ln X_i$, where d_i is the desired output for category i and X_i is the network output. See Bridle, (1991) for a complete description of this approach.

11.9 MODEL VERIFICATION

Perhaps one of the biggest problems many individuals have with neural models is how to quantify their performance. Statistical models often use the T test to establish confidence intervals at the 90 or 95 percent certainty level. This provides management with a number that inspires confidence in the model. Whether the T test results make sense, or the resulting confidence is justified, is irrelevant. The essential point is that T test results give a measure of belief in a model.

Just as the T test is applied to linear models, it can be applied as well to neural models. The only requirement is that the residual errors are approximately normally distributed. If the residuals meet this requirement, the T test can be validly applied to either neural or linear models. As an aside, when you are performing this test, it is essential that the data selected for the test have the same distribution as the main population. This is a nice way to summarize model performance and improve acceptance of neural models.

11.10 SUMMARY

Building a neural model is similar to building statistical models. In both instances, a thorough understanding of the model development process is essential as well as a good understanding of the modeling technology itself. This chapter has provided a basic structure for the model development process, highlighting key areas where the process often fails. An awareness of these issues, thoughtful analysis of results, and effective application of common sense make good neural models.

REFERENCES

Bridle, J. S. (1991). *Probabilistic Interpretation of Feedforward Classification Network Outputs, with Relationships to Statistical Pattern Recognition,* in NATO ASI Series, F68, *Neuro-Computing,* Springer-Verlag, New York.

Chatterjee, Samprit, and Bertram Price (1991). *Regression Analysis by Example,* 2d ed., John Wiley & Sons, New York.

Hanson, Stephen J., and David J. Burr (1988). "Minkowski-r Back-Propagation: Learning in Connectionist Models with Non-Euclidean Error Signals," *Neural Information Processing Systems,* Dana Z. Anderson (ed.), American Institute of Physics, New York.

Klimasauskas, Casimir C. (1992). "Accuracy and Profit in Trading Systems," *Advanced Technology for Developers,* vol. I, June 1992. High-Tech Communications, Sewickley, Pa.

Plutowski, Mark, and Halbert White (1992). *Selecting Concise Training Sets from Clean Data,* University of California, San Diego, February 1992.

Spirtes, Peter, Clark Glymour, and Richard Scheines (1993). *Causation, Prediction, and Search,* Springer-Verlag, New York.

Tukey, John W. (1977). *Exploratory Data Analysis,* Addison-Wesley, Reading, Mass.

P · A · R · T · 2

APPLICATIONS

CHAPTER 12

A MUTUAL INFORMATION-BASED LEARNING STRATEGY AND ITS APPLICATION TO RADAR

Andrew Ukrainec and Simon Haykin

Communications Research Laboratory,
McMaster University, Hamilton, Ontario, Canada

There is often a need to find features in data that are unique or that vary in some fashion from the dominant response. This situation arises in radar signal processing when there are two or more radar parameters that are simultaneously sensed from the environment. For example, a polarization-capable radar transceiver may receive both like- and cross-polar returns. The challenge is to make use of this joint information to discriminate features of interest in the environment.

The radar channels sensing the environment have much in common with each other. This common component is where most of the energy of the received signal lies. This may be termed the *dependent* component of the signal. However, much of the interesting information lies in components which differ from the dependent component in some fashion. This problem of separating dependent signal components from the received vector of signal components may be cast in the framework of statistical information measures.

The aim of this chapter is to show how mutual information-based measures can be used to find parameters of both linear and nonlinear neural networks, such that the overall output of these networks removes the dependent information component from the signal. First, a brief introduction is given to aspects of information theory—the relevant concepts are defined. Second, a solution to the problem is derived for a linear network that minimizes the mutual information at its output. By extending the results of the linear network, a nonlinear network based on *radial-basis functions* (*RBFs*) is proposed, along with a training algorithm that minimizes the mutual information between the outputs. Finally, an example application of the technique using a dual-polar radar system demonstrates the performance possibilities of these networks on the basis of real-life data.

12.1 INFORMATION THEORY DEFINITIONS

The fundamental quantities of information theory are defined as logarithmic measures of *probability density functions* (*PDFs*). Therefore, the information measures are of a statistical nature. Since the interest here is in processing continuous signals, the definitions given are those for continuous random variables. The differential entropy of a continuous random variable may be written as [1]

$$H(X) = \int_S f(x) \log \left(\frac{1}{f(x)} \right) dx = - \int_S f(x) \log f(x) \, dx \qquad (12.1)$$

where $f(x)$ is the PDF and S is defined as the support set, the set of values where $f(x) > 0$. The *relative entropy*, or, as it is sometimes called, the *Kullback-Leibler distance*, is defined as

$$D(f_1 \| f_2) = \int_{S_1} f_1(x) \log \frac{f_1(x)}{f_2(x)} \, dx \qquad (12.2)$$

where the support set S_1 of $f_1(x)$ contains the support of $f_2(x)$ for the measure to be finite. This measure can be thought of as an oriented measure of distance between two PDFs. A special case exists when the relative entropy between the joint probability density function $f_{X_1 X_2}(x_1, x_2)$ and the product of its marginal respective PDFs $f_{X_1}(x_1)$ and $f_{X_2}(x_2)$ is considered. The *mutual information I* between two random variables is therefore defined to be

$$I(X_1; X_2) = D(f_{X_1 X_2}(x_1, x_2) \| f_{X_1}(x_1) f_{X_2}(x_2))$$

$$= \int\int f_{X_1 X_2}(x_1, x_2) \log \frac{f_{X_1 X_2}(x_1, x_2)}{f_{X_1}(x_1) f_{X_2}(x_2)} \, dx_1 \, dx_2 \qquad (12.3)$$

Equivalently, in terms of differential entropies,

$$I(X_1; X_2) = H(X_1) - H(X_1 | X_2) = H(X_2) - H(X_2 | X_1) \qquad (12.4)$$

where $H(X_1)$ is the differential entropy of X_1 and $H(X_1 | X_2)$ is the conditional entropy of X_1 given X_2. Entropies $H(X_2)$ and $H(X_2 | X_1)$ are similarly defined. In communications theory, the mutual information is often used to measure the information capacity between the input and output of a noisy, band-limited channel.

Some properties that are useful to computing information-related quantities are now presented. The mutual information is equal to

$$I(X_1; X_2) = 0 \qquad (12.5)$$

if and only if X_1 is independent of X_2. The entropy of a random variable remains unchanged after translation $Y = X + k$, so that

$$H(Y) = H(X + k) = H(X) \qquad (12.6)$$

Under the linear transformation $Y = WX$, where X is a data matrix and W is a square matrix of weights, the entropy is changed such that

$$H(Y) = H(WX) = H(X) + \log(|W|) \qquad (12.7)$$

where $|W|$ is the determinant of W. For any continuous invertible transformation of a multivariate random variable $Y = F(X)$, the entropy change is equal to [2]

$$H(\mathbf{Y}) = H(\mathbf{X}) - E[\log |J_F(\mathbf{X})|] \tag{12.8}$$

where $J_F(\mathbf{X})$ is the Jacobian of the transformation.

12.2 LINEAR NETWORK

The objective is to use the principle of mutual information to find a linear transformation such that the outputs have the minimum mutual information measured between them. The linear network is an optimum processor where a gaussian probability density function describes the data. For the specific case of a Gaussian PDF, the differential entropy of a zero-mean, multivariate Gaussian distribution is found to be

$$H_G(X_1, X_2, \ldots, X_d) = H_G(\mathbf{X}) = \frac{1}{2} \log[(2\pi e)^d |\mathbf{R}|] \tag{12.9}$$

where $\mathbf{R} = E(\mathbf{X}\mathbf{X}^T)$ is the autocorrelation matrix of dimension $d \times d$. This also gives the upper bound on the differential entropy of continuous variables in that

$$H(\mathbf{X}) \leq H_G(\mathbf{X}) \tag{12.10}$$

for $\mathbf{X}$ zero mean, given the same autocorrelation matrix [1]. Assuming that the joint distribution is a bivariate Gaussian PDF, the mutual information is equal to [3]

$$I(X_1; X_2) = -\frac{1}{2} \log(1 - \rho_{x_1, x_2}^2) \tag{12.11}$$

where ρ_{x_1, x_2} is defined to be the correlation coefficient between x_1 and x_2. It is defined in terms of the pertinent correlation functions $R_{x_1, x_1}(0)$, $R_{x_2, x_2}(0)$, and $R_{x_1, x_2}(0)$ for zero lag as follows:

$$\rho_{x_1, x_2} = \frac{R_{x_1, x_2}(0)}{\sqrt{R_{x_1, x_1}(0) R_{x_2, x_2}(0)}} \tag{12.12}$$

In the Gaussian PDF case, minimizing the mutual information is equivalent to driving the outputs to being statistically uncorrelated.

The linear network architecture is shown in Fig. 12.1, the transformation for which can be written as

$$\mathbf{Y} = \mathbf{W}\mathbf{X} + \mathbf{w}_0 \tag{12.13}$$

where $\mathbf{X} = [\mathbf{x}_1 \mid \mathbf{x}_2]$ are the original data, $\mathbf{Y} = [\mathbf{y}_1 \mid \mathbf{y}_2]$ is the output of the network, $\mathbf{W}$ is the matrix of weights, and $\mathbf{w}_0$ is a constant bias vector. The desired weights may be learned by finding the solution to a variational problem with constraints [4]. The weights are computed by finding the solution to the gradient vector equation

$$\nabla_w I + \lambda \nabla_w J = \mathbf{0} \tag{12.14}$$

where I is the mutual information cost function and J is the constraint function that prevents trivial solutions (e.g., all weights equal to zero). The mutual information cost function that is to be minimized is therefore

$$C(\mathbf{W}) = I(Y_1; Y_2) + \lambda |\|\mathbf{W}\mathbf{W}^T| - 1| \tag{12.15}$$

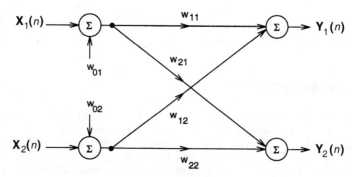

FIGURE 12.1 Linear neural network architecture.

The $\mathbf{w}_0$ is set equal to the negative of the mean, and therefore does not appear in the cost function. The constraint term is introduced to ensure that the output covariance is constant and equal to the input covariance. This is easily verified. From the properties of determinants, it is known that

$$|\mathbf{Y}\mathbf{Y}^T| = |\mathbf{W}\mathbf{X}\mathbf{X}^T\mathbf{W}| = |\mathbf{W}\mathbf{W}^T||\mathbf{X}\mathbf{X}^T| \qquad (12.16)$$

The property given in (12.7) shows that this is equivalent to keeping the input and output entropy constant. So long as the determinant of the transformation is kept constant, no change in entropy occurs from input to output.

The linear transformation can affect only the first- and second-order statistics. As a direct consequence of this fact, the best that can be expected is to decorrelate the input data. This is not as strong a condition as statistical independence. Independence implies uncorrelated behavior, but uncorrelated behavior does not imply independence, except for the special case of gaussian variates. From (12.11) it is known that the mutual information between two gaussian variates achieves a minimum when they are uncorrelated.

This task can therefore be reduced to finding a transformation that decorrelates the output. A well-known statistical technique based on eigenvector decomposition is called *principal-components analysis* (*PCA*) *projection* [5]. The PCA projection is a transformation that applies a linear orthogonal rotation to the original data, so as to remove the correlation between the dependent variables. We write the equivalent equations

$$\mathbf{Y} = \hat{\mathbf{W}}\mathbf{X} + \hat{\mathbf{w}}_0 \qquad \text{such that} \qquad E[\mathbf{Y}\mathbf{Y}^T] = \mathbf{R}_y \qquad (12.17)$$

where

$$R_y^{ii} = \sigma_i^2 \qquad R_y^{ii} = 0 \qquad i \neq j \qquad (12.18)$$

The weights are then determined from the eigenvector decomposition

$$\mathbf{R}_x = \mathbf{U}\mathbf{D}\mathbf{U}^T \qquad \mathbf{D} = \text{diag}(d_{ii}) \qquad i = 1, \dots, n \qquad (12.19)$$

The weight matrix is therefore set equal to the eigenvector matrix $\mathbf{U}$, and the $\mathbf{w}_0$ vector is set equal to the mean of the input data. A *singular-value decomposition* (*SVD*) may also be used [6].

The PCA approach has been cast into a connectionist framework, using a hebbian learning rule to achieve optimal (in the linear sense) unsupervised learning. Oja [7], Sanger [8], and others have demonstrated on-line versions of the PCA algorithm. The linear network has the advantage of being guaranteed (under reasonable conditions) to converge to a single global maximum. Haykin [9] provides an extensive survey of PCA learning techniques for neural networks. The Oja learning algorithm

$$\hat{\mathbf{w}}(n+1) = \hat{\mathbf{w}}(n) + \beta[\mathbf{x}(n)y(n) - \hat{\mathbf{w}}(n)y(n)^2] \quad (12.20)$$

is used to find the principal component. The parameter β is the learning rate parameter. The orthogonal component to the estimated principal component is given by

$$\hat{\mathbf{w}}_\perp = [-\hat{w}_2 \quad \hat{w}_1] \quad (12.21)$$

The weight matrix is given by

$$\hat{\mathbf{W}} = \begin{bmatrix} \hat{\mathbf{w}} \\ \hat{\mathbf{w}}_\perp \end{bmatrix} \quad (12.22)$$

12.3 NONLINEAR NEURAL NETWORK

The linear network is optimum in the special case that the data are described by a gaussian probability density function. To find a mapping that minimizes the mutual information at the outputs for a nonlinear network is much more difficult. However, the advantage of using a nonlinear network is that the network has more degrees of freedom to find a better mapping that satisfies the required conditions. The objective here is to use the mutual information principle to solve for the parameters of a RBF neural network.

The RBF network architecture is shown in Fig. 12.2. The inputs connect to a nonlinear hidden layer. The hidden layer, in turn, is connected to the output by a linear layer. The hidden layer nonlinear functions are of a type called *radially symmetric basis functions*. These functions can be chosen to be one of many different forms possible. Here only the gaussian form will be used. The nonlinear functionals in the hidden layer are given by

$$\phi_j(\mathbf{x}) = e^{-1/2(\mathbf{x} - \mathbf{c}_j)^T \mathbf{S}_j(\mathbf{x} - \mathbf{c}_j)} = e^{-1/2\|\mathbf{x} - \mathbf{c}_j\|_M^2} \quad (12.23)$$

where $\mathbf{x} \overset{\text{def}}{=} (x_1, \ldots, x_{N_x})^T$, $\phi_j(\mathbf{x})$ is the jth radial-basis function evaluated at the input vector $\mathbf{x}$, $\mathbf{c}_j$ is the jth RBF center, and $\mathbf{S}_j$ is the jth multidimensional width, or spread. The term following the factor $-\frac{1}{2}$ in the exponential is known as the *Mahalanobis metric*, or *weighted euclidean metric*. The functional form of the RBF network is therefore given by

$$y_i = \sum_{j=1}^{N_h} w_{ji}\phi_j(\mathbf{x}) + w_{0i} \quad (12.24)$$

where y_i is the ith output function evaluated for the input vector $\mathbf{x}$. The output can therefore be written as the vector $\mathbf{y} \overset{\text{def}}{=} (y_1, \ldots, y_{N_y})^T$. The parameter w_{ji} is the linear output weight corresponding to the jth hidden unit. The hidden layer has a total of N_h radial-basis functions. The weight w_{0i} is the bias term. Given a set of input data vectors and output data $\{\mathbf{x}(n), \mathbf{y}(n) \mid n = 0, \ldots, N-1\}$,

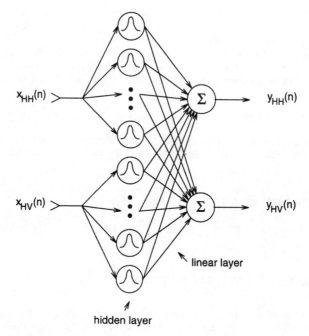

FIGURE 12.2   The radial-basis function neural network architecture.

$$
\mathbf{X}=\begin{pmatrix}\mathbf{x}^T(0)\\\mathbf{x}^T(1)\\\vdots\\\mathbf{x}^T(N-1)\end{pmatrix}\qquad
\boldsymbol{\Phi}=\begin{pmatrix}1\ \phi_1(\mathbf{x}(0)) & \phi_2(\mathbf{x}(0)) & \cdots & \phi_{N_h}(\mathbf{x}(0))\\1\ \phi_1(\mathbf{x}(1)) & & \ddots & \vdots\\ \cdots\cdots\cdots\cdots\cdots\cdots & & & \cdots\cdots\cdots\\1\ \phi_1(\mathbf{x}(N-1)) & \phi_2(\mathbf{x}(N-1)) & \cdots & \phi_{n_h}(\mathbf{x}(N-1))\end{pmatrix}
$$

$$
\mathbf{W}=\begin{pmatrix}\omega_{1,\mathrm{HH}} & \omega_{1,\mathrm{HV}}\\\omega_{2,\mathrm{HH}} & \omega_{2,\mathrm{HV}}\\\vdots & \vdots\\\omega_{N_h,\mathrm{HH}} & \omega_{N_h,\mathrm{HV}}\end{pmatrix}\qquad
\mathbf{Y}=\begin{pmatrix}y^T(0)\\y^T(1)\\\vdots\\y^T(N-1)\end{pmatrix}
$$

Rewriting (12.24) in matrix form gives

$$\mathbf{Y}=\boldsymbol{\Phi}(\mathbf{X})\mathbf{W} \tag{12.25}$$

12.3.1 Network Design Strategies

Various procedures have been used to estimate the centers and widths (or spread) of the hidden layer of RBF units from the data. These include nonadaptive, supervised and unsupervised learning techniques.

Several nonadaptive strategies have been used to determine the RBF centers and spread. The most straightforward choice for the location of the centers is to place them on an evenly spaced grid, spanning the input space. Unfortunately, a very large number of RBF units may be needed, since the number of units required grows exponentially with the dimensionality of the input space. As the dimensionality of the input grows, most of the input space becomes devoid of samples, and therefore a large percentage of the centers lie in an area where there are no data. Another more effective choice for the RBF centers is to set the centers equal to a random sampling of the input data. This strategy ensures that centers are located only in areas where there are data. It has been shown that as long as a sufficiently large number of centers are used, good prediction performance on a chaotic time series is achieved [10]. In either case, the RBF spreads are chosen by using some heuristic method.

Supervised adaptations of the RBF centers, spreads, and output weights using optimization techniques have been employed [11, 12]. This strategy can give a minimal RBF network configuration. Some of the disadvantages of using optimization techniques are the considerable computational cost, poor scaling of learning as the network complexity grows, and the presence of suboptimal local-minimum solutions. Lowe [11] points out that the same final error performance can be achieved by using a network with a larger number of nonadaptive centers, with the same generalization performance.

The investigations of hybridized unsupervised or supervised training schemes have shown promise [12–15]. Some of the advantages are the computational efficiency, good scaling of learning as network size grows, and faster convergence. The hybrid procedure consists of two stages of learning: An unsupervised clustering algorithm is used to determine the parameters of the hidden layer, followed by a supervised least-squares solution to the linear output weights. Moody and Darken [12, 13] suggest the use of the k-means clustering algorithm to find suitable positions for the centers. As a result, a smaller number of RBF units are required. After clustering, heuristic methods are used to choose the spreads of the RBF units. The k-means algorithm is an approximate version of the *maximum-likelihood* (*ML*) solution for determining the location of the means of a mixture density of component densities. The *expectation maximization* (*EM*) algorithm can be used to find the exact ML solution for the means and covariances of the density. A comparison of these two learning strategies on a classification problem was made by Nowlan [15, 16], with the EM algorithm shown to be superior. Saha and Keeler also studied the use of the k-means clustering for the adjustment of RBF centers, and they suggested an approach which they termed *extended metric clustering* [14], where clustering is done in an augmented input-output space. Once learning is complete, the cluster locations are projected back onto the input space and are used as the RBF unit centers. In recent studies by Ukrainec and Haykin [17, 18] the hybrid training was applied successfully to signal processing functions. It was shown that a combination of EM training and extended metric clustering, named *EMX clustering*, gave the best overall performance in the example prediction and cancellation signal processing problems.

The clustering concept is used here to learn the hidden layer parameters. The EM learning is performed in the two-dimensional input space $\mathbf{x} = (x_{HH}, x_{HV})$, and after the parameters have converged, the center and spread parameters are projected onto the x_{HH} and x_{HV} axes. This results in a one-dimensional RBF hidden layer. The linear layer then combines the localized representations to provide the desired mapping.

12.3.2   Unsupervised Clustering Algorithm

The expectation maximization (EM) algorithm is a general approach to iteratively computing the maximum-likelihood (ML) estimate of parameters of mixture density problems. This algorithm has had broad application in the areas of study of ML estimates from incomplete data [19], estimating mixture densities [20], and unsupervised clustering [21]. Here we will concentrate on the application of the EM algorithm to learn the RBF centers and spreads through unsupervised clustering.

A mixture distribution of Gaussian component densities is given by [21]

$$p(\mathbf{x}(n)|\theta) = \sum_{j=1}^{N_h} P(j)p(\mathbf{x}(n)|j,\theta_j) \qquad (12.26)$$

$$p(x(n)|j,\theta_j) = \frac{1}{(2\pi)^{d/2}|\Sigma_j|^{1/2}} \ e^{-1/2(x(n)-\mu_j)^T\Sigma_j^{-1}[x(n)-\mu_j]} \qquad (12.27)$$

where $\theta = (\theta_1, \ldots, \theta_{N_h})$ is the vector of parameters (means and covariances) to be estimated, d is the dimensionality of the multivariate Gaussian density, μ_j is the mean, and Σ_j is the covariance. The a priori probabilities $P(j)$ are called the *mixing parameters.*

The EM algorithm iteratively converges to a maximum of the likelihood function, yielding an estimate of the parameters of the component densities, as well as the mixing parameters $P(j)$. Although the algorithm is guaranteed to converge, there is no guarantee that it will converge to a global maximum. The update equations are as follows [21]:

$$\hat{P}(i) = \frac{1}{N} \sum_{n=0}^{N-1} \hat{P}(i|\mathbf{x}(n),\hat{\theta}) \qquad (12.28)$$

$$\hat{\mu}_i = \frac{\sum_{n=0}^{N-1} \hat{P}(i|\mathbf{x}(n),\hat{\theta})\mathbf{x}(n)}{\sum_{n=0}^{N-1} \hat{P}(i|\mathbf{x}(n),\hat{\theta})} \qquad (12.29)$$

$$\hat{\Sigma}_i = \frac{\sum_{k=0}^{N-1} \hat{P}(i|\mathbf{x}(n),\hat{\theta})[\mathbf{x}(n)-\hat{\mu}_i][\mathbf{x}(n)-\hat{\mu}_i]^T}{\sum_{k=0}^{N-1} \hat{P}(i|\mathbf{x}(n),\hat{\theta})} \qquad (12.30)$$

$$\hat{P}(i|\mathbf{x}(n),\hat{\theta}) = \frac{\hat{P}(i)p(\mathbf{x}(n)|i,\hat{\theta}_i)}{\sum_{j=1}^{N_h} \hat{P}(j)p(\mathbf{x}(n)|j,\hat{\theta}_j)} \qquad (12.31)$$

An additional step was added to these standard update equations to ensure that the algorithm learned localized representations. The step

$$\text{If } \hat{\sum}_i^{jj} > \sum_l^{jj} \text{ set the diagonal element } \hat{\sum}_i^{jj} = \sum_l^{jj} \qquad (12.32)$$

ensures that the spread is limited to a maximum given by Σ_l. Without this extra step, the algorithm may converge to solutions where one or more of the components of the mixture distribution span a large area of the sample space, overlapping other components. Although these are valid solutions, they are not desirable when the parameters are to be transferred to a RBF network that presupposes localized representations.

The equations describe a batch processing algorithm, where all the data are used for each iteration. An on-line version of the EM algorithm was suggested by Nowlan [16], where the density parameters can be continuously updated as new data become available. This may have application if the input space is slowly changing, and the representations need to be fine-tuned. For the purposes of this study, the batch update algorithm is used exclusively.

It is evident that the RBF given in (12.23) and the gaussian component density in (12.27) have almost the same form. It is hypothesized that the individually learned $\hat{\mu}_j$ of the component densities should give a good location for the centers of the RBF units. Likewise, the estimated covariances can give the required spread of the RBF units.

The hybrid learning procedure is therefore given as follows:

1. Choose the number of RBF units (and hence the number of component densities).
2. Initialize the density parameters.
3. Iterate the EM algorithm until convergence.
4. Transplant the estimated parameters of the component densities into the RBF units, so that $\mathbf{c}_j \leftarrow \hat{\mu}_j$ and $\mathbf{S}_j \leftarrow \alpha \hat{\Sigma}_j^{-1}$, where $0 < \alpha \leq 1$.
5. Forward-propagate the input data to the output of the RBF hidden layer.
6. Compute solution to linear weight layer.

The factor α is introduced to increase the spreads in order to smooth the interpolation performance of the network. As shown by Ukrainec and Haykin [17], the performance increases as α is decreased, although localization of response decreases.

12.3.3 Minimum Mutual Information Learning

Once the basis functions are trained using the unsupervised method described in the previous section, they are fixed and only the output layer of weights needs to be learned. The objective is to minimize the mutual information between the outputs, while keeping the output entropy fixed. The cost function is therefore

$$C(\mathbf{W}) = I(Y_{HH}; Y_{HV}) + \lambda |H(\mathbf{Y}) - H(\mathbf{X})| \tag{12.33}$$

where Y_{HH} and Y_{HV} are random variables whose sample values are denoted by $y_{HH}(n)$ and $y_{HV}(n)$, respectively. The constraint term explicitly ensures that the output entropy is constant and equal to the total input entropy. The advantage of using a nonlinear network over the linear network is the increased degrees of freedom in the mapping. The entropy of the output is given by

$$H(\mathbf{Y}) = H(\mathbf{X}) - E[\log|J_R(\mathbf{X})|] + \log|\mathbf{W}| \tag{12.34}$$

where $J_R(\mathbf{X})$ is the Jacobian of the hidden layer transformation. The RBF network has a computational advantage here over other neural networks, such as the multilayer Perceptron, in the sense that it has a set of fixed-basis functions, or, in other words, a nonadaptive hidden layer.

The numerical estimation of $I(Y_{HH}; Y_{HV})$ requires either an a priori assumed distribution model or a model-free estimate. A model-free estimate is computationally expensive (order $N \log N$ [22]) and must be recomputed on every iteration. Previous researchers Becker and Hinton [23] and Zemel and Hinton [24] have used the gaussian distribution model assumption when attempting to estimate mutual information. Preliminary studies done by Ukrainec and Haykin [25, 26] have shown that it is possible to use the Gaussian-based mutual information measure given in (12.11) as an estimate of the mutual information. The advantage is that it is easy to compute. However, since the distribution of the data was known to be non-Gaussian, it is also inaccurate. At best, it gives an upper bound estimate of the true mutual information. The property in (12.10) states that for a given autocorrelation function, the Gaussian distribution gives an upper bound on the differential entropy.

Using the Gaussian distribution assumptions of Eqs. (12.27) and (12.11) functions, we restate the cost function of (12.33) as

$$C(\mathbf{W}) = -\frac{1}{2}\log(1 - \hat{\rho}^2{}_{y_{\mathrm{HH}}, y_{\mathrm{HV}}}) + \lambda\|\hat{\mathbf{R}}_{y_{\mathrm{HH}}, y_{\mathrm{HV}}}| - |\hat{\mathbf{R}}_{x_{\mathrm{HH}}, x_{\mathrm{HV}}}| + J_{\mathrm{misc}}| \quad (12.35)$$

Under the Gaussian assumption, the entropy is proportional to the determinant of the autocorrelation function. The autocorrelation estimates of input $\mathbf{X}$ are given by $\hat{\mathbf{R}}_{x_{\mathrm{HH}}, x_{\mathrm{HV}}} = \mathbf{X}\mathbf{X}^T$, and similarly for output $\mathbf{Y}$. These estimates are also used to compute the correlation coefficient $\hat{\rho}^2{}_{y_{\mathrm{HH}}, y_{\mathrm{HV}}}$. Through experimentation it was found that putting additional constraints on the output mean, variance, and skew improved convergence and helped to avoid undesirable local minima. The term J_{misc} contains the sum of the additional constraints, such that

$$J_{\mathrm{misc}} = |\hat{\mu}_{y_{\mathrm{HH}}}| + |\hat{\mu}_{y_{\mathrm{HV}}}| + |\hat{\sigma}_{y_{\mathrm{HH}}} - \sigma_{y_{\mathrm{HV}}}| + |\hat{\gamma}_{y_{\mathrm{HH}}}| + |\hat{\gamma}_{y_{\mathrm{HV}}}| \quad (12.36)$$

The estimate of the means

$$|\hat{\mu}_{y_{\mathrm{HH}}}| + |\hat{\mu}_{y_{\mathrm{HV}}}| \quad (12.37)$$

is intended to ensure a zero-mean output. An equal output variance term

$$|\hat{\sigma}_{y_{\mathrm{HH}}} - \sigma_{y_{\mathrm{HV}}}| \quad (12.38)$$

is introduced to encourage a circularly symmetric distribution. Finally, the third-order moment, or skew, is constrained; the additional penalty term is

$$|\hat{\gamma}_{y_{\mathrm{HH}}}| + |\hat{\gamma}_{y_{\mathrm{HV}}}| \quad (12.39)$$

The quantity is normalized for the Gaussian distribution so that zero skew is equal to the skew of a Gaussian distribution, which has maximum entropy. In summary, constraints are introduced on the moments of the output so as to force the output to approximate a Gaussian PDF. A constrained optimization routine is used to minimize the cost function.

12.4 AN EXAMPLE APPLICATION

A novel *polarimetric radar for accurate navigation (PRAN)* system was invented at the Communication Research Laboratory, McMaster University. The system consists of a set of polarization rotating twist-grid retroreflectors situated along a confined waterway in known locations so that a ship equipped with a dual-polar incoherent marine radar can use the reflectors as beacons for navigation, even in inclement weather or after dark. The interested reader is referred to Haykin [27], who gives a complete historical perspective on the development of the PRAN system.

Despite the polarization diversity offered by such a radar target, depolarization allows significant cross-polar clutter to obscure the reflector return. Example sectors of a scan are shown in Figs. 12.3 and 12.4, for both like-polar (HH-pol) and cross-polar (HV-pol) channels. The subimages are referred to as the *DOFASCO* and *La Salle Park* sites (800×420 samples) and correspond to a physical area of approxi-

DOFASCO

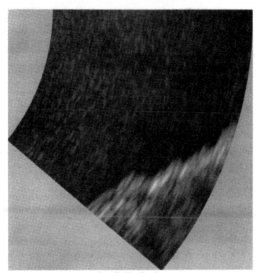

La Salle Park

FIGURE 12.3   The HH-pol subimages of interest.

mately $2100 \times 2100 = 4{,}410{,}000 \ \text{m}^2$. The data were recorded from a modified experimental marine radar system operating at X-band, with a *pulse repetition frequency* (*PRF*) of 3400 Hz, a nominal pulse width of 50 ns, and an antenna scan rate of 28 r/min. The reflector locations are noted on the HV-pol images.

The objective is to remove the energy contained in that part of the signal that is common to both channels. It is expected that one of the output channels will contain

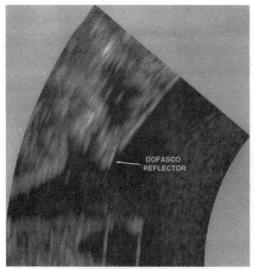

DOFASCO

La Salle Park

FIGURE 12.4   The HV-pol subimages with the locations
of the reflectors marked.

the dependent component of the signal (most of the clutter signal energy), and the
other channel the differing component (including the desired cross-polar target
response).

The resultant processed images are displayed to subjectively observe the success
of the respective method. A measurement based on the *target-to-clutter ratio* (*TCR*)

is now introduced as an objective method to judge the improvement given by the processing. The TCR estimate is given by the ratio of target power to clutter power. Since we are dealing with a log receiver with the output calibrated in dBm, the TCR is given by

$$\text{TCR} = \hat{\mu}_t - \hat{\mu}_c \quad \text{dBm} \tag{12.40}$$

where $\hat{\mu}_t$ is the estimated mean target response and $\hat{\mu}_c$ is the estimated mean clutter response. Figure 12.5 shows diagrammatically the PDFs and the estimated parameters for the corresponding target and clutter densities.

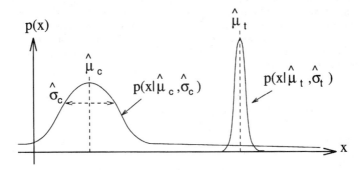

FIGURE 12.5   The target and clutter densities and the associated parameters used in calculating the normalized TCR figure of merit.

Unfortunately, the TCR estimate does not provide a good measure of target enhancement or visibility in this case. Various signal processing methods can scale the logarithmic data, resulting in a meaningless estimate of the TCR. To overcome this problem, a dimensionless measure based on the TCR is introduced as a figure of merit by which to judge the various processing methods. The *normalized TCR* (*NTCR*) is given as

$$\text{NTCR} = \frac{\hat{\mu}_t - \hat{\mu}_c}{\hat{\sigma}_c} \tag{12.41}$$

where $\hat{\sigma}_c$ is the estimated standard deviation of the clutter power in dBm. If we assume that the PDFs are Gaussian, then the NTCR is equivalent to the threshold used to calculate the probability of false alarm (P_{FA}) for this model, where

$$P_{FA} = Q(\text{NTCR}) = \frac{1}{2} \text{ erfc} \left(\frac{\text{NTCR}}{\sqrt{2}} \right) \tag{12.42}$$

where the Q function is itself defined by

$$Q(x) \triangleq \frac{1}{\sqrt{2\pi}} \int_x^\infty e^{-y^2/2} dy \tag{12.43}$$

and erfc($\cdot$) is the complementary error function [28].

The target and clutter estimates are summarized in Table 12.1 for the HV-pol subimages. The clutter patches were chosen to provide representative areas of clut-

TABLE 12.1 Estimated Parameters of Unprocessed HV-pol Subimages

	DOFASCO	La Salle Park
Target ($\hat{\mu}_t$, $\hat{\sigma}_t$)	(16.4, 0.3) dBm	(19.4, 0.6) dBm
Clutter ($\hat{\mu}_c$, $\hat{\sigma}_c$)	(2.2, 1.2) dBm	(−3.2, 3.9) dBm
TCR	14.2 dBm	22.6 dBm
Normalized TCR	12	6

ter from both sites. The clutter patch within the DOFASCO site is approximately 572 m in azimuth and 100 m in range, and the corresponding La Salle Park clutter patch is approximately 528 m in azimuth by 100 m in range. To make the estimate, the average clutter response within the patch areas is averaged, and then it is averaged over 28 scans to estimate a mean clutter level. The mean of the peak reflector target value is estimated by averaging the peak response within the reflector target cell area over the 28 scans.

12.4.1 Conventional Processing

The cell-averaging constant false-alarm rate (CA-CFAR) processor is in common use in radar systems. This conventional method provides a useful benchmark against which to compare the more advanced processing methods.

To derive a CFAR processor, the clutter process is assumed to be Rayleigh-distributed. The Rayleigh probability density function is given by

$$p(x) = \frac{2x}{\sigma^2} \exp\left(-\frac{x^2}{\sigma^2}\right) \qquad x > 0 \tag{12.44}$$

where x is the voltage amplitude and σ^2 is the variance. The ideal logarithmic receiver is described by the function

$$y = a \log bx \tag{12.45}$$

where a and b are scale factors. Under these assumptions, Croney [29] shows that the theoretical variance of the output is

$$\sigma_y^2 = \frac{a^2 \pi^2}{24} \tag{12.46}$$

which is independent of the input signal. The logarithmic receiver therefore has a CFAR-like operation, in the sense that clutter described by Rayleigh distribution results in a constant variance in the output. The mean level of the clutter, however, is a function of the input power and can be removed either by using a high-pass filter or averaging to estimate the mean level and subtracting it. The CA-CFAR model assumes that the clutter in the neighborhood of a cell under test is a stationary statistical process, with independent samples, and is representative of the clutter in the test cell. In practice, these statistical assumptions are often not consistent with the operating environment, resulting in a loss in performance.

To implement the desired cell-averaging operation, two-dimensional target masks and clutter masks are used. Two masks are defined: a 23 × 3 pixel mask for the target and a 69 × 9 pixel mask for the surrounding clutter, as shown in Fig. 12.6. The

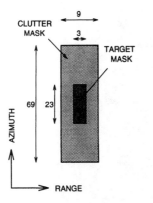

FIGURE 12.6 Target and clutter masks used in CA-CFAR processing.

target mask size was chosen to reflect the approximate size of the reflector target, and the clutter mask size was chosen to be large enough so as to provide a fair estimate of the clutter power, while at the same time being small enough so as to be in a stationary region of clutter. This is a tradeoff in CA-CFAR processing. The two masks are co-located, centered on the same pixel, the clutter mask having zero response where the target mask coincides with it. The pixels in the mask are all equally weighted, although this need not be the case. The masks are convolved with the image; the clutter-convolved result is subtracted from the target-convolved result. For a particular location in the image, the function can be expressed as

$$y = \sum_{i}^{N_t} w_i^t t_i - \sum_{i}^{N_c} w_i^c c_i \qquad (12.47)$$

were y is the output, t_i is the set of target pixels, c_i is the set of surrounding clutter pixels, w_i^t is the set of target pixel weightings, and w_i^c is the set of clutter pixel weightings. For the purposes of this study, no a priori information is used about the clutter orientation or distribution. The weights in the clutter mask are all assigned the value $w_i^c = 1/N_c$, for all i. Likewise, the weights in the target mask are all assigned the value $w_i^t = 1/N_t$.

The example images shown in Fig. 12.7 display a greater visibility after CA-CFAR processing. The NTCR results in Table 12.2 verify that the target detectability has marginally improved over that of the unprocessed HV-pol data.

TABLE 12.2 Estimated Parameters for CA-CFAR Processed HV-pol Subimages

	DOFASCO	La Salle Park
Target $(\hat{\mu}_t, \hat{\sigma}_t)$	(22.9, 0.3) dBm	(24.0, 0.9) dBm
Clutter $(\hat{\mu}_c, \hat{\sigma}_c)$	(2.8, 1.2) dBm	(−2.0, 3.7) dBm
TCR	20.1 dBm	26.0 dBm
Normalized TCR	16	7

12.4.2 Linear Network Solution

Linear networks based on principal-component analysis (PCA) have been used in the past to enhance the contrast and target-to-clutter ratio of polarization targets [30, 31]. The principal component is the vector direction that has the largest variance when the data are projected onto it. It is assumed that this projection will contain most of the clutter energy, and that the projection onto the direction orthogonal to the principal component $\mathbf{w}_\perp$ will contain the desired reflector target response.

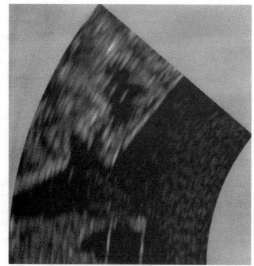

DOFASCO

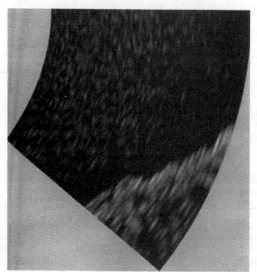

La Salle Park

FIGURE 12.7 Subimages after CA-CFAR processing.

A representative 200×200 pixel training subimage was chosen that did not overlap either subimage. After mean removal, the Oja algorithm was used to estimate the weight matrix. The subimages of interest were then processed by the linear network and viewed. The resultant orthogonal images did not contain an enhanced reflector target, but rather had a much enhanced sea clutter component. After study of the scatter plot of the output of the linear network, it was obvious that this is a result of the non-Gaussian nature of the distribution. The sea clutter data values are more densely represented than the land clutter values, and therefore the orthogonal transformation was biased in the direction of sea clutter. To overcome this problem, the orthogonal projection was manually biased so that a residual correlation remained. The scatter plot of the resulting output is shown in Fig. 12.8. This biased projection results in a residual correlation coefficient of approximately 0.53 in the output data, corresponding to a mutual information rate of approximately 0.1 bit.

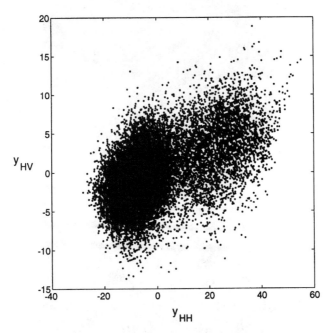

FIGURE 12.8   Scatter plot of the output of the linear network.

Figure 12.9 shows the processed subimages of interest, after additional CA-CFAR processing. The images clearly show an enhanced target. This is also reflected in the NTCR values found in Table 12.3, which are approximately double those of the previous CA-CFAR only processed results.

TABLE 12.3   Estimated Parameters of Linear Network Processed Subimages

	DOFASCO	La Salle Park
Target $(\hat{\mu}_t, \hat{\sigma}_t)$	(19.6, 1.38)	(22.2, 1.65)
Clutter $(\hat{\mu}_c, \hat{\sigma}_c)$	(4.26, 0.553)	(4.01, 1.08)
TCR	15.3	18.2
Normalized TCR	28	17

DOFASCO

La Salle Park

FIGURE 12.9 Subimages of linear network processed data.

12.4.3 RBF Neural Network Solution

In general, PCA techniques are applied against a single type of clutter background. The clutter process in these subimages can be thought of as a mixture distribution, where the differing regions of clutter require a different projection.

After initial explorations, a mixture density is learned by using the EM algorithm, as described in Eq. (12.3). Again, the same 200×200 clutter region is used for training. The scatter plot of the combined DOFASCO and La Salle Park input data is shown in Fig. 12.10, with the learned ellipsoidal standard deviations of the components of the mixture of Gaussian densities superimposed. The number of components in the density used to model the clutter is chosen to be seven, with two extra

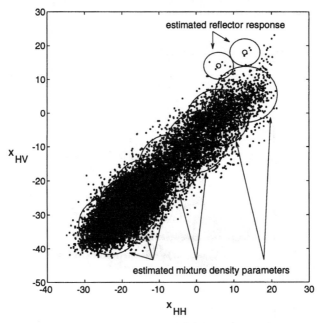

FIGURE 12.10   Scatter plot of the training data. The components of the estimated mixture densities are superimposed.

units introduced to represent the reflectors. These extra units were introduced manually in order to have a response from the target as well as clutter. The manual introduction was necessary since the number of target samples is underrepresented in the available data; a statistical learning method gives the target samples little weight. The locations of the centers are approximated from scatter plots of the target samples and are set equal to (13, 18) and (6, 14). The covariances are chosen to be circular, equal to $\Sigma = \mathrm{diag}(4, 4)$ dBm. Since the clutter and targets have been adequately modeled, the parameters of the two-dimensional mixture representations are projected onto both x_{HH} and x_{HV} axes, resulting in 18 one-dimensional RBF units. To improve the interpolation quality of the network, a factor of $\alpha = 0.01$ is applied to the clutter spread parameters.

The next step is the mutual information training to learn the weights. A subsampled data set from both regions is used. The data set is the same as shown in the scatter plots, with the same area coverage as the subimages, except subsampled in range by a factor of 4 and in azimuth by a factor of 10. The weights are initialized to approximate the same mapping as that of the linear network by solving for the RBF weights via least-squares fitting. The constrained optimization routine is used to minimize the cost function given by (12.35), subject to the aforementioned constraints. After convergence, the residual mutual information is estimated to be approximately 0.036 bit. The scatter plot of the output of the network is shown in Fig. 12.11. As can be observed, the data distribution is more clustered around a single point, rather than distributed over a large range, as in the scatter plot of the input data. Figure 12.12 shows the resultant nonlinear mapping learned by the RBF network. The inputs are along the x and y axes, and the z axis height is the output containing the enhanced cross-polar response.

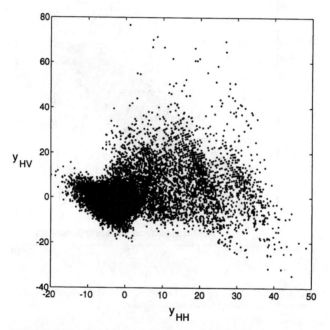

FIGURE 12.11 Scatter plot of the output of the RBF network.

The output of the network is processed by the CA-CFAR algorithm, as in the previous case. The resultant subimages in Fig. 12.13 show a much enhanced target visibility, in both areas. The clutter is generally well suppressed. The statistics in Table 12.3 verify the higher visibility of the target, showing that the enhancement is nearly twice that of the linear network.

12.5 SUMMARY

The statistical principle of mutual information is shown to be applicable to the successful training of linear and nonlinear networks. By minimizing mutual information between the outputs of the network, the dependent signal components may be separated from the differing signal components. For the case of a linear network, this

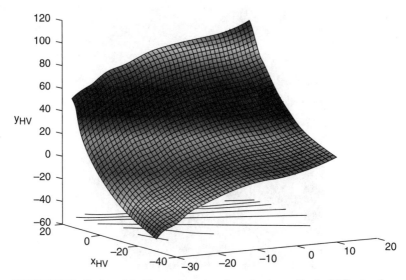

FIGURE 12.12 Surface plot of the nonlinear transformation learned by the RBF network.

condition is equivalent to decorrelating the output by using PCA techniques. For the case of the more general nonlinear mapping, a RBF network is proposed as an architecture. The RBF network is trained by using a novel hybrid method, where the hidden layer is determined via a mixture density modeling technique, and the output linear layer is learned by minimizing the mutual information cost function that is based on a Gaussian PDF assumption.

The processing was successfully demonstrated by using data from a dual-polarized radar experiment. The objective is to enhance radar returns from a retroreflector used for navigation. The like-polar clutter components of the signal are separated from the cross-polar component, yielding an enhanced reflector response, as indicated subjectively by the output images and objectively by a normalized TCR measure. Given the conventional CA-CFAR processing technique as a benchmark, the linear network was able to outperform the conventional technique by approximately a factor of 2, in terms of the normalized TCR measure. Furthermore, the RBF network was shown to be clearly superior, nearly doubling the performance achieved by the linear network.

However, there are several disadvantages to using nonlinear networks, in general. One is the manifestation of local minima during learning. With linear networks,

TABLE 12.4 Estimated Parameters of RBF Network
Processed Subimages

	DOFASCO	La Salle Park
Target $(\hat{\mu}_t, \hat{\sigma}_t)$	(84.4, 4.09)	(93.1, 6.22)
Clutter $(\hat{\mu}_c, \hat{\sigma}_c)$	(11.1, 1.58)	(10.7, 2.74)
TCR	80.4	82.4
Normalized TCR	46	30

DOFASCO

La Salle Park

FIGURE 12.13 Subimages of the RBF network processed data.

there is a guarantee of a single global minimum. This is not the case with nonlinear networks. The experience gained training these networks has shown that the more a priori information is used to design and train the network, the lower the probability of converging to a local-minimum solution. Another disadvantage is maintaining a one-to-one mapping. In the case of the linear network, as long as the weight matrix is full rank, we know that the mapping is invertible. However, with a nonlinear network, the nonlinear mapping must be exhaustively checked to see whether this condition has been violated. Currently, the training must be restarted, or the weights perturbed, if one of these conditions arises. Further research is needed to find learning algorithms that are more resilient to these possible problems and yet are computationally tractable. Despite the learning difficulties (it is the author's belief that they will be overcome), the mutual information-based learning strategy is a powerful one, and no doubt it will find ever-increasing success in applications that require the unsupervised learning of mappings.

REFERENCES

1. T. M. Cover and J. A. Thomas, *Elements of Information Theory*. New York: Wiley, 1991.

2. M. R. Walker and L. A. Akers, "Information-Theoretic Analysis of Finite Register Effects in Neural Networks," in *International Joint Conference on Neural Networks*, vol. 2. Piscataway, NJ: IEEE, 1992, pp. 666–671.

3. S. Kullback, *Information Theory and Statistics*. New York: Dover, 1968.

4. L. E. Franks, *Signal Theory*, rev. ed. Stroudsburg, PA: Dowden & Culver, 1981.

5. I. T. Jolliffe, *Principal Components Analysis*. New York: Springer-Verlag, 1986.

6. G. H. Golub and C. F. V. Loan, *Matrix Computations*. Baltimore, MD: Johns Hopkins University Press, 1983.

7. E. Oja, *Subspace Methods for Pattern Recognition*. Letchworth, United Kingdom: Research Studies Press, 1987.

8. T. D. Sanger, "An Optimal Principle for Unsupervised Learning," in *Advances in Neural Information Processing Systems*, vol. 1 (D. S. Touretzky, ed.). San Mateo, CA: Morgan Kaufmann, 1989.

9. S. Haykin, *Neural Networks: A Comprehensive Foundation*. New York: Macmillan & IEEE Press, 1994.

10. D. S. Broomhead and D. Lowe, "Multivariable Functional Interpolation and Adaptive Networks," *Complex Systems*, vol. 2, 1988, pp. 321–355.

11. D. Lowe, "Adaptive Radial Basis Function Nonlinearities, and the Problem of Generalization," in *First IEE International Conference on Artificial Neural Networks*, London: 1989, pp. 171–175.

12. J. Moody and C. J. Darken, "Fast Learning in Networks of Locally-Tuned Processing Units," *Neural Computation*, vol. 1, no. 3, pp. 281–294, 1989.

13. J. Moody and C. Darken, "Learning with Localized Receptive Fields," in *Proceedings of the 1988 Connectionist Models Summer School* (D. Touretzky, G. Hinton, and T. Sejnowski, eds.). San Mateo, CA: Morgan Kaufmann, 1989, pp. 133–143.

14. A. Saha and J. Keeler, "Algorithms for Better Representation and Faster Learning in Radial Basis Function Networks," Tech. Rep. ACT-NN-028-90, Microelectronics and Computer Technology Corporation, Austin, TX, January 1990.

15. S. J. Nowlan, "Maximum Likelihood Competitive Learning," in *Advances in Neural Information Processing Systems*, vol. 2 (D. S. Touretzky, ed.). San Mateo, CA: Morgan Kaufmann, 1990, pp. 574–582.

16. S. J. Nowlan, "Maximum Likelihood Competition in RBF Networks," Tech. Rep. CRG-TR-90-2, Connectionist Research Group, University of Toronto, Canada, February 1990.

17. A. Ukrainec and S. Haykin, "Signal Processing with Radial Basis Function Networks Using Expectation Maximization Algorithm Clustering," in *SPIE 36th International Symposium on Optical and Optoelectronic Applied Science and Engineering*, July 1991.

18. S. Haykin and A. Ukrainec, "Neural Networks for Adaptive Signal Processing," in *Adaptive System Identification and Signal Processing Algorithms* (N. Kalouptsidis and S. Theodoridis, eds.). New York: Prentice-Hall, 1993.

19. A. P. Dempster, N. M. Laird, and D. B. Rubin, "Maximum Likelihood from Incomplete Data via the EM Algorithm," *Proceedings of the Royal Statistical Society,* vol. 39, pp. 1–38, 1977.

20. R. A. Redner and H. F. Walker, "Mixture Densities, Maximum Likelihood and the EM Algorithm," *SIAM Review,* vol. 26, pp. 195–239, April 1984.

21. R. O. Duda and P. E. Hart, *Pattern Classification and Scene Analysis.* New York: Wiley, 1973.

22. A. M. Fraser and H. L. Swinney, "Independent Coordinates for Strange Attractors from Mutual Information," *Physical Review A,* vol. 33, pp. 1134–1140, February 1986.

23. S. Becker and G. E. Hinton, "Spatial Coherence as an Internal Teacher for a Neural Network," Tech. Rep. CRG-TR-89-7, Department of Computer Science, University of Toronto, Ontario, December 1989.

24. R. S. Zemel and G. E. Hinton, "Discovering Viewpoint-Invariant Relationships That Characterize Objects," in *Advances in Neural Information Processing Systems,* vol. 3 (R. P. Lippmann, J. E. Moody, and D. S. Touretzky, eds.). San Mateo, CA: Morgan Kaufmann, 1991.

25. A. Ukrainec and S. Haykin, "Application of Unsupervised Neural Networks to the Enhancement of Polarization Targets in Dual-Polarized Radar Images," in *25th Asilomar Conference on Signals, Systems & Computers,* Washington, D.C.: IEEE Computer Society, November 1991.

26. A. Ukrainec and S. Haykin, "Enhancement of Radar Images Using Mutual Information Based Unsupervised Neural Network," in *Canadian Conference on Electrical and Computer Engineering,* Toronto, Canada, pp. MA6.9.1–MA6.9.4, 1992.

27. S. Haykin, "Polarimetric Radar for Accurate Navigation," *Canadian Journal of Electrical and Computer Engineering,* vol. 17, no. 3, pp. 130–135, 1992.

28. J. M. Wozencraft and I. M. Jacobs, *Principles of Communication Engineering.* New York: Wiley, 1965.

29. J. Croney, "Clutter on Radar Displays—Reduction by Use of Logarithmic Receivers," *Wireless Engineer,* vol. 33, pp. 83–95, April 1956.

30. A. A. Swartz, H. Yueh, J. A. Kong, L. Novak, and R. T. Shin, "The Optimal Polarizations for Achieving Maximum Contrast in Radar Images," NASA Contractor Rep. NASA-CR-183349. Cambridge, MA: MIT, 1988.

31. E. Lewis, B. Currie, and S. Haykin, *Detection and Classification of Ice.* Letchworth, United Kingdom: Research Studies Press, 1987.

CHAPTER 13

SONAR SIGNAL PROCESSING AND CLASSIFICATION USING NEURAL NETWORKS

R. Paul Gorman

Member, Technical Staff,
AlliedSignal Microelectronics and Technology Center
Columbia, Maryland

13.1 SONAR ENVIRONMENT

Sonar applications cover a broad range of remote sensing objectives and environments. As a result, the processing and classification of sonar signals have required the use and development of a variety of signal processing tools and techniques. One's approach to detecting, processing, and classifying sonar signals depends greatly on the nature of the application. From a signal processing perspective, sonar applications are generally divided according to whether the sensing mode is active or passive. Active sonar applications are further divided into sector scan, which focuses on the detection and processing of individual sonar returns, and side (or forward) scan, which combines individual returns into sonar images. The processing and classification of sonar signals have traditionally relied on linear time-series analysis. More recent approaches to sonar signal processing and target classification have incorporated nonlinear techniques and, in the case of sonar imaging, have adopted traditional image processing and classification techniques.

All undersea sonar applications face similar signal processing challenges in attempting to accommodate the complex interaction between the acoustic signal and its medium, the ocean. From a signal processing and classification perspective, undersea sonar represents one of the most challenging application areas. The finite propagation speed of sound in water cannot be ignored, and the ocean channel is very nonideal. The signal processor must contend with signal distortions induced by frequency-dependent absorption, phase delay, multipath reverberation, as well as a host of unwanted and spurious background signals that defy simple characterization.

In spite of such complications, a great deal of progress has been realized through the application of linear signal processing techniques that necessarily impose unrealistic assumptions on the undersea sensing environment. More recently, the development of nonlinear techniques that can utilize a higher-order signal structure has begun to significantly extend this progress. Neural networks represent a generic nonlinear approach to sonar signal detection and classification that has been shown to be an effective tool in addressing sonar signal processing and classification.

This chapter reviews the application of neural networks to sonar signal processing and classification. We begin by examining some of the signal representation issues that arise in the application of neural networks to sonar classification problems. Representation issues specific to the three major application areas—active, passive, and imaging sonar—are covered. Next, we look at the various neural network models and optimization schemes that have been utilized in sonar signal classification experiments. Finally, we examine some of the experimental design issues relevant to the application of neural networks to classification problems in general and sonar applications in particular.

13.2 SIGNAL REPRESENTATION

The way in which information is presented to a neural network can largely determine the success of the application. Preprocessing is a procedure designed to produce a signal representation that accentuates information most relevant to classification. Normalization, also an issue associated with the application of neural networks, attempts to optimize the signal representation to take advantage of the network's intrinsic dynamic range. The specific methods adopted in the preprocessing phase of signal classification depend largely upon the type of application being addressed. We therefore cover signal representation issues specific to active, passive, and imaging sonar applications.

13.2.1 Preprocessing

Determining the form of the signal representation is largely a process of determining what is known and what is not known about a signal and its relevance to the classification problem at hand. Ideally, in the absence of any a priori knowledge concerning the information content of the signal, a representation would be chosen which retained all the signal information. Practically, however, some compromises are typically required to balance constraints associated with the classifier's dimension or number of degrees of freedom (number of connections in the case of a neural network) and the size of the data set available for training.

As a rule of thumb, the number of training set samples should exceed the classifier dimension by an order of magnitude. This is only an empirical rule of thumb and does not in any way derive from statistical arguments, since in cases where gaussian statistics apply, the number of samples required to accurately estimate the distribution of a given random vector increases exponentially with dimension. In practice, a neural network can easily possess over 100 degrees of freedom, and sonar databases are difficult and expensive to compile. In addition, distributions are highly nongaussian, and the theoretically optimal ratio of data samples to classifier dimension is not known a priori. It is therefore important to maintain a balance between maximizing the input information to a neural network classifier by simply increasing the number of input units and providing a sufficient number of training examples to the neural network to ensure proper generalization.

The network's convergence behavior can also be adversely affected by increasing its size (number of units, layers, connections) beyond certain limits. Therefore, for most applications, particularly those involving sampled time series or images, some decision must be made to limit or select the information presented to the neural network through a preprocessing or feature extraction stage. As a result, a wide variety of preprocessing techniques have been applied to the raw sonar time series or image to reduce the number of input samples and at the same time maintain signal information.

A frequently used technique for reducing the dimension of the input pattern is to transform a time series to a spectral domain. One of the first applications of neural networks to continuous signal classification involved a sonar target recognition problem.[1] In this study, the power spectral densities of the individual sonar returns were estimated, and the dimension of the signal was reduced by using a relatively small number of spectral bins. An interesting comparison of the power spectral versus a time-series signal representation is given by Guicking et al.[2] The problem posed was also a sonar target recognition problem, and the researchers found that the network trained more quickly when it was presented with the power spectrum as input. However, the performance of the network improved if it was presented with the raw time series. This is a classic example of the tradeoff between signal information and classifier size. The power spectrum eliminates any signal phase information which may carry important classification information.

A popular technique used to preprocess short-duration acoustic transients is the wavelet transform.[3] The wavelet transform attempts to model the transient signal in terms of a finite number of scaled basis functions which can be tailored to the class of signals

$$x(t) = \sum_j \sum_k c_{jk} h_{jk}(t) \qquad (13.1)$$

where $x(t)$ is the original time series, the c_{jk} are wavelet coefficients, and the $h_{jk}(t)$ are the wavelet kernels. The subscript j indexes the temporal position of the kernel, and k indexes the scale of the kernel. The wavelet coefficients are used as input to a neural network for training.

A recent study by Legitimus and Schwab[4] combined a wavelet transform with an autoregressive model[5] to represent acoustic events of very short duration (5 to 50 ms). This study also compared the performance of a neural network presented with the raw temporal signal. The number of neural network input units required to represent the transient as a raw temporal time series increased nearly an order of magnitude over the wavelet-based representation, and the performance of the network suffered as a result. It is not clear, however, whether the decrease in performance was due to convergence problems associated with the size of the network or to the fact that the size of the training set did not support the resulting increase in classifier dimension.

Another approach to signal representation uses a small number of signal features extracted from the signal or image. These signal features are typically identified empirically, and their extraction requires very specific preprocessing steps. Porto used a set of spectral ratios that were determined to be correlates of aural characteristics used by trained human listeners to distinguish sonar returns from minelike spheres and background clutter.[6] Frequently, sonar images are preprocessed by extracting shape and texture features. In a study conducted by Shazeer and Bello, sonar images were represented in terms of image texture characteristics which included the fractal dimension of the image.[7]

Neural networks are frequently used as a means of reducing the dimensionality of the signal through the application of unsupervised learning algorithms. Unsupervised algorithms adaptively cluster input patterns and can be used to compress the original signal into a feature space possessing fewer dimensions. These networks function in a way that is computationally similar to a nonlinear principal-components analysis.[8] As an example, Pridham and Hamilton use a *recirculation network*[9] as a feature extractor in a study involving the classification of sonar transients.[10] The recirculation network consists of two layers of nonlinear units. The input layer feeds information to the output layer, and the output layer feeds information back to the input layer. An unsupervised learning algorithm is used to adjust weights on connections to minimize the difference between the input pattern and the feedback pattern. The recirculation network is used as a feature extraction technique by using the minimum number of output units required to accurately reproduce the input pattern through the feedback connections. The output units then represent a feature set that can be presented to a classification neural network.

In all the above cases, the preprocessing step is used as a means to reduce the input dimension of the neural network classifier while retaining as much of the relevant signal information as possible. The neural network is capable of extracting high-order information from low-level signal representations like the time series or the raw image. Therefore, in the absence of any knowledge about the relevant signal information necessary for classification, it is always preferable to provide the network with as much of the original signal structure as possible. However, preprocessing can often improve network training time and convergence behavior and is very useful when knowledge about the signal can be applied to the selection of preprocessing techniques.

13.2.2 Normalization

The issue of normalization relates to the relationship between the maximum and minimum values of the network's nonlinearity and the intrinsic dynamic range of the optimization process. For example, the sigmoidal nonlinearity used in many of the multilayered Perceptron models typically limits the range of unit outputs to between −1.0 and +1.0. This range limitation coupled with the finite step size and iterative nature of the optimization process can limit the sensitivity or dynamic range of network classifiers. As a result, input patterns must be normalized to fully utilize that dynamic range without "clipping" the input signal. Depending on the amplitude variation and structural dynamic range of a given signal, this normalization may be linear or nonlinear. Normalization may also be hard-limited, forcing the maximum and minimum signal values to the limits of the input unit's range, or statistically limited, setting the variance of the signal to the limits of the unit's output range and the mean to its midpoint.

It is desirable, although not required, to set the ranges of units in each layer to be comparable. However, variable ranges can be accommodated as long as initial input weight ranges and learning rates are set accordingly, to allow proper convergence during the optimization process. For example, the input range could be twice the hidden-layer range and output layer range in a feedforward neural network by initializing the weights between the input and hidden layer, using a uniform distribution with half the range of the distribution to initialize the weights from the hidden layer to the output layer, and setting the learning rate for the hidden layer to half that of the output layer. Fitting the signal ranges properly to match the neural network's dynamic range will significantly improve the convergence behavior of the network, particularly for larger networks with multiple hidden layers.

13.2.3   Active Sonar Applications

The typical active sonar application involves the sonification of an undersea target and the detection and classification of the sonar return. Although side-scan and forward-scan sonars involve active sonification, we will deal with signal representation issues related to sonar imaging in a later section. The advantage of active applications is that the form of the sonification pulse is known a priori. Assuming that the background noise possesses gaussian statistics, we know that the optimal technique for detecting a known signal in noise employs a matched filter.[11] Neural networks have been shown to be effective as a detector when compared to the detection performance of the matched filter under nongaussian conditions.[12] The advantage of the neural network detector is that its performance is not as dependent on the nature of the background noise as is that of the matched filter.

Although the neural network can be used to detect the incoming sonar return, most active applications employ a preprocessing step as a prelude to signal classification. The preprocessing of the active return depends upon the design of the sonification pulse. It is often desirable to sonify targets with as much bandwidth as possible, since the response of complex targets can vary with frequency and the more spectral information received from the target the more characteristic the target signature becomes. Bandwidth is typically generated by using a very narrow pulse width or by using an FM chirp. The FM chirp can be used to generate both bandwidth and spectral power, and so it is used most often when signal bandwidth is a design objective. For broadband signals the power spectrum is used as the preprocessing technique of choice, even though the signal phase can carry significant information.

In a study by Ramani and Patrick, a pair of neural networks trained on different signal representations proved to perform better than the individual networks.[13] The networks were trained to recognize active sonar returns from four different species of fish and three types of debris. The sonification pulse width was 0.5 ms, and the pulse frequency was 420 kHz. One network was trained on the amplitude envelope of the returns, while a second network was trained on the output of a peak/trough detector. As distinct from the power spectrum representation, both of these preprocessors retained some temporal information.

13.2.4   Passive Sonar Applications

The ocean is literally alive with sounds generated by everything from cracking ice to whale cries. The character of these sounds varies widely in frequency, bandwidth, and duration. The typical passive sonar application involves the detection and classification of acoustic transients acquired through passive listening. Unlike the active case, there is no sonification pulse, and so the primary challenge of this class of sonar applications is to accommodate the variety of signals comprising the ocean's acoustic environment. As an example, Defense Advanced Research Project Agency compiled a database of passive signals that has served as the basis for many studies exploring the classification of passive sonar signals. The classes of passive signals in this data set vary in duration from 15 ms to 8 s and include everything from tonals to broadband clicks.

Because the nature of undersea acoustic transients varies so widely, accurate classification often requires the application of a variety of preprocessing techniques. Nonetheless, the presentation of the raw time series to a neural network has been considered in at least one case. In one recent study, Gorman used a time-delay network architecture to classify a variety of passive sonar signals.[14] The passive signals were classified as either natural or artificial events. Although all the signals possessed durations that far exceeded the temporal extent of the network's input layer, the network was able to detect the different classes with a high degree of accuracy. This temporal representation was chosen to explore the network's ability to extract detailed phase structure from short-duration signal segments whether the signal was a transient or a long-duration tonal. The time-delay architecture was used to capture information in sequences of these temporal segments.

The more conventional approach is to preprocess the passive signals in an attempt to reduce the amount of variability across signal classes. Pridham and Hamilton use the sequential application of various traditional techniques and network models to classify sonar transients.[15] They separate the classification process into four stages: detection, feature extraction, feature optimization, and classification. Recirculation networks are used for both the detection and the feature extraction phases. The recirculation network can be used as a signal detector by allowing the network to adapt to background noise and detecting significant deviations from the background as feedback errors.[16]

Pridham and Hamilton use a competitive learning network to optimize the feature set.[15] A competitive learning network either uses inhibitory connections within layers or maintains a fixed value for the sum of input weights to limit the network's response to those units that most strongly respond to a given input pattern. Competitive networks use an unsupervised learning strategy to cluster input patterns into similarity groups and are therefore commonly used as a feature extraction technique. Finally, a compound classifier network was used to classify the signals. The compound classifier network is a nonlinear kernel classifier (see below) that uses a clustering technique to determine the number and location of kernels in feature space.[18] Pridham compared this all-network approach to other traditional techniques and found that different combinations of techniques all produced good performance, but varied in their ability to classify particular classes of signals.

One way of visually representing passive sonar signals to allow human inspection is to compute the spectrum of the incoming signal and display the spectrum as a function of time in a "waterfall" type of display. This creates a gray-scale sonar image commonly called a *lofargram*. One study by Russo used the lofargram as the starting point for signal classification.[19] He chose a set of seven signal types based on lofargram signal shapes. These shape types were used to categorize the way that the spectral peak of different classes of passive sonar events varied as a function of time. Russo used a series of image processing techniques to transform the original gray-scale image to a time-frequency contour and then used a coding scheme referred to as a *chain code* to transform the contour into a sequence of symbols for input to a neural network. To obtain the sequence of symbols, the time-frequency contour was divided into linear segments. The orientation of each segment was quantized (e.g., down, left, up, right, etc.) producing a sequence of 180 orientations to represent the shape of the contour. The neural network was trained to convert this chain code sequence to one of the seven signal types.

13.2.5   Imaging Sonar

Side-scan and forward-scan sonars are classified as imaging sonars because they produce a two-dimensional sonar image (see Fig. 13.1). The side-scan image is produced by moving a sonar tow body at a given altitude above the sea floor while repeatedly transmitting and receiving a relatively high-frequency (100- to 600-kHz) sonar pulse. Each pulse sonifies a narrow swath perpendicular to the direction of motion. Each

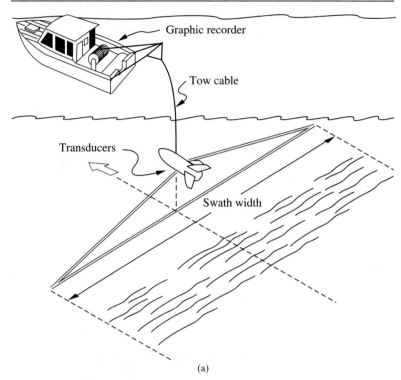

(a)

FIGURE 13.1 (*a*) The side-scan sonar is typically towed by a surface craft. The projector sends out a narrow beam to produce a single scan line of the side-scan image. The side-scan image is built up as the tow body is moved along a path perpendicular to the sonar beam and repeated sonar pulses sonify the sea floor.

scan line of the sonar image is produced by recording the power of the sonar return as a function of range, and each pulse produces a new scan line. Range resolution of the sonar image is determined by the pulse width, and resolution along the direction of motion is determined by the speed of the tow body and the beam width of the projector.

In the case of forward-looking imaging sonar, the image is produced by sonifying the region in front of the tow body and either mechanically or electronically scanning the hydrophone receiver to record power as a function of azimuth. Each scan of the receiver produces a scan line on the sonar image. Range resolution is determined by the scan rate of the receiver, and bearing resolution is determined by the beam width of the receiver.

Objects on the sea floor appear in the image as dark regions (high power) with a contiguous light region (low power) just down-range of the object. This light region is known as the *shadow region* and is produced as a result of the range gap between the top of the object and the sea floor behind the object (see Fig. 13.1*c*). The shape and texture of the dark region, as well as the shape of the shadow region, will vary from target to target and represent the primary image features used in automatic classification schemes. The resolution of the sonar image is a determining factor in

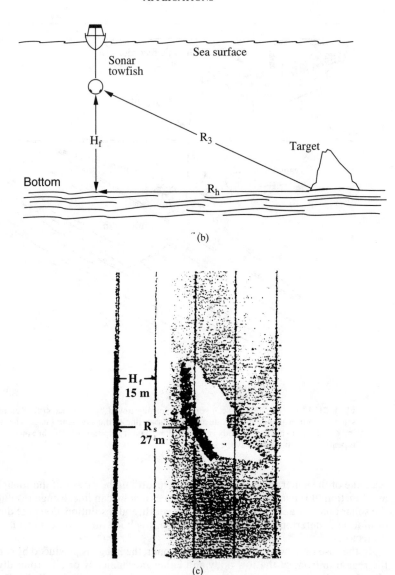

(b)

(c)

FIGURE 13.1 (*Continued*) (*b*) The tow body is pulled at a constant altitude above the sea floor H_f. The slant range to the target R_s determines the time required for the sonification pulse to return to the tow body hydrophones. This transit time determines the point along the image scan line at which the signal power is recorded. (*c*) This is a typical side-scan image. Side-scan targets are characterized by a dark region and a light region or "shadow" region just downrange of the target location.

the successful application of classification techniques to the sonar imaging problem. Therefore, as sonar imaging technology has improved, so has the ability of automatic classification schemes to accurately identify target types.

A study by Schweizer and Petlevich addresses the problem of classifying sidescan sonar images.[20] The authors apply three feature detection techniques in parallel as a preprocessing step. A region-growing technique is used to detect shadow and highlight, a statistical technique measuring gray-level distributions is used as a statistical-anomaly detector, and finally a neural network is used as an image feature detector. The neural network is trained to recognize six categories of images: background, shadow, highlight, shadow-highlight, anomaly, and texture. The outputs from these preprocessors are used as input to a second classifier neural network that determines whether the image represents a target of interest or background clutter. The redundant set of preprocessors is used to decrease the false-alarm rate. This study is a good example of using multiple preprocessing techniques tailored to extract specific types of pattern information.

13.3 NETWORK ARCHITECTURES AND OPTIMIZATION

There are as many variations on the standard feedforward neural network as there are types of signals. It can be a daunting task to select the appropriate model for a given classification problem. However, in spite of the seemingly endless generation of new network architectures and optimization algorithms, most models share certain fundamental characteristics that, when all is said and done, make these variants more similar computationally than distinct.

Generally, the neural network and all its related forms provide an adaptive mechanism for combining a set of nonlinearities in order to approximate a given nonlinear transformation. In principle, and most often in practice, the choice of nonlinearity makes little difference in terms of the capacity of a given network architecture to approximate a given transformation. There are many contrived problems which can be shown to benefit from the choice of nonlinearity in terms of the number of basis functions (nonlinearities) required to achieve a given accuracy. However, when one is addressing real-world problems such as sonar signal classification, the difference in performance from one model to the next is often of questionable significance.

Neural network architectures can be classified along a continuum between the standard *multilayered Perceptron* (*MLP*) networks and the nonlinear kernel classifier. Standard neural network classifiers are characterized by long training regimes and optimization algorithms that attempt to reduce the training time and eliminate local minima. The nonlinear kernel classifiers, which are interpolative versions of the nearest-neighbor classifier,[21] require little or no training, but must contend with balancing the number of basis functions with memory and classification speed constraints. While unsupervised optimization procedures are useful for signal clustering and feature extraction, the process of signal classification in most cases involves supervised learning algorithms such as gradient descent or genetic evolution. Even the nearest neighbor is supervised in the sense that all stored templates possess a predetermined class membership.

13.3.1 Neural Networks

The neural network classifiers include such variants as the pi-sigma and related networks, which attempt to explicitly represent higher-order correlations in the input pattern through multiplicative connections, and the time-delay and related architectures, which use various schemes to accommodate temporal pattern variations at a significant savings in the number of network parameters. Optimization algorithms for these architectures include standard gradient descent algorithms such as back propagation,[22] higher-order gradient descent techniques such as newtonian and quasi-newtonian methods,[23] as well as genetics-based algorithms which attempt to decouple optimization from a direct credit assignment scheme.[24]

Shin and Ghosh applied the pi-sigma architecture to the classification of sonar transients.[25] They show that the pi-sigma architecture can improve training time and performance over standard network architectures for a given data set. Improved training time is to be expected in cases where higher-order signal structure is relevant to the classification task. The pi-sigma architecture explicitly represents higher-order correlations, and therefore the extraction of such correlations from input patterns would be facilitated in comparison to the standard MLP, which must use additional layers of first-order units to represent higher-order structure.

The hierarchical or time-delay network architecture is also an important variant on the standard MLP.[26] In the study referred to in the last section, Gorman used the hierarchical architecture shown in Fig. 13.2 to classify sonar transients.[14] The time-scaling capability of the architecture was used to allow a temporal domain signal representation, and the study demonstrates that significant reduction in classifier size can be achieved without sacrificing classifier performance. A variation on this time-delay architecture was proposed by Venugopal et al. to classify sonar targets by using a side-scan sonar.[27] This study used the time-delay architecture to accommo-

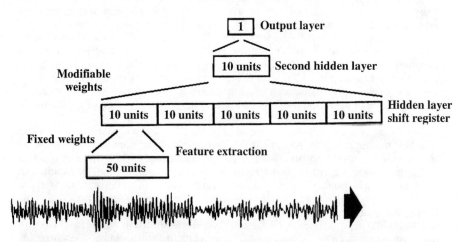

FIGURE 13.2 An example of a time-delay neural network. In this case, the network is used to classify sonar transients and is presented with the raw time-series data. A 50-unit input layer provides a short-duration temporal segment as input to the network. The input layer feeds forward to a 10-unit hidden layer. These ten hidden-unit states are shifted into the hidden-layer shift register as the next 50 samples are shifted into the input layer. The 5 sets of 10 hidden-layer units represent a compressed version of 250 time-series samples. All 50 hidden-layer unit states are fed forward to a second hidden layer and then to an output unit that produces the classification decision.

date sequences of sonar image scan lines. A statistical learning algorithm referred to as *Alopex* was used in place of the standard gradient descent algorithm to optimize network performance.[28]

The Alopex learning algorithm is a global optimization technique similar to the Boltzmann learning algorithm[29] that measures the statistical correlation between local weight changes and the global error gradient. This correlation derived from past updates is used to set a threshold determining the probability that a given weight will be increased or decreased during the current iteration. An improved time-delay architecture called the *FIR network* was recently developed by Wan.[30] This network retains the important time-scaling capabilities of the original architecture but significantly improves convergence behavior.

Genetic learning algorithms have also been applied to MLPs. Porto applied a neural network to the classification of active sonar returns from undersea targets and used an evolutionary or genetic type of learning algorithm to train the network.[6] The advantage of a genetic learning algorithm is that the explicit computation of the error gradient with respect to each adjustable weight is not necessary. In general, a genetic algorithm improves performance, in the case of classification problems, through the random combination of successful ancestor classifiers, while poor classifiers are discarded and therefore do not participate in the generation of future classifiers. Genetic optimization has been shown to be effective in a wide range of optimization environments.[31] Porto represented the weights of a MLP as a string of floating-point values which could then be utilized in an evolutionary optimization scheme. He started with 50 parent weight strings initialized according to a normal distribution with zero mean and normal variance. Offspring strings were generated by randomly adjusting the value of string elements (weights) with a variance proportional to the mean error of the parent. The network successfully learned to classify the targets with a 98 percent probability of correct classification.

These models all excel in nonlinear generalization. They require such an extraordinary amount of training because they compress the rarefied information contained in the training set into a set of weights achieving compression ratios of over three orders of magnitude. In the process, these models extract not only linear correlations among input values, but higher-order correlations as well, often rivaling in performance polyspectral techniques optimally tuned to extract such information.

13.3.2 Nonlinear Kernel Classifiers

The nonlinear kernel classifiers include *radial-basis function* (*RBF*) classifiers,[32] maximum-likelihood artificial neural networks,[33] and a variety of probabilistic neural networks.[34] All these models share a common template-based approach to classification. The main distinction between these classifiers and the nearest-neighbor classifier is their use of a nonlinear basis function or kernel as a means of interpolating between samples in the training set or set of templates. The standard nonlinear kernel classifier positions an identical basis function, typically a multidimensional gaussian or exponential kernel, at each training set pattern vector. The general form of the nonlinear kernel classifier can be given as follows:

$$f(\mathbf{x}) = \sum_{j} w_j G_j(\mathbf{x}) \tag{13.2}$$

$$G_j(\mathbf{x}) = G(\|\mathbf{x} - \mathbf{x}_j\|/\sigma_j) \tag{13.3}$$

where G_j is a nonlinear basis function whose centroid is given as $\mathbf{x}_j$ and whose width or spread is given as σ_j. The process of classification involves measuring the distance between the unknown pattern vector **x** and all the stored training vectors $\mathbf{x}_j$. This distance value serves as an argument to the basis function G_j positioned at $\mathbf{x}_j$, and a weighted sum of these basis functions determines the network's output $f(\mathbf{x})$.

In the case where class membership is required as an output, the probabilistic network dispenses with the weighted sum and uses a summation unit for each class. Only basis functions centered at templates from a particular class are summed into a summation unit. Class membership is determined by the summation unit with the largest output. Adaptive mechanisms can also be used to optimize the placement and spread of basis functions in order to reduce their number.[35] Some techniques also involve a vector quantization or clustering step, producing a set of cluster centroids as template vectors. The nonlinear kernel classifiers can achieve improved performance over a nearest-neighbor classifier in cases where relatively small training sets are used. As compared to neural network classifiers, nonlinear kernel classifiers are better at identifying patterns that do not fit any of the stored class distributions, and their classification strategy can be interpreted more easily. The most-quoted advantage of these models is their rapid training time.

Ghosh et al. developed an *adaptive kernel classifier* (*AKC*) for the classification of short-duration sonar transients.[36] The AKC is similar to the radial-basis function classifier in that it uses gaussian kernels; but the AKC defines an optimization procedure which allows the adaptation of kernel locations and dimensions (mean and variances). Ghosh uses a wavelet transform to preprocess six classes of acoustic transients. The performance of the AKC was compared to that achieved by various nonlinear kernel models. The AKC performed the best on the test data set.

Another example of a nonlinear kernel classifier is the *maximum-likelihood artificial neural system* (*MLANS*) developed by Perlovsky. The MLANS classifier is able to adaptively approximate arbitrary distributions through the use of a weighted sum of gaussians. Perlovsky applied the MLANS classifier to the classification of acoustic transients.[37] The transient was preprocessed to obtain a short-term spectral representation, and a MLANS classifier was developed to approximate the energy distribution in this domain. Perlovsky shows that the performance of the MLANS classifier approaches optimal information-theoretic bounds as the number of training samples increases.

13.3.3 Hybridism

Most of these adaptive nonlinear models can be shown to provide near-optimal performance where optimal benchmarks can be devised. Comparisons among models when applied to real-world sonar detection and classification problems generally bear out this equivalence. Nonetheless, variations in performance do occur, and the various classifier models can possess weaknesses and strengths which complement one another. Some of the most successful applications of neural network technology to real-world sonar problems have involved the use of multiple models whose combined output or sequential application served to enhance the performance over that of any single model. This is particularly true in cases where the types of patterns associated with the classification problem vary widely, as in passive sonar applications.

The study referred to above, conducted by Ghosh et al., applied network-based classifiers to the classification of six classes of acoustic transients. This study provides an excellent comparison of network models.[36] Ghosh et al. conclude the comparison with a recommendation that multiple models be utilized and a combination of their outputs be used to determine the class of the unknown transient. They show that superior performance can be achieved over the performance of individual models by using various methods for combining model outputs.

In some cases, neural networks can be used to preprocess patterns for input to another neural network or to a completely different type of classifier. Some problems are well suited to using a neural network to extract pattern features, which can then be processed by an expert system along with other symbolic factors to arrive at final interpretation or situation assessment. Lefebvre et al. introduce a hybrid model they call *Arachyde* which combines neural network feature extraction with knowledge-based decision making, and they apply their approach to the classification of acoustic signals.[38] Long-duration signals and short-duration transients were detected and processed separately. Autoregressive modeling and cepstral modeling were used to preprocess long-duration signals, and a wavelet transform was used to preprocess short-duration transients. Neural networks were employed in both cases to provide a signal-to-symbol transformation, and the final classification was accomplished by an expert system which used the output of the neural networks as input.

13.4 EXPERIMENTAL DESIGN ISSUES

13.4.1 Data Sets

The successful application of neural networks to sonar target classification problems has been hampered by the difficulties involved in acquiring sonar signals for experimentation. The application of adaptive techniques such as neural networks requires that the training set present an accurate portrayal of the classification problem and the operational environment. Although model-based studies have been conducted for active, passive, and imaging applications, they can only provide general insight into the nature of these problems and the effectiveness of neural networks to address them. Even the results of studies based on data collected in tanks or pools have not translated well to the actual ocean environment. The studies that have been the most relevant, providing the most insight into the requirements for robust sonar signal classification, have been based on sonar data sets collected under realistic conditions, and even the best of these data sets have been limited in size and scope.

When one is faced with a limited data set, the most effective approach to training an adaptive classifier is to divide the data set into a training set and a test set. The training set is used to develop the network model, and a distinct test set is presented to the trained network to determine whether the network can generalize from the patterns it has seen during training to patterns it has never seen before. Determining how best to divide a given set of data into a training set and a test set has often been problematic. The objective is to equalize the distribution of pattern classification features in the training and test sets. However, this is difficult to achieve in practice since it is generally not known a priori what the relevant classification features are.

In the absence of any knowledge concerning the distribution of classification features in the data set, it is best to randomly select a small percentage of the data set (typically 10 to 15 percent) to serve as a test set for a given experiment. To avoid potential bias in this selection process, it is also recommended that multiple experiments be conducted, a new test set be selected for each experiment, and all such test sets be disjoint subsets of the original data set. To obtain an overall estimate of the probability of classification error, one would average the error probability across all experiments.[39] Gorman and Sejnowski provide an example of this experimental paradigm in the application of neural networks to sonar target recognition.[1]

13.4.2 Experimental Parameters

The application of neural networks to signal processing or classification problems requires that consideration be given to a variety of experimental parameters, the values of which can significantly affect the convergence behavior of the chosen model. For instance, in the case of the standard MLP, the experimenter must choose the number of hidden layers, the number of units per hidden layer, the learning rate, the weight initialization range, and the momentum factor. The application of radial-basis functions requires the selection of the number of basis functions, the location of these functions if the number is less than the number of training patterns, and the scale of each basis function. While there are rules of thumb for deciding the value of these parameters and in some cases there are even adaptive procedures that can optimize the setting of these parameters, for most applications these decisions are made based on experience or intuition rather than in accordance with any formal criteria.

In selecting the values of those parameters related to the size and specific structure of the model, decisions are generally guided by the desire to minimize the size of the model. That is, select a model size that provides sufficient degrees of freedom to capture the underlying structure implicit in the training patterns and no more. Determination of the size and configuration is most often an empirical process. An initial model is chosen, and the asymptotic performance of the model is observed as the model parameters are varied. The size of the model is typically increased until there is no corresponding increase in performance. Conversely, the size can be decreased until a degradation in performance is observed. Performance on the test set is the most relevant criterion for making these decisions since it is the generalization of the model that must be optimized, not the performance on the training set.

In the vast majority of cases, a single layer of nonlinear units or hidden units will suffice in achieving the best possible performance. However, in some cases, particularly when the number of input and output units is small, the addition of hidden layers will enhance performance. Although, in principle, there is no need for more than a single hidden layer, in practice, adding a hidden layer can significantly reduce the number of hidden units per layer and improve convergence. In the case of time-delay architectures, additional hidden layers can significantly extend the temporal scale of the model, providing more signal history for use in the classification or prediction process.

Optimization parameters such as learning rate, weight initialization range, or momentum must also be chosen carefully. A learning rate that is too high can often cause oscillatory convergence behavior and adversely affect asymptotic performance. A learning rate and/or initial weight range that is too small can cause the network to flounder at the outset, producing asymptotic performance that is little better than that achieved by chance. The setting of these parameters is very problem-dependent and for the most part must be done empirically. The scale of the nonlinearity will often determine the appropriate ranges for these parameters. It is important to tune the optimization parameters to take full advantage of the dynamic range afforded by the model's nonlinearities, without causing the process to rapidly saturate.

13.4.3 Benchmarking

Since it is generally not possible to develop optimality criteria for most real-world sonar classification problems, it is often very important to apply a few models to a problem and compare performances. One model frequently used as a benchmark is the *nearest-neighbor classifier.* The nearest-neighbor classifier is simple in its implementation and provides Bayes-optimal decision boundaries in the limit as the number of training samples increases.[21]

In past comparative studies, well-tuned adaptive network classifiers have generally performed as well as, if not better than, the nearest neighbor. Since the nearest neighbor approaches optimal performance as a function of training set size, the neural network classifiers can be expected to achieve comparable performances. Poor relative performance on the part of the neural network in cases where the number of training patterns is sufficiently large often indicates that experimental parameters such as the size of the model or the optimization parameters are not appropriately set for the specific problem being addressed.

Comparative studies are also an important means of determining the best approach to a problem. Through an exploration of various network models and signal representations, a hybrid approach which combines models in a way that achieves better performance than any individual model may prove best. In the attempt to capture nonlinear signal structure, few theoretical guidelines for model selection are available to the researcher, and model development is primarily an empirical process.

REFERENCES

1. Gorman, R. P., and T. J. Sejnowski, "Learned Classification of Sonar Targets Using a Massively Parallel Network," *IEEE Transactions on Acoustics, Speech and Signal Processing,* vol. 36, no. 7, 1988, pp. 1135–1140.

2. Guicking, D., K. Gork, and H. Peine, "Recent Advances in Sonar Target Classification," SPIE vol. 1700, *Automatic Object Recognition,* II, 1992, pp. 2–15.

3. Rioul, O., and M. Vetterli, "Wavelets and Signal Processing," *IEEE Signal Processing Magazine,* vol. 8, no. 4, 1991, pp. 14–38.

4. Legitimus, D., and L. Schwab, "Experimental Comparison between Neural Networks and Classical Techniques of Classification Applied to Natural Underwater Transients Identification," in *Proceedings of IEEE Conference on Neural Networks for Ocean Engineering,* Washington, D.C., 1991, pp. 113–120.

5. Morf, M., B. Dickinson, T. Kailath, and A. Viera, "Efficient Solution of Covariance Equations for Linear Prediction," *IEEE Transactions on ASSP,* vol. 25, no. 5, 1977, pp. 429–433.

6. Porto, V., "Evolutionary Methods for Training Neural Networks for Underwater Pattern Classification," in *Proceedings of 24th Asilomar Conference on Signals, Systems and Computers,* vol. 2, Washington, D.C., *IEEE Computer Society,* 1990, pp. 1015–1019.

7. Shazeer, D., and M. Bello, "Minehunting with Multi-Layer Perceptrons," in *Proceedings of IEEE Conference on Neural Networks for Ocean Engineering,* Washington, D.C., 1991, pp. 57–68.

8. Linsker, R., "Self-Organization in a Perceptual Network," *Computer,* vol. 21, no. 3, 1988, pp. 105–117.

9. Hinton, G., and J. McClelland, "Learning Representations by Recirculation," in *Proceedings of IEEE Conference on Neural Information Processing Systems,* November 1988. Further note: Proc. of the IEEE Conference on Neural Networks for Ocean Engineering, is published by IEEE, New York, NY. The conference was held Aug. 1991 in Washington, D.C.

10. Pridham, R., and D. Hamilton, "Evaluation of Neural Network and Conventional Techniques for Sonar Signal Classification," in *Proceedings of IEEE Conference on Neural Networks for Ocean Engineering,* Washington, D.C., 1991, pp. 263–268.

11. Turin, G., "An Introduction to Matched Filters," *IRE Transactions on Information Theory*, vol. IT-6, 1960, pp. 311–329.

12. Ramamutri, V., S. Rao, and P. Gandhi, "Neural Detectors for Signals in Non-Gaussian Noise," *Proceedings IEEE International Conference on Acoustics, Speech and Signal Processing, vol. 1, Toronto, 1993*, pp. 481–484.

13. Ramani, N., and P. Patrick, "Fish Detection and Identification Using Neural Networks—Some Laboratory Results," *IEEE Journal of Oceanic Engineering*, vol. 17, no. 4, 1992, pp. 364–368.

14. Gorman, R. P., "Neural Networks and the Classification of Complex Sonar Signals," in *Proceedings of IEEE Conference on Neural Networks for Ocean Engineering*, Washington, D.C., 1991, pp. 283–290.

15. Pridham, R., and D. Hamilton, "Evaluation of Neural Network and Conventional Techniques for Sonar Signal Classification," in *Proceedings of IEEE Conference on Neural Networks for Ocean Engineering*, Washington, D.C., 1991, pp. 263–268.

16. Cottle, D., and D. Hamilton, "All Neural Network Sonar Discrimination System," in *Proceedings of IEEE Conference on Neural Networks for Ocean Engineering*, Washington, D.C., 1991, pp. 13–19.

17. Rumelhart, D., and D. Zipser, "Feature Discovery by Competitive Learning," in *Parallel Distributed Processing*, vol. 1: *Foundations*, D. E. Rumelhart and J. L. McClelland, eds., MIT Press, Cambridge, MA, 1986, pp. 151–193.

18. Batchelor, B., *Practical Approach to Pattern Classification*, Plenum Press, New York, 1974.

19. Russo, A., "Constrained Neural Network for Recognition of Passive Sonar Signals Using Shape," in *Proceedings of IEEE Conference on Neural Networks for Ocean Engineering*, Washington, D.C., 1991, pp. 69–76.

20. Schweizer, P., and W. Petlevich, "Automatic Target Detection and Cuing System for an Autonomous Underwater Vehicle (AUV)," in *Proceedings of the 6th International Symposium on Unmanned Untethered Submersible Technology*, 1989, pp. 359–371.

21. Cover, T., "Nearest Neighbor Pattern Classification," *IEEE Translation on Information Theory*, vol. IT-13, 1967, pp. 21–27.

22. Rumelhart, D., G. Hinton, and R. Williams, "Learning Internal Representations by Error Propagation," in *Parallel Distributed Processing*, vol. 1: *Foundations*, D. E. Rumelhart and J. L. McClelland, eds., MIT Press, Cambridge, MA, 1986, pp. 318–362.

23. Dennis, J., and R. Schnabel, *Numerical Methods for Unconstrained Optimization and Nonlinear Equations*, Prentice-Hall, Englewood Cliffs, NJ, 1983.

24. Holland, J., *Adaptation in Natural and Artificial Systems*, University of Michigan Press, Ann Arbor, 1975.

25. Shin, Y., and J. Ghosh, "The Pi Sigma Network: An Efficient Higher-Order Neural Network for Pattern Classification and Function Approximation," in *Proceedings of International Joint Conference on Neural Networks—1991—Seattle*, vol. 1, 1991, pp. 13–18.

26. Waibel, A., T. Hanazawa, G. Hinton, K. Shikano, and K. Lang, "Phoneme Recognition Using Time-Delay Neural Networks," *IEEE Transactions on Acoustics, Speech and Signal Processing*, March 1989.

27. Venugopal, K., A. Pandya, and R. Sudhakar, "Continuous Recognition of Sonar Targets Using Neural Networks," SPIE vol. 1471, *Automatic Object Recognition*, 1991, pp. 44–53.

28. Harth, E., and A. Pandya, "Dynamics of Alopex Process: Applications to Optimization Problems," in *Biomathematics and Related Computational Problems*, L. Ricciardi, ed., Reidel Publishing, Amsterdam, Holland, 1988.

29. Hinton, G., and T. Sejnowski, "Learning and Relearning in Boltzmann Machines," in *Parallel Distributed Processing*, vol. 1: *Foundations*, D. E. Rumelhart and J. L. McClelland, eds., MIT Press, Cambridge, MA, 1986, pp. 282–317.

30. Wan, E., "Time-Series Prediction by Using a Connectionist Network with Internal Delay

Lines," in *Time Series Prediction, Forecasting the Future and Understanding the Past*, A. Weigend and N. Gershenfeld, eds., Addison-Wesley, Reading, MA, 1994, pp. 195–217.

31. Davidor, Y., and H. Schwefel, "An Introduction to Adaptive Optimization Algorithms Based on Principles of Natural Evolution," in *Dynamic, Genetic, and Chaotic Programming*, S. Branko, ed., Wiley, New York, 1992, pp. 183–202.

32. Broomhead, D., and D. Lowe, "Multivariate Functional Interpolation and Adaptive Networks," *Complex Systems*, vol. 2, 1988, pp. 321–355.

33. Perlovsky, L., and M. McManus, "Maximum Likelihood Artificial Neural Systems (MLANS) for Adaptive Classification and Sensor Fusion," *Neural Networks*, vol. 4, 1991.

34. Specht, D., "Probabilistic Neural Networks," *Neural Networks*, vol. 3, 1990, pp. 109–118.

35. Musavi, M., W. Ahmed, K. Chan, K. Faris, and D. Hummels, "On the Training of Radial Basis Function Classifiers," *Neural Networks*, vol. 5, 1992, pp. 595–603.

36. Ghosh, J., L. Deuser, and S. Beck, "A Neural Network Based Hybrid System for Detection, Characterization, and Classification of Short-Duration Oceanic Signals," *IEEE Journal of Oceanic Engineering*, vol. 17, no. 4, 1992, pp. 351–363.

37. Perlovsky, L., "Model Based Classification of Transient Signals Using the MLANS Neural Network," in *Proceedings of IEEE Conference on Neural Networks for Ocean Engineering*, Washington, D.C., 1991, pp. 239–246.

38. Lefebvre, T., A. Lemer, and F. Dispot, "ARACHYDE: A Sensor-to-Situation Assessment Software Architecture for Passive Acoustic Signal Understanding," in *Proceedings of IEEE Conference on Neural Networks for Ocean Engineering*, Washington, D.C., 1991, pp. 255–262.

39. Toussaint, G., "Bibliography on Estimation of Misclassification," *IEEE Transaction on Information Theory*, vol. IT-20, 1974, pp. 96–104.

CHAPTER 14

NEURAL NETWORKS FOR SPEECH RECOGNITION

Jean-Paul Haton
Université Henri Poincaré
CRIN/INRIA-Nancy, France

14.1 INTRODUCTION

Automatic speech processing has been extensively investigated over the past fifty years or so. *Automatic speech recognition (ASR)* is one of the different topics which have attracted particular attention and research effort in this area. In spite of this and notwithstanding important progress and cumulated improvements, the performances of ASR systems, under natural and realistic conditions, are still far from the level that humans attain under similar conditions. ASR is still among the most challenging areas of artificial intelligence and pattern recognition.

The search for solution to the problem of automatic speech recognition has led to the development of a large number of techniques and models [1]. *Artificial neural networks (ANNs)* have also been applied over the past decade with some success. There is no surprise about this. Indeed, for a long time ANNs were successfully used to solve complex problems of pattern classification and recognition [2].

This chapter presents an overview of the different attempts to apply ANN techniques at various points of the speech recognition chain. Section 14.2 proposes a brief summary of the current state of ASR and reviews a number of unresolved issues. It also discusses reasons for the use of ANN in this domain. Section 14.3 focuses on the initial step of signal processing and feature extraction and considers the role of ANN at this level. Section 14.4 addresses the classical problem of speech pattern identification by neural networks and points out the limits of such methods. Section 14.5 presents and discusses hybrid models, the design of which is an important topic of ongoing research. Principally, hybrid models combine ANNs with stochastic models, especially with *hidden Markov models (HMMs)*. Combinations with symbolic models are also encountered. In the concluding section, we outline some future research perspectives.

14.2 A BRIEF OVERVIEW OF AUTOMATIC SPEECH RECOGNITION

The problem of ASR can be roughly described as the decoding of the information conveyed by a speech signal and its transcription into a set of characters. These characters can subsequently be used to perform various tasks such as producing a written form of the input speech, controlling a machine, accessing a database, and so on.

Figure 14.1 is an illustration of a general model for speech recognition. This model emphasizes the different tasks performed on the speech signal. Contrary to what the model suggests, the process of decoding does not proceed in a straightforward manner from the signal processing module through the intermediate modules and ending up with the language processing module, which yields a sequence of words forming a sentence. Rather, the decoding process involves interactions in both directions between the modules before a global interpretation is arrived at.

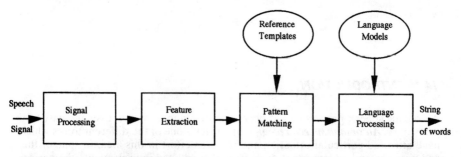

FIGURE 14.1   A general model of ASR.

The signal processing module derives from the sampled speech signal a representation which reduces the redundancy in the input speech, compensates for amplitude variations, subdues noise, etc. Next, the resulting representation is input to the feature extraction module, which produces parameters describing steady-state and transient components of speech.

The pattern-matching operation plays a central role in the overall recognition process. It attempts to match parts of an utterance against learned templates (which may contain words or sublexical units such as syllables and phones). To cope with changes in the rate and rhythm of speech utterances, the matching process is often aided by some efficient, nonlinear time alignment algorithms, like those based on dynamic programming [3]. The preliminary phase which derives representative reference patterns from the speech training data also requires powerful learning algorithms.

Finally, to cope with contextual dependencies, handle ambiguities in the interpretation of a part of a sentence, or solve the problem of nongrammatical phrases, the language processing module refers to and depends on several kinds of language models (phonological, syntactic, semantic, etc.).

Recognizing and understanding a spoken sentence is obviously a knowledge-intensive process which must take into account all the available pieces of information about the speech communication (models, rules, references, etc.). The amount of knowledge needed in each situation is naturally task-dependent. Thus, it takes less knowledge to recognize 10 digits than to understand a complete sentence in a pseudo-natural language comprising a 30,000-word vocabulary. Artificial intelligence knowledge-based architectures have proved quite successful principally at the language processing level but also in the case of acoustic-phonetic decoding of speech in which a speech wave is transcribed to some phonetic representation [4]. However, so far, stochastic models, especially the hidden Markov models, have produced the best-known performances in ASR [5].

ASR is a very difficult process. Associated difficulties may be best described in terms of characteristics of the tasks to be performed [6]. These include the number of speakers involved, nature of the utterance (continuous speech versus isolated utterance), size and complexity of the vocabulary, complexity of the language, and conditions and environment under which the ASR systems must operate.

1. *Number of speakers.* With more than one speaker, an ASR system must cope with the difficult problem of variability of speech from one speaker to another. It is no wonder that speaker-dependent systems, often optimized for a single speaker, achieve better recognition performances than do speaker-independent systems. For a wide range of applications, especially those involving the use of public telephone networks, ensuring speaker independence is, however, a necessity. This is usually achieved through the use of large speech databases as training data. There is still room for improvement, and progress is especially expected in the case of large vocabularies involving some thousands of words.

2. *Nature of the utterance.* Isolated word recognition systems impose on the speaker the need to insert artificial pauses between successive utterances. This avoids the difficult problem of having to segment the speech signal, which is by nature continuous. Continuous speech recognition systems, on the contrary, are able to cope with natural speech utterances in which words may be tied together and at times may be strongly coarticulated. A distinction should also be drawn between spontaneous speech and speech which is read. The problem of spontaneous speech is compounded by the possibility of pauses and false starts in the utterance, the use of words not found in the lexicon, etc. Problems like these are still awaiting satisfactory solution.

3. *Vocabulary size and complexity.* In general, increasing the size of the vocabulary decreases the recognition score. Small vocabularies may also be highly prone to confusion. A typical case is the set of spelled letters of the alphabet of any natural language.

4. *Language complexity.* With the exception of dictation machines which accept only syntactically correct sentences, the task of continuous-speech recognizers is simplified by limiting the number of possible utterances through the imposition of syntactic and semantic constraints. The difficulty of a task is often expressed in terms of its *perplexity*, which can be defined as the geometric mean of the number of lexicon terminals which can occur at any point in a sentence.

5. *Operational conditions and environment.* To date, most experiments have been conducted in quiet, ideal environments. The sites for real applications often present adverse conditions which can drastically alter system performances. Making room for noise and distortions of the speech signal due to environmental conditions, maintaining level of performance irrespective of the microphone used, achieving performance robustness vis-à-vis transmission line characteristics variability (e.g., telephone)—all the preceding constitute research areas still in their infancy.

By way of summary and at the risk of self-repetition, ASR remains a very difficult task. Significant results have indeed been obtained under laboratory or near-laboratory conditions [7]. Methods based on statistical modeling (especially HMMs) are reported to yield more than 99 percent accuracy for speaker-independent recognition of digits, more than 95 percent for the recognition of continuous sentences from a 1000-word vocabulary, etc. These performances fall rapidly once the systems are confronted with on-site conditions or have to cope with untrained users. Much therefore remains to be done before ASR can become operationally efficient for general use.

The fact that the basic problem of ASR is pattern recognition suggests the use of ANNs in this area. First, a fallacious reason to use ANNs is that the cortex is able to recognize speech and that ANNs represent crude models of the cortex. In fact, the cortex is known to operate in a manner different from ANNs. All the same, there are several good reasons in favor of using ANNs:

- ANNs can learn from examples, a feature particularly crucial for ASR.
- ANNs, unlike HMMs, do not require strong assumptions about the statistical properties of the input data.
- The ANN formalism is in general intuitively accessible.
- ANNs are capable of producing highly nonlinear functions of the inputs [8].
- ANNs have highly parallel and regular structures, making them especially suitable for high-performance hardware implementations.

14.3 SIGNAL PROCESSING AND FEATURE EXTRACTION USING ANNs

We now consider the use of ANNs in the front-end processing tasks of a speech recognizer involving signal processing and feature extraction. The current literature reports interesting applications in this area even though it is by no means the area where ANNs are most applied.

Conventional signal processing primarily resorts to linear methods. ANNs offer the potential of nonlinear processing. A *multilayer Perceptron* (*MLP*), e.g., has been used to derive an efficient solution for the least-mean-square algorithm used in adaptive filtering for correction estimation [9]. The authors reported that the MLP filter produces consistently lower bit errors than a linear transversal filter.

ANNs are also used to reduce the level of noise in a corrupted speech signal. The idea is to view speech enhancement as the process of transforming noisy speech to clean speech by some kind of mapping into a parametric space. ANNs can learn arbitrarily complex space mappings. An MLP-based system, e.g., has been tested successfully in an auditory preference test with human listeners [10]. Some improvements have been brought to the method since then. These improvements are based on the observation that it is easier to separate speech from noise at the output of a hidden layer of the network than to do so in the initial physical space [11].

ANNs can play a very useful role in the extraction of efficient features from the speech wave for speech recognition. This can be done in several ways. First, the different hidden layers of an MLP can be seen as producing new and more suitable internal representations of an input signal for the subsequent classification. This trainable feature extraction process is extensively investigated in Ref. 12. Classically, feature extraction in pattern recognition proceeds by data compression, using algorithms akin to data analysis like the Karhunen-Loeve expansion. It was shown that autoassociative MLPs with linear output units provide an efficient way of performing this transform [13].

Second, self-organizing ANNs and those endowed with the capability of unsupervised learning can be used for automatic extraction of relevant features from raw data. A classical example is the Kohonen feature map network [14], which is basically a two-layer, fully connected, feedforward network with lateral inhibition. This mapping preserves the phonotopic properties of the input speech signal [15]. This model can be used further for phone or word recognition, as we shall show in the subsequent development.

Biologically inspired models are also used for speech analysis. For instance, models of the ear have been used in the development of speech analyzers. Several models of the cochlea have been implemented, even under the form of VLSI circuit [16]. Binaural systems have also been proposed, especially to improve the intelligibility of speech in noisy environments [17].

14.4   NEURAL NETWORKS AS PATTERN CLASSIFIERS

14.4.1   Static Classifiers

ANNs have been widely applied in the classification of static speech patterns which are obtained through some kind of spectral analysis of isolated or presegmented words or phonemes [18]. In such cases, input data are considered as a single time-frequency pattern. MLPs are the most commonly used model in these experiments [19–22]. The results obtained for small vocabularies involving about 10 words compare favorably with the results of advanced HMM-based recognizers. The quality of these results has led to the suggestion that back propagation learning may have developed internal feature detectors capable of capturing some invariant acoustic events [20].

As in the case of the preceding systems, the decision part of a neuron in an MLP is commonly based on some kind of sigmoidal function. This is the case for the systems just presented. The use of gaussian functions has also been proposed [23], the basic idea being that of the *radial basis functions* (*RBFs*) [24]. In conventional MLPs, complex nonlinear decision surfaces are approximated by combining hyperplanes, whereas RBFs use more complex functions such as gaussian functions or higher-order polynomials. The two approaches have produced comparable results so far.

Other ANN models have also been used for speech pattern classification. The Kohonen feature map [25] in particular draws its inspiration from the topographic organization of the mammalian cortex. Here, the spatial organization of the cells in a network represents the organization of the projecting sensory surface. In the Kohonen model, the learning algorithm is unsupervised, and the development of the cell responses takes place in a self-organizing manner. The model is made up of two layers of cells—an input layer and a feature map layer, the cells of which receive data both from the input layer and from neighboring cells of the feature map. This lateral connectivity within the second layer is assumed to be identical for all cells and to be distance-dependent in the sense that the closer a cell is to a given cell, the greater its effect on the given cell.

The effect of the lateral connectivity during learning is a winner-take-all type of activity. For instance, a phoneme or a short word will correspond to the excitation of a small region of the map centered on a particular cell. This model was successfully used to recognize phonemes [15].

It is also possible to change learning based on a self-organizing feature map to a supervised learning algorithm by defining "target" cells in the map. The resulting *learning vector quantization* (*LVQ*) [26] is widely used in speech recognition.

Other feature map classifiers, such as the hierarchical feature map classifier which is similar to LVQ, have been tested for the recognition of vowel sounds [21]. In the hierarchical model, hidden nodes are used to compute kernel functions related to the euclidean distance between input data and the clusters represented by these nodes. As in LVQ, the combination of supervised and unsupervised learning drastically reduces the amount of training data needed.

14.4.2 Time-Sequence Processing

Speech is essentially a time-varying phenomenon. Since the basic connectionist formalism is not tailored for time-sequence input pattern processing, it was found necessary to develop partially satisfactory solutions to the problems posed by the temporal evolution of speech.

The simplest method consists of turning the dynamic speech pattern into a static spatial pattern in the form of a two-dimensional time-frequency spectrogram. This approach is valid for small vocabularies, as explained in Sec. 14.4.1. Efficient time-warping techniques such as dynamic programming can be adjoined to these models (see Sec. 14.4.3).

The specific problem of handling sequences of speech input vectors has been considered from different angles. One solution uses the *time-delay neural network* (*TDNN*) [27, 28]. A TDNN is an MLP with fixed time delays. Each cell of a TDNN weights the current input feature vector $f(t)$ as well as the N preceding vectors $f(t-n)$ (see Fig. 14.2).

Phoneme recognition and syllable spotting in continuous speech [29, 30] are examples of ASR tasks in which TDNNs have been applied successfully. Figure 14.3

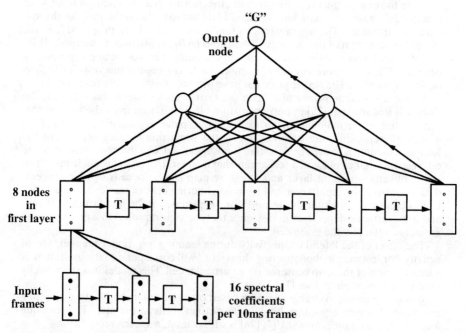

FIGURE 14.2   Cell connections in a time-delay MLP.

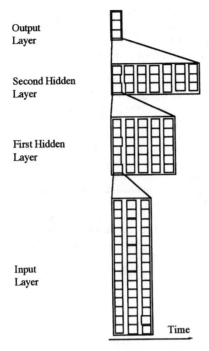

Output
Layer

Second Hidden
Layer

First Hidden
Layer

Input
Layer

Time

FIGURE 14.3 A TDNN for recognition of /b, d, g/. (*After [29].*)

shows the architecture of a TDNN designed for the identification of the English plosive consonants /b, d, g/.

Temporal sequences may also be handled by using recurrent networks. As illustrated in Fig. 14.4, such networks work on the principle that a recurrent internal state is a function of both the current input and the previous internal state.

A variety of recurrent networks have been designed and tried in ASR [31]. Their design often comprises a feedforward MLP with a time-delayed loop on the output and/or hidden units. For input sequences of sufficiently short duration, it is possible to solve the learning problem by replacing the recurrent network with an equivalent feedforward network obtained by unfolding over time [32]. This is the solution implemented in Ref. 33. Recurrent networks have also been implemented by using ANN models other than those involving MLPs. The Boltzmann machine with "carry units" [34] is an example of this type of implementation. The learning algorithm of this machine is based on a simulated annealing algorithm which turns out to be exceedingly time-consuming to be of practical use.

14.4.3 Dynamic Classifiers

ANN-based dynamic classifiers can be obtained by combining a *dynamic time-warping (DTW)* algorithm with static ANN models of the MLP type. In such sys-

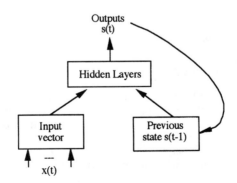

Outputs
s(t)

Hidden Layers

Input
vector

Previous
state s(t-1)

x(t)

FIGURE 14.4 Principle of a recurrent network.

tems, the outputs of the ANN are used as the local distance measure by the DTW algorithm. Results obtained with such a configuration show substantial improvements compared to those obtained with classical DTW systems.

Early examples of the preceding type of system for continuous speech recognition involving a 918-word vocabulary can be found in Ref. 35, while examples for the E-set recognition can be found in Ref. 36. A further example is provided by the *dynamic* (programming) *neural network* (*DNN*) described in Ref. 37. The DNN model is basically a time-delay MLP with back propagation learning, with the learning phase, however, requiring presegmentation of the speech data. The TDNN model has also been combined with DTW to yield the *multistate TDNN* (*MS-TDNN*) [38]. The principle of MS-TDNN is best described as a two-phase process. The first phase transforms the input signal by using a time-delay network while the second performs dynamic time alignment. Once again, learning requires segmented data. The NN-DP-LVQ proposed in Ref. 39 provides an enhanced performance in a multispeaker task involving a vocabulary of 30 French words. The proposed model comprises three modules, the first of which is a neural network which performs a time-independent transformation of the input data. The second module performs a dynamic alignment of temporal sequences, while the third is none other than a vector quantizer which produces the reference sequences.

14.4.4 New Cell Models for ANNs

Insight gained from psychology and from the neurosciences can help improve the ANN basic model. The Kohonen feature map is an example which combines lateral inhibition and the phonotopic property to produce an efficient model. Other new models developed for ASR present interesting features for speech processing. They have, however, not been tested on large speech databases as yet.

TDNN and dynamic models use an external representation of time. It is also possible to design neural models in which time is internally managed by the network [40]. Such models have been proposed for dealing with the task of time alignment [41, 42]. Neurons presented in these models are similar to those found in the retina vision process model. These models could be useful in ASR when associated with efficient learning algorithms.

The biological model of the cortical column [43] has also served as a basis for the design of a new ANN cell. This cell presents more sophisticated behavior than does the classical formal neuron and is capable of dealing with complex, symbolic situations. A cortical column-based ANN has been used to recognize phonemes in French [44].

14.5 HYBRID MODELS

14.5.1 Position of the Problem

As stated previously, HMMs are now widely used in ASR to recognize both isolated words and continuous sentences. These models produce very good results but suffer from a number of limitations which are mainly related to the strong hypotheses on which their optimization algorithms are based.

ANNs have also proved useful in the classification of speech patterns but require improvement in their ability to deal with the temporal and sequential nature of speech.

From what precedes, combining the time-domain modeling capability of HMMs with the discriminative power of ANNs can constitute an attractive solution. It is, however, not so easy to devise an adequate interface with which the respective qualities of the two models can be fully exploited. The next section presents a number of solutions found in the current literature.

14.5.2 Proposed Solutions

ANNs and HMMs can be made to cooperate in variety of ways in hybrid systems.

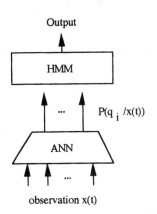

Output

$P(q_i /x(t))$

observation x(t)

FIGURE 14.5 Structure of a hybrid ANN-HMM system.

A large number of studies have concentrated on the use of ANNs as the front end for HMMs. It is proved in Refs. 31, 45, 46, and 47 that a properly trained MLP for pattern classification is asymptotically equivalent to an estimator of a posteriori class probability. Several experiments have confirmed the quality of this estimation. So from a practical point of view, the outputs of an ANN in a perfectly mastered framework are reliable. A hybrid system of this kind has the general structure presented in Fig. 14.5.

Estimators other than MLPs, especially recurrent networks and radial-basis functions, have also been used in such hybrid systems [48, 49].

The use of TDNNs was also investigated in Ref. 50. In the proposed system, a TDNN is incorporated into a Viterbi framework for performing time alignment. The outputs of the TDNN can then be normalized so as to deliver a posteriori probabilities which are then fed into an HMM.

Hybrid systems like those presented above are also reported to somewhat enhance the recognition performances of HMM systems [see, e.g., Ref. 51 for a test on the ARPA *resource management* (*RM*) task]. The implementation and use of these systems, however, are not straightforward, owing to the large number of parameters involved and the cost of computation. Moreover, the network must be trained with a sufficient amount of data to ensure convergence to a global minimum. A variety of solutions have been proposed. One solution uses the ANN to compute an additional set of symbols as transformed observations for the HMM [52]. A further improvement of this method is achieved through a global optimization of both the ANN and HMM [53]. This approach uses the gradient of the HMM optimization criterion with respect to the transformed observations to estimate the weights of the ANN connections. In another solution, the ANN is used not as a probability estimator, but as a labeler for a discrete-parameter HMM [54]. The authors see an MLP playing the role of assigning a phonetic label to each speech frame, which label is then passed on to the HMM. This amounts to vector quantization involving phonetic information. A similar idea is described in Ref. 55, but the ANN is trained by using an information-theory-based unsupervised training algorithm.

Another approach to ANN-HMM hybrid systems considers a unified paradigm for the two components. It is, e.g., proposed that the forward pass (hence the name of the method) of the Baum-Welch learning algorithm of HMMs in alpha networks [56] be viewed as a particular type of recurrent network. Other frameworks are also proposed in Refs. 57 and 58.

A further approach to hybrid system design considers ANNs as HMM postprocessors. This allows efficient combination of the time alignment capability of HMMs with the discriminative power of ANNs, a feature which has particular relevance to continuous speech recognition. Some systems feed sentences recognized by the HMM into the ANN [59, 60]. This solution works only for applications requiring a limited vocabulary. Another approach is to limit the number of hypotheses sent to the ANN as candidates elected by an N-best search algorithm [61–63].

The system described in Ref. 63, for instance, uses a *segmental neural network,* which is an ANN that accepts the acoustic frames of a phonetic segment as input and produces an estimation of the probability of a phoneme's corresponding to this segment. To be efficient, this network requires a reliable phoneme segmentation procedure. Figure 14.6 illustrates the principle of the system proposed by the authors.

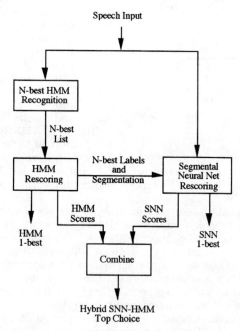

FIGURE 14.6 Principle of the hybrid SNN-HMM system. (*After [63].*)

A similar system was used in Ref. 64 to recognize connected spelled letters. This system is made up of two parts. The first is a second-order HMM [65] trained to recognize letters of the alphabet. The second is a *selectively trained neural network* (*STNN*) [66], basically an MLP. The latter incorporates acoustic-phonetic knowledge to help separate confusable letter pairs like /p/ and /t/, on one hand, and /m/ and /n/, on the other hand. The STNN focuses on the discriminative part of words, i.e., the area where the distinct acoustic information is localized. For instance, in the case of the plosive consonants /p/ and /t/, the discriminative part is made up of the shape of the burst and the vowel transitions.

Figure 14.7 illustrates how the system operates. The HMM provides an N-best response string with indications of word boundaries. These boundaries are then used by the STNN to localize the discriminative parts of words. It was shown that the combination of HMM and STNN substantially improves the identification of confusable letters both in English and in French.

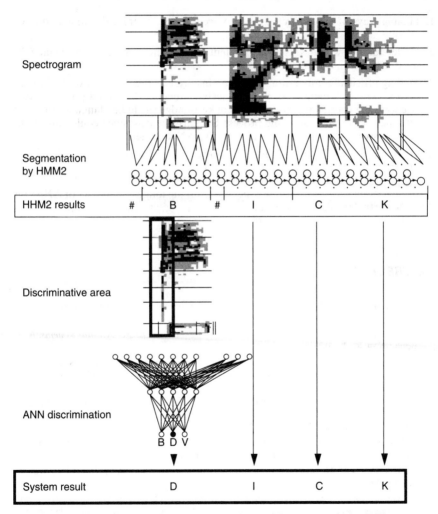

FIGURE 14.7   The recognition process of the hybrid HMM-STNN system. (*After [64].*)

14.6 CONCLUSION

Existing applications, though limited, have proved the potential of ANN technology for automatic speech processing. This chapter has mainly addressed the two aspects of speech analysis and recognition. The ANN technology is equally relevant to other aspects of automatic speech processing such as speech synthesis [67], speaker verification [68], and language acquisition [69].

Until now, ANNs in ASR have been used essentially as static recognizers. Existing architecture and associated learning procedures are not yet able to handle the temporal structure of speech totally satisfactorily. The following is a nonexhaustive list of important issues awaiting solution or under investigation:

1. Finding ways of efficiently taking into account the inherent dynamic nature of speech.

2. Understanding why ANNs yield excellent performances in some cases while failing drastically in others.

3. Finding efficient combinations of ANNs inspired by the structure of the human cortex. New architectures of interconnected subnetworks should provide effective ways of introducing diverse levels of knowledge (including language models) into the speech understanding process. Similarly, neuroscience could contribute in a decisive way to the design of innovative ANN models.

4. Designing more efficient, integrated hybrid systems which combine the ANN formalism with other formalisms, notably that of HMMs.

It is certainly too early to draw conclusions on the long-term impact of ANNs on ASR. Nevertheless, significant results are already available, and new improvements could be expected in the near future.

REFERENCES

1. L. R. Rabiner and B. H. Juang, *Fundamentals of Speech Recognition,* Prentice-Hall, Englewood Cliffs, NJ, 1993.

2. J. M. Mendel and K. S. Fu, eds., *Adaptive Learning and Pattern Recognition Systems,* Academic, New York, 1970.

3. H. Sakoe and C. Chiba, "Dynamic Programming Algorithm Optimization for Spoken Word Recognition," *IEEE Transactions on Acoustic, Speech and Signal Processing,* vol. 26, no. 1, pp. 43–49, 1978.

4. D. Fohr, *et al.,* "Knowledge-Based Techniques in Acoustic-Phonetic Decoding of Speech: Interest and Limitations," *International Journal of Pattern Recognition and Artificial Intelligence,* vol. 8, no. 1, pp. 133–153, 1994.

5. L. R. Rabiner, "A Tutorial on Hidden Markov Models and Selected Applications in Speech Recognition," *Proceedings IEEE,* vol. 77, no. 2, pp. 257–285, 1989.

6. H. Bourlard and N. Morgan, *Connectionist Speech Recognition: A Hybrid Approach,* Kluwer, Dordrecht, Netherlands, 1994.

7. H. Ney, "Progress in Large Vocabulary, Continuous Speech Recognition," in *Progress and Prospects of Speech Research and Technology,* H. Niemann, R. De Mori, and G. Hanrieder, eds., INFIX, 1994.

8. R. P. Lippmann, "An Introduction to Computing with Neural Nets," *IEEE Acoustic, Speech and Signal Processing Magazine*, vol. 4, no. 2, pp. 4–22, 1987.

9. G. J. Gibson, *et al.*, "Multilayer Perceptron Structures Applied to Adaptive Equalisers for Data Communications," *Proceedings IEEE International Conference on Acoustic, Speech and Signal Processing*, Glasgow, pp. 1183–1186, 1989.

10. S. Tamura and A. Waibel, "Noise Reduction Using Connectionist Models," *Proceedings of International Conference on Acoustic, Speech and Signal Processing*, New York, pp. 553–556, 1988.

11. S. Tamura and M. Nakamura, "Improvements to the Noise Reduction Neural Network," *Proceedings IEEE International Conference on Acoustic, Speech and Signal Processing*, Albuquerque, NM, pp. 825–828, 1990.

12. J. Elman and D. Zipser, "Learning the Hidden Structure of Speech," *JASA*, vol. 83, pp. 615–626, 1988.

13. H. Bourlard and Y. Kamp, "Auto-association by Multilayer Perceptrons and Singular Value Decomposition," *Biological Cybernetics*, vol. 59, pp. 291–294, 1988.

14. T. Kohonen, "Self-Organized Formation of Topologically Correct Feature Maps," *Biological Cybernetics*, vol. 43, pp. 59–69, 1982.

15. T. Kohonen, *et al.*, "Phonotopic Maps: Insightful Representation of Phonological Features for Speech Recognition," *Proceedings International Conference on Pattern Recognition*, Montreal, pp. 182–185, 1984.

16. R. F. Lyon and C. Mead, "An Analog Electronic Cochlea," *IEEE Transactions on ASSP*, vol. 36, pp. 1119–1134, 1988.

17. C. A. Mead, *et al.*, "Analog VLSI Model of Binaural Hearing," *IEEE Transactions on Neural Networks*, vol. 2, no. 2, pp. 230–236, 1991.

18. R. P. Lippmann, "Review of Neural Networks for Speech Recognition," *Neural Computation*, vol. 1, pp. 1–38, 1989.

19. R. P. Lippmann and B. Gold, "Neural Classifiers Useful for Speech Recognition," *First International Conference on Neural Networks*, vol. 4, IEEE, p. 417, 1987.

20. S. M. Peeling and R. K. Moore, "Experiments in Isolated Digit Recognition Using the Multi-layer Perceptron," Tech. Rep. 4073, Royal Speech and Radar Establishment, Malvern, Worcester, Great Britain, 1987.

21. W. M. Huang and R. P. Lippmann, "Neural Net and Traditional Classifiers," in *Neural Information Processing Systems*, D. Anderson, ed., American Institute of Physics, New York, 1988, pp. 387–396.

22. F. Yang, *et al.*, "Reconnaisance de mots isolés en utilisant un réseau de neurones," *Proceedings XVIIe J.E.P.*, Nancy, France, 1988, pp. 127–134.

23. T. Poggio and F. Gorosi, "A Theory of Network for Approximation and Learning," Rep. AI-1140, MIT Artificial Intelligence Laboratory, Cambridge, MA, 1989.

24. J. Moody, "Fast Learning in Multi-resolution Hierarchies," in *Advances in Neural Information Processing Systems*, D. S. Touretsky, ed., Morgan Kaufmann, San Mateo, CA, 1989.

25. T. Kohonen, "Clustering, Taxonomy and Topological Maps of Patterns," *Proceedings of the Sixth International Conference on Pattern Recognition*, pp. 114–128, 1982.

26. T. Kohonen, "Learning Vector Quantization," *First Annual International Neural Network Society Meeting*, p. 303, 1988.

27. A. Waibel, *et al.*, "Phoneme Recognition: Neural Networks vs. Hidden Markov Models," *Proceedings IEEE International Conference on Acoustic, Speech and Signal Processing*, New York, 1988, pp. 107–110.

28. K. J. Lang and G. E. Hinton, "The Development of the Time-Delay Neural Network Architecture for Speech Recognition," Tech. Rep. CMU-CS-88-152, Carnegie-Mellon University, Pittsburgh, PA, 1988.

29. A. Waibel, *et al.,* "Phoneme Recognition Using Time-Delay Neural Networks," *IEEE Transactions on ASSP,* vol. 37, no. 3, pp. 328–339, 1989.

30. H. Sawai, *et al.,* "Spotting Japanese CV—Syllables and Phonemes Using Time-Delay Neural Networks," *Proceedings IEEE International Conference on Acoustic, Speech and Signal Processing,* Glasgow, Scotland, pp. 25–28, 1989.

31. H. Bourlard and C. J. Wellekens, "Links between Markov Models and Multilayer Perceptrons," *IEEE Transactions on Pattern Anal. and Machine Intelligence,* vol. 12, pp. 1167–1178, 1990.

32. D. E. Rumelhart, *et al.,* "Learning Internal Representations by Error Propagation," in *Parallel Distributed Processing: Exploration of the Microstructure of Cognition,* vol. 1: *Foundations,* D. E. Rumelhart and J. M. McClelland, eds., MIT Press, Cambridge, MA, 1986.

33. R. I. Watrous and L. Shastri, "Learning Phonetic Features Using Connectionist Networks: An Experiment in Speech Recognition," *First International Conference on Neural Networks,* vol. 2, San Francisco, pp. 619–627, 1987.

34. R. W. Pragger, *et al.,* "Boltzmann Machines for Speech Recognition," *Computer Speech and Language,* vol. 1, pp. 2–27, 1986.

35. H. Bourlard and C. J. Wellekens, "Speech Pattern Discrimination and Multilayer Perceptrons," *Computer Speech and Language,* vol. 3, pp. 1–19, 1989.

36. D. J. Burr, "Experiments on Neural Net Recognition of Spoken and Written Text," *IEEE Transactions on ASSP,* vol. 36, pp. 1162–1168, 1988.

37. H. Sakoe, *et al.,* "Speaker-Independent Word Recognition Using Dynamic Programming Neural Networks," *Proceedings IEEE International Conference on Acoustic, Speech and Signal Processing,* Glasgow, Scotland, pp. 29–32, 1989.

38. P. Haffner, *et al.,* "Integrating Time Alignment and Neural Networks for High Performance Continuous Speech Recognition," *Proceedings IEEE International Conference on Acoustic, Speech and Signal Processing,* Toronto, Canada, pp. 105–108, 1991.

39. X. Driancourt, *et al.,* "Multilayer Perceptron, Learning Vector Quantization and Dynamic Programming: Comparison and Cooperation," *Proceedings IJCNN,* 1991.

40. S. Durand and F. Alexandre, "A Neural Network Based on Sequence Learning: Application to Spoken Digit Recognition," *Proceedings Neuro-Nimes Conference,* Marseilles, France, 1994.

41. S. J. Dehaene, *et al.,* "Neural Networks that Learn Temporal Sequences by Selection," *Proceedings National Academy Science, USA, Biophysics,* vol. 84, pp. 2713–2727, 1987.

42. M. K. Wong and H. W. Chen, "Toward a Massively Parallel System for Word Recognition," *Proceedings IEEE International Conference on Acoustic, Speech and Signal Processing,* sessions 37.4.1-37.4.4., 1986.

43. Y. Burnod, *An Adaptive Neural Network: The Cerebral Cortex,* Masson, Paris, France, 1988.

44. F. Guyot, *et al.,* "Toward a Continuous Model of the Cortical Column: Application to Speech Recognition," *Proceedings IEEE International Conference on Acoustic, Speech and Signal Processing,* Glasgow, Scotland, pp. 37–40, 1989.

45. J. J. Hopfield, "Learning Algorithms and Probability Distributions in Feed-Forward Networks," *Proceedings National Academy Science,* pp. 8429–8433, 1987.

46. H. Gish, "A Probabilistic Approach to the Understanding and Training of Neural Network Classifiers," *Proceedings IEEE International Conference on Acoustic, Speech and Signal Processing,* Albuquerque, NM, pp. 1361–1364, 1990.

47. M. D. Richard and R. P. Lippmann, "Neural Network Classifiers Estimate Bayesian *a Posteriori* Probabilities," *Neural Computation,* vol. 3, pp. 461–483, 1991.

48. S. Renals, *et al.,* "Connectionist Probability Estimation in the Decipher Speech Recognition System," *Proceedings IEEE International Conference on Acoustic, Speech and Signal Processing,* San Francisco, vol. 1, pp. 601–604, 1992.

49. E. Singer and R. Lippmann, "A Speech Recognizer Using Radial Basis Function Neural Networks in a HMM Framework," *Proceedings IEEE International Conference on Acoustic, Speech and Signal Processing,* San Francisco, vol. 1, pp. 629–632, 1992.

50. C. Dugast, *et al.,* "Combining TDNN and HMM on a Hybrid System for Improved Continuous-Speech Recognition," *IEEE Transactions on Speech and Audio Processing,* vol. 2, no. 1, pp. 217–223, 1994.

51. S. Renals, *et al.,* "Connectionist Probability Estimators in HMM Speech Recognition," *IEEE Transactions on Speech and Audio Processing,* vol. 2, no. 1, pp. 161–174, 1994.

52. Y. Bengio, *et al.,* "A Hybrid Coder for Hidden Markov Models Using a Recurrent Neural Network," *Proceedings IEEE International Conference on Acoustic, Speech and Signal Processing,* Albuquerque, NM, pp. 537–540, 1990.

53. Y. Bengio, *et al.,* "Global Optimization of a Neural Network–Hidden Markov Model Hybrid," *IEEE Transactions on Neural Networks,* vol. 3, no. 2, pp. 252–259, 1992.

54. P. Le Cerf, *et al.,* "Multilayer Perceptrons as Labelers for Hidden Markov Models," *IEEE Transactions on Speech and Audio Processing,* vol. 2, no. 1, 1994.

55. G. Rigoll, "Maximum Mutual Information Neural Networks for Hybrid Connectionist-HMM Speech Recognition Systems," *IEEE Transactions on Speech and Audio Processing,* no. 1, vol. 2, pp. 175–184, 1994.

56. J. S. Bridle, "Training Stochastic Model Recognition Algorithms as Networks Can Lead to Maximum Mutual Information Estimation of Parameters," in *Advances in Neural Information Processing Systems,* vol. 2, D. S. Touretzky, ed., Morgan Kaufmann, San Mateo, CA, 1990, pp. 211–217.

57. L. T. Niles and H. F. Silverman, "Combining Hidden Markov Models and Neural Network Classifiers," *Proceedings IEEE International Conference on Acoustic, Speech and Signal Processing,* Albuquerque, NM, pp. 417–420, 1990.

58. S. J. Young, "Competitive Training in Hidden Markov Models," *Proceedings IEEE International Conference on Acoustic, Speech and Signal Processing,* Albuquerque, NM, pp. 681–684, 1990.

59. D. N. L. Howell, "The Multi-layer Perceptron as a Discriminating Post Processor for Hidden Markov Networks," *Proceedings of Speech,* 7th FASE Symposium, 1988.

60. W. Y. Huang and R. P. Lippmann, "HMM Speech Recognition with Neural Net Discrimination," in *Advances in Neural Information Processing Systems,* vol. 2, Morgan Kaufmann, San Mateo, CA, 1990, pp. 194–202.

61. M. Ostendorf, *et al.,* "Integration of Diverse Recognition Methodologies through Reevaluation of the N-Best Sentence Hypotheses," *Proceedings of Defense Advanced Research Project Agency Speech and Natural Language Workshop,* Morgan Kaufmann, CA, 1991.

62. S. Austin, *et al.,* "Speech Recognition Using Segmental Neural Nets," *Proceedings IEEE International Conference on Acoustic, Speech and Signal Processing,* San Francisco, pp. 625–628, 1992.

63. G. Zavaliagkos, *et al.,* "A Hybrid Segmental Neural Net/Hidden Markov Model System for Continuous Speech Recognition," *IEEE Transactions on Speech and Audio Processing,* vol. 2, no. 1, pp. 151–160, 1994.

64. J. F. Mari, *et al.,* "Hidden Markov Models and Selectively Trained Neural Networks for Connected Confusable Word Recognition," *Proceedings ICSLP 94,* Yokohama, Japan, 1994.

65. J. F. Mari and J. P. Haton, "Automatic Word Recognition Based on Second-Order Hidden Markov Models," *Proceedings ICSLP 94,* Yokohama, Japan, 1994.

66. Y. Anglade, *et al.,* "Speech Discrimination in Adverse Conditions Using Acoustic Knowledge and Selectively Trained Neural Networks," *Proceedings IEEE International Conference on Acoustic, Speech and Signal Processing,* Minneapolis, MN, pp. 279–282, 1993.

67. T. J. Sejnowski and C. R. Rosenberg, "NETtalk: A Parallel Network that Learns to Read Aloud," Tech. Rep. JHU/EECS-86/01, Johns Hopkins University, Baltimore, MD, 1986.

68. Y. Bennani and P. Gallinari, "Connectionist Approaches for Automatic Speaker Recognition," *Proceedings ESCA Workshop on Automatic Speaker Recognition, Identification, Verification,* Martigny, France, pp. 95–102, 1994.

69. A. L. Gorin, *et al.,* "An Experiment in Spoken Language Acquisition," *IEEE Trans. on Speech and Audio Proceedings,* vol. 2, no. 1, part 2, pp. 224–240, 1994.

CHAPTER 15

NEURAL NETWORKS FOR CLASSIFICATION OF REMOTELY SENSED IMAGES

Fabio Roli and Sebastiano B. Serpico
DIBE, University of Genoa, Italy

Gianni Vernazza
DIEE, University of Cagliari, Italy

15.1 INTRODUCTION

At present, there is a growing interest in classification of remote-sensing images, thanks to the technological development of new sensors and the increasing importance of related applications. To this end, various approaches have been proposed, such as statistical, knowledge-based, and neural network methods.

The neural network approach has notable advantages: no need for a priori knowledge on statistical distribution of data, intrinsic parallelism, fast classification,[1] and so on. It is particularly attractive in the context of multisensor data classification, for it overcomes the main problem associated with most conventional classification methods based on multivariate models, i.e., difficulty with defining a single statistical model for different kinds of sensors.[2,3] *Artificial neural networks* (*ANNs*) (as well as other nonparametric classifiers) do not exhibit this drawback, for they are "data distribution-free."

On the other hand, well-known problems in the use of neural networks have to be faced: no general criteria for defining a suitable network architecture and dependence of classification results on training conditions (e.g., for a multilayer Perceptron); a general difficulty with interpreting the "network behavior" (the so-called opacity problem).[4] In this chapter, we deal with the use of neural networks for a supervised classification of multisensor remote-sensing images. In particular, we describe a new approach based on structured neural networks.

In the following section, we present an overview of previous work on the application of neural networks to remote-sensing data classification. Then we propose a type of structured neural network that makes it possible to interpret the network operation; e.g., the roles played by different sensors and by their channels can be explained and quantitatively assessed. This information is very useful, for it may be utilized by photointerpreters to validate a neural classifier.

As examples, we consider the applications of both the new proposed approach and two other well-known neural models to the classification of a multisensor (optical and radar) data set.

15.2 AN OVERVIEW OF ANNs FOR REMOTE-SENSING DATA CLASSIFICATION

15.2.1 Introduction

Classification of remote-sensing data has traditionally been performed by classical statistical methods (e.g., bayesian and k-nearest-neighbor classifiers). In recent years, the remote-sensing community has become interested in applying neural networks to data classification (the first attempts were described by Decatur).[5]

Although many types of neural network models could be applied to remote-sensing data classification,[6] most of the research work deals with few of them. In particular, the most widely used neural model is the *multilayer Perceptron (MLP)*. In the following, we provide an overview of previous work dealing with MLPs and other neural models.

15.2.2 Multilayer Perceptrons

This model[1,7–9] is based on multilayer feedforward networks trained by means of the *error back propagation* algorithm. Sigmoidal functions are usually adopted as nonlinear activation functions for neurons.

The first attempts to apply MLPs to the classification of remote-sensing data were described by Decatur.[5] He reported the results of an investigation into the applicability of MLPs to the classification of terrain radar images. He compared MLP performances with those of a bayesian classifier and found that significant improvements can be obtained by the MLP classifier.

Benediktsson et al. applied MLPs to the classification of multisource remote-sensing data (in particular, they used Landsat MSS and topographic data).[2] Classification performances were compared with those of a statistical parametric method that takes into account the relative reliabilities of the sources of data. They concluded that the relative performances of the two methods mainly depend on prior knowledge about the statistical distribution of data. MLPs are appropriate for cases where such distributions are unknown, for they are data-distribution-free. The considerable training time required is one of the main drawbacks of MLPs, compared with statistical parametric methods.

The use of an MLP for cloud classification using Landsat MSS images was described by Lee et al.[3] They proved that very high accuracy of cloud classification can be obtained by using a four-layer Perceptron. The reported results and comparisons with various statistical classifiers showed that textural information is basic to establishing the cloud type and cloud covering, especially if classification is performed by using an MLP.

Bischof et al. reported the application of a three-layer Perceptron for classification of Landsat TM data.[8] They showed that the MLP performs better than a bayesian classifier and that textural information can be integrated into the neural network classifier without the explicit definition of a texture measure. They also presented a "visualization" technique that aids in interpreting the network operation.

Dawson and Fung reviewed examples of the use of MLPs to perform retrieval of parameters and classification of remote-sensing data.[9] With regard to the latter task, they proposed an interesting combination of clustering algorithms and scattering models to train MLPs when no ground truth is available.

Heermann and Khazenie showed that optimized training algorithms can drastically reduce the training time taken by MLPs.[10] They presented an adaptive back propagation algorithm which reduced the training time to a reasonable level. Dawson et al. also described a fast-learning algorithm that decreased the training time by one or two orders of magnitude.[11] These results are important to make feasible the use of MLPs for classification of very large multispectral remote-sensing images.

Azimi-Sadjadi et al.[12] developed a structured neural network to classify radar images. The network architecture consists of four subnetworks (each for a different polarization of a radar signal) and of a final network which combines the subnetwork outputs to perform the decision task. All subnetworks are of the MLP type. The principal-components scheme is used to reduce the dimensionality of the feature space prior to application of the neural network. The reported results proved the advantages of a *combined-polarization architecture* that exploits the peculiarities of radar data.

Mascarilla et al.[13] translated the knowledge base of ICARE (an expert system for classification of multisource remote-sensing data) to a structured neural network. The network structure is based on a "one-network one-class" architecture. Each network is implemented by an MLP and is trained separately. This allows one to improve performances over those of the ICARE system.

15.2.3 Other Neural Models

An interesting kind of structured neural network was proposed by Ersoy et al.[14] The network architecture involves a number of stages consisting of two-layer networks. At the end of each stage, error detection is performed and a certain number of input vectors are rejected. Additional stages are automatically added to reconsider such vectors until satisfactory accuracy is obtained. Experiments were performed on multispectral and multisource remote-sensing data. A comparison with MLPs showed the superiority of the proposed neural network.

A similar kind of stage-based neural network, named the *consensual neural network,* was designed and tested on multisource data by Benediktsson et al.[15] The conceptual basis for this neural model lies in the framework of statistical consensus theory. This network, too, performed better than MLPs in the reported experiments. Moreover, it required a much faster training process.

Hwang et al.[16] presented a structured neural network to classify Landsat-4 Thematic Mapper data. Raw training data are preprocessed, class by class, to decorrelate and normalize them and to remove potential outliers. A *one-network one-class* architecture is proposed to improve data separation; each network is implemented by a *radial-basis function (RBF)* neural network. More satisfactory results were obtained from this structured neural network, as compared with MLPs and a bayesian classifier.

Salu and Tilton introduced a new neural network model, named the *binary diamond neural network,* for the classification of Landsat 4 TM data.[17] The binary diamond is a multilayer, feedforward neural network that learns from examples, in the one-shot mode. The reported results show that the binary diamond neural network performs much better than MLPs. The only drawback of this neural model seems to be the considerable use of memory.

15.3   AN APPROACH THAT ALLOWS INTERPRETATION OF NETWORK BEHAVIOR

The proposed method addresses the problem of supervised classification of multi-sensor remote-sensing data, under the assumption that the required image processing steps (correction, registration, and feature extraction) have been carried out previously by any techniques. In particular, we aim to solve such a problem by using neural networks whose behavior can be interpreted.

Our approach is based on multilayer Perceptrons trained by means of the back propagation algorithm. As a nonlinear activation function for neurons, we use a sigmoidal function, as is usually done for MLPs:

$$S(x) = (1 + e^{-x})^{-1} \tag{15.1}$$

which takes values over the range 0 to 1.

We adopt the notation given in Fig. 15.1, where n_i^l stands for the ith unit (i.e., the ith neuron) of the lth layer, b_i^l stands for its bias, and w_{ij}^l stands for the weight of the connection between such a unit and the jth unit of the $(l + 1)$st layer. (By default, we use the term *layer* to indicate a layer of neurons.) The input to n_i^l is denoted by net_i^l and the output from n_i^l by o_i^l. The output is computed as follows:

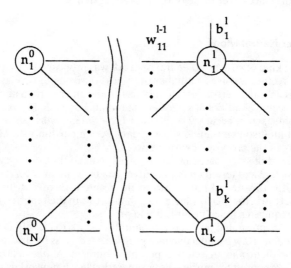

FIGURE 15.1 Notation adopted for the neurons, weights, and biases of a neural network.

$$o_i^l = S(\text{net}_i^l) = S\left(\sum_k w_{ki}^{l-1} o_k^{l-1} + b_i^l\right) \tag{15.2}$$

In this section, we describe an approach that is based on the use of structured architectures tailored to multisensor classification problems and on a simplified network representation that allows the role of each neuron to be understood. To understand the role played by each neuron in the determination of the network outputs, we suggest that one should keep separate the contributions of the different neurons, identify their processing tasks, and quantify the importance of their contributions.

15.3.1   Network Architecture

Keeping Neuron Contributions Separate by Treelike Architectures.   In a fully connected, layered ANN, all neurons of a layer contribute to the input to each neuron of the next layer. The resulting *distributed* information processing hinders the interpretation of the ANN behavior,[18] as it makes it difficult to separate the contributions of single neurons. Therefore, we propose the use of architectures in which the output of each hidden-layer neuron is fed as input to just one neuron of the next layer (later we explain why this condition is not necessary for input units). In this way, a *localist representation*[18] is obtained in which neuron contributions are kept separate.

An ANN with such an architecture is depicted in Fig. 15.2*a* for the case of a two-class problem. Even though the input unit can be connected to several units of the first hidden layer, we call it a *treelike network* (*TLN*) for simplicity. For a multiclass problem, the architecture that we propose is shown in Fig. 15.2*b:* a TLN like that in Fig. 15.2*a* is devoted to estimating the posterior probability of each class of data.[19] The outputs of all the TLNs are then compared by a *winner-takes-all* (*WTA*) decision block (Fig. 15.2*b*) that makes the final decision on classification.

An Architecture That Allows Identification of Neurons' Processing Tasks. According to our method, the architectures of the class-related TLNs in Fig. 15.2*b*

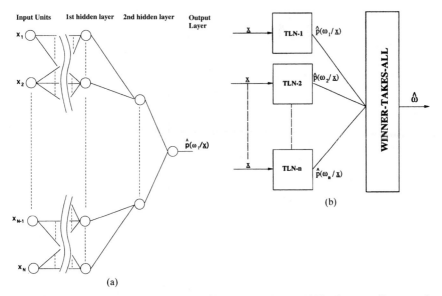

FIGURE 15.2   Network architectures used. (*a*) Example of a two-hidden-layer treelike network (TLN) used for two-class problems. The TLN output gives an estimate of the posterior probability specific for one of the two classes $p(\omega_1/\mathbf{x})$. The posterior probability for the other class is $1 - p(\omega_1/\mathbf{x})$. (*b*) As many treelike networks as the data classes considered are used for multiclass problems.

are all identical; therefore, in the following, we refer just to a single treelike architecture.

To facilitate the interpretation of the network behavior, architectures of the kind depicted in Fig. 15.3 are adopted, for they allow one to establish which aspect of available information is processed by each neuron. In particular,

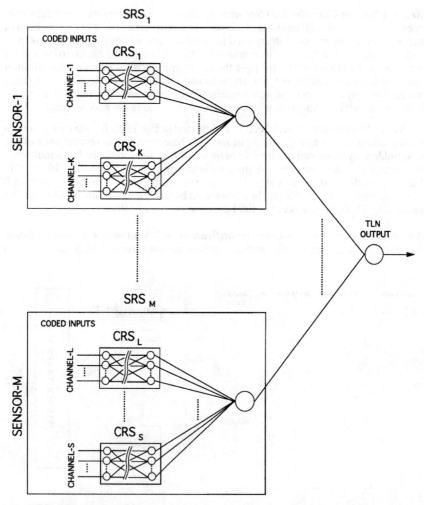

FIGURE 15.3 TLN architecture based on sensor-related subnetworks (SRSs) and channel-related subnetworks (CRSs).

- A *sensor-related subnetwork* (*SRS*) is devoted to each sensor; the task of the output neuron is to combine the outputs of the SRSs.

- Inside each SRS, a *channel-related subnetwork* (*CRS*) is devoted to each sensor; the task of the output neuron of each SRS is to combine the results of the processing performed by the CRSs.

- Each CRS imposes a constraint on the intensity values in a channel; the task of the neurons of a CRS is to contribute to constraint definition.

The architecture of the subnetworks devoted to constraint definition (that is, CRSs) can be designed according to the characteristics of the classification problem. CRSs must, however, meet the requirement of considering just one sensor channel at a time, in order to allow the interpretation of channel constraints.

15.3.2 A Simplified Representation

The TLNs with the above-defined architectures are first trained by the back propagation algorithm and then used to classify data. In addition, just for the purpose of interpreting the network behavior, we apply to the TLNs used for data classification the two transformations described in the following (details are given in App. 15A).

A Transformation That Makes Weights Correspond to the Importance of Neuron Contributions.   To interpret ANN behavior, it would be useful for the importance of each neuron to correspond to the weight of its output connection. Unfortunately, this does not always occur because (1) the outputs of some neurons may exhibit variations within a narrow subrange of their full output dynamics, (2) the importance of a connection entering a neuron also depends on the weights of the remaining connections entering the same neuron and on the related bias, and (3) the presence of both positive and negative weights in ANNs makes the evaluation of the importance of connections still more difficult.

To overcome the above difficulties, we apply a specific transformation to the representation of the TLNs. In App. 15A we define such a transformation and show that it provides an *equivalent network* (i.e., a network with an identical I/O characteristic). The properties of this network are as follows: the weights of connections are positive, the output dynamics is the same for all neurons, and weight and bias values are normalized. As a result, normalized weights become proportional to the importance of neurons in the network.

Piecewise-Linear Representation of Activation Functions and Channel Constraints.   The interpretation of the proposed TLNs may be facilitated by simplifying the representation of the neuron activation functions. To this end, the sigmoidal activation functions of neurons are replaced with piecewise-linear functions that approximate their behavior.

In addition, if we consider the contributions of a CRS to a neuron of the last hidden layer (Fig. 15.3) as a whole, we can relate the CRS to a single equivalent constraint, which is imposed on the intensity values in a sensor channel. This constraint can be approximated by a piecewise-linear function. To simplify the network representation, each CRS is then replaced with a single input neuron and a single equivalent neuron: The input neuron provides the intensity values in a sensor channel, and the equivalent neuron imposes the related piecewise-linear constraint on such values (Fig. 15.4). Thanks to this replacement, in the piecewise-linear representation, TLN architectures are actually of the treelike type.

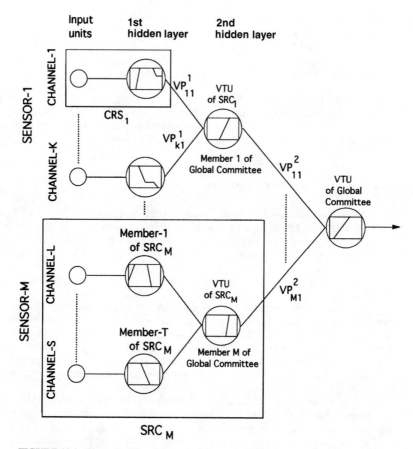

FIGURE 15.4 Piecewise-linear representation of the treelike network (PLTN) in Fig. 15.3. SRC stands for sensor-related committee; VPs (voting powers) are the normalized weights, and VTUs are the vote-taking units.

The I/O characteristics of a TLN in the piecewise-linear representation are not perfectly equivalent to those of the original TLN, due to the error on the piecewise-linear approximation.

15.4 INTERPRETATION OF TREELIKE NETWORKS

Applying the two proposed transformations to a TLN allows one to obtain a simplified representation (Fig. 15.4) with the following characteristics:

- Each channel-related subnetwork is represented by an input unit and a single equivalent neuron.
- All weights (denoted by $VP_{ij}{}^j$), from the first hidden layer up to the output one, are positive and normalized so that the sum of the weights of the connections enter-

ing each neuron may always be equal to a fixed value (that is, 1000). Biases are normalized, too.

- The output dynamics of each neuron but the output neuron are expanded up to the range [0, 1].
- The activation functions of all neurons are represented within piecewise-linear approximations.

We call a network represented in this way a *piecewise-linear treelike network* (*PLTN*) (Fig. 15.4).

15.4.1 Interpretation of Network Operation

The behavior of a PLTN can be interpreted by introducing the concept of *committees*, which judge the hypothesis that a pixel belongs to the class that the PLTN is devoted to. The whole network can then be interpreted as a hierarchical arrangement of committees that judge that hypothesis.

Input Units. They provide the intensity value of every pixel in each available sensor channel.

First Hidden Layer. Each equivalent neuron of the first hidden layer is a member of a *sensor-related committee* (Fig. 15.4) whose judgment of a constraint is based on the intensity values in a channel. If the constraint is fully satisfied (output equal to 1), then such a member gives all the "votes" available to it in favor of the aforesaid hypothesis. If the constraint is only partially satisfied, the member gives only a proportionally smaller part of the available votes. It gives no votes at all if the constraint is not satisfied (output equal to 0). The number of votes available to each member is given by the normalized weight of the output connection of the related neuron. The normalized weight is therefore called the *voting power* VP_{ij}^l.

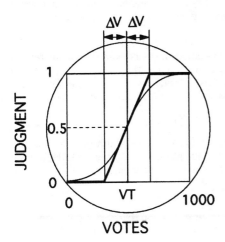

FIGURE 15.5 The majority rules of vote-taking units are defined by piecewise-linear approximations (thick line) for neuron activation functions (thin line). And ΔV is the delta votes, and VT is the voting threshold.

The votes of all the members of each sensor-related committee are collected by a neuron of the second hidden layer; this neuron plays the role of a *vote-taking unit* (*VTU*). The sum of such votes is always in the range [0, 1000], because the votes are normalized so that $\Sigma_i \mathrm{VP}_{ij}^l = 1000$ for any j and l. From Figs. 15.3 and 15.4, one can see that sensor-related committees represent the interpretations of sensor-related subnetworks.

Second Hidden Layer. The units of the second hidden layer are both the VTUs of sensor-related committees and the members of the *global committee*. Their judgments on the aforesaid hypothesis are based on their specific *majority rules*, applied to the sums of the votes of all the members of their sensor-related committees. Majority rules are defined by the piecewise-linear functions that approximate neuron activation functions in the simplified representation (Sec. 15.3.2). They are characterized by a *voting threshold* (*VT*) and by *delta votes* ΔV (Fig. 15.5). VT corresponds to the number of votes required to obtain a judgment equal to 0.5; and ΔV corresponds to the minimum decrease or increase in votes (with respect to VT) that makes a judgment reach 0.0 or 1.0, respectively. The judgments computed in this way are used by the members of the global committee to decide how many of their available votes (corresponding to their VPs) can be given to the current classification hypothesis.

Output Neuron.   The output neuron is the VTU of the global committee; therefore, it is devoted to collecting the votes of the members of this committee and to computing the final judgment, based on its specific majority rule. This majority rule is similar to those defined above (Fig. 15.5), except for the range of variations in the judgment, which can be a subrange of [0, 1].

15.4.2   Evaluation of Sensor and Channel Importance

The voting power of a member of a committee can be used directly to quantify the importance of that member in the context of its committee (i.e., the importance of a channel in a sensor-related committee or of a sensor in the global committee). To evaluate the importance of a channel for a TLN output, one has to take into account both the importance of that channel inside its sensor-related committee and the importance of the related sensor inside the global committee.

To select channels or sensors, one has to take into account also the behaviors of the majority rules. The same VP value may cause a larger or smaller variation in the related VTU output, depending on the majority rules. In particular, the ith sensor of a TLN can be disregarded, for classification purposes, if its votes do not change the output of the TLN appreciably. The maximum change induced by the ith sensor is equal to

$$SC_i = \min \{VP_{i1}^2 \,/\, 2\,\Delta V_1^3), \Delta J_1^3\} \qquad (15.3)$$

where VP_{i1}^2 is the voting power of the ith sensor, ΔJ_1^3 is the width (smaller than or equal to 1) of the output range of the VTU of the global committee, and ΔV_1^3 are the delta votes of such a VTU. Analogously, the maximum change in a TLN output due to the votes of the jth channel of the ith sensor is equal to

$$CC_j = \min \{ VP_{ji}^1 \,/\, 2\,\Delta V_i^2, 1 \} \cdot SC_i \qquad (15.4)$$

The two parameters SC and CC can be used to select sensors and related channels, respectively.

The evaluation of sensor and channel importance based on parameters VP, SC, and CC is meaningful for the TLN considered. It does not provide any general information about sensors and channels.

15.5   DATA

The considered data set referred to an agricultural area near the village of Feltwell (United Kingdom). We selected a section (250 × 350 pixels) of a scene acquired by two imaging sensors installed on an airplane: a Daedalus 1268 Airborne Thematic Mapper (ATM) scanner and a PLC-band, fully polarimetric, NASA/JPL synthetic

FIGURE 15.6 Multisensor image utilized for experiments: (*a*) channel 9 of the ATM sensor and (*b*) channel L-HV (band L, polarization HV) of the SAR sensor.

aperture radar (SAR) sensor. Images were registered by using the radar image as reference. Figure 15.6 shows channel 9 of the ATM sensor and channel L-HV (band L, polarization HV) of the SAR sensor. The ground truth was used to prepare a reference map to assess the classification accuracy. We considered the five numerically most representative agricultural classes (55,657 pixels). Agricultural fields were randomly subdivided into two disjoint sets; 5124 training pixels were taken from the fields of one set, 5820 test pixels from the fields of the other set.

Fifteen channels were selected to form a *feature vector* for each pixel: the six ATM channels corresponding to TM channels in the visible spectrum and in the infrared spectrum and the SAR channels in the HH, HV, and VV polarizations. Noise was reduced by applying a simple running-mean filtering to both the ATM (5×5 window) and the SAR (9×9 window) channels.

15.6 DATA REPRESENTATION AND NETWORK ARCHITECTURE

To use neural networks for pixel classification, the values of the spectral channels have to be mapped into a set of input units (*data representation* or *input coding* problem).[1,8] We adopted the simplest coding: one input unit per sensor channel. Each input unit was activated at a value equal to the intensity normalized to the range [0, 1].

Let us consider output coding. Each TLN has a single output neuron, which should provide an estimate of a posterior class probability. To this end, target outputs are set to 1 for pixels belonging to such a class; otherwise, they are set to zero.[19] Therefore, a specific training file for each TLN is utilized in the training phase.

The global architecture consists of five TLNs (one per data class) connected to a WTA block, as shown in Fig. 15.2*b*. Fifteen input units were defined: six devoted to the ATM channels and nine to the SAR channels. We adopted CRSs with one input neuron and two output neurons (Fig. 15.7*a*). Two SRSs were defined, one for the ATM sensor, the other for the SAR sensor. Therefore, each TLN is made up of four layers, with 15, 30, 2, and 1 units per layer, respectively (Fig. 15.7*a*).

15.7 EXPERIMENTAL RESULTS

In this section, we analyze the classification performances of the TLNs and of other well-known neural networks (i.e., fully connected MLPs and *probabilistic neural networks*) on the selected data set. Finally, we give an example of simplified representation and interpretation of the TLNs utilized to classify the data set. All considered classifiers are of the *supervised* type; for all of them, we utilized the same training set and assessed the performances on the same test set.

15.7.1 Classification Performances and Comparisons

Five TLNs with the same architecture as the one of the network in Fig. 15.7*a* were trained to estimate the posterior probabilities $p(\omega_i/\mathbf{x})$ of the five agricultural classes, given input vectors that characterize pixels. The back propagation learning procedure was used to this end. As a convergence criterion, we required a *mean square error (MSE)* smaller than 0.005. The TLNs were initialized with random weights; learning was stopped when the convergence was reached or after 400 *epochs*.[1] Learning was repeated at different *learning rates*,[1] that is, 0.1, 0.05, and 0.01. The resulting TLNs were first used to classify training pixels; to this end, the TLNs' outputs were combined by a WTA block, as in Fig. 15.2*b*. In terms of classification accuracy, the best results were obtained at the learning rate $\eta = 0.01$; that is, the overall accuracy was equal to 96.23 percent. The MSE decay at $\eta = 0.01$ is given in Fig. 15.8.

These TLNs were then used to classify test pixels. In this case, too, the TLN outputs were combined by the WTA block. Classification results on the test set are given in Table 15.1. The same neural classifier was then applied to the whole image, and pixels not belonging to the five agricultural classes considered were neglected. An overall accuracy of 86.46 percent was reached.

To give other examples of neural network applications, first we considered the same kind of ANNs (that is, MLPs) but with fully connected architectures, and we trained them by the same learning procedure. In particular, we considered six different architectures with one or two hidden layers and various numbers of units per layer. In all cases, the input units were 15, since we adopted the same input coding as for our TLNs. All the networks had 5 output units, since the *target* related to each training sample was obtained by setting to 1 the network output corresponding to the class to which the sample belonged and by setting to 0 the remaining four outputs. For classification purposes, each sample was assigned to the class corresponding to the output unit with the highest activation, without fixing any threshold. Results are summarized in Table 15.2 for two values of the learning rate ($\eta = 0.01$

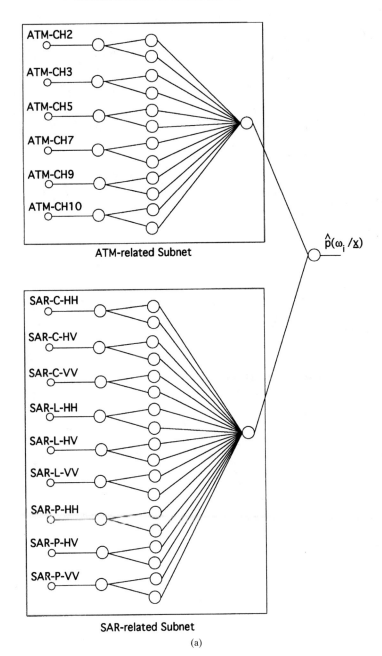

FIGURE 15.7 TLNs used to classify the selected multisensorial data set. (*a*) Architecture of the five treelike networks.

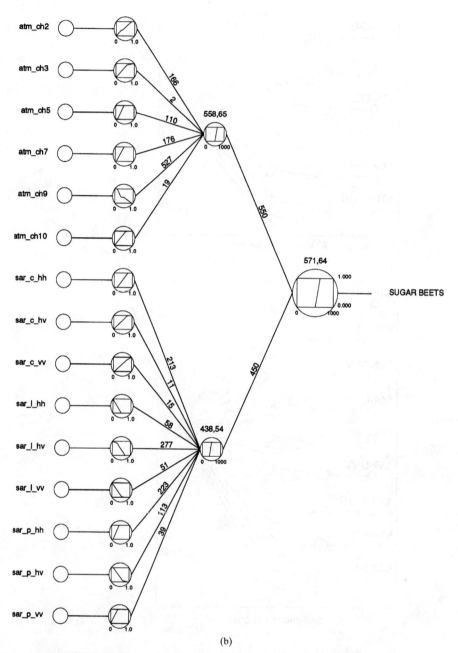

(b)

FIGURE 15.7   (*Continued*)   TLNs used to classify the selected multisensorial data set. (*b*) PLTN obtained for the class of sugar beets by training the original TLN and transforming its representation.

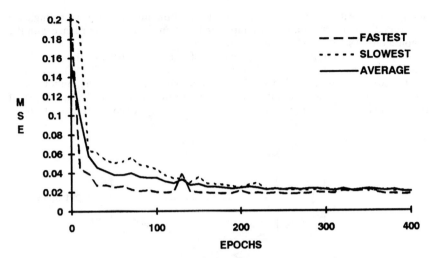

FIGURE 15.8 Mean square error (MSE) decay as a function of the number of training epochs. Three curves are shown: Two correspond to the TLNs with the slowest and fastest convergence speeds, respectively, and the third refers to the average MSE for the five TLNs.

TABLE 15.1 Classification of Test Samples by Using TLNs: Error Matrix

| | Classified as | | | | | |
True class	Sugar beets	Stubble	Bare soil	Potatoes	Carrots	Correctly classified, %
Sugar beets	2033	0	0	9	1	99.51
Stubble	41	1178	139	4	9	85.92
Bare soil	50	3	440	40	22	79.28
Potatoes	185	18	23	656	2	74.21
Carrots	189	0	1	50	727	75.18
Overall accuracy						86.49

TABLE 15.2 Percentages of Correctly Classified Pixels by Using Fully Connected Neural Networks

Architecture	Training set, $\eta = 0.01$, %	Test set, $\eta = 0.01$, %	Training set, $\eta = 0.05$, %	Test set, $\eta = 0.05$, %
15-15-8-5	98.7	79.9	98.5	86.3
15-30-15-5	98.0	82.7	98.7	79.9
15-7-5-5	96.9	82.3	98.1	76.1
15-15-5	97.3	87.9	98.7	86.0
15-30-5	97.2	88.2	98.8	86.2
15-8-5	96.5	89.6	98.0	82.3
Mean value	97.4	85.1	98.5	82.8

and $\eta = 0.05$). All the architectures were such that the number of weights might be much smaller than the number of samples in the training set, in accordance with the simplified rule suggested by Baum et al.[20]

As a further example of the application of neural networks to the considered classification problem, we utilized *probabilistic neural networks (PNNs)*.[21] A three-layer network was defined (Fig. 15.9), with a number of input units, a number of pattern units, and a number of output units equal to the numbers of features (15), of training pixels (5124), and of classes (5), respectively. Each pattern unit corre-

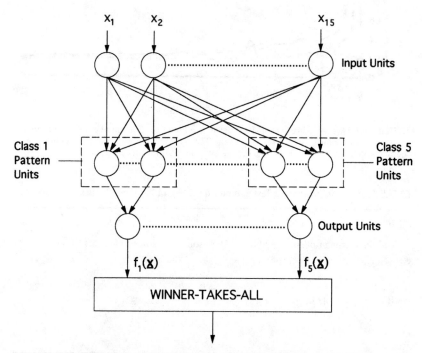

FIGURE 15.9 Architecture of the PNN considered as a further example of application of neural networks to the classification of the selected multisensorial data set.

sponded to a training pixel. The pattern units corresponding to the training pixels of the ith class contributed to the computation of the estimation $f_i(\mathbf{x})$ of the posterior probability of such a class $\hat{p}(\omega_i/\mathbf{x})$. A WTA block was then used to identify the most probable class. As input to the PNNs, we utilized the same inputs as for our TLNs (with no *normalization to unit length*)[21]; as a *smoothing parameter*[21] we adopted

$$\sigma = 0.1 \left(\frac{\nu}{M^{1/p}} \right)^{1/2} \tag{15.5}$$

where the coefficient 0.1 was experimentally found; ν is the average quadratic distance, in the feature space, between vectors of training samples and mean vectors of the related classes; M is the number of training pixels; and p is the number of features. Except for the empirical coefficient 0.1, the basis for Eq. (15.5) was provided

TABLE 15.3 Classification of Test Samples by Using PNNs: Error Matrix

True class	Sugar beets	Stubble	Bare soil	Potatoes	Carrots	Correctly classified, %
Sugar beets	1999	20	3	11	10	97.84
Stubble	43	1130	159	20	19	82.42
Bare soil	19	0	442	69	25	79.64
Potatoes	115	20	23	723	3	81.79
Carrots	84	0	0	17	864	89.35
Overall accuracy						88.62

(Classified as)

by the theory of nonparametric density estimation.[22] Table 15.3 gives, class by class, the classification accuracy obtained by using the PNNs; on the whole image, a classification accuracy of 88.68 percent was achieved.

Analysis of the above results suggests the following considerations:

• Compared with fully connected neural networks (Table 15.2), at each learning rate, the TLNs yielded accuracies on the test set that were better than or equal to the mean accuracy value computed for the different architectures considered. Even if we had chosen the neural network with the best performances on the training set (architecture: 15-30-5, $\eta = 0.05$), its classification accuracy on the test set would be very close to that obtained by the TLNs. Finally, an important advantage of the TLNs was that we did not need to perform experiments with different architectures.

• The probabilistic neural networks performed slightly better than the TLNs in terms of classification accuracy (a 2 percent difference on the test set). However, PNNs, as well as fully connected neural networks, have the drawback that classification criteria are not intelligible.

15.7.2 Network Interpretation

The simplified representation of a TLN (i.e., its PLTN) provides a synthetic view of the network behavior. As an example, in Fig. 15.7b the PLTN of the class of sugar beets is depicted. In particular, the optical and radar sensors are of comparable importance, since the related voting powers are $VP_{11}^2 = 550$ and $VP_{21}^2 = 450$, respectively. The votes of both sensor-related committees are necessary to provide a high network output, as the voting threshold is $VT_1^3 = 571$. Concerning sensor channels, among the ATM channels, channel 9 gives by far the most important contribution; channels 2, 5, and 7 are also very important; channel 10 gives a small contribution; and channel 3 is almost completely negligible. A similar analysis applies to SAR channels. Finally, channel constraints may be considered to analyze the requirements that must be met by the intensity values in sensor channels.

It is also interesting to select a sensor channel and compare the different PLTNs with respect to it. For example, in Fig. 15.10, we give the constraints on the intensities in ATM channel 9, for all the classes considered. Sugar beets should be dark, stubble light, bare soil dark, potatoes and carrots from medium gray to light gray.

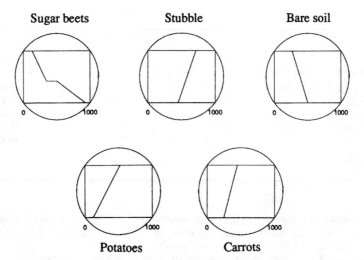

FIGURE 15.10 Constraints on intensity values in ATM channel 9 for all data classes. Such constraints represent the piecewise-linear approximations for equivalent neurons related to ATM channel 9 CRSs.

Such constraints determine the votes of just one member of the ATM-related committees of the five TLNs. Therefore, it is not necessary that they describe all the samples of the related class correctly. However, if a TLN involves many constraints that are not in agreement with a photointerpreter's a priori knowledge or with a visual image analysis by the user, then that TLN may be trained again with different random starting weights. This allows the TLN to converge to different final weights, which may correspond to a more consistent interpretation. In our case, the above constraints describe well the intensities of all the classes in ATM channel 9 (Fig. 15.6a), except for the class of bare soil. However, this class is well described by other constraints.

The importance of sensors and channels can be evaluated by consulting the values of parameters VP, SC, and CC. The SC and CC values in Table 15.4 can be compared with a threshold to decide which sensors and channels can be disregarded for each class. Such a threshold can be fixed on the basis of training data. Concerning sensors, ATM and SAR are always of similar importance and can never be neglected. As to channels, in our experiments, we checked that when we used a threshold equal to 0.15, classification accuracy on the training set remained substantially unchanged. In Table 15.4, negligible channels and sensors are marked with a star.

Finally, we selected a misclassified stubble field and checked, in the corresponding TLN, which members of the sensor-related committees wrongly denied their votes. We found that the members related to the ATM channels globally assigned about 500 votes to the pixels of the stubble field. This voting made the ATM-related committee assign no favorable votes at all (since the related voting threshold and delta votes were $VT_1^2 = 631$ and $\Delta V_1^2 = 39$, respectively). On the contrary, the pixels of this field received almost all votes from the SAR-related committee ($VP_2^2 = 499$), but this was not enough to have a high TLN output ($VT_1^3 = 778$ and $\Delta V_1^3 = 109$).

TABLE 15.4 Maximum Changes in TLN Outputs due to Sensor and Channel Contributions

A star indicates the channels that may be disregarded.

Channel	TLN				
	Sugar beets	Stubble	Bare soil	Potatoes	Carrots
atm-ch2	1.000	0.865	1.000	0.997	1.000
atm-ch3	0.015	0.213	0.023*	0.541	1.000
atm-ch5	0.845	0.981	1.000	0.997	1.000
atm-ch7	1.000	0.981	1.000	0.997	1.000
atm-ch9	1.000	0.981	1.000	0.997	1.000
atm-ch10	0.146*	0.981	1.000	0.578	1.000
sar-c-hh	1.000	0.040*	0.084	0.571	0.442
sar-c-hv	0.100*	0.007*	1.000	0.439	0.239
sar-c-vv	0.137*	0.172	0.102*	0.754	0.855
sar-l-hh	0.528	0.981	0.030*	0.997	1.000
sar-l-hv	1.000	0.981	0.132*	0.997	1.000
sar-l-vv	0.464	0.981	1.000	0.629	0.138*
sar-p-hh	1.000	0.251	1.000	0.997	1.000
sar-p-hv	1.000	0.522	0.174	0.845	1.000
sar-p-vv	0.355	0.178	0.054*	0.571	0.094*

Sensor	TLN				
	Sugar beets	Stubble	Bare soil	Potatoes	Carrots
ATM	1.000	0.981	0.685	0.997	1.000
SAR	1.000	0.981	1.000	0.997	1.000

15.8 DISCUSSION AND CONCLUSIONS

In this chapter, we have considered the application of different types of neural networks to the supervised classification of multisensor remote-sensing images. The performances of two well-known neural classifiers—MLPs and PNNs—have been evaluated and compared with those of the structured neural networks we have proposed.

Structured neural networks allow a tradeoff between classification accuracy and interpretation of the classifier operation. As stated in the previous section, a classifier based on the proposed neural networks can be outperformed (by some percentage) by probabilistic neural networks and can obtain an accuracy close to the average classification accuracy provided by the fully connected neural networks considered. On the other hand, our approach allows us to examine the operation of the developed neural classifier. In our experiment, we verified that there was good agreement between the *channel constraints* learned by TLNs and the responses of the cultivated land over both the optical and radar channels. The importance of the imaging sensors used and of the related channels has been evaluated with respect to the developed classifier. Finally, we have shown that misclassification errors can be explained by examining the network operation with respect to the feature vectors of misclassified pixels. This analysis can be used by photointerpreters to validate the operation of the neural classifier.

In a comparison between MLPs and PNNs, our experiments confirmed that such neural classifiers provide similar classification accuracies (PNNs performed slightly better). The main advantages of PNNs lie in a much faster training time (one-shot mode) and in the simplicity of the architecture configuration task. The only limitation of PNNs is that the size of the network and the classification time grow proportionally to the size of the training set. In general, all considered neural classifiers have provided satisfactory performances. Similar performances on the considered multisensor data set can be obtained by statistical nonparametric methods. (An additional experiment, not reported in this chapter, showed that the k-nearest-neighbor classifier obtains a classification accuracy of 89.85 percent on the test set.[23]) These results, in agreement with the conclusions drawn by other remote-sensing researchers (Sec. 15.2), confirm that neural networks constitute a valid alternative to traditional statistical classifiers.

ACKNOWLEDGMENTS

The authors wish to thank Prof. S. Ridella for his helpful comments. The work was supported in part by the Italian Space Agency (ASI) and by the Programma Nazionale di Ricerca sulle Tecnologie per la Bioelettronica (MURST-PNTB). Thanks are also due to Hunting Technical Services Ltd. for providing the ATM images.

APPENDIX 15A

In this appendix, we give three propositions (Sec. 15A.1) and describe the algorithms adopted for the piecewise-linear approximations for neuron activation functions and channel constraints (Sec. 15A.2). The results of these two parts have been used to develop the transformation (Sec. 15A.3) to simplify the representation of treelike networks. Proofs of propositions and details of algorithms are given by Serpico and Roli.[23]

15A.1 Propositions

Proposition 1: Changing the Signs of Weights.   Let us consider the weights of the connections starting from the hidden units of a multilayer feedforward neural network with sigmoidal activation functions and a treelike architecture. The sign of any such weights can be changed [Eq. (15.6)] without changing the I/O characteristic of the network, provided that the compensations in Eqs. (15.7) to (15.9) are introduced (Fig. 15.11):

$$w_{ij}^{l} \rightarrow w_{ij}^{+l} = -w_{ij}^{l} \tag{15.6}$$

$$b_{j}^{l+1} \rightarrow b_{j}^{+l+1} = b_{j}^{l+1} + w_{ij}^{l} \tag{15.7}$$

$$b_{i}^{l} \rightarrow b_{i}^{+l} = -b_{i}^{l} \tag{15.8}$$

$$w_{ki}^{l-1} \rightarrow w_{ki}^{+l-1} = -w_{ki}^{l-1} \qquad \text{for all } k \in [1, n] \tag{15.9}$$

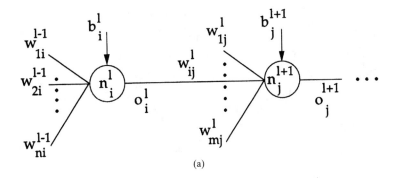

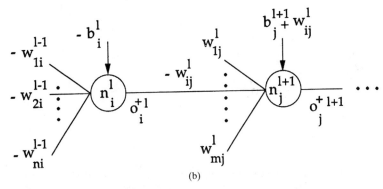

FIGURE 15.11 Procedure to change the sign of a weight w_{ij}^l of a TLN. (*a*) Part of the original TLN; (*b*) the same part of the TLN after application of the procedure.

where the apex + indicates the variables involved in the above changes.

In particular, it is easy to prove that

$$o_i^{+l} = 1 - o_i^l \qquad o_j^{+l+1} = o_j^{l+1} \tag{15.10}$$

which imply proposition 1, due to the treelike architecture.

Proposition 2: Expanding Output Dynamics. Let o_i^l be the output of any unit n_i^l but the output unit of a multilayer feedforward neural network with a treelike architecture and a sigmoidal activation function (Fig. 15.12*a*). Let θ_i^l and ϕ_i^l be the minimum and maximum values of o_i^l, respectively, for any possible value of the input vector **x** to the network [Eq. (15.11)]. The output dynamics $[\theta_i^l, \phi_i^l]$ of n_i^l can always be expanded into the range $[0, 1]$ through the transformation in Eq. (15.13), without changing the I/O characteristic of the network, provided that the changes in Eqs. (15.14) and (15.15) are made (Fig. 15.12*b*):

$$\theta_i^l = \min_x \{o_i^l\} \qquad \phi_i^l = \max_x \{o_i^l\} \tag{15.11}$$

$$\Delta o_i^l = \phi_i^l - \theta_i^l \tag{15.12}$$

$$o_i^l = S(\text{net}_i^l) \rightarrow o'_i^l = f'_i^l(\text{net}_i^l) = \frac{S(\text{net}_i^l) - \theta_i^l}{\Delta o_i^l} \tag{15.13}$$

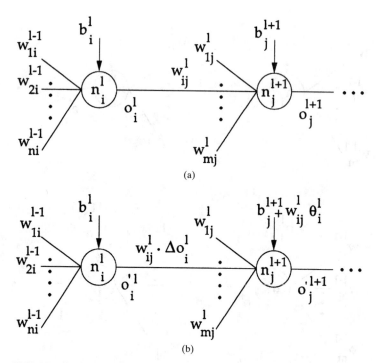

(a)

(b)

FIGURE 15.12 Procedure to expand the dynamics of a neuron of a TLN. (*a*) Part of the original TLN; (*b*) the same part of the TLN after application of the procedure.

$$w_{ij}^l \rightarrow w'^l_{ij} = \Delta o_i^l w_{ij}^l \tag{15.14}$$

$$b_j^{l+1} \rightarrow b'^{l+1}_j = b_j^{l+1} + w_{ij}^l \theta_i^l \tag{15.15}$$

where $f_i'^l$ is the activation function of the unit n_i^l in the modified network; net_i^l is the input to unit n_i^l and is the same for both networks; and the apex indicates the variables that are involved in the above changes. Note that Eq. (15.13) involves the definition of a specific activation function $f_i'^l(net_i^l)$ for unit n_i^l.

Proposition 3: Scaling Weights and Biases. The biases and the weights of the input connections to a neuron n_i^l of a multilayer feedforward neural network can be scaled by a multiplicative factor A_i^l [Eq. (15.16)] without changing the I/O characteristic of the network, provided that a compensation [Eq. (15.17)] is introduced to the activation function of the neuron:

$$w_{ki}^{l-1} \rightarrow w''^{l-1}_{ki} = A_i^l w_{ki}^{l-1} \qquad b_i^l \rightarrow b''^l_i = A_i^l b_i^l \tag{15.16}$$

$$f_i^l(net_i^l) \rightarrow f''^l_i(net''^l_i) = f_i^l(net''^l_i/A_i^l) \tag{15.17}$$

where the double apexes indicate the variables of the modified network that have been changed, compared with the original network. This proposition, too, involves a modification to the activation function of the unit n_i^l [Eq. (15.17)].

15A.2 Piecewise-Linear Approximations

Algorithm 1: Piecewise-Linear Approximation for Modified Sigmoidal Functions.
A modified sigmoidal function, obtained by applying in sequence the expansion in
Eq. (15.13) and the scaling in Eq. (15.17) to the activation function of a generic unit
n_i^l, is a monotonically increasing function whose values are within the range $[0, 1]$.
Therefore, such a function can be approximated by a linear function with saturation
at 0 and 1. In particular, as a linear function, we utilize the straight line tangent to the
modified sigmoidal function at the point where this function is equal to 0.5. Such a
piecewise-linear function may be characterized, in a comprehensible way, by the
quantities y_0 and Δy (Fig. 15.13a).

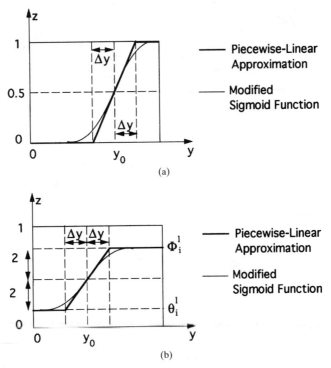

FIGURE 15.13 Piecewise-linear approximations for a modified sigmoidal
function. (a) Approximation for an *expanded and scaled* sigmoidal function;
(b) approximation for a *scaled* sigmoidal function (with no expansion).

A modified sigmoidal function, obtained by applying just the scaling in Eq.
(15.17) [and not the expansion in Eq. (15.13)] to the activation function of a generic
unit n_i^l, can be approximated in a similar way (Fig. 15.13b). In this case, the piecewise-linear function may be characterized by $y_0, \Delta y, \theta_i^l$ and ϕ_i^l: the meanings of y_0 and
Δy are depicted in Fig. 15.13b, and θ_i^l and ϕ_i^l are the quantities defined in Eq. (15.11).

Algorithm 2: Piecewise-Linear Approximation for Channel Constraints. Each CRS in a TLN can be replaced with an *equivalent neuron* whose activation function provides a piecewise-linear approximation for the channel constraint implemented by the CRS. For the type of CRS used for the experiments described in Sec. 15.7, the basic steps of the procedure for generating the equivalent neuron are given in the following. As an example, we make reference to the CRS of the first channel of the first sensor (Fig. 15.14a):

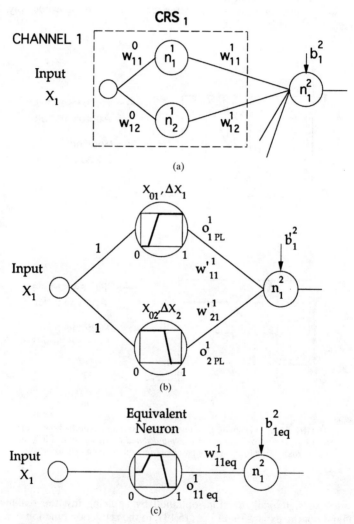

FIGURE 15.14 Replacement of a channel-related subnetwork (CRS) with a single equivalent neuron. (*a*) Architecture of the CRSs adopted for experiments; (*b*) piecewise-linear approximations for the activation functions of neurons n_1^1 and n_2^1; (*c*) replacement of n_1^1 and n_2^1 with an equivalent neuron. As an example, the first channel of the first sensor is considered.

**** STEP 1:   MAKING WEIGHTS POSITIVE ****
      **** (based on Proposition 1) ****

        For l=2, 1, -1
          For i=1, N_l
            For j=1, N_{l+1}
            If $w_{ij}^l < 0$ Then change_sign_&_compensate (w_{ij}^l)
                                   Else continue
            End
          End
        End

**** STEP 2:   TURNING CRS INTO EQUIVALENT NEURONS****
      **** (based on Algorithm 2) ****

        For k=1, N_0
            Turn_CRS_into_Eq_Neuron_&_compensate (CRS_K)
        End

**** STEP 3:   EXPANDING DYNAMICS OF 2nd H.L NEURONS ****
      **** (based on Proposition 2) ****

        For j=1, N_2
            Expand_&_compensate (n_j^2)
        End

**** STEP 4:   WEIGHTS AND BIAS NORMALIZATION ****
      **** (based on Proposition 3) **** '

        For l=2, 3
                For j=1, N_l
                $A_j^l = 1000 / \Sigma_i\, w_{ij}^{l-1}$
                Scale_weights_bias_&_activ_fun (n_j^l, A_j^l)
                End
        End

**** STEP 5:   PIECEWISE LINEAR APPROXIMATION FOR ****
      **** ACTIVATION FUNCTIONS ****
      **** (based on Algorithm 1) ****

        For l=2, 3
                For j=1, N_l
                Apply_PL_approx_to_activ_fun (n_j^l)

                End
        End

FIGURE 15.15 Control flow of the transformation that simplifies the representation of a treelike network. Here N_l is the number of neurons in the lth layer, and N_0 is the total number of sensor channels.

- Expansion of the output dynamics of n_1^1 and n_2^1 (proposition 2)
- Scaling of the weights and biases of n_1^1 and n_2^1 so that $w''_{11}{}^0 = w''_{21}{}^0 = 1$ (proposition 3)
- Piecewise-linear (PL) approximations for the activation functions of n_1^1 and n_2^1 (Fig. 15.14b)
- Replacement of n_1^1 and n_2^1 with a single equivalent neuron with the activation function

$$C_1(x_1) = w'_{11}{}^1 o_{1\,\mathrm{PL}}^1(x_1) + w'_{21}{}^1 o_{2\,\mathrm{PL}}^1(x_1) \tag{15.18}$$

- Expansion of the dynamics of such an equivalent neuron (proposition 2) (Fig. 15.14c)

As a result, the activation function of the equivalent neuron becomes

$$f_{1\mathrm{eq}}(x_1) = \frac{C_1(x_1) - \min_{x_1}\{C_1(x_1)\}}{\max_{x_1}\{C_1(x_1)\} - \min_{x_1}\{C_1(x_1)\}} \tag{15.19}$$

which defines a constraint on channel x_1. It can be easily seen that the activation function $f_{1\mathrm{eq}}(x_1)$ is piecewise-linear, is made up of five (or fewer) linear pieces, and is normalized to the range $[0, 1]$.

15A.3 Transformation to Simplify TLN Representation

The transformation used to simplify the representation of treelike networks for the purpose of interpreting the network behavior is based on five progressive steps which, starting from a TLN, generate a PLTN equivalent to the original TLN, except for the piecewise-linear approximations for the neuron activation functions and for the channel constraint functions (the term *equivalent* refers to the I/O characteristics of TLNs). We recall that the architecture of a PLTN is depicted in Fig. 15.4, and its characteristics have been defined in Sec. 15.4.

The control flow of the transformation is given in Fig. 15.15. Each of its progressive steps is based on a procedure that implements one of the network modifications defined in the propositions or in the algorithms described in Secs. 15A.1 and 15A.2. Note that, at the third step, the procedure to expand the dynamics of the neuron activation function is applied to the units of the second hidden layer only. In particular, the activation function of the output unit must be left unchanged, otherwise the comparison of the class-probability estimates performed by the WTA block would be distorted. As to the fifth step, piecewise-linear functions are defined by parameters y_0 and Δy (Fig. 15.13); these parameters correspond, respectively, to the quantities VT and ΔV defined for majority rules.

REFERENCES

1. Hertz, J., A. Krogh, and R. G. Palmer, *Introduction to the Theory of Neural Computation*, Addison-Wesley, Advanced Book Program, Reading, MA, 1991.

2. Benediktsson, J. A., P. H. Swain, and O. K. Ersoy, "Neural Network Approaches versus Statistical Methods in Classification of Multisource Remote-Sensing Data," *IEEE Transactions on Geoscience and Remote Sensing*, vol. 28, no. 4, pp. 540–552, July 1990.

3. Lee, J., R. C. Weger, S. K. Sengupta, and R. M. Welch, "A Neural Network Approach to Cloud Classification," *IEEE Transactions on Geoscience and Remote Sensing*, vol. 28, no. 5, pp. 846–855, September 1991.

4. Chandrasekaran, B., and A. Goel, "From Numbers to Symbols to Knowledge Structures: Artificial Intelligence Perspectives on the Classification Task," *IEEE Transactions on Systems, Man, and Cybernetics*, vol. 18, no. 3, pp. 415–424, May/June 1988.

5. Decatur, S. E., "Applications of Neural Networks to Terrain Classification," *Proceedings of the International Joint Conference on Neural Networks '89*, held in Washington, D.C., vol. 1, 1989, pp. 283–288.

6. Lippmann, R. P., "An Introduction to Computing with Neural Networks," *IEEE Acoustics, Speech and Signal Processing Magazine*, vol. 4, no. 2, pp. 4–22, April 1987.

7. Rumelhart, D. E., J. L. McClelland, and the PDP Research Group, *Parallel Distributed Processing*, vols. 1, 2, MIT Press, Cambridge, MA, 1986.

8. Bischof, H., W. Schneider, and A. J. Pinz, "Multispectral Classification of Landsat-Images Using Neural Networks," *IEEE Transactions on Geoscience and Remote Sensing*, vol. 30, no. 3, pp. 482–490, May 1992.

9. Dawson, M. S., and A. K. Fung, "Neural Networks and Their Applications to Parameter Retrieval and Classification," *IEEE Geoscience and Remote Sensing Society Newsletter*, September 1993, pp. 6–14.

10. Heermann, P. D., and N. Khazenie, "Classification of Multispectral Remote Sensing Data Using a Back-Propagation Neural Network," *IEEE Transactions on Geoscience and Remote Sensing*, vol. 30, no. 1, pp. 81–88, January 1992.

11. Dawson, M. S., A. K. Fung, and M. T. Manry, "Sea Ice Classification Using Fast Learning Neural Networks," *Proceedings of 1992 IEEE International Geoscience and Remote Sensing Symposium*, Houston, TX, May 1992, pp. 1070–1071.

12. Azimi-Sadjadi, M. R., S. Ghaloum, and R. Zoughi, "Terrain Classification in SAR Images Using Principal Components Analysis and Neural Networks," *IEEE Transactions on Geoscience and Remote Sensing*, vol. 31, no. 2, pp. 511–515, March 1993.

13. Mascarilla, L., E. H. Zahzah, and J. Desachy, "Neural Network Classifiers Based on Geocoded Data and Multispectral Images for Satellite Image Interpretation," *Proceedings Fifth International Conference, CAIP '93*, Budapest, Hungary, pp. 830–837, September 1993.

14. Ersoy, O. K., and D. Hong, "Parallel, Self-Organizing, Hierarchical Neural Networks," *IEEE Transactions on Neural Networks*, vol. 1, no. 2, pp. 167–178, June 1990.

15. Benediktsson, J. A., O. K. Ersoy, and P. H. Swain, "A Consensual Neural Network," *Proceedings of the 1991 International Geoscience and Remote Sensing Symposium*, Espoo, Finland, June 3–6, 1991, pp. 2219–2222.

16. Hwang, J. N., S. R. Lay, and R. Kiang, "Robust Construction Neural Networks for Classification of Remotely Sensed Data," *Proceedings of World Congress on Neural Networks*, WCNN '93, Portland, OR, July 11–15, 1993, vol. 4, pp. 580–584.

17. Salu, Y., and J. Tilton, "Classification of Multispectral Image Data by the Binary Diamond Neural Network and by Nonparametric, Pixel-by-Pixel Methods," *IEEE Transactions on Geoscience and Remote Sensing*, vol. 31, no. 3, pp. 606–617, May 1993.

18. Hinton, G. E., "Preface to the Special Issue on Connectionist Symbol Processing," *Artificial Intelligence*, vol. 46, no. 1–2, pp. 1–4, November 1990.

19. Gish, H., "A Probabilistic Approach to the Understanding and Training of Neural Network Classifiers," *Proceedings of 1990 IEEE International Conference on Acoustic, Speech, and Signal Processing*, April 3–6, 1990, pp. 1361–1364.

20. Baum, E. B., and D. Haussler, "What Size Network Gives Valid Generalization," *Neural Computation*, vol. 1, pp. 151–160, 1989.

21. Specht, D. F., "Probabilistic Neural Networks," *Neural Networks,* vol. 3, pp. 109–118, 1990.

22. Fukunaga, K., *Introduction to Statistical Pattern Recognition,* 2d ed., Academic Press, New York, 1990, chap. 6.

23. Serpico, S. B., and F. Roli, "Classification of Multisensor Remote-Sensing Images by Structured Neural Networks," *IEEE Transactions on Geoscience and Remote Sensing*, vol. 33, no. 3, pp. 562–578, May 1995.

CHAPTER 16

NEURAL NETWORKS FOR HANDWRITTEN CHARACTER RECOGNITION

Qiang Gan
Department of Biomedical Engineering,
Southeast University, Nanjing, China

Ching Y. Suen
Centre for Pattern Recognition and Machine Intelligence
(CENPARMI), Concordia University, Montreal, Canada

Handwritten character recognition has long been one of the most interesting and successful research areas in pattern recognition and machine intelligence. Neural networks, used not only as classifiers but also as feature extractors, are making the dream of real industrial applications of unconstrained handwritten character recognition come true in the near future. In this chapter, the contents are limited to off-line recognition, because the neural network approach to on-line recognition has not been shown to be particularly advantageous over the conventional methods. After the state of the art in off-line recognition of handwritten characters is reviewed, the back propagation neural network for handwritten character recognition is presented. The important factors that influence its generalizability, such as the architecture, activation function, and probability distribution of weight values, are discussed. The best performance on some commonly used databases is given to demonstrate its power in recognizing handwritten characters. Although the back propagation neural network is the most successful one for pattern recognition, several other kinds of neural networks have been applied to handwritten character recognition with promising properties. The progress in handwritten character recognition made by Neocognitron, associative memory networks, and the ART network is introduced. A comparison of the performance of neural networks with other classifiers is given, and some problems yet to be solved in this field are pointed out.

16.1 STATE OF THE ART IN OFF-LINE RECOGNITION OF HANDWRITTEN CHARACTERS

Many *optical character recognition* (*OCR*) systems have been developed during the last two decades, but more work is still required before human performance can be matched in a meaningful way. The key to high recognition performance is the ability to detect and utilize the distinctive features of the characters, but these features are extremely difficult to define. Although there exist a number of methods for feature extraction and classification, it is probably safe to say that no simple scheme is likely to satisfy the requirements in real industrial applications. Since each method has its own strengths and weaknesses, it can be deduced that performance can be improved significantly by combining several classifiers. A neural network is not only an excellent feature extractor and classifier, but also a good combiner. It is also a learnable recognizer with high adaptability in realistic applications.

16.1.1 Conventional Methods Based on Explicitly Defined Feature Extraction

Although some underlying factors which determine the true identity of handwritten characters remain untractable by conventional methods of feature extraction, measurable and visible features such as the density of points, moments, mathematical transforms, crossing counts, loops, endpoints, junctions, arcs, concavities, and convexities can lead to a good classification.

The conventional pattern recognition process can be modeled by the simple sequence of operations: preprocessing, feature extraction, and classification. Most important is feature selection and extraction on which most efforts of the traditional methods have been focused. Features can be roughly divided into two types: statistical and structural. In general, structural features include more information of characters, and the structural approach often outperforms the statistical one. However, structural features are difficult to define and sensitive to different data sets. In other words, one set of features that leads to high performance on a certain database may fail to give good results on another database. As far as a simple scheme is concerned, among a lot of methods proposed so far for numeral classification, the best efforts have resulted in 90 to 95 percent recognition rates with 1 to 3 percent substitution rates [1].

Combination of multiple algorithms has proved itself to be an effective way of improving the recognition performance. In this approach, the outcomes of several methods are combined according to majority voting or some more complex rules. Here the rationale is to design and combine algorithms to reinforce one another, thus relying on more extensive, diversified, and complementary sources of information concerning the problem to be solved. Kimura and Shridhar [2] combine two algorithms to achieve very good classification of handwritten numerals. Using a training set of 3000 samples and a distinct testing set of 17,394 samples, they examined two parallel and four sequential combinations of the algorithms. Their best results were obtained with a parallel combination: recognition rates of 96.23, 95.08, and 89.55 percent were achieved with corresponding substitution rates of 0.25, 0.13, and 0.07 percent, respectively. A multiexpert system for recognizing totally unconstrained handwritten numerals has been developed by the research team at CENPARMI of Concordia University [3]. It consists of four methods labeled as experts, all of which have achieved high recognition rates and low substitution rates. Three are based on features extracted from skeletons of numerals, and one makes use of features from contours. All these algorithms are trained on 4000 samples from the CENPARMI database of the U.S. Zip codes and are tested on another separate set of 2000 digits in the same database. A recognition rate of 93.05 with 6.95 percent rejection and 0.0 percent substitution has been achieved by combining the four algorithms. This is the best result ever reported in the literature.

The research is continuing on several fronts, aimed at stretching the limits and improving the performance of the traditional handwriting recognition approaches. They may be summarized as follows: improving feature extraction, discovering the intrinsic properties of characters, incorporating human knowledge into the recognition system, etc. It seems very hard to make breakthroughs in the above aspects in the near future. On the other hand, neural networks, with a lot of novel characteristics, are becoming more and more attractive in their applications to handwritten character recognition.

16.1.2 Neural Network Approach

Recently, the application of neural networks to recognize characters and other types of patterns has resurfaced, because neural networks can overcome some deficiencies of the conventional pattern recognition methods and have achieved excellent results. As indicated above, feature extraction is crucial to pattern classification. However, the traditional feature extractor usually contains most of the problem-dependent information and is rather specific to the problem at hand. It requires most of the design effort, and it determines the performance to a large extent. The classifier, on the other hand, often incorporates a trainable module and contains little a priori knowledge about the task. Neural network is generally a statistical method. However, a structured neural network can be considered as an approach bridging the gap between purely statistical and purely structural methods. It can be used not only as the feature extractor but also as the classifier. The rules to extract features and the decision functions for classification are determined by learning. They may be very abstract and complex. To design a neural network requires a large set of examples, but not much a priori knowledge about the task.

The back propagation neural network has shown itself to be very successful for handwritten character recognition [4]. With a suitable and adequate number of features as the input, it almost takes the role of a multiple classifier-combiner. The performance can match the best results reported. Even with pixel images as the input, the neural network can extract features and classify them at a remarkable recognition rate. It gives one of the best results among a number of methods proposed.

Although other kinds of neural networks have not outperformed the back propagation neural network in handwriting recognition, they provide new mechanisms and show promising performance, especially in some particular environment. In the following subsections, several typical neural networks for handwritten character recognition are introduced and discussed.

16.2 BACK PROPAGATION NEURAL NETWORK

A back propagation neural network is composed of several layers of interconnected elements, each of which computes a weighted sum of its inputs and transforms it into an output by a nonlinear function. The weights are determined by a learning algorithm called *back propagation* [5]. It has an exceptional ability to learn by examples, but the ability to recognize patterns outside the training set is most interesting. The problem of generalization is discussed first; then the AT&T network proposed by LeCun et al. [6] is introduced.

16.2.1 On the Generalizability

Naturally, the quantity and quality of the training samples are key factors which influence the generalization performance [4, 7]. However, it is often difficult to collect a desirable set of training samples in many applications. There exist some results on the size of a network which gives valid generalization. Baum and Haussler derived an inequality to describe the relationship between the number of training samples and the number of neurons and weights for a feedforward network of linear threshold functions [8]. The result is difficult to use in network design, because the inequality can withstand great changes of its parameters and there are limitations which may conflict with the requirement in practical applications. There has been a neural network design principle that the number of training samples should be approximately 10 times the number of independent weights [9]. According to this principle, a very, very huge training set is often needed. A rule of thumb for obtaining good generalization has also been put forward, which states that one should use the smallest system that will fit the training samples [10]. In our understanding, the smallest system means a neural network with the smallest capacity which is dependent on both the network size and the accuracy of the weights, although smallest network size was often sought in the design of neural network classifiers in some papers. The influence of the activation function on the generalization was seldom studied before, but it is an important part of the neural network and a key factor affecting the performance.

In many realistic applications of pattern classification, people are interested in not so much the raw recognition rate as the number of rejections necessary to reach a given level of accuracy. In general, the rejection criterion of neural network classifiers is based on the difference between the two most-active outputs corresponding to the input pattern. If this value is less than a given threshold, this pattern is rejected. However, the output values of the neural network after training are often relatively high or relatively low. To arrive at a given accuracy, a high threshold value is often needed. As a result, the recognition rate will be reduced considerably. One possible way of preventing this is to modify the activation function.

When a neural network is trained by examples, an important consideration in practice concerns how well the neural network generalizes to patterns that are never seen in the training set. For this purpose, the neural network is expected to be tolerant to small changes in input. Based on this point of view, the following criterion for generalization of the neural network classifier is helpful to the design of a back propagation network [11]:

> Under the constraint that training patterns have to be correctly classified, the smaller the partial derivative of the output with respect to the input, the better the neural network can generalize. In other words, the output should be as insensitive to input changes as possible, but has to be sensitive enough to be able to classify the training patterns correctly.

For simplicity of description, the following formulation of a back propagation neural network classifier is used:

$$y_{ki} = f(x_{ki}) \qquad y_{k0} = 1.0$$

$$x_{ki} = \sum_{j=0}^{M_k - 1} w_{kij} y_{(k-1)j} \tag{16.1}$$

$$y_{1j} = x_j \qquad y_{10} = 1.0$$

$$k = 2, 3, \ldots, K; i = 1, 2, \ldots, M_k$$

The meanings of the variables in the above equations are given in Table 16.1.

TABLE 16.1 Definitions of Variables in Back Propagation Neural Network Classifier

Variable	Description
x_j	Input to neural network
x_{ki}	Input to ith neuron of layer k
y_{ki}	Output of ith neuron of layer k
$f(x)$	Activation function of neurons
w_{kij}	Connection weight between ith neuron of layer k and jth neuron of layer $k-1$
w_{ki0}	Bias of ith neuron of layer k
k	Layer index
K	Number of layers in neural network (including input and output layers)
M_k	Number of neurons in layer k

The partial derivative of the output with respect to the input can be derived as follows:

$$\frac{\partial y_{km}}{\partial x_j} = \frac{\partial y_{Km}}{\partial x_{Km}} \sum_{n=1}^{M_K - 1} w_{Kmn} \frac{\partial y_{(K-1)n}}{\partial x_{(K-1)n}} \sum_{i=1}^{M_K - 2} w_{(K-1)ni} \frac{\partial y_{(K-2)i}}{\partial x_j} \tag{16.2}$$

$$m = 1, 2, \ldots, M_K; j = 1, 2, \ldots, M_1$$

For a three-layer neural network ($K = 3$), we have

$$\frac{\partial y_{3m}}{\partial x_j} = \frac{\partial y_{3m}}{\partial x_{3m}} \sum_{n=1}^{M_2} w_{3mn} \frac{\partial y_{2n}}{\partial x_{2n}} w_{2nj} \tag{16.3}$$

where $\partial y_{3m}/\partial x_{3m}$ and $\partial y_{2n}/\partial x_{2n}$ are the derivatives of the activation functions in the output layer and the hidden layer, respectively. Obviously the generalization performance is affected by many factors, such as the activation function, number of hidden nodes, and probability distribution of the weight values. To achieve high performance, we have to take these factors into account in the design of the network.

16.2.2   AT&T Network

A multilayer locally connected architecture is used in the AT&T neural network, which has several advantages according to the above criterion. It was regarded as one of the most powerful neural network classifiers. Compared with the standard back propagation network, it consists of many fewer free parameters and can extract local features of characters by itself.

A typical network architecture is shown in Fig. 16.1. The network consists of four hidden layers named H1, H2, H3, and H4. Layers H1 and H3 are weight-sharing feature extractors, while H2 and H4 are averaging and subsampling layers. The dimension of the input patterns is 16×16, but the actual input is 28×28 to avoid boundary overlaps. There are 10 units in the output layer. The units in each layer are arranged in two-dimensional planes except for the output layer.

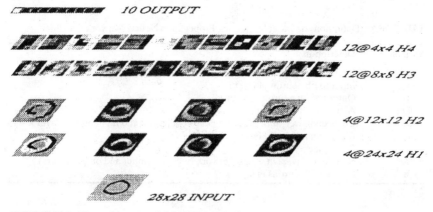

FIGURE 16.1   The architecture of the AT&T network.

Hidden layer H1 is composed of four groups or feature maps of 24×24 units. Each unit takes its inputs from a 5×5 neighborhood on the input plane. The receptive fields of units in this layer overlap. All the units in a map use the same set of 26 weights (including the bias). The units in another map share another set of 26 weights. There are 100 independent weights and 4 independent biases in H1.

Layer H2 consists of four planes of 12×12 units. Each unit takes inputs from 2×2 units on the corresponding plane in H1. The receptive fields do not overlap. All the units in a map have the same weight value and the same bias. Therefore, H2 performs a local averaging and a 2:1 subsampling of H1 in each direction. There are four independent weights and four independent biases in H2.

Layer H3 is composed of 12 feature maps. Each map contains 8×8 units. The connection scheme between H2 and H3 is quite similar to the one between the input plane and H1, but slightly more complicated because each unit receptive field is composed of one or two 5×5 neighborhoods.

Layer H4 plays the same role as layer H2. It consists of 12 planes of 4×4 units. The output units are fully connected to layer H4. In total, there are 4635 units and 98,442 connections but only 2578 independent parameters.

The AT&T network can be trained by the back propagation algorithm, which needs trivial modification because of the weight-sharing technique. After training on a set of 7291 handwritten plus 2549 printed digits, the network was tested on a set of 2007 handwritten digits. Figure 16.2 shows some typical numerals in the database. The result on the testing set is 9 percent rejection for 1 percent error. The architecture described above is a typical one. Actually, it can be modified in many ways, such as the number of layers and feature maps, the means of weight sharing, etc. The performance is expected to be further improved.

FIGURE 16.2   Typical numerals in database used by AT&T network.

16.3   NEOCOGNITRON

Neocognitron is a neural network model for visual pattern recognition proposed by Fukushima in 1980 [12]. It represents one of the crowning achievements of neuro-computing to date. The application of Neocognitron has shown very good results in handwritten character recognition, especially its deformation-invariant property [13].

16.3.1   Structure of Network

Neocognitron is a multistage hierarchical network consisting of several layers of neuronlike cells. There are forward connections between cells in adjoining layers. Some are variable and can be modified by learning. Its architecture for alphanumeric character recognition is shown in Fig. 16.3, where each rectangle represents a two-dimensional array of cells. After the input layer, indicated by U_0, a layer consisting of cells called *S cells* is followed by a layer of cells called *C cells*. These layers of S cells and C cells are arranged alternatively and are denoted by U_{sl} and U_{cl}, respectively, where l represents the stage. The layer of C cells at the highest stage is the output layer. The S cells are capable of extracting features, and the C cells are inserted to allow for position errors in the features. In this functional aspect, the architecture is similar to that of the AT&T network to some extent.

Each layer of S cells or C cells is divided into subgroups called *cell planes*. The cells in each cell plane are arranged in a two-dimensional array. Incidentally, each layer of S cells contains subsidiary inhibitory cells called V cells, which are not shown

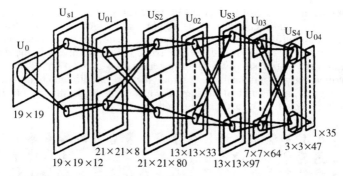

FIGURE 16.3   Architecture of Neocognitron.

explicitly in Fig. 16.3. The number of cells in each layer is designed to decrease with the order of the stage, because the cells in higher stages usually have larger receptive fields and the neighboring cells receive similar signals.

The connections to the cells in a cell plane are constrained to be homogeneous: All the cells in a cell plane have connections of the same spatial distribution, in which only the positions of the preceding cells shift in parallel with the position of the cells in the cell plane. This is an application of a weight-sharing mechanism.

Figure 16.4 illustrates how the cells are connected in the network. Connections converging to feature-extracting S cells are variable and are reinforced by training. An S cell is activated only when a particular feature is presented at a certain position in the input layer. Connections from S cells to C cells are fixed and invariable. Each C cell receives signals from a group of S cells which extract the same feature. A C cell is activated if at least one of these S cells is active. Therefore, the C cell's response results in lower sensitivity to the shift in position of the input pattern. At a lower stage, local features are extracted, which are gradually integrated into more global features at the higher stages. Finally, in the output layer, each C cell integrates all the information of the input pattern and responds to only one specific pattern.

16.3.2   Training Algorithm

Neocognitron can be trained by either supervised learning or unsupervised learning. The former leads to higher recognition performance than the latter, but its training patterns have to be carefully designed. The Neocognitron for handwritten character recognition is trained by supervised learning.

For the sake of clarity and better understanding of the architecture, the mathematical formulation of Neocognitron is briefly introduced as follows: The notations $u_{sl}(\mathbf{n}, k_s)$, $u_{cl}(\mathbf{n}, k_c)$, and $u_{vl}(\mathbf{n})$ are used to represent the outputs of the S cell in layer U_{sl}, the C cell in layer U_{cl}, and the V cell, respectively, where $\mathbf{n}$ is a two-dimensional set of coordinates indicating the position of the cell's receptive-field center in the input layer U_0; k_s is a serial number of the S cell plane changing from 1 to K_{sl}; and k_c is a serial number of the C cell plane changing from 1 to K_{cl}. The outputs of the different cells are calculated according to Eqs. (16.4) to (16.6).

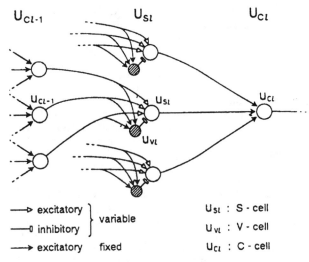

FIGURE 16.4   Connections of cells in Neocognitron.

$$u_{sl}(\mathbf{n}, k_s) = r_l(k_s)\varphi \left\{ \frac{1 + \sum_{k_c = 1}^{K_{cl} - 1} \sum_{\mathbf{v} \in A_l} a_l(\mathbf{v}, k_c, k_s)u_{cl - 1}(\mathbf{n} + \mathbf{v}, k_c)}{1 + r_l(k_s)[1 + r_l(k_s)]^{-1}b_l(k_s)u_{vl}(\mathbf{n})} - 1 \right\} \quad (16.4)$$

$$u_{vl}(\mathbf{n}) = \left\{ \sum_{k_c = 1}^{K_{cl} - 1} \sum_{\mathbf{v} \in A_l} c_l(\mathbf{v}) \left[u_{cl - 1}(\mathbf{n} + \mathbf{v}, k_c) \right]^2 \right\}^{1/2} \quad (16.5)$$

$$u_{cl}(\mathbf{n}, k_c) = \psi \left[\sum_{k_s = 1}^{K_{sl}} j_l(k_s, k_c) \sum_{\mathbf{v} \in D_l} d_l(\mathbf{v})u_{sl}(\mathbf{n} + \mathbf{v}, k_s) \right] \quad (16.6)$$

where $\varphi(x) = x$ (if $x \geq 0$) or $\varphi(x) = 0$ (if $x < 0$) and $\psi(x) = \varphi(x)/[1 + \varphi(x)]$. And A_l and D_l denote the receptive-field areas of S cells and C cells, respectively. In Fig. 16.3, the size of A_l, D_l, and D_4 is 3×3; A_2 to A_4 and D_3 is 5×5; and D_2 is 7×7. Also $r_l(k_s)$ is a positive parameter which determines the efficiency of the inhibitory input to the S cell and controls the selectivity in feature extraction. Here $j_l(k_c, k_s)$ represents the condition under which the outputs of several S cell planes are joined and connected to a single C cell plane. And $a_l(\mathbf{v}, k_c, k_s)$ and $b_l(k_s)$ are the weights of the variable excitatory and inhibitory connections, respectively. Also $c_l(\mathbf{v})$ and $d_l(\mathbf{v})$ denote the fixed excitatory connection weights, which are positive and monotonically decreasing functions of $\mathbf{v}$.

The training process is performed step by step from the lower stages to the higher stages, and all the stages are trained with the same procedure. The training patterns for different layers are different, but all the training patterns enter the input layer. The lower layers respond to them and then provide inputs to the layer currently being trained. With supervised learning, the seed cells are manually selected and marked in the training patterns. At the beginning, all the variable connection weights are set to zero. During the training, a_l ($\mathbf{v}$, k_c, k_s) and b_l (k_s) are modified according to the following equations:

$$\Delta a_l(\mathbf{v}, k_c, k_s^*) = q_l c_l(\mathbf{v}) \, u_{c\,l\,-\,1}(\mathbf{n}^* + \mathbf{v}, k_c) \tag{16.7}$$

$$\Delta b_l(k_s^*) = q_l u_{v\,l}(\mathbf{n}^*) \tag{16.8}$$

where q_l is a positive constant affecting the speed of reinforcement and the asterisk represents a seed cell selected. It is obvious that the amount of reinforcement of each connection weight to the seed cell is proportional to the intensity of the response of the cell from which the relevant connection is leading. According to the convention of homogeneous connection in a cell plane, other cells in the same cell plane have the same set of connection weights as the seed cell. Now we are concerned about how to design the training patterns to achieve good results. It should be carefully considered. Readers can find an example set of the training patterns used by Fukushima for alphanumeric character recognition in Ref. 13.

The training takes a very short time compared with the back propagation algorithm, but it often takes a couple of seconds to recognize a character on a Sun Sparc station. This would be a major weakness of Neocognitron in industrial applications. Figure 16.5 illustrates some examples of deformed input patterns which Neocognitron can recognize correctly. It is clear that Neocognitron is insensitive to scale change, shift in position, distortion, and noise. In recent years, Neocognitron has been further improved and applied to both recognition and segmentation of cursive handwriting [14].

16.4   ASSOCIATIVE MEMORY NETWORKS

Neural networks based on associative learning have been widely applied to pattern recognition. There were attempts to utilize Hopfield-type neural networks for handwritten character recognition [15], but no remarkable results were obtained in large-scale applications. Dystal (*d*ynamically *st*able *a*ssociative *l*earning) is an artificial neural network based on features of neurobiological learning and memory, which has been shown to be very competitive in handwriting recognition [16].

Dystal is composed of output neuronal elements and patches (similar to the bottom-up memories or clusters in the ART network). The network has separate input pathways for the input pattern called *CS* (conditioned *stimulus*) inputs and expected output called *UCS* (*unconditioned stimulus*) inputs. Each output neuronal element is connected through patches to a subset of the CS inputs, called the *receptive field*, and one of the UCS inputs. A patch consists of (1) a patch vector which is the average value of similar CS input patterns, (2) the expected value of the UCS associated with that CS, and (3) a weight that reflects the frequency of utilization of the patch. Each patch belongs to a single-output neuronal element, and every patch of an output neuronal element is connected to the same subset of CS inputs. The subsets of the CS inputs are often determined by a random mechanism.

When a CS pattern is input, the output of a neuronal element equals the product of the similarity between the CS and the most similar patch and the expected value of the UCS of the patch. All the values of the CS and UCS inputs and the neuronal outputs are normalized to the range between −0.5 and 0.5. In practice, if the value of only one of the output elements is greater than zero, then the input pattern is classified (may be correct or incorrect); otherwise it is rejected.

FIGURE 16.5 Some examples of deformed patterns which Neocognitron recognizes correctly

All the patterns that Dystal learns are collectively stored in its entire set of patches. To train Dystal is to create or modify patches. Prior to training, no patch exists. Training is initiated by the presentation of a CS pattern and the associated UCS input. Each output neuronal element compares the portion of the CS pattern within its receptive field to any preexisting patches based on a certain similarity measure. Suppose there are Q patches, represented by $P^j, j = 1, 2, \ldots, Q$. The similarity between the CS input I and the patch P^j is calculated as follows:

$$S^j = \text{corr}(P^j, I) = \frac{\sum_i (P_i^j - \text{MP}^j)(I_i - \text{MI})}{\sqrt{\sum_i (P_i^j - \text{MP}^j)^2 \sum_i (I_i - \text{MI})^2}} \qquad (16.9)$$

where P_i^j is the value of the ith element of the jth patch vector; MP^j is the mean value of the elements of patch P^j; I_i is the value of the ith element of the CS input; and MI is the mean value of the elements of the CS input. The UCS input is also compared with the expected values of the UCS in the preexisting patches. Among those patches with matching UCS expected values, a patch P^m with the greatest similarity S^m is selected. In the subsequent step, either a new patch is created or an existing patch is updated, depending on the value of S^m. In general, if S^m is less than a predefined threshold T_c, then the incoming CS pattern is not sufficiently similar to an existing patch and a new patch is created. Otherwise, all three parts of patch P^m are modified according to the following rules:

$$P_i^m(t) = \frac{(t-1)P_i^m(t-1) + I_i}{t} \tag{16.10}$$

$$U^m(t) = \frac{(t-1)U^m(t-1) + \text{UCS}(t)}{t} \tag{16.11}$$

$$W^m(t) = a[1 - W^m(t-1)] + W^m(t-1) \tag{16.12}$$

$$W^k(t) = (1-b)W^k(t-1) \qquad k \neq m \tag{16.13}$$

where t is the number of patterns that have activated the patch; $P_i^m(0) = U^m(0) = W^m(0) = 0$; a is the learning increment; and b is the learning decrement. As t increases, the effect that a novel CS input pattern has on the patch decreases. Therefore, patch modification eventually ceases for stationary distributions of the inputs. Note that, unlike other networks, the weights of Dystal are not used in the computation of the output of a neuronal element. They are used in patch merging and patch deletion, which reduce the number of existing patches. Readers can find how to do that in Ref. 16.

The testing is done in almost the same way as the training. During testing, the CS input patterns are presented alone without a UCS input pattern. This comprises three steps: computation of the similarities between the CS input pattern and the patches, selection of a patch with the maximum similarity, and the product of the maximum similarity and the expected value of the UCS for that patch.

Dystal has been tested on handwritten character recognition problems. The database used in the experiment consists of 10,964 handwritten ZIP code digits, which is divided into a training set of 2000 digits and a testing set of 8964 digits. The digits are size-normalized to 22×16 pixel images. Each training pattern is presented only once, and the order of pattern presentation is random. The testing results in a 97.8 percent accuracy with 89.1 percent of testing patterns classified. Although Dystal has not outperformed the back propagation network, it has a number of desirable properties, including a theoretical storage capacity of b^n nonorthogonal memories, where b is the number of discrete values and n is the number of output neurons; a computational complexity of $O(N)$; monotonic convergence in the training; etc.

16.5 ART NETWORK

In the neural networks mentioned above, the supervised learning mechanism is applied. During training, a desired output pattern is required, or a seed cell should be manually identified when an input pattern is presented to the network. The network can carry out recognition only after the training is finished. The *adaptive resonance theory* (ART) network makes use of unsupervised learning algorithm, showing new properties such as that both training and recognition take place at the same time. There are three generations of ART networks developed to date, called *ART-1, ART-2,* and *ART-3,* respectively. The ART-1 network allows for two-value inputs only. ART-2 can handle real-number inputs. In ART-3, a biochemical reaction-diffusion process is introduced for the purpose of robustness. In this subsection, we present the application of the ART-2 network in handwritten character recognition [17–19].

ART-2 consists of two functionally complementary subsystems, the attentional subsystem and the orienting subsystem. It is able to classify an input pattern, either familiar or unfamiliar, into one of a number of categories depending on a certain similarity measure between the pattern and the stored classes, which is automatically generated. If an input pattern matches one of the stored classes within a pre-specified tolerance, it will be regarded as a familiar pattern. The attentional subsystem will adjust the stored class to make it more like the input pattern. Otherwise, the orienting subsystem will create a new category by storing the input pattern. This process is similar to that of Dystal, but the matching mechanism and the storage format are different. In addition, it is not necessary to have expected output patterns corresponding to input patterns in training.

Let $\mathbf{X} = \{x_j, j = 1, 2, \ldots, N\}$ and $\mathbf{Y} = \{y_i, i = 1, 2, \ldots, M\}$ be the input and output vectors of the network respectively. Also N is the dimension of the input patterns, and M is the number of total categories in the output layer. The dynamics of the network can be mathematically described as follows:

$$
y_i = \begin{cases} 1 & \text{if } i = I \\ 0 & \text{otherwise} \end{cases} \tag{16.14}
$$

$$
t_I = \max\{t_i, i = 1, 2, \ldots, M\} \tag{16.15}
$$

$$
t_i = \sum_{j=1}^{N} w_{ij} p_j \tag{16.16}
$$

$$
p_j = u_j + d w'_{jI} \tag{16.17}
$$

$$
u_j = \frac{v_j}{e + |\mathbf{V}|} \tag{16.18}
$$

$$
v_j = f(q_j) + b f(s_j) \tag{16.19}
$$

$$
s_j = \frac{p_j}{e + |\mathbf{P}|} \tag{16.20}
$$

$$
q_j = \frac{z_j}{e + |\mathbf{Z}|} \tag{16.21}
$$

$$
z_j = x_j + a u_j \tag{16.22}
$$

$$
i = 1, 2, \ldots, M; j = 1, 2, \ldots, N
$$

where $f(x) = x$ if $x > \theta$ or $f(x) = 0$ if $0 \le x \le \theta$; I represents the index of the output element which maximally corresponds to the input pattern; $|\mathbf{V}|$, $|\mathbf{P}|$, and $|\mathbf{Z}|$ are the norms of vectors $\mathbf{V} = \{v_j, j = 1, 2, \ldots, N\}$, $\mathbf{P} = \{p_j, j = 1, 2, \ldots, N\}$, and $\mathbf{Z} = \{z_j, j = 1, 2, \ldots, N\}$, respectively; $a, b, d, e,$ and θ are parameters; and w_{ij} and w'_{ji} are bottom-up and top-down connection weights, respectively. Variables $p_j, u_j, v_j, s_j, q_j,$ and z_j, which describe positive feedbacks, normalizations, and nonlinear transforms in the input layer, will stabilize before they can be transmitted to the output layer, represented by t_i and y_i. When they are stabilized, $\mathbf{U} = \{u_j, j = 1, 2, \ldots, N\}$ denotes the bottom-up pattern, and $\mathbf{P}$ is the top-down template selected. The connection weights will be updated or initialized depending on whether the input pattern is familiar or unfamiliar, i.e., whether $\mathbf{U}$ and $\mathbf{P}$ are satisfactorily matched or not. We use the following vector to describe the similarity between $\mathbf{U}$ and $\mathbf{P}$:

$$\mathbf{R} = \frac{\mathbf{U} + c\mathbf{P}}{e + |\mathbf{U}| + c|\mathbf{P}|} \tag{16.23}$$

where c is a parameter. If $|\mathbf{R}| > \rho$, a vigilance parameter taking values between 0 and 1, the connection weights are updated according to the following rules. Otherwise, a new category is created in the output layer, and its connection weights are initialized.

$$w_{ij}(k+1) = \begin{cases} w_{ij}(k) + d[p_j(k) - w_{ij}(k)] & \text{if } i = I \\ w_{ij}(k) & \text{otherwise} \end{cases} \tag{16.24}$$

$$w'_{ji}(k+1) = \begin{cases} w'_{ji}(k) + d[p_j(k) - w'_{ji}(k)] & \text{if } i = I \\ w'_{ji}(k) & \text{otherwise} \end{cases} \tag{16.25}$$

In general, the initial values are set to $w_{ij}(0) = 1/\sqrt{M}$ and $w'_{ji}(0) = 0$.

ART-2 can be used for handwritten numeral and Chinese character recognition. In the network design, parameters a, b, c, d, e, θ, and ρ are determined through a lot of experiments. Although ART-2 itself has the ability to extract features, it is favorable to have feature inputs as in Refs. 18 and 19. Using a database of 3755 training Chinese characters and 7510 testing patterns, ART-2 obtained a recognition rate of 92 percent in classifying the testing patterns. To sufficiently confirm the power of the ART network in handwritten character recognition, more experimental results are expected.

16.6 CONCLUSION

It is often difficult to compare different approaches in handwritten character recognition, because the results in the literature are based on different databases, and even on the same database the results are not sufficiently convincing owing to the lack of a standard database. However, there is a lot of evidence which shows that neural networks are competitive among various methods of handwriting recognition and even perform better than the conventional approaches [4, 20, 21]. As far as a single method is concerned, the recognition rate of the neural network can match that of any other method, and neural networks often have the advantages of high recognition rate and low memory requirement. What is more, the hard labor to search for features in a data set can be avoided in the neural network classifier design. In neural networks, feature extraction and classification are interactive. In general, feature extraction is based on a weight-sharing mechanism or some kind of similarity measure. The features extracted by neural networks may be both structural and statistical, and it is not necessary to define them clearly. Needless to say, the neural network is a complementary approach of the traditional methods based on explicitly defined feature extraction. Very rapid progress is being made in the neural network area, and various new neural network models are emerging. It can be expected that neural networks will take a very important role in putting the handwritten character recognition technology into real industrial applications on a large scale.

REFERENCES

1. Suen, C. Y., R. Legault, C. Nadal, M. Cheriet, and L. Lam, "Building a New Generation of Handwriting Recognition Systems," *Pattern Recognition Letters,* **14:** 303–315, 1993.

2. Kimura, F., and M. Shridhar, "Handwritten Numerical Recognition Based on Multiple Algorithms," *Pattern Recognition Letters,* **24**(10): 969–983, 1991.

3. Suen, C. Y., C. Nadal, R. Legault, T. A. Mai, and L. Lam, "Computer Recognition of Unconstrained Handwritten Numerals," *Proceedings of the IEEE,* **80**(7): 1162–1180, 1992.

4. Martin, J. A., and J. A. Pittman, "Recognizing Hand-Printed Letters and Digits Using Back Propagation Learning," *Neural Computation,* **3:** 258–267, 1991.

5. Rumelhart, D. E., G. E. Hinton, and R. J. Williams, "Learning Internal Representations by Error Propagation," in *Parallel Distributed Processing: Explorations in the Microstructure of Cognition,* vol. 1, Bradford Books, Cambridge, MA, 1986, pp. 318–362.

6. LeCun, Y., et al., "Constrained Neural Network for Unconstrained Handwritten Digit Recognition," *Proceedings of the International Workshop on Frontiers in Handwriting Recognition,* Montreal, 1990, pp. 145–152.

7. Kressel, U. H.-G., "Impact of the Learning Set Size in Handwritten Digit Recognition," *Proceedings of the International Conference on Artificial Neural Networks,* vol. 2, Espoo, Finland, 1991, pp. 1685–1689.

8. Baum, E. B., and D. Haussler, "What Size Net Gives Valid Generalization?" *Neural Computation,* **1:** 151–160, 1989.

9. Hush, D. R., and B. G. Horne, "Progress in Supervised Neural Networks: What's New Since Lippmann?" *IEEE Signal Processing Magazine,* **10**(1): 8–39, 1993.

10. Reed, R., "Pruning Algorithms—A Survey," *IEEE Transactions on Neural Networks,* **4:** 740–747, 1993.

11. Gan, Q., and C. Y. Suen, "A Neural Network Classifier with Valid Generalization Performance," *Journal of Southeast University,* **24**(4): 1–6, 1994.

12. Fukushima, K., "Neocognitron: A Self-Organizing Neural Network Model for a Mechanism of Pattern Recognition Unaffected by Shift in Position," *Biology Cybernetics,* **36**(4): 193–202, 1980.

13. Fukushima, K., and N. Wake, "Handwritten Alphanumeric Character Recognition by the Neocognitron," *IEEE Transactions on Neural Networks,* **2**(3): 355–365, 1991.

14. Fukushima, K., and T. Imagawa, "Recognition and Segmentation of Connected Characters with Selective Attention," *Neural Networks,* **6:** 33–41, 1993.

15. Zhang, M., "A Study on Associative Memory Classifier and Its Application in Character Recognition," Ph.D. thesis, Concordia University, Montreal, Canada, 1992.

16. Blackwell, K. T., T. P. Vogl, S. D. Hyman, G. S. Barbour, and D. L. Alkon, "A New Approach to Hand-written Character Recognition Letters," *Pattern Recognition,* **25**(6): 655–666, 1992.

17. Carpenter, G. A., and S. Grossberg, "ART 2: Self-Organization of Stable Category Recognition Codes of Analog Input Pattern," *Applied Optics,* **26**(23): 4919–4930, 1987.

18. Carpenter, G. A., and S. Grossberg, "Comparative Performance Measures of Fuzzy ARTMAP, Learned Vector Quantization, and Backpropagation for Handwritten Charac-

ter Recognition," *Proceedings of International Joint Conference on Neural Networks '92,* Baltimore, MD, vol. 1, 1992, pp. 794–799.

19. Gan, K. W., and K. T. Lua, "Chinese Character Classification Using an Adaptive Resonance Network," *Pattern Recognition Letters,* **25**(8): 877–882, 1992.

20. Lee, Y., "Handwritten Digit Recognition Using *K* Nearest-Neighbor, Radial Basis Function and Back Propagation Neural Nets," *Neural Computation,* **3:** 440–449, 1991.

21. English, T. M., M. P. Gomez-Gil, and W. J. B. Oldham, "A Comparison of Neural Network and Nearest-Neighbor Classifiers of Handwritten Lower-case Letters," *Proceedings of the IEEE ICNN,* New York, vol. 3, 1993, pp. 1618–1621.

CHAPTER 17
NEURAL NETWORKS FOR BROADCAST SCHEDULING IN TELECOMMUNICATIONS

Nirwan Ansari
Gangsheng Wang
Center for Communications and Signal Processing
New Jersey Institute of Technology, Newark

17.1 NEURAL NETWORKS IN TELECOMMUNICATIONS—AN OVERVIEW

A neural network consists of a large number of simple, identical, and interconnected processing elements called *neurons,* operating in parallel. The synaptic interconnection strength from neuron i to neuron j is determined by a weight, w_{ij}. The computational function of a neural network is primarily determined by the connection topology among the neurons, by the connection strengths, and the type of processing performed in each neuron. A properly constructed neural network can implement high-level functions, such as classification and constrained optimization. One of the reasons that neural networks have aroused considerable interest is their parallelism. Since a neural network has a highly interconnected structure and all of the neurons operate in parallel, the information processing can be widely distributed across the whole structure. The parallel structure provides high-speed computation and robustness.

Neural networks have been successfully applied to telecommunications in recent years. In the telecommunications area, many complicated optimization and adaptive control problems arise as the demand and sophistication of the area grows. Conventional strategies may no longer meet the new challenges. One of the applications of neural networks in telecommunications is regression and classification, where the outputs are estimated from a set of input variables. The estimation criterion is established in such a way that the difference between the estimated output pattern and the desired one is minimized. This is done by learning algorithms which modify the weights in the neural network so as to minimize the difference. In Ref. 1, Hiramatsu presents a neural network approach to the asynchronous transfer mode (ATM) traffic control in which the backpropagation neural network is applied to adaptively control call admission and link capacity. Hiramatsu uses backpropagation to learn the relationship between the offered traffic and the quality of service (QOS) by on-line training. The adaptability provided by the neural network is very useful to optimize the overall ATM traffic control system. In Ref. 2, Goodman and Ambrose describe the application of learning algorithms to communication network management. Yang [3] applies the error backpropagation training algorithm to an echo canceller which provides the parallel distributed echo cancellation for digital transmission systems. Other learning algorithms on channel equalization, image quantization, and network routing can be found in Refs. 4 to 8. Another application of neural networks in telecommunications is constrained optimization, where the problem is to find a solution that satisfies a set of constraints while minimizing cost. For this type of problem, neural networks provide a parallel method of quickly searching the space of possible solutions. In Ref. 9, Goudreau and Giles propose a neural network routing scheme to establish point-to-point communication in an interconnection network. The problem is posed as a constrained optimization problem, and is solved by a Hopfield net. Amin and Gell [10] apply the Hopfield dynamic model to the switching problem in telecommunications. Other constrained optimization approaches based on the Hopfield model are given in Refs. 11 to 13. The Hopfield model is generally used to solve optimization problems, but it may get stuck in a local minimum. At this point, simulated annealing (SA) provides an effective way to escape from local minima. SA is an extension of a local search, and it allows state transitions from a state with lower cost to one with higher cost with a certain probability. Thus, getting stuck in local minima may be avoided in the search for optimal solutions. In Ref. 14, Ansari demonstrates how to manage traffic and increase the throughput of a circuit switched satellite communication network by simulated annealing and self-organization. The two neural networks are used to find the global optimal map configurations. In Ref. 15, Duque-Antón et al. address the problem of channel assignment by simulated annealing. The objective is to find interference-free channel assignments which yield the maximum channel utilization.

Neural networks have been widely used in telecommunications. In constrained optimization, there is a class of difficult problems known as NP-complete problems, where no polynomial algorithms have been found to search for the optimal solutions. Neural networks have provided an alternative way to solve this class of optimization problems. In this chapter, we will present the mean field annealing approach to an NP-complete problem, and the broadcast scheduling problem in packet radio networks.

17.2 BROADCAST SCHEDULING
IN TDMA SYSTEMS

Packet radio (PR) is a technology that applies the packet switching technique to the broadcast radio environment. In a PR network, each station is equipped with a transmitter/receiver and a control unit. Stations communicate with each other via broadcast radio. The control unit performs the packet switching functions. In order to provide communication over a wide geographic area, the multihop store-and-forward broadcast packet radio network has been proposed. In this type of network, connectivity between neighboring stations is established. All stations employ omni-directional antennas and share a high-speed radio channel. When a station is intended to transmit, it broadcasts through its antenna to all of its neighboring stations. Each neighboring station receives the transmission and absorbs the packets addressed to it. If a station receives a packet which is not designated to it, it will store the packet in the buffer and send it out whenever channel access is allocated to this station. Therefore, for any two distant stations where direct connectivity does not exist, the intermediate stations act as repeaters and perform store-and-forward functions. The typical example of the multihop store-and-forward packet radio network is the PRNET sponsored by the Advanced Research Projects Agency (ARPA) [16]. It permits mobile communication over a wide geographic area, provides efficient multiaccess for bursty-type traffic, allows coexistence with different systems in the same frequency band, and offers antijam protection. In a multihop PR network, since a single channel (usually broadband) is shared by all users, the transmission for each station must be scheduled to avoid any collision or interference. The single radio channel can then be shared by all stations in both time and space domains. A multiaccess protocol, namely, spatial time-division multiple access (TDMA), can be used to schedule conflict-free transmission [17].

In the spatial TDMA network, time is divided into frames which consist of fixed-length time slots. Any two stations that may collide or interfere with each other must be scheduled to transmit at different time slots, while stations some distance away may be arranged to transmit at the same time slots without causing interference. Since the primary objective of the PR network is to provide high throughput with low delay, a scheduling scheme must provide a schedule which can achieve maximum transmissions as well as lower delay. For a fixed-topology PR network in which locations of stations are fixed, the problem is to schedule a frame in which each station transmits at least once. Additional transmissions can be added into the frame if the addition does not cause any collision. The scheduled frame repeats in the time domain. The optimal schedule is the frame pattern that has the minimum length (the number of time slots in a frame) and provides the maximum number of collision-free transmissions. Such a scheduling problem has been shown to be NP-complete, which implies that a good algorithm rarely exists. In this chapter, an approximation algorithm based on mean field annealing (MFA) is presented to solve the scheduling problem. In Sec. 17.3, the scheduling problem is stated. The MFA theory is reviewed in Sec. 17.4. In Sec. 17.5, MFA is applied to solving the optimal scheduling problem. Numerical examples are given and the resulting performance is evaluated in Sec. 17.6. Conclusions are made in the last section.

17.3 PROBLEM FORMULATION

A PR network can be represented by a graph $G = (V,E)$, where the vertices in V are network stations and E is a set of edges. We assume that the network has a fixed topology. The total traffic passing through station i consists of packets received from other stations which will be routed through station i and the packets from the terminals attached to it. The spatial TDMA protocol is adopted in which a single wideband channel is shared by all stations of the network. Time is divided into unit-length slots. Each frame consists of a fixed number of time slots. Data can be transmitted in successive frames. The transmission time of stations in a frame is scheduled to avoid any collision. We are concerned with the fixed assignment of transmission for stations in a frame. Once the optimal frame pattern (the order of transmissions) is determined, the frame is repeated in the time axis. Without loss of generality, we assume that a time slot is equal in length to the amount of time for a station to transmit one packet over the channel. We also assume that all stations have the same transmission range R and they are synchronized. Zero capture is assumed, i.e., when some stations receive two or more overlapping packets, regardless of the difference of received signal power between the stations, collision occurs and all of the packets are destroyed. For any two stations $i, i' \in V$, if the distance between them is less than R, they can receive the packets transmitted from each other. Therefore, there exists an undirected edge $e = (i,i') \in E$ incident to station i and i', and the two stations are one hop apart. If $(i,i') \notin E$ and there is an intermediate station j such that $(i,j) \in E$ and $(i',j) \in E$, then station i and i' are two hops apart. The topology of a PR network can be described by an $(N \times N)$ symmetric binary matrix C, where $N = |V|$ is the number of stations in the network. The matrix $C = [c_{ij}]$ $(i, j = 1, \ldots, N)$, also known as the *connectivity matrix*, is defined by

$$
c_{ij} = \begin{cases} 1 & \text{if } (i,j) \in E \text{ and } i \neq j \\ 0 & \text{otherwise} \end{cases} \tag{17.1}
$$

To ensure that a packet is correctly received in a station, the following constraints must be satisfied:

1. A station cannot be in both the transmission and reception status simultaneously; i.e., if $(i,i') \in E$, station i and i' must be scheduled to transmit in different time slots.

2. A station is not allowed to receive two or more transmissions simultaneously; i.e., if $(i, j) \in E$, $(j, k) \in E$, but $(i, k) \notin E$, station i and k must transmit in different time slots in order to avoid collision in station j.

In short, a station and its one-hop or two-hop neighboring stations must be scheduled to transmit in different time slots.

We can form a new $(N \times N)$ matrix called the *compatibility matrix* $F = [f_{ij}]$ from matrix C, where

$$
f_{ij} = \begin{cases} 1 & \text{if stations } i \text{ and } j \text{ are one hop or two hops apart} \\ 0 & \text{otherwise} \end{cases} \tag{17.2}
$$

Note that F is symmetric $(f_{ij} = f_{ji})$ and $f_{ii} = 0$. Therefore, for any two stations i and j, if $f_{ij} = 0$, both stations can transmit in the same slot with no collision. We assume that each frame consists of M time slots. In a frame, each station must be scheduled to transmit at least once (one time slot). Additional transmissions can be arranged provided that the addition does not cause collision. We use an $(M \times N)$ matrix $S = [s_{ij}]$ to express a transmission schedule, where

$$
s_{ij} = \begin{cases} 1 & \text{if station } j \text{ transmits at the } i\text{th slot in a frame} \\ 0 & \text{otherwise} \end{cases} \tag{17.3}
$$

Let ρ_k be the channel utilization for station k. Then

$$
\rho_k = \frac{\text{number of transmission slots assigned to station } k}{\text{frame length}} = \frac{\sum_{i=1}^{M} s_{ik}}{M} \tag{17.4}
$$

The channel utilization for the whole network, ρ, is given by

$$
\rho = \frac{1}{N} \sum_{j=1}^{N} \rho_j = \frac{1}{NM} \sum_{i=1}^{M} \sum_{j=1}^{N} s_{ij} \tag{17.5}
$$

The objective of scheduling transmission in a frame is to resolve transmission collision. An optimal schedule is the one which has the minimum frame length and provides the maximum channel utilization.

Denote S' as a set of collision-free schedules where $S' = \{S^1, \ldots, S^N\}$, and each feasible schedule S^i is an $M \times N$ matrix defined by Eq. (17.3). Define ρ_{S^i} as the channel utilization achieved by schedule S^i. Therefore, the optimal scheduling problem is described as follows:

Find the optimal schedule $S^{\text{opt}} \in S'$ so that

1. It has the minimum frame length M.

2. It satisfies the constraints

$$\sum_{i=1}^{M} s_{ij}^{\text{opt}} \geq 1 \qquad (j = 1, 2, \ldots, N), \tag{17.6}$$

and

$$\sum_{k=1}^{M} \sum_{i=1}^{N} \sum_{j=1}^{N} f_{ij} s_{ki}^{\text{opt}} s_{kj}^{\text{opt}} = 0 \tag{17.7}$$

3. It yields the maximum channel utilization; i.e.,

$$\rho_{S^{\text{opt}}} = \max_{S^i \in S'} \rho_{S^i} \tag{17.8}$$

For a given M and N, there are 2^{MN} schedule configurations. An exhaustive search for the optimal schedules is prohibitive when M and N get larger. It has been shown that the scheduling problem falls into the class of difficult optimization problems known as NP-complete [18, 19]. For an NP-complete optimization problem, the computational complexity becomes intractable as the problem size gets larger. The reason for this difficulty is that the computational time grows exponentially with the problem size. Therefore, it is suggested that some approximation algorithms should be used for NP-complete problems. An efficient algorithm should be the one that can find the suboptimal solutions which are close to the best and involve much less computational effort. Since neural networks have shown great promise in solving such optimization problems, we will present an efficient approximation algorithm based on neural networks in Sec. 17.5.

For a given PR network, the minimum frame length depends on the topology of the network and is generally unknown. However, a tight lower bound for a frame length can be found analytically, thus allowing one to estimate the minimum required frame length.

By defining the degree of a vertex i as the number of edges incident to it and denoting the degree as $\deg(i)$, we have the following lemma:

Lemma 17.1.   The frame length M satisfies

$$M \geq X(G) + 1 \tag{17.9}$$

where

$$X(G) = \max_{\forall i \in V} \deg(i) \tag{17.10}$$

Proof: It is obvious that $\deg(i)$ equals the number of one-hop neighbors of station i. Denote $B(i)$ as the set of one-hop neighbors of station i. For any two stations $j, j' \in B(i)$, since $c_{ij} = 1$ and $c_{ij'} = 1$, station j and j' are one-hop neighbors if $c_{jj'} = 1$ and two-hop neighbors if $c_{jj'} = 0$. According to the constraints mentioned above, station i and all its $\deg(i)$ one-hop neighbors must be arranged to transmit in different distinct time slots in order to obtain collision-free transmissions. Any two stations $j, j' \in B(i)$ cannot transmit in the same slot. Therefore, the required number of time slots for transmission for station i and its one-hop neighbors is $\deg(i) + 1$, and the least required number of time slots of a frame for the network, $\Delta(G)$, is given by

$$\Delta(G) = X(G) + 1 = \max_{\forall i \in V} \deg(i) + 1 \qquad (17.11)$$

Equation (17.11) provides only a lower bound for the frame length. For a given network, the frame length for any of the collision-free schedules is always greater than or equal to $\Delta(G)$, i.e., the inequality $M \geq \Delta(G)$ holds.

The real frame length for an optimal schedule depends on the topology of a network. For certain networks, a feasible schedule with exact frame length $\Delta(G)$ may not exist. Therefore, a longer frame length is required. The example shown in Fig. 17.1 is used to illustrate this point. In Fig. 17.1, two networks and the corresponding optimal schedules are given. In Fig. 17.1a, $X(G) = 2, \Delta(G) = 3, M = X(G) + 1 = 3$, and the equality $M = \Delta(G)$ holds. In Fig. 17.1b, however, $X(G) = 2, \Delta(G) = 3, M = 4$, and the inequality $M > \Delta(G)$ holds. Thus, the feasible schedule with the frame length $\Delta(G)$ does not exist. From this example, we can see that the minimum required frame length is dependent on the connectivity of a network, and cannot be predetermined. The lower bound for the frame length in Eq. (17.9) provides useful information when collision-free transmissions are scheduled. We can start to search for the optimal schedules with a frame length equal to the lower bound $\Delta(G)$. If no feasible schedules with this length can be found, we will increase the frame length, and

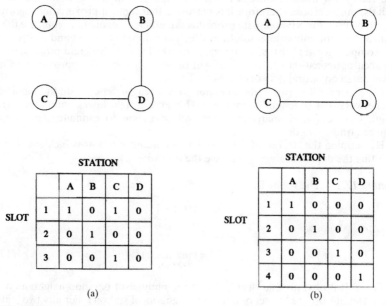

FIGURE 17.1   PR networks and their transmission schedules.

then search further for the feasible solutions. In this way, the scheduled frame length would be minimized. Once the frame length is determined, the optimal scheduling procedure will continue until a collision-free schedule with maximum channel utilization, defined in Eq. (17.5), is found. This schedule provides the optimal solution for the scheduling problem. In Sec. 17.5, we will discuss how to use neural networks to solve such an optimal scheduling problem.

17.4 MEAN FIELD ANNEALING THEORY

The class of NP-complete problems is usually characterized by optimization over a combinatorial set of configurations (the system state space). An exact search for the optimal configuration requires a computing effort which increases exponentially with the problem size. Therefore, finding exact optimal solutions becomes intractable as the problem size gets larger. No efficient method for exact solutions with deterministic polynomial computing time has been found for this class of optimization problems. Since many optimization problems are classified as NP-complete, many polynomial heuristic approaches have been developed to find near-optimal solutions, but the heuristic algorithms are usually problem-specific: an effective heuristic algorithm for one NP-complete problem might not be suitable for another. In the past few years, neural network approaches have shown encouraging results in solving general NP-complete problems [20–24]. The pioneering work, which attempted to solve the classic NP-complete problems, such as the traveling salesperson problem (TSP) and content-addressable memory (CAM) by neural networks, was done by J. J. Hopfield [25–27]. In the Hopfield neural network model, the energy function is proposed to reflect the terms to be optimized as well as the constraints. A system configuration is represented by the states of neurons. Each neuron i has two states: $s_i = 0$ (off) and $s_i = 1$ (on). The energy function should be formulated in such a way that the configuration with the minimum energy yields the optimal solution for an optimization problem. After initializing the states of neurons, a certain dynamic iteration procedure is executed to update neurons. The evolution of neurons' states results in a decrement of energy. The iterative process continues until no further energy improvement can be found. Then the system state with the minimum energy provides the solution.

17.4.1 Hopfield Energy Function

In Refs. 25 to 27, Hopfield proposed a neural network model to solve discrete combinatorial optimization problems. In this model, a neural network consists of N distributed processing devices called *neurons*. Each neuron is modeled as a nonlinear device (operational amplifier). The output s_i for neuron i is related to its input u_i with a sigmoid function $s_i = g(u_i)$, where s_i can take on any value between 0 and 1. For a binary neural network, $s_i \in \{0,1\}$, the energy function is given by

$$E(\mathbf{s}) = -\frac{1}{2} \sum_{i=1}^{N} \sum_{j=1}^{N} T_{ij} s_i s_j - \sum_{i=1}^{N} I_i s_i \qquad (17.12)$$

where T_{ij} describes the synaptic connection from neuron j to neuron i and I_i is the external input current to neuron i. Note that T_{ij} is symmetric ($T_{ij} = T_{ji}$) and $T_{ii} = 0$.

The dynamics of the ith neuron is given by

$$C_i \frac{du_i}{dt} = \sum_j T_{ij} s_j - \frac{u_i}{R_i} + I_i \tag{17.13}$$

where R_i and C_i are the input resistance and capacitance of neuron i.

Through the iteration of u_i with time according to Eq. (17.13), u_i will finally reach the stable state and will not change further with time. Then the decoding of the final states of the neurons according to $s_i = g(u_i)$ provides the solution, which should yield the minimum energy. Although convergence is guaranteed, the network usually gets stuck in local minima and is highly sensitive to the initial condition.

17.4.2   Simulated Annealing

Generally, a set of configurations or solutions in an optimization problem is represented by a state vector of neurons $\mathbf{s} = \{s_1, \ldots, s_N\}$. An energy function $E(\mathbf{s})$ establishes the correspondence between state and energy. The optimization procedure is to search for the system state which has global minimum energy, and the decoding of the state yields an optimal solution. Simulated annealing [28] is an effective scheme to find a global minimum of $E(\mathbf{s})$. Annealing is the physical process in which a solid is heated up until it melts, then is cooled down slowly until it settles in its ground state. During this process, the energy of the solid is minimized and the energy of the system is minimal in the ground state. SA is the simulation of the physical annealing process in searching for the optimal solution for a combinatorial optimization problem. SA combines gradient descent with a stochastic process. It avoids getting stuck in poor local minima by occasionally allowing "uphill moves" to the states with higher energy. The probability of a system being in a state $\mathbf{s}'$ with energy $E(\mathbf{s}')$ is given by a *Boltzmann distribution*:

$$\Pr\{\mathbf{s}'\} = \frac{1}{Z(T)} \exp\left(-\frac{E(\mathbf{s}')}{T}\right) \tag{17.14}$$

where T is a parameter called temperature, $Z(T)$ is the partition function, which is defined as

$$Z(T) = \sum_{\mathbf{s}} \exp\left[-\frac{E(\mathbf{s})}{T}\right] \tag{17.15}$$

and $\mathbf{s}$ is the state vector of neurons. In SA, the transition probability from one state $\mathbf{s}'$ to state $\mathbf{s}''$ is given by the *Metropolis criterion*:

$$\Pr\{\mathbf{s}' \rightarrow \mathbf{s}''\} = \begin{cases} 1 & \text{if } E(\mathbf{s}'') \leq E(\mathbf{s}') \\ f[\text{rad}, \exp(E(\mathbf{s}') - E(\mathbf{s}'')/T)] & \text{otherwise} \end{cases} \tag{17.16}$$

where rad is a random number uniformly distributed in the interval $(0, 1)$ and $f(x,y) = 1$ if $x < y$ and $f(x,y) = 0$, otherwise.

From Eq. (17.16), it can be seen that SA is a generalization of a local search. SA performs a local search among a specific subset of the state space. Whenever the search is getting stuck in a local minimum, SA allows uphill climbing from the local minima with a probability decided by Eq. (17.16). Therefore, SA keeps the local search feature while allowing the search to escape from local minima. Through proper control of the temperature T from high to low, the transition probability is gradually decreased and finally, the system would fall onto the state with global minimum energy.

17.4.3 Mean Field Annealing

While SA provides a scheme to obtain a global minima, it might be very time-consuming in finding the equilibrium state at each temperature. To reduce the computational effort in obtaining equilibrium at each temperature, MFA can be used. Instead of the probabilistic state transitions in SA, the MFA relaxes the averages of states to their equilibrium (i.e., the operation of **s** is replaced by its average $< \mathbf{s} >$). Since the mean calculation involves much less computational effort than the stochastic operation in SA, MFA relaxes the system to its equilibrium at each temperature much faster than SA does. Many applications of MFA [20–24] have shown that MFA requires 1 to 2 orders of magnitude less computing time than SA while maintaining the same optimization performance.

For a binary neural network, the energy function is described by the Hopfield model defined in Eq. (17.12). The average energy is given by

$$< E(\mathbf{s}) > = < -\frac{1}{2} \sum_i \sum_j T_{ij} s_i s_j - \sum_{i=1}^{N} I_i s_i > = -\frac{1}{2} \sum_i \sum_j T_{ij} < s_i s_j > - \sum_{i=1}^{N} I_i < s_i >$$

(17.17)

When the number of neurons is large, the dependence of any single neuron on other neurons can be neglected, and therefore we have the approximation:

$$< s_i s_j > = < s_i > < s_j >$$

(17.18)

Thus,

$$< E(\mathbf{s}) > = -\frac{1}{2} \sum_i \left[\sum_j T_{ij} < s_j > +2 I_i \right] < s_i >$$

(17.19)

and

$$h_i^{MFT} = -\frac{\partial < E(\mathbf{s}) >}{\partial < s_i >} = \sum_j T_{ij} < s_j > + I_i$$

(17.20)

where h_i^{MFT} is the mean field affecting s_i. The average of each signal neuron i at temperature T is given by

$$< s_i >_T = \sum_{s_i = 0}^{1} s_i \Pr \{s_i\} = \sum_{s_i} s_i \frac{\exp (h_i^{MFT} s_i / T)}{1 + \exp (h_i^{MFT} s_i / T)}$$

$$= \frac{\exp (h_i^{MFT}/T)}{1 + \exp (h_i^{MFT}/T)} = \frac{1}{2} \left[1 + \tanh \left(\frac{h_i^{MFT}}{2T} \right) \right]$$

(17.21)

From the above equations, we can see that the stochastic process of SA is replaced by a set of deterministic equations. The evolution of the ith neuron in MFA is given by

$$v_i(t + \Delta t) = < s_i(t + \Delta t) > = \frac{1}{2} \left[1 + \tanh \left(-\frac{1}{2T} \cdot \frac{\partial E}{\partial v_i(t)} \right) \right]$$

(17.22)

The MFA algorithm starts iterations at a high temperature. Each neuron is initialized to $s_i = 0.5 \pm \delta$, where δ is a small random value introduced to break the system balance. At each temperature, a neuron i is randomly selected from the set of neurons and updated according to Eq. (17.22). The iteration continues until a fixed point (equilibrium state) is found. This procedure is called the *relaxation operation*. Then the temperature T is lowered and the relaxation operation is repeated until freezing occurs [at a very low temperature, the iteration freezes and s_i converges to either 0 or 1 regardless of the scale of h_i^{MFT} (see Eq. (17.21)]. The decoding of the averages of all neurons provides the optimal solution.

17.5 THE OPTIMAL SCHEDULING ALGORITHM BASED ON MFA

To solve the optimal scheduling problem described in Sec. 17.3 by using MFA, we first need to map the channel utilization to be maximized and the constraints into an energy function. We assume that the frame length is M and there are N stations in a PR network. $M \times N$ neurons are required to represent a schedule. Each neuron s_{ij} $(i = 1, \ldots, M; j = 1, \ldots, N)$ is defined in Eq. (17.3). The energy function is given by

$$E = -\frac{W_1}{2}\left(\frac{1}{NM} \sum_{i=1}^{M}\sum_{j=1}^{N} s_{ij}^2 \right) + \frac{W_2}{2} \sum_{k=1}^{M}\sum_{i=1}^{N}\sum_{j=1}^{N} f_{ij}s_{ki}s_{kj} + W_3 \sum_{i=1}^{M}\sum_{j=1}^{N} s_{ij}(1 - s_{ij})$$

$$(17.23)$$

Weights $W_i > 0$, $i = 1, 2, 3$. The first term in Eq. (17.23) is the negatively weighed channel utilization. The second term is a penalty function for constraint violations. When the constraint is satisfied, it becomes zero. The third term is used to force neurons to converge to either 0 or 1 (if all $s_{ij} = 0$ or 1, the third term equals zero). The mean field of neuron ij is

$$h_{ij}^{MFT} = -\frac{\partial E}{\partial v_{ij}} = \frac{W_1}{NM} \cdot v_{ij} - W_2 \sum_{k=1}^{N} f_{jk}v_{ik} - W_3(1 - 2v_{ij}) \qquad (17.24)$$

where

$$v_{ij} = <s_{ij}>$$

The iteration of the neuron average is given by

$$v_{ij}(t + \Delta t) = \frac{1}{2}\left\{ 1 + \tanh\left[\frac{1}{2T}\left(\frac{W_1}{NM} \cdot v_{ij} - W_2 \sum_{k=1}^{N} f_{jk}v_{ik} - W_3(1 - 2v_{ij}) \right) \right] \right\}$$

$$(17.25)$$

Then the MFA iteration proceeds until freezing occurs. Since the exact frame length is unknown, we can start to schedule the frame with length $\Delta(G)$, the lower bound of the frame length shown in Eq. (17.9). The proposed scheduling algorithm includes three steps:

Step 1. Presetting neurons. Find the station p which has the maximum degree $X(G)$, then set the initial frame length $M = \Delta(G)$ as defined in Eq. (17.11), and assign station p and its one-hop neighboring stations $j \in B(p) = \{k : c_{pk} = 1\}$ to the different distinct time slots. That is, $v_{1p} = 1$, $v_{ij} = 1 \; \forall j \in B(p) \; (i = 2, \ldots, \Delta(G))$. For the ith slot, since $v_{ij} = 1$, the neuron k with $f_{jk} = 1$ must be set to $v_{ik} = 0$ to resolve collisions [see Eq. (17.7)]. The preassigned neurons no longer need to be updated and their states will be used to update the other neurons.

Step 2. Performing the MFA iterations based on Eq. (17.25). The frame length M is set to $M = \Delta(G)$. The iteration continues until freezing occurs and the freezing state provides the maximum channel utilization within the frame length M.

Step 3. Applying the heuristic algorithm for unassigned stations. After completing the above two steps, some stations might remain unassigned for transmission due to the collision-free constraint. The number of unassigned stations depends on the topology of the network. Usually, after the first two steps, only a few stations are unassigned. Extra time slots are needed to arrange the transmissions. The following heuristic algorithm is adopted to minimize the number of extra time slots: Denote the unassigned stations as $U = \{U_1, \ldots, U_q\}$.

1. Sort the stations in U in a descending order of station degree such that $\deg(U_i) \geq \deg(U_{i+1})$.
2. Add a time slot for the frame, and assign the stations in U to transmit in the slot. The priority of assigning stations' transmission is based on the order of U; i.e., the priority of U_i is greater than that of U_{i+1}. The stations arranged in the slot must be conflict-free. Repeat the above procedure until U is null.
3. The actual frame length M equals $\Delta(G)$ plus the number of added time slots.
4. Check the stations which have been assigned to transmit in the first $\Delta(G)$ time slots. If any of the stations can transmit in the added time slots without conflict, assign the transmissions of the stations in the corresponding time slots.

After the three steps are completed, the optimal schedule represented by $v_{ij} \; \forall i, j$ is translated into the actual transmission assignment (i.e., $v_{ij} = 1$ means that station j can transmit in slot i).

To illustrate the scheduling algorithm, we use the network shown in Fig. 17.2a as an example, and the results in each step are shown in Fig. 17.2b and c. For this network, after the first two steps, all stations have been arranged. Therefore, the third step is not executed.

17.6 NUMERICAL EXAMPLES AND PERFORMANCE ANALYSIS

In MFA, the proper selections of weights W_i and the annealing schedule (the way that temperature T is lowered) will guarantee that a feasible and optimal solution can be found. We will not go through the details of selecting these parameters in this chapter. In our example, the weights are set as $W_1 = 5NM$, $W_2 = 2$, $W_3 = 1$, and a simple annealing schedule $T_k = \alpha T_{k-1}$ ($\alpha < 1$) is adopted. When the following stopping criterion is achieved, the annealing process terminates and the decoding of $\mathbf{v} = [v_{ij}]$ provides the optimal solution:

$$\frac{1}{NM} \left(\sum_i \sum_j v_{ij}^{(k)} - \sum_i \sum_j v_{ij}^{(k-1)} \right)^2 \leq \delta \qquad (17.26)$$

where $v_{ij}^{(k)}$ is the value of v_{ij} at equilibrium state at temperature T_k and δ is a small positive value.

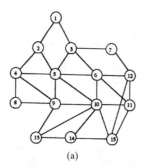

(a)

STATION

SLOT	1	2	3	4	5	6	7	8	9	10	11	12	13	14	15
1	0	0	0	0	1	0	0	0	0	0	0	0	0		
2	0	0	0	0	0	1	0		0	0	0	0	0	0	0
3		0	0	0	0	0	0	1	0	0		0	0	0	
4	0	0	0	0	0		0	0	1	0	0	0	0	0	
5		0		0	0	0		0	0	1	0	0	0	0	
6		0	0	0		0	0	0	0		1	0	0		
7			0	0		0	0	0	0	0	0	1	0		
8			0	0	0		0	0	0	0	0	0	0	1	

(b)

STATION

SLOT	1	2	3	4	5	6	7	8	9	10	11	12	13	14	15
1	0	0	0	0	1	0	0	0	0	0	0	0	0	0	0
2	0	0	0	0	0	1	0	1	0	0	0	0	0	0	0
3	1	0	0	0	0	0	0	0	1	0	0	1	0	0	0
4	0	0	0	0	0	0	1	0	0	1	0	0	0	0	0
5	0	0	0	1	0	0	0	0	0	0	1	0	0	0	0
6	0	0	1	0	0	0	0	0	0	0	0	0	1	0	0
7	0	1	0	0	0	0	1	0	0	0	0	0	0	1	0
8	1	0	0	0	0	0	0	1	0	0	0	0	0	0	1

(c)

FIGURE 17.2 (*a*) 15-station network; (*b*) the first step; (*c*) the second step.

Three PR networks with 15, 30, and 40 stations are scheduled in our numerical examples. The 15-station network is shown in Fig. 17.2*a* and the 40-station network in Fig. 17.3*a*. The scheduling results for the two networks are shown in Figs. 17.2*c* and 17.3*b*. For the three networks, $X(G) = 8, 9, 8$, and the scheduled frame lengths are 8, 10, and 9 respectively. It can be seen from these that the MFA algorithm is effective in searching for the optimal schedule with the minimum frame length.

The performance of the resulting schedules can be evaluated by two criteria: channel utilization and average time delay. The following assumptions are made:

1. Packets have a fixed length, and the length of a time slot equals the time required to transmit a packet.

2. The interarrival time for each station *i* is statistically independent from other stations, and packets arrive according to a Poisson process with a rate of λ_i packets/slot. The total traffic in station *i* consists of the traffic incoming from other stations and the data from terminals attached to it. Packets are stored in buffers in each station and the buffer size is infinite.

3. The probability distribution of the service time of station *i* is deterministic and statistically independent from other stations. The average service rate is μ_i packets/slot.

4. Packets can be transmitted only at the beginning of each time slot.

Under the above assumptions, a network can be modeled as N $M/D/1$ queues, where N is the number of stations. According to the Pollaczek-Khinchin formula [29], the average delay for each queue *i* is given by

$$D_i = \overline{X_i} + \frac{\lambda_i \overline{X_i^2}}{2(1 - \rho_i)}, \qquad (17.27)$$

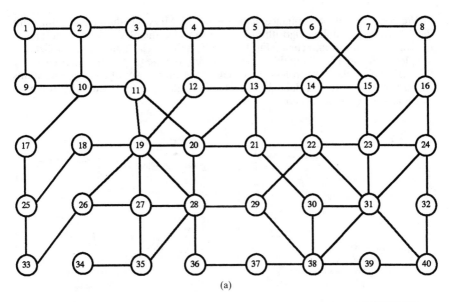

(a)

station / time slot	1	2	3	4	5	6	7	8	9	10	11	12	13	14	15	16	17	18	19	20	21	22	23	24	25	26	27	28	29	30	31	32	33	34	35	36	37	38	39	40
1	1	0	0	0	0	0	0	0	0	0	1	0	0	1	0	1	0	0	0	0	0	0	0	0	0	0	0	0	0	0	0	1	0	1	0	1	0	0	0	1
2	0	1	0	0	0	1	0	1	0	0	0	1	0	0	0	0	0	0	0	0	0	1	0	0	1	0	0	0	0	0	0	0	1	0	1	0	0	1	0
3	0	0	0	0	0	0	0	1	0	1	0	0	1	0	0	0	1	0	0	0	0	0	0	0	0	0	0	0	1	0	1	0	0	0	1	0	0
4	1	0	0	0	1	0	1	0	0	0	0	0	0	0	0	1	0	1	0	0	0	0	0	0	0	0	0	1	0	1	0	0	1	0	0	1	0	0	0
5	0	0	0	1	0	0	1	0	1	0	1	0	0	0	0	0	0	0	0	1	0	1	0	0	0	0	0	0	0	0	1	0	0	1	0	0
6	0	0	1	0	0	0	0	1	1	0	0	0	0	0	1	0	0	0	0	0	0	0	0	1	0	0	0	1	0	1	0	1	0	1	0	0	0	0
7	1	0	0	1	0	0	1	0	0	0	0	0	0	0	0	0	1	0	0	0	1	0	0	1	0	0	1	0	0	0	0	0	0	0	1	0	0	0
8	1	0	0	1	0	0	1	0	0	0	0	0	0	0	0	1	0	0	0	0	1	0	0	0	0	1	0	0	0	0	1	0	0	0	0	0	0	1	0
9	1	0	0	1	0	0	1	0	0	0	0	0	0	0	0	1	0	0	0	0	0	1	0	1	0	0	1	0	0	0	1	0	0	0	0	0

(b)

FIGURE 17.3 The network with 40 stations and its transmission schedule.

where $\overline{X}_i = 1/\mu_i$, average service time for station i
 $\rho_i = \lambda_i/\mu_i$, utilization factor for station i
 $\overline{X_i^2}$ = second moment of service time for station i

Since the service time is deterministic, the variance equals zero, and thus

$$\overline{X_i^2} = \overline{X_i}^2 = \frac{1}{\mu_i^2} \tag{17.28}$$

and

$$\mu_i = \frac{\sum_{j=1}^{m} v_{ji}}{M} \quad \text{packets/slot} \tag{17.29}$$

The total time delay is given by

$$D = \frac{\sum_{i=1}^{N} \lambda_i D_i}{\sum_{i=1}^{N} \lambda_i}. \tag{17.30}$$

We compare the performance achieved by the MFA scheduling algorithm with the other two scheduling algorithms [19, 30], in which the objective of scheduling is to achieve the maximum channel utilization. The time delay and channel utilization are plotted in Fig. 17.4. From this figure, it is seen that the time delay experienced by the MFA schedule is much less than that of the other two scheduling algorithms which have the same time delay, but the channel utilization achieved by MFA is a little bit less than the other two.

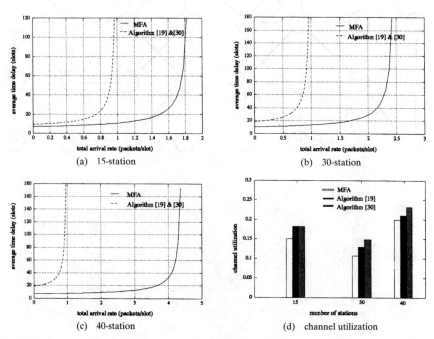

FIGURE 17.4   Performance comparison for different algorithms.

17.7   CONCLUSIONS

In this chapter, we presented an efficient broadcast scheduling algorithm based on MFA neural networks. As indicated, the TDMA broadcast scheduling in a PR network is an NP-complete combinatorial optimization problem. We first map the channel utilization to be maximized and the collision-free constraints onto an energy function, and then the MFA procedure is applied to searching for the optimal solutions. To reduce the computational complexity, we divide the algorithm into three steps. In the first step, the solution space is reduced by presetting some neurons according to the topology of the scheduling network. The preset neurons need not be further updated, and their values can be used to update other neurons. In the second step, the MFA procedure is executed to maximize channel utilization. At the end of the execution, a solution with near-maximal channel utilization can be found. After the first two steps, some stations might not be assigned to transmit in any slots. To arrange the unassigned stations, additional time slots are needed. In the last step, a heuristic method is used to arrange the transmissions of the unassigned stations. This step guarantees that the additional number of time slots is minimal. Since neural networks provide a parallel computing strategy, the proposed scheduling algorithm will obtain the optimal solution faster than other heuristic algorithms. Numerical results have shown that the proposed algorithm can find the shortest collision-free frame schedule while providing the maximum channel utilization. The average time delay is much smaller than that of the other two algorithms.

REFERENCES

1. A. Hiramatsu, "ATM traffic control using neural networks," in *Neural Networks in Telecommunications* (Yuhas and Ansari, eds.), pp. 63–89, Kluwer Academic Publishers, 1994.

2. R. M. Goodman and B. Ambrose, "Applications of learning techniques to network management," in *Proc. of the International Workshop on Applications of Neural Networks to Telecommunications* (Alspector, Goodman, and Brown, eds.), pp. 34–44, Lawrence Erlbaum Associates Publishers, 1993.

3. D. Yang, "An echo canceller based on the multi-layer LTBP neural network," *Proc. of GLOBLECOM'92*, pp. 1298–1302, December 1992.

4. W. Refai, N. Zaibi, and G. Kane, "Image transmission based on neural network approaches," *Proc. of GLOBLECOM'92*, pp. 1315–1318, December 1992.

5. R. Lancini and F. Perego, "Frame adaptive vector quantization with neural networks," *Proc. of GLOBLECOM'92*, pp. 1310–1314, December 1992.

6. P. Chang and B. Yeh, "Nonlinear communication channel equalization using wavelet neural networks," *Proc. of ICNN'94*, pp. 3605–3610, June 1994.

7. T. X. Brown, "Neural networks for adaptive equalization," in *Proc. of the International Workshop on Applications of Neural Networks to Telecommunications* (Alspector, Goodman, and Brown, eds.), pp. 34–44, Lawrence Erlbaum Associates Publishers, 1993.

8. T. Martinez and G. Rudolph, "A learning model for adaptive network routing," in *Proc. of the International Workshop on Applications of Neural Networks to Telecommunications* (Alspector, Goodman, and Brown, eds.), pp. 183–187, Lawrence Erlbaum Associates Publishers, 1993.

9. M. W. Goudreau and C. L. Giles, "Routing in random multistage interconnection networks," in *Neural Networks in Telecommunications* (Yuhas and Ansari, eds.), pp. 37–61, Kluwer Academic Publishers, 1994.

10. S. Amin and M. Gell, "Constrained optimization for switching using neural networks," in *Proc. of the International Workshop on Applications of Neural Networks to Telecommunications* (Alspector, Goodman, and Brown, eds.), pp. 106–111, Lawrence Erlbaum Associates Publishers, 1993.

11. C. Pham and T. Ogunfunmi, "Multiple-symbol differential detection of M-DPSK using neural network," *Proc. of ICNN'94*, pp. 3559–3564, June 1994.

12. S. Neuhauser, "Hopfield optimization techniques applied to routing in computer networks," in *Proc. of the International Workshop on Applications of Neural Networks to Telecommunications* (Alspector, Goodman, and Brown, eds.), pp. 203–209, Lawrence Erlbaum Associates Publishers, 1993.

13. D. Kunz, "Channel assignment for cellular radio using neural networks," *IEEE Trans. on Vehicular Technology*, pp. 188–193, vol. 40, no. 1, February 1991.

14. N. Ansari, "A neurocomputing approach to optimizing the performance of a satellite communication network," in *Neural Networks in Telecommunications* (Yuhas and Ansari, eds.), pp. 349–365, Kluwer Academic Publishers, 1994.

15. M. Duque-Antón, D. Kunz, and B. Rüber, "Cellular mobile communication design using self-organizing feature maps," in *Neural Networks in Telecommunications* (Yuhas and Ansari, eds.), pp. 211–232, Kluwer Academic Publishers, 1994.

16. R. Kahn, S. Gronemeyer, J. Burchfiel, and R. Kunzeman, "Advances in packet radio technology," *Proc. IEEE,* vol. 66, no. 11, pp. 1468–1496, Nov. 1978.

17. L. Kleinrock and J. Silvester, "Spatial reuse in multihop packet radio networks," *Proc. IEEE,* vol. 75, no. 1, pp. 156–167, January 1987.

18. E. Arikan, "Some complexity results about packet radio networks," *IEEE Trans. on Information Theory,* vol. IT-30, pp. 681–685, July 1984.

19. A. Ephremides and T. V. Truong, "Scheduling broadcasts in multihop radio network," *IEEE Trans. on Communications,* COM-38, pp. 456–460, April 1990.

20. C. Peterson, "A mean field theory learning algorithm for neural networks," *Complex System,* vol. 1, pp. 995–1019, 1987.

21. C. Peterson, "Applications of mean field theory neural networks," Dept. of Theoretical Physics, Technical Report CS-1153, University of Lund, pp. 1–27, August 1989.

22. C. Peterson and J. Anderson, "Neural networks and NP-complete optimization problems: a performance study on the graph bisection problem," *Complex Systems,* vol. 2, pp. 59–71, 1988.

23. C. Peterson and E. Hartman, "Explorations of the mean field theory learning algorithm," *Neural Networks,* vol. 2, pp. 475–494, 1989.

24. C. Peterson and B. Soderberg, "A new method for mapping optimization problems onto neural network," *International Journal of Neural Systems,* vol. 1, no. 1, pp. 3–22, May 1989.

25. J. J. Hopfield and D. W. Tank, "Neural computation of decisions in optimization problems," *Biological Cybernetics,* vol. 52, no. 4, pp. 141–156, 1985.

26. J. J. Hopfield, "Neural networks and physical systems with emergent collective computational abilities," *Proceedings of the National Academy of Science,* vol. 79, pp. 2541–2554, 1982.

27. J. J. Hopfield, "Neurons with graded response have collective computational properties like those of two-state neurons," *Proceedings of the National Academy of Science,* vol. 81, pp. 3088–3092, May 1984.

28. E. Aarts and J. Korst, *Simulated Annealing and Boltzmann Machine—A Stochastic Approach to Combinatorial Optimization and Neural Computing,* John Wiley & Sons, 1989.

29. D. Bertsekas and R. Gallager, *Data Networks,* Prentice-Hall, 1987.

30. G. Wang and N. Ansari, "A neural network approach to broadcast scheduling in multihop radio networks," *Proc. of ICNN'94,* pp. 4699–4704, June 1994.

CHAPTER 18

APPLICATIONS OF NEURAL NETWORKS IN SEMICONDUCTOR MANUFACTURING PROCESSES

Gary S. May, Ph.D.
School of Electrical & Computer Engineering
Georgia Institute of Technology, Atlanta

18.1 INTRODUCTION

The fabrication of integrated circuits and related devices is extremely expensive. In fact, the last decade has seen semiconductor manufacturing become so capital-intensive that only a few very large companies can participate. A typical state-of-the-art high-volume manufacturing facility today costs several hundred million dollars, which represents a factor of over 1000 increase over the cost of a comparable facility 20 years ago (Fig. 18.1) [1]. If this trend continues at its present rate of increase, facility costs are projected to exceed the total annual revenue of any of the four leading U.S. semiconductor companies by the turn of the century [2].

As a result of rising costs, the challenge before semiconductor manufacturers today is to offset such large capital investment with a greater amount of technological innovation in the actual fabrication processes themselves. The objective now is to make use of the latest developments in computer hardware and software technology to enhance manufacturing methods which have become prohibitively expensive. In effect, this effort in *computer-integrated manufacturing of integrated circuits* (IC-CIM) is aimed at optimizing the cost-effectiveness of integrated circuit manufacturing in the same manner in which *computer-aided design* (CAD) has dramatically impacted the economics of circuit design.

Under the overall heading of reducing manufacturing cost, several subtasks have been identified. These include increasing chip fabrication yield, reducing product cycle time, maintaining consistent levels of product quality and performance, and improving the reliability of processing equipment [3]. Unlike the manufacture of discrete parts such as electrical appliances, where relatively little rework

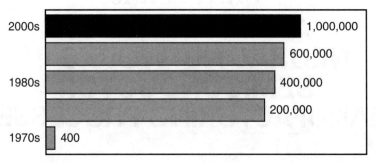

FIGURE 18.1 Graph of rising integrated circuit fabrication costs in thousands of dollars over the last two decades [1].

is required and greater than a 95 percent yield on sellable product is realizable, the manufacture of very large scale integrated (VLSI) circuits faces unique obstacles. For example, semiconductor fabrication processes consist of hundreds of sequential steps, and yield loss may potentially occur at every step. Therefore, IC manufacturing processes typically realize yields on the order of 20 to 80 percent of sellable product. The problem of low yield is particularly severe for new fabrication sequences.

However, the implementation of effective IC-CIM systems offers the promise of alleviating such problems. Table 18.1 summarizes the results of a 1986 study by Toshiba which analyzed the use of IC-CIM techniques in the production of 256K dynamic random-access memory (RAM) circuits [4]. It was shown in this study that the utilization of CIM techniques improved the manufacturing process on each of the four relevant productivity metrics.

TABLE 18.1 Results of 1986 Toshiba Study

Productivity metric	No CIM	With CIM
Turnaround time	1.0	0.58
Integrated unit output	1.0	1.50
Average equipment uptime	1.0	1.32
Direct labor hours	1.0	0.75

Because of the large number of steps involved, maintaining product quality in an IC manufacturing facility requires the strict control of literally hundreds or even thousands of process variables. The interdependent issues of high yield, high quality, and low cycle time have been addressed in part by the ongoing development of several critical capabilities in state-of-the-art IC-CIM systems: in-situ process monitoring, process/equipment modeling, real-time closed-loop process control, and equipment malfunction diagnosis. The emphasis of each of these activities is to increase throughput and reduce yield loss by preventing potential misprocessing, but each presents significant engineering challenges in their effective implementation and deployment.

18.2   THE ROLE OF NEURAL NETWORKS

Recently, there has been an explosion in the use of artificial neural networks in various manufacturing applications [5], and the semiconductor manufacturing arena is no exception to this trend. Neural networks have emerged as a powerful technique for assisting IC-CIM systems in performing process monitoring, modeling, control and diagnosis functions. Because of their inherent learning ability, adaptability, and robustness, neural nets have been used to solve problems that have heretofore resisted solutions by other more traditional methods.

The name *neural network* stems from the fact that these systems mimic the behavior of biological neurons, but the neural networks used in semiconductor manufacturing actually have little to do with biology. However, they do share some of the advantages that biological organisms have over standard computational systems. Neural networks are capable of performing highly complex mappings on noisy and/or nonlinear data, thereby inferring very subtle relationships between diverse sets of input and output parameters. Moreover, these networks can also generalize well enough to learn overall trends in functional relationships from limited training data.

There are several neural network architectures and training algorithms eligible for manufacturing applications. *Hopfield networks,* for example, have been used for solving combinatorial optimization problems such as optimal scheduling [6]. However, the *backpropagation* (BP) algorithm is the most generally applicable and thus far the most popular in semiconductor manufacturing. Feedforward neural networks trained by BP (referred to herein as *BP neural networks*) consist of several layers of simple processing elements called *neurons* (Fig. 18.2). These rudimentary processors are interconnected in such a way that information relevant to input/output mappings is stored in

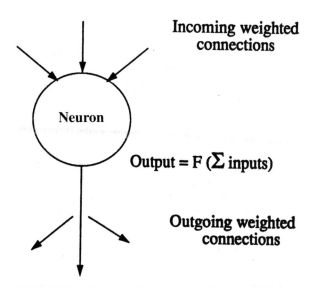

FIGURE 18.2   Schematic of a single neuron. The output of the neuron is a function of the weighted sum of its inputs, where F is a sigmoid function [8]. *(Copyright 1993 IEEE.)*

the weight of the connections between them. Each neuron contains the weighted sum of its inputs filtered by a sigmoid transfer function. The layers of neurons in BP networks receive, process, and transmit critical information regarding the relationships between the input parameters and corresponding responses (Fig. 18.3). In addition to the input and output layers, these networks incorporate one or more "hidden" layers of neurons which do not interact with the outside world, but assist in performing nonlinear feature extraction tasks on information provided by the input and output layers.

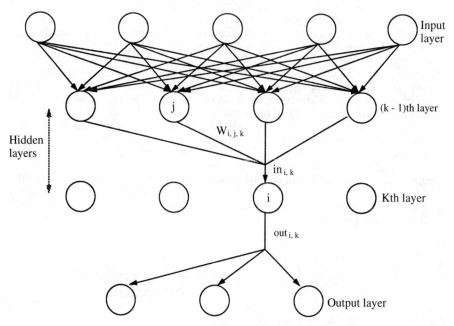

FIGURE 18.3   BP neural network showing input, output, and hidden layers [8].

In the BP learning algorithm, the network begins with a random set of weights. An input vector is presented and fed forward through the network, and the output is calculated by using this initial weight matrix. Next, the calculated output is compared to the measured output data, and the squared difference between these two vectors determines the system error. The accumulated error for all the input-output pairs is defined as the euclidean distance in the weight space, which the network attempts to minimize. Minimization is accomplished via the *gradient descent* approach, in which the network weights are adjusted in the direction of decreasing error. It has been demonstrated by several authors that if a sufficient number of hidden neurons are present, a three-layer BP network can encode any arbitrary input-output relationship [7].

18.3   PROCESS MODELING

The ability of neural networks to learn input/output relationships from limited data is quite beneficial in semiconductor manufacturing, where a plethora of highly nonlinear fabrication processes exist, and experimental data for process modeling is expensive to obtain. Several researchers have recently reported noteworthy successes in using neural networks to model the behavior of a few key fabrication processes [8–11]. In so doing, the basic strategy is usually to perform a series of statistically designed characterization experiments, and then to train BP neural nets to model the experimental data. The process characterization experiments typically consist of a factorial or reduced factorial exploration of the input parameter space, which may be subsequently augmented by a more advanced experimental design. Each set of input conditions in the design corresponds to a particular set of measured process responses. This input/output mapping is precisely what the neural network learns.

As an example of this procedure, Himmel and May of the Georgia Institute of Technology used BP neural networks to model ion-assisted plasma etching, a process widely used in semiconductor manufacturing [8]. Plasma etching is the removal of patterned layers of material by reactive gases in an ac discharge (Fig. 18.4) [12]. Because

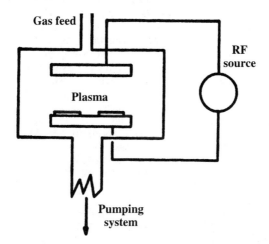

FIGURE 18.4 Simplified schematic of plasma etching system. Plasma etching is a popular process which can be modeled using neural networks [12].

of the popularity of this process, considerable effort has been expended developing reliable models which relate the response of process outputs (such as etch rate or etch uniformity) to variations in input parameters (such as pressure, radio-frequency (rf) power, or gas composition). These models are required by semiconductor manufacturers in order to predict etch behavior under an exhaustive set of operating conditions with a very high degree of precision. However, plasma processing involves highly complex and dynamic interactions between reactive particles in an electric field. As a result of this inherent complexity, approaches to plasma etch modeling which preceded the advent of neural networks had met with limited success.

Plasma process modeling from a fundamental physical standpoint is usually done by computationally expensive numerical simulation methods which produce ion distribution profiles within the plasma. However, not only does long computation time render these simulators too inefficient for real-time manufacturing applications, but the connections between microscopic ion profiles and macroscopic responses like etch rate are not yet clearly understood. Other modeling efforts have focused on statistical *response surface methods* (RSM) [13]. RSM models can predict etch behavior under a wide range of operating conditions, but they are most efficient when the number of process variables is small (i.e., six or less). The large number of experiments required to adequately characterize the many significant variables in processes like plasma etching is costly and usually prohibitive, forcing experimenters to choose a reduced set of variables to manipulate. Since plasma etching is a highly nonlinear process, this simplification tends to reduce the accuracy of the RSM models.

Himmel and May compared RSM to BP neural networks for modeling the etching of polysilicon films in a carbon tetrachloride (CCl_4) plasma. To do so, they characterized the process by varying rf power, chamber pressure, electrode spacing, and gas composition in a partial factorial design, and trained the neural nets to model the effect of each combination of these inputs on etch rate, uniformity, and selectivity. Afterwards, they found that the neural network models exhibited 40 to 70 percent better accuracy (as measured by *root-mean-square* (rms) error) over RSM models and required fewer training experiments. Furthermore, the results of this study also indicated that the generalization capabilities of the neural models were superior to their conventional statistical counterparts. This fact was verified by using both the RSM and "neural" process models to predict previously unobserved experimental data (or "test" data). Neural networks showed the ability to generalize with an RMS error 40 percent lower than the statistical models even when built with fewer training data.

The Georgia Tech process models were derived using internally developed neural network simulation software. This package, called the Object-Oriented Neural Network Simulator (ObOrNNS), consists of approximately 5300 lines of C++ code in which various C++ data structures (or *classes*) mirror the structure and functionality of biological neurons. The simulator uses an X-window-based interface and is custom-designed for semiconductor manufacturing applications. Typical network training times for process modeling with the ObOrNNS package range from 30 to 60 seconds, depending on the size of the network.

Investigators at DuPont Electronics in Wilmington, Del., and AT&T Bell Laboratories in Murray Hill, N.J., have likewise reported positive results using neural nets for plasma etch modeling. Mocella et al. of DuPont also modeled polysilicon etching, and found that BP neural nets consistently produced models exhibiting better fit than second- and third-order polynomial RSM models [9]. Moreover, they too found that their neural process models effectively generalized test data. In addition, this group has since developed a PC-based neural network data analysis package called Design Advisor/Neural Analyzer (DANA) [10]. DANA, which is used for understanding and optimizing physical processes, provides users with specific guidance for designing experiments for subsequent neural network modeling. Originally implemented to analyze plasma etch data from designed experiments and historical data from photomask manufacturing, this software has resulted in significant process upgrades. As a result, the package was recently licensed to the NeuralWare Corporation of Pittsburgh.

At Bell Labs, Rietman and Lory modeled tantalum silicide/polysilicon etching of the gate of metal-oxide-semiconductor (MOS) transistors [11]. This group has successfully used data from an actual production machine to train neural nets to predict the amount of silicon dioxide remaining in the source and drain regions of the devices after the etch. They subsequently used their neural etch models to analyze the sensitivity of this etch response to several input parameters, which provided much useful information for process designers. They found, for example, that the most significant parameters in the polysilicon portion of the etch process were gas flow and induced dc bias, whereas chamber pressure had a lesser impact.

Other manufacturing processes besides plasma etching have also benefited from the neural network approach. Specifically, chemical vapor deposition (CVD) processes, which are also nonlinear, have been modeled effectively [14–16]. Nadi et al. at the University of California at Berkeley combined BP neural nets and influence diagrams for both the modeling and recipe synthesis of low-pressure CVD (LPCVD) of polysilicon [14]. Bose and Lord, also of Bell Labs (from the Princeton, N.J., facility) demonstrated that neural networks provided appreciably better generalization than regression-based models of silicon CVD [15]. Similarly, Han et al. of Georgia Tech developed neural process models for the plasma-enhanced CVD (PECVD) of silicon dioxide films used as interlayer dielectric material in multichip modules [16].

18.3.1   Modifications to Standard Backpropagation in Process Modeling

In each of the above examples, standard implementations of the error backpropagation algorithm have been employed to perform process modeling tasks. However, innovative modifications of standard BP have also been developed for certain other applications of semiconductor process modeling. In one case, BP has been combined with *simulated annealing* to enhance model accuracy. In addition, a second adjustment has been developed which incorporates knowledge of process chemistry and physics into a semiempirical or hybrid model, which has advantages over the purely empirical black-box approach described above. These two variations of BP are described below.

Neural Networks and Simulated Annealing in Plasma Etch Modeling.   Kim and May [17] used neural networks to model etch rate, etch anisotropy, spatial variations in etch rate (i.e., uniformity), and etch selectivity in a low-pressure form of plasma etching called *reactive ion etching* (RIE). The modeled RIE process consisted of the removal of silicon dioxide films by a chloroform (CHF_3) and oxygen plasma in a Plasma Therm 700 series dual chamber RIE system operating at 13.56 MHz. The process was initially characterized via a 2^4 factorial experiment with three center-point replications augmented by a central composite design [18]. Factors varied included pressure, rf power, and two gas flow rates.

The data from this experiment were used to train specially modified backpropagation neural networks. The alteration of the backpropagation algorithm resulted in significantly improved network prediction accuracy. The specific technique used modified the rule used to update network weights during training. The new rule combined a memory-based weight update scheme with the well-known *simulated annealing* procedure used in combinatorial optimization [19].

The rationale for this new rule is as follows: neural network training rules adjust synapse strengths to satisfy the constraints given to the network. In the standard BP algorithm, the weight update mechanism at the $(n + 1)$th iteration is given by:

$$w_{ijk}(n + 1) = w_{ijk}(n) + \eta \, \Delta w_{ijk}(n) \qquad (18.1)$$

where w_{ijk} is the connection strength between the jth neuron in layer $(k - 1)$ and the ith neuron in layer k, Δw_{ijk} is the calculated change in that weight which reduces the error function of the network, and η is the learning rate. Equation (18.1) is known as the *generalized delta rule*. Kim and May's new *K-step prediction* rule, however, modifies the generalized delta rule by using portions of previously stored weights in predicting the next set of weights. This new update scheme is expressed as

$$w_{ijk}(n+1) = w_{ijk}(n) + \eta \, \Delta w_{ijk}(n) + \gamma_K w_{ijk}(n-K) \qquad (18.2)$$

The last term in the above expression provides the network with a degree of "long-term memory" [20]. The integer K determines the number of sets of previous weights stored and the γ_K factor allows the system to place varying degrees of emphasis on weight sets from different training epochs. Typically, larger values of γ_K are assigned to more recent weight sets. Appropriate values for these parameters are determined experimentally.

This memory-based weight update scheme is combined with a variation of simulated annealing. In thermodynamics, annealing is the slow cooling procedure which enables nature to find the minimum energy state. In neural network training, this is analogous to using the following "thermo-squashing" function in place of the usual sigmoid:

$$\frac{1}{1 + \exp - \left[\dfrac{\text{net}_{ik} + \beta_{ik}}{\lambda T_0} \right]} \qquad (18.3)$$

where net_{ik} is the weighted sum of neural inputs and β_{ik} is the neural threshold. Network "temperature" gradually decreases from an initial value T_0 according to a decay factor λ (where $\lambda < 1$), effectively resulting in a time-varying gain for the network transfer function (Fig. 18.5). Annealing the network at high temperature early

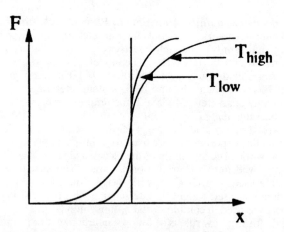

FIGURE 18.5 Plot of thermo-squashing function as temperature is decreased [17].

on leads to rapid location of the general vicinity of the global minimum of the error surface. The training algorithm will then remain within the attractive basin of the global minimum as the temperature decreases, preventing any significant uphill excursion. When used in conjunction with the K-step weight prediction scheme outlined above, this approach has been termed *annealed K-step prediction.*

In [17], BP neural networks were trained using annealed K-step prediction as described above. The training data for these networks consisted of the trials from the 2^4 factorial array plus the three center-point replications. The remaining axial trials from the central composite characterization experiment were used as test data for the models. A comparison of the annealed K-step training rule and the generalized delta rule was also performed. Network performance was measured by its rms error. The prediction errors are shown in Table 18.2. The % *improvement* column in this table refers to the improvement obtained using the annealed K-step training rule.

TABLE 18.2 Network Prediction Errors

Etch response	Error (K-step)	% improvement
Etch rate	8.0 Å/min	57.3
Uniformity	0.3 %	53.8
Anisotropy	3.9 %	51.1
Selectivity	0.12	59.8

For the K-step prediction rules, best results were achieved for $K = 2, \gamma_1 = 0.9, \gamma_2 = 0.08$, $T_0 = 100$, and $\lambda_0 = 0.99$. It is clear that annealed K-step prediction significantly improves network prediction ability. It is also clear that the neural process models developed can predict these responses with a very high degree of accuracy.

Semiempirical Process Modeling Using Hybrid Neural Networks.   Nami et al. [21] recently developed a semiempirical model of the metal-organic chemical vapor deposition (MOCVD) process based on hybrid neural networks. This effort was motivated by the fact that although neural process models offer advantages in both accuracy and robustness over statistical models, they still possess a shortcoming in that their empirical derivation offers little insight into the underlying physical understanding of the process being modeled. This problem can be overcome by the development of a neural process model which incorporates partial knowledge regarding the first-principles relationships inherent in the process being modeled. In so doing, the hybrid model combines the best aspects of physical and empirical black-box modeling methods.

The model in [21] was constructed by characterizing the MOCVD of titanium dioxide (TiO_2) films through the measurement of deposition rate over a range of deposition conditions. This was accomplished by varying both susceptor and source temperature, flow rate of the argon carrier gas for the precursor (titanium tetra-iso-propoxide, or TTIP), and chamber pressure. After characterization, a modified BP (or hybrid) neural network was trained to determine the value of three adjustable fitting parameters in an analytical expression for the TiO_2 deposition rate. In so doing, the researchers developed a general-purpose methodology for deriving semiempirical neural process models which take into account prior knowledge of the underlying process physics.

The first step in the hybrid modeling technique involves the development of an analytical model. For TiO_2 deposition via MOCVD, this was accomplished by applying the continuity equation to reactant concentration as the reactant of interest is transported from the bulk gas and incorporated into the growing film. Under these conditions and several key assumptions, it can be shown that the average deposition rate R is given by the following general expression [22]:

$$R = \frac{M}{\rho} N \frac{D}{\delta} \frac{N_u}{1 + N_u} C_b \qquad (18.4)$$

where N_u is the Nusselt number for mass transport, M is the molecular weight of the deposited film, ρ is the specific density of the film, D is the diffusion coefficient of the reactant gas, N is Avogadro's number, and C_b is the fixed concentration of reactant at the boundary layer interface.

After some additional manipulation and substitution of suitable values for the relevant physical constants, the final form of the specific deposition rate equation for TiO_2 becomes

$$R = 4.4 \frac{A e^{-\Delta E/kT}}{1 + \left[\dfrac{6.9 \times 10^{-5}}{D_0} T^{-0.926} P Q^{-0.5} A e^{-\Delta E/kT} \right]} \frac{PP_e}{P - P_e} \frac{v}{Q} \qquad (18.5)$$

where
R = average deposition rate, µm/h
A = preexponential factor related to the molecular "attempt rate" of the growth process
ΔE = activation energy, cal/mole
D_0 = diffusion coefficient of TTIP at 300°K and 1.0 atm
k = Boltzmann's constant
T = susceptor temperature, degrees Kelvin
P = reactor chamber pressure, mtorr
v = carrier gas flow rate, standard cm³/min
Q = total flow rate, standard cm³/min
P_e = equilibrium pressure of reactant in the carrier gas (a function of the source temperature)

For accurate prediction of deposition rate, the three unknown physical parameters that need to be estimated are D_0, A, and ΔE. The estimation of these parameters was accomplished with hybrid neural networks as explained below.

In standard backpropagation learning, gradient descent minimizes the network error E by adjusting the weights by an amount proportional to the derivative of the error with respect to previous weights. In its simplest form, the weight update expression is the generalized delta rule given by Eq. (18.1), where

$$\Delta w_{ijk}(n) = -\frac{\partial E}{\partial w_{ijk}} \qquad (18.6)$$

The gradient of the error with respect to the weights is calculated for one pair of input-output patterns at a time. After each computation, a step is taken in the opposite direction of the error gradient, and the procedure is iterated until convergence is achieved.

For the hybrid approach, the network structure corresponding to the deposition of TiO_2 by MOCVD has inputs of temperature, total flow rate, chamber pressure, source pressure, precursor flow rate, along with the actual (measured) deposition rate R_a. The outputs are the unknown physical constants: D_0, A, and ΔE. These outputs are fed into the physical deposition rate expression [Eq. 18.5], the predicted deposition rate R_p is computed, and the result is compared with the actual (measured) deposition rate (see Fig. 18.6). The error signal in this case is defined as

$$E = 0.5(R_p - R_a)^2 \tag{18.7}$$

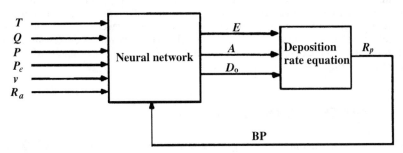

FIGURE 18.6   Illustration of the hybrid neural network process modeling architecture [21].

Since the expression for predicted deposition rate is differentiable, the new error gradient can be computed by using the chain rule as

$$\frac{\partial E}{\partial w_{ijk}} = \left(\frac{\partial E}{\partial R_p} \right) \left(\frac{\partial R_p}{\partial \text{out}_{ik}} \right) \left(\frac{\partial \text{out}_{ik}}{\partial w_{ijk}} \right) \tag{18.8}$$

where out_{ik} is the calculated output of the jth neuron in the kth layer. The first partial derivative in Eq. (18.8) is $(R_p - R_a)$, and the third is the same as that of standard BP. The second partial derivative is computed individually for each unknown parameter to be estimated. For example, referring back to Eq. (18.5), the partial derivative of the predicted deposition rate with respect to activation energy is

$$\partial R_p / \partial \Delta E = 4.4 \frac{-\dfrac{1}{kT} A e^{-\Delta E/kT}}{1 + \left(\dfrac{6.9 \times 10^{-5}}{D_0} T^{0.926} PQ^{-0.5} A e^{-\Delta E/kT} \right)} \frac{PP_e}{P - P_e} \frac{v}{Q} \tag{18.9}$$

The partial derivatives for the other two parameters are computed in a similar manner, and after error minimization using this modified form of BP, values of the three fitting parameters for the TiO$_2$ MOCVD process are known explicitly.

It has been previously mentioned that purely empirical neural networks require less training data to derive accurate process models than statistical techniques. Since hybrid neural networks rely on network training to predict only portions of a physical model, they require even less training data [23]. In Ref. 21, the hybrid network was trained in only 10 training experiments. A three-layer neural network with six inputs, eight hidden neurons, and three outputs (a 6-8-3 structure) proved to be the best network architecture for this case. After error minimization, the values of the diffusion coefficient D_0, the preexponential constant A, and the activation energy ΔE were determined to be 0.07×10^{-4} m^2/s, 0.878 m/s, and 6325 cal/mole, respectively.

Once trained, the hybrid neural network was subsequently used to predict the deposition rate for four additional MOCVD runs which constituted a test data set, not a part of the original experiment. The rms error of the deposition rate model predictions using the estimated parameters for the three remaining test vectors was only 0.66 μm/h. The measured rate for these experiments was approximately 8 μm/h, so this prediction error represented very good agreement. The hybrid neural network approach therefore represents general-purpose methodology for deriving semiempirical neural process models which take into account the underlying process physics. It is anticipated that such hybrid models will offer advantages in interpolation and extrapolation over other experimental techniques whenever approximate physical models are available.

18.4 PROCESS OPTIMIZATION

In semiconductor manufacturing applications, neural-network-based optimization has been undertaken from two fundamentally different viewpoints. The first uses statistical methods to optimize the neural process models themselves. The goal of this approach is to determine the proper network structure and set of BP learning parameters to minimize network training error, prediction error, and training time. The second approach to optimization focuses on using neural process models to optimize a given semiconductor fabrication process or determine specific process recipes to achieve a desired response [14, 34].

18.4.1 Network Optimization

The problem of optimizing network structure and values of the BP learning parameters for a given semiconductor process modeling application has been addressed by both Kim and May for plasma etch modeling [24] and Han et al. in modeling plasma-enhanced CVD [16]. Each used essentially the same approach: performing a statistically designed experiment in which network structure and learning parameters are varied in a systematic way, and using the results of this experiment to derive the optimal neural process model.

Although they offer advantages in both accuracy and predictive ability over other methods, neural process models contain several adjustable learning parameters whose proper values are unknown prior to model development. In addition, the structure of the network can be modified by adjusting the number of layers as well as the number of neurons per layer. As a result of the many possible combinations of these variables, the optimal network structure and values of network parameters for a given modeling application are not always clear. To increase the benefits of this modeling strategy, a systematic means of selecting an optimal set of parameters and network structure is an essential requirement. Among the most critical optimality issues for neural process models are learning capability, prediction (or generalization) capability, and convergence speed.

Neural network architecture is determined by the number of layers and number of neurons per layer. Usually, the number of input-layer and output-layer neurons is uniquely determined by the number of process inputs and responses in the modeling application. However, specifying the number of hidden-layer neurons is less obvious. It is generally understood that an excessively large number of hidden neurons may significantly increase training time and give poorer prediction of unfamiliar facts. Aside from network architecture are issues of optimal learning rate, initial weight range, momentum, and training tolerance.

A number of previous efforts at obtaining the optimal network structure have been described in the literature [25–27]. Other researchers have studied the effects of BP learning parameters on network performance [28–30]. However, the consideration of interactions between parameters has been lacking in most of the previous work in neural network optimization. Furthermore, much of the existing effort in this area has focused on improving networks designed to perform classification and pattern recognition tasks. The optimization of networks which model continuous nonlinear processes (such as those in semiconductor manufacturing) has not been adequately addressed. In Ref. 24, Kim and May presented an experiment designed to provide a comprehensive evaluation of all relevant learning and structural network parameters. The goal was to design an optimal neural network for a specific semiconductor manufacturing problem: modeling the etch rate of polysilicon in a CCl_4 plasma.

To develop the optimal neural process model, these researchers designed a *D-optimal* experiment [31] to investigate the effect of six factors: the number of hidden layers, the number of neurons per hidden layer, training tolerance, initial weight range, learning rate, and momentum. *D*-optimal designs give flexibility in designing experiments not provided by classical designs (such as factorial designs). Moreover, they provide the best quality of design when an experiment contains both qualitative and quantitative factors. A *D*-optimal design was therefore ideal for this experiment, since it involved both quantitative (or continuous) learning parameters as well as qualitative (or discrete) structural parameters.

This experiment determined how the structural and learning factors affect network performance and provided an optimal set of parameters for a given set of performance metrics. The network responses optimized were learning capability, predictive capability, and training speed. The experiment consisted of two stages. In the first stage, statistical experimental design was employed to fully characterize the behavior of the etch process [32]. Etch rate data from these trials was used to train neural process models. Once trained, the neural models were subsequently used to predict the etch rate for 12 additional test wafers. Prediction error for these additional wafers was also computed, and these two measures of network performance, along with training time, were used as experimental responses to optimize the neural etch rate model as the structural and learning parameters were varied in the second stage (which consisted of the *D*-optimal design).

Individual Network Parameter Optimization.   Independent optimization of each performance characteristic was then performed with the objective of minimizing training error, prediction error, and training time. A constrained multicriteria optimization technique based on the Nelder-Mead simplex search algorithm [33] was implemented in order to do so. The optimal parameter set was first found for each criterion individually, irrespective of the optimal set for the other two. The results of the independent optimization are summarized in Table 18.3.

Several interesting interactions and tradeoffs between the various parameters emerged in this study. One such tradeoff can be visualized in two-dimensional (2-D) contour plots such as those in Figs. 18.7 and 18.8. Figure 18.7 plots training error against training tolerance and initial weight range with all other parameters set at their optimal values. Learning capability improves with decreased tolerance and wider weight distribution. Intuitively, the first result can be attributed to the increased precision required by a tight tolerance. In addition, the larger initial spread in randomized weights gives the network greater tunability in mimicking the

TABLE 18.3 Optimized Network Inputs for Independent Optimization

Parameter	Training error	Prediction error	Training time
Hidden layers	1	1	1
Neurons/hidden layer	6	9	3
Training tolerance	0.08	0.13	0.09
Initial weight range	±2.00	±1.04	±1.00
Learning rate	2.78	2.80	0.81
Momentum	0.35	0.35	0.95
Optimal value	239 Å/min	162 Å/min	37.3 s

patterns in the training data. Figure 18.8 plots network prediction error versus the same variables as in Fig. 18.7. As expected, optimum prediction is observed at high tolerance and a narrow initial weight distribution. The latter result implies that the interaction between neurons within the restricted weight space while the network is training is a primary stimulus for improving prediction. Thus, although learning degrades with a wider weight range, generalization is improved. Also, with a larger tolerance, the BP algorithm is more capable of extrapolating the nonlinear relationships embedded in the trained network beyond the training data.

Collective Network Parameter Optimization. The parameter sets in Table 18.3 are useful to obtain optimized performance for a single criterion, but can provide unacceptable results for the other two. For example, the parameter set which minimizes training time yields very high training and prediction errors. Since it is not desirable to train three different networks corresponding to each performance metric for a given neural process model, it becomes necessary to optimize all network inputs simultaneously. This may be accomplished by implementing a suitable cost function such as

$$\text{Cost} = K_1\sigma_t^2 + K_2\sigma_p^2 + K_3 T^2 \qquad (18.10)$$

where σ_t is the network training error, σ_p is the prediction error, and T is the training time. The constants K_1, K_2, and K_3 are weights representing the relative importance of each performance measure.

Typically, prediction error is the most important quality characteristic, followed by training error. For modeling applications, a network need not be trained frequently, so training time is not as critical a consideration. To optimize the above cost function, the values chosen by Kim and May for these constants were $K_1 = 10, K_2 = 100$, and $K_3 = 1$. Optimization was again performed, this time on the overall cost function. The results of this collective optimization appear in Table 18.4.

The parameter values in Table 18.4 yield the minimum cost according to Eq. (18.10). Thus, a three-layer network with three hidden-layer neurons exhibits optimal behavior for the plasma etch modeling application. Optimal learning for this network is accomplished with a tight training tolerance, moderate initial weight distribution, high learning rate, and a small momentum term. This combination results in a training error of 412 Å/min, a prediction error of 340 Å/min, and a training time of 292 s. While this represents only marginally acceptable performance, these values may be tuned further by adjusting the cost function constants K_i and the optimization constraints until suitable performance is achieved.

The determination of an optimal set of network training parameters is required for any domain-specific neural process model. The results of this study provide gen-

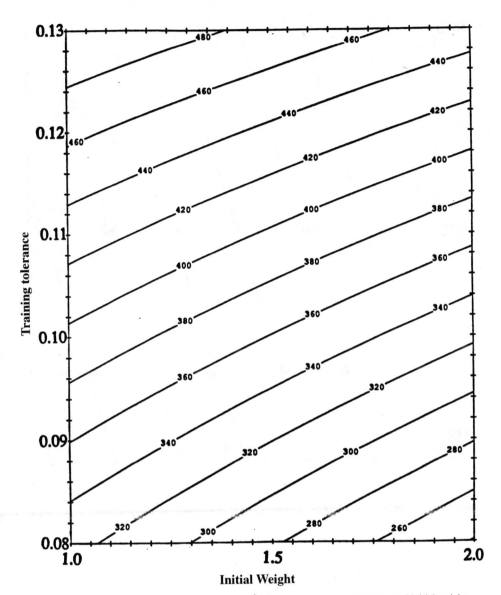

FIGURE 18.7 Contour plot of training error (Å/min) versus training tolerance and initial weight range [24]. (Learning rate = 2.8, momentum = 0.35, neuron number = 6, layer number = 1.) *(Copyright 1994 IEEE.)*

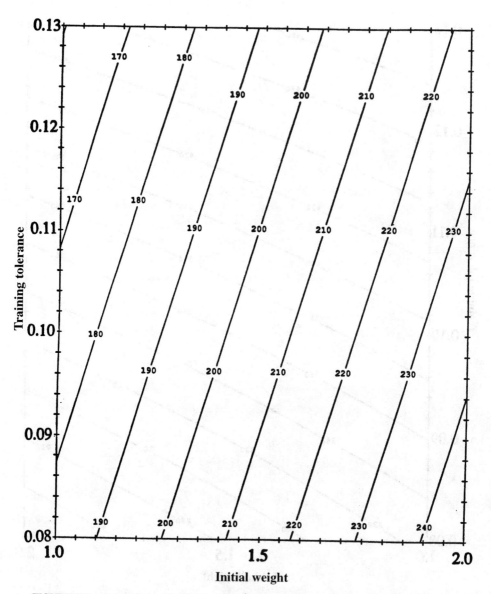

FIGURE 18.8   Contour plot of prediction error (Å/min) versus training tolerance and initial weight range [24]. (Learning rate = 2.8, momentum = 0.35, neuron number = 6, layer number = 1.) *(Copyright 1994 IEEE.)*

erally applicable rules of thumb for neural process modeling with BP networks, especially for the independently optimized parameter sets based on a single performance measure. Moreover, this method provides a systematic procedure for the adjustment of BP neural network parameters in any given modeling application.

TABLE 18.4   Optimized Network Inputs for
Collective Optimization

Parameter	Optimized value
Hidden layers	1
Neurons/hidden layer	3
Training tolerance	0.095
Initial weight range	±1.50
Learning rate	2.80
Momentum	0.35

18.4.2 Process Optimization

A natural extension of neural process modeling is using these models to optimize
the processes (as opposed to the networks) or to generate specific process recipes.
This type of optimization is designed to produce designated target output responses
based on the functional relationship between controllable input parameters and
process responses supplied by the neural process models. To illustrate the importance of process optimization, consider the PECVD of silicon dioxide films used as
interlayer dielectrics in multichip modules [16]. In this process, one would like to
grow a film with the lowest dielectric constant, best uniformity, minimal stress, and
lowest impurity concentration possible (Fig. 18.9). However, achieving these goals
usually requires a series of tradeoffs in growth conditions. Optimized neural process
models can help a process engineer navigate the complex response surface and provide the necessary combination of process conditions (temperature, pressure, gas
composition, etc.) or find the best compromise among potentially conflicting objectives to produce the desired results. Essentially, this requires using the neural process
model in reverse.

Such process optimization activities have been undertaken by both Nadi et al. of
the University of California at Berkeley [14] and Han and May of Georgia Tech [34]
using slightly different approaches. The Berkeley researchers used the generalization capabilities of neural nets configured as an associative memory to successfully
generate novel recipes for polysilicon LPCVD. They were able to synthesize process
recipes to meet two specific practical objectives. These new recipes were created by
generalizing the information used in developing neural network models of the
LPCVD process. The first recipe was for a zero-stress polysilicon film, and the second was for a uniform deposition rate over an entire production lot in a batch process under the condition of significant source gas depletion down the length of the
furnace tube. Both recipes were synthesized from the neural LPCVD models using
a stochastic optimization routine called ALOPEX, which is very similar to simulated
annealing [35]. The output of the generated recipes was confirmed by experiment
with excellent results.

In Ref. 34, Han and May used neural process models for the PECVD process
to synthesize other novel process recipes. To characterize the PECVD of silicon
dioxide (SiO_2) films, they first performed a 2^{5-1} fractional factorial experiment with
three center-point replications [16]. Data from these experiments were used to
develop neural process models for SiO_2 deposition rate, refractive index, permittivity, film stress, wet etch rate, uniformity, silanol concentration, and water concentration. The recipe synthesis procedure was then performed to generate the necessary
deposition conditions to obtain specific film qualities, including zero stress, 100 percent uniformity, low permittivity, and minimal impurity concentration. This synthesis

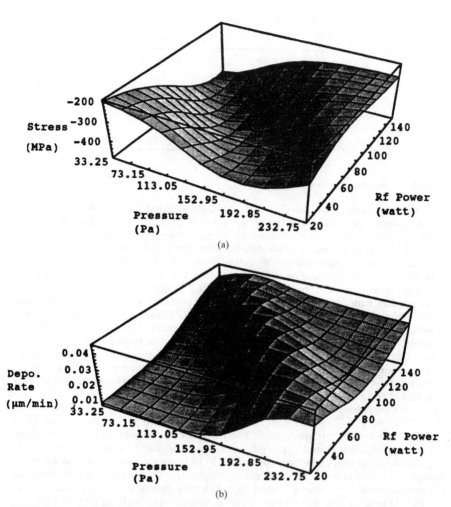

FIGURE 18.9 Examples of response surfaces generated by the application of neural process modeling to PECVD silicon dioxide films. (*a*) Deposition rate vs. chamber pressure and rf power; (*b*) film stress versus chamber pressure and rf power. These surfaces are typical of those that must be effectively searched in order to locate the optimal growth conditions [16]. (SiH_4 = 300 sccm, N_2O = 650 sccm, temp. subst. = 300°C.)

procedure was unique in that it utilized *genetic algorithms* to search the response surfaces for the appropriate recipe.

Genetic algorithms (GAs) were first proposed by John Holland at the University of Michigan in 1975 [36]. GAs are guided stochastic search techniques based on the mechanics of genetics. They use three operations found in natural genetics to guide their trek through the search space: *selection, crossover,* and *mutation.* Using these operations, GAs are able to search through large, irregularly shaped spaces such as those in Fig. 18.9 quickly, requiring only objective function value information (detailing the quality of possible solutions) to guide the search. This is an inviting characteristic, considering that the majority of commonly used search techniques require derivative information, continuity of the search space, or complete knowledge of the objective function to guide their search. Furthermore, GAs take a more global view of the search space than many methods currently encountered in engineering optimization.

In computing terms, a genetic algorithm maps a problem onto a set of binary strings, each string representing a potential solution. The GA then manipulates the most promising strings in searching for improved solutions. A GA operates typically through a simple cycle of four stages:

1. Creation of a population of strings
2. Evaluation of each string
3. Selection of "best" strings
4. Genetic manipulation, to create the new population of strings

During each computational cycle, a new generation of possible solutions for a given problem is produced. At the first stage, an initial population of potential solutions is created as a starting point for the search process. Each element of the population is encoded into a string (the "chromosome"), to be manipulated by the genetic operators. In the next stage, the performance (or *fitness*) of each individual of the population is evaluated. Based on each individual string's fitness a selection mechanism chooses mates for the genetic manipulation process. The selection policy is responsible for assuring survival of the most fit individuals.

Binary strings are typically used in coding genetic searches. A common method of coding multiparameter optimization problems is concatenated, multiparameter, mapped, fixed-point coding [37]. Using this procedure, if an unsigned integer x is the decoded parameter of interest, then x can be mapped linearly from $[0, 2^l]$ to a specified interval $[U_{min}, U_{max}]$ (where l is the length of the binary string). In this way, both the range and precision of the decision variables can be controlled. The precision π of this coding may be calculated as

$$\pi = \frac{U_{max} - U_{min}}{2^l - 1} \tag{18.11}$$

To construct a multiparameter coding, as many single parameter strings as required can simply be concatenated. Each coding may have its own sublength (i.e., its own U_{max} and U_{min}). Figure 18.10 shows an example of a two-parameter coding with four bits in each parameter.

The string manipulation process employs genetic operators to produce a new population of individuals ("offspring") by manipulating the genetic "code" possessed by members ("parents") of the current population. It consists of *selection,*

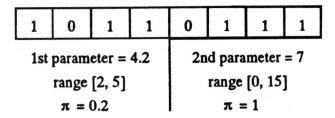

FIGURE 18.10   Example of multiparameter binary coding.

crossover, and *mutation* operations. *Selection* is the process by which strings with high fitness values (i.e., good solutions to the optimization problem under consideration) receive larger numbers of copies in the new population. In one popular method of selection, strings with fitness value F_i are assigned a proportionate probability of survival into the next generation. This probability distribution is determined according to

$$P_i = \frac{F_i}{\Sigma F} \qquad (18.12)$$

Thus, an individual string whose fitness is n times better than another's will produce n times the number of offspring in the subsequent generation. Once the strings have reproduced, they await the actions of the crossover and mutation operators.

The *crossover* operator takes two chromosomes and interchanges part of their genetic information to produce two new chromosomes (see Fig. 18.11). After the crossover point has been randomly chosen, portions of the parent strings ($P1$ and $P2$) are swapped to produce the new offspring ($O1$ and $O2$) based on a specified crossover probability. *Mutation* is motivated by the possibility that the initially defined population might not contain all the information necessary to solve the problem. This operation is implemented by randomly changing a fixed number of bits every generation according to a specified mutation probability (see Fig. 18.12). Typical values for the probabilities of crossover and bit mutation range from 0.6 to 0.95 and 0.001 to 0.01, respectively. Higher rates disrupt good string building blocks more often, and for smaller populations, sampling errors tend to wash out the predictions.

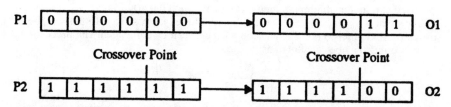

FIGURE 18.11 The crossover operation.

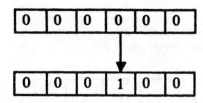

FIGURE 18.12 The mutation operation.

For the synthesis of PECVD recipes in [34], Han and May set the probabilities of crossover and mutation to 0.6 and 0.01, respectively. A population size of 100 was used in each generation. Each of the five process input parameters was coded as a 40-bit string, resulting in a total chromosome length of 200 bits. The desired output characteristics of the SiO_2 films to be produced were reflected in the fitness function:

$$F = \frac{1}{1 + C(y)} \qquad (18.13)$$

The cost function $C(y)$ is given by

$$C(y) = \Sigma_r |y_d - y| \qquad (18.14)$$

where y_d are the desired process responses, y are the process responses dictated by the current choice of input parameters coded in the 200-bit string, and r is the number of responses. The GA generated a population of 100 possible solutions in each generation. These solutions (which are input recipes represented by concatenated 40-bit substrings) were decoded and fed into the neural process models. The fitness of the solutions was evaluated using Eq. (18.13) for each population. Maximization of F was continued for 500 generations.

Genetic algorithms were used to synthesize process recipes which represent highly desirable film properties. This synthesis procedure was unique in that none of the desired characteristics appeared in the original training data for the neural process models. The film properties to be obtained included 100 percent uniformity, 0 percent impurity (silanol and water) concentration, low dielectric constant, and zero residual stress. The recipes generated to produce such films, along with the simulated process outputs (as predicted by the neural process model) are shown in Table 18.5.

TABLE 18.5   PECVD Recipes Generated by Genetic Algorithms

Desired characteristic	Simulation results
100% Uniformity	100%
Low dielectric constant	3.12
0% impurities	0.43% water, 1.69% silanol
Zero residual stress	56.21 MPa

The synthesis procedure was successful in nearly every case. Note that in the case of residual stress and impurity concentration, for example, the algorithm could not find zero points on the response surface, indicating that the neural process model predicts that no input recipe can achieve these goals given the constraints on the search space. At the time of this writing, these simulation results are being verified by experiment.

For multiproduct semiconductor manufacturing environments, equipment utilization tends to be low, partly due to the time needed to design and fine-tune process recipes. This task is further complicated by the fact that recipes must often balance process objectives and equipment limitations. To facilitate more effective manufacturing, process recipes must yield results that are insensitive to process and equipment variations. Thus, recipe generation and optimization procedures can provide invaluable assistance to process engineers when they are considering the design of the optimal combination of process conditions to obtain specific objectives.

18.4.3   Optimization of Model-Building Experiments

Yet another optimization task involves optimizing the actual experimental conditions used to *build* neural process models. In fact, a major question yet to be answered in using neural nets for semiconductor process modeling concerns determining the proper number and sequence of experiments to run. Although for statistical regression techniques (such as RSM), there exists a well-established theoretical basis for designing experiments, the same can not be said for neural-net-based process modeling. Since the acquisition of experimental data can be costly for semiconductor processes, the amount and type of experiments required for proper characterization and the conditions under which this data are obtained are critical concerns.

Research by Boning and White [38] at the Massachusetts Institute of Technology Microsystems Technology Laboratory and Laboratory for Information and Decision Systems is aimed at addressing these issues by identifying a general methodology for the use of optimal experimental design techniques in conjunction with neural network learning. The goal is to determine whether optimal experimental design can provide the necessary information regarding the proper process conditions under which experiments should be conducted, thereby defining a suitable data set for subsequent function approximation using neural networks.

18.5 PROCESS MONITORING AND CONTROL

As a result of consistent demands on semiconductor manufacturers to produce circuits with increased density and complexity, stringent process control has become an issue of growing importance. Efficient and robust process control techniques require accurate monitoring of the ambient process conditions which characterize a given fabrication step. Historically, statistical process control (SPC) has been used to achieve the necessary level of control. This method is designed to minimize costly misprocessing by applying control charts to monitor fluctuations in critical process variables [39]. Although SPC techniques are able to detect undesirable process shifts, they are usually applied off line. These techniques, therefore, suffer from the drawback of being incapable of detecting shifts until after the process step in question is complete. This delay can result in the fabrication of devices that do not conform to required specifications. Recently, neural networks have been used to address these issues from two different perspectives: (1) monitoring the variation in manufacturing process conditions for real-time SPC [40] and (2) developing real-time, closed-loop process control schemes which use in-situ process sensors make on-line adjustments in process set points. Each of these techniques is discussed below.

18.5.1 Process Monitoring and Statistical Process Control

The objective of real-time SPC is to take advantage of the availability of on-line sensor data from semiconductor fabrication equipment in order to identify process shifts and out-of-control equipment states and generate real-time malfunction alarms. This offers the benefit of on-line process monitoring for generating alarms at the very onset of a shift. The application of real-time SPC is complicated, however, by the correlated nature of the sensor data. Traditional SPC is based on the assumption that the data to be monitored in controlling a process is *identically independent and normally distributed* (IIND). This assumption is not valid, however, when applied to real-time data. These data are often nonstationary (subject to mean and variance shifts), auto-correlated (dependent on data from previous time points), and cross-correlated (dependent on the values of other concurrently measured parameters).

In Ref. 40, Baker et al. addressed these difficulties by employing neural networks to develop time series models which filtered cross- and autocorrelation from real-time sensor data. In other prior research efforts, neural network-based control charts demonstrated significantly improved performance over traditional Shewhart control charts in preventing Type II errors (i.e., missed alarms) and detecting small process shifts [41]. Such superiority was attributed to neural networks' abilities to learn arbitrary mappings of complex nonlinear data sequences, handle noisy and corrupted data, and simultaneously monitor multiple process variables. Furthermore, neural networks have been applied to predict the behavior of chaotic time series. In Ref. 42, *ontogenic* neural networks (i.e., those that modify their own topology during training) were successfully used to predict continuous-valued aperiodic functions such as the Mackey-Glass equation. In Ref. 43, recurrent neural networks were able to model time series in short-term load forecasting of electrical power systems when statistically based models proved inadequate. Finally, wavelet neural networks (or *wavenets*) have been used as a modified version of the wavelet transform to predict time series in signal processing applications [44].

In applying this methodology to semiconductor manufacturing, Baker et al. developed a real-time equipment monitoring system that transfers data from a reactive ion etching system to a remote workstation. The processes monitored were the etching of aluminum by chloroform (CHF_3) and boron trichloride (BCl_3). The parameters monitored included gas flow rates, rf power, temperature, pressure, and dc bias. Data sampled at 50 samples/second was used to train backpropagation neural networks. The trained networks were then used both to forecast the time series data and to generate a malfunction alarm when the sampled data did not conform to its specification within a designated tolerance.

Time Series Modeling. Conventional SPC techniques are based on the assumption that data generated by a controlled process are IIND. The IIND assumption, however, is not valid for applying control charts directly to data acquired real-time, since real-time data is nonstationary, autocorrelated, and cross-correlated. Time series modeling is employed to account for correlation in real-time data. The purpose of a time series model is to describe the chronological dependence among sequential samples of a given variable. Passing raw data through time series filters results in residual forecasting error which is IIND. Therefore, once an adequate time series model has been developed, it can legitimately be used for SPC. One of the most basic time series models is the univariate Box-Jenkins autoregressive moving average (ARMA) model [45].

Data collected from modern semiconductor manufacturing equipment can also be represented by means of time series models, and Baker et al. showed that neural networks may be used to generalize the behavior of a time series. They referred to this new genre of time series model as the *neural time series* (NTS) model. As with statistical time series models such as ARMA, once an NTS model is developed, the forecast data can be used on conventional control charts. However, unlike the ARMA family of models, the NTS model is capable of simultaneously filtering both auto- and cross-correlated data. In other words, the NTS model can account for correlation among several variables being monitored simultaneously.

The neural network used to model the RIE process was trained off line on data acquired when the process was under control. The parameter of interest was the BCl_3, but the same methodology could be extended to any other process variable. The NTS network was trained to model the BCl_3 flow using a unique sampling technique which involved training the network to forecast the next BCl_3 value from the behavior of 10 past values. The network was trained on a subset of the total autocorrelated data which consisted of the first 11 out of every 100 samples. To quantify the performance of the trained network, it was then tested on 11 midrange samples (samples 51–61, 151–161, etc.) out of every 100.

Autocorrelation among consecutive BCl_3 measurements was accounted for by simultaneously training the network on the present value of the BCl_3 and 10 past values. Cross-correlation among the BCl_3 and the other six parameters was modeled by including as inputs to the NTS network the present values of the temperature, pressure, incident and reflected rf power, chlorine, and the BCl_3 itself. The resulting network topology therefore had 17 input neurons, 10 hidden neurons, and a single output neuron (see Fig. 18.13). The future value of the BCl_3 at time $(t + T)$ was forecast at the network output (where T is the sampling period).

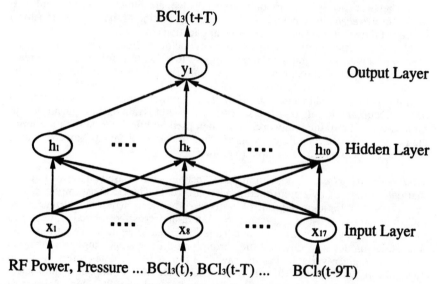

FIGURE 18.13   NTS network structure [40]. *(Copyright 1995 IEEE.)*

Figure 18.14 shows the measured and NTS model predictions of the BCl_3 data. Each point on the graph represents one out of every 100 samples, beginning with sample 61. (Recall that samples 51–61, 151–161, etc. were used as test data for the trained network.) The NTS model very closely approximates the actual value. Even when there are drastic changes in the BCl_3, the NTS network was able to quickly adapt. This technique yielded an excellent rms error of 1.40 standard cm^3/min. This small error indicates that the sampling rate of 50 samples/second was probably higher than what was actually required. In fact, since only 10 percent of this data was needed to build very accurate NTS models, the sampling rate could theoretically have been reduced to as low as 5 samples/second.

Malfunction Detection.   The NTS model can be used to generate a real-time alarm signal when sampled process data does not conform to its previously established pattern, indicating a possible equipment malfunction or other out-of-control state.

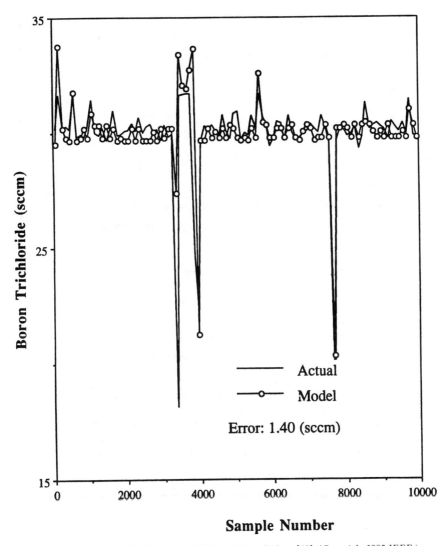

FIGURE 18.14   Measured BCl_3 flow and NTS model predictions [40]. *(Copyright 1995 IEEE.)*

This capability was demonstrated on an actual RIE malfunction. In this case, aluminum was etched in a chloroform and chlorine gas mixture. The malfunction consisted of an unstable feed condition in the CHF_3 mass flow controller. Figure 18.15 is a plot of the gas flows during the period leading up to the malfunction. Although the Cl_2 flow appears to fall out of compliance at the 200th sample, this was not the cause of the malfunction. The true cause may be discerned by observing the behavior of the CHF_3 several samples earlier and comparing the instability of its flow to the more stable and consistent readings exhibited by the Cl_2 during the same time span.

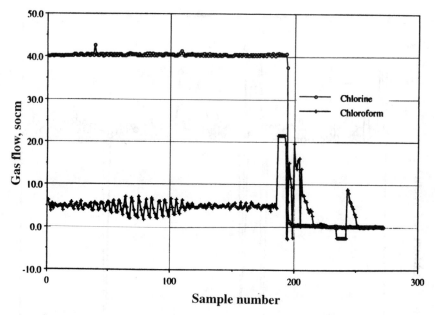

FIGURE 18.15 Chlorine and chloroform flow rates for an aluminum etch step just prior to an equipment malfunction [40]. *(Copyright 1995 IEEE.)*

A careful study of this situation then reveals that the chloroform mass flow controller was not able to regulate the gas flow correctly, and consequently the RIE control circuitry aborted the process, thus causing the Cl_2 to shut off.

The on-line application of the NTS model was used to generate an alarm signal warning of the impending CHF_3 out-of-control condition even before the RIE aborted itself. Recall that the NTS model acts as a filter to remove autocorrelation and cross-correlation from the raw process data. Thus, the residuals which result from computing the difference between NTS model predictions and the measured values of the CHF_3 flow are IIND random variables. As a result, these residuals can be plotted on a standard Shewhart control chart in order to identify process shifts. In this case, alarm generation was based on the well-known Western Electric Rules, which are summarized below [39]:

1. One data point plots outside the 3-σ control limits.

2. Two out of three consecutive points plot beyond the 2-σ warning limits.

3. Four out of five consecutive points plot 1 σ or beyond from the centerline.

4. Eight consecutive points plot on one side of the centerline.

Although this malfunction eventually broke all these rules, the violation of Rule 4 was invoked to generate the malfunction alarm. The data from the RIE malfunction was fed into the NTS network with CHF_3 serving as the forecast parameter. Figure 18.16 demonstrates that the NTS model once again closely resembled the actual data sequence until the malfunction occurred, at which point the CHF_3 instability became too great and the NTS model predictions diverged from the measurements. Figure 18.17 shows the measurement residuals resulting from the difference between the

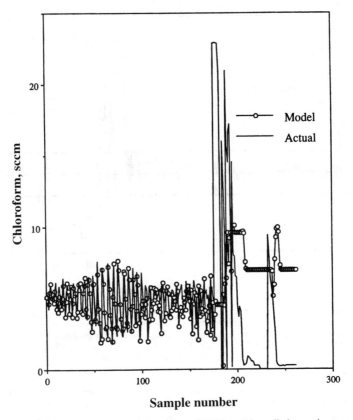

FIGURE 18.16   Measured CHF$_3$ flow and NTS model predictions prior to RIE malfunction [40]. *(Copyright 1995 IEEE.)*

NTS model predictions and the actual sensor data. When eight consecutive points in the data sequence are plotted on one side of the centerline (which occurred at the 18th sample), the NTS network immediately responded by signaling an alarm.

At the point where the NTS alarm is generated, the value of the mean shift in CHF$_3$ flow was merely 0.25σ, which indicates that the NTS model is quite sensitive to small shifts. For the same malfunction, the internal RIE process control circuitry did not respond until significantly later (at about the 170th sample). The rapid NTS response time can be instrumental in the identification of incipient equipment faults and the prevention of subsequent misprocessing. This illustrates an important trade-off that occurs when the data sampling rate is chosen. Even though the chosen rate of 50 samples/second proved to be unnecessary to build an accurate NTS model, this high rate can ensure that malfunction detection is nearly immediate.

18.5.2 Closed-Loop Process Control

Since neural networks excel in modeling processes with complex dynamics, they have also been successfully applied to the real-time, closed-loop control of a diverse array

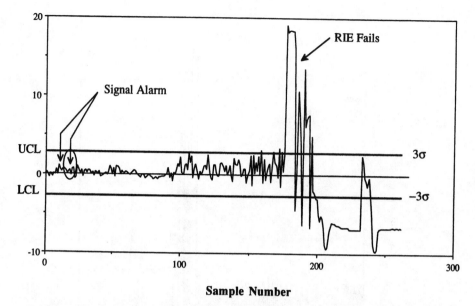

Sample Number

FIGURE 18.17 Measurement residuals from NTS model before RIE malfunction plotted on a 3σ control chart. The first arrow indicates the beginning of an 8-point sequence of data which plots above the centerline, which is a violation of the Western Electric Rules. The second arrow (circled) indicates where an alarm is generated by the NTS model [40]. *(Copyright 1995 IEEE.)*

of such processes, including arc welding [46], machining operations [47], lithographic color printing [48], and even linear accelerator beam positioning [49]. Neural nets are well-suited to process control since they can be used to build predictive models from multivariate sensor data generated by process monitors. It therefore comes as no surprise that neural-network-based control techniques are also appearing in semiconductor manufacturing. In fact, the Kopin Corporation of Taunton, Mass., has used neural network control techniques to reduce dopant concentration and deposition thickness errors in solar cell manufacturing by more than a factor of two [50].

This strategy is also being pursued by Rietman et al. of AT&T Bell Laboratories, who have designed a neural network to compute in real time the overetch time for a plasma gate etch step [51]. This time computation was based on a neural network mapping of the mean values of fluctuations about control variable set points as well as an in-situ optical emission monitor. By monitoring a single optical emission wavelength during etching, the researchers were able to infer information regarding etch rate, etch uniformity, pattern density, and cleanliness of the reaction chamber. In neural network training, vectors representing process "signatures" inherent in the emission trace and set points were mapped to the ideal etch time for a desired oxide thickness. This training procedure is illustrated in Fig. 18.18. The backpropagation network used to perform the control operation consisted of 36 input nodes, five hidden-layer neurons, and one output.

This system has been learning on line since mid-1993. During this time, the network has trained on many thousands of wafers. After months of close observation, the network was eventually turned loose for independent control of a production etcher. This has eliminated the need for human intervention in determining the

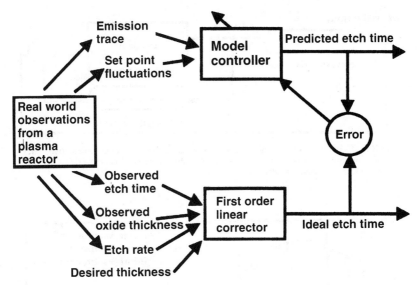

FIGURE 18.18   Illustration of training method for wafer-to-wafer neural network control of a plasma gate etch [51].

proper overetch time. In the opinion of the Bell Labs engineers, in addition to reducing process variation, increasing yield, and reducing manufacturing cost, this functional adaptive controller has the potential to extend the useful life of the processing equipment, since design rules continue to shrink and greater demands are constantly being placed on equipment performance.

University research groups are also participating in these efforts. The group at MIT under the direction of Boning is also focused on the development and analysis of in-situ sensing and control methods for the plasma etch process [38]. They are currently investigating a combined approach using compression of real-time optical emission and mass spectroscopy data and neural-network-based fitting algorithms for correlating multivariate sensor data for etch diagnostics and control. May and the Georgia Tech researchers, on the other hand, are pursuing a control scheme that will utilize two backpropagation neural networks operating in unison: one trained to emulate the process in question, and another trained to learn the inverse dynamics of the process and perform the control operation [52].

In this arrangement, neural process models must be available which both predict the process outputs based on a set of operating conditions (*forward* models) *and* those which can determine the appropriate set of operating conditions based on a desired output response (*reverse* models). If these conditions are met, then the process control technique may be implemented as shown in Fig. 18.19. Here, the measured process output is compared to that of a forward neural process model (the process *emulator*). The error signal generated by this comparison is then fed to the reverse neural model, which performs the control operation to keep the process output at its desired level. This control architecture allows both the emulator and controller networks to be trained continuously on line.

Figure 18.20 provides simulation results showing the application of the dual neural network feedforward/feedback control scheme. In this case, a noisy process

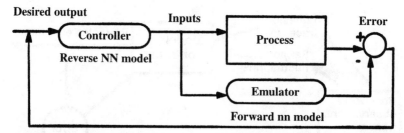

FIGURE 18.19 Illustration of adaptive process control scheme using two back-propagation neural networks: a forward network (labeled *emulator*) and a reverse network (*controller*) [50]. *(Copyright 1994 IEEE.)*

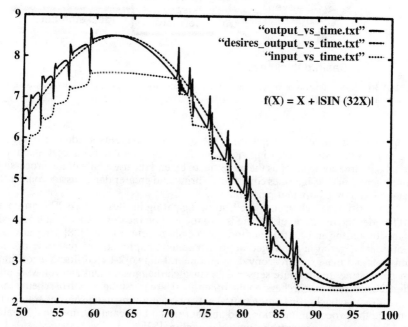

FIGURE 18.20 Simulation results for feedforward/feedback control scheme.

has been simulated by the nonlinear function $f(x) = x + |\sin 32x|$, and the control objective was to force the simulated process output to follow a sinusoidal trajectory. This figure shows the desired process output, simulated process output and controlled input for this single-input, single-output system. It can be seen that the controller forces the process to follow the desired trajectory quite well, given the nonlinear behavior of the function. It is therefore anticipated that this scheme will also achieve acceptable performance in an actual process control application, where the desired output is usually a static set point, rather than a time-varying sinusoid.

18.6 PROCESS DIAGNOSIS

Neural networks have been widely used in process monitoring and diagnosis [5, 53], primarily in mechanical machining operations such as cutting or injection molding. For example, Burke and Rangwala discussed a neural network approach for tool conditioning in metal cutting [54]. Wasserman et al. used neural networks to detect and measure small cracks in the shafts of rotating machines [55]. Recently, neural nets have also begun to appear in the area of electronics systems diagnosis. Murphy and Kagle utilized the pattern identification capabilities of neural networks for the recognition of electronic malfunctions [56]. In keeping with this trend of growing popularity, the use of neural nets for process diagnosis in semiconductor manufacturing is also gaining attention. The approaches that have been undertaken by researchers in this area include diagnosis at three distinct levels of the manufacturing process: (1) the equipment level, (2) the circuit level, and (3) the wafer level.

18.6.1 Equipment Level Diagnosis

In a recently initiated joint venture sponsored by Sematech, NeuroDyne (a neural net software firm located in Cambridge, Mass.), Texas Instruments (in Dallas), and Lam Research Corporation (a plasma etch equipment manufacturer in Fremont, Calif.) are examining the application of neural-network-based in-situ diagnostic schemes to plasma etching in TI's IC fabrication environment. The goal of this program is the combined implementation of data compression and neural-net-based fault detection and identification into a Lam etcher [38]. This group is employing a hybrid scheme which involves using neural networks in tandem with traditional expert-system approaches to diagnosis. Such techniques can effectively serve to offset the weaknesses of each method when used alone [57]. Traditional expert systems excel at reasoning from previously viewed data, while neural networks can extrapolate analyses and perform generalized classification when new scenarios arise.

The hybrid scheme is also the strategy being employed by Kim and May at Georgia Tech, who are developing a working prototype for real-time, automated malfunction diagnosis of IC fabrication equipment. The system is being implemented on a Plasma Therm 700 series RIE, with the ultimate objective of outlining general diagnostic strategy that is applicable to other rapid single-wafer processes. Diagnostic systems which rely on postprocess measurements and electrical test data alone cannot rapidly detect process shifts and also identify process faults. Since unreliable equipment causes product quality to be jeopardized, it is essential to diagnose the root causes for the malfunctions quickly and accurately. May and Spanos have previously developed a real-time diagnostic system which integrates evidence from various sources using the Dempster-Shafer rules of *evidential reasoning* [58].

In an extension of this work, Kim and May have integrated neural networks into this knowledge-based expert system. Diagnosis is conducted by this system in three chronological phases: the *maintenance* phase, the *on-line* phase, and the *in-line* phase. Neural networks are being used in the maintenance phase to model equipment maintenance history and component reliability. For on-line diagnosis in the case of previously encountered faults, neural networks are used to encode the fault patterns as in Ref. 40. Finally, neural process models of RIE response variables (such as etch rate) derived from prior experimentation are used to analyze the in-line measurements, and identify the most suitable candidate among possible faulty input parameters (i.e., pressure, gas flow, etc.).

Hybrid neural expert systems offer the advantage of easier knowledge acquisition and maintenance, besides allowing implicit knowledge to be extracted (through neural network learning) with the assistance of explicit expert rules. The only perceived disadvantage in neural expert systems is that, unlike other rule-based systems, the somewhat nonintuitive nature of neural networks can make it difficult to provide the user with explanations about how diagnostic conclusions are reached [5]. However, these barriers are lessening as more and more successful systems are demonstrated and become available. It is anticipated that the coming decade will see neural networks integrated firmly into diagnostic software in newly created fabrication facilities.

18.6.2 Circuit Level Diagnosis

At the integrated circuit level, Plummer has developed a *process control neural network* (PCNN) to identify faults in bipolar operational amplifiers (or *op amps*) based on electrical test data [59]. This network exploits the capability of neural nets to interpret multidimensional data and identify clusters of performance within such a data set. This provides enhanced sensitivity to sources of variation which may not be distinguishable from observing traditional single-variable control charts. Given a vector of electrical test results as input, the PCNN can evaluate the probability of membership in each set of clusters, which represent different categories of circuit faults. The network can then either report the various fault probabilities, or select the most likely fault category.

Representing one of the few cases in semiconductor manufacturing in which backpropagation networks are not employed, the PCNN is formed by replacing the output layer of a probabilistic neural network with a Grossberg layer (Fig. 18.21). In the probabilistic network, input data is fed to a set of pattern nodes. The pattern layer is trained using weights developed with a Kohonen self-organizing network. Each pattern node contains an exemplar vector of values corresponding to an input variable typical of the category it represents. If more than one exemplar represents a single category, the number of exemplars reflects the probability that a randomly selected pattern will be included in that category. The proximity of each input vector to each pattern is computed, and the results are analyzed in the summation layer.

The Grossberg layer functions as a lookup table. Each node in this layer contains a weight corresponding to each category defined by the probabilistic network. These weights reflect the conditional probability of a cause belonging to the corresponding category. Outputs from the Grossberg layer then reflect the products of the conditional probabilities. Together, these probabilities constitute a Pareto distribution of possible causes for a given test result (which is represented in the PCNN input vector). The Grossberg layer is trained in a supervised manner, which requires that the cause for each instance of membership in a fault category must be recorded beforehand.

Despite its somewhat misleading name, Plummer applied the PCNN in a diagnostic (as opposed to a control) application. In Ref. 59, a popular circuit simulation package called *SPICE* was used to generate two sets of highly correlated input/output op amp test data, one representing an in-control process and the other a process grossly out of control. Even though the second data set represented faulty circuit behavior, its descriptive statistics alone gave no indication of suspicious electrical test data. Training the Kohonen network using electrical test results from these data sets produced four distinct clusters (representing one acceptable and three faulty states).

With the Kohonen exemplars serving as weights in the pattern layer, the PCNN was then used to identify one of the three possible out-of-control conditions: (1) low

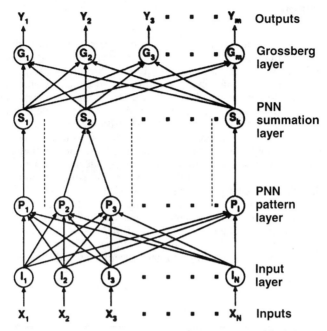

FIGURE 18.21 Process control neural network [59].

npn beta; (2) high *npn* beta and low resistor tolerance; or (3) high *npn* beta and high resistor tolerance. The summation layer of the PCNN reported the conditional probability of each of these conditions as well as the probability that the op amp measurements were acceptable for each input pattern of electrical test data. The PCNN realized a 93 percent level of accuracy in overall diagnosis, and correctly sounded alarms for 86 percent of the out-of-control cases (no false alarms were generated). The PCNN was therefore shown to be an exceptional adaptive diagnostic tool.

18.6.3 Wafer Level Diagnosis

In another diagnostic application, Sikka of Intel's Artificial Intelligence Laboratories in Santa Clara has used BP neural networks for wafer map analysis [60]. To do so, a technique was developed to detect and characterize spatial features on gray scale cumulative wafer maps acquired at the final wafer sort step. These cumulative maps are obtained by summing the contents of several individual wafer maps, each consisting of the pass/fail status of each tested die on the wafer. Defects from certain process steps produce characteristic spatial features on the cumulative maps. The Intel *wafer map analyzer* (WMA) software combines standard image processing (to enhance features and extract specific attributes) with neural networks (to determine categories and locations of the extracted attributes) to reduce the need for impractical and lengthy visual wafer inspection. In so doing, this system, accurate to nearly 100 percent, can assist with diagnostic troubleshooting by providing warning signs of potential equipment failures in key process steps.

18.7 SUMMARY

In semiconductor manufacturing, process and equipment reliability directly influence cost, throughput, and yield. Over the next several years, significant process modeling and control efforts will be required to reach projected targets for future generations of microelectronic devices and integrated circuits. Computer-assisted methods will provide a strategic advantage in undertaking these tasks, and among such methods, neural networks have certainly proven to be a viable technique.

Thus far, neural networks have not yet become routine in semiconductor manufacturing at the process engineering level. In fact, the use of neural networks at the present time is probably at a comparable point in its evolution to that of statistical experimental design or Taguchi methodology a decade ago, and now statistical methods such as these have become pervasive in the industry. The outlook for neural nets is therefore similarly promising. New applications are appearing and software is constantly being developed to meet the needs of these applications (see Table 18.6). The overall impact of neural-network-based techniques in this field depends primarily on fundamental awareness of their capabilities and limitations, coupled with a commitment to their implementation. With each new successful application, neural networks continue to gain acceptance, and thus their future is bright.

TABLE 18.6 Summary of Neural Network Applications in Semiconductor Manufacturing

	Process modeling	Process optimization	Monitoring and control	Process diagnosis	Commercial product
Corporations:					
AT&T	×		×		
DuPont	×				×
Kopin			×		
Intel				×	
TI/NeuroDyne/Lam			×	×	
Universities:					
Georgia Tech	×	×	×	×	
MIT		×	×	×	
University of California, Berkeley	×	×			

REFERENCES

1. G. Amelio, "Managing the Integration of Semiconductor Manufacturing," *International Semiconductor Manufacturing Sciences Symp.*, July 1993.

2. P. Losleben, "Semiconductor Manufacturing in the 21st Century: Capital Investment vs. Technological Innovation," *Proc. 12th IEEE/CHMT International Electronic Manufacturing Technology Symp.*, Oct., 1990.

3. M. Moslehi et al., "Single-Wafer Integrated Semiconductor Device Processing," *IEEE Trans. Electron Devices*, vol. 39, no. 1, January 1992.

4. D. Hodges, L. Rowe, and C. Spanos, "Computer Integrated Manufacturing of VLSI," *Proc. 11th IEEE/CHMT International Electronic Manufacturing Technology Symp.*, September 1989.

5. S. Huang and H. Zhang, "Artificial Neural Networks in Manufacturing: Concepts, Applications and Perspectives," *IEEE Trans. Component Packaging and Manufacturing Technology,* Part A, vol. 17, no. 2, June 1994.

6. J. Hopfield and D. Tank, "Neural Computation of Decisions in Optimization Problems," *Biological Cybernetics,* vol. 52, 1985.

7. R. Lippman, "An Introduction to Computing with Neural Nets," *IEEE ASSP Magazine,* April 1987.

8. C. Himmel, and G. May, "Advantages of Plasma Etch Modeling Using Neural Networks Over Statistical Techniques," *IEEE Trans. Semiconductor Manufacturing,* vol. 6, no. 2, May 1993.

9. M. Mocella, J. Bondur, and T. Turner, "Etch Process Characterization Using Neural Network Methodology: A Case Study," *SPIE Proc. Module Metrology, Control and Clustering,* vol. 1594, 1991.

10. A. Owens and M. Mocella, "An Experimental Design Advisor and Neural Network Analysis Package," *Proc. IEEE International Workshop on Artificial Neural Networks,* September 1991.

11. E. Rietman and E. Lory, "Use of Neural Networks in Semiconductor Manufacturing Processes: An Example for Plasma Etch Modeling," *IEEE Trans. Semiconductor Manufacturing,* vol. 6, no. 4, November 1993.

12. D. Manos and D. Flamm, *Plasma Etching: An Introduction,* San Diego: Academic Press, 1989.

13. G. Box and N. Draper, *Empirical Model-Building and Response Surfaces,* New York: Wiley, 1987.

14. F. Nadi, A. Agogino, and D. Hodges, "Use of Influence Diagrams and Neural Networks in Modeling Semiconductor Manufacturing Processes," *IEEE Trans. Semiconductor Manufacturing,* vol. 4, no. 1, February 1991.

15. C. Bose and H. Lord, "Neural Network Models in Wafer Fabrication," *SPIE Proc. Applications of Artificial Neural Networks,* vol. 1965, 1993.

16. S. Han, M. Ceiler, S. Bidstrup, P. Kohl, and G. May, "Modeling the Properties of PECVD Silicon Dioxide Films Using Optimized Back-Propagation Neural Networks," *IEEE Trans. Component Packaging and Manufacturing Technology,* vol. 17, no. 2, June 1994.

17. B. Kim and G. May, "Modeling Reactive Ion Etching of Silicon Dioxide Films Using Neural Networks," *Proc. 1994 Electronic Components and Technology Conf.,* May 1994.

18. G. Box, W. Hunter, and J. Hunter, *Statistics for Experimenters,* New York: Wiley, 1978.

19. S. Kirkpatrick, C. Gelatt, and M. Vecchi, "Optimization by Simulated Annealing," *Science,* vol. 220, May 1983.

20. L. Nadel, L. Cooper, P. Culicover, and M. Harnish, *Neural Connections, Mental Computation,* Cambridge, Mass.: MIT Press, 1989.

21. Z. Nami, A. Erbil, and G. May, "Semi-Empirical MOCVD Modeling Using Neural Networks," *Proc. 1994 SPIE Conf. on Microelectronics Manufacturing,* October 1994.

22. C. Van Den Brekel and A. Jansen, "Morphological Analysis in Chemical Vapor Deposition Processes, I," *J. Crystal Growth,* vol. 43, 1978.

23. D. Psichogios and L. Ungar, "A Hybrid Neural Network—First Principles Approach to Process Modeling," *AIChE Journal,* vol. 38, no. 10, October 1992.

24. B. Kim and G. May, "An Optimal Neural Network Process Model for Plasma Etching," *IEEE Trans. Semiconductor Manufacturing,* vol. 7, no. 1, February 1994.

25. M. Gutierrez, J. Wang, and R. O. Grondin, "Estimating Hidden Units for Two-Layer Perceptrons," *Proc. IEEE International Conf. on Artificial Neural Networks,* 1989.

26. S. Kung and J. Hwang, "An Algebraic Projection Analysis for Optimal Hidden Units Size and Learning Rates in Back-Propagation Learning," *Proc. IEEE International Conf. on Artificial Neural Networks,* 1988.

27. D. Fogel, "An Information Criterion for Optimal Neural Network Selection," *IEEE Trans. Neural Networks,* vol. 2, no. 5, September 1991.

28. S. Venkatesh, "The Science of Making ERORS: What Error Tolerance Implies for Capacity in Neural Networks," *IEEE Trans. Knowledge and Data Engineering,* vol. 4, no. 2, April 1992.

29. D. Nguyen and B. Widrow, "Improving the Learning Speed of 2-Layer Neural Networks by Choosing Initial Values of Adaptive Weights," *Proc. International Joint Conf. on Neural Networks,* vol. 3, 1990.

30. R. White, "The Learning Rate in Back-Propagation Systems: An Application of Newton's Method," *Proc. International Joint Conf. on Neural Networks,* vol. 1, 1990.

31. Z. Galil and J. Kiefer, "Time- and Space-Saving Computer Methods, Related to Mitchell's DETMAX, for Finding D-Optimum Designs," *Technometrics,* vol. 22, August 1980.

32. G. May, J. Huang, and C. Spanos, "Statistical Experimental Design in Plasma Etch Modeling," *IEEE Trans. Semiconductor Manufacturing,* vol. 4, no. 2, May 1991.

33. J. Nash, *Compact Numerical Methods for Computers,* Bristol, 1979.

34. S. Han and G. May, "Modeling the Plasma Enhanced Chemical Vapor Deposition Process Using Neural Networks and Genetic Algorithms, *Proc. 6th IEEE International Conf. on AI Tools,* New Orleans, November 1994.

35. E. Harth and A. Pandya, "Dynamics of the ALOPEX Process: Applications to Optimization Problems," *Biomathematics and Related Computational Problems,* 1988.

36. J. Holland, *Adaptation in Natural and Artificial Systems,* Ann Arbor: University of Michigan Press, 1975.

37. D. Goldberg, *Genetic Algorithms in Search, Optimization and Machine Learning,* Reading, Mass.: Addison Wesley, 1989.

38. D. Boning and D. White, private communication, April 1994.

39. D. Montgomery, *Introduction to Statistical Quality Control,* New York: Wiley, 1991.

40. M. Baker, C. Himmel, and G. May, "Time Series Modeling of Reactive Ion Etching Using Neural Networks," *IEEE Trans. Semiconductor Manufacturing,* vol. 8, no. 1, February 1995.

41. H. Yazici and A. Smith, "Neural Network Control Charts for Location and Variance Process Shifts," *Proc. 1993 World Congress on Neural Networks,* vol. I, 1993.

42. D. Nelson, D. Ensley, and S. Rogers, "Prediction of Chaotic Time Series Using Cascade Correlation: Effects of Number of Inputs and Training Set Size," *SPIE Conf. on Applications of Neural Networks,* vol. 1709, 1992.

43. H. Mori and T. Ogasawara, "A Recurrent Neural Network Approach to Short-Term Load Forecasting in Electrical Power Systems," *Proc. 1993 World Congress on Neural Networks,* vol. I, 1993.

44. S. Rao and R. Pappu, "Nonlinear Time Series Prediction Using Wavelet Networks," *Proc. 1993 World Congress on Neural Networks,* vol. IV, 1993.

45. G. Box and G. Jenkins, *Time Series Analysis: Forecasting and Control,* San Francisco: Holden-Day, 1976.

46. K. Anderson, G. Cook, and K. Gabor, "Artificial Neural Networks Applied to Arc Welding Process Modeling and Control," *IEEE Trans. Industrial Applications,* vol. 26, 1990.

47. S. Hattori, M. Nakajima, and Y. Katayama, "Fuzzy Control Algorithms and Neural Networks for Flatness Control of a Cold Rolling Process," *Hitachi Review,* vol. 41, no. 1, 1992.

48. M. Lam, P. Lin, and L. Bain, "Modeling and Control of the Lithographic Offset Color Printing Process Using Artificial Neural Networks," *Neural Networks in Manufacturing and Robotics,* ASME, vol. 57, 1992.

49. D. Nguyen, M. Lee, R. Sass, and H. Shoaee, "Accelerator and Feedback Control Simulation Using Neural Networks," *Proc. IEEE Particle Accelerator Conf.,* 1991.

50. G. May, "Neural Networks Aid IC Manufacturing," *IEEE Spectrum,* September 1994.

51. E. Rietman, S. Patel, and E. Lory, "Neural Network Control of a Plasma Gate Etch: Early Steps in Wafer-to-Wafer Process Control," *Proc. 15th International Electronic Manufacturing Technology Symp.,* October 1993.

52. C. Himmel, T. Kim, A. Krauss, E. Kamen, and G. May, "Real-Time Predictive Control of Semiconductor Manufacturing Processes Using Neural Networks," *Proc. 1995 American Control Conference,* June 1995.

53. T. Sorsa, H. Koivo, and H. Koivisto, "Neural Networks in Process Fault Diagnosis," *IEEE Trans. Systems, Man, and Cybernetics,* vol. 21, no. 4, 1991.

54. L. Burke and S. Rangwala, "Tool Condition Monitoring in Metal Cutting: A Neural Network Approach," *J. Intelligent Manufacturing,* vol. 2, no. 5, 1991.

55. P. Wasserman, A. Unal, and S. Haddad, "Neural Networks for On-line Machine Condition Monitoring," in *Intelligent Enginering Systems Through Artificial Neural Networks,* New York: ASME Press, 1991.

56. J. Murphy and B. Kagle, "Neural Network Recognition of Electronic Malfunctions," *J. Intelligent Manufacturing,* vol. 3, no. 4, 1992.

57. D. Hillman, "Integrating Neural Nets and Expert Systems," *AI Expert,* June 1990.

58. G. May and C. Spanos, "Automated Malfunction Diagnosis of Semiconductor Fabrication Equipment: A Plasma Etch Application," *IEEE Trans. Semiconductor Manufacturing,* vol. 6, no. 1, February 1993.

59. J. Plummer, "Tighter Process Control with Neural Networks," *AI Expert,* October 1993.

60. D. Sikka, "Automated Feature Detection and Characterization in Sort Wafer Maps," *Proc. International Joint Conference on Neural Networks,* 1993.

CHAPTER 19

MODELING QUARTERLY RETURNS ON THE FTSE: A COMPARATIVE STUDY WITH REGRESSION AND NEURAL NETWORKS

A. N. Refenes
P. Bolland
London Business School
Department of Decision Science

We examine the use of neural networks as an alternative to classical linear approaches for modeling and forecasting asset prices. Partly a tutorial, partly a review, this chapter gives an introduction to investment management, provides a formulation of neural learning which is synergetic rather than competitive to theory formulation, and reviews some ongoing research and applications in investment management. We compare neural networks with multiple linear regression in the context of modeling quarterly returns on the Financial Times Stock Exchange (FTSE) All Share Index. Neural networks outperform multiple linear regression in out-of-sample forecasting accuracy. This result and subsequent sensitivity analysis supports the hypothesis of the existence of nonlinear relationships between the economic variables and Index returns, even though the classical regression analysis procedure fails to spot any obvious nonlinearities.

19.1 INTRODUCTION

Neural networks is a field of research which has enjoyed a rapid expansion and great popularity in both the academic and industrial research communities. Neural networks are essentially statistical devices for performing inductive inference. From the statistician's point of view they are analogous to nonparametric, nonlinear regression models. The novelty about neural networks lies in their ability to model nonlinear processes with few (if any) *a priori* assumptions about the nature of the generating process. This is particularly useful in investment management, where much is assumed and little is known about the nature of the processes determining asset prices.

The prevailing wisdom among financial economists is that price fluctuations not due to external influences are dominated by noise and are modeled as wholly *stochastic* processes. Consequently we try to understand the nature of noise and develop tools for predicting its effects on asset prices. It is possible, however, that these remaining price fluctuations, to a large extent, are due to deterministic but *nonlinear* processes at work in the market place. Therefore, given appropriate tools, it is possible to understand much of the market's price structure on the basis of partially *deterministic* but *nonlinear* dynamics.

Nonlinear modeling techniques are the subject of increasing interest from practitioners in quantitative asset management with neural networks assuming a prominent role. Neural networks are being applied to a number of "live" systems in financial engineering and have shown promising results. Various performance figures are being quoted to support these claims but there is rarely a comprehensive investigation of the nature of the relationship that has been captured between asset prices and their determinants. The absence of explicit models makes it difficult to assess the significance of the estimated model and the possibility that any short-term success is due to "data mining".

In Sec. 19.2, we formulate neural learning in a framework similar to additive nonlinear regression. This provides an explicit representation of the estimated models and enables modelers to use a rich collection of analytic and statistical tools to test the significance of the various parameters in the estimated neural models. The methodology encourages the use of modern financial economics theory on market dynamics to investigate the plausibility of the estimated models and to analyze them in order to separate the nonlinear components of the models which are invariant through time from those that reflect temporary (and probably unrepeatable) market imperfections.

In Sec. 19.3 we review the process of quantitative investment management and explain how and where neural networks can be applied to enhance the process. The key idea here is that a particular portfolio will depend on the universe of assets under consideration and the properties of those assets at that time. The main proposition of prevailing theories [e.g., arbitrage pricing theory (APT)] is that the return of each asset can be explained by a set of (economic and other) factors and can be computed a *linear* function of each asset's exposure to these factors. In later sections of this chapter we challenge this hypothesis and provide experimental evidence to show that a *nonlinear* estimate based on a simple backpropagation network is more accurate. We also give some specific examples of using neural networks in the financial markets.

In Sec. 19.4, we introduce the topic of forecasting quarterly returns on the FTSE All Share index which will serve as our benchmark for evaluating linear against nonlinear modeling methodologies and describe the data and setup for our experimental analysis.

In Sec. 19.5 we use linear regression analysis to estimate quarterly returns on the FTSE All Share, on the basis of a universe of economic and financial factors. We concentrate on variable selection and we demonstrate the methodological considerations which are an integral part of the model construction process.

With the phase of variable selection concluded, Sec. 19.6 uses those variables to evaluate the performance of neural networks against the linear approach. We show that neural networks give significant performance improvements over linear models, even though the classical linear analysis fails to detect any obvious nonlinearities. This is supported by the sensitivity analysis on the neural models.

19.2 NEURAL NETWORKS AND NONPARAMETRIC REGRESSION

There many ways to interpret neural "learning." The common formulation gives a *geometric* interpretation, e.g., Weigend et al. (1991). Although this is quite useful in developing efficient learning procedures, the formulation is, however, incapable of supporting an explicit representation of the relationship that has been learned between input and response vectors. The absence of an explicit model makes it difficult to assess the significance of the estimated model and the possibility that any short term success may be due to data mining. In this section we show that it is possible to provide a theoretical framework for analyzing the computational properties of neural networks by making use of statistical estimation theory. To demonstrate how these principles can be applied, we shall give a formulation of neural computation which is directly analogous to *additive nonparametric nonlinear regression* models and for which there is a rich collection of analytic and statistical tools.

19.2.1 Nonparametric Statistical Inference

Much of the work on neural networks has been compared to nonparametric statistical inference (Amari, 1990). Geman et al. (1992) formulated the problem in a statistical framework and showed that the machine learning task of constructing an internal representation between input and response vectors is analogous to nonparametric regression. They also showed that among *all possible representations* (i.e., functions of the input space), the regression is the *best* estimator of the response space, i.e., it is conditioned on the input observations in the sense of the least square error. Bayesian estimation theory has also been used to study neural learning and to aid in the construction of parsimonious models [Weigend et al., 1991].

One important area of statistical estimation theory which has been overlooked is recent developments in the field of nonparametric nonlinear regression. Much of the work in so-called *additive nonlinear regression models* such as Alternating Conditional Expectation (ACE) and Additivity and Variance Asymptotic Stabilization (AVAS) (Leontief, 1947; Breiman and Friedman, 1985; Hardle, 1989) can be shown to be similar to feedforward networks. The main strength of these models derives from the fact that they provide an *explicit* representation of the structure of the estimated models which is very important in analyzing the properties of the estimators. Consider, for example, the simple ACE model for nonparametric nonlinear regression. Given a set of observations (i.e., training set), ACE attempts to estimate (i.e., learn) a function of the form:

$$\theta(y_i) = \phi_1(x_{ip}) + \phi_2(x_{ip}) + \cdots + \phi_p(x_{ip}) + r_i \qquad (19.1)$$

where $\theta, \phi_1, \ldots, \phi_p$ are smooth nonlinear transformations estimated from the data $(y_i, x_{i1}, \ldots, x_{ip})$ $i = 1, \ldots, p$, and r_i are the residuals. The estimation procedure may choose the nonlinear transformations $\theta, \phi_1, \ldots, \phi_p$ in a way that maximizes the correlation between $\theta(y_i)$ and $\phi_1(x_{ip}) + \phi_2(x_{ip}) + \cdots + \phi_p(x_{ip}) + r_i$ (or in a way that minimizes the residual mean square error). In either case the end effect bears a striking resemblance to learning by error backpropagation with ordinary least squares and linear output units.

This similarity will be explored in the next section to produce a framework for representing neural learning in the same framework as additive nonlinear regression.

19.2.2 Neural Networks as Nonparametric Multiplicative Regression

Consider the family of neural networks with asymmetric sigmoids as the nonlinear transfer function. For simplicity, we consider networks with two layers of hidden connections as shown in Fig. 19.1 with A and B denoting input variables, Y denoting the output variable, α_0, α_1, β_0, β_1 denoting the connection weights from the input units to the hidden layer, and γ_0, γ_1 denoting connections from the hidden units to the output unit.

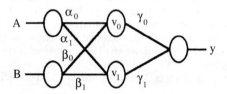

FIGURE 19.1 Feedforward network with two layers of hidden units.

The task of the training procedure is to estimate a function between input and response vectors. The function is parameterized by the network weights and the transfer function and takes the form:

$$y = \frac{1}{1 + e^{-(\gamma_0 v_0 + \gamma_1 v_1)}} \qquad (19.2)$$

where v_0 and v_1 are the outputs of the intermediate hidden units similarly parameterized by the weights between the input and hidden layers. Ignoring the bias components we have

$$v_0 = \frac{1}{1 + e^{(-\alpha_0 A + \beta_0 B)}} \quad \text{and} \quad v_1 = \frac{1}{1 + e^{-(\alpha_1 A + \beta_1 B)}} \qquad (19.3)$$

Let us illustrate how the task of the learning procedure can be compared to that of additive nonlinear regression as defined in Eq. (19.1) by assuming, without loss of generality, that on a network with linear units at the output level:

$$y = \gamma_0 v_0 + \gamma_1 v_1 = \gamma_0 \frac{1}{1 + e^{-(\alpha_0 A + \beta_0 B)}} + \gamma_1 \frac{1}{1 + e^{-(\alpha_1 A + \beta_1 B)}} \qquad (19.4)$$

In investment management applications, it is common to apply smoothing transformations to the input and output variables prior to training, in order, for example, to remove the effect of statistical outliers. A commonly used transformation is the logarithmic operation. Typically, instead of estimating $y = f(A, B)$, one would use the reversible transformation $\ln(y) = f(\ln (A), \ln (B))$. With this transformation, the exponential term can be rewritten as

$$e^{(\alpha_0 \ln(A) + \beta_0 \ln(B))} = e^{(\ln(A^{\alpha_0}) + \ln(B^{\beta_0}))} \qquad (19.5)$$

$$= e^{\ln(A^{\alpha_0} B^{\beta_0})}$$

$$= A^{\alpha_0} B^{\beta_0}$$

Using Eq. (19.5), it is easy to show that Eq. (19.4) can be rewritten as the sum of two products:

$$\ln (y) = \gamma_0 \frac{A^{\alpha_0}B^{\beta_0}}{A^{\alpha_0}B^{\beta_0} + 1} + \gamma_1 \frac{A^{\alpha_1}B^{\beta_1}}{A^{\alpha_1}B^{\beta_1} + 1} \tag{19.6}$$

Overall we have six parameters $\{\alpha_0, \alpha_1, \beta_0, \beta_1,$ and $\gamma_0, \gamma_1\}$, ignoring the constants, i.e., biases. The task of the learning procedure is to estimate the parameters in a way that minimizes the residual least square error. In the general case for networks with n hidden units and m input variables, Eq. (19.6) takes the form:

$$\ln (y) = \gamma_0 \frac{A^{\alpha_0}B^{\beta_0}\cdots M^{\mu_0}}{A^{\alpha_0}B^{\beta_0}\cdots M^{\mu_0} + 1} + \gamma_1 \frac{A^{\alpha_1}B^{\beta_1}\cdots M^{\mu_1}}{A^{\alpha_1}B^{\beta_1}\cdots M^{\mu_1} + 1} + \cdots + \gamma_n \frac{A^{\alpha_n}B^{\beta_n}\cdots M^{\mu_m}}{A^{\alpha_n}B^{\beta_n}\cdots M^{\mu_m} + 1}$$

$$\tag{19.7}$$

Thus neural learning is analogous to searching the function space defined by the terms of Eq. (19.7) and the range of the permissible values for the parameters. This formulation is strikingly similar to the formulation of additive nonlinear nonpara-metric regression (Hardle, 1989; Breiman and Friedman, 1985), and it allows us to apply the analytic and statistical tools that have been developed in the field of additive nonparametric regression for the class of neural networks of a similar structure.

19.3 ACTIVE INVESTMENT MANAGEMENT AND NEURAL NETWORKS

The ultimate goal of any investment strategy is to maximize returns with minimum risk. In the framework of modern portfolio management theory, this is achieved by constructing a portfolio of investments which is weighted in a way that achieves maximum return at minimum risk. The construction of such an optimal portfolio requires *a priori* estimates of asset *returns* and *risk*.

Traditionally, in line with the efficient market hypothesis, it has been assumed that returns are random and that the best prediction for tomorrow's return is today's return. Over a longer period, expected returns were calculated by averaging histori-cal returns. The prediction error was considered as unpredictable noise and so asset risks were estimated by the standard deviation of historical returns. More recently, with multiple-factor capital asset pricing model (CAPM) and APT, the idea has emerged that asset returns might be influenced by a number of factors. This new approach involves three stages:

- *Factor analysis.* In this stage, practitioners attempt to identify factors which have an influence on asset prices (and/or returns).

- *Estimating returns of the different assets.* In this stage, practitioners attempt to esti-mate asset prices on the basis of the above factors.

- *Portfolio construction and optimization.* In this stage, given estimates of returns, the problem is to find portfolio weights which maximize the global return of the portfolio and minimize its risk.

We review these stages in more detail in order to describe the limitations of the clas-sical approaches and to identify how and where neural networks can be used to enhance the process.

19.3.1 Factor Analysis

There are two principal ways to select factors that might have an influence on asset prices. The first is to use the experience, knowledge, and judgment of financial economists. This is a perfectly acceptable approach, but it suffers from the disadvantage of building *high bias* into subsequent models. The second way is by factor analysis. The main methodologies in this approach typically involve principal component analysis, stepwise regression, or discriminant analysis. They are applied on the raw data and known factors and/or financial ratios. Both the regression and the principal component analysis (PCA) techniques are based on linear models. Unfortunately, this might bias the selection of the determinant factors by excluding those that have a nonlinear influence on the return (e.g., threshold effect).

An alternative approach is to use neural networks to perform nonlinear dimensionality reduction and sensitivity analysis. This might be useful when the influences of the individual factors on asset returns are not constant in time and depend on the value of the other factors. One of the ways in which neural networks can be used in nonlinear factor analysis is recording multidimensional data in a representation of reduced dimensionality with minimal information loss. This can be achieved by training a neural network to learn the identity map through a so-called bottleneck (see Fig. 19.2).

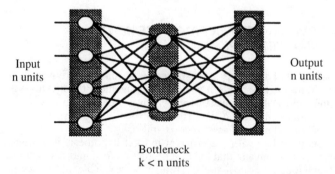

Input
n units

Output
n units

Bottleneck
k < n units

FIGURE 19.2 General architecture of autoassociative networks for dimensionality reduction.

The idea of using autoassociative networks for dimensionality reduction is quite straightforward. If we construct a network with n inputs, a single hidden layer of, say, k units, and n outputs, the network computes a transformation from input to output. If the n inputs represent n lags of a time series and the n outputs are the same values, we can compute weight values to (exactly) reproduce the input without loss of information. If the number of hidden units k *is less than* n and we are still able to reproduce the input without any loss of information, then it can be shown that, under appropriate conditions, the activation values of the k units in the hidden layer will compute the first k principal components of the data. The obvious extension is to add more hidden layers between input and earlier hidden layers for nonlinear encoding. For a complete treatment see DeMers (1992) and Oja (1991). This is a simple way of nonlinear factor analysis, but like all such models it may suffer from *high variance* due to the changing dynamics of the data-generating process.

An obvious alternative to autoassociative backpropagation networks is the use of unsupervised learning algorithms such as self-organizing feature maps. By constraining the dimensionality of the output grid, a similar effect can be achieved.

19.3.2 Estimating Returns

With multiple-factor CAPM and APT, practitioners explain asset returns as a weighted combination of the different factors as shown in the following equation:

$$R_i = a_i + b_{i1}f_1 + b_{i2}f_2 + \cdots + b_{in}f_n + \varepsilon_i \tag{19.8}$$

where R_i = return of asset i
       f_j = determinant factors
       b_{ij} = exposure of asset i to factor j
       ε_i = nonpredictable part of the return, i.e., the error of the model

However, there is no reason to assume that the relationship between asset returns and their determinants is additive and linear as presumed in Eq. (19.8). In other words, it is highly possible that these remaining price fluctuations ε are due to some extent to *nonlinear* processes at work in the market place. Therefore it might be possible with nonlinear models such as neural networks to understand much of the market's price structure on the basis of completely or partially *deterministic* but *nonlinear* dynamics.

The case for the existence of nonlinear dependencies in the context of financial markets can be made by using a mix of observations on market microstructure, feedback effects in market prices, and empirical observations. Nonlinear dependencies may be explained in terms of nonlinear feedback mechanisms in price movements alone. When the price of an asset becomes too high, self-regulating forces usually drive the price down. If the feedback mechanism is nonlinear, then the correction will not always be proportional to the amount by which the price deviates from the asset's real value. It is not unreasonable to expect such nonlinear corrections in the financial markets; they can be explained by the study of market psychology where it is understood that investors and markets overreact to bad news and underreact to good news. There are many participants in the financial markets with complex motivations, reactions, and interrelationships. It would be a miracle if these complexities always average out to give an aggregate linear feedback. Once nonlinear feedback mechanisms are introduced in the market description, many price fluctuations could be explained without reference to stochastic effects.

It is generally accepted that market imperfections, such as taxes, transaction costs, and the timing of the information reaction introduces nonlinearities in the capital markets. Although information arrives randomly to the market, market participants respond to such information with lags due to transaction costs for example. In other words, market participants do not trade every time news arrives to the market; rather, they trade whenever it is economically possible. This leads to clustering of price changes. Furthermore, nonlinearities are observed when announcements of important factors are made less often than the sampling frequency. For example, weekly money supply announcements will cause nonlinearities in daily but not in monthly data.

The prevailing capital market model is based on the rationality of individual investors. In other words, it is assumed that investors are risk-averse, unbiased when they set their subjective probabilities, and always react to information as it is received. The implication is that the data-generating process is linear. In practice, however, investors may well be risk-seeking instead of risk-averse when, for example, taking gambles to minimize their losses. Moreover, they may have excessive faith in their own forecasts, thus introducing bias in their subjective probabilities, and they may not react to information instantaneously but delay their response until their peers reveal their preferences. These points question the rationality not only of individual investors but of the market as a whole, since the market is an aggregation of individuals. Therefore linear models may not be adequate in explaining market behavior.

Nonlinear models such as neural networks may provide a more reliable method of modeling asset returns, because they make no *a priori* assumption about the nature of the relationship between R_i and the selected factors f_j. The neural network approach is to model R_l as a nonlinear combination of factor exposures [see for example Eq. (19.7)]. Having done so, one can then compute the expected returns (as a nonlinear function of the different factors) and estimate the risk of the asset as the prediction interval of the model.

19.3.3 Portfolio Optimization

It is possible to optimize a portfolio in a manner directly analogous to standard mean-variance optimization. The model prediction is used in place of the historical mean and the prediction interval replaces the historical variance. Correlations between asset prices are taken into account by calculating the correlation of the prediction errors of the model when applied to different stocks.

The expected return of the portfolio is the weighted average of the predicted returns of individual securities in the portfolio. The expected risk σ_p of the portfolio is determined by three factors: the prediction standard error σ_i for each security in the portfolio, the correlation ρ_{ij} between the prediction errors for each pair of securities in the portfolio, and the proportion X_i of each security represented in the portfolio:

$$\sigma_p = \sqrt{\sum_{i=1}^{N} X^2_i \sigma^2_i + 2 \sum_{i=1}^{N-1} \sum_{j=i+1}^{N} X_i X_j \rho_{ij} \sigma_i \sigma_j} \qquad (19.9)$$

We can then construct a portfolio of assets that provides the highest return at a given level of risk or, alternatively, the minimum risk at a given level of return.

Besides, it is possible to run a complete risk analysis by using the neural network for a scenario simulation. A complete risk analysis is very important in constructing the portfolio because predicting a single most likely rate of return is not entirely satisfactory. In fact, the expected return represents only a few points on a continuous curve of possible combinations of future happenings. It is a bit like trying to predict the outcome in a two-dice game by saying that the most likely outcome is a seven. The description is incomplete because it does not tell us about all the other returns that could happen.

Once the network has estimated the relationship between the stock returns and the different factors, it is possible to use it to simulate the market for the different scenarios. Thus it is possible to compute the probability distribution for the return of each stock given the probability distribution of each scenario, and also the prediction interval of the model. Because of the possible nonlinearities of the modeled relationship, the return probability distribution may not be normal. It is therefore dangerous to handle these returns in terms of historical expected return and standard deviation.

However it is possible to construct portfolios on the basis of several criteria. For example, one might be interested in:

- Selecting stocks that have a probability of less than 10 percent of having a negative return over the next month
- Constructing a portfolio with maximum expected return for minimum level of risk or, alternatively, the minimum risk at a given level of return
- Constructing a portfolio which is immune against interest and/or exchange rate risk or, alternatively, making the portfolio sensitive to interest and/or exchange rate changes

The advantage of dynamical systems such as neural networks rests in the ability of constructing a portfolio according to the current state of the market and economic variables rather than on the basis of past correlations and standard deviation of stock prices. Markets move together because they are sensitive at a same level to certain factors. These sensitivities might not be constant in time. This is why a good diversification should not take into account the past correlation between stocks but the sensitivity of these stocks to certain factors and the probability that these factors will change.

19.3.4 Applications of Neural Networks to Investment Management

Neural networks have been applied extensively to all three stages of investment management. Comprehensive reviews can be found in Refenes (1993, 1994), Trippi and Turban (1993), and Azoff (1994). In this section we give a brief overview of ongoing research and application development at the Neuroforecasting Unit, London Business School.

1. *Tactical asset allocation.* This project deals with tactical allocation between asset classes: bonds *versus* equities *versus* cash. It is initially intended for the United Kingdom markets and, at a later stage, the international and global level. The aim is to estimate expected differential returns on the basis of (up to 17) economic variables which are then used to construct an optimal portfolio. A detailed description can be found in Zapranis and Refenes (1994).

2. *Futures price sensitivity to volume, and open interest.* This project tries to identify the relationship between price changes and changes in volume and open interest in futures contracts. The aim is to confirm (or, more difficult, refute) the hypothesis that there indeed exists a relationship and to investigate if this can be used for forecasting or trading purposes (Bolland and Refenes, 1994).

3. *Tactical intraday currency trading.* This project is developing technical systems for tactical intraday currency trading in selected markets. Neural networks are used to identify and generate optimal buy/sell signals. The networks are used to track price movements in the major European currencies and to identify appropriate trading opportunities.

4. *Factor models for equity investment.* Using a bottom-up approach, this project tries to model stock returns on the basis of a preselected universe of fundamental and technical factors. These models are then used as part of a larger portfolio management system (Refenes, Bentz, and Burgess, 1994).

5. *Modeling and trading concurrent futures indices.* The task here is to estimate differential returns of European futures indices on the basis of technical indicators.

Once differential returns are estimated, and the associated risk is known, investments can be weighted among the indices to maximize return for given risk tolerances (Burgess, 1994).

6. *Forecasting volatility for option pricing.* The task here is to produce estimates of implied volatility to be used in the context of option pricing for futures contracts. High-frequency tick data from the Spanish markets is being used to develop the methodology (Miranda-Gonzales, 1994).

An example of investment management based on neural networks is described in the next section. In this description we deal with the first two phases in the investment management process: variable selection and the estimation of expected returns.

19.4 MODELING QUARTERLY RETURNS WITH LINEAR REGRESSION

We use monthly data on economic variables to estimate quarterly returns on the FTSE All Share Index. These economic variables are to be selected from a universe of 12 variables and we use stepwise regression to reduce them to a manageable level and create a parsimonious model. The factors selected through the stepwise regression are then used to estimate quarterly returns. For the estimate we compare the performance of linear regression against a feedforward ordinary least squares (OLS) network. Clearly this comparison is rather unfair to the network since the predictive variables have already been selected in a way that best suits the linear regression model. It is therefore probable that those factors explain only the linear part of the relationship. Nevertheless, since our purpose is to show that even in these restricting conditions a nonlinear estimator can still give a better model, we shall ignore this underlying bias.

A 3-month time horizon was chosen for the modeling process. The data were provided and collated by Henderson Financial Management. It consisted of monthly data from micro- and macroeconomic indicators described in Table 19.1. The majority of indicators were available from 1975 to 1994. Our objective was to predict 3-month changes in FTSE. We chose 11 variables which analysts commonly use to gauge long-term movements in the FTSE. Data were taken at the end of the month. For some of the variables, only the previous month's data were available. The various lags are specified in Table 19.1. Several methods are available to make the 3-month-ahead predictions:

- Iterated monthly prediction
- Three-month predictions using 3-month time step
- Three-month prediction using a monthly time step

Iterating a forecast deteriorates the accuracy, and using 3-month time steps diminishes the size of data set, therefore the third option was chosen. The dependent variable was the 3-month percentage change in FTSE All Share Index.

The number of independent variables, as will become apparent in the next sections, is rather large. The forecasting literature is full of examples where models including as many as 20 explanatory variables achieve a correlation coefficient as high as 0.995. However, this good fit may be spurious and does not necessarily mean that the model will give good forecasts. The idea is to end up with a reduced set of independent variables which is more useful in model construction than the full set.

TABLE 19.1 Universe of Factors Influencing Quarterly Returns

Name	Code	Transform	Mar	Apr	May	Jun	Jul	Aug	Sep
FTSE All Share price index	FTALLSH	3M % diff.							Y
FTSE All Share dividend yield	FTALLSH(DY)	Level				X1			
DS total market—P/CSH flow ratio	TOTMKUK(PC)	Log				X2			
DS total market—PER	TOTMKUK(PE)	Log				X3			
Gross redemption yield on gilt-edged stocks (average)	UKMEDYLD	Level				X4			
Eurocurrency STER 3 months—middle rate	ECUK£3M	Level				X5			
Money supply M0 calendar month level CURA	UKMO....B	3M % diff.			X6				
Volume of retail sales—total VOLA	UKRETTOTG	3M % diff.			X7				
Output of production industries—manufacturing VOLA	UKMANPRDG	3M % diff.			X8				
Shorter leading composite index	UKOCSHLD	Level	X9						
Retail prices index, all items—annual inflation rate	UKRPANNL	1Y % diff.			X10				
London gold bullion, $/fine oz—CLOSE	GOLDBLN	3M % diff.				X11			

DS = data stream
P/CSH = price/cash flow
CURA = currency
VOLA = volume
STER = sterling
MO = money supply 0
PER = price to earnings ratio

19.5 STEPWISE VARIABLE SELECTION WITH BACKWARD REGRESSION

In the variable selection phase we use multiple linear regression to estimate the linear relationship between the independent variables x_i^j and the dependent variable v. The least-squares technique is used to estimate the coefficients b_i in an equation of the form

$$y_{t+\tau} = b_0 + b_1 x_{t-\tau_1}^1 + b_2 x_{t-\tau_2}^2 + \cdots + b_n x_{t-\tau_n}^n + \varepsilon_t \qquad (19.10)$$

where ε denotes a random disturbance term and τ is a time lag. The regression coefficient b_i represents the expected change in y associated with a one-unit change in the ith independent variable.

A regression was run without any selection process to compare with the backward selection process. The backward stepwise method starts with all variables in the model and deletes variables one at a time. The criterion for the retention of variables is to select the ones which reduce the sum of squared errors the most, and have significant t statistics. Three data sets were used, all employing the same test set 1991 to 1994. The first contained all data from 1975 to 1990; the second contained data from 1983 to 1990; the third contained only data from 1987 to 1990. The results were compared to determine how stable the relationships are and to see if nonstationarity is a problem. The results shown below are for the full data set.

The regression model produced by backward stepwise elimination is shown in Table 19.2. It is clear from the t values associated with the variables that the model as a whole is significant. The sample R^2 is high, showing that there is a significant amount of information in the independent variables. The Durbin-Watson statistic suggests autocorrelation in the residuals. A full analysis of the residual-correlations is given in Fig. 19.3. The cause of such high autocorrelation is the method of modeling we are applying. As we are predicting a 3-month time horizon yet using monthly data, there is significant overlap between input variables.

In Fig. 19.3 we see that the 3-month difference between April and July also contains some of the change between May and August and between June and September. Therefore adjacent months will have similar values, so any error in predicting one month will be similar to the error in predicting the next. In Fig. 19.4 we see that there is significant correlation for the first two lags and then only very small correlation. This is as we would expect, and so the anomalous Durbin Watson statistic can be ignored.

TABLE 19.2 Multivariate Regression 1975–1990 (6 Variables)

Parameter	Estimate	Error	Statistic	P value
CONSTANT	46.9551	29.8313	1.57402	0.1172
FTALLSH_DY	5.62115	5.62115	2.26776	0.0245
PE_LNTOTMK	−17.7588	9.15271	−1.94028	0.0539
UKM0_B3ML1	−0.41633	0.154529	−2.69419	0.0077
UKMEDYLD	−1.72005	0.824885	−2.0852	0.0384
UKRPANLL1	−0.532632	0.17668	−3.01466	0.0029
R^2	20.6558			
R^2(adjusted for degrees of freedom)	18.5229			
Standard error of estimate	9.08617			
Mean absolute error	6.86843			
Durbin-Watson statistic	0.661927			

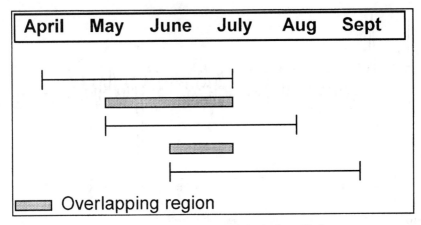

FIGURE 19.3   Overlapping regions cause autocorrelation in the residuals.

Figures 19.5 and 19.6 show the in-sample fit produced by the multiple linear regressions (MLR). It is clear that the MLR has picked out the average and only a small amount of the variance, with the majority of the predictions being positive. Ideally the scatter plot (Fig. 19.6) should produce a straight line going through the points $(1, 1)$ and $(-1, -1)$.

Before proceeding further, it is desirable to test the assumptions of regression to see if it is possible to make any improvements. The main areas of investigations include:

1. Testing for serial correlations in the residuals. The presence of such correlations may indicate that there is a systematic error component which could be modeled separately through, for example, an error correction term.

2. Testing for obvious nonlinear transformations of the input variables. Such transformations may lead to a nonlinear but parametric model.

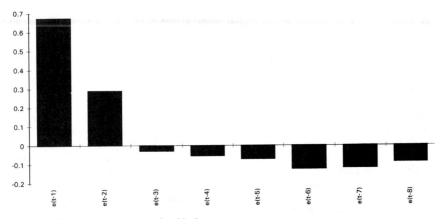

FIGURE 19.4   Autocorrelation of residuals.

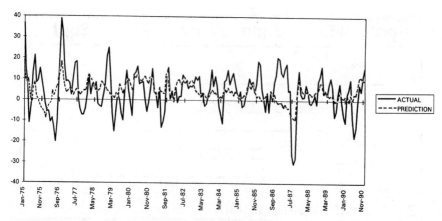

FIGURE 19.5   Stepwise regression 1975–1990.

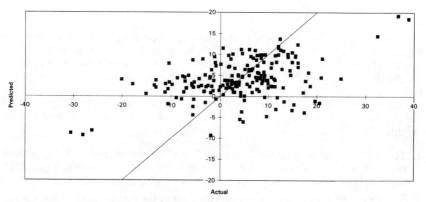

FIGURE 19.6   Scatter plot of predicted versus actual, 1975–1990.

3. Investigating the effects of influential observations in the data set. The effects can be dealt with in various ways, such as robust regression methods.
4. Investigating the effects of possible nonstationarity in the data.

19.5.1   Testing the Assumptions of Regression Analysis

The assumptions of regression analysis are linearity, constant variance, independence of the residuals, and normality. We test all of these assumptions. The most basic type of residual plot is shown in Fig. 19.7, the residuals versus the predicted values. As we can see, the residuals fall within a generally random pattern, although the main body of points appears to have somewhat negative correlation. Furthermore, because Y is a sequential variable, we can use this plot to see if any pattern emerges. Clearly this is not the case where the effect of carryover from one observation to the other makes the residuals not independent.

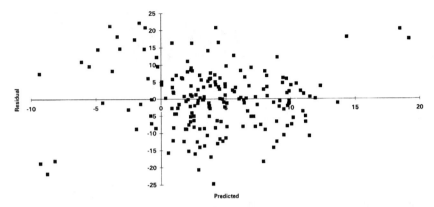

FIGURE 19.7   Residuals versus predicted values.

We assess the assumption of linearity through the analysis of the residuals and the partial regression plots. Figure 19.7 does not exhibit any obvious nonlinear pattern to the residuals, thus indicating that the overall equation is indeed linear. But we must also be certain that each predictor variable's relationship is linear as well, to ensure its best representation in the equation. To do so, we use the partial regression plots for all predictor variables in the equation.

As we can see from Figs. 19.8 to 19.12, there are no clear and strong linear relationships between Y and any of the independent variables, thus the variables are not expected to have strong effects in the regression equation. What is also clear from these plots is the clusters of outliers that give an impression of linearity. Furthermore, these plots do not give any clear indication about any specific nonlinear transformation we might use to achieve linearity.

To test for normality of the residuals, we constructed the normal probability plot. It was observed that the values do not fall exactly along the diagonal. Any systematic departures were only slight. The shape of the normal probability plot indicated a nonpeaked distribution.

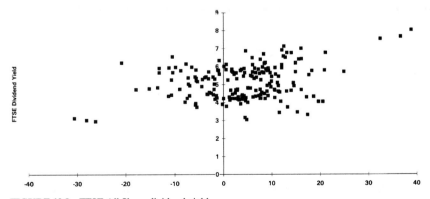

FIGURE 19.8   FTSE All Share dividend yield.

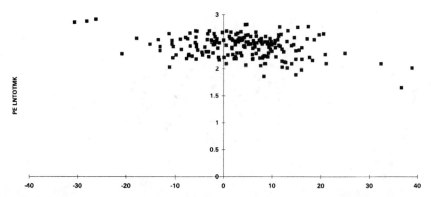

FIGURE 19.9 U.K. data stream total market—price to earnings ratio.

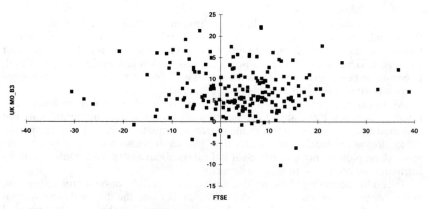

FIGURE 19.10 U.K. money supply M0 calendar month level currency.

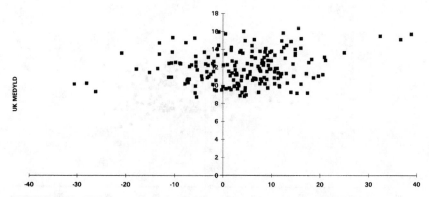

FIGURE 19.11 U.K. gross redemption yield on medium dated gilt-edged stocks (average).

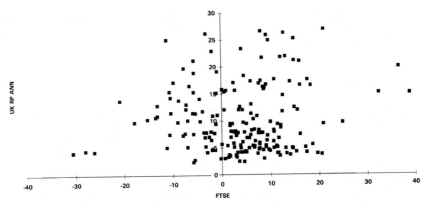

FIGURE 19.12   U.K. retail prices index—all items, annual inflation rate.

19.5.2   The Effects of Influential Observations

Influential observations include all the observations that have a disproportionate effect on the regression results. Potentially, they include outliers and leverage points, but may include other observations as well. Outliers are observations that have residual values and can only be identified with respect to a specific regression model, while leverage points are observations that are distinct from the remaining observations in terms of their independent-variable values. Table 19.3 gives the outliers and leverage points which correspond to the regression equation discussed in the preceding sections and to the data used to derive that equation.

These observations could be due to errors, or they could be valid but exceptional observations explainable by extraordinary situations. The recommended course of action is to remove or transform them or to use robust modeling methodologies. The main problem is that using monthly data means that any major

TABLE 19.3   Unusual Residuals

Row	Observed	Predicted	Residual	Studentized residual
1	36.6787	19.1621	17.5166	2.06
10	14.9248	−3.31869	18.2435	2.10
19	−20.7769	4.00052	−24.7774	−2.84
20	−10.4547	7.86942	−18.3241	−2.07
22	38.8592	18.4739	20.3854	2.39
23	32.3901	14.3695	18.0207	2.07
49	24.9709	4.23876	20.7322	2.35
143	20.5779	−1.60587	22.1838	2.51
144	19.6965	−1.15643	20.8529	2.35
148	17.4499	−3.89001	21.3399	2.41
151	−26.185	−8.19558	−17.9894	−2.05
152	−30.5503	−8.77929	−21.771	−2.49
153	−28.0096	−9.314	−18.6956	−2.14
186	−17.8523	2.86809	−20.7204	−2.33

outlier will be tripled, so if any removal of points is to be done we must ensure that all of the three are removed together [see Bolland (1994) for ways to deal with influential observations].

19.5.3 The Effect of Nonstationarities

Broadly speaking, a time series is said to be stationary if there is no systematic change in mean (no trend), if there is no systematic change in variance, and if strictly periodic variations have been removed. In real world applications, nonstationary data are common, resulting in poor model fit and/or poor forecasting ability. Another common source of concern in application development is what has become known as *model nonstationarity*. This refers to gradually or abruptly changing relationships between the explanatory variables and the dependent variables even in cases when we are dealing with relatively stationary time series. There is very little difference in the in-sample fit produced, and several of the variables remain the same in all the models.

19.5.4 Generalization with MLR Models

We mentioned before that the data for the period January 1991 to February 1994 were withheld for out-of-sample testing. For all models we obtained forecasts for the dependent variable in that period. The correlation coefficients between the actual and the forecasted figures are shown in the captions for Figs. 19.13 and 19.14.

The out-of-sample statistics are in line with the in-sample fit. Both the scatter plot and Fig. 19.11, however, do show a bias in that the MLR generally predicts positive returns.

19.5.5 Model Stability

A final step in our model selection process for linear regression is to examine the stability of the relationships discovered over the different data sets. With data stretching back to 1975, the question we ask is, How valid is such old data? As we believe that the older data are more likely to be less relevant, the older data were the first to be removed in testing for stability.

The aim of this investigation was to discover the variables whose relationship remained stable over time and whose significance was high. Also we wished to achieve a set of variables that would produce consistent out-of-sample results for different training sets.

Initially all the data from 1975 to 1990 were used to build the regression models. The data set was reduced one point at a time by removing the oldest observation. This removal of points was repeated until only 4 years' data remained. The data were normalized so that each input variable had a mean of zero and a standard deviation of one. For each data set a new regression model was calculated and recorded. Also, out-of-sample predictions for the period 1991 to 1994 were calculated.

Initially all the variables selected in the backward stepwise elimination process were included. Subsequently subsets of these variables were investigated. The

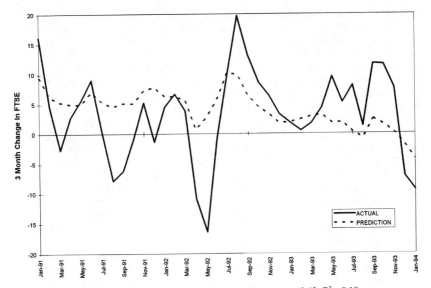

FIGURE 19.13 Predicted versus actual in cross validation set: $\rho = 0.43$, $R^2 = 0.19$.

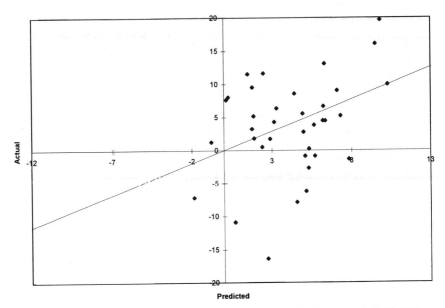

FIGURE 19.14 Scatter plot of predicted versus actual in cross validation set: $\rho = 0.43$, $R^2 = 0.19$.

method for choosing the subsets was similar to backward elimination; that is, the criteria for elimination were consistency and level of t statistic of the variables. The coefficient of each variable was also used to guide removal. As the variables were normalized the size of their coefficient directly related to their relative importance in the models. It was noted that the coefficients of several variables changed in a correlated manner as the data set was reduced. The t statistics also moved together, most notably for variables which were themselves correlated. Collinearity in the variables made the selection of variables by their t statistics more difficult.

During this selection process, composite multiplicative variables were included. These were FTSE*DY and FTSE/PE. It should be noted that this explicit identification of composite variables is strictly only necessary in our linear analysis, since neural networks are capable of learning such representation without explicit specification because there is no assumption of independence between input variables (in fact quite the reverse is true in a fully connected network).

Figures 19.15 and 19.16 show the coefficients of the variables as the data set is decreased. It is clear to see that with more variables the model changes rapidly, also the t statistics for the larger model (Figure 19.17) show large variability. When the variables have been reduced the model produced is much more stable, and we can see from Fig. 19.18 that the significance of the variables selected remains high for all data sets. The rationale behind this approach is to give preference to variables that are significant over time (and thus more likely to represent fundamental economic laws).

As the size of the data set decreased, the variability in the coefficient and t statistics increased. The model became increasingly unstable as the 1987 crash began to dominate the data set.

The out-of-sample performance was also calculated, although it was not used in the selection of variables for elimination. Nevertheless the presence of all variables contributes little or nothing to the overall out-of-sample performance.

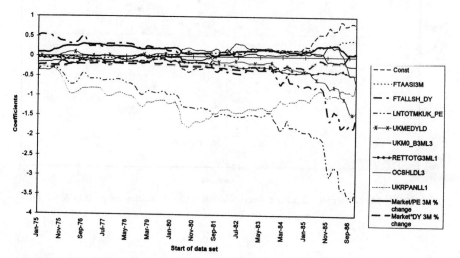

FIGURE 19.15 Variable coefficient variance through time (all variables).

Variables Coefficents

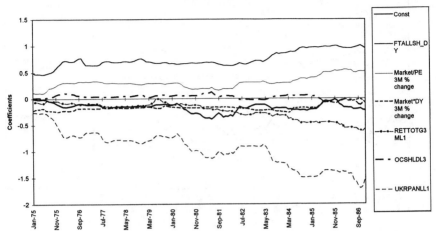

FIGURE 19.16   Variable coefficient variance through time (selected variables).

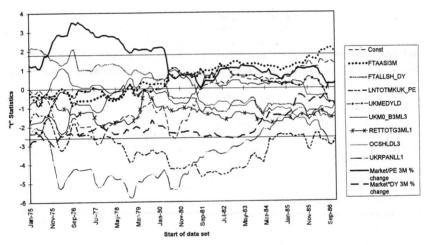

FIGURE 19.17   Variable *t* statistic variance with time (all variables).

19.6   MODELING QUARTERLY RETURNS WITH NEURAL NETWORKS

The regression analysis showed that the linear relationships remained stable over the entire length of the data set. Also it gave direct information on the most significant linear relationships. This information may not be directly relevant to nonlinear analysis, so a variable selection process was undertaken. In the area of tactical asset allocation we would not expect highly nonlinear functions between independent and dependent variables. Rather we would expect low-order nonlinear relationships

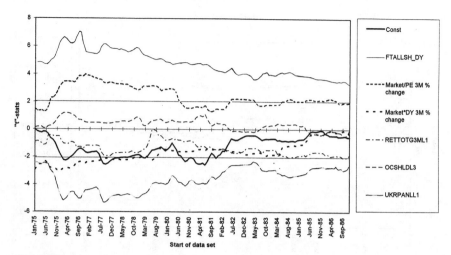

FIGURE 19.18   Variable *t* statistic variance with time (selected variables).

or bounded linear responses and interaction effects between variables. The methodology employed was to start with a large number of inputs and remove data in the same order as observed in the linear selection process. Careful analysis of the model and investigation of the both in- and out-of-sample performance allowed for the identification of variable interaction and possible nonlinear relationships which regression analysis might have failed to indicate.

The training set is the same as that for linear regression (1975–1990). To avoid overfitting we use relatively small network architecture of the feedforward 10-4-1. An initial analysis shows that the least mean square error in the training set trails off after approximately 700 iterations. Leaving out the four least-significant variables (as identified by the regression analysis) has little effect. The relatively small sample size (180 observations in-sample and a further 40 observations for the period 1991–1994) does not leave much room for a comprehensive analysis with different training, cross validation, and ex-ante testing. We choose to fix the architecture to a simple 10-4-1 structure and use a fixed learning rate (0.1) and no momentum term. We also choose to run 30 training runs using training times between 700 and 2000 iterations, and investigate the mean and standard deviation of these networks. These are clearly not optimal network parameters, but provided that there is little variability in the predictions of the 30 networks, they will give us a good insight into whether there are any low-order nonlinear relationships. Subsequent sensitivity analysis will be used to investigate the nature of these nonlinearities.

Figures 19.19 and 19.20 show the out-of-sample performance of a 10-4-1 network trained for 1500 epochs. The values of the correlation (between actual and predicted) ρ and R^2 remain quite stable with the 30 training runs (see Table 19. 4).

The results are consistent with many of the networks not only of different training times in the range 800 to 1800 iterations but also with different inputs and topologies with 3, 4, and 5 hidden units.

To understand the difference between the linear model and the relationships that were fitted by the networks, a simple sensitivity analysis was conducted. Each input in turn was varied across its range while the remaining inputs were held at their

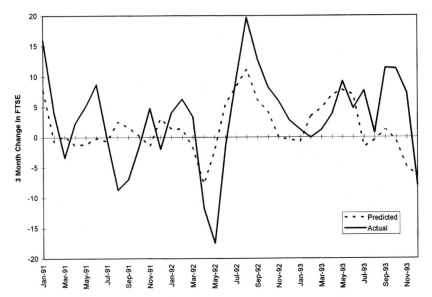

FIGURE 19.19   Out-of-sample prediction with OLS backpropagation: $\rho = 0.55$, $R^2 = 0.24$.

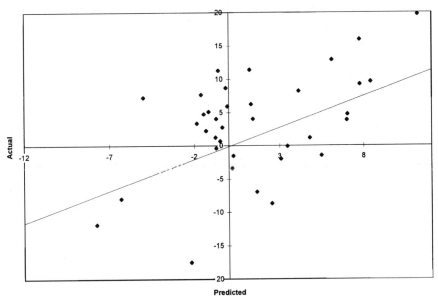

FIGURE 19.20   Scatter plot of actual versus predicted with OLS backpropagation: $\rho = 0.55$, $R^2 = 0.24$.

TABLE 19.4 Summary of Results—Mean and Standard
Deviation for 30 Runs (NN).

	Regression	NN
Correlation	0.436	0.541 (0.021)
R^2	0.190	0.292 (0.045)
Directional changes	63%	65%

means and the network's response was recorded. This method allows us to examine slices of the overall relationship fitted, although it gives no indication of interaction effects. Many of the variables had only a linear effect on the dependent variable, although several were found to have nonlinear relationships. The results of sensitivity analysis were compared across different sets of input variables, topologies, and training time and were seen to change little. Figures 19.21 to 19.23 provide some examples of the response of a typical network to some of the more influential input variables.

Figure 19.22 shows the response of the index to unit changes of the FTSE/price-earnings (PE) ratio. Overall this is consistent with the positive coefficient estimated by the regression. This is not surprising, as the independent variable already contains an element of index prices. Thus, when PE changes in the positive direction, this is partially due to the fact that prices increase (or earnings decrease, but since earnings are revised only at a lower frequency the dominant component is expected to be price increases). The network response indicates that large negative PE changes (probably) due to downward earnings revisions cause negative price changes.

The response of the network model to changes in the annual inflation rate is also consistent with the negative regression coefficient. Note the logistic effect at the tails of the reversed sigmoid.

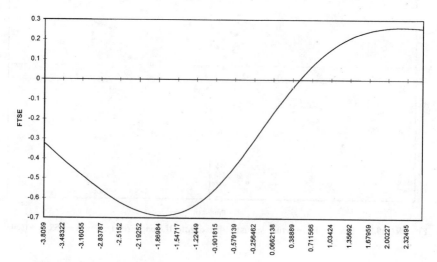

FIGURE 19.21 Predicted change in FTSE versus FTSE/PE.

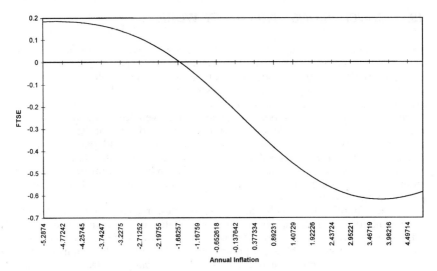

FIGURE 19.22 Predicted change in FTSE versus change in annual inflation rate.

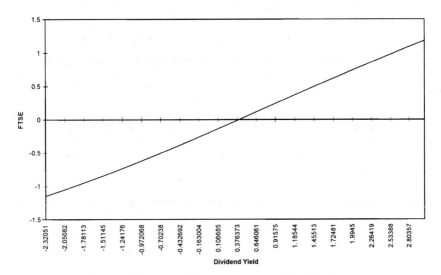

FIGURE 19.23 Predicted change in FTSE versus change in dividend yield.

Finally the network response to changes in dividend yields is also consistent with the positive coefficient in the regression model. Overall, the neural model is consistent with the linear analysis. The improvements in modeling performance can be accounted for by the relatively small but significant nonlinearities such as the logistic effect in Fig. 19.20 and the quadratic effect on the negative side of the PE range.

19.7 CONCLUSIONS AND FUTURE WORK

There are strong reasons to believe that the relationships between asset prices and their determinants are determined by nonlinear processes. Neural networks provide a suitable methodology for modeling this type of relationship. However, the development of successful applications is not a straightforward task. It requires the synergetic combination of expertise in financial engineering and network engineering. Many problems of neural modeling remain unresolved. These include improving robustness to statistical outliers, discontinuous data, and weak nonstationarity, and dealing with serial correlation and multicollinearities in the independent variables. These areas are currently the subject of intensive research in the statistical, mathematical, and econometric sciences. Nevertheless, even in its current state of development, neurotechnology has demonstrated that with careful use it is capable of providing more accurate models.

Nonstationarities are usually handled with brute-force techniques which require large numbers of simulations. The major representative of these kinds of approaches is the *window,* where models are fitted in rolling windows of fixed size. The window size is a parameter and the appropriate value is determined by extensive experimentation. Another approach is the class of *robust backpropagation* algorithms, which replace the scalar error with an error *suppressor* function. In this context a *time-sensitive* cost function could be used to assign more weight to the most recent observations. The appropriate parameters of the suppressor function are also determined with extensive experimentation.

Assigning confidence intervals to forecasts is a problem very much related to the stability of the model performance in and out of sample over different periods. *Jackknifing,* or *leave-one-out cross validation,* is a technique frequently used to determine the stability of a model. According to this technique, a model is fitted on the available data, leaving out only one observation, which is subsequently used for *cross validation.* The procedure is reiterated until all observations have been used as cross validation points. The problem with this approach is that, although it can be used for estimating confidence intervals for forecasts, if nonstationarities are present these intervals are probably going to be so wide that they will not be useful for any practical purposes. Other more sophisticated (but probably less practical) approaches include calculation of confidence intervals for the forecasts, on the basis of several assumptions for the residuals and the data used to derive the model. The problem here is that very rarely are all these assumptions met.

The most common technique for variable selection is a form of indirect sensitivity analysis, where a variable is substituted usually with its mean, and its relevance to the dependent variable (and the model) is evaluated by the observed effect on the residuals. Other analysts decide the importance of independent variables by ranking them according to a sensitivity coefficient which is derived by a variety of methods (e.g., by perturbing the inputs and observing the effect on the output). We believe that the direct calculation of the partial derivatives of the outputs with respect to the inputs is a far superior technique which can be used to assess the importance of each individual variable and observe how it changes over time.

Clearly, all these issues are interdependent. Handling the above problems and producing a reliable and practical model is neither a straightforward nor an easy procedure. And, furthermore, these are not problems associated only with neural network techniques or particular algorithms for updating the synaptic strengths. In the future, estimation of error gradients may be replaced by more efficient algorithms. Instead, new algorithms may hop over, contract, vibrate, or flatten the unknown weight-error surface, but the analyst will still have to tackle the problems mentioned above.

REFERENCES

Amari, S., "The mathematical foundations of neural computing," *IEEE Trans. on Neural Networks,* 1990.

Azoff, M. E., *Neural Network Time Series Forecasting of Financial Markets,* John Wiley & Sons, 1994.

Bolland, P. and A. N. Refenes, "Analysis of the relationship between volume, open interest and futures prices," *Proc. NnCM '94 Neural Networks in the Capital Markets,* Caltech, Pasadena, November 17–18, 1994.

Bolland, P., "Tactical asset allocation with neural networks," working paper, NeuroForecasting Unit, London Business School, 1994.

Breiman, L., and J. Friedman, "Estimating optimal transformations for multiple regression and correlation," *Journal of the American Statistical Association,* **80,** 580–619, 1985.

Burgess, A. N., "Principled variable selection for neural networks: an application on cointegration of European equity indices, in C. Dumir and N. Mead (eds.), *Proc. 2nd International Conference: Advances in FX and Interest Rate Forecasting.* London, February 1994.

DeMers, D., "Dimensionality reduction for nonlinear time series," *Proc. SPIE 1766,* "Neural and stochastic methods for image and signal processing," San Diego, 1992.

Geman, S., E. Beienenstock, and R. Doursat, "Neural networks and the bias/variance dilemma," *Neural Computation,* **4,** 1–58, 1992.

Hardle, W., *Applied Nonparametric Regression,* Econometric Society Monographs, Cambridge University Press, 1989.

Leonfief, W., "Introduction to a theory of the internal structure of functional relationships," *Econometrica,* **15,** 361–73, 1947.

Miranda-Gonzales, F., "Intra-day volatility forecasting for option pricing using a neural network approach," *Proc. NnCM'94, Neural Networks in the Capital Markets,* Caltech, Pasadena, November 17–18, 1994, also submitted to *International Journal of Forecasting.*

Oja, E., "Data compression, feature extraction, and autoassociation in feed forward neural networks," in T. Kohonen et al. (eds), *Artificial Neural Networks,* Elsevier, New York, pp. 737–745, 1991.

Refenes, A. N. (ed.), "Neural networks in the capital markets," NnCM'93, *Proc. First International Workshop, Neural Networks in the Capital Markets,* London Business School, November 1993.

Refenes, A. N., "Neural networks for investment management," *Journal of Finance and Communication,* **8,** 95–101, April 1994.

Refenes, A. N. (ed.), *Neural Networks in the Capital Markets,* John Wiley & Sons, Chichester, England, 1994.

Refenes A. N., Y. Bentz, and N. Burgess, "Neural networks in investment management," *FICOM Journal of Finance and Communication,* special issue on New Investment Technology and Issues, 1994.

Refenes, A. N., Y. Bentz, A. N. Burgess, and A. D. Zappranis, "Backpropagation with differential least squares and its application to financial time series modelling," *Proc. Snowbird '94,* April 1994.

Trippi, R., and E. Turban (eds.), *Neural Networks in Finance and Investment: Applying Artificial Intelligence to Improve Real-World Performance,* Probus Publ. Co., Chicago, 1992.

Wahba, G., "Optimal convergence properties of variable knot, kernel and orthogonal series methods for density estimation," *Annals of Statistics,* **3,** 15–29.

Weigend, A. S., D. Rumelhart, and B. Huberman, "Generalisation by weight elimination applied to currency exchange rate prediction," *Proc. IJCNN'91,* IEEE Press, New York, 1991.

Zapranis, A. D., and A. N. Refenes, "Investment management: Neural and regression models in tactical asset allocation," in M. Arbib (ed.), *The Handbook of Brain Theory and Neural Networks,* The MIT Press, Cambridge, Mass., 1994.

CHAPTER 20

APPLICATION OF NEURAL NETWORKS AND FUZZY LOGIC IN NONDESTRUCTIVE EVALUATION OF MATERIALS

C. H. Chen
Electrical and Computer Engineering Department
University of Massachusetts, Dartmouth

20.1 INTRODUCTION

The role of neural networks in improving the capability of nondestructive evaluation of materials (NDE) will be examined in this chapter. Particular emphasis is placed on ultrasonic NDE using neural networks. The use of fuzzy logic in NDE is still in its infancy but will also be discussed. In the last few years, as a result of renewed interest in artificial neural networks (hereafter, *neural networks*), there has been a significant increase in using neural networks for NDE as described in the Bibliography. The ultrasonic NDE application of neural networks has included defect classification and characterization and crack depth estimation. Neural networks have also been used in eddy-current NDE with significant improvement over the traditional classifier. An assessment of the advantages and disadvantages of neural network NDE is presented in the chapter. The many uncertainties experienced in NDE problems can be suitably described by using the fuzzy set idea, and the decisions made with fuzzy logic often are better than those made by other methods such as statistical decision theory and expert system methodology.

In this chapter the term nondestructive evaluation is considered equivalent to nondestructive testing (NDT), which is also called nondestructive inspection (NDI) in some literature. NDE methods include ultrasonics, eddy current, radiography, magnetics, microwaves, and visual inspection.

20.2 *NEURAL NETWORKS IN ULTRASONIC NDE*

Neural networks are trained to learn through experience represented by the training data set or historical data. The networks are inherently nonlinear, hence have the ability to capture the underlying nonlinearity typical in NDE problems. The robustness property of the networks is particularly important to NDE, as the defect characteristics vary considerably among specimens. Since the networks derive their classification and prediction capability from training, mathematical modeling of the data is not required. In fact, the best feature of the neural network is that it lets the data speak for themselves and thereby frees us from the burden of having to guess [1]. Data fusion, i.e., merging data from various NDE methods, can be easily performed with neural networks. Neural networks are perfectly made for very large scale integration (VLSI) implementation, and thus are quite suitable for real-time NDT system implementation.

NDE systems using neural networks must be computer-based. An example of ultrasonic NDE which fully integrates neural networks into the system is the one we have developed for the Information Research Laboratory; the block diagram is shown in Fig. 20.1. Neural networks are a key part of the Interactive Ultrasonic Nondestructive Evaluation (IUNDE) system, version 2.3. Other systems making significant use of neural networks are the ICEPAK of Tektrend International, Montreal,

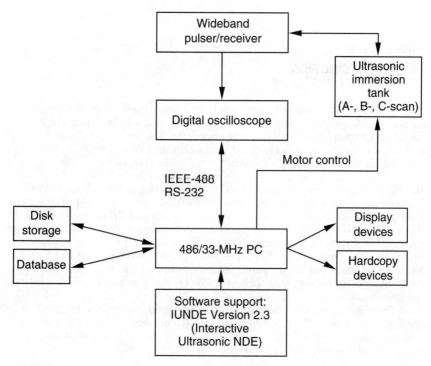

FIGURE 20.1 The block diagram of an interactive ultrasonic NDE system. Neural network is part of IUNDE 2.3.

and TestPro of Informetrics, Silver Spring, Md., U.S.A. In our system, the software package IUNDE directs data acquisition, filtering, and feature extraction, and relies on neural networks for most classification tasks [2].

Though most studies demonstrate similar performance between neural networks and the traditional methods, improvement in the network learning algorithms has now made it possible to achieve better classification and prediction results by using suitably chosen neural networks. For example, our recently developed class-sensitive neural network (CSNN) [3] can offer at least 6 percent improvement in classification over the popular backpropagation-trained network, in underwater acoustics [4] and stock market [5] problems. With proper parameter selection, the backpropagation-trained network (BPN) itself can provide more than 10 percent improvement over the traditional nearest neighbor decision rule (NNDR) in a defect classification experiment with composite materials [6]. The C-scan images of two graphite-epoxy specimens are shown in Fig. 20.2. The classification results are given in Table 20.1.

We now discuss the disadvantages of neural networks. A general problem with neural network applications is that training or learning time may be too long. There are a number of algorithms that offer significant reduction in training time, but the time required may still be too large for most applications. For NDE, the networks can always be pretrained and the subsequent classification or estimation takes an insignificant amount of time. Fast algorithms are needed so that the updated input data can be included in retraining. Actually, for NDE the more serious problem is that a good-sized training data set may not be available. Network algorithms are needed that can perform well with small data sets. For the problem that the system may not converge to the absolute minimum (in mean square error), there are solu-

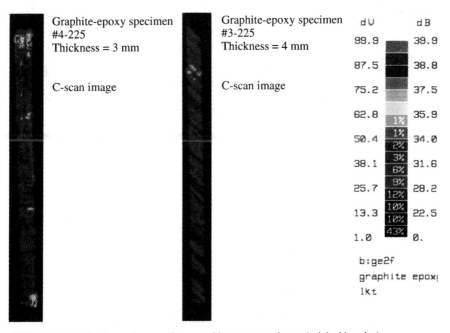

FIGURE 20.2 The C-scan images of two graphite epoxy specimens (original in color).

TABLE 20.1 NN Performance Comparison

	NNDR	BPN	CSNN
Percentage correct	62.81	77.33	78.06
Standard deviation	4.64	2.23	1.54

The results are based on averaging over 20 experiments of the ultrasonic B-scan data. Note that CSNN has lower standard deviation in performance estimate and is thus more reliable.

tions available now. Therefore the advantages far outweigh the disadvantages in view of the rapid progress in neural network studies. Neural networks should be fully utilized to improve the capability of modern NDT systems.

20.3 NEURAL NETWORKS FOR EDDY-CURRENT NDE

Actually the early adaptive system proposed by Mucciardi [7] is a form of neural network with application to eddy-current NDE. More recently Udpa and Udpa [8] presented classification results obtained by implementing a multilayered neural network using the backpropagation algorithm. The eddy-current signals were represented by a parametric model using the Fourier descriptor method. Thus the preprocessing stage enables the model to be invariant under translation, rotation, and scaling of the input data and also achieves a significant amount of data compression. A set of eight Fourier descriptors served as input to the backpropagation-trained neural networks. Four defect classes were assumed. The classification result based on a very limited number of samples was slightly better than the use of the K-means clustering algorithm.

The simplicity of using neural networks with waveform and image data such as the ultrasonic and eddy-current NDE signals is an important factor that will make greatly increased use of neural networks attractive not just for classification, but also for prediction, filtering, control, and estimation as needed in various NDE tasks.

20.4 FUZZY LOGIC IN NDE SYSTEMS

To describe uncertainty, randomness characterized by probability theory and random variable is not the only form available. In the 1960s a mathematical tool was developed to formulate and deal with other forms of uncertainty and came to be known as *fuzzy set theory;* it was first introduced by Zadeh [9, 10]. Essentially, fuzzy set theory provides a natural approach in dealing with problems in which the transition between membership and nonmembership of the classes of objects is gradual rather than abrupt, and the source of imprecision is the absence of sharply defined class membership rather than the presence of random variables. The theory provides us a methodology for dealing with phenomena that are vague, imprecise, too complex, and too ill-defined to be susceptible to analysis by conventional mathematical approaches. For an introduction of the fuzzy set theory, the readers are referred to Klir and Folger [11].

In this section, one example is presented on the use of a fuzzy system [12] to evaluate and predict flexural strength and density of NASA 6Y silicon nitride ceramic. The fuzzy system was built using the data from 273 silicon nitride modulus-of-rupture bars which were tested at room temperature, and 135 bars which were tested at 1370°C. The input fuzzy sets were defined by three points: nitrogen pressure p, sintering time st, and milling time mt, while the output fuzzy sets have two elements: flexural strength s and density d. Different fuzzy sets were defined for room temperature and 1370°C. The grades of memberships were normalized. The normalization was performed at every step of prediction. The resulting membership grades were combined by means of generalized mean operation to produce the resulting fuzzy sets.

By using 60 percent of data for training and the rest for testing, the resulting fuzzy sets for 1370°C temperature were determined; they are listed in Table 20.2. The data are randomly selected to form training and testing set combinations A to E. The graphical explanation of the method used for fuzzy prediction is shown in Fig. 20.3. The k fraction of the measure, where $k \, \varepsilon \, (0,1)$, is either added to or subtracted from the generalized grades of memberships of the output parameters; k is 0.1 for Fig. 20.3. This results in the predicted values for flexural strengths and density. Among the collected samples, batch number 6Y25 is considered optimal, as it represents the optimum combination for the processing variables from the available data set. Table 20.3 shows the overall results of prediction for 1370°C with 60 percent training. Note that the prediction errors for 6Y25 are zero.

TABLE 20.2   The Resulting Fuzzy Sets, after Generalized Mean Operation, for 1370°C, 60 Percent Training

Combination	Strength, MPa	Density, g/cm³	Milling time, h	Sintering time, h	Pressure, MPa
A	0.93	0.98	0.65	0.68	0.74
B	0.93	0.99	0.65	0.74	0.74
C	0.94	0.99	0.26	0.78	0.84
D	0.93	0.98	0.26	0.68	0.74
E	0.91	0.98	0.67	0.56	0.63

SOURCE: After Cios et al. [12] with permission.

TABLE 20.3   Overall Results for 1370°C (2500°F), 60 Percent Training

Combination	Strength-average % error for all test vectors	Strength-% error for 6Y25	Density-average % error for all test vectors	Density % error 6Y25
A	6.3	0	5.7	0
B	4.3	0	4.3	0
C	3.3	0	3.0	0
D	6.3	0	0.7	0
E	6.7	0	2.7	0
Combined average % error	5.4	0	3.3	0

SOURCE: After Cios et al. [12] with permission.

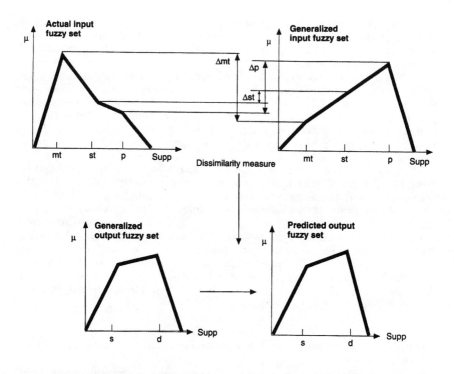

The generalized input fuzzy set consists of grades of membership obtained by generalized mean operation performed on normalized values of input parameters: milling time *mt*, sintering time *st*, and pressure *p* (note that these fuzzy sets differ for different combinations of training data). The actual input fuzzy set represents normalized values of a particular input. The dissimilarity measure based on the Hamming distance is used and the elementwise differences are summed up. The *k*-fraction of the measure is then added to the grades of membership of the generalized output fuzzy set (a fuzzy set obtained by generalized mean operation performed on normalized values of output parameters: strength *s* and density *d*), resulting in the predicted output fuzzy set. The grades of memberships of the latter are then compared with the actual normalized output.

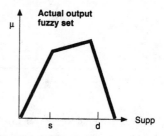

FIGURE 20.3 A graphical explanation of the method used for fuzzy set prediction. *(After Cios et al. [12] with permission.)*

20.5 COMPARISON BETWEEN RBF NEURAL NETWORK AND FUZZY SETS

It is always of interest to make comparisons among traditional methods, neural networks, and fuzzy logic. However, rigorously speaking, the comparison results are valid only under certain specified conditions for the data studied. With this in mind, it is useful to show a comparison between the powerful radial basis function (RBF) neural network and the fuzzy sets (FS) for the NDE problem considered in the previous section. The results, as reported in Cios et al. [12, 13], are shown in Figs. 20.4 and 20.5. They concluded that fuzzy sets are better at modeling less precise relationships existing between the processing variables and strength, which are due to statistical variations in the manufacturing process. The more precise relationship between the processing variables and density was modeled better (in terms of error) by neural networks. Developers of ceramics could achieve higher strength and density, and shorten the processing time, by using fuzzy sets and neural networks in a hybrid system. The former can help to capture imprecise relationships which are due to unavoidable variations in the manufacturing process; the latter can capture more precise, although still very complex, relationships, according to these authors.

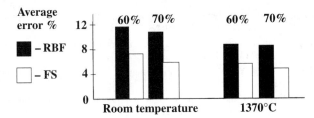

FIGURE 20.4 Average errors in predicting strength using radial basis function neural network (RFB) and fuzzy sets (FS). *(After Cios et al. [12] with permission.)*

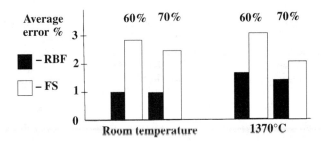

FIGURE 20.5 Average errors in predicting density using radial basis function neural network (RBF) and fuzzy sets (FS). *(After Cios et al. [12] with permission.)*

20.6 CONCLUDING REMARKS

Neural networks and fuzzy logic are only beginning to be used in various NDE problems, with various degrees of success. However, it can now be concluded that both can contribute significantly to nondestructive testing problems and the related manufacturing process. Listed in the Bibliography in chronological order are the publications from 1989 to 1994. The increase in publications is expected to continue in the foreseeable future as more activities on neural networks, fuzzy logic, and hybrid systems as applied to NDE are reported in the literatures. Future research and development efforts are likely to include real-time and/or on-line systems.

ACKNOWLEDGMENT

I thank Dr. K. J. Cios and Dr. A. Vary for permission to use their materials presented in Secs. 20.4 and 20.5.

REFERENCES

1. S. Haykin, "Intelligent signal processing," invited lecture at the NATO Advanced Research Workshop on Advances of Signal Processing in Nondestructive Evaluation of Materials, Univ. Laval, Quebec City, Canada, August 17–20, 1993.

2. C. H. Chen, "A high resolution ultrasonic spectroscopy system for nondestructive evaluation," *Proc. ASNT Fall Conf.,* Boston, September 1991, pp. 61–64.

3. C. H. Chen and G. H. You, "Class-sensitive neural network," *Neural, Parallel Scientific Computing,* vol. 1, no. 1, March 1993.

4. C. H. Chen, B. Bosworth, and J. Sikorski, "Neural networks for active sonar classification", *U.S. Navy Journal of Underwater Acoustics,* April 1993.

5. C. H. Chen, "Neural networks for financial market prediction," *Proc. IEEE WCNN,* Orlando, June 1994.

6. C. H. Chen, "Application of artificial intelligence in NDE," in *Advances in Signal Processing for Nondestructive Evaluation of Materials,* X. P. V. Malague (ed.), Kluwer Academic Publishers, 1994, pp. 241–249.

7. A. N. Mucciardi, "Elements of learning control systems with applications to industrial process," *Proc. IEEE Conf. on Decision and Control,* New Orleans, 1972.

8. L. Udpa and S. S. Udpa, "Eddy current defect characterization using neural networks," *Materials Evaluation,* vol. 48, pp. 342–353, March 1990.

9. L. Zadeh, "A theory of approximate reasoning," in *Machine Intelligence,* vol. 9, J. K. Hayes, D. Michie, and L. I. Mikulich (eds.), pp. 149–194, Wiley, 1979.

10. L. Zadeh, "Fuzzy sets," *Information and Control,* vol. 8, pp. 338–353, 1965.

11. G. J. Klir and T. A. Folger, "Fuzzy Sets, Uncertainty, and Information," Prentice-Hall, 1988.

12. K. J. Cios, G. Y. Baaklini, A. Vary, and L. M. Sztandera, "Using fuzzy sets in the prediction of flexural strength and density of silicon nitride ceramics," *Materials Evaluation,* May 1994, pp. 600–606.

13. K. J. Cios, G. Y. Baaklini, A. Vary, and R. E. Tjia, "Radial basis function network learns ceramic processing and predicts related strength and density," *Journal of Testing and Evaluation,* pp. 343–350, 1994.

BIBLIOGRAPHY

Note: RQNDE stands for the annual meeting of *Review of Progress in Quantitative Nondestructive Evaluation.* The proceedings have been edited by Donald O. Thompson and Dale E. Chimenti and published by Plenum Press. The 1993 RQNDE Meeting was held at Brunswick, Maine, August 2–6, 1993. The 1994 RQNDE Meeting was held at Snowmass Village, Colo., July 31–August 5, 1994. The following list is arranged according to the date of publication.

1. A. R. Baker and C. G. Windsor, "The classification of defects from ultrasonic data using neural networks: the Hopfield method," *British NDT International,* pp. 97–105, 1989.

2. C. H. Chen, "Applying and validating neural network technology for nondestructive evaluation of materials," *IEEE SMC Society Conf. Proc.,* Cambridge, Mass., November 1989.

3. L. Udpa and S. S. Udpa, "Eddy current defect characterization using neural networks," *Materials Evaluation,* vol. 48, pp. 342–353, March 1990.

4. J. M. Mann, et al., "Inversion of uniform field eddy current data using neural networks," in RQNDE vol. 9A, pp. 681–688, 1990.

5. T. Ogi et al., "A neural network applied to crack type recognition," in RQNDE vol. 9A, pp. 689–696, 1990.

6. K. Shahani, L. Udpa, and S. S. Udpa, "Time delay neural networks for classification of ultrasonic NDT signals," in RQNDE vol. 11A, 1992, pp. 663–700.

7. M. Kitahara et al., "Neural network for crack-depth determination from ultrasonic backscatter data," in RQNDE, vol. 11A, 1992, pp. 701–708.

8. L. M. Brown, et al., "Graphite epoxy defect classification of ultrasonic signatures using statistical and neural network techniques," in RQNDE, vol. 11A, 1992, pp. 677–684.

9. C. H. Chen and G. G. Lee, "Neural networks for ultrasonic NDE signal classification using time-frequency analysis," *Proc. IEEE ASSP Conf.,* Minneapolis, April 1993.

10. K. J. Cios, G. Y. Baaklini, and A. Vary, "Soft computing in design and manufacturing of advanced materials," *Proc. International Gas Turbine and Aeroengine Congress and Exposition,* Cincinnati, May 1993.

11. K. J. Cios, E. A. Mayer, A. Vary, and H. E. Kautz, "Neural network methods in analysis of acousto-ultrasonic data," *Proc. Second International Conf. on Acousto-Ultrasonics,* Atlanta, June 1993.

12. L. M. Brown, J. S. Lin, and R. W. Newman, "Signature classification development system," ASME, June 1993.

13. C. P. Chiou, L. W. Schmerr, and R. B. Thompson, "Statistical detection for ultrasonic NDE," RQNDE Meeting, August 1993.

14. T. Stepinski, "Restoration of eddy current images with neural networks," RQNDE Meeting, August 1993.

15. D. S. Forsyth, A. Fahr and C. E. Chapman, "An evaluation of artificial neural networks for the classification of eddy current signals," RQNDE Meeting, August 1993.

16. M. Takadoya et al., "Depth estimation of inclined surface-breaking crack by a neural network," RQNDE Meeting, August 1993.

17. S. Nair, L. Udpa, and S. S. Udpa, "Radial basis functions network for defect sizing," RQNDE, vol. 12A, 1993.

18. M. Takadoya et al., "Crack-depth determination by a neural network with a synthetic training data set," RQNDE, vol. 12A, 1993.

19. C. H. Chen, "Neural networks for defect characterization of composite materials using time-frequency transforms," RQNDE Meeting, August 1993.

20. E. Segal, Y. Merlis, and Y. Segal, "Adhesive bond classification by neural nets," RQNDE Meeting, August 1993.

21. I. N. Komsky, K. Zgonc, and J. D. Achenbach, "Application of an adaptive signal classifier to the quantitative characterization of fatigue cracks using a self-compensating ultrasonic technique," RQNDE Meeting, August 1993.

22. M. Davis and W. D. Rummel, "The use of neural network tools in decision processing of nondestructive evaluation data," RQNDE Meeting, August 1993.

23. D. David, et al., "Sequoia: artificial intelligence applied to infrared thermography inspection of composite aerospace structures," RQNDE Meeting, August 1993.

24. I. Grabec, W. Sachse, and D. Grabec, "Intelligent processing of ultrasonic signals for process control applications," *Materials Evaluation,* August 1993, pp. 1174–1182.

25. C. H. Chen, "Application of artificial intelligence in NDE," NATO Advanced Research Workshop on Advances of Signal Processing in Nondestructive Evaluation of Materials, Univ. Laval, Quebec City, Canada, August 17–20, 1993.

26. C. H. Chen, "Pattern recognition in nondestructive evaluation of materials," in *Handbook of Pattern Recognition and Computer Vision,* C. H. Chen, L. F. Pau, and P. S. P. Wang (eds.), World Scientific Publishing, September 1993.

27. H. B. Smart, J. A. Johnson, and C. J. Einerson, "The role of intelligent systems in weld process control," *Materials Evaluation,* October 1993, pp. 1166–1173.

28. P. J. Sinebaugh, "A general purpose image analysis inspection," in *Advanced Materials and Process Technology for Mechanical Failure Prevention, Proc. 48th MFPG Meeting,* Wakefield, Mass., pp. 393–401, April 1994.

29. K. J. Cios, G. Y. Baaklini, A. Vary, and L. M. Sztandera, "Using fuzzy sets in the prediction of flexural strength and density of silicon nitride ceramics," *Materials Evaluation,* May 1994, pp. 600–606.

30. W. D. Rummel and M. Davis, "Neural network applications laboratory at the San Antonio Air Logistics Center," RQNDE Meeting, August 1994.

31. K. Zgonc and J. D. Achenbach, "Crack characterization using a neural network classifier trained with data obtained from finite element models," RQNDE Meeting, August 1994.

32. L. M. Brown and R. Denale, "Knowledge-based NDE system," RQNDE Meeting, August 1994.

33. H. Hoshikawa and K. Koyama, "Flaw depth classification in eddy current tubing inspection by using neural network," RQNDE Meeting, August 1994.

34. J. Yim, S. S. Udpa, L. Udpa, M. Mina, and W. Lord, "Neural network approaches to data fusion," *RQNDE Meeting,* August 1994.

35. H. Tretout et al., "An evaluation of artificial neural networks applied to infrared thermography inspection of composite aerospace structures," RQNDE Meeting, August 1994.

36. J. H. Xu and D. L. Birx, "Neural network based pattern recognition for defect detection of load slots," RQNDE Meeting, August 1994.

37. E. R. Doering, "Fuzzy membership function for volumetric defect signatures in digital radiographs," RQNDE Meeting, August 1994.

38. K. J. Cios, G. Y. Baaklini, A. Vary, and R. E. Tjia, "Radial basis function network learns ceramic processing and predicts related strength and density," *Journal of Testing and Evaluation,* pp. 343–350, 1994.

CHAPTER 21
FUZZY LOGIC FOR HOME APPLIANCES

Noboru Wakami
Hiroyoshi Nomura
Shoichi Araki
Central Research Laboratories
Matsushita Electric Industrial Co., Ltd.
Kyoto, Japan

21.1 INTRODUCTION

Fuzzy logic has been applied to many kinds of home appliances in Japan since 1990. Fuzzy logic makes home appliances intelligent and easy to operate by dealing with qualitative knowledge of experts.

In this chapter, we discuss the following three topics:

1. *Application to a washing machine.* In this section, we introduce an application of fuzzy inference to a washing machine. This fuzzy washing machine went on sale in 1990. It triggered a flood of applications of fuzzy inference to many kinds of home appliances in Japan.

2. *Applications to image processing.* In this section, we introduce an electronic image stabilizer for a video camera and an air-conditioning system with a pyroelectric infrared-ray detector. The video camera can detect unstable support (hand jitter) by fuzzy inference, and the air-conditioning system can identify the number of occupants in a room from thermal images taken by the pyroelectric infrared-ray detector using a fuzzy clustering algorithm.

3. *Self-tuning methods of fuzzy rules by neural networks.* Fuzzy inference enables home appliances to be intelligent easily. However, when the number of input variables and fuzzy rules increases, it is difficult to design the fuzzy rules. In order to overcome this problem, we developed some methods to tune fuzzy rules by a learning function of neural networks. In this section, we introduce the self-tuning methods of fuzzy rules and their application.

21.2 APPLICATION TO A WASHING MACHINE

In this section, we explain a fully automatic washing machine, which is the first application of fuzzy inference in the Japanese home appliances market [1]. This washing machine went on sale in 1990. It triggered a flood of applications of fuzzy inference to many kinds of home appliances (vacuum cleaner, air conditioner, microwave oven, etc.) in Japan.

In order to wash clothes skillfully and easily, we applied fuzzy inference to the washing machine, based on the basic principle of laundering: "When dirt has been removed, washing is stopped."

Using fuzzy inference, the optimum washing time is determined from output of a wash sensor. The wash sensor measures the dirtiness of the laundry by detecting the transmittance of the wash water with an optical sensor. The mechanism of the wash sensor and the functions realized by the fuzzy inference are introduced in the following.

21.2.1 Mechanism of the Wash Sensor

Figure 21.1 shows the composition of the washing machine. The wash sensor is installed near the drain valve. Figure 21.2 shows the mechanism of the wash sensor

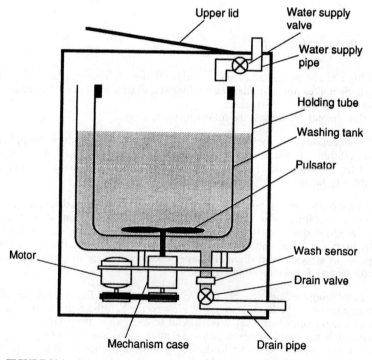

FIGURE 21.1 Composition of a washing machine.

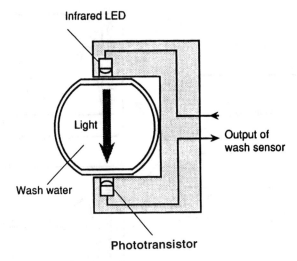

FIGURE 21.2 The wash sensor.

in detail. The wash sensor consists of an infrared light-emitting diode (LED) and a phototransistor. The light beam generated by the infrared LED, passing through the wash water in the pipe, enters the phototransistor. The phototransistor produces a voltage in proportion to the intensity of the light. This voltage is the output of the wash sensor, and indicates the transmittance of the wash water.

The change of the output of the wash sensor over time is shown in Fig. 21.3. When washing is started, the dirt in the clothes is gradually washed out and the wash water becomes dirty, causing the transmittance of wash water to decrease as shown in Fig. 21.3a. The rate of decrease of the transmittance depends on the quality of the dirt, being fast for muddy dirt and slow for oily dirt (Fig. 21.3b). This is because muddy dirt is removed easily by the mechanical force of the water flow produced by rotation of the pulsator, while oily dirt is not adequately removed until the detergent takes effect.

When most of the dirt in the clothes has been removed, the transmittance of the wash water approaches a state of saturation. The transmittance at saturation is lower, the greater the dirtiness of the clothing, while the transmittance is higher, the less the dirtiness of the clothing (Fig. 21.3c).

21.2.2 Fuzzy Inference in the Washing Machine

It is difficult to obtain the optimum relation between dirtiness and washing time experimentally, because there are a great many kinds of dirtiness (wash sensor output patterns), and collecting detailed experimental data for all such types would be nearly impossible. In addition, since the wash mechanism in the washing machine is not well understood and the relation between dirtiness and wash time is not linear, it is difficult to obtain a unique numerical formula relating them. Therefore, in order to determine the wash time from the output of the wash sensor, we employed the fuzzy inference. Using fuzzy inference, the relation between the dirtiness and the wash time is expressed by linguistic rules, and the nonlinear property of the relation is approximated by an interpolation function of the fuzzy inference.

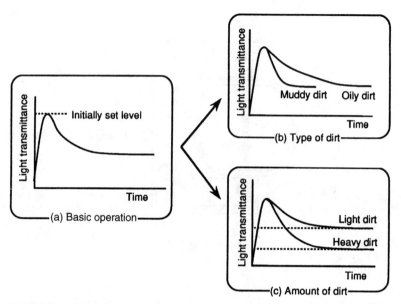

FIGURE 21.3   Wash sensor output change.

Figure 21.4a shows a diagram of the fuzzy inference in the washing machine, and Fig. 21.4b explains input/output variables used in the fuzzy inference. From the time until the transmittance reaches saturation, T_s (which is related to the quality of dirt), and the output level at saturation, V_s (which is related to the amount of dirt), the remaining wash time W_t is determined by fuzzy inference.

Some fuzzy rules to determine the wash time are

- If the transmittance V_s is low and the saturation time T_s is long, then the wash time W_t is very long ($T4$).

- If the transmittance V_s is high and the saturation time T_s is short, then the wash time W_t is very short ($T3$).

Table 21.1 shows the rule table, where $T1$ to $T6$ are wash times. Figure 21.5 shows the membership functions used in the fuzzy rules. In this case, we employed a simplified fuzzy inference [2] in which the consequent part of the fuzzy rule is expressed by a real number. Therefore, the simplified fuzzy inference makes it possible to simplify the inference operations and tuning of the membership function

TABLE 21.1   Rule Table

	V_s		
T_s	Low	Middle	High
Short	$T1$	$T2$	$T3$
Long	$T4$	$T5$	$T6$

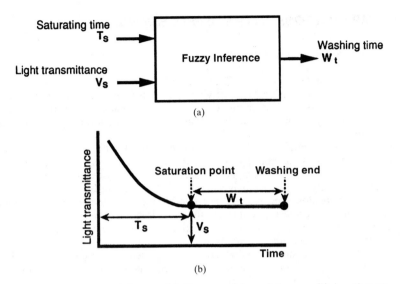

FIGURE 21.4   Fuzzy inference. (*a*) Diagram of fuzzy inference; (*b*) input/output variables.

and to reduce the amount of required memory. In this case, the creation of rules and the tuning of membership functions were carried out according to skilled launderers' know-how.

By applying the fuzzy inference to the fully automatic washing machine, the nonlinear relation between the degree of dirtiness and the wash time can be expressed by rules, making it possible to determine the optimum wash time based on the amounts and types of dirt detected by the wash sensor.

As a result of using fuzzy inference, excessive washing or inadequate washing can be prevented, and a savings of both energy and time can be realized.

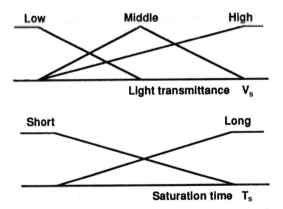

FIGURE 21.5   Membership functions.

21.3 *APPLICATIONS TO IMAGE PROCESSING*

21.3.1 Application to a Video Camera

Recently fuzzy logic has been actively applied to televisions and videotape
recorders, among the various types of video equipment. Particularly in video cameras, many functions (the automatic focus control, automatic iris control, etc.) have
been improved by fuzzy logic. In this section, we explain another application to a
video camera, electronic image stabilization [3, 4, 5].

Since the video camera has become very small and light recently, we can use it
more conveniently than conventional heavy ones. However, as video cameras
become smaller and lighter, the camera movement caused by hand jitter grows more
noticeable, making recorded images unpleasant. Particularly, when the lens is
zoomed in to take close-ups, even a small amount of camera movement is magnified
on the screen. Furthermore, people want to use their video cameras even in a vibrat-
ing environment such as inside a car or a train. Therefore, a camera movement correction function has become indispensable.

An S-VHS-C–type single-hand video camera, placed in the market in June 1990,
is equipped with a camera movement correction function. We call the correction
function an *electronic image stabilizer.*

The function is realized by two technologies: digital video signal processing and
fuzzy logic. Figure 21.6 shows a block diagram of the electronic image stabilizer system. The system consists of a motion-detection large-scale integration chip (LSI), an
interpolation processing LSI, a field memory, and an 8-bit microprocessor. The fuzzy
inference is executed in the microprocessor. This sequence occurs in the video camera:

1. Analog video signals are transformed into digital signals and stored in the field
   memory.

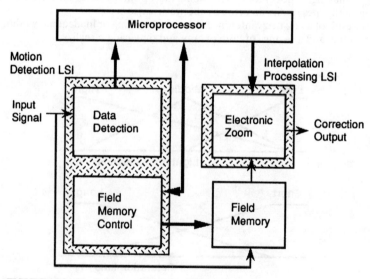

FIGURE 21.6   Block diagram of camera-vibration correction function.

2. These digital signals are processed to extract motion vectors by the motion-detection LSI. The motion vectors are derived from the correlation between the movement of images.

3. The field memory readout position is controlled in accordance with the detected motion vectors to compensate the shaky pictures.

4. The compensated image is enlarged by the electronic zoom function in the interpolation processing LSI.

Figure 21.7 shows the compensation principle of the image stabilizer. In this figure, a shaky image of a dog in front of a house is the input image; the dog is not walking. The lower image is the present image, and the upper image is the preceding image that is stored in the field memory. Comparing these two images, we can derive motion vectors from a correlation measure. According to the motion vectors, the cutout image of the next frame is shifted in the field memory. Then, this cut-out image is enlarged up to the original frame size by means of the electrical zoom function.

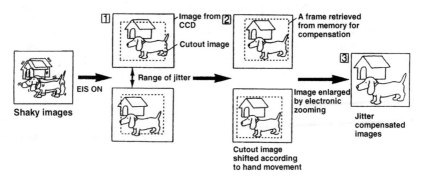

FIGURE 21.7   The principle of camera movement correction.

However, there is a problem in the electric image stabilizer system. If in Fig. 21.7, the dog is walking and there is no shaking due to camera movement, the movement of the dog is used to derive the motion vectors. Since the compensation of images is made against the motion vectors, the system will produce strange images—the dog appears to stop and the background unnaturally shakes according to the dog's motion vector. So, we must discriminate between hand movement and a moving object.

In order to distinguish shaky pictures, we employed fuzzy inference. Figure 21.8 shows examples of the fuzzy rules. When only the object moves differently in the frame, movement is judged to be caused by a moving object. When the entire picture frame is being shifted in an identical direction, the movement is judged to be caused by unstable holding.

By applying fuzzy inference, the cause of shaky picture is discriminated between unstable holding and a moving object. The electronic image stabilizer can compensate the shaky image from this inference result.

Using the electronic image stabilizer with fuzzy inference, we can take stable pictures any time without the influence of hand jitter. Furthermore, this electronic image stabilizer makes stable shooting possible even while walking or riding in a car or train.

Rule1:
IF   different motion vectors are detected
        and their difference becomes larger
THEN   a moving object exists in the picture.

Rule2:
IF   most of the motion vectors are in the same
        direction,
        and their difference is small
THEN   the movememt in the image is due to
        hand jitter.

FIGURE 21.8 Fuzzy rules.

21.3.2 Application to an Air-Conditioning System

We have equipped air-conditioning systems with "eyes." In order to realize more comfortable thermal environment, we have to detect not only physical environmental conditions (air temperature, humidity, etc.) but also the information about occupants in a room (the number, positions, etc.). A pyroelectric infrared-ray detector was developed to take a thermal image inside a room [6]. We introduced a segmentation algorithm for a thermal image to identify the number and positions of occupants by a fuzzy logic [7, 8].

Structure of the Pyroelectric Infrared-Ray Detector. The schematic structure of the pyroelectric infrared-ray detector is shown in Fig. 21.9. The sensor consists of a

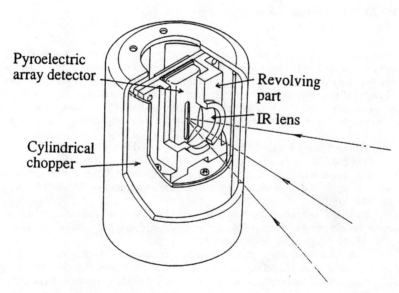

FIGURE 21.9 Infrared-ray detector.

one-dimensional linear pyroelectric array detector, a horizontal scanning mechanical body, a silicon infrared-ray (IR) lens, and a mechanical chopper. The array detector, which has eight elements, and the IR lens are united in a revolving part that scans horizontally. The part is located in the center of a cylindrical chopper. The chopper has three windows, so it opens and closes at 60° intervals, three times for one rotation. The revolving part and the chopper are linearly rotated at a constant rate ratio. A two-dimensional thermal image is produced as the vertical array detector scans horizontally. An example of a thermal image and the corresponding visual image is shown in Fig. 21.10a and b. The thermal image is composed of 8 × 20 elements. Each element has a value of temperature expressed by 8 bits.

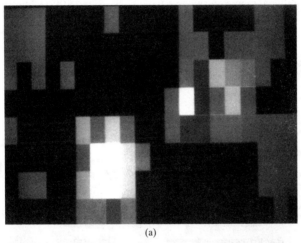

(a)

(b)

FIGURE 21.10 An example of an image. (a) Thermal image; (b) corresponding visual image.

Segmentation Algorithm for Thermal Images.   A segmentation algorithm to identify the number of occupants is described here. The algorithm consists of three procedures: removal of background, identification of each occupant, and region growing. Our approach is based on the fact that the temperature of occupants is higher than that of background and each occupant has a local temperature peak in an image. We explain our algorithm using the image shown in Fig. 21.10a.

   Removing Background Using the Fuzzy C-Means Algorithm.   A fuzzy c-means algorithm (FCM) is applied to remove background, or to distinguish occupants from background in a thermal image. Clustering of FCM is performed on a data set of temperature of 8×20 elements of an image. Figure 21.11 shows an example of clustering results. The elements which belong to the cluster whose weighted mean temperature is the highest with high membership value are selected as the component of regions representing occupants. As shown in Fig. 21.11, selected elements depend on the thresholding level of membership value. Therefore, we set the thresholding level at 0.5 to roughly distinguish occupants from background at first. Figure 21.12 shows the initial selected elements as the components of occupants.

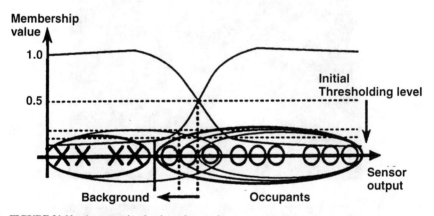

FIGURE 21.11   An example of a clustering result.

   Identifying the Number of Occupants.   In order to distinguish each occupant, local temperature peaks in an image are located from among elements selected as occupants. A particular element searches for an element which has the maximum temperature among its eight neighbors. If the temperature of the searched element is higher than the particular one, the searched one is taken as the parent of the particular one. The result of peak location is shown in Fig. 21.13. An arrow linked between two elements points to the parent. Elements with no parent are local peaks of temperature. A distinct peak surrounded by a circle is regarded as the representative element of an occupant. Each peak is given a distinct label such as a natural number. Every element selected as a component of occupants is given the same label as its parent. As shown in Fig. 21.14, the region composed of the elements which have the same label represents one occupant.

   Region-Growing Algorithm.   The region-growing algorithm resolves the regions of occupants into an image. It is performed by lowering the thresholding level of the

Search step

FIGURE 21.12 — Initial selected elements.

Element number	1	2	3	4	5	6	7	8	9	10	11	12	13	14	15	16	17	18	19	20
1	81	84	82	64	68	74	75	80	74	72	73	69	85	75	76	77	77	80	83	75
2	78	82	82	71	73	71	63	73	72	62	72	68	78	78	69	83	86	84	83	76
3	80	72	82	74	82	73	70	71	74	62	55	59	96	101	111	(132)	(118)	84	71	68
4	71	75	77	65	71	75	72	72	66	42	38	80	(164)	(162)	(131)	113	86	74	68	66
5	78	76	69	55	63	(120)	(151)	(135)	93	66	66	79	107	108	98	93	91	81	82	80
6	53	69	77	32	50	(149)	(215)	(207)	(133)	84	73	70	70	67	63	65	73	78	84	78
7	54	78	87	51	47	(121)	(186)	(197)	(138)	77	71	58	66	70	72	65	69	82	89	85
8	62	72	76	57	65	79	92	102	86	64	65	56	64	67	64	72	73	76	82	73

Search step

FIGURE 21.13 — Peak location.

Element number	1	2	3	4	5	6	7	8	9	10	11	12	13	14	15	16	17	18	19	20
1	81	84	82	64	68	74	75	80	74	72	73	69	85	75	76	77	77	80	83	75
2	78	82	82	71	73	71	63	73	72	62	72	68	78	78	69	83	86	84	83	76
3	80	72	82	74	82	73	70	71	74	62	55	59	96	101	111	(132)	118	84	71	68
4	71	75	77	65	71	75	72	72	66	42	38	80	(164)	162	131	113	86	74	68	66
5	78	76	69	55	63	120	151	135	93	66	66	79	107	108	98	93	91	81	82	80
6	53	69	77	32	50	149	(215)	207	133	84	73	70	70	67	63	65	73	78	84	78
7	54	78	87	51	47	121	186	197	138	77	71	58	66	70	72	65	69	82	89	85
8	62	72	76	57	65	79	92	102	86	64	65	56	64	67	64	72	73	76	82	73

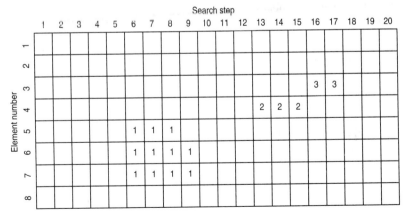

Search step

Element number	1	2	3	4	5	6	7	8	9	10	11	12	13	14	15	16	17	18	19	20
1																				
2																				
3																3	3			
4													2	2	2					
5						1	1	1												
6						1	1	1	1											
7						1	1	1	1											
8																				

FIGURE 21.14 — Initial label.

membership value of elements to be regarded as occupants under the restriction that the number of occupants determined by locating peaks is not changed. Figure 21.15 shows the result of region growing.

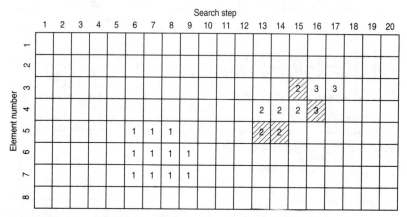

FIGURE 21.15 Result of region growing.

Method of Locating Occupants. In this section, we describe a method to find the positions of occupants. If their positions can be located, we can control the airflow direction in various situations. For example, it is possible to prevent the cool air from reaching occupants when the air conditioner starts to heat. Positions of occupants in a room can be easily calculated from the distance L_{so} between the infrared-ray sensor and occupants. In general, the output of the sensor becomes low and the position of occupants in an image rises to the upper part of the image as the distance L_{so} becomes long. On the other hand, as the distance L_{so} becomes short, the output becomes high and the position descends to the lower part of the image. However, it is difficult to express this relationship in a simple model. Therefore, we tried to identify the relationship among the distance L_{so}, the output of the local temperature peak, and its element number using fuzzy rules.

Figure 21.16 shows a room layout for the experiment. The sensor is set 2.3 m high from the floor and its declination angle is 28°. We generated nine fuzzy rules for the estimation of the distance L_{so} [9]. Reasoning results are shown in Table 21.2. Average error between the estimated value and real value is less than 0.1 m. This result shows that the fuzzy inference can estimate the distance L_{so} with desirable accuracy.

21.4 SELF-TUNING METHODS FOR FUZZY RULES

As mentioned above, the fuzzy inference enables home appliances to be intelligent. However, when the numbers of input variables and rules increase, it is difficult to design fuzzy rules. In conventional fuzzy systems, human operators have to deter-

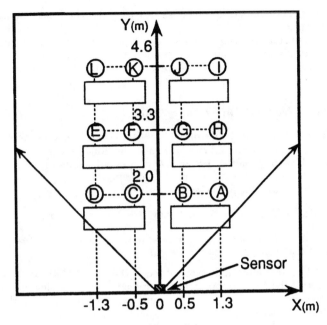

FIGURE 21.16   Room layout for experiment.

TABLE 21.2   Reasoning Results for Distance

Position	Peak temp.	Element no.	Reasoning result	Real distance
A	182	6	2.58	2.63
A	188	6	2.52	2.63
B	203	6	2.35	2.34
B	193	6	2.48	2.34
C	207	6	2.36	2.34
C	201	6	2.41	2.34
D	209	6	2.34	2.63
D	184	6	2.56	2.63
E	173	4	3.57	3.72
E	161	4	3.68	3.72
F	175	4	3.55	3.52
F	176	4	3.55	3.52
G	168	4	3.61	3.52
G	161	4	3.68	3.52
H	167	4	3.62	3.72
H	167	4	3.62	3.72
I	129	3	4.86	4.91
I	131	3	4.84	4.91
J	128	3	4.87	4.76
J	138	3	4.78	7.76
K	131	3	4.84	4.76
K	125	3	4.89	4.76
L	136	3	4.80	4.91
L	121	3	4.92	4.91

mine the rules and membership functions by trial and error; it takes much time to optimize the rules.

In order to overcome this problem, we developed some methods to design fuzzy rules automatically by a learning function of neural networks. In this section, we introduce these self-tuning methods of fuzzy rules and their application.

21.4.1　Neural-Network-Driven Fuzzy Control

Neural-network-driven fuzzy control (NNDF) [10, 11] is a method to combine fuzzy inference and a neural network directly. Membership functions in the fuzzy rules are expressed by backpropagation-type neural networks [12]. From the input-output data, the NNDF can derive the fuzzy rules automatically.

The NNDF employs the following rule format.

$$\text{Rule } i\text{: If } (x_1, \ldots, x_m) \text{ is } A^i \text{ then } y^i \text{ is } N\,N_i(x_1, \ldots, x_m) \tag{21.1}$$

where i is a rule number, $x_1, \ldots, x_m$ are input variables, A^i is a fuzzy set, y^i is an output variable, and NN_i is a neural network.

Figure 21.17 shows a block diagram of the NNDF. The NNDF consists of plural neural networks. The NN_{mem} represents a neural network expressing the antecedent parts of the fuzzy rules. The $NN_1, \ldots, NN_n$ represents the neural networks expressing the consequent parts of the fuzzy rules, where n is the total number of rules. The neural network for the antecedent parts, NN_{mem}, outputs $\mu_{A^i}, i = 1, \ldots, n$, which are membership values of the fuzzy set A^i. The neural networks for the consequent parts, $NN_1, \ldots, NN_n$, outputs $y^i, \ldots, y^n$.

The output of NNDF is calculated from the following equation:

$$y = \frac{\displaystyle\sum_{i=1}^{n} \mu_{A^i} * y^i}{\displaystyle\sum_{i=1}^{n} \mu_{A^i}} \tag{21.2}$$

The desirable output value for a pth input data $(x_{1p}, \ldots, x_{mp})$ is expressed by y'_p, and a pair of the input data and the desirable output value $(x_{1p}, \ldots, x_{mp}, y'_p)$ are called *input-output data*.

From the plural input-output data, the NNDF creates the fuzzy rules according to the following procedure.

1. The input-output data $(x_{1p}, \ldots, x_{mp}, y'_p), p = 1, \ldots, P$ are divided into n clusters using a conventional hierarchical clustering method. The input-output data that belongs to the ith cluster is expressed by $(x^i_{1p}, \ldots, x^i_{mp}, y'^i_p)$, and a vector $(R_{1p}, R_{2p}, \ldots, R_{np})$ is determined for each input-output data from the following equation.

$$\begin{cases} R_{kp} = 1.0 & k = i \\ R_{kp} = 0 & k \neq i \quad k = 1, \ldots, n \end{cases} \tag{21.3}$$

2. From the input data $(x_{1p}, \ldots, x_{mp})$ and the vectors expressing the result of clustering $(R_{1p}, R_{2p}, \ldots, R_{np})$, the neural network NN_{mem} is trained with the backpropagation algorithm. Figure 21.18 is a diagram that shows the determination process of the membership function in the antecedent part.

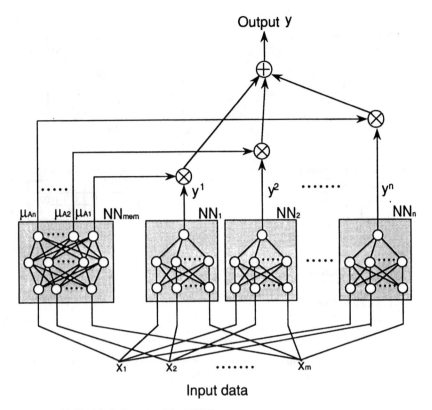

FIGURE 21.17   Block diagram of the NNDF.

3. From the input-output data $(x_{1p}^i, \ldots, x_{mp}^i, y_p'^i)$ contained in the ith cluster, the neural network NN_i of the consequent part of the ith rule is trained by backpropagation $(i = 1, \ldots, n)$.

Using this procedure, the NNDF can determine the membership functions from the input-output data.

As described above, the NNDF can create the fuzzy rules from given input-output data by means of the neural networks.

21.4.2   Self-Tuning by a Delta Rule

Next, we explain another self-tuning method [13, 14], that is, tuning fuzzy rules by a delta rule. The delta rule is a kind of learning algorithm of a neural network [12].

This self-tuning method has the following rule format:

$$\text{Rule } i: \quad \text{If } x_1 \text{ is } A_{i1} \text{ and } \cdots \text{ and } x_m \text{ is } A_{im}$$

$$\text{then } y \text{ is } w_i \tag{21.4}$$

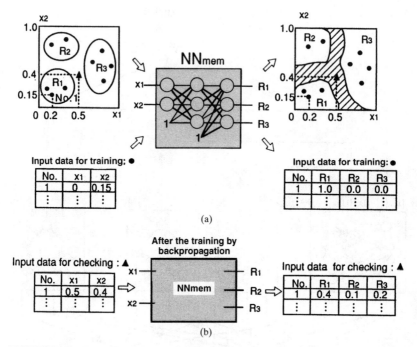

FIGURE 21.18 Determination of the membership function of the antecedent part. (a) Learning process; (b) determination of a membership value.

where i is a rule number $(i = 1, \ldots, n)$; $x_1, \ldots, x_m$ are input variables; A_{ij} is a fuzzy set; and w_i is a real number. This is the simplified fuzzy inference rule. The membership function in the antecedent part has a triangular form as shown in Fig. 21.19.

The output y of the fuzzy inference is derived from the following equations:

$$\mu_i = \prod_{j=1}^{m} \mu_{A_{ij}}(x_j) \tag{21.5}$$

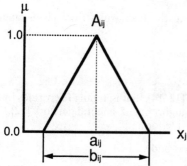

FIGURE 21.19 Membership function.

$$y = \frac{\displaystyle\sum_{i=1}^{n} \mu_i \cdot w_i}{\displaystyle\sum_{i=1}^{n} \mu_i} \tag{21.6}$$

where $\mu_{A_{ij}}$ is a membership function of the fuzzy set A_{ij} and μ_i is a membership value of ith rule.

Figure 21.20 shows a block diagram of this self-tuning method. The simplified fuzzy inference can be expressed by the three-layered network structure, which has processing units (○), a fuzzy set A_{ij}, and a real number w_i (□). The

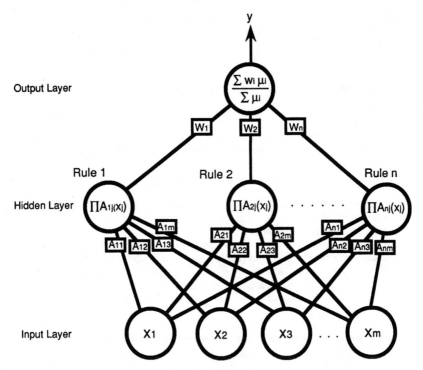

FIGURE 21.20 Block diagram of self-tuning by the delta rule.

processing unit of the output layer derives the weighted average according to Eq. (21.6), and the processing units of the hidden layer calculate the membership value μ_i by Eq. (21.5). In this method, the tuning parameters indicated by □ are iteratively adjusted by the delta rule to minimize the following objective function E:

$$E = \frac{1}{2} (y' - y)^2 \qquad (21.7)$$

The objective function is the difference between the output y of fuzzy inference and the desirable output y'.

The parameters w_i of the consequent part and the a_{ij}, b_{ij} of the membership function are iteratively optimized by the delta rule. The learning rules of the parameters are

$$a_{ij}(t+1) = a_{ij}(t) - K_a \cdot \frac{\partial E}{\partial a_{ij}} \qquad (21.8)$$

$$b_{ij}(t+1) = b_{ij}(t) - K_b \cdot \frac{\partial E}{\partial b_{ij}} \qquad (21.9)$$

$$w_i(t+1) = w_i(t) - K_w \cdot \frac{\partial E}{\partial w_i} \qquad (21.10)$$

where t is the number of tuning iterations and K_a, K_b, K_w are constants.

Since this method employs the simplified fuzzy inference operation and simple triangular membership function, the tuning speed of this method is faster than the NNDF.

21.4.3 Improvement by a Genetic Algorithm

The NNDF and self-tuning by the delta rule have two common problems:

1. The learning algorithm of the neural network cannot escape from a local optimum in the tuning process, therefore the self-tuning methods may not be able to obtain optimum rules.
2. The self-tuning methods cannot determine the total number of rules automatically.

In order to solve these problems, we improved the self-tuning method by means of a genetic algorithm [15, 16]. The genetic algorithm (GA) is an optimization method developed from the theory of biological evolution [17]. The most advantageous feature of the GA is that it offers the possibility to escape from a local optimum because of probabilistic operations such as a crossover and mutation.

In the GA, a solution candidate s_r which optimizes an objective function $E(s_r)$, called the *fitness function,* is searched for. The solution candidate is expressed by a string called an *individual,* and a set of individuals is called a *population S.*

The rule format of this method is the same as for self-tuning by the delta rule. The membership functions take a triangular shape, and the width of each membership function is defined to be the length between the centers of neighboring membership functions, as shown in Fig. 21.21. The arrangement of membership functions can be expressed in terms of a string consisting of 0's and 1's, wherein the center position of each membership function is expressed by 1. The string can be provided for each of the input variables. A string combining the strings provided for each input variable is considered as an individual s_r in the GA. Therefore, an individual expresses a fuzzy rule set.

In this method, we employ a kind of information criterion [18] as a fitness function. The fitness E is expressed by the following equation:

$$E = P \cdot \log \left[\frac{1}{P} \sum_{p=1}^{P} (y'_p - y_p)^2 \right] + 2N_p \qquad (21.11)$$

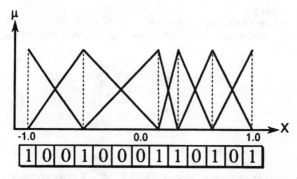

FIGURE 21.21 Membership functions expressed by an individual.

where y'_p is a desirable output data for the pth input data, y_p is an output of the fuzzy inference performed to the same pth input data, P is the total number of data, and N_p is the number of tuning parameters in the rules.

Using this setting of the individual and the fitness, the optimal number of membership functions and the center positions of these are searched by the GA. The algorithm to search for the optimum rules is shown in the following and in Fig. 21.22.

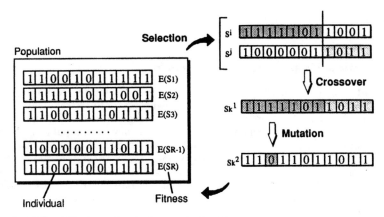

FIGURE 21.22 Operations in the genetic algorithm.

1. All individuals in the population $S(t)$ of the 0th generation ($t = 0$) are initialized by random numbers.

2. From an individual s_r in the population $S(t)$, the arrangement and the shape of membership functions in the antecedent parts are determined, and the consequent parts of its rules are optimized by the delta rule according to Eq. (21.10). For these antecedent parts and consequent parts, the fitness value E for the individual s_r is obtained by Eq. (21.11). With repetition of this algorithm, the fitness value $E(s_r)$ is obtained for all individual ($s_r, r = 1, \ldots, R$) in the population $S(t)$.

3. Two individuals $s_i(t)$ and $s_j(t)$ are selected out from the population $S(t)$ in accordance with a selection probability $P_s(s_r)$. The selection probability P_s for the individual with superior fitness value is set at a larger value, while the selection probability P_s for the individual with inferior fitness value is set at a smaller value. Therefore, the individuals having superior fitness value are selected frequently.

4. A crossover operation is applied to the selected two individuals. The crossover consists of selecting a boundary in strings at random, and exchanging the blocks of strings about the boundary. The individual produced by this operation is nominated as a new individual $s_k^1(t)$.

5. A mutation operation is applied to $s_k^1(t)$. By this, each element of the individual $s_k^1(t)$ is reversed according to a probability of P_m. In Fig. 21.22, the third element from the left end is reversed by the mutation.

6. By repeating steps 3 to 5, the population of the next generation, $S(t + 1)$, having many new individuals, is created.

7. The number of the generation, t, is incremented by one, and steps 2 to 6 are repeated until the population converges.

With this method, the number of fuzzy rules and the membership functions are determined automatically, and the possibility to escape from local optimums in the tuning process is obtained.

21.5 APPLICATION OF A SELF-TUNING METHOD FOR FUZZY RULES

In this section, we introduce an application to a refrigerator of a self-tuning method for fuzzy rules.

21.5.1 Stable Temperature Control in a Refrigerator

The self-tuning technique is applied to temperature control in a refrigerator [19]. In order to keep food fresh for a long period, it is necessary to restrain temperature fluctuation in the freezer compartment (FC). The temperature fluctuation is caused by heat shock, which occurs when the door is opened, new food is put in, and ambient temperature rises. The heat shock includes five factors: heat quantity, heat distribution, heat fluctuation of foods, airflow into the refrigerator, and ambient temperature around the refrigerator. We installed two thermal sensors at different positions in the FC and one thermal sensor on the outside of the refrigerator to detect these factors. From the average FC temperature T_r, the difference T_d between the output of the two inside sensors, and the ambient temperature T_a, the setting temperature T_s in the FC is determined by fuzzy inference. The fuzzy rules to control the setting temperature T_s are

1. If T_r is small and T_d is small and T_a is low then T_s is very small.

2. If T_r is small and T_d is middle and T_a is low then T_s is small.

3. If T_r is small and T_d is big and T_a is low then T_s is small.

$$\vdots$$

27. If T_r is big and T_d is big and T_a is high then T_s is big.

The membership functions of antecedent parts and the real-number values of consequent parts in the above rules are optimized by the delta rule. The optimized membership functions and rules are shown in Figs. 21.23 and 21.24.

Figure 21.25 shows the profile of the temperature in the FC controlled by optimized fuzzy rules when new food is put into the FC, where the new food has a higher temperature than the FC. The optimized fuzzy rules limit the temperature rise of food already in the refrigerator to 50 percent and shorten the restoration time to 60 percent compared to the conventional refrigerator.

21.6 CONCLUSIONS

In this chapter, we discussed the following three topics: (1) an application to a washing machine, (2) applications to image processing, and (3) self-tuning methods for fuzzy rules. All these applications of fuzzy logic have been successful in adding new functions and improving the control result compared with the conventional machines.

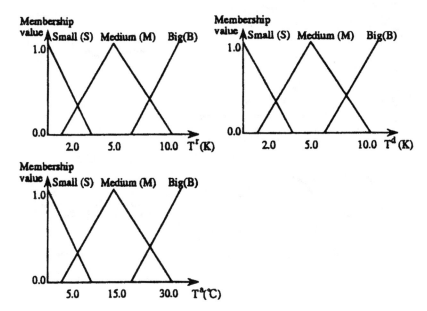

FIGURE 21.23 Optimized membership functions.

T_S : Setting temperature

T_r		S			M			B		
T_d		S	M	B	S	M	B	S	M	B
T_a	L	1.7	2.0	2.0	3.2	2.6	2.0	4.5	3.2	2.5
		(VS)	(S)	(S)	(B)	(M)	(M)	(VB)	(VB)	(B)
	M	1.6	2.1	2.0	2.6	2.5	2.5	3.2	2.6	2.2
		(VS)	(S)	(S)	(M)	(M)	(M)	(VB)	(B)	(B)
	H	1.5	1.7	2.0	3.0	2.5	2.0	2.0	2.0	2.0
		(VS)	(VS)	(S)	(M)	(M)	(S)	(B)	(B)	(B)

FIGURE 21.24 Optimized fuzzy rules.

In Japan, applications of fuzzy logic have been increasing since 1990, and research is being carried out on not only the control problem but also on information retrieval, the human interface, etc. We believe that fuzzy logic will be evolved by fusion with other methods (for example, neural networks, genetic algorithms, chaos, etc.) and the basic concept of fuzzy logic will be applied to still more products in many fields.

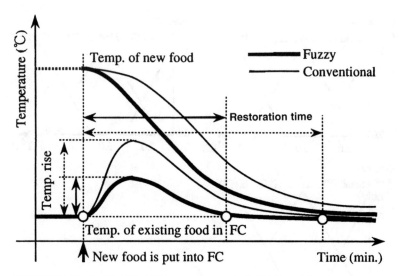

FIGURE 21.25 Profile of the FC temperature controlled by fuzzy inference.

REFERENCES

1. S. Kondo and M. Kiuchi, "Introduction to the AISAIGO DAY FUZZY (NA-F50Y5) fully automatic washing machine," *Journal of Japan Society for Fuzzy Theory and Systems,* vol. 2, no. 3, pp. 112–114, 1990 (in Japanese).

2. M. Maeda and S. Murakami, "Self-tuning fuzzy logic controller," *Transactions of the Society of Instrument and Control Engineers,* vol. 24, no. 2, pp. 191–197, 1988 (in Japanese).

3. Y. Egusa, H. Akahori, A. Morimura, and N. Wakami, "An electronic video camera image stabilizer operated on fuzzy theory," *Proceedings of the IEEE International Conference on Fuzzy Systems,* pp. 851–858, 1992.

4. Y. Egusa, H. Akahori, A. Morimura, and N. Wakami, "An application of fuzzy set theory for an electronic video camera image stabilizer," *IEEE Transactions on Fuzzy Systems,* vol. 3, no. 3, pp. 351–356, 1995.

5. K. Uomori, A. Morimura, H. Ishii, T. Sakaguchi, and Y. Kitamura, "Automatic image stabilizing system by full-digital signal processing," *IEEE Transactions on Consumer Electronics,* vol. 36, no. 3, pp. 510–519, 1990.

6. N. Yoshiike, K. Arita, and K. Morinaka, "Human information sensor," *Proceedings of the 7th International Conference on Solid-State Sensor and Actuators,* pp. 1015–1018, 1993.

7. S. Araki, H. Nomura, and N. Wakami, "Segmentation of thermal images using the fuzzy c-means algorithm," *Proceedings of the IEEE Second International Conference on Fuzzy Systems,* pp. 719–724, 1993.

8. S. Araki, N. Wakami, K. Morinaka, and N. Yoshiike, "Segmentation of occupants in thermal images using the fuzzy clustering algorithm and its application to identification of their number, positions and activities," *Proceedings of the 36th Conference on Automatic Control,* pp. 379–382, 1993 (in Japanese).

9. S. Araki, H. Nomura, I. Hayashi, and N. Wakami, "A self-generating method of fuzzy inference rule," *Proceedings of the International Fuzzy Engineering Symposium,* pp. 1047–1058, 1991.

10. I. Hayashi, H. Nomura, and N. Wakami, "Artificial neural network driven fuzzy control and its application to the learning of inverted pendulum system," *Third IFSA Congress,* pp. 610–613, 1989.

11. H. Takagi and I. Hayashi, "NN-driven fuzzy reasoning," *International Journal Approximate Reasoning,* Vol. 5, No. 3, pp. 191–212, 1991.

12. D. E. Rumelhurt, G. E. Hinton, and R. J. Williams, "Learning Internal Representations by Error Propagation," *Parallel Distributed Processing,* pp. 318–362, 1986.

13. H. Nomura, I. Hayashi, and N. Wakami, "A self-tuning method of fuzzy reasoning by delta rule and its application to a moving obstacle avoidance," *Journal of Japan Society for Fuzzy Theory and Systems,* vol. 4, no. 2, 1992 (in Japanese).

14. H. Nomura, I. Hayashi, and N. Wakami, "A learning method of fuzzy inference rules by descent method," *Proceedings of the IEEE International Conference on Fuzzy Systems,* pp. 203–210, 1992.

15. H. Nomura, I. Hayashi, and N. Wakami, "A Self-tuning method of fuzzy reasoning by genetic algorithm," *Proceedings of the International Fuzzy System and Intelligent Control Conference,* pp. 236–245, 1992.

16. H. Nomura, I. Hayashi and N. Wakami, "A learning method fusing fuzzy reasoning and genetic algorithm," *Proceedings of IMACS/SICE International Symposium on Robotics, Mechatronics and Manufacturing Systems,* pp. 16–20, 1992.

17. D. E. Goldberg, "Genetic algorithms in search, optimization and machine learning," Addison Wesley, 1989.

18. H. Akaike, "A new look at the statistical model identification," *IEEE Transactions on Automatic Control,* vol. AC-19, no. 6, 1974.

19. M. Maeda, S. Mori, K. Endo, and H. Hayashi, "Stable temperature control by neuro-fuzzy control method," *Proceedings of the Second FAN Symposium,* pp. 31–32, 1992 (in Japanese).

CHAPTER 22
A FUZZY LOGIC CONTROLLER TO DRILL SMALL HOLES

Mark E. Dreier
William L. McKeown
H. Wayne Scott
Bell Helicopter Textron, Inc.
Fort Worth, Texas

This chapter describes the application of fuzzy logic to a difficult manufacturing task, that of drilling small lubrication holes into hardened transmission gears. Commercially available fuzzy logic software and hardware, some simple interface hardware, and a low-end personal computer were combined with a modified drill press to create an automated drilling system. The rule base used five rules to control downfeed rate as a function of drill speed. Eleven additional rules handled start-up, parking, and through-the-part detection. Results indicate a dramatic reduction in setup time, drilling operation cycle time, rework time, and broken drills.

22.1 THE MANUFACTURING TASK

The manufacturing task was to drill small (0.030-in.) diameter lubrication holes in transmission gear shafts made of carburized steel with Rockwell hardnesses of R_C 41 to R_C 43. See Fig. 22.1. Oil is introduced to the inside of the shaft from a spray bar. Centrifugal force causes the oil to flow out through the lubrication hole to the bearing. Before fuzzy logic was used to control this process, a human operator drilled the holes manually. Drill breakage, which was not uncommon, required expensive reworking or scrapping of the part. The problem was to develop a method to reduce the rework and scrap rate.

Our justification for using fuzzy logic control, rather than classical control, was based in part on a desire to try this new technology, and in part on a review of the problem that showed that a classical controller would be difficult to apply.

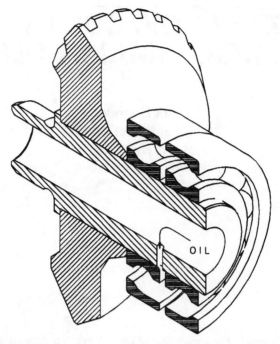

FIGURE 22.1 Typical method for lubricating bearings in gear assembly.

22.2 PROBLEM DESCRIPTION

Before the drilling operation could be improved, the existing method was studied to learn how a manual operation was successfully conducted. The problem was divided into two parts: knowledge acquisition and mechanical description.

22.2.1 Knowledge Acquisition

An interview with an experienced drill press operator revealed that there is one major problem in drilling small holes: judging the downfeed rate. The consequences of too low or too high a rate are

Downfeed rate	Consequence
Too low	The part will work-harden, preventing further penetration.
Too high	The drill will break.

The operator said he used the sound and feel of the drill to control the downfeed rate. The sound implied a certain rotor speed which implied a load on the drill. The feel of the resistance in the press handle helped him command the downfeed rate.

His rules were easy to express but difficult to quantify. For instance, a rule like this was common: "Start out hard at first to break through the skin, then back off some, but not too much, to continue." From the interview and our own experience, the following rules emerged:

1. If the drilling is not aggressive enough, the steel work hardens and the drill will dull and break.
2. If the drilling is too aggressive at first contact, the drill can break.
3. If the rotor speed slows too much, the drill can break.

22.2.2 Mechanical Description

The fuzzy-logic-controlled drill press, Fig. 22.2, is similar to the manual press. The drill speed set point is dialed in through a potentiometer mounted on the motor housing. A high-gain drill speed controller maintains drill speed to tight tolerance, no matter the load on the drill. However, the drill press was modified somewhat to accommodate fuzzy logic control. It was equipped with a stepper motor that controls the downward or upward displacement of the drill. It also had a simple drill speed sensor attached, and the gain on the drill speed controller was reduced so that the speed would slow with increasing load on the drill.

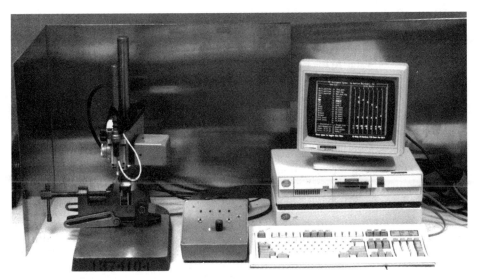

FIGURE 22.2 Fuzzy-logic-controlled drill press.

22.3 BUILDING THE CONTROLLER

The fuzzy logic controller comprises a low-end personal computer, fuzzy logic software, a signal converter, an interface board, and a rotational speed sensor.

22.3.1 The Software/Hardware

An inexpensive, commercially available fuzzy logic software/hardware controller package was purchased. The controller allows 64 rules and 16 terms. It uses fixed-point arithmetic and triangular membership functions or their logical complements. The software features a graphical editor that places and sizes the membership functions on the universe of discourse. The rules were written with a matrix that joins fuzzified terms in conjunction only. Defuzzification uses the *max of min* method.

The controller card fits a standard IBM PC or compatible expansion slot. Besides the fuzzy logic processor, the card also provides the analog-to-digital (A/D) and digital-to-analog (D/A) signal converters.

The controller package had some initial problems:

1. The maximum width of fuzzification membership functions required a more dense rule structure than was needed in this application.

2. We had to tie up production hardware while we experimented with rules because no closed-loop dynamic simulation was available.

3. The controller required a signal to propagate through the hardware for up to three fuzzify-infer-defuzzify cycles before the expected action of a rule could be observed. This pipeline effect was overcome with an interface that is described next.

22.3.2 Drill/Controller Interface

The interface board addresses several problems. First, it normalizes and maps a portion of the rotor speed so that the sensed value of the unloaded drill always appears as the nominal value to the rules. The drill speed is measured in tens of thousands of revolutions per minute, with expected variations in the hundreds. The controller allows only 8 bits to represent analog signals. Eight bits cannot provide the required precision over such a wide domain. Therefore, the interface includes a potentiometer that maps the unloaded drill speed value to the rule indicating no load. Now, variations of a few hundred revolutions per minute from nominal could be mapped in 8 bits with sufficient precision. This mapping means just one set of rules can be used no matter what the initial drill speed setting is. The operator merely selects the desired speed with the potentiometer mounted on the drill, and then adjusts the potentiometer on the interface panel until a red/green light-emitting diode (LED) shows amber, indicating the speed is nominal.

The second function of the interface panel is to provide two discrete signals, the *drill* and *retract* commands. The drill command generates an input signal to a latch. Once the drill button is pressed, the drill operation remains in effect until the drill goes through the part or until the retract command interrupts the latch. The retract command sets a latch that causes the drill to move up until it is fully retracted or until the drill button is pressed, interrupting the retract cycle and causing the drill cycle to begin again. Both latches were implemented in the fuzzy logic software.

The third interface function is to generate the stepper motor signal. The stepper motor controls how far the drill penetrates the part. With each positive pulse, the drill moves down 0.0004 in. A negative pulse moves the drill up 0.0004 in. Thus, the rate of the stepper motor pulse signal controls downfeed. But, since the update rate from the fuzzy software is the same regardless of the rule output, the stepper motor pulse rate had to be generated in the interface. The solution was to use an integrator with threshold detection on the output. The output of the downfeed rules is an integer value between −128 and +127, with −128 indicating a high retraction rate and +127 indicating a high downfeed. A zero value does not necessarily indicate zero downfeed, however. Some bias is built in so that zero produces a moderate retract command. The integer value becomes the input to the integrator. When the output of the integrator exceeds an upper threshold, a positive pulse is sent to the stepper motor and the integrator is reset to an initial condition of zero. A similar process occurs when the output goes more negative than a lower threshold. Thus, the greater the magnitude of the input to the integrator, the more frequently it sends a stepper motor pulse and the faster the drill moves down or up.

The fourth function of the interface board is to provide a signal that represents the drill speed. The drill speed sensor is made from a small iron bar and a magnetic pickup. The iron bar is mounted to the top of the drill axle and spins with the drill. The magnetic pickup is mounted nearby on the nonrotating frame of the drill, and in the same horizontal plane as the spinning iron bar. As the iron bar spins near the pickup, the magnetic flux is perturbed and a voltage variation is sensed. The amplitude of the generated voltage is proportional to the time rate of change of the magnetic flux, which itself is proportional to the rotor speed. This simple method to measure rotational speed eliminates the need for peak detection or elaborate timing circuits.

The last function of the interface board is to defeat the pipeline effect that the hardware creates before it produces an output signal. This is necessary because compound rules that combine discrete signals and analog signals often do not fire if the discrete signal is not used at the moment it is sensed. A simple lag filter ensures that a discrete signal lingers long enough at its high value to fill the pipeline.

22.4 RULE DEVELOPMENT

Five rules are used to control the downfeed from the sensed rotational speed. They command an aggressive downfeed rate when the drill speed is nominal or indicates some loading. As loading increases, the speed decreases, and the commanded downfeed decreases at an accelerated rate. When the speed droops to a low value, the downfeed rate is suddenly changed to a high retract rate. The nonlinear derivative of downfeed rate with respect to drill speed, combined with reduced gain on the speed controller, produces a limit cycle that is commonly called called *peck drilling:* the drill press retracts the drill enough to clear the chips out of the hole and let the speed recover, then starts again with an aggressive downfeed. What is more important, the nonlinear control law prevents the drill press from finding an equilibrium point (zero downfeed rate) that would work-harden the steel. The five rules used are

1. If RPM is LOAD_0, then DOWNFEED is −75
2. If RPM is LOAD_1, then DOWNFEED is −75
3. If RPM is LOAD_2, then DOWNFEED is −40
4. If RPM is LOAD_3, then DOWNFEED is 0
5. If RPM is LOAD_4, then DOWNFEED is 0

The conclusion singletons were determined by trial and error. A value of −75 in the rules corresponds to a large commanded downfeed. A value of zero corresponds to a moderate commanded retract rate.

The membership functions that fuzzify drill speed are overlapping triangles that center at the following points:

Function	Center
LOAD_0	245
LOAD_1	225
LOAD_2	205
LOAD_3	165
LOAD_4	133

Each triangular function has a maximum width of 32 on either side of the center position and a maximum height of 32, giving the membership functions a slope of ±1, depending on which side of the function center the variable to fuzzify falls. The functions LOAD_0 and LOAD_1 overlap at location 235, LOAD_1 and LOAD_2 overlap at location 215, etc. The resulting function of downfeed versus drill speed is roughly parabolic, with rapid decrease of downfeed after initial contact, followed by a slowing downfeed afterward until a lower limit on acceptable speed error is reached. After that point, the downfeed command becomes a rapid retract command. This behavior matches the verbal rules expressed earlier.

Other rules were written to detect when the drill goes through the part and when it is parked in the fully retracted position, and to create software latches to command downfeed or retraction with just a momentary press of the *drill* or *retract* buttons. In total, only 16 rules controlled the entire operation.

22.5 TESTING AND CALIBRATION

The drill was tested with various speeds, drill sizes, and hardnesses to determine the optimum speed for drill life. Heat-treated slugs with hardnesses of R_C 41 to R_C 43 were used. Over 400 holes were drilled and only two drills broke. During the tests, we regularly drilled 25 holes with a single drill using the fuzzy logic controller. The average time to drill a hole was 3 minutes. When performed manually, the drill cycle required an average of 5 minutes, and could manage no more than two to three holes before the drill dulled. A high drill speed (12,000 r/min) and cobalt-tipped drills worked best. This is the combination that entered production.

22.6 RESULTS

The fuzzy-logic-controlled drill press is being used on the production line now, and the results are impressive. The amount of rework has been reduced 95 percent because drill breakage has been virtually eliminated. This was the primary goal. However, some additional benefits were realized. The amount of time needed to drill a hole has decreased 24 percent, and the setup time has decreased 40 percent. The setup time needs some explanation. Before the gear is drilled, it is set up in a jig that aligns it with a bushing that guides the drill. Since the number of broken drills has decreased, the number of times the gear must be set up in the jig has decreased.

22.7 FURTHER DEVELOPMENTS
AND CONCLUSIONS

Additional development has taken place since the system was introduced. To overcome some of the limitations of the original software and hardware, we developed a new fuzzy logic software package called FULDEK, an acronym for Fuzzy Logic Development Kit. FULDEK enables the user to design fuzzy rules with many different kinds of membership functions, then test those rules in a closed-loop simulation of the plant and controller. FULDEK also produces customized software control laws.

From our experience, we conclude:

1. It was easy and inexpensive to develop a fuzzy logic control system to control a drill press for drilling small holes.

2. We did not require expensive parameter identification of the drilling process to write the rules. The rules were intuitive.

3. The fuzzy-logic-controlled drill press does not require a computer engineer to run it. In fact, after only a few minutes, the operator who originally drilled the small holes by hand had mastered the new drill press. Initial skepticism and fear yielded to praise and acceptance after the first few holes were drilled.

4. Fuzzy logic is not applicable in all cases. From Refs. 1, 2, and 3, we developed the simple test below to determine if a fuzzy-logic-based controller is a good candidate.

Test for Fuzzy Logic Control Candidates

- Is the process difficult to model?

- Is the item to be controlled difficult to sense, or are the feedback signals difficult to sense?

- Is the control of the process intuitive?

- Are the sensors prone to noise, reliability, and accuracy problems?

- Do experienced operators perform better than inexperienced operators?

If one answers most (a fuzzy concept itself) of the questions with yes, then fuzzy logic may be an alternative to classical control techniques.

SUGGESTIONS FOR FURTHER READING

Jamshidi, M., Vadiee, N., and Ross, T. J., *Fuzzy Logic and Control, Software and Hardware Applications,* Prentice Hall, Englewood Cliffs, N.J., 1993.

Kosko, B., *Neural Networks and Fuzzy Systems, A Dynamical Systems Approach to Machine Intelligence,* Prentice Hall, Englewood Cliffs, N.J., 1992.

If you would like more information regarding FULDEK, write to Dr. Mohammad Jamshidi, TSI Enterprises, P.O. Box 14155, Albuquerque, NM 87191-4155.

REFERENCES

1. Williams, Tom, "Fuzzy Logic Is Anything But Fuzzy," *Computer Design Magazine,* pp. 113–127, April 1992.
2. Berardinis, L. A., "Clear Thinking On Fuzzy Logic," *Machine Design Magazine,* pp. 46–52, April 23, 1992.
3. Chiu, Stephen, et al., "Fuzzy Logic for Control of Roll and Moment for a Flexible Wing Aircraft," *IEEE Control Systems Magazine,* pp. 42–44, June 1991.

ARCHITECTURES
AND SYSTEMS

CHAPTER 23

HARDWARE FUZZY INFERENCE SYSTEMS— ARCHITECTURE, DESIGN, AND IMPLEMENTATION

Donald L. Hung*

Department of Electrical Engineering
Gannon University, Erie, Pennsylvania

23.1 INTRODUCTION

The kernel of any fuzzy-logic-based system is the fuzzy inference engine which carries out the required computation for fuzzy approximate reasoning. In most realized fuzzy applications, fuzzy inference algorithms were implemented in software and executed on standard processors. Although this approach is, in general, more economical and may cope with a large variety of application problems, many real-time applications (e.g., robotics, image and speech processing) require very high processing speeds that only specially designed hardware fuzzy inference systems can provide.

Following the early works reported by Togai and Watanabe [12], Watanabe et al. [17], and Yamakawa et al. [19–21], in recent years a number of hardware fuzzy inference systems have been implemented or proposed [1–6, 8, 10–11, 14–18]. These reported works reflect the diversity in technologies related to hardware design: digital [1–2, 4–5, 8, 11–13, 16–18], analog [3, 10, 19–20], mixed-signal [14–15], dedicated fuzzy hardware [1, 3, 5, 13, 17], fuzzy processor [16, 18], custom ASIC chip [3, 8, 12, 19], programmable-device based [4–5], and standard-device based [11]. Commercial products are also available, such as the FC110 fuzzy processor from Togai InfraLogic, the NLX22X fuzzy controller from NeuroLogix, and the Fuzzy-166 processor from Siemens and Inform. Due to the demand for real-time applications and the available VLSI technology, it is expected that interest in special fuzzy inference hardware will continue to grow.

To design a hardware fuzzy inference system that can outperform standard processors, its architecture must be specially arranged based on the algorithms it intends to execute. Therefore, the hardware designer must be able to understand and be intimately familiar with the fuzzy inference algorithms.

---

*Now with Electrical Engineering and Computer Science Department, Washington State University—Tri Cities, Richland, Washington.

In Sec. 23.2, we discuss fuzzy inference algorithms based on the *generalized modus ponens* (*GMP*) and their architectural mapping. Following the discussion, design and implementation issues are discussed in Sec. 23.3. Then in Sec. 23.4 a design example is provided. Finally, Sec. 23.5 concludes this chapter.

23.2 GMP-BASED FUZZY INFERENCE MECHANISM AND ARCHITECTURAL MAPPING

23.2.1 Basic Terminology

The GMP-based fuzzy inference rule is the most widely adopted fuzzy inference mechanism in practical applications. It is stated thus:

Premise 1:   If input is A, then output is B.

Premise 2:   Input is A' (23.1)

Consequence: Output is B'.

Here A, B, A', and B' are fuzzy sets.

Premise 1 in (23.1) is described by the fuzzy implication function $R = A \rightarrow B$, where R is a fuzzy relation. Due to the richness of fuzzy operators and fuzzy implication functions, about 40 different fuzzy inference methods have been proposed in the literature [7]. In practice, most applications adopt the "mini" implication method which is based on the mini-operation rule:

$$\mu_R(u, v) = \min \left[\mu_A(u), \mu_B(v)\right]: \quad u \in U, v \in V \qquad (23.2)$$

In (23.2), $\mu_R(u, v)$, $\mu_A(u)$, and $\mu_B(v)$ are membership functions of R, A, and B, respectively, and U and V are universes of discourse of A and B, respectively.

With the observed input A', the *consequence* in (23.1) is determined by the fuzzy composition $B' = A' \circ R = A' \circ (A \rightarrow B)$, where the symbol $\circ$ stands for the max-* fuzzy composition and the symbol $*$ stands for some conjunctive fuzzy operator. In practice, *max -min* is the most commonly used fuzzy composition method, and with it, the membership function value of B' can be computed as

$$\mu_{B'}(v) = \max \min \left[\mu_{A'}(u), \mu_R(u, v)\right] \quad u \in U, v \in V \qquad (23.3)$$

where $\mu_{B'}(v)$ and $\mu_{A'}(u)$ are membership functions of B' and A', respectively.

Also seen in practical applications are fuzzy implication methods based on product operation and fuzzy composition methods based on the "max product" operation. In this case the min operator in Eqs. (23.2) and (23.3) must be replaced by the *prod* operator, where the symbol *prod* stands for multiplication.

The above fuzzy inference procedure handles a *single-input, single-output* (*SISO*) system. In reality, we have to deal with *multiple-input, multiple-output* (*MIMO*) systems. The expression for a GMP-based MIMO fuzzy inference system with n inputs and m outputs is

$$(B'_1, B'_2, \ldots, B'_m) = (A'_1, A'_2, \ldots, A'_n) \circ [(A_1 \times A_2 \times \cdots \times A_n) \rightarrow (B_1, B_2, \ldots, B_m)]$$
$$(23.4)$$

where the symbol $\times$ stands for fuzzy cartesian product. For a detailed discussion of fuzzy operators and inference mechanisms, see Refs. 7, 9, and 22.

Expression (23.4) is read as follows:

Premise 1   If inputs are A_1 and A_2 and . . . and A_n, then outputs are $B_1, B_2, \ldots, B_m$.

Premise 2   The observed inputs are A'_1 and A'_2 and . . . and A'_n.

Consequence   The inferred outputs are $B'_1, B'_2, \ldots, B'_m$.

GMP-based inference is especially suitable for practical applications because of its forward data-driven nature. In most of the practical applications, the GMP-based inference is one level; i.e., the inferred outputs are not fed back for chained reasoning. Therefore, outputs $B_1, B_2, \ldots, B_m$ in (23.4) are logically independent of one another. As a consequence, the MIMO fuzzy inference system represented by (23.4) can be decomposed into m independent *multiple-input, single-output (MISO)* subsystems:

$$B'_i = (A'_1, A'_2, \ldots, A'_n) \circ [(A_1 \times A_2 \times \cdots \times A_n) \to B_i] \qquad \text{for } i = 1, 2, \ldots, m \quad (23.5)$$

This idea is illustrated by Fig. 23.1. With this understanding, we focus our attention on MISO fuzzy inference systems in the rest of our discussion. To simplify the notation, our discussion will be based on the simple two-input, one-output fuzzy inference system shown in Fig. 23.2. The concepts, however, can be extended to MISO fuzzy inference systems of any size.

The system's input-output (I/O) relation is shown in Fig. 23.2a. Note that for a fuzzy inference system, its inputs and outputs are fuzzy linguistic variables, each of which is characterized usually by several fuzzy linguistic values (fuzzy sets). For instance, if we let the input variable A stand for temperature, then it can be characterized as A (temperature) = {A_1 (low), A_2 (medium), A_3 (high)}. Figure 23.2b shows the membership functions associated with the fuzzy linguistic values for each of the input and output variables. Together they form the *I/O database*. For the given system, when the I/O database is defined, one can specify up to nine different inference rules, such as

If A is A_1 and B is B_1, then C is C_3.

If A is A_2 and B is B_2, then C is C_2.

The matrix in Fig. 23.2c shows a possible set of nine different inference rules. The collection of all specified inference rules is called the *inference rule base*. The database combined with the rule base forms the fuzzy inference system's *knowledge base*.

23.2.2 Basic Fuzzy Inference Algorithm and Architecture

Note that the membership functions in the input and output spaces are normally overlapped (see Fig. 23.2b), which means that with a given observation, multiple inference rules could be activated (fired). As we stated in Sec. 23.2.1, distinct consequents (outputs) inferred from a one-level forward data-driven fuzzy inference system are logically independent. To apply this concept to our system, only those inference rules that produce the same consequent (now it is a specific fuzzy linguistic value) need to be aggregated. For the given system, we have the following:

$$C'_1 = (A' \times B') \circ \{[(A_2 \times B_3) \to C_1] \parallel [(A_3 \times B_2) \to C_1] \parallel [(A_3 \times B_3) \to C_1]\}$$

$$(23.6a)$$

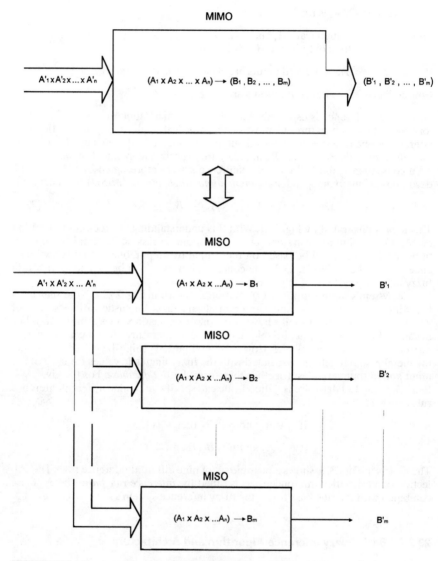

FIGURE 23.1 Decomposition of a MIMO fuzzy inference system.

$$C_2' = (A' \times B') \circ \{[(A_1 \times B_3) \to C_2] \,\|\, [(A_2 \times B_2) \to C_2] \,\|\, [(A_3 \times B_1) \to C_2]\}$$

$$(23.6b)$$

$$C_3' = (A' \times B') \circ \{[(A_1 \times B_1) \to C_3] \,\|\, [(A_1 \times B_2) \to C_3] \,\|\, [(A_2 \times B_1) \to C_3]\}$$

$$(23.6c)$$

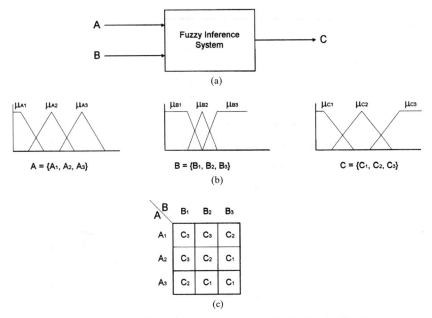

FIGURE 23.2   A simple fuzzy inference system. (a) System, (b) database, (c) rule base.

where the symbol $\|$ stands for an appropriate aggregation operator and the most fre-
quently used one is the max operator.

Since Eqs. (23.6a to c) have the same structure, to save space we list the step-by-
step algorithm only for Eq. (23.6a).

Algorithm 1 (Basic)

1. Execute
$$R_{11} = (A_2 \times B_3) \rightarrow C_1$$
$$R_{12} = (A_3 \times B_2) \rightarrow C_1 \qquad \text{implication}$$
$$R_{13} = (A_3 \times B_3) \rightarrow C_1$$

2. Execute $\quad R_{1\_total} = R_{11} \| R_{12} \| R_{13} \qquad$ rule aggregation

3. Execute $\quad C'_1 = (A' \times B') \circ R_{1\_total} \qquad$ composition

An architectural mapping of the algorithm for the entire system is shown in Fig. 23.3,
where block 1 corresponds to the part of the algorithm listed above. Figure 23.3 also
indicates that the GMP-based fuzzy inference algorithm is intrinsically parallel; i.e.,
all inference rules triggered by the same observed inputs can be executed simultaneously. This is why conventional von Neumann-type processors are intrinsically
inadequate for executing fuzzy inference algorithms when the processing speed is
critical. Because most of the practical applications require a crisp value as the output
of a fuzzy inference system, some defuzzification function must be performed at the
output stage of the system, as shown in Fig. 23.3.

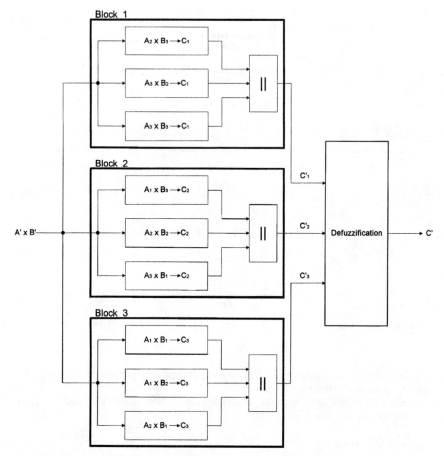

FIGURE 23.3   Basic architecture of a MISO fuzzy inference system.

23.2.3   Algorithm and Architecture Variations

In the basic fuzzy inference algorithm discussed in Sec. 23.2.2, if the fuzzy implication is based on a conjunctive operator such as *min* or *prod,* and if the rule aggregation is based on either the *max* or the *mini* operation, then the fuzzy implication $\rightarrow$ is distributive to the rule aggregation ‖. For the given system, algorithm 1 can be modified as follows:

Algorithm 2 (When $\rightarrow$ Is Distributive to ‖)
1. Execute $P = (A_2 \times B_3) \,\|\, (A_3 \times B_2) \,\|\, (A_3 \times B_3)$.
2. Execute $R_{1\_\text{total}} = P \rightarrow C_1$.
3. Execute $C'_1 = (A' \times B') \circ R_{1\_\text{total}}$

The architecture inside each block in Fig. 23.3 should be rearranged accordingly.

In the basic fuzzy inference algorithm discussed in Sec. 23.2.2, if the fuzzy composition is based on either the *max min* or the *max prod* operation, and if the rule aggregation is based on the *max* operation, then the fuzzy composition ∘ is distributive to the rule aggregation ∥. In this case, algorithm 1 can be rewritten as follows:

Algorithm 3 (When ∘ Is Distributive to ∥)

1. Execute $\quad R_{11} = (A_2 \times B_3) \to C_1$

$\qquad\qquad\quad R_{12} = (A_3 \times B_2) \to C_1$

$\qquad\qquad\quad R_{13} = (A_3 \times B_3) \to C_1$

2. Execute $\quad (A' \times B') \circ R_{11} = C'_{11}$

$\qquad\qquad\quad (A' \times B') \circ R_{12} = C'_{12}$

$\qquad\qquad\quad (A' \times B') \circ R_{13} = C'_{13}$

3. Execute $\quad C'_1 = C'_{11} \parallel C'_{12} \parallel C'_{13}$

Note that so far we discussed fuzzy inference algorithms and their architectural mapping at a conceptual level where no detailed operator is specified. Readers can verify that for certain operators the inference unit $(A' \times B') \circ [(A_i \times B_j) \to C_1]$ in algorithm 3 will possess a one-antecedent sliced structure. For instance, if we choose the *mini* operation for the fuzzy implication $\to$ and the *max min* for the fuzzy composition ∘, since the *mini* operation is distributive to the *max* operation, we will have

$$(A' \times B') \circ [(A_i \times B_j) \to C_1] = \min \{A' \circ (A_i \to C_1), B' \circ (B_j \to C_1)\} \quad (23.7)$$

and the detailed computation can be carried out by

$$\mu_{C'_{1k}} = \min\{[\min(\max \min (\mu_{A'}, \mu_{A_i}), \max \min (\mu_{B'}, \mu_{B_j}))], \mu_{C_1}\} \quad (23.8)$$

For the given system, k can be 1, 2, and 3 with appropriate values of i and j determined by the rule base. With Eq. (23.8), a more detailed implementation of block 1 in Fig. 23.3 can be constructed, as shown in Fig. 23.4, where the rightmost max block corresponds to the aggregation operation ∥. A graphical interpretation of (23.8) is given in Fig. 23.5. In this case the system has two inference rules: If A_1 and B_1, then C_1; and if A_2 and B_2, then C_2. The rightmost part of Fig. 23.5 shows the result z_0 obtained from the defuzzification procedure, which will be discussed later.

Similarly, if we choose the product operation for the fuzzy implication $\to$ and the *max prod* for the fuzzy composition ∘, then Eqs. (23.7) and (23.8) should be changed to

$$(A' \times B') \circ [(A_i \times B_j) \to C_1] = \text{prod} \{A' \circ (A_i \to C_1), B' \circ (B_j \to E)\} \quad (23.9)$$

and

$$\mu_{C'_{1k}} = \text{prod}\{[\text{prod}(\max \text{prod} (\mu_{A'}, \mu_{A_i}), \max \text{prod} (\mu_{B'}, \mu_{B_j}))], \mu_{C_1}\} \quad (23.10)$$

respectively. In Eq. (23.9), E is a unit vector with the same dimension as C_1. Expression (23.10) provides another way to construct the fuzzy inference system.

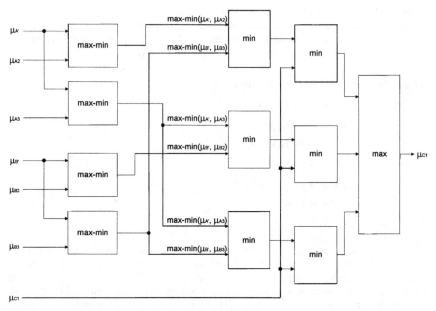

FIGURE 23.4   A possible realization of block 1 in Fig. 23.3.

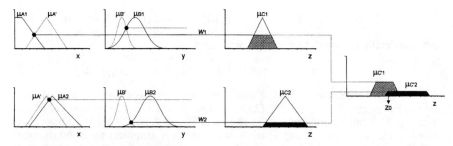

FIGURE 23.5   A graphical interpretation of the concept of Eq. (23.8).

23.3   DESIGN AND IMPLEMENTATION CONSIDERATIONS

Today's semiconductor technology and design automation tools provide the hardware designer with a large set of selections. Beyond these, in designing hardware fuzzy inference systems, there are many technical considerations related to fuzzy technology itself. This section brings these issues into discussion.

23.3.1   Digital versus Analog

The main advantages of digital circuits compared to their analog counterparts are accuracy and robustness to noise and temperature. In addition, significant advances in the digital field (technology, device, and electronics design automation tool) during the past 10 years have made the design, verification, and implementation process of a digital system more efficient than that of an analog system. However, digital circuits are relatively slower and can be much more complex if multiplication and division functions need to be included. On the other hand, analog circuits are faster and allow much simpler implementation of arithmetic functions. Analog circuits are also more efficient in area and consume less power than their digital counterparts. Their main drawback is that they lack accuracy and reliability. Currently mixed-signal (analog-digital) design is gaining more attention, and fuzzy hardware should benefit from this technology. For instance, many practical fuzzy inference systems include the popular *center-of-gravity* (*COG*) based defuzzification function which requires both multiplication and division that can significantly reduce the system's overall throughput if the COG part is implemented in digital circuitry. In mixed-signal design, an analog COG can be implemented easily, which will not only increase the system's throughput but also substantially reduce the system's area and complexity.

23.3.2   Dedicated Fuzzy Hardware versus Fuzzy Processor

The tradeoff between dedicated hardware and the processor is a tradeoff between performance and flexibility. As usual, hardware deliberately designed for solving a specific problem can achieve very high processing speeds while sacrificing its flexibility. As mentioned earlier, due to the diversity of fuzzy operators, for GMP-based fuzzy inference alone many different inference algorithms exist. A fully dedicated fuzzy inference hardware is application-specific; i.e., it is designed based on a specific fuzzy inference algorithm for solving a specific application problem. Among the numerous fuzzy inference algorithms, the one based on Eq. (23.8) has been widely adopted in practical applications owing to its simplicity and versatility. Therefore, dedicated fuzzy inference hardware based on this algorithm has the advantage of being less complex and able to support a large class of application problems, if its knowledge base is not fixed and its size is large enough. In contrast to dedicated fuzzy hardware, a fuzzy processor intends to support a certain class of fuzzy inference algorithms for solving a large variety of problems with different knowledge bases and sizes, by simply changing its stored program. It should be able to provide better performance than conventional processors and be more flexible than dedicated fuzzy hardware. To pay for this flexibility, a fuzzy processor is usually slower for a specific fuzzy inference algorithm than dedicated hardware purposely designed for that one, and its internal circuits (especially the control logic) are usually more complex than those for the dedicated fuzzy hardware. By connecting to a standard host processor, dedicated fuzzy hardware can gain some flexibility, such as knowledge base updating. To do so, the control logic of the dedicated fuzzy hardware needs to be enhanced without substantially increasing its complexity. The dedicated fuzzy hardware then acts as a fuzzy accelerator or coprocessor.

23.3.3   Targeting Technology

In designing any hardware systems, the designer has to decide which technology (application-specific integrated circuits, multichip module, programmable device, processor-based, etc.) the design should target, based on tradeoffs among cost, performance, and turnaround time. With much higher initial cost and much longer turnaround time, full custom ASIC can provide the highest density and the best performance. Therefore it is the target for mature designs with large volumes in demand. In the 1990s, rapidly developing user-programmable technology [field-programmable gate arrays (FPGAs), complex programmable logic devices (CPLDs), and programmable interconnections] has become a very attractive choice to design engineers. The short turnaround time delivered by this technology makes it especially suitable for design prototyping and fast implementation. Note that many of the user-programmable devices are in-circuit reprogrammable. This feature may have the potential to allow fuzzy hardware designers to design autonomous or adaptive hardware fuzzy inference systems.

23.3.4 Adaptability

For a fuzzy inference system, adaptability means the capability to update its knowledge base (both database and rule base) automatically. When the fuzzy hardware is dedicated for a fixed application, its knowledge base is fixed and therefore all fuzzy inference computation (e.g., computation inside the blocks in Fig. 23.3) can be precalculated and stored in lookup tables. This approach may deliver the highest speed with the simplest circuitry while completely giving up the system's adaptability. To support adaptation, a hardware fuzzy inference system needs to be designed in such a way that its database (usually stored in memory) must be updatable (writable), its rule base (usually determined by interconnections) must be selectable (switchable), and the adaptation action must be controlled by a decision-making unit, either locally or through external communication. Currently adaptive fuzzy inference is still at the research stage and is under intensive study.

23.3.5 Defuzzification Method

A defuzzification function aggregates the inference results with respect to all output membership functions and produces a crisp inferred overall result (refer to Figs. 23.3 and 23.5). As mentioned earlier in this chapter, certain defuzzification functions are required by most practical applications. Among many existing defuzzification methods, the COG method is highly successful and widely adopted. With this method the crisp output is computed by

$$z_0 = \Sigma w_i z_i / \Sigma w_i \qquad (23.11)$$

for all fired rules indicated by i (please refer to Fig. 23.5 for the definition of w_i). If the design is completely digital, the hardware and the computation time required by the COG part often exceed those required by the inference part. Systems with small size and limited resolution may be able to avoid the multiplication and division circuitry required by the COG method through a table lookup approach. (This will be discussed in the design example in Sec. 23.4.) A simplified version of the COG method, known as the *truth value fuzzy inference* (*TVFI*) method, can significantly reduce the storage and computation required by the regular COG method. The TVFI method is based on the assumption that all output membership functions possess symmetric shapes. Therefore the z_i's in (23.11) are only the center values in the universe of discourse of output membership functions. Other alternatives include using analog COG methods and considering other defuzzification functions that are more suitable for digital implementation while still able to provide satisfactory defuzzification results.

23.3.6 Crisp Inputs

In a large class of fuzzy applications, the observed inputs are crisp. In fuzzy logic, crisp values are treated as full-scale fuzzy singletons. From a hardware point of view, this can greatly simplify the *max-min* operation shown in Eq. (23.8), as illustrated in Fig. 23.6. In digital design, this operation can be implemented via a table search: Values of an input membership function can be prestored in memory, and digitized crisp values of the observed input serve as the addresses for memory access.

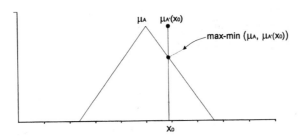

FIGURE 23.6 Crisp input x_0 as a fuzzy singleton.

23.3.7 Number of Fired Rules

For an n-input fuzzy inference system, if each input is characterized by m membership functions, at any time the observed inputs can cause up to m^n fired rules (if the m membership functions are all overlapped in the input space). From a hardware point of view, even for m and n with moderate values, the demand for hardware resources can be tremendous if the architecture is intended to have a high degree of parallelism. Experience shows that for many practical applications, an overlapping degree of 2 with the maximum overlap (cross-point value of two adjacent membership functions) around 0.5 is appropriate. With this constraint, the number of possible fired rules reduces to 2^n. The designer should keep in mind that, even with this reduction, when designing a multiple-input fuzzy inference hardware with highly parallel architecture, the required hardware resources grow exponentially with the number of inputs n. Since usually $2^n \ll m^n$, another problem concerns the designer: While maintaining a high degree of parallelism, how can one optimize the design by keeping only the circuitry needed for processing 2^n fired rules? In general, this is not an easy problem to solve. But for m and n with small values, rule reduction criteria can be easily found, as will be shown in the design example discussed in Sec. 23.4.

23.4 DESIGN EXAMPLE—A DIGITAL FUZZY INFERENCE ENGINE

Based on the discussion in previous sections, this section offers a design example with some implementation details.

23.4.1   Overall System

The designed system is a digital hardware fuzzy inference engine, and its features are summarized below:

Number of inputs	2
Number of outputs	1
Number of membership functions	3 per input/output
Input resolution	4 bits
Output resolution	8 bits
Membership function resolution	4 bits
Number of inference rules supported	9
Inference mechanism	GMP
Implication operator	Mini
Composition operator	Max-min
Defuzzification method	TVFI
Adaptability	Through host microprocessor
Observed inputs	Crisp, digitized
Overlapping degree	2
Maximum overlap	0.5

The overall block diagram of the digital fuzzy inference engine is shown in Fig. 23.7. In the data section, the input table and the min module correspond to the max min block and the min block in Fig. 23.4, respectively; the max module selects the fired inference rules and produces their weights w_i, based on the current sample of the observed input values; the product table is a lookup table which produces the products (values of $w_i z_i$) corresponding to the weights. Note that since the membership functions have only 4-bit resolution, with the TVFI defuzzification method, all possible $w_i z_i$ values for a particular z_i (the system uses 4 bits to identify 9 distinct z_i values separated 16 units apart from each other) can be precalculated and stored in the

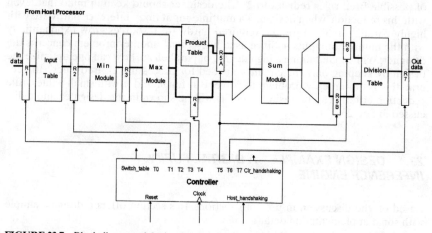

FIGURE 23.7   Block diagram of the hardware fuzzy inference engine.

product table, which has values of w_i as the addresses; thus the use of multiplication circuitry can be avoided. To reduce hardware resources, the sum module is shared by the w_i inputs and the $w_i z_i$ inputs, and a partial pipeline is formed here; i.e., while the module is adding up the Σw_i, values of $w_i z_i$ are being fetched from the product table. The Σw_i and $\Sigma w_i z_i$ are finally latched to form the address bus to the division table, which stores the precalculated $\Sigma w_i z_i / \Sigma w_i$ values. In this way, the division circuitry is also eliminated. Note that the division table depends on only the widths of Σw_i and $\Sigma w_i z_i$. As long as its address bus is wide enough to cover the width of the concatenated Σw_i and $\Sigma w_i z_i$, this lookup table is independent of changes in the knowledge base of the inference engine. The registers (R1 through R7) are inserted into the data path to facilitate the implementation of pipelines. The control section in Fig. 23.7 is a *finite-state machine (FSM)* which controls operations of the data path by generating the following basic commands:

- Latch the system inputs (control signal T1).
- Latch the min module inputs (control signal T2).
- Latch the max module inputs (control signal T3).
- Latch the w_i inputs to the sum module (control signal T4).
- Latch the Σw_i outputs from the sum module (control signal T5).
- Latch the $w_i z_i$ inputs to the sum module (control signal T5).
- Latch the $\Sigma w_i z_i$ outputs from the sum module (control signal T6).
- Latch the division table outputs (control signal T7).

For adaptability, the fuzzy inference engine can be connected to a host processor. The control logic is responsible for communicating with the host processor through hand-shaking signals *host_handshaking* and *clear_handshaking* and generates the *switch_table* signal accordingly. Note that the knowledge base of this system can be completely updated by rewriting the input table and the product table. The basic configuration of the FSM can be easily modified for pipelining the above operations with different overlapping stages. Readers may notice that the rule aggregation function was not implemented in this system. The reason is that when the COG defuzzification method is used, the absence of the rule aggregation function will not cause noticeable differences in the final results.

23.4.2   Implementation Information

The fuzzy inference engine was targeted to the Xilinx XC4000 Family FPGA; building blocks of the main modules in the system's data path are introduced below.

Input Table.   This module contains twelve 16×4 bit static RAM (XC4000 macro RAM 16×4) in parallel to store the input membership function values. Six are for normal operation; another six belong to the secondary memory bank for on-line adaptation. Each of the 16×4 SRAMs can be accessed by both the related sensor input and the host processor, and switching between the memory banks is controlled by the inference engine's control logic, as shown in Fig. 23.8.

Min Module.   This module contains nine identical "mini" blocks (constructed by using XC4000 macros COM4 and X74-257) that execute in parallel. Each of the mini blocks selects the minimum from its two 4-bit inputs, as shown in Fig. 23.9.

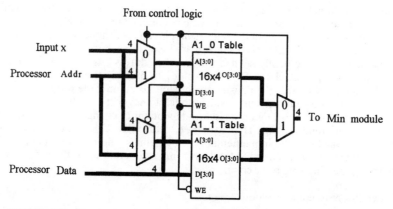

FIGURE 23.8   The storage of a membership function in the input table.

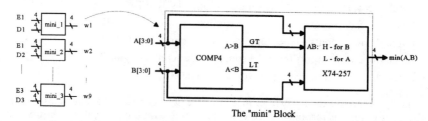

The "mini" Block

FIGURE 23.9   The min module.

Max Module.   For a sample of observed input values, at most four inference rules can be fired in this system. To select the four fired inference rules among a possible set of nine, the rule reduction criterion was derived and shown in Fig. 23.10. The max function in this figure is implemented in a way very similar to the mini blocks shown in Fig. 23.9.

Product Table.   This module includes memory blocks (constructed by using the Xilinx FPGA on-chip resources) that store the $w_i z_i$ values correspondent to the weights and some decoding logics that allow only the weights of the fired inference rules to access the table. Figure 23.11 shows part of the data flow within the max module and the product table which illustrates how these two modules work together. For simplicity, the secondary memory block for adaptation is not shown.

Sum Module.   This module produces the two sums Σw_i and $\Sigma w_i z_i$. It consists of two levels of adders (XC4000 macros ADD8 and ADD12) in a tree structure, as shown in Fig. 23.12.

Division Table.   For the designed hardware fuzzy inference engine, the $w_i z_i$ values are stored in 8-bit binary (integer) format, the maximal widths for Σw_i and $\Sigma w_i z_i$ are 5 and 9 bits (integers), respectively. The division table was implemented by using a separate Cypress CY7C251 16K $\times$ 8 EPROM with 50-ns access time. Again, this module is independent of the rest of the system.

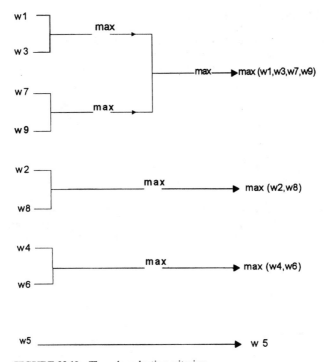

FIGURE 23.10   The rule reduction criterion.

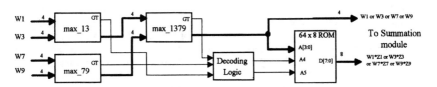

FIGURE 23.11   Part of the connected max module and the product table.

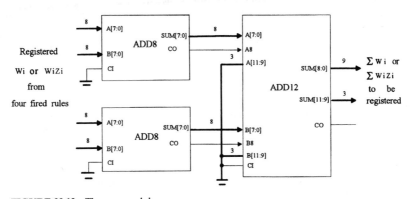

FIGURE 23.12   The sum module.

23.4.3 Performance Results

The system (except the division table) was implemented on a single Xilinx XC4008-6 FPGA with 6-ns delay per *configurable block* (*CLB*). Including the access time for the division table, performance obtained with three different versions of the control logic is listed below:

System clock	Pipelining	Inference per second
10 MHz	None	1.43 M
40 MHz (15 wait states)	T1, T7	1.90 M
10 MHz	T1, T2, T3, T4, T7	3.30 M

Throughput of the fully pipelined version can be increased by using a faster system clock and inserting wait states. Note that the listed performance can be further improved by targeting the design to other technologies or to the same device with a higher-speed grade.

23.5 CONCLUSIONS

In Sec. 23.2 we discussed from a hardware designer's viewpoint the GMP-based fuzzy inference mechanism, algorithms, and their architectural interpretations at a high level. Since a hardware fuzzy inference system often needs to meet performance demands that standard processors cannot adequately deliver, the parallel nature of the fuzzy inference algorithms is emphasized. Architecture for the most popular fuzzy inference algorithm based on mini implication and max-min composition was discussed in detail. Although it is impossible to discuss the detailed architecture for each individual fuzzy inference algorithm resulting from some specific fuzzy operators, a clear understanding of the general algorithm and its correspondent high-level architectural mapping will offer hardware designers a useful guideline in their design efforts. Many technical issues related to fuzzy hardware design were discussed in Sec. 23.3. A concrete design example based on the previous sections was given in Sec. 23.4, and some detailed implementation information was provided. The testing results show that the performance of the hardware fuzzy inference engine, with a design based on appropriate architectural interpretation and technical handling of the selected fuzzy inference algorithm, was greatly superior to the performance of the standard processors, as measured in fuzzy inferences per second.

REFERENCES

1. W. D. Detloff, K. E. Yount, and H. Watanabe, "A Fuzzy Logic Controller with Reconfigurable, Cascadable Architecture," *Proceedings of 1989 IEEE International Conference on Computer Design: VLSI in Computers and Processors,* 1989, pp. 474–478.
2. M. A. Eshera and S. C. Barash, "Parallel Rule-Based Fuzzy Inference on Mesh-Connected Systolic Arrays," *IEEE Expert,* Winter 1989, pp. 27–35.
3. S. Guo and L. Peters, "A Reconfigurable Analog Fuzzy Logic Controller," *Proceedings of the 3d IEEE International Conference on Fuzzy Systems,* Orlando, FL 1994, pp. 124–128.

4. D. L. Hung and W. F. Zajak, "Implementing a Fuzzy Inference Engine Using Field Programmable Gate Array," *Proceedings of the 6th IEEE International ASIC Conference,* Rochester, NY, 1993, pp. 349–352.

5. D. L. Hung, "Custom Design of a Hardware Fuzzy Logic Controller," *Proceedings of the 3d IEEE International Conference on Fuzzy Systems,* Orlando, FL, 1994, pp. 1781–1785.

6. C. Isik, "Inference Hardware for Fuzzy Rule-Based Systems," in *Fuzzy Computing,* M. M. Gupta and T. Yamakawa, eds., Elsevier Science Publishers B. V. (North Holland), Amsterdam, The Netherlands, 1988, pp. 185–194.

7. C. C. Lee, "Fuzzy Logic in Control Systems: Fuzzy Logic Controller, Part II," *IEEE Transactions on Systems, Man, and Cybernetics,* vol. 20, no. 20, pp. 419–435, 1990.

8. M-H. Lim and Y. Takefuji, "Implementing Fuzzy Rule-Based Systems on Silicon Chips," *IEEE Expert,* February 1990, pp. 31–45.

9. M. Mizumoto and H. Zimmermann, "Comparison of Fuzzy Reasoning Methods," *Fuzzy Sets and Systems,* vol. 18, pp. 253–283, 1982.

10. A. Sanz, "Analog Implementation of Fuzzy Controller," *Proceedings of the 3d IEEE International Conference on Fuzzy Systems,* Orlando, FL, 1994, pp. 279–283.

11. Sujal Shah and Ralph Horvath, "A Hardware Digital Fuzzy Inference Engine Using Standard Integrated Circuits," *Proceedings of the 1st International Conference on Fuzzy Theory and Technology,* Durham, NC (Publisher: Duke University), October 1992, pp. 109–114.

12. Masaki Togai and Hiroyuki Watanabe, "Expert System on a Chip: An Engine for Real-Time Approximate Reasoning," *IEEE Expert,* vol. 1, pp. 55–62, 1986.

13. Masaki Togai and S. Chiu, "A Fuzzy Logic Chip and a Fuzzy Inference Accelerator for Real-Time Approximate Reasoning," *Proceedings of the 17th International Symposium on Multiple-Valued Logic,* 1987, pp. 25–29.

14. J. Tombs, A. Torralba, and L. G. Franquelo, "Design of a Fuzzy Controller Mixing Analog and Digital Techniques," *Proceedings of the 3d IEEE International Conference on Fuzzy Systems,* Orlando, FL, 1994, pp. 1755–1758.

15. A. P. Ungering, K. Thuener, and K. Goser, "Architecture of a PDM VLSI Fuzzy Logic Controller with Pipelining and Optimized Chip Area," *Proceedings of the 2d IEEE International Conference on Fuzzy Systems,* vol. 1, 1993, pp. 447–452.

16. A. P. Ungering, H. Bauer, and K. Goser, "Architecture of a Fuzzy-Processor Based on an 8-Bit Microprocessor," *Proceedings of the 3d IEEE International Conference on Fuzzy Systems,* Orlando, FL, 1994, pp. 297–301.

17. H. Watanabe, W. D. Detloff, and K. E. Yount, "A VLSI Fuzzy Logic Inference Engine for Real-Time Process Control," *IEEE Journal of Solid-State Circuits,* vol. 25, no. 2, pp. 376–382, 1990.

18. H. Watanabe, "RISC Approach to Design Fuzzy Processor Architecture," *Proceedings of the International Conference on Fuzzy Systems,* 1991, pp. 120–127.

19. T. Yamakawa and T. Miki, "A Current Mode Fuzzy Logic Integrated Circuit Fabricated by the Standard CMOS Process," *IEEE Transactions on Computers,* vol. C-35, no. 2, pp. 161–167, 1986.

20. T. Yamakawa and K. Sasaki, "A Simple Fuzzy Computer Hardware System Employing Min and Max Operations—A Challenge to 6th Generation Computer," in *Proceedings of the 2d IFSA Congress,* Tokyo, Japan, July 1987.

21. T. Yamakawa, "Fuzzy Microprocessors—Rule Chip and Defuzzifier Chip," *Proceedings of the International Workshop on Fuzzy System Applications,* Iizuka, Japan, August 1988, pp. 51–52.

22. H.-J. Zimmermann, *Fuzzy Set Theory and Its Applications,* 2d ed., Kluwer Academic Publishers, Dordrecht, Netherlands, 1991.

CHAPTER 24
REACTIVE CONTROL USING FUZZY LOGIC

Enrique H. Ruspini
*Artificial Intelligence Center, SRI International,
Menlo Park, California*

A number of control and multistage decision problems involve complex systems that operate in uncertain environments. In these problems, the controller must address both needs to attain a number of explicitly stated goals and implicit requirements to respond to unexpected events. In many cases the control problem is further complicated by the unreliable, imprecise, and vague nature of the information describing the system state, its behavior, and the nature of the operational environment.

In this chapter we present a fuzzy logic approach for the treatment of this class of control problems. This approach is based on the combination of *purposive* behaviors seeking explicit goals, with *reactive* behaviors intended to respond, in robust fashion, to unforeseen circumstances.

This approach is based on the context-dependent activation of special constructs called *control structures,* which correspond to sets of fuzzy if-then rules. Inferential operations performed on these control structures result in the computation of *desirability measures,* which quantify the utility associated with the activation of each control action from the viewpoint of a specific goal or objective. Desirability measures corresponding to multiple, possibly conflicting, goals are then combined to arrive at a combined desirability distribution. The actual control value sent to the plant is then computed by the use of defuzzification methods. We illustrate this approach to reactive control with examples from its application to the control of an autonomous mobile robot.

24.1 INTRODUCTION

In many control and multistage decision applications, there exist requirements that go beyond the mere production of a control strategy which seeks explicit regulation goals. In these problems, the underlying systems operate under conditions of uncertainty that make impossible the prediction of changes to the environment where the system operates. Under these conditions, any policy without sufficient flexibility is bound to be of little use because typically dynamic environmental changes will prevent further utilization of the policies recommended by the plan.

If a dynamic control problem is thought of as the regulation of the behavior of a system, then we may classify such behavior as being essentially *purposive* (e.g., fabricate as many components as possible, given resource constraints) or *reactive* (e.g., stop scheduling a malfunctioning machine). Each of the just-mentioned components of a control policy is required to ensure successful performance of a robust controller. Purposive behaviors are obviously required to ensure that the system attains its goals. Reactive behaviors, on the other hand, are intended to provide responsiveness to a myriad of possible but difficult-to-predict environmental changes. Finally, adequate activation and blending techniques are needed to ensure a smooth transition between behaviors and to permit partial attainment of goals while responding to evolving circumstances.

In such a view of the control problem, the specification of a control strategy is equivalent to the identification of purposive and reactive behaviors, and of procedures to activate, deactivate, and integrate (or *blend*) them.

The requirement to trade off a degree of goal attainment with responsiveness is essential to ensure that incompatible goals, sought by various possible modes of operational behavior, may be successfully integrated. In a typical scheduling problem, e.g., demands to maintain a production rate may be traded off with requirements to attain a minimum level of safety (i.e., within bounds, delays may be permitted if they decrease malfunction risk).

The concepts, tools, and structures of fuzzy logic provide a convenient framework for the treatment of this class of control and decision problems. First, restrictions on control choices and system behavior may be expressed by means of possibility distributions that define relaxable or *elastic* constraints that quantify the adequacy of solutions from a variety of viewpoints [1]. Second, rational bases for the selective relaxation of certain goals or constraints in favor of others may be expressed through logical rules that explicitly describe context-dependent tradeoff considerations. This reliance on methods inspired by the inferential machinery of knowledge-based systems facilitates the explanation of the rationale utilized to arrive at specific control recommendations. Finally, fuzzy logic is well suited, by design, to represent imprecise and vague aspects of knowledge about the system and its operational environment.

In this chapter, we present a fuzzy-logic-based approach for the control of complex systems operating in uncertain environments. The primary goal of this approach is the development of controllers capable of reacting to unforeseen environmental circumstances while still pursuing, to the best possible extent, a number of designer-specified objectives.

These controllers govern the execution of a number of controlled system processes called *behaviors*. Behaviors that seek explicit goals, called *purposive behaviors*, are combined with those concerned with responding to unforeseen circumstances—*behavior blending*. In a typical application, several behaviors may be active at any time. Fuzzy logic techniques blend the control policies corresponding to these multiple, possibly conflicting, behaviors to arrive at a recommended action that trades off considerations about the context-dependent importance of each behavior. Unlike approaches based on the optimization of global measures of performance, the procedures to be used to determine the recommended control action are explicitly stated by means of context-dependent vague rules.

The conceptual foundation of this approach is provided by the notion of *control structure*. Informally, a control structure is a function that computes the desirability of each possible control action as a function of the current state. The output of these calculations, or the *desirability measure,* is a possibility distribution defined over the control space.

In Sec. 24.2 we discuss the semantic bases of our approach, which rest on an interpretation of fuzzy logic as a formal system concerned with notions of utility and preference. Section 24.3 describes the control approach, introducing the computational structures utilized to represent goals and to compute desirability measures.

Our approach is illustrated in Sec. 24.4 by means of examples drawn from experiments with the control of the local motion of an autonomous mobile robot.[†]

24.2   TRUTH AS UTILITY

The foundations of our approach to reactive control are provided by semantic models of fuzzy logic as logics of similarity and utility [11, 12]. Our interpretation of fuzzy logic as a logic concerned with issues of utility is strongly influenced by seminal ideas of Bellman and Zadeh [1, 5], being also influenced by the *logics of preference* proposed by Rescher [7], where the truth value (usually measured in a [0, 1] scale) of a constraining proposition p represents the desirability of p coming about, or, in other words, the degree by which p is a "good thing."

Our approach extends the original ideas of Bellman and Zadeh, proposing specific techniques to represent and deal with multiple, possibly conflicting, objectives and to combine elementary behaviors intended to attain them. A significant aspect of our approach is the explicit representation of context-dependent metarules to govern this behavioral integration. Furthermore, our approach is based on formal results relating the notions of possibility and similarity [10, 11] that facilitate the derivation of rule sets (control structures) for the computation of desirability measures.

Our methodology also differs from previous multivalued-logic-based formulations, such as Rescher's, in a number of regards.

In our formulation, e.g., each of the formal logic expressions that states either the characteristics of the system or constraints placed on its behavior is associated with a utility measure that evaluates the adequacy of solutions as measured from the perspective of the constraint of all other things being equal. This constraint-specific interpretation differs from that of Rescher where utilities are functions that measure the "global" desirability of a proposition's being true, regardless of context. These global measures are given, in Rescher's approach, by an average of context-specific desirability values. This assumption leads to the unwarranted conclusion that such functions must behave as probability distributions.

Our approach also permits the introduction of generalized, graded modalities, thus allowing the representation of ignorance about the potential utility of certain choices.

24.2.1   Desirability Measures

In our formulation [11, 12], following the original suggestions of Bellman and Zadeh, a number between 0 and 1 is assigned to every pair (solution, constraint).

[†]This application of fuzzy logic to the development of a robot motion controller is the result of the collaboration of various scientists at the Artificial Intelligence Center of SRI International, including, in addition to the author, N. Helft, K. Konolige, D. Musto, K. Myers, A. Saffiotti, and L. Wesley.

This number represents the relative desirability of that solution from the viewpoint of that constraint. Both constraints requiring attainment of some goal (e.g., reach point P in less than 5 s) and constraints on control or state variable values (e.g., the speed should be less than 2 ft/s) are represented by the same type of measure of desirability of the state of affairs, as are laws describing system behavior and observations about the state of the system. In the case of the latter elements of information, the corresponding utility functions measure the extent of the potential errors if the actual system being modeled does not, in fact, satisfy the model's assumptions.

From such a perspective, each constraint is a function that measures the extent by which each solution—strictly corresponding in our semantic model to the notion of *possible world* or *possible state of affairs*—satisfies that constraint. From the viewpoint of a single constraint, solutions that are ideal in the sense that they are deemed totally adequate from such a limited outlook are given a desirability measure of 1, while those not worthy of being considered are given a value of 0. Intermediate values between 0 and 1 indicate the relative adequacy or *usefulness* of the solution.

Returning now to the notion of *universe of discourse* as a nonempty conventional set $\mathcal{U}$ having as members the solutions of a system analysis problem, we may simply define a *desirability measure* as a function $\mathbf{D} : \mathcal{U} \mapsto [0,1]$, that is, a fuzzy set of the universe of discourse $\mathcal{U}$.

Desirability measures are natural extensions of the concept of *hard* or *crisp* constraint. If w is a solution in $\mathcal{U}$, then the value $\mathbf{D}(w)$ may also be thought of as the truth value of the proposition "The solution w is satisfactory from the viewpoint of $\mathbf{D}$."

24.2.2 Combination of Desirability Measures

In a typical system analysis problem, it is often required that solutions be acceptable from the perspective of several constraints. It is often convenient to model such a requirement as the logical conjunction $\mathbf{D}_1 \wedge \mathbf{D}_2 \wedge \cdots$ of several desirability measures.

Clearly, a solution w that is acceptable from the viewpoint of two desirability measures $\mathbf{D}$ and $\mathbf{D}'$ should also be deemed adequate from any measure that represents their logical conjunction. If rational requirements are placed on the nature of such a combination function, then it may be shown that the desirability of a conjunction of two desirabilities $\mathbf{D}$ and $\mathbf{D}'$ is given by the expression

$$(\mathbf{D} \wedge \mathbf{D}')(w) = \mathbf{D}(w) \otimes \mathbf{D}'(w) \qquad w \text{ in } \mathcal{U}$$

where $\otimes$ is a *triangular norm*.

Similar considerations show that the desirability of the disjunction of two desirabilities $\mathbf{D}$ and $\mathbf{D}'$ is given by

$$(\mathbf{D} \vee \mathbf{D}')(w) = \mathbf{D}(w) \oplus \mathbf{D}'(w) \qquad w \text{ in } \mathcal{U}$$

where $\oplus$ is a *triangular conorm*.

The logical notion of negation is generalized by nonincreasing *complementation* functions $\sim$ from $[0,1]$ into $[0,1]$ that, in addition, satisfy $\sim 0 = 1$ and $\sim 1 = 0$.

In our formulation, the logical operator $\rightarrow$ is generalized by the *pseudoinverse* or *residuation* operator $\oslash$, that is,

$$(\mathbf{D} \rightarrow \mathbf{D}')(w) = \mathbf{D}'(w) \oslash \mathbf{D}(w)$$

where the pseudoinverse $\oslash$ of a T norm $\otimes$ is defined by the expression

$$a \oslash b = \sup \{c : b \otimes c \leq a\}$$

The importance of the residuation operation and its role in the tautology

$$(\mathbf{D} \otimes (\mathbf{D} \to \mathbf{D}')) \to \mathbf{D}'$$

which generalizes the classical modus ponens have been pointed out by Trillas and Valverde [15].

In our methodology, implication operators play a central role in the inferential process of reactive controllers, which are primarily collections of if-then fuzzy rules. The applicability of a particular rule $R \equiv A \to B$, for example, may be measured by the extent $S \to A$ of matching between the antecedent A of R and the present state S.

24.3 CONTROL STRUCTURES

The notion of control structure was first introduced in the context of autonomous mobile agent applications [9]. In this type of application, a control structure was closely related to the intuitive notion of *landmark* or *place* [6]. Control structures were used to quantify the degree of desirability of potential control actions, as promoters of a specific goal, within the vicinity of such landmark or perceivable environmental feature. Although the emphasis was placed primarily on motion actions, control structures were conceived as general mechanisms that promoted a variety of perceptual, communication, and computation activities. For example, control structures may activate, in certain situations, a variety of sensors in order to better identify the position of the mobile agent in its workspace. In other situations—when the agent is deemed to be adequately localized—the control structures may deemphasize perceptual observation in favor of other activities such as motion.

Control structures were also conceived as the basic link between global objectives of a system (e.g., reach an intersection) and the numerical specification of the extent by which, given a certain context, a particular action promoted attainment of that objective. If one were seeking to reach the end of a corridor, e.g., actions that move the robot parallel and at a safe distance from a wall would be preferred to those that would place the robot in danger of collision or that would not result in significant motion in the desired direction.

The high-level architecture of the controllers based on control structures is strongly influenced by the layered, behavior-subsumption architectures of Brooks [3]. In these autonomous agent architectures, behaviors are organized into layers or hierarchical levels of increasingly complex actions, with behaviors at higher levels in the architecture controlling the simpler behaviors at the lower level, enabling or inhibiting their execution.

Our formulation—strongly dependent on utilitarian concepts and on numerical quantifications of the degree by which certain outcomes are preferred to others—regards notions such as constraints, goals, and behaviors as conditions capable of being achieved to various degrees. Behaviors, e.g., may be executed at various levels of performance quality (e.g., the quality of a plan to follow a wall may be measured by performance indexes that are a function of the time required to reach the physical end of the wall).

Deliberations made on the basis of current knowledge lead to the formulation of a *plan* to attain the system goals. Rather than being a sequence of prespecified actions, a plan is a collection of control structures that act as instructions for a fuzzy inferential machine. This inferential machine computes the required desirability measures.

Plans may be ranked numerically by means of fuzzy-logic-based techniques that measure the extent by which the plan directives (i.e., control structures) promote the desired goals. Plans may also be decomposed hierarchically into subplans, i.e., collections of behaviors (and associated control structures) intended to accomplish dependent subgoals.

In our robotic application, a number of traditional *artificial intelligence (AI)* planning techniques have been used to develop plans as collections of control structures that promote subgoals such as following a wall or crossing a door threshold.

Once a plan to achieve one or more objectives has been formulated, the corresponding control structures are input to an inferential machine that computes the desirability of potential control actions as a function of the current state. Control structures, usually specified as sets of if-then rules, are then employed by this inferential engine to compute the required desirability measures.

In our robotic applications, two major classes of fuzzy if-then rules are specified within a control structure:

1. *Control rules* of the form "If the state is A, then the control is in B," where A and B are fuzzy sets (of state and controls, respectively).

2. *Contextual metarules* of the form "If the state is S, then the desirability of activating (or deactivating) the control structure C is α," which measure the importance of activating a rule in a given context. Examples of these types of rules include constraints such as "do not start following wall until you are in the vicinity of point P," "stop following wall if obstacle is sensed," and "if the load is balanced, then proceed along wall." These elements of knowledge, suggested by the interpretation of Berenji et al. [2] of metarules as statements of priorities and dependencies between subgoals, provide the rational bases for metalevel reasoning about tradeoffs between conflicting goals

Rules in the first class essentially specify the adequacy of actions as a function of the state of the agent and the state of its environment, while those in the second class rank actions on the basis of the extent by which the plan subgoals have been accomplished. In our robotic applications, rules of the first type are used primarily to define the desired behavior around specific landmarks, while those in the second class are employed primarily to specify priorities and temporal activation sequences.

Control structures are the basic knowledge blocks utilized by a fuzzy inferential machine that computes the desirability of potential control actions. Each control structure is intended to promote a *behavior* that attains or maintains a goal or subgoal, such as following a wall. At any given time, several behaviors, each seeking a specific goal, may be active in the fuzzy controller. For example, behaviors to follow a wall and to sense open office doors may both be active at the same time.

When several such behaviors are active (i.e., the corresponding control structures are active), the inferential engine utilizes metarules in the second class to trade off between their multiple requirements, seeking to "blend" them so as to promote each active behavior to the best possible degree. In our robotics application, the inferential engine chooses the course of action that best satisfies all active behaviors. The degree of satisfaction is measured by the extent by which a fuzzy predicate—defining the context of applicability—matches the present state.

Control structures include both rule sets seeking explicit goals and promoting behaviors intended to attain them, and rule sets that are intended to reactively respond whenever certain events are observed or sensed. In our mobile agent application, the first type of purposive control structure regulates behaviors such as "follow a wall" or "reach an intersection," while the second controls reactive behaviors such as "avoid an obstacle" or "confirm your location."

Depending on the current operational context and the metarules included in each control structure, the inferential engine determines the relative applicability and importance of each potential control action. In the immediate vicinity of an obstacle, e.g., control structures intended to steer the robot away from a collision course prevail over those seeking purposeful behaviors. As the danger of collision is reduced, the reactive control structures are slowly deactivated and the inferential engine assigns importance to other active structures.

The actual fuzzy logic functions performed by the inferential controller are the generalized modus ponens—mapping evidence about the state into a blended desirability measure—and defuzzification—producing a single control value deemed to summarize such desirability distribution. Specific formulations of the functions utilized in our mobile agent experiments are discussed in detail by Saffiotti et al. [14, 13].

24.4 EXPERIMENTS

The planning and control of the actions of a mobile autonomous agent provide a good example of the applicability of the fuzzy logic approach discussed in previous sections. The scope of our approach extends, however, beyond robotics applications since it relies on general methods for the attainment of multiple, possibly conflicting, objectives, the combination of numerical control with conventional AI planning methods, and the processing of approximate maps.

These techniques and concepts, suitably enhanced and adapted to this particular domain of application, were implemented in the mobile robot platform of the Artificial Intelligence Center (AIC) [14, 13]. The resulting controller was evaluated in numerous in-house experiments and in the first international robotics competition of the American Association for Artificial Intelligence [4].

The AIC mobile robot is a custom-built platform, with a height of 1 m and a diameter of 0.6 m, which operates in an indoor environment. The robot moves and turns, using two independently powered wheels. The maximum linear velocity of the robot is about 0.5 m/s. The mobile agent sensors include sonars, wheel encoders, and a video camera. Flakey also has several on-board computers, dedicated to low-level sensor interpretation, motor control, and radio communication with an off-board Sparc station. Although it is possible to run the high-level interpretation and control processes on board, they are normally performed remotely for programming convenience.[†]

The control of the actions of a mobile agent is a foremost example of a problem of system control under conditions of imprecision and uncertainty. These inconvenient features of knowledge present themselves in this problem in a variety of ways which include lack of precise and complete information about the environment; inherent noise, errors, and observational limitations of on-board sensors; imprecision and failure of robot actions; and inability to predict the dynamic characteristics of the environment.

The layered architecture described in Sec. 24.3 was implemented by a fuzzy controller with capabilities for reactive and purposive control seeking to attain multiple, possibly conflicting, objectives. In this architecture, control structures are typically

---

[†]Recent reconfigurations of the device have resulted in the incorporation of an on-board Sparc workstation that performs control and other high-level functions.

associated with environmental features capable of being discerned by the robot's sensors.

Control structures were implemented by fuzzy if-then rules of the form

$$\text{IF } A_i \text{ THEN } C_i$$

where A_i is a fuzzy predicate defined over state variables and C_i is a fuzzy set of control values. The rules are utilized to approximate a desirability function associated with a behavior. For example, a collision avoidance behavior, intended to keep the robot safely away from occupied areas, may include the following rule:

IF obstacle-close-on-right AND NOT obstacle-on-left,

THEN turn slow-left

If a rule set $\mathfrak{R} = \{R_1, \ldots, R_n\}$ is active and if the state is s, the controller, recurring to the generalized modus ponens, computes the desirability distribution[†]

$$\text{Des}_{\mathfrak{R}}(s, c) = (A_1(s) \otimes C_1(c)) \oplus \cdots \oplus (A_n(s) \otimes C_n(c))$$

The actual control $\hat{c}$ sent to the plant is then chosen by the centroid defuzzification method.

In the AIC controller implementation, a control structure is defined by a triple

$$S = \langle A, \text{Des}, C \rangle$$

where A is a virtual or real object in the robot's workspace, des is a function that specifies the desirability of potential control actions as a function of the relations between the state of the robot and the characteristics of that object, and C is a fuzzy predicate describing the *context* where the structure is applied. In the actual implementation, a typical desirability measure is computed that uses 4 to 8 rules based on 4 to 20 predicates.

For example, the following control structure—

$$\langle \text{CP}, \text{Go-To-CP}, \text{near(CP)} \rangle$$

where CP is a control point, i.e., a fuzzy location in state space, the associated measure Go To CP gauges the adequacy of potential control actions in terms of their ability to guide the robot from its present state to CP, and the context near(CP) specifies where this control structure should be activated—was utilized in our experiments to generate a behavior steering the robot to CP.

In general, several control structures may be active at any time. Each control structure, by itself, induces a behavior leading to attainment of its corresponding goal. When several structures are present, the corresponding behaviors are blended by generation of a context-dependent combined-desirability measure.

In the simplest blending scheme, when the n control structures $\{S_1, \ldots, S_n\}$, with corresponding desirability measures $\{\text{Des}_1, \ldots, \text{Des}_n\}$ and contexts $\{C_1, \ldots, C_n\}$, are active, they are combined by using the expression

$$\text{Des}(s,c) = (\text{Des}_1(s,c) \otimes C_1(s)) \oplus \cdots \oplus (\text{Des}_n(s,c) \otimes C_n(s))$$

[†]In the actual implementation, $\otimes$ and $\oplus$ are the min T norm and max T conorm, respectively.

The actual control value is then chosen by using centroid defuzzification.

Figure 24.1 illustrates the actual execution of a plan to guide the robot to a specified office. The following four control structures are the central part of the plan:

S1 = ⟨Obstacle, KEEP-OFF, near(Obstacle)⟩

S2 = ⟨Corr2, FOLLOW, ¬near(Obstacle) ∧ at(Corr2) ∧ ¬near(Corr1)⟩

S3 = ⟨Corr1, FOLLOW, ¬near(Obstacle) ∧ at(Corr1) ∧ ¬near(Door5)⟩

S4 = ⟨Door1, CROSS, ¬near(Obstacle) ∧ near(Door5)⟩

Note that while one is following the first corridor, a purposeful behavior FOLLOW is blended with the KEEP-OFF behavior, resulting in a trajectory that traverses the hallway while avoiding obstacles. At point *a*, an obstacle has been detected, and the KEEP-OFF behavior dominates, causing the robot to turn. As the obstacle is left behind, the FOLLOW behavior regains importance, guiding the robot from point *b*. The solid lines in Fig. 24.2 show, for each behavior, the level of activation at points *a* and *b* for each of these two behaviors. The blended controls are shown in the third line at the bottom of each figure.

ACKNOWLEDGMENTS

The author benefited from discussions with H. Berenji, N. Helft, K. Konolige, J. Lowrance, D. Ruspini, A. Saffiotti, L. Valverde, D. Musto, and L. Zadeh.

Results of the application of the ideas presented in this chapter, together with a number of associated developments in the areas of self-localization, map interpretation, intelligent device architecture, and planning, which led to the results presented

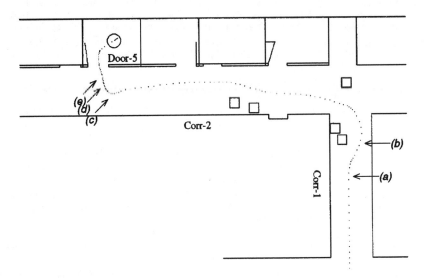

FIGURE 24.1 Plan execution.

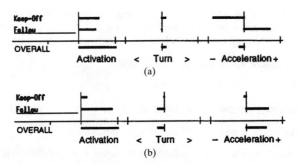

FIGURE 24.2   Behavior blending.

in Sec. 24.4, are the joint work of the author with colleagues at the Artificial Intelligence Center of SRI International, including A. Saffiotti, K. Konolige, K. Myers, N. Helft, L. Wesley, and D. Musto.

This work was partially supported by the U.S. Air Force Office of Scientific Research under contract no. F49620-91-C-0060. Additional support was provided by SRI International.

REFERENCES

1. R. E. Bellman and L. A. Zadeh, "Decision-Making in a Fuzzy Environment," *Management Science,* 17:B141–B164, 1980.

2. H. Berenji, Y.-Y. Chen, C.-C. Lee, J.-S. Jang, and S. Murugesan, "A Hierarchical Approach to Approximate Reasoning-Based Controllers for Dynamic Physical Systems," in P. P. Bonissone and M. Henrion, eds., *Proceedings of the Sixth Conference on Uncertainty in Artificial Intelligence,* Morgan Kaufmann Publishers, San Mateo, CA, 1990, pp. 362–369.

3. R. A. Brooks, "A Robust Layered Control System for a Mobile Robot," in P. H. Winston and S. A. Shellard, *Artificial Intelligence at MIT,* vol. 2: *Expanding Frontiers,* MIT Press, Cambridge, MA, 1990, pp. 2–27.

4. C. Congdon, M. Huber, D. Kortenkamp, K. Konolige, and K. Myers, et al., "CARMEL vs. Flakey: A Comparison of Two Winners," *AI Magazine,* 14(1):49–57, Spring 1993.

5. D. Dubois and H. Prade, "Criteria Aggregation and Ranking of Alternatives in the Framework of Fuzzy Set Theory," in H. J. Zimmermann, L. A. Zadeh, and B. R. Gaines, eds., *Fuzzy Sets and Decision Analysis,* North-Holland, Amsterdam, 1984, pp. 209–240.

6. B. J. Kuipers, "Modeling Spatial-Knowledge," *Cognitive Science,* 2:129–153, 1978.

7. N. Rescher, "Semantic Foundations for the Logic of Preference," in N. Rescher, ed., *The Logic of Decision and Action,* Pittsburgh, PA, 1967.

8. E. H. Ruspini, "Fuzzy Logic in FLAKEY," in *Proceedings of the 1990 International Conference on Fuzzy Logic and Neural Networks* (*IIZUKA '90*), Fuzzy Logic Systems Institute, Iizuka, Kyushu, Japan, 1990.

9. E. H. Ruspini and D. C. Ruspini, "Autonomous Vehicle Planning Using Fuzzy Logic," in *Proceedings of the IEEE Round Table on Fuzzy and Neural Systems and Vehicle Applications,* Tokyo, Japan, November 1991.

10. E. H. Ruspini, "Approximate Reasoning: Past, Present, Future," *Information Sciences,* 57–58:297–317, 1991.

11. E. H. Ruspini, "On the Semantics of Fuzzy Logic, *International Journal of Approximate Reasoning,* 5:45–88, 1991.

12. E. H. Ruspini, "On Truth and Utility," in R. Kruse and P. Siegel, eds., *Symbolic and Quantitative Approaches to Uncertainty,* Springer, New York, 1991.

13. E. Ruspini, A. Saffiotti, and K. Konolige, "Progress in Research on Autonomous Vehicle Motion Planning," in J. Yen and R. Langari, eds., *Industrial Applications of Fuzzy Logic,* CRC/IEEE Press, New York, 1995.

14. A. Saffiotti, K. Konolige, and E. H. Ruspini, "A Multivalued Logic Approach to Integrating Planning and Control," *Artificial Intelligence,* forthcoming, 1995.

15. E. Trillas and L. Valverde, "On Mode and Implication in Approximate Reasoning," in M. M. Gupta, A. Kandel, W. Bandler, and J. B. Kiszka, eds., *Approximate Reasoning and Expert Systems,* North-Holland, Amsterdam, 1985, pp. 157–166.

CHAPTER 25

A HYBRID FUZZY EXPERT SYSTEM SHELL FOR AUTOMATED MEDICAL DIAGNOSIS

Elisabetta Binaghi
Maria Grazia Montesano
Anna Rampini
ITIM—Istituto per le Tecnologie Informatiche
Multimediali—C.N.R., Milano, Italy

Iacopo Cerrani
Dipartimento di Scienze dell' Informazione
Università degli Studi di Milano, Milano, Italy

The authors propose a hybrid fuzzy expert system shell for automated medical diagnosis. The system supports a strategy to acquire and represent medical knowledge, combining the use of fuzzy sets as the representational framework with fuzzy learning techniques, neural networks, and structured interviews for the generation of medical diagnostic knowledge.

An intelligent multiwindow interface is implemented, which relieves the user of the technicalities of encoding knowledge, allowing information to be entered in the form of visual representations which correspond to the way physicians formulate diagnostic tasks.

The authors also describe an application of this hybrid fuzzy expert system shell in the diagnosis of hyperandrogenism in women. In the intricate clinical presentation of the pathology concerned, some indicators, such as hematochemical parameters, can be easily determined, while the assessment of hirsutism, essential for the formulation of diagnostic judgments, is instead a complex, sophisticated task.

All the steps taken in the acquisition and representation of the clinical signs, diagnostic classes, and rules related to the diagnosis of hirsutism are presented in detail together with the numerical results and a quantitative evaluation of the overall approach.

25.1 INTRODUCTION

The field of artificial intelligence in medicine has been dominated by the academic sector, where the orientation of researchers in addressing the problem of diagnostic systems has not favored the commercial exploitation in this field and actual employment of knowledge-based systems in clinical diagnosis.

System accuracy has been too limited, and system operation too complicated, requiring the transfer of complex technology, together with the broad implementation and standardization of hospital information systems.

There is, however, a growing demand for these tools and a corresponding increase in projects for the automatic analysis and interpretation of clinical data to support decision-making activities in specific medical domains [1].

Current research in knowledge-based systems focuses on the development of expert system shells, or system-building tools in general, which can (at least theoretically) be adapted to different applications by simply replacing the knowledge base, without altering the implemented reasoning mechanisms [2]. Fuzzy set [3] techniques are widely used in the solution of practical problems in medicine. The current literature provides various examples of medical expert systems with fuzzy inference models and of medical applications which use fuzzy expert system shells to provide for human flexibility and variability in formulating diagnostic judgments, while ensuring a rigorous, quantitative interpretation of the knowledge underlying the diagnostic process concerned [4].

A major objective in designing these systems has been the development of fuzzy-logic-based knowledge acquisition strategies which can actively help experts in defining the conceptual model of the diagnostic processes and in translating medical knowledge to a machine-readable expression.

In this context, the neural network approach has received renewed attention in recent years. This approach, unlike the rule-based approach which relies on expert input, offers the advantage of a knowledge base derived directly from accumulated data [5]. But since in medicine both these sources of information are extremely important, it would seem a good idea to incorporate both approaches into a single comprehensive framework [6, 7].

To this end the authors propose a hybrid software environment for automated support in medical diagnosis that guarantees high system accuracy in producing diagnostic judgments, because it deals with knowledge acquisition by actually building a model of the expert's cognitive processes and can be easily and economically tailored to different diagnostic situations by changing and/or adding domain modeling without altering the overall decision-making scheme.

In particular, an integrated set of modules has been designed to fulfill these basic requirements:

- Formalize and store, in a unified framework, expert-derived and data-derived knowledge (usually multiple criteria, the description of clinical signs, subjective decision attitudes) in forming a diagnosis in a given medical domain, in order to provide an objective, explicit, and deterministic assessment of the cognitive decision-making process involved.

- Organize human-machine communication, using an intelligent interface through which the large amount of information required at each step of the knowledge acquisition and representation process is exchanged in a form close to the mental representation of human experts, using natural expressions and graphical forms.

- Support the physician by suggesting graduated soft diagnostic judgments, based upon patients' descriptions of their clinical signs, and by explicitly explaining how these conclusions are reached.

- Achieve new insight in the medical fields in which applications are developed, creating conditions for the communication and discussion of methods, criteria, and results among physicians by comparison with those of automated diagnostic strategies.

25.2 ACQUISITION AND REPRESENTATION OF MEDICAL DIAGNOSTIC KNOWLEDGE

In diagnosis, considered a cognitive process, the description of clinical signs and subsequent decision activity is based not on a mass of numbers, but on *elicitation links* [8] between linguistic descriptions of clinical signs and qualitative diagnostic judgments. Medical experts do not use formal languages for reasoning and for representing knowledge in their domains. The formal basis lies in deeper theory, such as physics, and their expression of this complexity may be subject to imprecision and vagueness. However, physicians have developed fairly stable procedures and a generally accepted language for representing clinical knowledge and reasoning with it. The causal relation between clinical signs and diagnostic classes may be difficult to assess directly: in most cases this relationship is the result of simpler relationships between clinical signs and subdiagnostic classes, and between these and the final diagnostic classes. In other words, the support for a decision may depend on supports for several different criteria and the degree of satisfaction of other subcriteria, and so on.

Consequently, the strategy we propose for the acquisition and representation of medical knowledge is hybrid, combining the use of fuzzy sets as the representational framework with fuzzy learning techniques, neural networks, and structured interviews for the generation of medical diagnostic knowledge. Figure 25.1 shows the architecture of the strategy proposed.

The strategy is organized to preserve the advantages of symbolic and connectionist techniques and overcome their disadvantages. Symbolic stages support knowledge-based techniques for gathering and processing information, which may be imprecise, incomplete, or unreliable, with methods of fuzzy reasoning. The ability to learn in an uncertain environment is enhanced by incorporating a neural stage where knowledge is derived directly from accumulated case data through the use of a supervised learning algorithm.

The literature presents various solutions to the problem of identifying a suitable network topology, but none can be adopted as a general method. In most cases the best solution is empirical and problem-dependent or is derived from experience. In the strategy proposed here, a hybrid stage supports the definition of network topology by directly deriving input, hidden, and output units from the structure of decision rules generated in the symbolic stage.

A second hybrid stage concludes the overall strategy. At this level, knowledge stored in network connections is encoded in symbolic form.

Even if the connectionist stage successfully addresses the problem of generation of a knowledge base, it cannot satisfactorily represent the experts' decision-making activity. The acquired knowledge is stored in network connections, but since it is not formalized in an explicit way, it is not documentable.

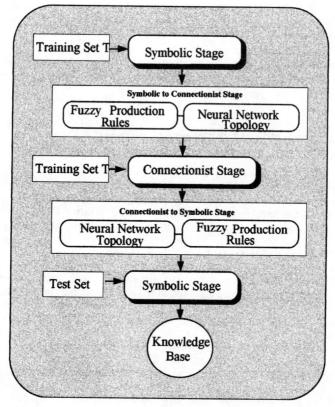

FIGURE 25.1 The hybrid strategy for the acquisition and representation of knowledge.

Since the resulting set of rules is a refinement of the decision rules generated in the previous symbolic stage, we may expect an increase in accuracy.

25.2.1 Symbolic Stage

The fuzzy representation model interprets qualitative concepts involved in the diagnostic problem as fuzzy sets. In particular, clinical signs and diagnostic classes can be interpreted as linguistic variables, and their description is represented as a fuzzy declarative proposition in the form "X is A," where X is the linguistic variable representing a given sign, while A is a term which belongs to the term set of the linguistic variable and denotes a fuzzy set in a given universe of discourse U, characterized by the membership function $\mu_A(u)$ where $u \in U$. The set U contains all the possible numerical or, more generally, crisp values assumed by X. The fuzzy set denoted by A defines a possibility distribution of X [9].

In this context, the first acquisition task at the symbolic stage is to elicit and interpret expert data to characterize fuzzy declarative propositions regarding the problem under investigation. A relaxed strategy is essential here to preserve the variability of expert opinions, but at the same time an objective procedure which can quantify and aggregate expert answers must be introduced.

The elicitation strategy must take into account the fact that, due to the nature of fuzziness, not all people will evaluate a subjective attribute identically; different answers will be collected from different assessors. It is important that the group of experts selected for the elicitation session share concepts and hold well-defined opinions on element membership in the fuzzy sets in question [10].

Elicited data are interpreted as membership functions of the fuzzy sets concerned. In our approach, the construction of membership functions proceeds from the selection of an appropriate group and is based on a statistical survey [11].

The second task of the symbolic stage is to generate a draft version of diagnostic rules describing how combinations of clinical signs relate to diagnostic classes [12]. Diagnostic rules can be formalized and stored in terms of fuzzy production rules structured as evaluation-decision pairs. The antecedent of a fuzzy production rule combines fuzzy declarative propositions to express a multifactorial clinical situation; the consequent part contains judgmental knowledge expressed in terms of a declarative proposition which assesses a linguistic judgment for a given diagnostic class. The general structure of a fuzzy production rule is

$$R_i\text{: If } E_i \text{ then } (D_1 \text{ is } S_{1,i}) \text{ and} \ldots \text{ and } (D_K \text{ is } S_{K,i}) \tag{25.1}$$

where E_i is a compound fuzzy declarative proposition of the form

$$(X_1 \text{ is } A_{1,j1}) \text{ and} \ldots \text{ and } (X_n \text{ is } A_{n,jn}) \tag{25.2}$$

The term $(X_h \text{ is } A_{h,jh})$ represents the linguistic description of the medical sign X_h, where

$$1 \leq h \leq n \qquad n = \text{number of clinical signs concerned}$$

$$1 \leq j_h \leq J_H \qquad J_H = \text{cardinality of term set related to } X_h$$

In proposition (25.1), when $1 \leq k \leq K$, D_k belongs to a predefined set of diagnostic classes, each class is treated as a linguistic variable, and $S_{k,i}$ is a term expressing the degree of satisfaction with which a diagnostic conclusion may be inferred.

The evaluation of the rule antecedent produces different degrees of evidence, aggregated according to both the aggregation operator that corresponds to the logical connective *and* and the relative importance of the clinical signs. Different aggregation operators are proposed in the fuzzy decision-making framework to represent the experts' decision attitudes in aggregating different criteria and reaching an overall decision [13]. At this stage the selection of the aggregation operator and identification of the relative importance of signs are performed by structured interviews with experts, leaving to the connectionist stage the refinement of these parameters.

The complexity of a real medical domain makes it difficult to elicit diagnostic rules directly from experts; with an interview technique there is always the risk that the knowledge elicited may be an artifact produced under the pressure of questioning. To avoid this, our strategy supports an empirical learning procedure for the automatic generation of a draft version of the rules and fuzzy neural network techniques for a complete refinement of them. A minimally complete training set is used for the empirical learning to reduce complexity in generation. The property of minimal completeness is ensured by a homogeneous sampling of the universe of discourse with few examples supporting each antecedent-consequence relationship. The algorithm adopts a method of induction based on a direct application of fuzzy reasoning operators. In particular, the problem of learning fuzzy production rules is formulated in terms of how to automatically induce, from a training set of already diagnosed clinical cases, the strength of implication $S_{k,i}$ for each rule R_i and for a given diagnostic class D_k. A detailed description of the approach may be found in Refs. 14 and 15.

25.2.2 Integration from Symbolic to Connectionist Stage

The output of the symbolic stage is a draft version of the domain knowledge base and consists of a set R of decision rules. These are used to infer the initial topology of a three-level feedforward neural network.

The cardinality of the input and output nodes of the network is equal to the sum of the linguistic terms introduced for the domain concerned; the cardinality of the hidden level is $|R|$, equal to the number of decision rules generated. The connections among network levels are also inferred by the rules' structure, as described in the following example. Let

R_i: If $(X_1$ is $A^i_{1,j1})$ and ... and $(X_n$ is $A^i_{n,jn})$ Then $(D_1$ is $S_{1,i})$ and ... and $(D_K$ is $S_{K,i})$

R_y: If $(X_1$ is $A^y_{1,j1})$ and ... and $(X_n$ is $A^y_{n,jn})$ Then $(D_1$ is $S_{1,y})$ and ... and $(D_K$ is $S_{K,y})$

be two elements of set R. This infers a neural network with the topology described in Fig. 25.2 where the yth hidden neuron represents the antecedent of the yth production rule. If we connect each rth hidden neuron to its corresponding input and output neurons, when $1 \le r \le |R|$, we obtain a partially connected neural network which reflects both the knowledge base obtained at the symbolic stage and, as a consequence, the experts' cognitive processes in the aggregation of criteria and decision classes.

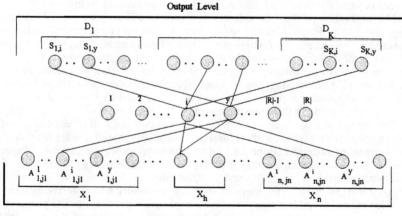

FIGURE 25.2 Network topology.

25.2.3 Connectionist Stage

The objective of the connectionist stage is to learn the parameters of the network by means of a back propagation learning algorithm [16]. In accordance with Krishna-puram and Lee [17], we use fuzzy set-theoretic aggregation functions as activation functions in the network. Fuzzy aggregation functions implement logical aggregation connectives to represent the possible decision attitudes of a decision maker, who combines the descriptions of observables and makes a selection from a set of decision actions. The network first assumes as an activation function those operators used in the generation of symbolic rules. In this context the connectionist learning procedure may be reformulated as the search for the most adequate aggregation connectives, appropriately refining the connectives introduced in the symbolic stage.

Two general, parametric operators have been investigated and used in our strategy to address decision-making problems with decision criteria that are mutually compensable [18]: the generalized mean operator and the hybrid operator.

The Activation Function as Generalized Mean Operator. The generalized mean operator has the following general form [19]:

$$g(x_1, x_2, \ldots, x_m, p, w_1, w_2, \ldots, w_m) = \left(\sum_{i=1}^{m} w_i x_i^p \right)^{1/p}$$

where, when $1 \leq i \leq m$, the coefficients w_i represent the relative importance of each decision criterion x_i in the symbolic fuzzy framework and $\sum_{i=1}^{m} w_i = 1$. In the connectionist stage, the coefficients represent the weights that must be learned by the network.

If we define the following sets

$$I = \bigcup_{h=1}^{n} T_{X_h} = \{x_1, x_2, \ldots, x_m\} \qquad \rightarrow \text{set of input nodes}$$

$$O = \bigcup_{k=1}^{K} T_{D_k} = \{y_1, y_2, \ldots, y_z\} \qquad \rightarrow \text{set of output nodes}$$

$$H = \{h_1, h_2, \ldots, h_{|R|}\} \qquad \rightarrow \text{set of hidden nodes}$$

in which T_{X_h} is the term set associated with the clinical sign X_h and T_{D_k} is the term set associated with the decision class D_k, then the activation of the kth hidden neuron and of the jth output neuron has the following general form:

$$A_k = \left(\frac{\sum_{i=1}^{m} w_1[i][k]^2}{\sum_{i=1}^{n} w_1[i][k]^2} \, x_i^{p_1} \right)^{1/p_1} \qquad A_j = \left(\frac{\sum_{i=1}^{|R|} w_2[i][j]^2}{\sum_{i=1}^{|R|} w_2[i][j]^2} \, h_i^{p_2} \right)^{1/p_2}$$

In the connectionist stage, the network must learn the weights' connections w_1 and w_2 (i.e., the relative importance of each criterion) and, at each level, the proper aggregation connective, i.e., the values of parameters p_1 and p_2, for which the network converges.

The Activation Function as Hybrid Operator. The hybrid operator has the form [20]

$$g(x_1, x_2, \ldots, x_m, \gamma, \delta_1, \delta_2, \ldots, \delta_m) = \left(\prod_{i=1}^{m} x_i^{\delta_i} \right)^{1-\gamma} \left[1 - \prod_{i=1}^{m} (1 - x_i)^{\delta_i} \right]^{\gamma}$$

where the x_i values are inputs to the nodes and the δ_i are the weights related to inputs $(\sum_{i=1}^{m} \delta_i = m)$. The γ parameter $(0 \leq \gamma \leq 1)$ reflects the node's behavior: We see that when γ is close to 1, the neuron functions as an element of "union" whereas when γ is close to 0, the input is an element of "intersection."

The power of the hybrid connective lies in its flexibility in modeling various decision attitudes, choosing the right tradeoff between the union and the intersection elements.

The hybrid operators described above are used as an activation function in the back propagation learning algorithm to train the network.

The classic back propagation learning algorithm has been modified to improve learning accuracy and accelerate the training phase. The central concept of the approach is to introduce a "superfluous" hidden neuron H_{sup}, totally connected with the input and output neurons and activated only when the network processes those elements of the training set that make a significant contribution to error, and to retard the network convergency. To simulate this situation in the network, the unit H_{sup} introduced must assume the value 1; otherwise, the activation of H_{sup} is equal to zero. Figure 25.3 shows the resulting network topology.

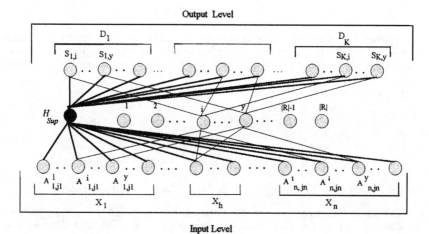

FIGURE 25.3   Introduction of the superfluous node at the intermediate level.

The error of H_{sup} is then evaluated according to the formula

$$E_{H_{\text{sup}}} = V_{H_{\text{sup}}} - H_{|R| + 1}$$

where $V_{H_{\text{sup}}}$ is the expected value of H_{sup} (that is 1 or 0) and $H_{|R| + 1}$ is the activation of H_{sup} calculated by means of the back propagation algorithm.

25.2.4   Integration from Connectionist to Symbolic Stage

In the final connectionist to symbolic stage, the topology and parameters of the trained neural network are used to infer the final set R' of decision rules in the knowledge base. This determines a refinement of the initial set of rules, reducing the number of rules and providing a final appropriate interpretation of the logical connective *and* in the rule antecedents.

25.3 A FUZZY EXPERT SYSTEM SHELL

A hybrid system-building tool for decision support in medical diagnosis has been designed and implemented on the basis of the strategy presented above. Figure 25.4 represents the modular architecture of the system. Each module implements a specific task of the strategy and is organized in other submodules. The interaction between the system and the user is supported by a user-friendly interface which frees the user of the technicalities of encoding knowledge and allows information to be entered as visual representations which correspond to the way physicians seem to think about diagnostic tasks.

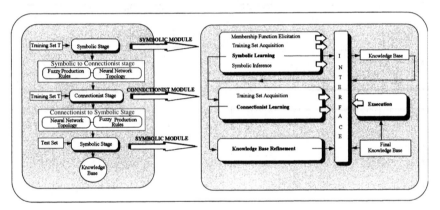

FIGURE 25.4   System architecture.

25.3.1 Application: Diagnosis of Hyperandrogenism

A detailed description of an application in the domain of hyperandrogenism in women gives a clearer idea of how the expert system shell works. In the complex clinical presentation of this pathology, various indicators, such as hematochemical parameters, are easily determined, while the assessment of hirsutism, which is essential for the formulation of diagnostic judgments, is an intricate and sophisticated task.

The question is usually approached as if there were a clear dividing line between hirsutism and normality, and it is based on visual inspection of several body sites. Body hair growth is, however, a graded characteristic. The problem of assessment becomes a matter of selecting suitable sites for study and the choice of a method for grading hair growth in any given site.

The methods commonly used for grading hair growth are based on a crisp evaluation of visual signs, providing numerical gradings for each site. Hair growth is scored according to the sum of the gradings obtained [21].

The resulting discrepancies and unpredictable subjectivity of expert opinions have suggested that a fuzzy medical expert system could better guarantee an objective, explicit, and deterministic support to the diagnostic process.

The overall diagnostic problem underlying this application can be broken down into a hierarchy of metadiagnostic tasks:

- First level: Clinical assessment of hirsutism—visual evaluation of three clinical signs (density, consistency, area) in nine different body sites. A metadiagnosis is made for each body site.
- Second level: Global diagnosis of hirsutism—aggregation of first-level diagnostic judgments.

A sequence of machine-aided steps characterizes the overall knowledge acquisition and representation process. The automated support of the diagnosis of hirsutism considers nine sites (Fig. 25.5) which, in the cognitive process, are evaluated as metasigns.

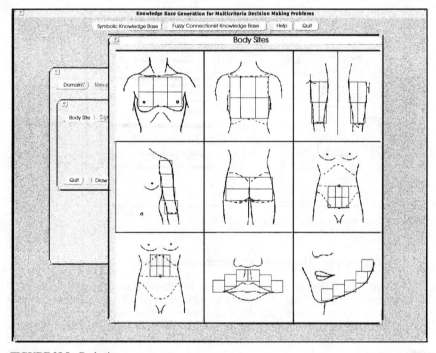

FIGURE 25.5 Body sites.

For each body site, the clinical signs listed in Fig. 25.6 are introduced. Clinical signs are encoded in the system knowledge base as linguistic variables. The linguistic qualification of the sign *density* of the chin body site is illustrated in Fig. 25.7. The linguistic terms introduced are valued as fuzzy sets.

The difficulties encountered in creating fuzzy sets for these signs are due principally to the global visual perception underlying the clinical evaluation. Visual data, in the form of scenes and pictures, are often processed in visual terms alone, without any

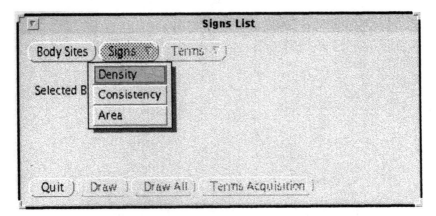

FIGURE 25.6   Clinical signs.

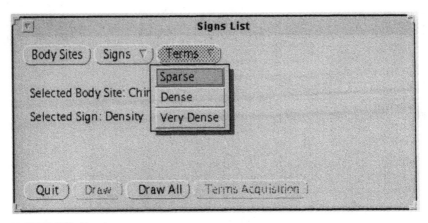

FIGURE 25.7   Density term set.

corresponding translation or recording as verbal labels or representations [22]. This is a crucial aspect in the elicitation of fuzzy sets for the sign *area*. Experts are unable to qualify it linguistically and require contextual information before they can provide reliable evaluations. We addressed the problem by implementing a graphical interface displaying all the elements of the body as parts of an integrated whole, and not as separate and independent items. Figure 25.8 shows the interface window designed for the acquisition of membership functions related to the sign *area* evaluated in the chin site.

The global region of interest was divided into five items, and progressive combinations of these items were displayed. They constituted the range on which the membership functions for the linguistic terms *nonsignificant, medium,* and *significant* were defined. Because it was impossible to procure explicit descriptions of the sign *area,* these terms were semantically related to a *metadiagnosis* in which the experts evaluated (together with the *area, consistency,* and *density*) parameters. Employing the membership function exemplification method [23], the experts were then asked to express the compatibility of each term with each combination of items by answering yes or no and assigning a number from 0 to 5 to indicate the degree of

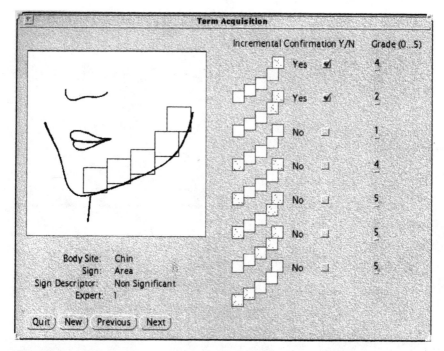

FIGURE 25.8   Elicitation of the membership function of fuzzy sets for the sign *area*.

confidence in the answer. The collected data were then processed to produce the representative value $\mu_t(x)$ of the membership function for the term t and the combination of area items x using the formula

$$\mu_t(x) = \frac{1}{2} + d \times \frac{r}{10}$$

where $d-1$ if the answer was yes and $d = 0$ if the answer was no. The degrees $\mu_t(x)$, quantifying each expert's opinion of the compatibility between the linguistic term t and the crisp value assumed by the clinical sign concerned, were aggregated. Several measures were used to group the different answers; among these were the mean, median, expected value, and fuzzy expected value. Of all these, only the fuzzy expected value seemed to give consistent results: Extreme values did not greatly affect it, as they did the other measures, and it provided, despite the great variability in answers, a measure indicative of a general trend [24].

Figure 25.9 shows membership functions for the sign *density* obtained by applying a spline-based fitting operation on the representative values computed with the fuzzy expected value.

At the symbolic and connectionist levels, the system must be provided with a training set of examples for the generation of rules and network training. The interface window that supports experts in this phase can be seen in Fig. 25.10. Figure 25.11 shows the pop-up widget that supports the user in rule generation. Some 30 fuzzy production rules were generated for each body site.

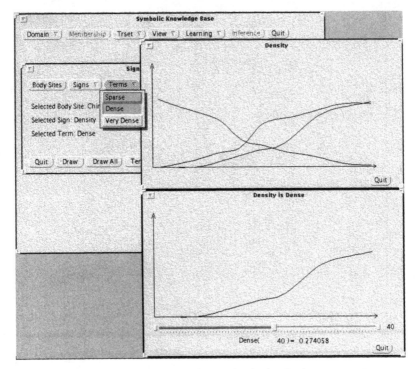

FIGURE 25.9 Membership function of fuzzy sets for the sign *density*.

At the end of the symbolic stage, a deductive inference mechanism (Fig. 25.12) can be selected to test the performance of the tentative knowledge base that has been generated. The main window at the connectionist stage of the strategy is shown in Fig. 25.13.

The network topology has been automatically defined by the system; the user must introduce, by means of a text-field widget, only some learning coefficients.

25.3.2 Results

The application to the diagnosis of hyperandrogenism provides a quantitative and a qualitative evaluation of the knowledge acquisition and representation strategy described in this chapter.

Table 25.1 shows the numerical results for the first level of the overall diagnostic process. It lists for each body site the magnitude of the different training sets evaluated at the symbolic and connectionist stages and the magnitude of the test sets used in the connectionist stage. The evaluation procedure uses the training data to measure the learning power and the testing data to measure the testing power. The results produced a mean diagnostic accuracy of 88.5 percent in the training phase and 84.5 percent in test phase.

The overall diagnosis was made by aggregating the metadiagnostic results shown above; this implied the definition of a new neural network. Final diagnostic system

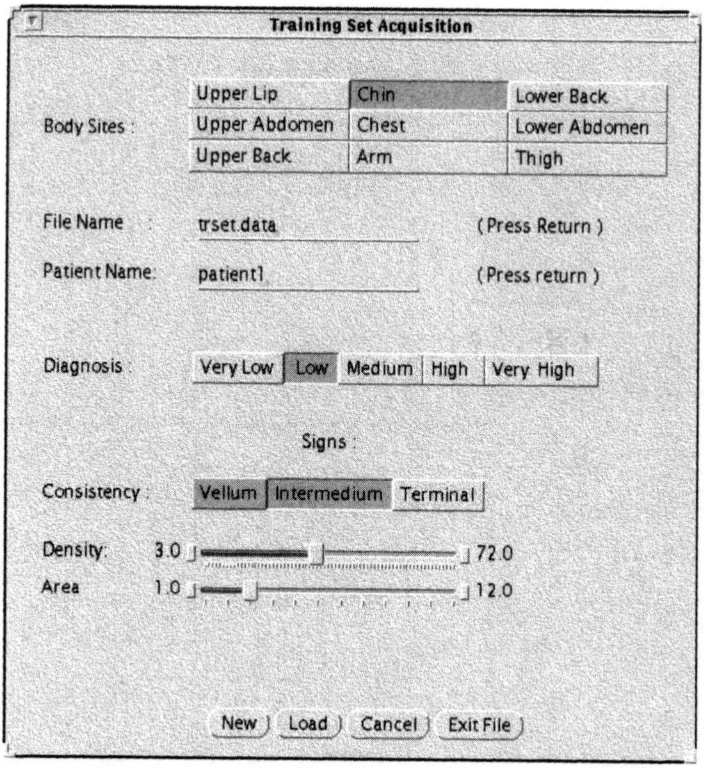

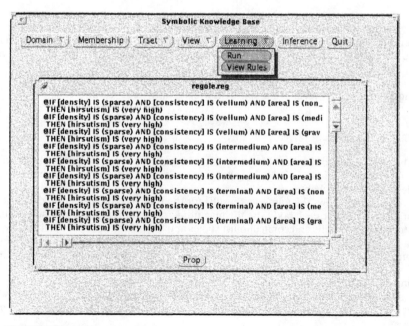

FIGURE 25.10 Training set acquisition.

FIGURE 25.11 Rule generation.

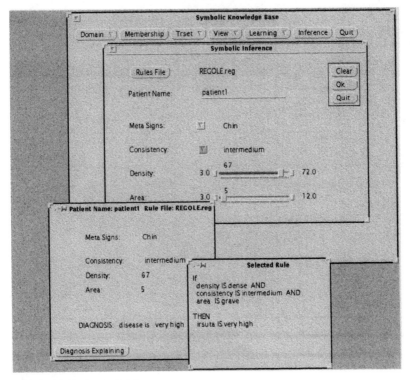

FIGURE 25.12 Symbolic inference.

results have been compared with clinical diagnosis regarding 100 cases. The results coincided in 83.8 percent of cases.

Note that the results shown above have been reached by applying the generalized mean operator as an activation function in the networks. Despite its major accuracy in other domains, the second operator investigated has given some implementation troubles due to its analytical form.

25.4 CONCLUDING REMARKS

Medical diagnosis has been considered a cognitive process and modeled within a hybrid fuzzy logic framework. This made it possible to handle the inherent fuzziness of medical concepts and to formalize expert-derived and data-derived knowledge in a relaxed form, close to the mental representation of physicians.

The application developed has proved the flexibility and efficiency of the hybrid strategy in automating the diagnostic process. It also demonstrates the efficiency of the implemented shell in developing a specific application. Some drawbacks of the hybrid method must, however, be mentioned: Its dependence on the goodness of the data available for training the network limits the predictability of its performance in specific applications. But it provides all the advantages of the integration of symbolic

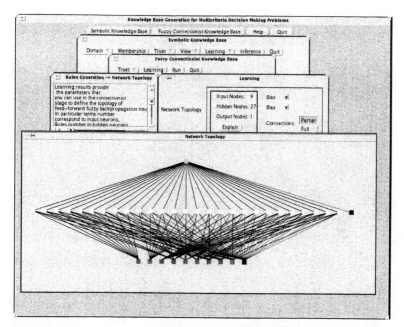

FIGURE 25.13   From rule generation to network topology.

and connectionist techniques. The symbolic representation of medical diagnostic knowledge is enhanced by the automatic refining of the aggregation operators and identification of the relative importance of the clinical signs involved. The network becomes an optimal tool, using the symbolic structure of diagnostic rules to infer its initial topology.

TABLE 25.1   Results

Body sites	Symbolic stage		Connectionist stage			
	Training set	Rules	Training set	Test set	Learning power, %	Testing power, %
Chin	40	27	74	40	88	84
Chest	60	27	126	40	87	84
Arm	50	27	99	40	90	87
Upper lip	40	27	41	20	90	85
Upper back	60	27	126	55	88	83
Lower back	60	27	126	55	90	85
Upper abdomen	60	27	126	55	87	83
Lower abdomen	60	27	126	55	90	85
Thigh	60	27	126	55	87	85

REFERENCES

1. Szolovits, P., R. S. Patil, and W. B. Schwartz, "Artificial Intelligence in Medical Diagnosis," *Annals of Internal Medicine,* vol. 108, pp. 80–87, 1988.

2. Binaghi, E., O. De Giorgi, G. Maggi, T. Motta, and A. Rampini, "Computer-Assisted Diagnosis of Post-Menopausal Osteoporosis Using a Fuzzy Expert System Shell," *Computer and Biomedical Research,* vol. 26, pp. 498–516, 1993.

3. Zadeh, L. A., "Fuzzy Sets," *Information and Control,* vol. 8, pp. 338–353, 1965.

4. Binaghi, E., "Fuzzy Logic-Based Tools for the Acquisition and Representation of Knowledge in Biomedical Applications," in A. N. Venetsanopulos and S. Tzafestas, eds., *Fuzzy Reasoning in Information, Decision and Control Systems,* MBISE series, Kluwer Academic Publishers, Dordrecht, Netherlands, 1993, pp. 529–551.

5. Kandel, A., and G. Langholz, eds., *Hybrid Architectures for Intelligent Systems,* CRC Press, Boca Raton, FL, 1992.

6. Machado, R. J., and A. F. Rocha, "A Hybrid Architecture for a Fuzzy Connectionist Expert System," in A. Kandel and G. Langholz, eds., *Hybrid Architecture for Intelligent Systems,* CRC Press, Boca Raton, FL, 1992, pp. 135–152.

7. Hudson, D. L., M. E. Cohen, P. W. Banda, and M. S. Blois, "Medical Diagnosis and Treatment Plans Derived from a Hybrid Expert System," in A. Kandel and G. Langholz, eds., *Hybrid Architecture for Intelligent Systems,* CRC Press, Boca Raton, FL, 1992, pp. 329–344.

8. Pedrycs, W., "Fuzzy Sets in Pattern Recognition: Methodology and Methods," *Pattern Recognition,* vol. 23, pp. 121–146, 1990.

9. Zadeh, L. A., "PRUF—A Meaning Representation Language for Natural Languages," in E. H. Mamdani and B. R. Gaines, eds., *Fuzzy Reasoning and Its Applications,* Academic Press, London, 1981, pp. 1–58.

10. Hall, L., S. Szabo, and A. Kandel, "On the Derivation of Memberships for Fuzzy Sets in Expert Systems," *Information Science,* vol. 40, pp. 39–52, 1986.

11. Civanlar, M. R., and H. J. Trussel, "Constructing Membership Functions Using Statistical Data," *Fuzzy Sets and Systems,* vol. 18, pp. 1–13, 1986.

12. Binaghi, E., "A Fuzzy Logic Inference Model for a Rule-Based System in Medical Diagnosis," *Expert System,* vol. 7, pp. 134–141, 1990.

13. Zimmermann, H. J., and P. Zysno, "Latent Connectives in Human Decision Making," *Fuzzy Sets and Systems,* vol. 4, pp. 37–51, 1980.

14. Binaghi, E., "Empirical Learning for Fuzzy Knowledge Acquisition," in *Proceedings of 2d International Conference on Fuzzy Logic and Neural Networks,* IIzuka, Japan, 1992, pp. 245 251

15. Binaghi, E., "Learning of Uncertainty Classification Rules in Medical Diagnosis," in R. Kruse, ed., *Symbolic and Quantitative Approaches to Uncertainty,* 548, Lecture Notes in Computer Science, Springer-Verlag, New York, 1991, pp. 115–119.

16. Rumelhart, D. E., G. E. Hinton, and R. J. Williams, "Learning Internal Representation by Error Propagation," in D. E. Rumelhart and J. L. McClelland, eds., *Parallel Distributed Processing,* MIT Press, Cambridge, MA, 1986, pp. 319–362.

17. Krishnapuram, R., and J. Lee, "Fuzzy Set-Based Hierarchical Networks for Information Fusion in Computer Vision," *Neural Networks,* vol. 5, pp. 335–350, 1992.

18. Dubois, D., and H. Prade, "A Review of Fuzzy Set Aggregation Connectives," *Information Science,* vol. 36, pp. 85–121, 1985.

19. Dyckhoff, H., and W. Pedrycz, "Generalized Means as a Model of Compensation Connectives," *Fuzzy Sets and Systems,* vol. 14, pp. 147–158, 1984.

20. Zimmermann, H. J., and P. Zysno, "Decision and Evaluations by Hierarchical Aggregation of Information," *Fuzzy Sets and Systems,* vol. 10, pp. 243–260, 1983.

21. Ferriman, D. M., and J. D. Gallwey, "Clinical Assessment of Body Hair Growth in Women," *Journal of Clinical Endocrine Metabolism,* vol. 21, pp. 1440–1447, 1961.

22. Freedman, J., and R. N. Haber, "One Reason Why We Rarely Forget a Face," *Bulletin of Psychonomic Sociology,* vol. 3, pp. 107–109, 1974.

23. Chameau, J., and J. Santamarina, "Membership Functions I: Comparing Methods of Measurements," *International Journal of Approximate Reasoning,* vol. 1, pp. 288–317, 1987.

24. Pal, S. K., "Fuzzy Tools for the Management of Uncertainty in Pattern Recognition, Image Analysis Vision and Expert Systems," *International Journal of System Science,* vol. 22, pp. 511–549, 1991.

CHAPTER 26

CEREBELLAR MODEL ARITHMETIC COMPUTER

W. Thomas Miller, III
Filson H. Glanz
Robotics Laboratory
University of New Hampshire, Durham

This chapter discusses the *cerebellar model arithmetic computer* (*CMAC*), a neural network based on the concept of sensory encoding using local receptive fields. The chapter opens by describing the characteristics, advantages, and disadvantages of CMAC and by giving some guidelines on when CMAC is appropriate to use for an application. The original Albus CMAC is described next so that the user has a basic understanding of how CMAC works. This section and the following one are organized in such a way that computer code can be written from the description. Then these variations on the Albus CMAC are described and advantages and disadvantages are given: weight center placements, nonrectangular basis functions, and input space adaptation. There follows a section on the general capabilities of CMAC, answering the questions, How much can it learn? How well can it learn? How well can it generalize? and What can it learn? A subsequent section discusses configuring CMAC for your application, including information on input scaling, and approaches to the training of the CMAC. Finally, a listing of applications with references classified by area and a general References section are presented.

26.1 BACKGROUND

This chapter covers the cerebellar model arithmetic computer, or CMAC, which is a type of neural network based on the Perceptron of Rosenblatt [1] as interpreted by Albus [2]. In this section we will give a short description of CMAC, including some of its characteristics, advantages, and disadvantages and when it is appropriate or not to use. There follows a short history of CMAC and a comparison of CMAC to other neural networks. In subsequent sections we will explain how the standard CMAC works (outlined so code could be written from the explanation), discuss a few variations on CMAC, explore the general capabilities of CMAC, comment on configuring

CMAC for your application, and provide a listing of some of the known applications of CMAC in the literature.

26.1.1 A Short Description of CMAC Characteristics

Here are some of the characteristics of CMAC:

- Real inputs (but quantized) and real outputs (analog or quantized)
- Built-in local generalization
- Can be trained in practical time (training time does not increase radically with dimension)
- Uses least mean square training and has been proved to converge to the one minimum error
- Can learn a wide variety of functions with some approximation
- Obeys output superposition
- Can get errors down to the level of the input sensor quantization in real systems
- Can imprint-learn in one training cycle under certain conditions

Advantages and Disadvantages. CMAC has a number of advantages. Because of its fast convergence it is appropriate for real-time use. Because the error surface has no local minima, it can learn nonlinear functions at least approximately. There is little learning interference due to the nature of its local generalization.

Disadvantages include the fact that hashing collisions can cause a noise or interference in learning if they are not handled correctly. CMAC has some biological rationale, but is not a true biological model. Furthermore, heavily scaled versions of previously learned inputs do not generalize, but must be learned.

When Is CMAC Appropriate to Use? CMAC has a great advantage in applications to real-time control because of its computational speed. Furthermore, applications with large numbers of inputs (say, 10 to 256) and large input spaces can be realized more easily with CMAC. Other situations where CMAC is advantageous include situations where local generalization is appropriate, where generalization in time is appropriate, or where incremental learning is appropriate. CMAC is *not* appropriate in situations where one expects to get good generalization from a heavily scaled version of a vector which has been already trained, as might be expected for a standard Perceptron [1] or Adaline [3] if the output nonlinearity is appropriate. Nor is it appropriate as a pure biological model. In batch off-line training, CMAC loses some of its advantage because speed is not so important, but still its generalization characteristics may be advantageous. For very large numbers of input components, CMAC is not especially good because generalization cannot be made large enough without leading to too much computation and memory storage.

26.1.2 History and Background of CMAC

James Albus developed CMAC while doing his dissertation research in the early 1970s, and he published several comprehensive papers [4–6] and a book [7] on his broad concepts of CMAC in the late 1970s. This work was the outgrowth of his biological study of the brain and was based on the Perceptron of Rosenblatt [1]. In the early 1980s, a group in Germany [8, 9] started describing the use of CMAC for some control applications, especially chemical control where speed is not so important a consideration (control periods of seconds). Also in the early 1980s our group at the University of New Hampshire [10] rediscovered CMAC in the literature (or, more accurately, discovered that the standard description in most literature surveys—that CMAC was impractical—was in fact wrong). It was shown that CMAC not only was practical but also solved many problems that the multilayer Perceptron could not do in real time. More recently, there have been several other groups working on various aspects of CMAC theory and application (see Sec. 26.6).

26.1.3 CMAC in Relation to Other Neural Networks

A comparison of CMAC to multilayer Perceptrons (using back propagation), or MLPs, shows that local generalization is characteristic of CMAC while global generalization characterizes MLPs. This means less learning interference and no hope of generalization for inputs distant from any training vector when CMAC is used, but there is the possibility of generalization for distant inputs when MLPs are used. It also means that CMAC can imprint and one-step learn where MLPs cannot. Also, CMAC training takes orders of magnitude less time than MLP training. Furthermore, MLP training may converge to a local minimum whereas the CMAC error surface has a single minimum.

Radial-basis function (*RBF*) neural networks have much in common with CMAC. They both have local generalization and a compact set of bases and receptive fields. But CMAC has many standard bases placed in a standard, regular array while RBFs use a minimum number put at the best places in a data-driven, adaptive approach.

A comparison of CMAC to Hopfield networks shows that CMAC is a feedforward network which can be used with feedback while the Hopfield network is by nature a feedback network. The training of a Hopfield network is a pure calculation (not iterative) while CMAC training is an iterative process. This also means that Hopfield training is by nature a batch process while CMAC is a natural on-line network.

It is not possible to compare CMAC to the many specific networks crafted by neural network researchers. However, it is worth mentioning that CMAC, because of its unique structure, can be thought of as a large number of individual neurons connected in local physical areas according to the region in the input space. This means that those neurons which correspond in a particular generalization region act as if they were biological neurons close together in the neural system.

26.2 THE ALBUS CMAC

In this section we review the basic operating principles of the CMAC neural network as proposed by Albus [2, 4–7]. We then present a mathematical description of the conventional CMAC in a form intended to facilitate software implementation. The notation used is somewhat different from that in the original Albus papers, but the set of equations presented is numerically equivalent to the original Albus algorithm.

26.2.1   General Operation of the Albus CMAC

The operation of the Albus CMAC [2, 4–7, 11] can be most easily described in terms of a large set of overlapping, multidimensional receptive fields with finite boundaries (Fig. 26.1). Any input vector falls within the range of some of the local receptive fields (the excited receptive fields), and falls outside of the range of most of the receptive fields. The response of the CMAC neural network to a given input is the average of the responses of the receptive fields excited by that input, and is not affected by the other receptive fields. Similarly, neural network training for a given input vector affects the adjustable parameters of the excited receptive fields, but does not affect the parameters of the remaining majority of receptive fields.

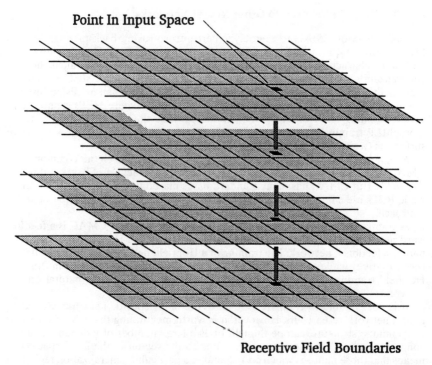

Point In Input Space

Receptive Field Boundaries

FIGURE 26.1   Albus CMAC receptive field distribution for two-dimensional input with generalization $C = 4$.

Figure 26.1 depicts the organization of the receptive fields of a typical Albus CMAC neural network with a two-dimensional input space. The total collection of receptive fields is divided into C subsets, drawn as parallel layers in the figure (parallel N-dimensional hyperspaces for a network with N inputs). The receptive fields in each of the layers have rectangular boundaries and are organized so as to span the input space without overlap. Each input vector excites one receptive field from each layer (shown by the projecting vertical bar in the figure), for a total of C excited receptive fields for any input. Each layer of the receptive field is identical in organization, but each layer is offset relative to the others in the input hyperspace. The width of the receptive fields produces input generalization, while the offset of the adjacent layers of receptive fields produces input quantization. The ratio of the width of each receptive field (input generalization) to the offset between adjacent layers of receptive fields (input quantization) must be equal to C for all dimensions of the input space. The integer parameter C is called the *generalization parameter*.

This organization of the receptive fields guarantees that only a fixed number C of receptive fields are excited by any input. However, the total number of receptive fields required to span the input space can still be large for many practical problems. On the other hand, it is unlikely that the entire input state space of a large system would be visited in solving a specific problem. Thus it is not necessary to store unique information for each receptive field. Following this logic, most implementations of the Albus CMAC include some form of pseudorandom hashing, so that only information about receptive fields that have been excited during previous training is actually stored.

Each receptive field in the Albus CMAC is assumed to be an on/off type of entity. If a receptive field is excited, its response is equal to the magnitude of a single adjustable weight specific to that receptive field. If a receptive field is not excited, its response is zero. The CMAC output is thus the average of the adjustable weights of the excited receptive fields. If nearby points in the input space excite the same receptive fields, they produce the same output value. The output changes only when the input crosses one of the receptive field boundaries (Fig. 26.1). The Albus CMAC neural network thus produces piecewise-constant outputs.

The implementation of the Albus CMAC logically proceeds as follows:

1. Identify the C receptive fields excited by the input.
2. Find the C adjustable weights for those receptive fields in a pool of stored weights.
3. Compute the average of the C adjustable weights.

26.2.2 Albus CMAC Computation

Consider a classic Albus CMAC neural network with a real-valued input vector

$$\mathbf{S} = <s_1, s_2, \ldots, s_N> \tag{26.1}$$

in an N-dimensional input space. Assume that the generalization parameter (the number of simultaneously excited receptive fields for each input) is C. The first step of the CMAC computation is to form a normalized integer input vector $\mathbf{S}'$ by dividing each component s_j of the input vector by an appropriate *quantization parameter* Δ_j.

$$\mathbf{S}' = <s_1', s_2', \ldots, s_N'> = <\text{int}\left(\frac{s_1}{\Delta_1}\right), \text{int}\left(\frac{s_2}{\Delta_2}\right), \ldots, \text{int}\left(\frac{s_N}{\Delta_N}\right)> \tag{26.2}$$

The width of each receptive field along the jth axis is equal to $C * \Delta_j$ in the original input space and is equal to C along all axes in the normalized input space.

The next step of the CMAC computation is to form the vector addresses, $\mathbf{A}_i$ of the C receptive fields which contain the input point $\mathbf{S}'$:

$$\mathbf{A}_i = <s_1' - [(s_1' - i) \,\%\, C], s_2' - [(s_2' - i) \,\%\, C], \ldots, s_N' - [(s_N' - i) \,\%\, C]> \quad i = 1, 2, \ldots, C$$

$$= <a_{i1}, a_{i2}, \ldots, a_{iN}> \tag{26.3}$$

where % represents the modulus operator and the index i references the C parallel layers of receptive fields. And $\mathbf{A}_i$ is the normalized N-dimensional address of one corner of the hypercubic region spanned by the single excited receptive field in layer i. Due to the properties of the modulus operator, the receptive field address components in the above equation are only valid for $s_j' - i$ positive. A similar expression can be easily formulated, however, for $s_j' - i$ negative.

Since the total number of receptive fields in a space of dimension N can be quite large, the receptive field addresses $\mathbf{A}_i$ are typically considered as virtual rather than physical addresses. The next step of the CMAC computation is to form the scalar physical addresses A_i' of the actual adjustable weights to be used in the output computation:

$$A_i' = h(a_{i1}, a_{i2}, \ldots, a_{iN}) \tag{26.4}$$

In this equation, $h(\ldots)$ represents any pseudorandom hashing function which operates on the components a_{ij} of the virtual addresses of the receptive fields, producing uniformly distributed scalar addresses in the physical weight memory of size M (see Sec. 26.3.3).

Finally, the CMAC scalar output $y(\mathbf{S})$ is just the average of the addressed weights:

$$y(\mathbf{S}) = \frac{1}{C} \sum_{i=1}^{C} W[A_i'] \tag{26.5}$$

A vector CMAC output is produced by simply considering the weight memory locations to contain vector rather than scalar values and by performing a vector rather than scalar average in the above equation. The weight memory W can contain integer or real values, depending on the desired implementation.

Network training is typically based on observed training data pairs $\mathbf{S}$ and $y_d(\mathbf{S})$, where $y_d(\mathbf{S})$ is the desired network output in response to the vector input $\mathbf{S}$. The memory training adjustment ΔW is given by

$$\Delta W = \beta * [y_d(\mathbf{S}) - y(\mathbf{S})] \tag{26.6}$$

where the same value ΔW is added to each of the C memory locations $W[A_i']$ accessed in the computation of $y(\mathbf{S})$. This is equivalent to the well-known LMS adaptation rule for linear adaptive elements. And β is a constant *training gain*. If β is 1.0, the weights are adjusted to force the network output $y(\mathbf{S})$ to be exactly equal to the training target $y_d(\mathbf{S})$. If β is 0.5, the network output is adjusted to fall halfway between the old output value and the training target. If β is 0.0, the weights are not changed.

Figure 26.2 shows the results of training a single-input, single-output conventional CMAC neural network using a test nonlinear function. The piecewise-constant nature of the approximation is obvious. The granularity of the piecewise-constant approximation is dependent on the adjustment Δ_j used for the input vector quantization.

26.3 EXTENSIONS TO THE ALBUS CMAC NEURAL NETWORK

In this section we discuss extensions to the conventional Albus CMAC neural network. When appropriate, modifications to the equations of Sec. 26.2.2 are presented

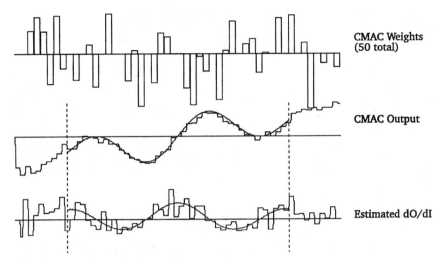

FIGURE 26.2 Results of training a single-input, single-output Albus CMAC on a test nonlinear function. Both the CMAC output and the estimated derivative of the CMAC output with respect to the input are shown against the ideal values for the test function.

in a form intended to facilitate software implementation. When all these extensions are implemented, the algorithms and learning system performance can be quite different from that of the conventional Albus CMAC. However, the extensions are faithful to the original learning system concepts of Albus and thus are still appropriately called CMAC algorithms. Note that some of the frequently described limitations of CMAC (such as learning only integer mappings) are in fact characteristics specific to the original Albus algorithm and are neither properties of nor limitations of the general CMAC concept.

26.3.1 Organization of Receptive Fields

The descriptions in Sec. 26.2 apply to the classic Albus CMAC [2, 4–7]. Research at the University of New Hampshire [12–14] and elsewhere [14, 15] has investigated alternative lattice arrangements for the receptive fields which provide more uniform local generalization in higher-dimensional input spaces. Figure 26.1 and the corresponding text present the arrangement of the receptive fields used in the conventional CMAC implementation. This mapping has three key features which it is desirable to retain:

1. Each input in the multidimensional input state space falls into exactly the same number of receptive fields (C), and this number of overlapping fields is not dependent on the dimensionality N of the space or the total size M of the physical weight memory.

2. Regardless of the operating point in multidimensional space, a change of one quantization level Δ_j in any input parameter causes exactly one active receptive field to become inactive and one new receptive field to become active. This provides for uniform quantization within the space.

3. The receptive fields are arranged in a geometrically regular way, such that the coordinates of the C excited receptive fields for any input can be easily determined in software, or generated in hardware, without having to compare to independent coordinates stored for each of the very many receptive fields.

The conventional Albus CMAC implementation (Figs. 26.1 and Fig. 26.3) achieves these properties by offsetting the parallel layers of receptive fields along hyperdiagonals in the input space [the effect of the $s_j' - i$ terms in Eq. (26.3)]. All inputs fall within the same number of receptive fields. However, some inputs fall near the centers of several receptive fields while other inputs fall near the centers of no receptive fields. This results in inhomogeneous and anisotropic generalization within the input state space. Ideally, the distribution of receptive fields should be uniform in the multidimensional input space unless prior knowledge of the function to be learned dictates otherwise.

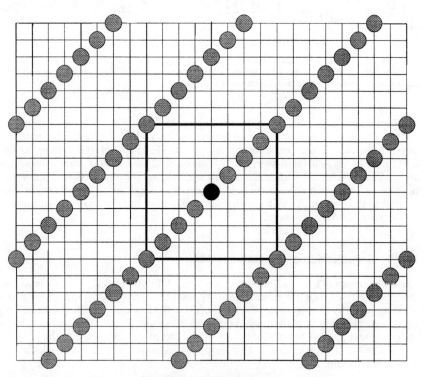

Albus CMAC Mapping
Generalization C = 8
Displacement Vector = <1,1>

FIGURE 26.3 Example of Albus CMAC receptive field distributions for a two-dimensional input and generalization of $C = 8$. Each shaded circle represents the center of a receptive field. The center and boundary of a single receptive field are darkened for reference.

The above three desirable features of the CMAC mapping can be used to place constraints on the possible arrangements of receptive fields, through which new arrangements can be generated. For the following discussion, assume that the N-dimensional input space has been normalized by using Eq. (26.2) such that the widths of the receptive fields relative to all N components of the input are equal to C (the generalization parameter). The first and third items above suggest that the arrangement should be periodic in the normalized input space, with period C. This is equivalent to assuming that the receptive fields will be arranged in C parallel layers, each with nonoverlapping receptive fields, as shown in Fig. 26.1, and that only the offsets of each layer relative to the others can be varied when new receptive field distributions are generated. In this case, the distribution of receptive fields throughout the space is uniquely defined by the arrangement of C receptive field centers in an N-dimensional hypercube of side C (referred to as the *reference hypercube*), with one receptive field centered at the corner of the hypercube (coordinate $<0, 0, \ldots, 0>$).

The individual receptive fields are hypercubes of side C in the normalized input space, and C receptive field centers are located inside any region bounded by a hypercube of side C. Item 2 in the above list (uniform segmentation of the space) is thus achieved only if the C receptive field centers are spaced uniformly (with integer separation) when projected onto each of the N axes of the reference hypercube. Any arrangement which satisfies these criteria qualifies as a CMAC mapping, according to the three items above. However, many of the possible arrangements (such as the conventional CMAC mapping) have locally nonuniform distributions.

Parks and Militzer [15] studied the arrangement of receptive fields in CMAC networks, using distance between nearest neighbors as the evaluation criterion, based on the assumption that the most uniform distribution would have the greatest distance between nearest neighbors (given a fixed receptive field density in the space). They further assumed that the receptive field centers were arranged in a lattice defined by a *displacement vector*

$$\mathbf{D} = <d_1, d_2, \ldots, d_N> \tag{26.7}$$

such that the coordinate of the ith receptive field in the reference hypercube was

$$<(i * d_1) \% C, (i * d_2) \% C, \ldots, (i * d_N) \% C> \qquad i = 1, 2, \ldots, C \tag{26.8}$$

In these terms, the conventional CMAC would be defined by a lattice displacement vector of

$$\mathbf{D}_{\text{Albus}} = <1, 1, \ldots, 1> \tag{26.9}$$

They performed an exhaustive search of such lattice arrangements for various values of C and N, and they developed tables of best displacement vectors according to their nearest-neighbor distance criterion.

We have developed a simple heuristic for selecting similar displacement vectors for any values of C and N which provide lattice arrangements equivalent to those found by Parks and Militzer [14] without performing a search [12–14]. First, we choose the set of integers in the range 1 to $C/2$ which are not factors of C or integer products of factors of C (the value 1 can be included in the set). These are the candidate values for the displacement vector components (guaranteeing uniform projection of the centers on the axes of the reference hypercube), from which N must be selected. If there are more than N candidate values, we choose N (there are multiple nearly equivalent arrangements). If there are less than N candidates, the best that can be done is to use all the candidate values with a minimum number of repetitions of any one value. However, the resulting mapping will be diagonalized (locally nonuniform) in some projections to lower-dimension spaces. A better solution in this case is to increase C, in order to achieve at least N candidates for the displacement vector.

For a CMAC with a three-dimensional input and a generalization of 16, the candidate values for the displacement vector are 1, 3, 5, and 7. A typical displacement vector might be <1, 3, 5> which would produce receptive field locations at <0, 0, 0>, <1, 3, 5>, <2, 6, 10>, and so forth, within the reference cube. Figures 26.3 and 26.4 show examples of receptive field distributions for conventional Albus CMAC and modified CMAC neural networks with a two-dimensional input and a generalization C of 8.

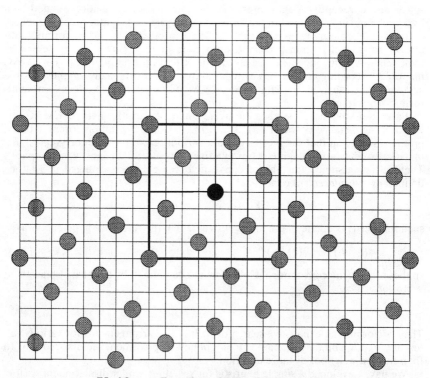

Uniform Lattice CMAC Mapping
Generalization C = 8
Displacement Vector = <1,3>

FIGURE 26.4 Example of a modified CMAC receptive field distribution for a two-dimensional input and generalization of $C = 8$. Each shaded circle represents the center of a receptive field. The center and boundary of a single receptive field are darkened for reference.

The CMAC computations described in Sec. 26.2.2 can be easily modified to accommodate the displacement vector approach to specifying receptive field placement. In this case, the virtual addresses of the excited receptive fields are given by

$$\mathbf{A}_i = <s'_1 - \{[(s'_1 - i) * d_1] \% C\}, s'_2 - \{[(s'_2 - i) * d_2] \% C\}, \ldots, s'_N$$

$$- \{[(s'_N - i) * d_N] \% C\}>$$

$$= <a_{i1}, a_{i2}, \ldots, a_{iN}> \qquad i = 1, 2, \ldots, C \tag{26.10}$$

in place of Eq. (26.3). Due to the properties of the modulus operator, the receptive field address components in the above equation are valid only for $(s'_j - i) * d_j$ positive. A similar expression can be easily formulated, however, for $(s'_j - i) * d_j$ negative.

It is impossible to quantify the improvement in performance to be gained in the general case by using a relatively uniform lattice of receptive fields, rather than the diagonalized arrangement used by Albus. In our experience, a more uniform arrangement of receptive fields typically provides learning system performance equal to or better than that achieved in the same application by using the Albus arrangement (sometimes substantially better), with relatively little increase in computational effort. We typically select C to be the smallest power of 2 which is equal to or greater than $4*N$, in which case a good displacement vector is simply the first N odd integers [12].

26.3.2 Receptive Field Sensitivity Functions

We have also investigated CMAC networks with graded, rather than all-or-none, receptive field sensitivity functions [12–14], as have others [16]. In this case, the CMAC output is influenced more by receptive fields for which the input vector is near the center of the active range and is influenced less by receptive fields for which the input is near the limits of the active range. The CMAC output is then a weighted average of the C addressed adjustable parameters, rather than a simple average as in Eq. (26.5). This provides a continuous function approximation (rather than the piecewise-constant function approximation shown in Fig. 26.2). Any function which is maximum at the center and decreases smoothly to near zero at the edges is satisfactory (e.g., linear decrease) for generating continuous outputs. Smooth outputs require that the slope of the function also approach zero near the receptive field edges (e.g., cubic spline, gaussian). The critical issue is how to form the multidimensional receptive field sensitivity function from the one-dimensional primitives.

An obvious choice would be to simply base the receptive field sensitivity function on the radial distance from the center of the receptive field. Although there is substantial evidence supporting the use of radial-basis functions for general system approximation [17, 18], the fixed, relatively sparse distribution of receptive fields inherent in CMAC-family networks must be considered. In the normalized input space defined in the previous section, each CMAC receptive field spans the interior of a hypercube of side C. The distance from the center to the nearest edge (the center of a face of the hypercube) of the receptive field is $C/2$, while the distance from the center to the farthest edge (a corner of the hypercube) is $N^{1/2}C/2$. A radial-basis function which tapers to a small value at the nearest edge of the receptive field will be very small in most of the corner region, confining the significant response to a limited region of the hypothetical receptive field. On the other hand, if the radial-basis function tapers to a small value at the corner, it will have a significant output at the nearest edge of the receptive field, which is counter to the objective of a tapered receptive field.

A second alternative is to use the distance from the input point to the nearest face of the receptive field as the single parameter in the sensitivity function (rather than the radial distance from the center). This provides a receptive field sensitivity function which is maximum at the center and which has the same value at all points on its boundary. The sensitivity function will be continuous throughout the receptive field, but will have discontinuous slopes along select hyperplanes. We have found this to be the preferred alternative for CMAC neural networks [12]. Figure 26.5 shows two-dimensional gaussian receptive field sensitivity functions for radially symmetric and minimum-distance-to-edge metrics. Figure 26.6 shows the results of training a single-input, single-output modified CMAC neural network with gaussian receptive fields, by using the same test nonlinear function as in Fig. 26.2. The improvement in the approximation is obvious.

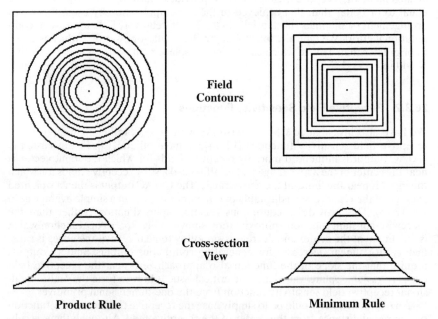

FIGURE 26.5 Two-dimensional gaussian receptive field sensitivity functions for radially symmetric (product rule) and minimum-distance-to-edge (minimum rule) metrics.

The CMAC computations described in Secs. 26.2.2 and 26.3.1 can be easily modified to accommodate nonconstant receptive field sensitivity functions. Let a_{ij} represent the jth component of the receptive field virtual address $\mathbf{A}_i$ in the normalized input space, as given in Eq. (26.10). Let s_j'' represent the jth component of the real-valued, normalized input vector $\mathbf{S}''$:

$$\mathbf{S}'' = <s_1'', s_2'', \ldots, s_N''> = <\frac{s_1}{\Delta_1}, \frac{s_2}{\Delta_2}, \ldots, \frac{s_N}{\Delta_N}> \qquad (26.11)$$

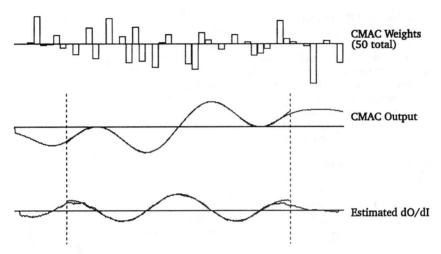

CMAC Weights (50 total)

CMAC Output

Estimated dO/dI

FIGURE 26.6 Results of training a single-input, single-output modified CMAC neural network with gaussian receptive fields. Both the CMAC output and the estimated derivative of the CMAC output with respect to the input are shown against the ideal values for the test function.

The corresponding faces of the receptive field occur at $s_j'' = a_{ij} - 0.5$ and $s_j'' = a_{ij} + C - 0.5$ in the normalized space. For an arbitrary input point, the minimum distance δ_i to any face of receptive field i is then given by

$$\delta_i = \min(s_i'' - a_{ij} + 0.5, a_{ij} + C - 0.5 - s_i'') \qquad j = 1, 2, \ldots, N \qquad (26.12)$$

In this case, $\delta_i = 0$ corresponds to any point on a face of the receptive field, while $\delta_i = C/2$ corresponds to the single point at the center of the receptive field. And δ_i varies linearly along any linear path from any point on a face of the receptive field to the point at the center. Equation (26.5) can then be modified to give the new CMAC output:

$$y(\mathbf{S}) = \frac{\displaystyle\sum_{i=1}^{C} f(\delta_i) * W[A_i']}{\displaystyle\sum_{i=1}^{C} f(\delta_i)} \qquad (26.13)$$

In Eq. (26.13), $f(\delta_i)$ represents the one-dimensional primitive which forms the basis of the receptive field *sensitivity function*. In practice, $f(\delta_i) = \delta_i$ is a simple and effective choice for the sensitivity function, producing piecewise-planar approximations.

Finally, Eq. (26.6), which describes the weight adjustment during training, must be replaced by

$$\Delta W_i = \beta * [(y_d(\mathbf{S}) - y(\mathbf{S})] * f(\delta_i) * \frac{\displaystyle\sum_{n=1}^{C} f(\delta_n)}{\displaystyle\sum_{n=1}^{C} f^2(\delta_n)} \qquad (26.14)$$

Note that Eq. (26.6) described a weight adjustment ΔW which was added equally to each of the C adjustable weights representing the C excited receptive fields, while in Eq. (26.14) the weight adjustment ΔW_i for each receptive field is scaled by the magnitude of the receptive field sensitivity function $f(\delta_i)$. If $f(\delta_i) = 1$ for all δ_i, Eqs. (26.13) and (26.14) reduce to Eqs. (26.5) and (26.6).

It is obvious from comparing Eqs. (26.5) and (26.6) to Eqs. (26.13) and (26.14) that the implementation of nonconstant receptive field sensitivity functions requires an increase in computational effort. Thus, in many cases the simpler case of $f(\delta_i) = 1$ is preferable, even though it results in piecewise-constant CMAC outputs. When a continuous CMAC output is important, we generally use $f(\delta_i) = \delta_i$, which results in piecewise-planar CMAC outputs. We have also experimented with cubic spline and truncated gaussian functions for $f(\delta_i)$. Paradoxically, learning system performance is usually worse when these higher-order sensitivity functions are used for input dimensions greater than 2. We feel that this results from their much smaller magnitude near the edges of the receptive field, which dominates the receptive field volume in higher-dimension spaces. In applications we thus use either constant or linear sensitivity functions. Note that when nonconstant sensitivity functions are used, the arrangement of receptive fields (Sec. 26.3.1) is critical to good performance. In such cases, near-uniform arrangements of receptive fields always provide substantially better learning system performance [12] than the diagonalized arrangement used by Albus.

26.3.3 Receptive Field Hashing Considerations

As discussed in Sec. 26.2.1, the total number of receptive fields required to span a multidimensional space (C times) is often too large for practical implementation in terms of the storage required for the adjustable weights of all possible receptive fields. On the other hand, it is unlikely that the entire input state space of a large system would be visited in solving a specific problem. Thus it is only necessary to store information for receptive fields that are excited during training. Following this logic, most implementations of CMAC neural networks include some form of pseudorandom hashing to transform the vector virtual address $\mathbf{A}_i$ of an excited receptive field to a scalar address A_i' of the corresponding weight storage.

The major requirement of the hashing function is that the generated addresses A_i' be uniformly distributed in the range M of the available physical memory addresses, even for small changes in $\mathbf{A}_i$. In software implementations of CMAC, we have primarily used a simple hashing algorithm based on previously generated random number tables:

$$A_i' = \left(\sum_{j=1}^{N} T_j[a_{ij} \% R_j] \right) \% M \qquad (26.15)$$

where each T_j represents a table of uniformly distributed random values with R_j total table entries. Here, R_j effectively limits the dynamic range of the jth component of the normalized input vector, due to wraparound of the table index. This hashing algorithm is numerically efficient and produces a good approximation to uniformly distributed addresses in the range from 0 to $M - 1$, as long as the dynamic range of the pseudorandom numbers in the tables is at least M. Note that a single bit change in any component of $\mathbf{A}_i$ can cause a large change in A_i', as desired. In our experience, the quality of the hashing produced is sensitive to the quality of the uniform random number generator used to fill the T_j tables, but is not sensitive to the specific seed selected when a good random number generator is used.

Hashing collisions are defined by

$$A'_n = A'_m \quad \text{for} \quad \mathbf{A}_n \neq \mathbf{A}_m \tag{26.16}$$

This has the effect of introducing learning interference, in the sense that training adjustments to two distinct and possibly distant receptive fields affect the same adjustable weights. In many implementations of CMAC (including that described originally by Albus), hashing collisions are ignored. This is often reasonable since the CMAC outputs are averages over several receptive fields (there is no specific desired response for any single receptive field), and since the goal is often to approximate a target function rather than to reproduce it exactly. In essence, CMAC training involves satisfying coupled equations by using the available adjustable weights. Hashing collisions increase the coupling between equations (possibly slowing training convergence), but do not necessarily preclude finding a satisfactory solution. Of course, if hashing collisions are too frequent, the coupled set of training equations can become greatly overdetermined, with no satisfactory solutions.

The probability of no hashing collisions when training a single example of novel data is approximately

$$P_{\text{no coll}} = \left(1 - \frac{M_u}{M}\right)^C \tag{26.17}$$

where M_u/M represents the fraction of the available weight storage that has been affected by previous training. Clearly, for reasonable values of the generalization parameter C, the probability of collision-free training is low unless the utilization of available storage is very low. Thus, collision-ignorant hashing is best suited to applications which provide opportunity for repetitive training in order to resolve the additional coupling due to hashing collisions during training. This could involve repetitive off-line training for a pattern recognition application using a fixed training set, or it could involve continuous on-line training (and thus retraining) in a control application. The advantage to collision-ignorant hashing in applications involving on-line training is that old information, which is not reinforced in subsequent training and which may no longer be useful, will eventually be completely overwritten and will not tie up storage resources. Complete saturation of the storage capacity will never occur, in the sense that new information can always be learned (although possibly at the expense of previously trained information).

Collision-free hashing generally involves storing some unique identifier of the virtual receptive field (such as its virtual address $\mathbf{A}_i$) along with each adjustable weight or weight vector, so that collisions can be detected and thus avoided. While hashing collisions may be eliminated, storing unique identifiers can result in a substantial increase in the amount of storage per receptive field, offsetting the reduction in storage which was the original motivation for hashing. Collision-resistant hashing can provide a compromise by storing a pseudorandom hashing tag, derived from the receptive field virtual address $\mathbf{A}_i$, along with each adjustable weight or weight vector. Collisions can then be detected and avoided reliably (but not certainly) by comparing the stored hashing tag with the value derived from the new address. If the tags do not match, the CMAC weight memory is searched sequentially until either a tag match or an unallocated location (blank tag) is found.

In our implementation of collision-resistant hashing, we generate the hashing tag by using the same pseudorandom generator used for address mapping [Eq. (26.15)], but with different random tables and with a different constant k in the final modulus [M in Eq. (26.15)]. Assuming that all detected collisions can be avoided, the probability of no hashing collisions when training a single example of novel data is then approximately

$$P_{\text{no coll}} = \left(1 - \frac{1}{k} * \frac{M_u}{M}\right)^C \tag{26.18}$$

where k represents the dynamic range of the hashing tag. In contrast to the collision-ignorant hashing [Eq. (26.17)], the probability of collision-free training is high even if the utilization of available storage is high, assuming a reasonably large value of k. Thus, collision-resistant hashing provides essentially the same performance as collision-free hashing, typically with substantially less storage per receptive field. Collision-resistant hashing is best suited to applications which require long-term retention of previously trained information in the presence of subsequent training of novel data, without reinforcement of previously trained examples (no learning interference). This could involve pattern recognition applications where it may be desirable to train new examples of certain classes as they are encountered, or control applications which require sequential skill learning. The disadvantage to collision-resistant hashing in applications involving on-line training is that old information, which may no longer be useful, will tie up storage resources indefinitely. This can lead to complete saturation of the storage capacity.

26.3.4 Weight Magnitude Normalization

The output of the CMAC neural network for any input is an average over C adjustable weights. During training, individual weights are adjusted in order to reduce the error in the average. However, there are an infinite number (or, in practice, a very large number) of combinations of weight values which will produce the same average. As a result, training provides only indirect control of weight magnitude.

This can be a problem during applications which require continuous on-line training. After the neural network training converges to a low error, residual error and sensor noise can cause continual small adjustments to the weights. These residual adjustments may average to zero over time for the CMAC output and yet not average to zero over time for individual weights. Some weights may drift toward large positive values while others drift toward large negative values, while maintaining good output performance in terms of averages over C weights. These unnecessarily large weights can eventually cause problems, however, in terms of increased error from hashing collisions and weight saturation for weight implementations with limited dynamic range.

The problem can be fixed by placing a penalty on large weight magnitudes during training (similar to the weight decay concept used as part of training for some other neural networks). Since the CMAC output is an average over multiple weights, an appropriate magnitude regularization is to penalize individual weights for varying from the average. The weight adjustment equation [Eq. (26.6)] is then replaced by

$$\Delta W_i = \beta_1 * [\, y_d(\mathbf{S}) - y(\mathbf{S})\,] + \beta_2 * \{\, y(\mathbf{S}) - W\,[A'_i]\} \tag{26.19}$$

where separate training gains are used to individually emphasize the importance of the supervised learning versus the weight magnitude normalization. We generally select β_2 to be at most equal to $\beta_1/4$, since good output performance is generally the most important. Note that Eq. (26.6) described a single weight adjustment ΔW which was added equally to the C adjustable weights representing the C excited receptive fields, while in Eq. (26.19) the weight adjustment ΔW_i is different for each weight. A similar modification can be added to Eq. (26.14) for training when nonconstant receptive field sensitivity functions are used.

26.3.5 Variable Input Quantization

One limitation of the CMAC algorithms described in previous sections is that quantization and generalization are fixed in the input space by the constants Δ_j and C (Δ_j is the quantization interval and $C * \Delta_j$ is the generalization width for input component j). In some problems, it may be desirable to have fine quantization and narrow generalization in some regions of the input space, with coarse quantization and broad generalization in other regions. If these regions can be identified in advance, the s_j/Δ_j terms in Eqs. (26.2) and (26.11) can be replaced by a more general $w_j(s_j)$, where each $w_j(\ )$ is a fixed nonlinear warping function specific to each input.

If appropriate regional variations in quantization and generalization cannot be determined in advance, it may be possible to represent input warping functions by using models with adaptable parameters and to adapt the warping functions during neural network training. Our laboratory and others have done preliminary experiments on adaptive input space warping, but no detailed information has yet been published. At least two general approaches have been proposed. In one approach, warping functions at the CMAC inputs are adapted in order to directly reduce the CMAC output error (using back propagation of the error through the CMAC element). In a second approach, warping functions at the CMAC inputs are adapted in order to reduce the gradient of the estimated variance of the CMAC output error.

An alternative approach to this problem was reported by Moody [19]. He proposed using a multiresolution CMAC in which the receptive fields in each layer in Fig. 26.1 were of different size. The layer with the largest receptive fields was trained first, followed by the layer with the next-largest receptive fields, and so forth. In this way, broad generalization could be achieved where appropriate by the initial training of the large receptive fields, and fine details could be learned during the later training of the small receptive fields. Better learning system performance can be obtained by using complete CMACs in parallel, each with a different resolution [13], rather than single layers of different-size receptive fields as proposed by Moody. The drawback to the multiresolution approach (relative to input space warping) is that the smallest receptive fields are placed everywhere in the space, even though there may be only a limited region that actually requires fine quantization. Thus, the memory utilization is unnecessarily high.

26.4 GENERAL CAPABILITIES OF CMAC

How much can a CMAC learn, how well can it learn, how well can it generalize, and what can it learn? In this section we discuss what is known about the capabilities and behavior of CMAC. The material is a result of what we have learned over 10 years of using CMAC, what we have determined in research we conducted over those years, and what we have found in the literature on CMAC. We discuss such topics as the sampling and reconstruction that take place due to the fixed receptive field weight centers of CMAC and how this relates to Nyquist sampling theory; the capacity of

CMAC as determined by experiment and bolstered by the logic of simultaneous equations; the generalization characteristics of CMAC; and the types of functions that CMAC can learn.

26.4.1 CMAC Function Reconstruction and Nyquist

CMAC Receptive Field Centers.   As seen earlier (Sec. 26.2), although all inputs in the input range are legal input components, a subset of points in the input space is specified as the CMAC receptive field weight centers. The CMAC algorithm used specifies the arrangement of these centers. The number of centers is equal to the number of weights in the neural network. These centers are the points at which interpolation functions are placed in order to reconstruct a multidimensional learned function. Each center has an associated weight which is used as the weighting factor for the reconstruction function. Although any point in the input space (any input vector) can be learned, only C (generalization size) points can be learned in any hypercube of side C in the input space. CMAC training adjusts C weights at each training of a sample point (training vector). In essence, the centers are equivalent to sampling points of the learned function, only instead of one point per sample there are (in general) C points per C samples. Thus Nyquist sampling applies to CMAC function learning.

Multidimensional Nyquist Sampling.   Nyquist sampling [20] applies to a frequency-limited function and guarantees that the appropriate samples can be used to reproduce the function exactly. This is done by ensuring that the spectrum of the sampled function—which is a periodically extended version of the spectrum of the continuous learned function—will allow the recovery of the original spectrum of the continuous function by being sure the repeated elements do not overlap. In one dimension, recovery of the original spectrum is done by multiplying the spectrum of the sampled points by a rectangular pulse placed over the baseband part of the spectrum. In the time domain, this is equivalent to convolving the samples with the inverse transform of the rectangular pulse—a $(\sin x)/x$ function. The result is that the original function is exactly reproduced from the samples by properly weighting and summing the regularly placed $(\sin x)/x$ functions. The weights are the sample heights. If the spectrum falls off rapidly enough but is not band-limited, the function will not be perfectly recovered, but the approximation can be good enough for practical purposes.

Nyquist sampling in multidimensional space [21, 22] consists of assigning points in the space as sample points of the function in such a way that in the frequency domain a frequency-limited function will have its spectrum repeated but will not overlap. Of course, the function being learned will influence the best placement of sample points (receptive field centers). For a generic placement, a spherically symmetric spectrum makes sense. This leads to closest multidimensional sphere packing placement of samples in the frequency domain as the optimum in this generic case. The inverse transform of these points would be the corresponding sample array for the CMAC centers. However, there is no guarantee that these center points end up on integer points in the input space, so approximations are necessary. We have shown that the procedure described in Sec. 26.3.1 generates CMAC receptive field centers which are good approximations to the optimal locations predicted by multidimensional sampling theory.

An example shows the effect of the center placement on the ability to learn a function, in this case a two-dimensional sinusoid. If the standard Albus CMAC receptive field centers are being used, then a two-dimensional sinusoid with lines of constant maxima running parallel to the lines of CMAC centers is not learned as well (nor does it generalize as well) as a sinusoid with the lines of constant maxima running perpendicular to the lines of centers (see Fig. 26.3).

26.4.2 Capacity: How Many Input Vectors Can a CMAC Learn?

It is natural to be curious about how many training vectors a CMAC can learn. The answer, of course, depends on what CMAC is being used and what *being learned* means. One might expect that the characteristics of the function being learned might be critical. We now look at this question experimentally and then explain the results in light of our knowledge of how CMAC works.

Experimental Results. Figure 26.7 shows average experimental results [23, 24] of training numbers of training vectors with components generated from a uniform random number generator. Each point is the average of about 20 runs. Points represent runs with parameters as follows: generalization size = 10, 50, 100; physical memory size = 200, 500, 1000; N = 10, 25. Figure 26.7 shows the normalized final training summed square error versus the number of training vectors normalized by the memory size. The normalized summed squared error would be unity if all CMAC weights were zero, and zero if all the training vectors were perfectly learned. The data show that if the number of training vectors is small relative to the memory size, then the error is zero; and as the number of training vectors approaches the memory size, the error starts to grow. Similar results hold for "correlated" inputs and inputs taken as samples of multidimensional sinusoids.

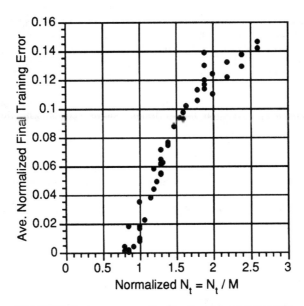

FIGURE 26.7   Average normalized final training error versus the number of training vectors normalized by the memory size.

The conclusion is that the capacity of CMAC is about equal to the memory size!

Further experiments show that the capacity is not strictly the memory size but the smallest of the physical memory size and the number of *available weights,* i.e., the number of weight centers encompassed by the input vectors. In most real applications, the memory size will be the smaller of the two and will represent the capacity.

Number of Available Weights.   If the training vectors are taken from the whole multidimensional input space and all the R_i are equal to R, then the number of available weights is approximated by

$$M_A = \frac{(R + C - 1)^N}{C^{N-1}} \qquad (26.20)$$

where, as used earlier in this chapter, R is the range of the input components, C is the generalization size, and N is the input dimension. The exact expression is much more complicated and not included here [13, 25].

Clearly, since R is usually large (for example, 32,000), for N more than 4, this is much bigger than a practical memory size. These expressions are maximum values. With inputs restricted to smaller regions of input space, the number of available weights would be proportionally smaller. The number of available weights could be smaller than or larger than the physical memory size. The CMAC capacity is the minimum of these two values.

Simultaneous Equations.   Why is the capacity of CMAC about equal to the number of weights that can be used? The explanation can be found in the mechanism of CMAC. For each input vector CMAC must iteratively find C weights that add to equal the desired output. Each input vector has its own C weights, with some possible weights shared with other inputs. The C weights would be exactly the same only if two quantized inputs were exactly the same. The upshot of all this is that CMAC is trying to solve a set of simultaneous equations, and if the number of equations is greater than the number of weights, there is only a small probability of a solution (the equations are highly dependent). If there are fewer training vectors than weights, there is a high probability of solution. This is seen in Fig. 26.7.

Hashing Variations.   The use of hashing in CMAC leads to a slight degradation of the capacity results discussed above. Although there is a certain amount of physical memory allotted for the CMAC to use, not all those memory slots actually get picked by the hashing algorithm. Since the hashing algorithm uses a random number generator, this is a probabilistic situation. It is as if we had a bucket for each memory location and a ball for each weight value, and the balls were thrown randomly into the buckets. If there were as many balls as buckets, we still would not necessarily end up with one ball per bucket. Some buckets would have two balls (hashing collisions), and others would have none. The expected value of the number of buckets used is given by [25]

$$M_E = M\left[1 - \left(\frac{M-1}{M}\right)^{M_A}\right] \qquad (26.21)$$

and the variance is given by

$$\sigma_{ME}^2 = M\left[1 - \left(\frac{M-1}{M}\right)^{M_A}\right] + \frac{M}{2}\left[1 - 2\left(\frac{M-1}{M}\right)^{M_A} - \left(\frac{M-2}{M}\right)^{M_A}\right] \qquad (26.22)$$

where M is the physical memory size and M_A is the number of available weights.

The comforting thing about this result is that the standard deviation is small in practical cases, meaning that no matter what random number seed is used, the CMAC will perform about the same. At least you do not have to worry about picking the exactly right seed to get good results, as long as you have a good random number generator!

26.4.3 Generalization

Generalization is the capability of giving the right response to an input that has not been seen before (trained on before). It implies that there is a *correct* response, so there must be an implied continuity if you are dealing with functions, an implied shape if you are dealing with shapes, etc. The question is, How well does CMAC generalize? To find out experimentally, one must choose a function to experiment with—and there are so many functional forms! The correct answer is needed to compare the CMAC response and get an error rate. Rather than arbitrarily picking a function, there is a line of reasoning that leads us to using sinusoids to do generalization experiments. Because there is a range R for the components of the inputs, the input space in N dimensions is R^N, finite in extent. Therefore multidimensional *Fourier series* apply, and any function on the input space can be written as a sum of sinusoids, all of which are harmonics of a fundamental. And because of CMAC's output *superposition property*, if CMAC can learn the sinusoids and generalize, it can learn the function and generalize.

Figure 26.8 shows the average normalized generalization error versus the normalized number of training vectors $N_t * C/M$, where N_t is the number of training vectors, C is the generalization, and M is the physical memory size. These data are the result of experiments built on the ideas of the last paragraph [24–26]. In particular, the desired output functions were multidimensional sinusoids. The result of note here is that the generalization error goes rapidly to zero as the normalized number of training vectors is increased. Although there were assumptions and conditions in these experiments, the results are consistent with our experience in using CMAC for real-time robot control applications and for signal processing, pattern recognition, handwriting recognition, and speech recognition.

26.4.4 Types of Functions That CMAC Can Learn

What functions can CMAC learn? All functions? A few functions? We would like to know that if we use CMAC in an application, it will learn the unknown function at least fairly well. We know by logic that CMAC cannot learn every possible function, since in every C-sided hypercube in normalized input space there are C^N possible inputs and only about C weights. So only about C of those functions can be learned. On the other hand, experience with using CMAC for 10 years has shown us that in real situations CMAC will converge to low enough error if we pick the correct values for generalization, learning rate, and memory size and set up the problem so the inputs make sense. Can we say any more about this important question?

Brown et al. [27–29] show that there is a class of functions that an arbitrary CMAC can learn. That is the class of additive functions, i.e., functions that are a linear combination of one-dimensional functions. Brown has proved a number of theorems about CMAC learning capabilities. These, of course, mean *exact* learning—no error. If low error is acceptable, then the set of learnable functions is yet larger.

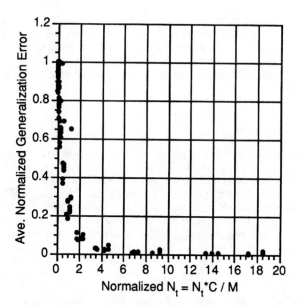

FIGURE 26.8 Average normalized generalization error versus the normalized number of training vectors for selected data points, where the normalization factor is the number of available weights divided by the generalization C.

As seen under the capacity discussion above, experiments with random vectors lead to a high percentage of the randomly generated functions being learned as long as sufficient memory is available. Furthermore, we have found that multidimensional sinusoids (see below) and rectangular pulses can be learned, although the pulses are slightly rounded off by the CMAC. Also mentioned above was the fact that years of experience have indicated that for all practical purposes CMAC can approximately learn functions we have run across in real-time hardware problems.

Figure 26.9 is the result of simulation experiments [25, 26] and shows a plot of normalized generalization error which is equal to the normalized training error versus normalized harmonic number ($K*C/R$) for CMACs trained on sinusoids. Notice that the errors are small as long as $K*C/R$ is less than about 0.5, which corresponds to sinusoids with half wavelength greater than the receptive field width. These results are for two dimensions only. The $N = 3$ results are similar, but higher-dimension results are not available. Notice that if the input component range R is represented by 16 bits, then $R = 65,536$ and even a large wave number sinusoid can be learned with low error. This explains why multidimensional rectangular pulses can be learned with only slight smoothing.

Coupling these results with the output superposition and Fourier series ideas shows that spatially band-limited target functions can be approximated by a CMAC with constant receptive field sensitivity functions if the receptive field width is less than the minimum spatial wavelength of the target function. When a CMAC with linearly tapered receptive field sensitivity functions is used, the receptive field width must be less than twice the minimum spatial wavelength. These are theoretical lim-

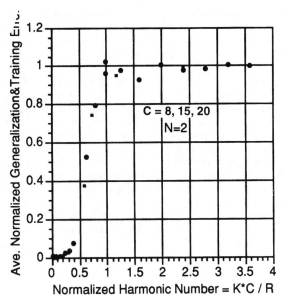

FIGURE 26.9   Average normalized generalization and training error versus normalized harmonic number for $C = 8, 15, 20; N = 2$.

its, and as demonstrated in the previous paragraph, functions with longer spatial wavelengths can generally be learned with lower error.

26.5 CONFIGURING CMAC FOR YOUR APPLICATION

In this section we record some guidelines for setting up a CMAC to use for a particular application. Experience in trying CMAC on different problems is invaluable, but these guidelines should give a starting place for what to think about.

26.5.1 General Applications

Determining the Type of Inputs.   When you are starting to think about an application, first consider what information is available to the neural network and what is needed physically in order to determine the output. No neural network can learn a result without the appropriate information. The functional form of the result is not required, but an understanding of the input data that are necessary for the result is important. For example, if two inputs to a recognition system have the same input vectors exactly, even though they are in different classes, then it will not be possible to classify both those inputs correctly. As another example, learning the kinematics of a system requires only position measurements, but learning the dynamics requires position, velocity, and acceleration in general. Also be conscious that some past values of inputs (held in a shift register) might be necessary for learning. An example would be trying to learn the output of a filter, where the system output is the convolution of the input and the system function (system with memory).

Input Component Scaling.   For physical problem inputs, it is desirable to adjust the quantization levels Δ_j to be equal to the smallest change in an input vector component that is of importance, and to adjust $C*\Delta_j$ to be the largest change in an input vector component that should still be related at the output. As mentioned in Sec. 26.4.4, experimental results and theoretical considerations suggest that CMAC is capable of learning to represent spatially band-limited functions, where the minimum spatial wavelength is greater than $C*\Delta_j$ (greater than $\frac{1}{2}C*\Delta_j$ when linearly varying receptive field sensitivity functions are used). This can be used in selecting input vector scaling, if information about the spatial frequency content of the target function is available. Note that Δ_j is independent for each component of the input vector, while C has the same value for all components of the input vector. It is often necessary to resort to trial-and-error testing to determine the best scaling for the input vector components.

26.5.2   Approaches to Training CMAC

Training Mode.   A number of training modes might be used in any situation. For example, there may be a fixed number of training vectors, and then training may be on-line, where each pattern is presented and trained on in a sequence. On the other hand, training may be *batch* training, where all the vectors are trained collectively off-line. The latter is often used with multilayer Perceptron training using back propagation. In sequential training it is important to not present the inputs in exact cyclic order, or else a limit cycle may result instead of the minimum-squared-error solution. Any slight randomness will avoid this problem.

   In contrast to the fixed number of training vectors situation, one may just put the CMAC in an input stream and let it train on any vectors that come along. This is the common training situation for real-time control situations or in signal processing applications. In this case there is no fixed number of training vectors, and the vectors are not repeated cyclically.

Training Gain.   The *training gain* is the factor between 0 and 1 that assigns how much of the training error is corrected in any one training cycle. The value of the training gain depends on the nature of the use of CMAC. In real-time noisy environments, the training rate should be small, say below 0.1. In other training situations, values between 0.25 and 1.0 may be appropriate. Notice that if the training vectors are outside of each other's generalization distance, then a training gain of 1.0 will be equivalent to imprint learning in that the vectors will be learned in one training cycle.

   In situations where one seeks to find the absolute lowest training error, we have found that changing the training gain in a systematic way is useful. Our system is as follows: If the summed squared error increases, then the training gain is multiplied by a training gain rate factor less than 1 in order to slow the learning. Usually the squared error will then decrease steadily but will eventually increase again. Again the training gain is multiplied by the rate factor. The best rate factor depends on the type of problem. If the factor is too small, then the learning will get slow too fast and training will never go anywhere. If the rate is too high, the lowest possible squared error will never be reached. We often use a rate factor between 0.6 and 0.9.

Choosing the Generalization Size.   Once one has chosen the type of inputs needed for the problem at hand, the dimension of the space of inputs is specified. Then the size of the generalization parameter must be chosen. The higher the number of dimensions of the input space, the higher the generalization should be. Considerations from multidimensional sampling theory (Sec. 26.4.1) suggest that selecting C greater than or equal to $4*N$ is appropriate for learning space spanning functions with N inputs. A problem with N inputs may be on a lower-dimension subspace and would not require as high a C. But the type of inputs and the nature of the function being learned (the desired output) influence the value. The farther apart the training inputs are in the input space, the larger the generalization will have to be. Probably one will have to pick a reasonable initial value and then train and test the system. If inputs close to a training vector should have a similar response and do not, then increase the generalization by a factor of 2; if inputs far from any training vector give a response similar to a training vector, then cut the generalization by a factor of 2. We have found that changes in generalization size by anything less than a factor of 2 tend not to make much difference in the quality of learning.

In real-time control situations, it has been found that there is a generalization in time from one control cycle to the next because the system is moving deferentially through the state space. This results in a system responding well even on the first time through a sequence because the response on the next cycle is related to the response on the current cycle. One way to pick the generalization size in these situations is to log some data from the system and adjust the generalization to a value larger than the distance moved in the state space from one control cycle to the next. This procedure has worked well at the University of New Hampshire Robotics Laboratory [30].

Note that changes made to the generalization parameter C directly influence input vector scaling (Sec. 26.5.1).

Amount of Memory Required.   The amount of physical memory that is assigned to the CMAC for a given problem depends on the number of training vectors required, the size of the generalization parameter, and the amount of generalization error that is acceptable (see Figs. 26.7 and 26.8). The number arrived at from these figures is really the amount of memory used, not the amount assigned to the task. Because of hashing coding collisions, we have found that a minimum of twice the memory-used number gives a reasonable value for physical memory. This doubling keeps the collisions down to a value small enough that troubles do not often occur.

Imprint Learning.   Because of CMAC's local learning, it is capable of instant learning as long as the training vectors are outside of each other's generalization distance. In that case, if the training gain is 1.0 and the number of training vectors is below capacity, then the vectors are learned in one training cycle, thus being analogous to imprint learning in some animals.

26.6   AN OUTLINE OF APPLICATIONS AND THEORY LITERATURE

Over the years there have been a large number of attempts to use CMAC for real applications, in simulated applications, and in demonstration projects. Below is a listing of as many of those applications as we have found. There are others that we know of but have been unable to obtain, and there have undoubtedly been some oversights (our apologies!). These are organized by application with a list of references. Headings for theory papers and hardware papers are also included.

- Control (including robotics)
  Kinematics [10, 31–40]
  Dynamics [30, 33, 34, 36, 41–45]
  Unstable plant [34]
  Time delay in plant [46]
  Adaptive critic [47–50]
  Walking (biped and quadruped) [35, 36, 38, 43, 44, 51]
  Dynamic programming [52]
  Chemical systems [9, 53–57]
  Optimal [52, 58, 59]
  Mobile [60]
  Manipulator/robot [5, 10, 30–33, 45, 61–66]
  Fuzzy [27, 28, 67–69]
- Manufacturing, CIM, tool fault [39, 70–72]
- Pattern recognition
  Nearest-neighbor methods [73]
  Character recognition [23, 74]
  Handwriting recognition [74]
- Signal processing [23, 75–77]
- Biomedical [2, 68, 77–81]
- Others
  Physics detectors [82]
  Geophysical [83–85]
  Ultrasonics [86]
  Color correction [87]
- Theory [12, 14–16, 25, 27–29, 57, 88–100]
- Hardware implementation [87, 101–103]

REFERENCES

1. F. Rosenblatt, *Principles of Neurodynamics,* New York: Spartan, 1962.
2. J. S. Albus, "Theoretical and Experimental Aspects of a Cerebellar Model," Ph.D. dissertation, University of Maryland, 1972.
3. B. Widrow, "Generalization and Information Storage in Networks of Adaline 'Neurons,' " *Self-Organizing Systems,* M. C. Yovits, ed., Washington: Spartan, 1962, pp. 435–461.
4. J. S. Albus, "Data Storage in the Cerebellar Model Articulation Controller," *Trans. ASME, Journal of Dynamic Systems, Measurement and Control,* vol. 63, no. 3, pp. 228–233, 1975.

5. J. S. Albus, "A New Approach to Manipulator Control: The Cerebellar Model Articulation Controller (CMAC)," *Transactions of the ASME, Journal of Dynamic Systems, Measurement and Control,* vol. 63, no. 3, pp. 220–227, 1975.

6. J. S. Albus, "Mechanisms of Planning and Problem Solving in the Brain," *Mathematical Biosciences,* vol. 45, pp. 247–293, 1979.

7. J. S. Albus, *Brains, Behavior, and Robotics,* Peterborough, NH: Byte Books/McGraw-Hill, 1981.

8. E. Ersu, "A Learning Mechanism for an Associative Storage System," *IEEE International Conference on Cybernetics and Society,* Atlanta, GA, pp. 26–28, 1981.

9. H. Tolle and E. Ersu, *Neurocontrol,* Berlin: Springer-Verlag, 1992.

10. W. T. Miller, "A Nonlinear Learning Controller for Robotic Manipulators," *Proceedings of the SPIE: Intelligent Robots and Computer Vision,* vol. 726, pp. 416–423, 1986.

11. W. T. Miller, F. H. Glanz, and L. G. Kraft, "CMAC: An Associative Neural Network Alternative to Backpropagation," *Proceedings of the IEEE,* vol. 78, pp. 1561–1567, 1990.

12. W. T. Miller, E. An, F. H. Glanz, and M. J. Carter, "The Design of CMAC Neural Networks for Control," *Adaptive and Learning Systems,* vol. 1, New Haven, CT: Yale University, pp. 140–145, 1990.

13. P.-C. E. An, "An Improved Multi-dimensional CMAC Neural Network: Receptive Field Function and Placement," Ph.D. dissertation, University of New Hampshire, 1991.

14. P.-C. E. An, W. T. Miller, and P. C. Parks, "Design Improvements in Associative Memories for CMAC," *International Conference on Artificial Neural Networks—1991, Proceedings* Helsinki, Finland, vol. 2 (Publisher: North Holland, The Netherlands), pp. 1207–1210, 1991.

15. P. C. Parks and J. Militzer, "Improved Allocation of Weights for Associative Memory Storage in Learning Control Systems," *IFAC Design Methods of Control Systems,* Zurich, Switzerland [publisher: IFAC (International Federation of Automatic Control)], pp. 507–512, 1991.

16. S. H. Lane, D. A. Handelman, and J. J. Gelfand, "The Theory and Development of Higher-Order CMAC Neural Networks," *IEEE Control Systems Magazine,* pp. 23–30, April 1992.

17. T. Poggio and F. Girosi, *A Theory for Approximation and Learning,* MIT Al Laboratory, Rep. 1140, Massachusetts Institute of Technology, Cambridge, MA, July 1989.

18. J. Moody and C. Darken, "Learning with Localized Receptive Fields," Connectionists Models Summer School, 1988.

19. J. Moody and C. J. Darken, "Fast Learning in Networks of Locally-Tuned Processing Units," *Neural Computation,* vol. 1, pp. 281–294, 1989.

20. A. V. Oppenheim and R. W. Schafer, *Discrete-Time Signal Processing,* Englewood Cliffs, NJ: Prentice-Hall, 1989.

21. D. Peterson and D. Middleton, "Sampling and Reconstruction of Wave-Number Limited Functions in N-Dimensional Euclidean Spaces," *Information and Control,* vol. 5, pp. 279–323, 1962.

22. D. E. Dudgeon and R. M. Mersereau, *Multidimensional Digital Signal Processing,* Englewood Cliffs, NJ: Prentice-Hall, 1984.

23. F. H. Glanz, W. T. Miller, and L. G. Kraft, "An Overview of the CMAC Neural Network," *IEEE Conference on Neural Networks for Ocean Engineering,* Washington, DC, pp. 301–308, 1991.

24. F. H. Glanz and J. Yang, "Experimental Parameter Studies for the CMAC Neural Network," *International Joint Conference on Neural Networks—1991,* Seattle, WA, 1991.

25. F. H. Glanz, "CMAC Mechanism and Behavior," UNH Robotics Laboratory, Rep. ECE. IS. 94.07, University of New Hampshire, Durham, NH, October 1994.

26. X. J. Yang, "Experimental Parameter Studies for the CMAC Neural Network," MS thesis, University of New Hampshire, 1993.

27. M. Brown and C. Harris, *Neurofuzzy Adaptive Modelling and Control,* Hemel Hempstead, United Kingdom: Prentice-Hall, 1994.

28. M. Brown, "Neurofuzzy Adaptive Modelling and Control," Ph.D. dissertation, Southampton University, 1993.

29. M. Brown, C. J. Harris, and P. C. Parks, "The Interpolation Capabilities of the Binary CMAC," *Neural Networks,* vol. 6, pp. 429–440, 1993.

30. W. T. Miller, R. P. Hewes, F. H. Glanz, and L. G. Kraft, "Real-Time Dynamic Control of an Industrial Manipulator Using a Neural-Network-Based Learning Controller," *IEEE Transactions on Robotics Automation* vol. 6, pp. 1–9, 1990.

31. W. T. Miller, "A Learning Controller for Nonrepetitive Robotic Operations," *Proceedings of the Workshop on Space Telerobotics,* Pasadena, CA, vol. 2, pp. 273–281, 1987.

32. W. T. Miller, "Sensor Based Control of Robotic Manipulators Using a General Learning Algorithm," *IEEE Transactions on Robotics Automation,* vol. RA-3, pp. 157–165, 1987.

33. W. T. Miller, F. H. Glanz, and L. G. Kraft, "Application of a General Learning Algorithm to the Control of Robotic Manipulators," *International Journal of Robotics Research,* vol. 6, pp. 84–98, 1987.

34. W. T. Miller and C. M. Aldrich, "Rapid Learning Using CMAC Neural Networks: Real Time Control of an Unstable System," *5th IEEE International Symposium on Intelligent Control,* Philadelphia, PA, pp. 465–470, 1990.

35. W. T. Miller, III, "Real-Time Neural Network Control of a Biped Walking Robot," submitted to *IEEE Transactions on Automatic Control,* 1993.

36. W. T. Miller, III, "Real-Time Control of a Biped Walking Robot," *World Conference on Neural Networks,* Portland, OR, vol. 3, pp. 153–156, 1993.

37. H. Werntges, "Delta Rule-Based Neural Networks for Inverse Kinematics," *1990 International Joint Conference on Neural Networks,* San Diego, CA, vol. 3, pp. 415–420, 1990.

38. Y. Lin and S.-M. Song, "Kinematic Control and Coordination of Walking Machine Motion Using Neural Networks," *1991 IEEE International Joint Conference on Neural Networks (IJCNN '91),* Singapore, pp. 248–253, 1991.

39. Z. Geng and L. S. Haynes, "Neural Network Solution for the Forward Kinematics Problem of a Stewart Platform," *Robotics and Computer-Integrated Manufacturing,* vol. 9, pp. 485–495, 1992.

40. Z. Geng and L. Haynes, "Neural Network Solution for the Forward Kinematics Problem of a Stewart Platform," *1991 IEEE International Conference on Robotics and Automation,* Sacramento, CA, vol. 3, pp. 2650–2655, 1991.

41. R. P. Hewes and W. T. Miller, "Practical Demonstration of a Learning Control System for a Five Axis Industrial Robot," *Proceedings of the SPIE: Intelligent Robots and Computer Vision—Seventh in a Series,* Cambridge, MA, vol. 1002, pp. 679–685, 1989.

42. W. T. Miller and R. P. Hewes, "Real Time Experiments in Neural Network Based Learning Control during High Speed Nonrepetitive Robotic Operations," *Proceedings of the Third IEEE International Symposium on Intelligent Control,* Arlington, VA, pp. 513–518, 1988.

43. W. T. Miller, P. J. Latham, and S. M. Scalera, "Bipedal Gait Adaption for Walking with Dynamic Balance," *IEEE American Control Conference,* Boston, 1991.

44. W. T. Miller, III, "Learning Dynamic Balance of a Biped Walking Robot," *IEEE International Conference on Neural Networks,* Orlando, FL, vol. 5, pp. 2771–2776, 1994.

45. A. Eskandarian, N. E. Bedewi, B. Kramer, and A. J. Barbera, "Dynamic Modeling of Robotic Manipulators Using an Artificial Neural Network," *Journal of Robotic Systems,* vol. 11, pp. 41–56, 1994.

46. A. V. Sebald and J. Schlenzig, "Minimax Design of Neural Net Controllers for Highly Uncertain Plants," *IEEE Transactions on Neural Networks,* vol. 5, pp. 73–82, 1994.

47. C.-S. Lin and H. Kim, "Selection of Learning Parameters for CMAC-Based Adaptive Critic Learning," *International Conference on Artificial Neural Networks in Engineering,* pp. 153–160, 1992.

48. C.-S. Lin and H. Kim, "CMAC-Based Adaptive Critic Self-Learning Control," *IEEE Transactions on Neural Networks,* vol. 2, pp. 530–533, 1991.

49. R. O. Shelton and J. K. Peterson, "Controlling a Truck with an Adaptive Critic Temporal Difference CMAC Design," *Third Workshop on Neural Networks: Academic/Industrial/NASA/Defense,* Auburn, AL, SPIE vol. 1721, pp. 195–206, 1993.

50. R. O. Shelton and J. K. Peterson, "Controlling a Truck with an Adaptive Critic CMAC Design," *Simulation,* vol. 58, pp. 319–326, 1992.

51. W. T. Miller, P. J. Latham, and S. M. Scalera, "Bipedal Gait Adaptation for Walking with Dynamic Balance," *IEEE American Control Conference,* Boston, 1991.

52. J. K. Peterson and R. O. Shelton, "Use of CMAC Neural Architectures in Obstacle Avoidance," *3d Workshop on Neural Networks: Academic/Industrial/NASA/Defense,* Auburn, AL, vol. 1721, pp. 187–194, 1993.

53. E. Ersu and X. Mao, "Control of pH Using a Self-Organizing Control Concept with Associative Memories," *International IASTED Conference on Applied Control and Identification,* Copenhagen, Denmark, 1983.

54. E. Ersu and J. Militzer, "Real-Time Implementation of an Associative Memory-Based Learning Control Scheme for Non-Linear Multivariable Processes," *1st Measurements and Control Symposium on Applications of Multivariable Systems Techniques,* Plymouth, United Kingdom, pp. 109–119, 1984.

55. E. Ersu, ed., *On the Application of Associative Neural Network Models to Technical Control Problems,* Springer-Verlag, New York, 1984, pp. 90–93.

56. S. Gehlen and J. Kreuzig, "Learning by Interpolating Memories for Modelling of Fermentation Processes," *Advanced Control of Chemical Processes '91,* Toulouse, France, pp. 273–278, 1991.

57. L. Xu, J.-P. Jiang, and J. Zhu, "Supervised Learning Control of a Nonlinear Polymerization Reactor Using the CMAC Neural Network for Knowledge Storage," *IEE Proceedings: Control Theory and Application,* vol. 141, pp. 33–38, 1994.

58. J. K. Peterson, "On-Line Estimation of Optimal Control Sequences," *International Conference on Artificial Neural Networks in Engineering,* pp. 579–584, 1992.

59. R. Carlson, C. Lee, and K. Rothermel, "Real Time Neural Control of an Active Structure," *International Conference on Artificial Neural Networks in Engineering,* pp. 623–628, 1992.

60. T. Fukuda, F. Saito, and F. Arai, "Study on the Brachiation Type of Mobile Robot (Heuristic Creation of Driving Input and Control Using CMAC)," *12th International Conference on Soil Mechanics and Foundation Engineering,* Rio de Janeiro, Brazil, vol. 2, pp. 478–483, 1989.

61. W. T. Miller, III, L. G. Kraft, and F. H. Glanz, "Real Time Comparison of Neural Network and Traditional Adaptive Controllers," *The Yale Conference on Adaptive Control,* May 20–22, 1992, Yale University, New Haven, CT, pp. 99–104.

62. H. Kano and K. Takayama, "Learning Control of Robotic Manipulators Based on Neurological Model CMAC," *11th Triennial World Congress of the International Federation of Automatic Control,* Tallinn, USSR, vol. 5, pp. 249–254, 1991.

63. Y. Jin, T. Pipe, and A. Winfield, "Stable Neural Network Control for Manipulators," *International Joint Conference on Neural Networks,* Nagoya, Japan, vol. 3, pp. 2775–2778, 1993.

64. Z. Geng and L. S. Haynes, "Dynamic Control of a Parallel Link Manipulator Using a CMAC Neural Network," *Computers & Electrical Engineering,* vol. 19, pp. 265–276, 1993.

65. Z. Geng and L. S. Haynes, "Dynamic Control of a Parallel Link Manipulator Using a CMAC Neural Network," *IEEE International Symposium on Intelligent Control,* Arlington, VA, pp. 411–416, 1991.

66. T.-Y. Kuc and K. Nam, "CMAC Based Iterative Learning Control of Robot Manipulators," *28th IEEE Conference on Decision and Control,* Tampa, FL, vol. 3, pp. 2613–2618, 1989.

67. G. Calcev, "Self-Tuning Neurofuzzy Controller," *IEEE International Symposium on Intelligent Control,* Chicago, pp. 577–580, 1993.

68. J. Nie and D. A. Linkens, "Fuzzified CMAC Self-Learning Controller," *Second IEEE International Conference on Fuzzy Systems,* San Francisco, pp. 500–505, 1993.

69. J. Ozawa, I. Hayashi, and N. Wakami, "Formulation of CMAC-Fuzzy System," *IEEE International Conference on Fuzzy Systems—Fuzz-IEEE,* San Diego, CA, pp. 1179–1186, 1992.

70. H. Park and H. S. Cho, "CMAC-Based Learning Controller for Pressure Tracking Control of Hydroforming Processes," *Winter Annual Meeting of the American Society of Mechanical Engineers,* Dallas, TX, pp. 101–106, 1990.

71. J. Lee and B. M. Kramer, "Analysis of Machine Degradation Using a Neural Network Based Pattern Discrimination Model," *Journal of Manufacturing Systems,* vol. 12, pp. 379–387, 1993.

72. J. Lee and B. Kramer, "On-Line Fault Monitoring and Detection Using an Integrated Learning and Reasoning Approach," *Japan-USA Symposium on Flexible Automation,* San Francisco, vol. 1, pp. 235–242, 1992.

73. N. Ramesh and I. K. Sethi, "Nearest Neighbor Classification Using CMAC," *IEEE International Conference on Neural Networks,* Orlando, FL, vol. 5, pp. 3061–3066, 1994.

74. W. T. Miller, III, K. F. Arehart, S. M. Scalera, and H. L. Gresham, "On-Line Hand-Printed Character Recognition Using CMAC Neural Networks," *World Conference on Neural Networks,* Portland, OR, July 12–15, 1993, pp. IV10–IV13.

75. F. H. Glanz and W. T. Miller, "Deconvolution Using a CMAC Neural Network," *Proceedings of the First Annual Meeting of the International Neural Network Society,* Boston, p. 440, 1988.

76. F. H. Glanz and W. T. Miller, "Deconvolution and Nonlinear Inverse Filtering Using a Neural Network," *International Conference on Acoustics and Signal Processing,* Glasgow, Scotland, vol. 4, pp. 2349–2352, 1989.

77. E. Wilson and J. LaCourse, "Analyzing Biological Signals with CMAC, a Neural Network," *1991 IEEE 17th Annual Northeast Bioengineering Conference,* Hartford, CT, pp. 3–4, 1991.

78. S. Gehlen, M. Hormel, and S. Bohrer, "A Learning Control Scheme with Neuron-Like Associative Memories for the Control of Biotechnological Processes," *Neural Networks,* Nimes, France, 1988.

79. D. Bergantz and H. Barad, "Neural Network Control of Cybernetic Limb Prostheses," *Annual International Conference of the IEEE Engineering in Medicine and Biology Society,* New Orleans, LA, vol. 3, pp. 1486–1487, 1988.

80. A. V. Sebald, C. A. Sebald, and J. Schlenzig, "Use of Neural Net Control Strategies in Difficult Adaptive Control Problems: Closed Loop Control of Drug Infusion," *23d Annual Asilomar Conference on Signals, Systems and Computers,* Pacific Grove, CA, vol. 1, pp. 342–345, 1989.

81. D. J. Wasser, D. W. Hislop, and R. N. Johnson, "Evaluation of a Neural Network for Fault-Tolerant, Real-Time, Adaptive Control," *Images of the Twenty-First Century,* vol. 11: *Annual International Conference of the IEEE Engineering in Medicine and Biology,* Seattle, WA, pp. 2027–2028, 1989.

82. G. Simpson and K. Reinhard, *A New Approach to Event Location,* University of New Hampshire—GRO-Compter Group, Rep. COM-TN-UNH-F70-044, June 9, 1988.

83. A. Hagens and J. H. Doveton, "Application of a Simple Cerebellar Model to Geologic Surface Mapping," *Computers & Geosciences,* vol. 17, pp. 561–567, 1991.

84. G. Simpson and K. Li, *Artificial Neural Networks: Solutions to Problems in Remote Sensing,* Rep. EOS-92/00(16000)-RP-001 Earth Observation Sciences, Ltd. (EOS) March 1993.

85. D. Verrall and G. Simpson, *Neural Networks for Meteosat Cloud Classification,* Rep. EOS-92/078-RP-001, Earth Observation Sciences, Ltd. (EOS), October 1992.

86. Daarla and Zhao, "A Learning Algorithm for a CMAC-Based System and Its Application to Classification of Ultrasonic Signals," *Ultrasonics,* vol. 32, pp. 91–98, 1994.

87. R.-C. Wen, et al., "A CMAC Neural Network Chip for Color Correction," *IEEE International Conference on Neural Networks,* Orlando, FL, vol. 3, pp. 1943–1948, 1994.

88. J. S. Albus, "A Theory of Cerebellar Functions," *Mathematical Biosciences,* vol. 10, pp. 25–61, 1971.

89. E. Ersu and H. Tolle, "A New Concept for Learning Control Inspired by Brain Theory," *IFAC 9th World Congress,* Budapest, Hungary, (publisher: International Federation of Automatic Control), 1984.

90. E. Ersu and H. Tolle, "Hierarchical Learning Control—An Approach with Neuron-Like Associative Memories," *IEEE Conference on Neural Information Processing Systems,* Denver, CO, 1988.

91. D. Ellison, "On the Convergence of the Multidimensional Albus Perceptron," *The International Journal of Robotics Research,* vol. 10, pp. 338–357, 1991.

92. Y.-F. Wong, "CMAC Learning Is Governed by a Single Parameter," *IEEE International Conference on Neural Networks,* San Francisco, vol. 1, pp. 1439–1443, 1993.

93. N. E. Cotter and T. J. Guillerm, "The CMAC and a Theorem of Kolmogorov," *Neural Networks,* vol. 5, pp. 221–228, 1992.

94. M. Brown and C. J. Harris, "The Modelling Abilities of the Binary CMAC," *IEEE International Conference on Neural Networks,* Orlando, FL, vol. 3, pp. 1335–1339, 1994.

95. S. Yao and Z. Bo, "Learning Convergence of CMAC in Cyclic Learning," *International Joint Conference on Neural Networks,* Nagoya, Japan, vol. 3, pp. 2583–2586, 1993.

96. Y. Jin, A. G. Pipe, and A. Winfield, "Stable Neural Control of Discrete Systems," *IEEE International Symposium on Intelligent Control,* Chicago, pp. 110–115, 1993.

97. J. Moody and C. Darken, "Speedy Alternatives to Back Propagation," *International Neural Network Society First Annual Meeting,* Boston, p. 202, 1988.

98. N. E. Cotter and O. N. Mian, "A Pulsed Neural Network Capable of Universal Approximation," *IEEE Transactions on Neural Networks,* vol. 3, pp. 308–314, 1992.

99. S. Lane, D. Handelman, and J. J. Gelfand, "Higher-Order CMAC Neural Networks—Theory and Practice," *American Control Conference,* Boston, vol. 2, pp. 1579–1585, 1991.

100. E. Ersu and H. Tolle, eds., *Learning Control Structures with Neuron-Like Associative Memory Systems,* VCH Verlagsgesellschaft mbH, pp. 417–438, 1988.

101. W. T. Miller, B. A. Box, E. C. Whitney, and J. M. Glynn, "Design and Implementation of a High Speed CMAC Neural Network Using Programmable Logic Cell Arrays," in *Advances in Neural Information Processing Systems,* vol. 3, R. P. Lippmann, J. E. Moody, and D. S. Touretzky, eds., Morgan Kaufmann, San Mateo, CA, pp. 1022–1027, 1991.

102. B. Yang, "A VLSI Implementation of the CMAC Neural Network," MS thesis, University of New Hampshire, 1992.

103. A. Kolez and N. M. Allinson, "Realisation of a Modified CMAC Architecture Using Reconfigurable Logic Devices," *3d Workshop on Neural Networks: Academic/Industrial/NASA/Defense,* Auburn, AL, SPIE vol. 1721, pp. 195–206, 1993.

CHAPTER 27

LEARNING IN NEURAL NETWORKS: VLSI IMPLEMENTATION STRATEGIES

Tuan A. Duong
Silvio P. Eberhardt*
Taher Daud
Anil Thakoor
Center for Space Microelectronics Technology,
Jet Propulsion Laboratory,
California Institute of Technology, Pasadena

Fully parallel hardware neural network implementations may be applied to high-speed recognition, classification, and mapping tasks in areas such as vision, or can be used as low-cost self-contained units for tasks such as error detection in mechanical systems (e.g., automobiles). Learning is required not only to satisfy application requirements, but also to overcome hardware-imposed limitations such as reduced dynamic range of connections. A learning algorithm may be implemented in hardware, in which case the application merely needs to provide training data (for supervised learning); or the hardware implements only a feedforward operation, in which case learning is under the control of a host computer that applies input patterns and updates connections according to the error of the measured outputs (i.e., hardware-in-the-loop learning). The latter method is useful if the network needs to be trained only once for an application, since it greatly simplifies the hardware, but at the cost of greater learning time and the requirement for a host computer.

Following a review of the emerging hardware implementation strategies for neural network learning reported in the literature, this chapter details a new architecture and supervised learning algorithm: *cascade back propagation* (*CBP*). It combines powerful features from other algorithms such as *cascade correlation* (*CC*)

---

* Present address: Department of Engineering, Swarthmore College, Swarthmore, Pennsylvania.

and *error back propagation* (*EBP*) and is particularly suited to problems of image and data classification and object discrimination. CBP is a constructive architecture in which a neuron (processing unit) is sequentially added to the network, and gradient descent is used to permanently fix the weights connected to that neuron, both input and output. Each new neuron has connections to the inputs and to each preceding neuron's output; thus each added neuron implements a hidden layer. The addition of each successive neuron provides the system with an opportunity to further reduce the mean-squared error. Because the average number of connections to a neuron is small, learning is quite fast.

Currently, the system is implemented by using analog CMOS VLSI and hardware-in-the-loop learning. To adapt the architecture for hardware with limited synaptic dynamic range, the maximum synaptic conductivity associated with later neurons is reduced, thus effectively reducing the synaptic quantized step size. Simulations and tests with analog CMOS VLSI hardware suggest that the system is capable of learning difficult problems (such as six-input parity and image classification) with synaptic quantizations as low as 5 bits, as opposed to the 8 to 16 bits required for EBP and CC learning algorithms.

27.1 INTRODUCTION

Modern general-purpose computers allow simulation of almost any neural network architecture and learning algorithm, and there is little doubt that such simulations in many cases afford the easiest and most cost-effective approach for neural network applications. However, there are major application areas that require or benefit from custom neural hardware. Custom hardware is necessary in cases where the required throughput is greater than can be sustained on available computers, due either to very large network size or the need for short (real-time) learning or response intervals. At the other extreme, a simple network used in a mass-produced commodity such as an automobile may only be cost-effective as a single-chip stand-alone neural system. In between, one might envision many applications where inexpensive, self-contained black box neural hardware performs tasks such as fault detection, actuator control, and adaptive home environmental regulation, to name just a few.

The field of neural network hardware is still in its infancy. Perhaps the only well-established neural hardware is the computer plug-in *accelerator board* that is capable of rapidly calculating such common neural primitives as multiply-accumulate, while other computational tasks are performed by the main processor. Despite the fact that dedicated neural chip sets have been on the market for close to a decade [1, 2], few custom neural systems have found their way into commercial products [3, 4]. In this chapter we review the most common technologies and techniques for implementing custom neural systems, and we give an example from our own work of an analog neural system capable of learning. We also stress the point that many of the learning algorithms that have been developed for computer-based simulations are not directly compatible with hardware, and so any hardware development effort must have as its centerpiece the development of a compatible learning algorithm.

The basic task of a neural network hardware (or hardware simulator) is independent of the implementation technology and can be divided into the following modes: (1) *mapping* a specified neural architecture onto the hardware while taking stock of the number of inputs, outputs, etc.; (2) *learning*—calculation and programming of synaptic connections (and possible network architecture) so that the network will perform desired mappings from input to output; and (3) *operation*—upon application of a complete set of inputs, the hardware must provide the results for the required input-to-output mapping.

Let us consider the computational load required by learning, evaluation, and operation. For serial simulations, the following algorithm applies to many learning methodologies:

1. while (network has not reached desired performance level)
{
   2. for (each training vector)
   {
     apply input vector
     3. for (each layer)
     {
       4. for (each neuron in layer)
       {
         5. for (each synapse connecting to neuron)
         {
           multiply activation by synapse weight
           accumulate result into neuron's input
         }
         calculate neuron's activation
       }
     }
     read outputs
     calculate error at output
     perform weight updates
   }
}.

Note that the weight-update sequence may require many more computations than the operation pass (loops 3 to 5), depending on the learning algorithm. Due to the nested nature of the loops, the computational load can increase dramatically with increased problem complexity (giving more loop 1 passes), increased network size (increasing loop 3, 4, and 5 passes), or a complex learning algorithm (increased computation in the inner loops). For example, a 2-2-1 network requiring, say, 100 passes to learn the exclusive-OR problem (2 bit parity) would require on the order of

$$(100 \text{ training passes}) \times (4 \text{ training patterns}) \times (2 \text{ passes}) \times$$
$$(3 \text{ layers}) \times (2 \text{ neurons/layer}) \times (2 \text{ synapses/neuron}) = 9600 \text{ operations}$$

where it is assumed that weight-update and operation passes have equivalent complexity (2 passes). Applying this simplistic model to 3-, 5-, and 8-bit parity, assuming that the number of hidden units is the same as the number of input layer units and the required number of training passes increases to 500, 2000, and 10,000, we see that the required numbers of operations are, respectively, 216×10^3, 9.6×10^6, and 983×10^6. It is obvious that larger applications would benefit tremendously if calculations could be carried out in a parallel fashion.

Nevertheless, the general-purpose computer simulation that carries out these calculations one at a time is near ideal in all respects save response time and, in some cases, cost. The computer can be programmed to implement almost any architecture and any learning algorithm, and signals are represented with high precision and dynamic range by floating-point variables. The same is not true of custom hardware: Networks are often limited in size, support only certain classes of architecture, and represent signals and weights with limited precision and (possibly) with large noise components. Thus, the success of a hardware implementation depends critically upon a judicious balance of the many tradeoffs involved in selecting a hardware technology, designing the circuits, fixing classes and sizes of architectures that will be supported, and crafting a compatible learning algorithm.

While we focus in this chapter on the most popular implementation technologies, namely, *complementary metal-oxide semiconductor* (*CMOS*) analog and digital, with signals that are continuous-valued (or quantized to many levels), we should mention several other technologies that have been reported in the literature for neural hardware implementations. Optical [5], thin-film [6–9], and charge-coupled device [10, 11] technologies have all been used to implement neural networks, but they require rather elaborate or specialized fabrication processes. A technology that uses standard CMOS, and that more closely models biological neural *wetware* functions, is pulse-mode circuits. Pulse-mode networks represent signals by the duty cycle or firing rate of pulse trains [12–15]. Weights, however, are generally stored by using analog or digital memories. A primary advantage of pulse-mode circuits lies in their space-efficient processing circuits, which combine analog circuit characteristics such as a few transistors per processing element and fully parallel implementations with small-size transistors. A possible advantage—and the primary disadvantage—of this approach is that dynamic range is traded off with time. Otherwise, pulse-mode circuits tend to exhibit the same difficulties as analog networks [16]. Several smaller-scale pulse-mode networks have been built and furnished with a learning algorithm [13, 15].

In the following sections, we hope to give the reader an appreciation of the characteristics of the more dominant technologies employed for neural implementations, including strengths and weaknesses that dictate the form of the implementations. Since our discussion of learning requires addressing details of hardware implementations, hardware is treated first. Issues having to do with learning, and in particular the incompatibility of many learning algorithms with limited-precision hardware, are then discussed. We present in detail a new learning algorithm, *cascade back propagation* (*CBP*), that is compatible with hardware implementations, and we give results from learning experiments conducted with CBP. In addition, we describe a further refinement in the learning algorithm and give simulation results to show that the method is particularly useful for reduced weight resolution, and therefore, suitable for analog hardware implementations.

27.2 HARDWARE OVERVIEW

One key characteristic that distinguishes different implementations is the level of parallelism. A neural network program running on a personal computer or workstation has no parallelism beyond engaging integer and floating-point processor units simultaneously. At any time, the general-purpose processor is calculating one synaptic weighting, the activation function of one neuron, or one connection update. Many custom digital implementations (and software implementations executing on a parallel computer system) follow this model in a semiparallel way: Each processing element calculates a subset of the network's connections and neuron activations. Throughput is increased by sharing the task over multiple processors. Further gains may be achieved by designing specialized custom processors optimized for the neural tasks required. However, there is often a tradeoff among speed of execution, network size, and generality, so that the more specialized processors are usually faster, but support only a limited number of architectures and learning algorithms.

The highest level of parallelism is achieved by implementing each synapse and each neuron as a distinct circuit. While fully parallel digital networks are rare in digital implementations, due to the silicon-hogging nature of digital weighting, aggregation, and activation-function lookup circuits, full parallelism is the rule in analog and other nondigital implementations, in part because multiplexing is more expensive, noise-prone, and difficult in the analog domain. Also, custom circuits that store weights, perform weighting, and implement neurons tend to be significantly smaller when implemented as analog rather than digital circuits, because the physics of semiconductor circuits can be exploited to obtain neural functionalities in a highly space- and power-efficient manner [17, 18].

Because both analog and digital technologies have their own particular inherent advantages, neither has yet come to dominate. The state of the art of hardware implementations can be abstracted from Table 27.1, which presents an overview of many of the hardware implementations that have been prototyped to date. For each design, the table includes, if available in the literature, specifications such as architecture size, speed, and learning algorithm supported. Most of the features listed in the table will be discussed in the following sections [19].

27.3 DIGITAL IMPLEMENTATIONS

Digital circuits, because of their high noise immunity and the resulting capacity to transfer information perfectly intact, are well suited to time-multiplexing. Partially parallel systems, with a handful of custom synapse and neuron circuits, can be constructed, allowing a flexibility that is difficult to achieve in analog technology: A given neuron circuit or synapse multiplier can calculate one, ten, or even thousands of neurons or connections within one pass with parallel processing. Thus, as long as sufficient memory for weight storage is available, almost any size neural architecture may be mapped onto a fixed number of processors. Bandwidth—often measured in *millions of connections per second* (*MCPS*) for data processing operation and *millions of connection updates per second* (*MCUPS*) for learning—remains relatively constant for such a circuit. Thus, the operation throughput—the reciprocal of the time lag between application of an input and availability of the output—is also inversely related to the complexity of the architecture that is mapped onto such a time-multiplexed system.

Most digital designs are indeed multiplexed, for the simple reason that a fully parallel digital system is impractical for all but small architectures, since each connection in the network generally requires silicon-hogging multiplier and adder circuits. Also, it would be wasteful to incorporate into each neuron circuit an activation-function lookup table, when the speed of the system is limited by not the lookup time, but the multiply-accumulate synaptic weighting and aggregation calculations. However, a moderately large fully parallel digital system, described below, has been constructed that uses eight 5-in silicon wafers [20].

Another advantage is that digital circuits are scalable—as fabrication technologies (which are often geared toward digital requirements) improve, circuits can be made ever smaller, allowing more processors on a chip, while simultaneously decreasing the execution time. Analog circuitry may not scale down to the same degree, because noise may increase as feature size is reduced. For example, transis-

TABLE 27.1 A Comprehensive Survey and Compilation of Hardware Implementations of Neural Networks Reported in Literature [19]

Electronic neural network chips—Commercially available, under development, and/or imaginary

Company	Reference number	Chip	First silicon	Technology source	Sponsor	No. of transistors	Connection updates/s (CUPS)
Adaptive Solutions Inc. (Beaverton, OR)	NN22, NN26	1) CNAPS prototype	12/90	Codesigner Inova MicroElec.	Venture Funds		2.50E + 08
	NN28	2) CNAPS-1064		(IME Med bankrupt in 1991)		1.40E + 07	1.00E + 08
American Neurologic (Sanford, FL)		1) Prototype 2) NLX-220	1992				
AT&T Bell Labs (Holmdel, NJ)	NN11	1) ANNA		SDC	US Army	180,000	
Bell Communications Research Corp., Inc. (Morristown, NJ)	NN46		In progress				
Boeing Defense & Space (Seattle, WA)		1) AVPS-POC2					
CA Institute of Technology (Pasadena, CA)	NN77 NN77 NN79	1) Contour-length 2) Figure ground 3)			NSF, ONR, and RISC DAPRA/ NSF		
CalTech & JH Univ. (Pasadena, CA)	NN90				RIA-NSF, MOSIS, HP		
Center for Neural Engr. at USC (LA, CA)	NN07	1) Analog VLSI			DARPA, TRW, & Samsung		
CISC—Univ. of Michigan (Ann Arbor, MI)	NN06	1) 16 Channel CMOS			NIH	7,100	
Computational NN Center (Lyngby, Denmark)	NN14	1) Neuron chip					
Echelon Corporation (Palo Alto, CA)	NN18 NN18	1) MC143120 2) MC143150					

Connections/s (CPS)	Semiconductor technology	Clock speed	No. of neurons	No. of weights	Algorithms supported	Circuit type	Partners	Miscellaneous
1.60E + 09	0.8μ CMOS		64		BP		Mitsubishi Elec., Sharp, Meideneha	(buggy)
1.28E + 09	0.8μ CMOS	20 MHz	64		LVQ2	Digital		Used in server with up to 512 processors
							Samsung	Suspended neural work Fuzzy processor
1.00E + 10	0.9μ CMOS	20 MHz	8	4,096		Mixed A/D		For OCR
2.50E + 08	2μ CMOS	10 MHz	40	960		Hybrid		Cascadable
	2μ CMOS		2,304			Analog	Tanner Research	Dynamic wire technology
	2μ CMOS					Analog	RISC	for vision circuitry
	2μ CMOS		6		EGD, K-W	Analog		
	2μ CMOS n-well						C. Mead	
	2μ CMOS double polysil.	1.024 MHz	33	252	EKF	Analog		For communication receiver applications
	3μ CMOS 1 metal/1 poly	10 MHz						80-mW power dissipation
	CMOS		100	10,000		Analog		Arbitrary topology
							Motorola & Toshiba	External data bus Self-contained memory (EEPROM, SRAM, ROM)

TABLE 27.1   (*Continued*)   A Comprehensive Survey and Compilation of Hardware Implementations of Neural Networks Reported in Literature [19]

Electronic neural network chips—Commercially available, under development, and/or imaginary

Company	Reference number	Chip	First silicon	Technology source	Sponsor	No. of transistors	Connection updates/s (CUPS)
Ecole Polytech/ Fed. Laus (Lausanne, Switzerland)	NN60	1) L-Neuro 1.0				160,000	
Fujitsu (Kawasaki, Japan)	NN31 NN70	1) 2)	1988 In progress				
General Dynamics (Pomona, CA)	NN23, NN32	1) AXON 1	1990				
Hitachi, Ltd. (Tokyo, Japan)	NN30	1) Prototype	1989				
	NN17, NN27	2) 1024 Prototype	In progress	Central Research Laboratory			
Hughes Research Lab (Malibu, CA)	NN74	1) 3D Wafer					
Hughes Tech. Center (Carlsbad, CA)	NN27		In progress				
HNC (San Diego, CA)	NN26,NN28	1) SNAP	1992		US Army/ Ft. Monmouth	90,000 gates	6.25E + 06
	NN26,NN28	2) VIP	1992		DARPA	110,000 gates	1.00E + 08
Intel (Santa Clara, CA)	NN13,NN28, NN40,NN53	1) ETANN (80170NX)	1989	Naval Weapons Center			1.20E + 09
	NN20,NN28 NN82	2) Ni 1000	?/93		DARPA/ONR	3.70E + 06	
Irvine Sensors Corp.(Costa Mesa, CA)	NN19,NN25, NN43	1) 3DANN			BMDO/IST, ONR		
JPL (Pasadena, CA)	NN01, NN84 NN02, NN03 NN47	1) Path planner 2) Neuron-synapse building block 3) Asset manager 4) Associative memory					
King's College (London, UK)	NN04	1) pRAM			SERC	39,000 gates	
Korea Telecom (Seoul, Korea)		1) URAN					
Matsushita Electric (Osaka, Japan)		1) QNC				27,000 gates	5.00E + 06

Connections/s (CPS)	Semiconductor technology	Clock speed	No. of neurons	No. of weights	Algorithms supported	Circuit type	Partners	Miscellaneous
2.56E + 07	1.6µ CMOS		64	960	BP, Kohen., Hebbian			Real-time robotics applications
	2µ Bi-CMOS		50		BP	Digital Analog		Dispersion problems
1.20E + 09			40					Technology transferred to E-metrics (Ontario, CA)
	0.8µ CMOS		576	1,152				
1.37E + 09	0.5µ CMOS	3.9 MHz	1,024	1.00E + 06		Digital		75-mW power dissipation
2.4E + 09 2.04E + 10	3-D WSI							Vision integration net and back propagation net
1.00E + 07	EEPROM		300	100,000			NOSC (San Diego)	
8.00E + 07	1.0µ CMOS gate array		4		BP/CP, SOM, LVQ2,	Digital		Designed to work in 16 chip sets (1.28E + 09 cps)
3.2E + 08— 1.28E + 09	1.0µ CMOS gate array		64		ART,PNN, and others	Digital		Two chip sets (ViP-1 and ViP-2)
2.00E + 09			64	10,240	BP/RBP Madaline III			
1.00E + 10	0.8µ EEPROM	25 MHz	1,024	2.56E + 05	RCE	Digital	Nestor	ATC applications
3.40E + 10		50 MHz	16,384			Analog		Human eye and brain emulator
6.00E + 09	2µ CMOS n-well	7 MHz	600			Digital		
5.00E + 08	2µ CMOS p-well		32	992	Cascade BP	Analog		Currently being commercialized
	2µ CMOS 2µ CMOS		1,600		Cascade BP	Analog Hybrid		Stores 128 patterns of dimension 16
	1µ CMOS		256					Up to 5 chips can be linked
2.00E + 09	1.2µ CMOS		14-225	3,596		Digital		
2.05E + 10	1.2µ double metal CMOS		4,736	2.00E + 06				Weights are stored off chip

TABLE 27.1   (*Continued*)   A Comprehensive Survey and Compilation of Hardware
Implementations of Neural Networks Reported in Literature [19]

Electronic neural network chips—Commercially available, under development, and/or imaginary

Company	Reference number	Chip	First silicon	Technology source	Sponsor	No. of transistors	Connection updates/s (CUPS)
Melco-Mitsubishi Electric (Hyogo, Japan)	NN08	1) NN LSI circuit		LSI Labs			
Micro Computing Lab(Lausanne, Switzerland)	NN15 NN15	1) GENES HN8 2) GENES HH8	1990 1991			380,000 800,000	
Micro Devices (Lake Mary, FL)	NN38, NN53	1) MD 1220 (neural bit slice)					
MIT Lincoln Laboratory (Lexington, MA)	NN91	1) NNC2					
Neural Semiconductor (Irvine, CA)	NN36, NN53	1) CNU3232S	1992				
Neural Technologies, Ltd. (Petersfield, England)	NN41, NN45	1) NiSP					
North Carolina University (Raleigh, NC)	NN12, NN34	1) TinMANN			IBM	4,000	
NTT LSI Laboratories (Kanagawa, Japan)	NN09	1) PDN Model				15,500 gates 582,400 trans.	
Oxford Computer, Inc. (Oxford, CN)	NN42	1) OBL Chip					
Ricoh, Ltd. (Tokyo, Japan)	NN23	1) RN-100	4/90				4.00E + 07
	NN23	2) RN-200	7/92			200,000 gates	1.50E + 09
Siemens, AG (Munich, Germany)	NN21 NN61, NN65, NN67, NN83	1) MA-16 prototype 2) MA-16	1992		Esprit	610,000 gates 510,000	4.00E + 08
Stanford University (Stanford, CA)	NN81				NASA	400,000	3.50E + 08
Sydney Univ. EE (Sydney, Australia)	NN59 NN80	1) Kakadu 2) WATTLE					
Synaptics, Inc. (San Jose, CA)	NN42, NN69 NN76	1) I-1000 neural eye 2) RBF chip			DITRD		
Tohoku Univ. (Sendai, Japan)	NN73	1) Neuron MOS transistor(vMOS)					
Toshiba (Tokyo, Japan)	NN24, NN75 NN24, NN75	1) Synapse chip 2) Neuron chip				150,000 11,000	1.80E + 09
Toyoshi Univ. of Tech.(Toyoshi, Japan)	NN64						

Connections/s (CPS)	Semiconductor technology	Clock speed	No. of neurons	No. of weights	Algorithms supported	Circuit type	Partners	Miscellaneous
8.00E+04	0.8μ CMOS		400	40,000	Boltzmann	Analog		
1.10E+08		10 MHz	16		Hopfield		SFIT	4 × 4 chip set
1.00E+09		40 MHz	24		Hebbian	Digital		
1.00E+07			8			Digital		Weights stored in external memory
1.92E+09	2μ CCD/CMOS dm-dps	10 MHz		980		Digital		Tech. based on charge-coupled device
		25 MHz	32	1,024		Digital		$500/chip 100,000 patterns/s
							Smith Industries	
1.95E+05	2μ CMOS p-well	15 MHz	1		Kohonen, Markovian	Digital		
8.00E+09	0.8μ CMOS	15.6 MHz	13	832		Digital		Low-power chain-reaction (LCR) architecture
	Submicron CMOS				unrestricted			
8.00E+07		10 MHz	1	8				
3.00E+09	0.8μ CMOS	12 MHz	16	256		Digital		To be used in photocopier
4.00E+08	1.0μ CMOS	25 MHz (demo)	128	65,536	unrestricted	Digital		$2K/chip
8.00E+08	1.0μ CMOS	50 MHz	16+	16+		Digital		Signal preprocessing
	1.2μ CMOS	125 MHz	32	20,480	Boltzmann	Digital		
						Analog		20-μW power consumption
	1.2μ CMOS		10	84	CSA	Analog		
						Analog		<100 mW
	2μ CMOS	90 kHz				Analog		For radial basis function
	Double poly silicon CMOS							Logic design using floating-gate PD
	0.8μ double metal CMOS	50 MHz		576	Amari-Hopfield	Analog		Layered neural net Two chip set (neuron & synapse chip work together)
	0.8μ dm CMOS		24		BP, Hebbian	Analog		
					BP			Based on optoelectronic integrated circuit model

TABLE 27.1 (*Continued*)   A Comprehensive Survey and Compilation of Hardware Implementations of Neural Networks Reported in Literature [19]

Electronic neural network chips—Commercially available, under development, and/or imaginary

Company	Reference number	Chip	First silicon	Technology source	Sponsor	No. of transistors	Connection updates/s (CUPS)
TRW (San Diego, CA)	NN29		In progress				
Univ. of California & ICSI (Berkeley, CA)	NN16	1) SPERT	In progress		ONR & NSF		1.00E + 08
Univ. of Delaware (Newark, DE)	NN86						
Univ. of Edinburgh (Edinburgh, Scotland)	NN78	1) EPSILON					
Univ. of Minnesota (Duluth, MN)	NN58						
Univ. of Southern Calif. (Los Angeles, CA)	NN63	1) Early vision					
	NN68	2) Video motion detector					
Univ. of Tsukuba (Tsukuba, Japan)	NN62	1) Pulse density modulating (PDM) chip					
Univ. of Waterloo (Waterloo, Ont., Can.)	NN85						
Univ. of WI-Platteville (Platteville, WI)	NN57	1) Neural network controller	1992				
Washington St. Univ. (Pullman, WA)	NN87	1) PWTA					
Westinghouse (Baltimore, MD)	NN27, NN33	1) MSPSE	1993	Elec. Design, Inc. Analog Devices	ARPA		

Optoelectronic neural network chips—Commercially available, under development, and/or imaginary

JILA— University of CO (Boulder, CO)	NN88	1) Photorefractive ring resonator			ONR & AFOSR		
JPL (Pasadena, CA)	NN50	1) Optoelectronic system					
Mitsubishi Electric Corp. (Hyogo, Japan)	NN05, NN10, NN66	1) Optical neural chip	1988	Central Research Laboratory			
Tel-Aviv Univ. (Tel-Aviv, Israel)	NN71						
Accurate Automation Chattanooga, TN	NN51	1) Sparse MIMD AAC NNP					
Adaptive Solutions, Inc. (Beaverton, OR)	NN43	1) CNAPS/VME16					
	NN55	2) CNAPS/PC board	1994		ARPA		

Connections/s (CPS)	Semiconductor technology	Clock speed	No. of neurons	No. of weights	Algorithms supported	Circuit type	Partners	Miscellaneous
	1.0μ CMOS							
1.00E + 11	MOSIS CMOS	50 MHz		64	BP			
						Analog		VLSI neuromorph
3.60E + 08	1.5μ CMOS dmsp			3,600		Analog		Pulse stream neural state signaling
	2.0μ CMOS			9	BEP	Analog		LSI prototype
1.80E + 10	1.2μ CMOS		5			Analog		Multiple neuro-processor chip
8.32E + 10	1.2μ CMOS		25	675		Analog		
						Digital		High scalability
	0.8μ BiCMOS					Mixed A/D		
	2.0μ CMOS		17	15		Analog		Control applications
					Hopfield			
	0.6μ CMOS	33 MHz				Digital		To be used in RAH-66
					Lotka-Volterra			
1.00E + 12						Analog		Robotic vision and pattern recognition
1.00E + 12		10 MHz	32	1024	BP	Analog		Neuron density is 2000/cm²
								Four quadrant matrix-vector multiplier
1.40E + 08		33 MHz	8,000	32,000		Hybrid		Single/multi-processor environment
		20 MHz						16 processors 1.3 BOPS 6.4 BOPS
			128					

TABLE 27.1 A Comprehensive Survey and Compilation of Hardware
Implementations of Neural Networks Reported in Literature [19]

Electronic neural network chips—Commercially available, under development, and/or imaginary

Company	Reference number	Chip	First silicon	Technology source	Sponsor	No. of transistors	Connection updates/s (CUPS)
Adaptive Solutions Inc. (Beaverton, OR)	NN22, NN26	1) CNAPS prototype	12/90	Codesigner Inova MicroElec.	Venture Funds		2.50E + 08
	NN28	2) CNAPS-1064		(IME Med bankrupt in 1991)		1.40E + 07	1.00E + 08
American Neurologic (Sanford, FL)		1) Prototype 2) NLX-220	1992				
AT&T Bell Labs (Holmdel, NJ)	NN11	1) ANNA		SDC	US Army	180,000	
Bell Communications Research Corp., Inc. (Morristown, NJ)	NN46		In progress				
Boeing Defense & Space (Seattle, WA)		1) AVPS-POC2					
CA Institute of Technology (Pasadena, CA)	NN77 NN77 NN79	1) Contour-length 2) Figure ground 3)			NSF, ONR, and RISC DAPRA/ NSF		
CalTech & JH Univ. (Pasadena, CA)	NN90				RIA-NSF, MOSIS, IIP		
Center for Neural Engr. at USC (LA, CA)	NN07	1) Analog VLSI			DARPA, TRW, & Samsung		
CISC—Univ. of Michigan (Ann Arbor, MI)	NN06	1) 16 Channel CMOS			NIH	7,100	
Computational NN Center (Lyngby, Denmark)	NN14	1) Neuron chip					
Echelon Corporation (Palo Alto, CA)	NN18 NN18	1) MC143120 2) MC143150					

Connections/s (CPS)	Semiconductor technology	Clock speed	No. of neurons	No. of weights	Algorithms supported	Circuit type	Partners	Miscellaneous
1.60E + 09	0.8μ CMOS		64		BP		Mitsubishi Elec., Sharp, Meideneha	(buggy)
1.28E + 09	0.8μ CMOS	20 MHz	64		LVQ2	Digital		Used in server with up to 512 processors
							Samsung	Suspended neural work Fuzzy processor
1.00E + 10	0.9μ CMOS	20 MHz	8	4,096		Mixed A/D		For OCR
2.50E + 08	2μ CMOS	10 MHz	40	960		Hybrid		Cascadable
	2μ CMOS		2,304			Analog	Tanner Research	Dynamic wire technology for vision circuitry
	2μ CMOS					Analog	RISC	
	2μ CMOS		6		EGD, K-W	Analog		
	2μ CMOS n-well						C. Mead	
	2μ CMOS double polysil.	1.024 MHz	33	252	EKF	Analog		For communication receiver applications
	3μ CMOS 1 metal/1 poly	10 MHz						80-mW power dissipation
	CMOS		100	10,000		Analog		Arbitrary topology
							Motorola & Toshiba	External data bus Self-contained memory (EEPROM, SRAM,

TABLE 27.1 (*Continued*)   A Comprehensive Survey and Compilation of Hardware Implementations of Neural Networks Reported in Literature [19]

Reference list: Artificial neural network chips and boards

Ref. no.	Article title	Reference title/organization	Author	Date
NN01	Rectangular Array of Digital Processors for Planning Paths	JPL New Tech Report NPO-18727	Tawel, R.	Dec. 1993
NN02	Cascaded VLSI Chips Help Neural Network to Learn	JPL New Tech Report NPO-18645	Duong, T., et al.	Dec. 1993
NN03	Non-Volatile Array of Synapses for Neural Network	JPL New Tech Report NPO-18578	Kemeny, S.	Dec. 1993
NN04	The pRAM: An Adaptive VLSI Chip	IEEE Transactions on Neural Networks	Clarkson, T. G.	May 1993
NN05	Optical Learning Neurochip with Internal Analog Memory	Applied Optics	Nitta, Y.	Mar. 1993
NN06	A 16-Channel CMOS Neural Stimulating Array	IEEE Journal of Solid-State Circuits	Tanghe, S. J	Dec. 1992
NN07	A Programmable Analog VLSI NN Processor for Communication Receivers	IEEE Transactions on Neural Networks	Choi, J.	May 1993
NN08	A Refreshable Analog VLSI NN Chip with 400 Neurons and 40K Synapses	IEEE Journal of Solid-State Circuits	Arima, Y.	Dec. 1992
NN09	A High-Speed Digital NN Chip with Low-Power Chain-Reaction Architecture	IEEE Journal of Solid-State Circuits	Uchimura, K.	Dec. 1992
NN10	Melco's Neural Chip; Holography Research	IEEE Micro	Kahaner, D. K.	Aug. 1992
NN11	Application of the ANNA NN Chip to High-Speed Character Recognition	IEEE Transactions on Neural Networks	Sackinger, E.	May 1992
NN12	The TinMANN VLSI Chip	IEEE Transactions on Neural Networks	Melton, M. S.	May 1992
NN13	The MOD 2 Neurocomputer System Design	IEEE Transactions on Neural Networks	Mumford, M. L.	May 1992
NN14	An Analog CMOS Chip Set for NNs with Arbitrary Topologies	IEEE Transactions on Neural Networks	Lansner, J. A.	May 1993
NN15	A Generic Systolic Array Building Block for NNs with On-Chip Learning	IEEE Transactions on Neural Networks	Lehmann, C.	May 1993
NN16	The Design of a Neuro-Microprocessor	IEEE Transactions on Neural Networks	Wawrzynek, J	May 1993
NN17	A Single 1.5V Digital Chip for a 10⁶ Synapse Neural Network	IEEE Transactions on Neural Networks	Watanabe, T.	May 1993
NN18	Echelon: Networking Control	IEE Review	Heath, S.	Oct. 1992
NN19	Neural Network System to Stimulate Human Brain and Eye	Defense Electronics	K., L. A.	Oct. 1993
NN20	Darpa Gets Neural Chip from Intel	Electronic Engineering Times	Johnson, R. C.	Feb. 1993
NN21	Siemens Fields Big, Fast Neural IC	Electronic Engineering Times	Johnson, R. C.	Dec. 1992
NN22	Adaptive Adapts Its CNAPS Chip	Electronic Engineering Times	Wirbel, L.	Mar. 1993
NN23	Ricoh Announces Neural Microchip	Electronic Engineering Times	Yoshida, J	Jul. 1992
NN24	Neural IC Beefed Up	Electronic Engineering Times		Sept. 1992
NN25	3-D Stacking Used to Build Neural Network	Electronic Engineering Times	Wirbel, L.	Sept. 1992
NN26	Neural Chips Pour 100M 'cups'	Electronic Engineering Times	Johnson, R. C.	Oct. 1992
NN27	Neural Microchips Go Commercial	Electronic Engineering Times	Johnson, R. C.	June 1992
NN28	Working with Neural Networks	IEEE Spectrum	Hammerstrom, D.	July 1993
NN29	Raytheon Dealing for TRW's IC Business	Electronic Engineering Times	Gold, M.	June 1992
NN30	Hitachi Neural Prototype Thinks, Learns Quickly		Reinhardt, A.	
NN31	Fujitsu Plays Cops 'N Robbers to Apprehend Expert AI	Electronic Engineering Times	Johnson, R. C.	Feb. 1989
NN32	GD Claims Neural Chip Breakthrough	Military & Aerospace Electronics	Adams, C.	Apr. 1993
NN33	Westinghouse Readies Neural Network Computer	Military & Aerospace Electronics	Keller, J	July 1989
NN34	TinMANN: The Interger Markovian Artificial Neural Network	Computer Science Laboratory	Van den Bout, D. E.	Dec. 1987
NN35	Electronic Neural Network Chips	Applied Optics	Jackel, L. D.	Feb. 1993
NN36	Neural Network Resource Guide	AI Expert	Shaw, J	
NN37	Introducing the MM32K-AT	Current Technology, Inc.	Current Tech.	
NN38	MD1220—Neural Bit Slice	Micro Devices	Internet DL	Feb. 1994
NN39	Neural Network Solutions	Intel	Intel	
NN40	80170NX—ETANN	Intel	Intel	Mar. 1993
NN41	PCs Get Neural-Net Training	Electronic Engineering Times	Woolnough, R.	Aug. 1992
NN42	Are Artificial Neural Networks Finally Ready for Market?	Electronics	Manuel, T.	Aug. 1988
NN43	Neural Nets Carve a Niche in Military Systems	Military & Aerospace Electronics	Keller, J.	Feb. 1994

	Title	Author	Source	Date
NN44	Hardware: Accelerator Card for Neural Net Training	Johnson, R. C.	PCAI	Dec. 1993
NN45	In Britain, Neural Nets Are Bursting Out All Over	Bylinsky, G.	Electronic Engineering Times	Nov. 1992
NN46	Computers that Learn by Doing	Daud, T.	Fortune	Sept. 1993
NN47	A Neuroprocessor for Asset Management		JPL, Calif. Institute of Technology	1987
NN48	The Retina: An Approachable Part of the Brain	Dowling, J. E.	Belknap/Harvard Univ. Press	1992
NN49	Neurons and Networks: An Introduction to Neuroscience	Dowling, J. E.	Belknap/Harvard Univ. Press	Nov. 1990
NN50	Fast Feature-Recognizing Optoelectronic System	Thakoor, S.	NASA Technical Briefs	1993
NN51	Sparse MIMD Neural Network Processor	AAC	Accurate Automation Corp.	May 1994
NN52	Neural Networks		PCAI	1993
NN53	Advanced Methods in Neural Computing	Wasserman, P. D.	Van Nostrand Reinhold	
NN54	A Massively-Parallel SIMD Processor for Neural Network/Machine Vision	Glover, M. A.	Current Technology, Inc.	Feb. 1994
NN55	ARPA Awards $2 Million for Massively-Parallel PC	Rayner, B.	Military & Aerospace Electronics	July 1993
NN56	Product Showcase: Accelerate Your Train		AI Expert	1993
NN57	On the Design of a Neural Network Chip for Control Applications	Narathong, C.	Proceedings—IEEE Inter. Symp. C&S	1993
NN58	Modular Analog CMOS LSI for Feedforward NN with On-Chip BEP Learning	Wang, Y.	Proceedings—IEEE Inter. Symp. C&S	1993
NN59	Low Power Trainable Analog Neural Network Classifier Chip	Leong, P.	Proceedings—IEEE CIC Conference	Sept. 1993
NN60	Neural Accelerator for Parallelization of Back-Propagation Algorithm	Franzi, E.	Microprocessing and Microprogramming	1993
NN61	Architecture and VLSI Design of a VLSI Neural Signal Processor	Ramacher, U.	Proceedings—IEEE Inter. Symp. C&S	Feb. 1992
NN62	PDM Digital Neural Network System	Hirai. Y.	Electronics & Communications in Japan	Apr. 1993
NN63	VLSI Neuroprocessor for Image Restoration	Lee, J-C	Journal of VLSI Signal Processing	Nov. 1992
NN64	Optoelectronic Adaptive Device and Its Learning Performance	Kanamori, K.	Electronics & Communications in Japan	June 1993
NN65	General-Purpose Signal Processor Architecture for Neurocomputing	Ramacher, U.	Journal of VLSI Signal Processing	Mar. 1993
NN66	Optical Neuro-Devices	Kyuma, K.	Optoelectronics—Devices & Technics	Feb. 1993
NN67	Design of a General-Purpose Neural Signal Processor	Beichter, J	Neurocomputing	Mar. 1993
NN68	VLSI Neuroprocessors for Video Motion Detection	Lee, J-C	IEEE Transactions on Neural Networks	Sept. 1992
NN69	Neural Nets are Starting to Make Sense	McDonald, J. A.	Biosensors & Bioelectronics	Fall 1993
NN70	Analog Neurochip and Its Applications to Multilayered Artificial NN	Masumoto. D.	Fujitsu Scientific and Technical Journal	1993
NN71	Four-Quadrant Optical Matrix Vector Multiplication Machine as a NNP	Abramson, S.	Proceedings of SPIE	July 1993
NN72	Programmable Parallel Digital Neurocomputer	Shimokawa, Y.	IEICE Transactions on Electronics	Mar. 1993
NN73	Neuron MOS Binary-Logic Integrated Circuits—Part I	Shibata, T.	IEEE Transactions on Electron Devices	1993
NN74	3-D Wafer Stack Neurocomputing	Campbell, M. L.	IEEE Inter. Conf. on Wafer Scale Integration	Dec. 1993
NN75	Neuro Chips with On-Chip BP and/or Hebbian Learning	Takeshi. S.	IEEE Journal of Solid-State Circuits	1993
NN76	An Analog VLSI Chip for Radial Basis Functions	Platt, J. C.	ANIPS 5	1993
NN77	Object Based Analog VLSI Vision Circuits	Koch, C.	ANIPS 5	1993
NN78	Generic Analog Neural Computation—The EPSILON Chip	Churcher, S.	ANIPS 6	1994
NN79	A Learning Analog NN Chip with Continuous-Time Recurrent Dynamics	Cauwenberghs, G.	ANIPS 6	1994
NN80	WATTLE: A Trainable Gain Analogue VLSI Neural Network	Coggins, R.	ANIPS 6	1994
NN81	Digital Boltzmann VLSI for Constraint Satisfaction and Learning	Peterson, A. M.	ANIPS 6	1994
NN82	Intel and Nestor to Commercialize Neural-Net Chip	Bara. N.	BYTE	Mar. 1994
NN83	Special Chips Are at the Core of World's Fastest Neuro-Computer	Gosch. J	Electronics	Jan. 1993
NN84	High-Speed Path Planning	Kemeny, S.	JPL	1994
NN85	An Improved Programmable NN and VLSI Architecture Using BiCMOS . . .	Zhang, D.	Proceedings—1994 Int NN Society AM	June 1994
NN86	Analog VLSI Neuromorph with Spatially Extensive Dendritic Tree	Elias, J. G.	Proceedings—1994 Int NN Society AM	June 1994
NN87	VLSI Implementation of a Pulse-Coded Winner-Take-All Network	Meador, J. L.	Proceedings—1994 Int NN Society AM	June 1994
NN88	Optical Implementation of a Self-Organizing Feature Extractor	Anderson, D. Z.	ANIPS 4	1992
NN89	A Neurocomputer Board Based on the ANNA Neural Network Chip	Sackinger, E.	ANIPS 4	1992
NN90	A Contrast Sensitive Silicon Retina with Reciprocal Synapses	Boahen, K. A.	ANIPS 4	1992
NN91	CCD Neural Network Processors for Pattern Recognition	Chiang, A. M.	ANIPS 4	1992

tor edge effects may become more pronounced as transistors are made smaller, resulting in larger voltage offsets. Also, electromagnetic pickup from adjacent wires may increase as wires are deposited closer to each other, and larger temperature variations may occur as current densities and fluctuations increase. As noise levels increase, it can be expected that noise-intolerant learning algorithms will fail and that noise-tolerant algorithms will take longer to learn. However, the analog-digital tradeoff will still be decided based on the type of application, requirement of precision, power consumption, processing time, and silicon real estate.

Recent innovations in digital design and fabrication technologies have already been applied to neural networks, making possible several of the larger-scale designs in Table 27.1. *Wafer-scale integration* (*WSI*) has been used to implement a single integrated circuit on a 5-in-diameter wafer, implementing 576 time-multiplexed neuron circuits with associated synapses, using 40 million transistors [21]. The wafer was mapped with a fully connected network implementing, without learning, the 16-city traveling salesperson problem. A solution was obtained after only 0.1 s, giving a throughput of 1.2 *giga connections per second* (*GCPS*). An even more ambitious implementation involved a battery of eight 5-in wafers as a WSI neural network with 1000 neurons [20]. EBP learning was incorporated into the hardware, giving a maximum weight-update rate (with all neurons used) of 2 GCUPS. The system was initially used for signature verification and stock price prediction, and it was found that the hardware learned 1 to 3 times as fast as a simulation running on a Hitachi S-820 supercomputer. While these two designs illustrate how rapidly new digital technologies can be adapted to neural networks, note that WSI systems would be quite expensive, even if mass-produced.

27.4 ANALOG IMPLEMENTATIONS

Given the "messy" analog electronic circuit milieu of time-invariant offset voltages and currents, induced and generated noise, drift, and temperature dependence, it is rather remarkable that analog networks can be made to function at all! However, biological *wetware* is at least as noisy a medium, and certainly nature has found a way to overcome the noise effects sufficiently that neural systems can exhibit highly discriminatory behavior. Carver Mead has argued that the physical characteristics of (subthreshold) analog circuits model closely those of biological neural tissue [18]. This suggests that once we know the learning algorithms employed by biological neural systems, we may be able to directly apply these to analog hardware. Moreover, even with current analog hardware, it appears that the collection of noisy and imprecise neurons and synapses can behave with much higher accuracy than can the individual components [22]. Thus, the challenge is to find the architectures and algorithms that best learn a task, while reducing the effects of the underlying circuit nonidealities. However, investigators are also attempting to "clean up" analog circuits by reducing noise components, in one case by automatically canceling offset voltages [23].

Most analog neural implementations developed so far show marked similarities (Fig. 27.1). Inputs, coded as voltages to take advantage of a wire's ability to distribute voltage, are routed to one multiplier circuit for each synaptic connection. Each multiplier derives the other input from a memory cell in which is stored that synapse's weight. Multiplier output signals, representing the weight inputs for the next layer of neurons, are coded as currents to take advantage of a wire's ability to aggregate currents. Finally, neuron circuits apply a nonlinear activation function to the aggregated

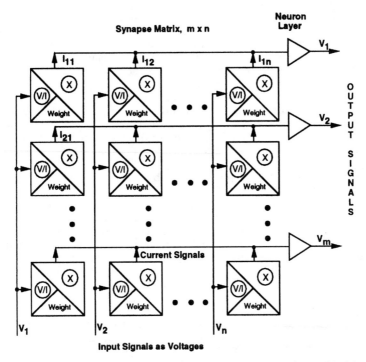

FIGURE 27.1   A schematic block diagram showing the synapse (square blocks) and neuron (triangles) functions and signal flow. For maximum generality, outputs could be connected on-chip to inputs, and a feedforward network could be mapped onto this architecture by nulling synapses leading from any layer to the neurons in the same or earlier layer(s).

weighted inputs, and supply a voltage output that can be routed to the next layer of multipliers or used as system output.

From this description, it can be inferred that a primary advantage of analog implementations is that the aggregation operation is essentially performed by the interconnection wiring, whereas in digital implementations, each synapse output must be aggregated to the appropriate neuron input network by using one adder time slot. Another advantage of many analog implementations is that the dynamic range of analog circuitry is limited by the noise characteristics, not the number of bits, as in digital circuits. Thus, whereas a semicustom digital network may be limited to fixed 8-bit weight resolution by the designers, analog networks may reach 10 bits of resolution, with stochastic (noise) effects that may additionally serve to mitigate some of the problems associated with hard-quantized networks and learning. For example, in cases where a neuron is clipped during learning, a digital weight-update signal to the synapses feeding that neuron may always be zero, whereas an analog update signal with noise may succeed in dislodging the neuron, thus bringing the network out of a local minimum.

Several primary differences beyond mere circuit detail serve to distinguish implementations and have major effects on system performance and capabilities. First and foremost is the network architecture. Either the architecture can be fixed, in which case only subsets of that particular hard-wired architecture may be mapped onto the chip, or programming circuitry can be added to allow some flexibility in routing synapses to neurons and perhaps controlling the number of layers in the network. Because such programming circuitry can take up a significant part of a chip's silicon real estate, the total number of usable synapses and neurons per unit silicon area will be correspondingly lower. The most general architecture is the fully connected recurrent network, in which each neuron's output is routed through synapses to each neuron's input. By setting all feedback synapses to zero, any feedforward network can be mapped onto this architecture. While the network is very general, at least one-half the synapses are unused in a feedforward network, and likely many more, since it appears that many synapses are unnecessary even in feedforward networks [24].

A paradigm that has proved popular is the building-block approach [25], where several chips can be interconnected in different ways to obtain a good measure of architectural flexibility. For example, synapse arrays can be implemented on independent chips, or each chip could implement one layer of a feedforward network. Large networks could be constructed by tying many chips together. Disadvantages of this approach are the added chip and interchip wiring costs and the throughput penalties resulting from the capacitances associated with chip pins.

A second difference between implementations lies in the method used to store connection weights. Currently, three mechanisms are being exploited: digital memory with analog converter, capacitive charge retention, and floating gate. While digital weight storage does not have the drift problems of the other methods and allows fast downloading from the computer, it is space-intensive since a *digital-to-analog converter (DAC)* must be furnished on-chip for each weight, and resolution is limited to about 6 bits [24, 26]. Storing weights as charge on capacitors [27] is relatively space-efficient, but requires that leaked-off charge be periodically replaced, either by interspersing learning cycles with feedforward passes [28, 29] or by storing weights digitally and sequentially refreshing the charge by using one or more off-chip DACs [30]. Finally, floating-gate memories [1, 31] store charge with nonvolatility, using *electrically erasable programmable read-only memory (EEPROM)* technology. The charge can be nondestructively and continuously monitored by special transistor structures. Charges are added or removed by quantum-mechanical tunneling, a process that is slow and may require voltages that over time damage the storage device. Nevertheless, floating-gate memories hold much promise for single-chip stand-alone neural networks with on-chip learning, particularly where fast learning is not required.

The third and final major factor distinguishing analog learning implementations is the support for learning. On-chip learning support ranges from none, as is the case with feedforward hardware networks where learning is executed solely by computer, to sophisticated stand-alone systems where the learning portions of the chip may far exceed in size the feedforward execution portions. This topic will be pursued extensively in a later section.

Let us consider in greater depth a typical analog implementation. The majority of analog designs to date used the charge storage mechanism for weight memories, with a sample-and-hold gate controlled by select logic, as shown in Fig. 27.2. External address lines are decoded to allow random access of a synapse. This closes the sample-and-hold for that synapse and allows the voltage from external computer-controlled digital-to-analog converters (DACs) to be applied to a capacitor that stores the weight. (Thus, strictly speaking, the weights are actually stored in the computer's memory in high-resolution binary form, and the capacitors just serve as a temporary store.) The alternate capacitive memory mechanism, which is employed

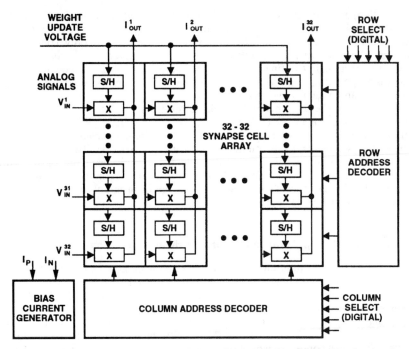

FIGURE 27.2   Block diagram of a capacitor refresh 32 × 32 synapse chip showing the arrangement of individual synapse cells with signal flow and row and column decoders.

by networks that must periodically learn in order to refresh weights, employs circuits that add or extract a quantum of charge from the capacitor [32]. In either case, the weights are applied to a multiplier circuit that continually performs the weighting function. Unfortunately, multiplier circuits require a number of sizable transistors if linearity, uniformity between circuits, and a large dynamic range are desired, limiting synaptic circuit density to the order of 10^3 to 10^4 synapses per square centimeter. Since the number of synapses is the limiting factor determining the size of most fully parallel networks, the use of simpler nonlinear multipliers has been proposed, along with a learning scheme tolerant of the nonlinearities [33]. Fairly linear response has also been obtained by using simpler weighting circuits [34]. Synaptic outputs, coded as currents, are simply and highly efficiently aggregated by the wires that connect them to their corresponding neuron input. Analog semiconductor physics can also bestow an advantage in the neuron circuit—a sigmoidal activation function can be efficiently implemented by little more than a differential transistor pair.

Let us highlight just two of the significant number of analog implementations that have been developed. (Additional citations are given in Sec. 27.5.) One AT&T neural system is particularly interesting because it is an analog-digital hybrid that is being used for character recognition [35]. With a recognition rate of one handwritten character every millisecond, the system was faster by two orders of magnitude than a (serial) *digital signal processor* (*DSP*) optimized for neural calculations. A 20 × 20 pixel image was applied to four network layers mapped onto an analog chip that implements 130,000 connections, and a final fifth layer was implemented serially on a DSP, using an additional 3000 connections. Learning was performed off-line by a workstation, and weights were downloaded to the system's memories. The analog network used the capacitor-charge method for buffering weights. Weights were quantized to 6 bits, and neuron activations were represented with only 3 bits, including sign. The relatively few quantization levels necessitated a final learning step where the weights in the final layer were retrained on-line. The recognition error rate was 5.3 percent, compared to rates of 4.9 and 2.5 percent for full dynamic-range simulations and human subjects, respectively.

One of the earlier commercially available products was Intel's *electrically trainable analog neural network* (*ETANN*) chip, released in 1990 [36]. Each ETANN 80170W chip comprises 64 neurons and 10,240 floating-gate synapses onto which can be mapped recurrent or multilayer feedforward networks. The chip must be plugged into a socket on a development system for learning, using one of the many supported learning algorithms. While learning is slow due to the floating-gate technology, ETANN has nevertheless heralded the age of program-rarely, moderately sized, stand-alone analog neural network chips.

27.4.1   The Jet Propulsion Laboratory Hardware Approach

At the Jet Propulsion Laboratory (JPL), we have developed a variety of building-block chips, some of which use digital weight storage and others use capacitor storage [26, 30]. Learning has been demonstrated with both designs [24, 37]. In this chapter, we highlight one of the chip sets, which incorporate hybrid *multiplying digital-analog converter* (*MDAC*) synapses, on which we have implemented learning. Each synapse (Fig. 27.3) consists of a 7-bit digital memory that can be randomly accessed by a host computer, a 6-bit digital-to-analog converter using scaled current mirrors, a circuit to convert the input voltage to a current in order to drive the converter's current mirror network, and a programmable current-steering network such that the synapse can be programmed to be excitatory or inhibitory. Each synapse circuit is 200×200 μm in a 2-μm CMOS fabrication process.

The neuron circuit is slightly more complex (Fig. 27.4). To avoid a speed penalty resulting from having to charge and discharge large summing-node capacitances (especially if these nodes are routed between chips), the potential of each current-summing *network* node is held constant by the corresponding neuron circuit. This is achieved by the neuron's input stage: A differential transistor pair Q19-Q20 amplifies the deviation of the summing node from ground (i.e., one-half the 10-V power supply potential) and causes the generation of a current that opposes the sum current, forcing the potential of the sum node to remain at ground. This compensating current is mirrored, inverted, and applied to an output transimpedance node. The transimpedance, and thus the neuron's sigmoidal slope (i.e., gain), can be controlled over a wide range by a programmable current mirror circuit (Q14). Programmable neuron gain is useful for normalizing the neuron's response for the number of input synapse connections [30, 38]. This design resulted in a wide-range, variable-gain neuron.

These circuits were combined on two chips with two types of architectures. One type implements a 32×32 crossbar network of 1024 synapses; the other is similar except that the main diagonal consists of neuron circuits. These two types of chips can be cascaded and programmed to form larger, fully connected, partially connected, or feedforward layered networks. A variety of network architectures (with standard synapse and neuron characteristics) can be constructed with this chip set. To map a feedforward network onto a chip set that is wired to be fully connected, all synapses leading to a previous layer are simply nulled. Respective synapses on two

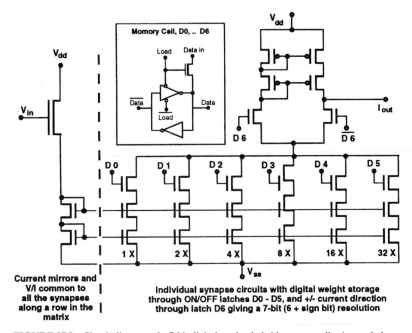

FIGURE 27.3   Circuit diagram of a 7-bit digital-analog hybrid synapse cell using scaled current mirrors to implement a monotonic programmable scaling circuit. The inset shows schematically the digital circuit for weight storage.

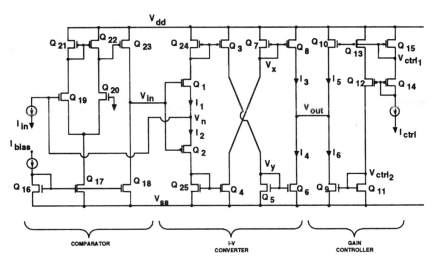

FIGURE 27.4   Circuit diagram of a wide-range variable-gain neuron with sigmoidal transfer characteristics. The stages of voltage-to-current conversion, comparator, and gain controllers are shown. Input potential is kept constant to avoid capacitive charge delay, and the gain control stage allows programming of sigmoidal slope.

chips can even be paralleled together to increase the number of synaptic quantization steps [38]; the outputs of the two synapses are wired in parallel, and the synapses on the chip with the most-significant bits are provided with 64 times the transconductance of the respective synapses with less significant bits. Sign bits are programmed together. While the response of such stacked synapses may not increase monotonically with binary weight count, it is advantageous with some learning schemes to have the additional levels of weight quantization.

27.4.2   A Technology of the Future: Three-Dimensional Die Stacking

JPL is currently evaluating an approach that may allow the construction of very large analog or analog/digital neural systems. Noting that size of the VLSI networks is often limited by the available silicon area (where area, in turn, is constrained by increasing cost and decreasing reliability as die size increases), the possibility exists that functioning silicon dies can be interconnected by stacking to form compact, three-dimensional structures. A cube, constructed from scores of thinned dies, occupies approximately the same footprint as a standard die. In addition to the tremendous processing power afforded by such a dense *integrated circuit* (*IC*) cube, hybridization of a three-dimensional IC stack to an image sensor array would enable spatially parallel signal processing to be performed on image data at extremely high data rates. As shown in Fig. 27.5, an architecture has been conceptualized which combines the spatially parallel three-dimensional imager cube with neural network processing for the first time, promising tremendous speed and network size enhancements over conventional two-dimensional VLSI techniques [39]. While the feasibility of such stacking technologies has been demonstrated [40], many challenges must be faced in developing such a cube, including heat control, the development of software tools that can follow connections in the third dimension, and, of course, the development of an appropriate neural-based architecture.

A particularly challenging application that requires the tremendous processing capability afforded by such a three-dimensional neural image processing cube is missile defense, which specifies spatial-temporal recognition of both point and resolved targets at extremely high speed (milliseconds). A reconfigurable neural network architecture, properly trained, may discriminate targets from clutter or classify targets once resolved. By mating a 64×64 image sensor to a stack of 64 neural network ICs so that each row in the imager array is attached to one IC, each with a different set of weights, a variety of image processing tasks could be performed in parallel at extremely high speeds and in an extremely small package. Neural network inputs could be controlled by a sequencer circuit that controls signal flow along 64 common bus lines. A novel sequencer circuit comprises a switching matrix that allows a small window (for example, 8×8) from the imager to be input to any IC in the stack.

To limit power dissipation to about 2 W for the entire IC stack, the synapse and neuron circuits described above were redesigned to support lower operating currents and power supply rails and a concomitant fourfold speed increase. The expected computation rate for a 64-die stack incorporating these synapses and neurons would be 10^{12} *connections per second* (*CPS*), and it could be increased to 10^{18} CPS when a 1024×1024 focal-plane array imager becomes available and as the three-dimensional stacking technology matures further. The synapse circuit is similar to the earlier version, except that it utilizes single transistor current mirrors rather than the cascode current mirrors of the previous design. The neuron circuit, shown in Fig. 27.6, consists of a very simple variable-gain transconductance opera-

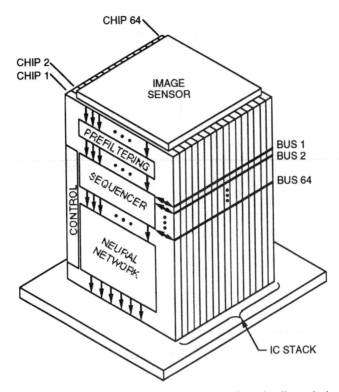

FIGURE 27.5 Conceptual diagram of a three-dimensionally stacked multichip module integrated with a two-dimensional focal plane array. All the sensor array contacts are bump-bonded to the chip stack under them. Interconnections (including controls and power) at the neural network chips are brought out along the edges to the connecting busbars.

tional amplifier without compensation capacitor. Neuron gain is varied by adjusting the amplifier bias current. Figure 27.7 shows the two-quadrant synapse output characteristics of the hardware as a function of stored weights with voltage V_{in} as a parameter. The combined synapse-neuron characteristics are shown in Fig. 27.8 as a family of sigmoidal curves with different slopes obtained by variation of the gain voltage. These circuits were modeled with a PSPICE circuit simulation tool, and experimental results correlate closely with simulation. Simulation results indicate an average power consumption of less than 30 mW per chip (or less than 2 W for a 64-chip stack) at the 4-MHz operation rate.

27.5   *LEARNING IN HARDWARE SYSTEMS*

A general-purpose computer can be programmed to execute any reasonably sized architecture and any conceivable learning algorithm. The dynamic range of weights and signals traversing the simulated network, coded with floating-point variables, is

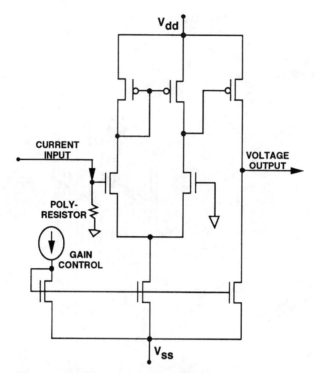

FIGURE 27.6   Circuit diagram for a high-speed and compact variable-gain neuron cell. A feedforward time < 150 ns per synapse-neuron pass is more than an order-of-magnitude improvement over previous design with a 6- to 7-ms delay.

sufficiently large that quantization effects very rarely affect learning or operation. Unfortunately, the opposite is true of most analog or digital hardware implementations: Signals and/or weights must be implemented with limited quantized levels of resolution and dynamic range. Studies suggest that for most learning algorithms, a reduced dynamic range will adversely affect (or even inhibit) learning. For operation, however, reducing the dynamic range of weights and signals to a few bits often does not greatly affect the result [17, 41]. A direct implementation of the ever-popular error back propagation algorithm, e.g., requires 12 to 16 bits of weight quantization [42]. However, major modifications of EBP may function reliably for at least some problems with as few as 8 bits of weight precision [43].

Learning with analog hardware poses a second challenge: how to structure a learning algorithm to be less sensitive to the noise sources inherent in analog circuits. Such sources can be dynamic, with wide-ranging frequency components (including low-frequency drifts), or time-invariant, as in the fixed offset signals generated within every analog circuit. Furthermore, noise sources are not necessarily uncorrelated: Noise in power busses may affect circuit outputs in diverse ways. As mentioned above, in some cases noise can assist learning by introducing a stochastic component to weight updates. However, offsets can be a major problem, as can correlated noise sources.

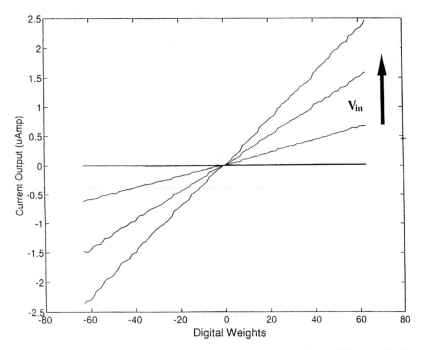

FIGURE 27.7 Synapse output current as a function of synaptic weights (±63 levels) with different input voltages V_{in} (1.5, 1.9, 2.4, and 2.8 V).

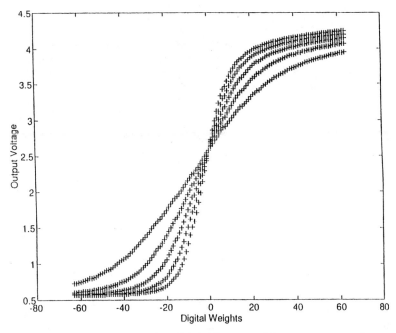

FIGURE 27.8 Synapse-neuron sigmoidal transfer curves giving neuron output voltage as a function of synaptic weights (±63 levels) with neuron gain as a parameter.

Thus, a primary challenge that faces the hardware designer is to find a hardware-compatible learning algorithm. We will focus here on a few leading examples of supervised learning algorithms that appear to be most promising for hardware learning [44]. For the many applications that do not require fast learning (including situations where the weights are fixed for the life of the network), learning may be under the control of a computer. Digital networks of modest size can often be faithfully simulated by using floating-point variables, and the resulting weights can be quantized and mapped onto the hardware. Such an approach may not work for analog networks unless offsets and other noise sources are measured and incorporated into the simulation. Instead, a simple but time-intensive gradient-descent method that has been employed is *hardware-in-the-loop learning* (*HILL*) [28, 45–47]. HILL systems use a computer to set the analog input values to the hardware, measure the outputs, and reprogram weights. A training token is applied to the network, and the output is compared to the target vector. Each neuron output or weight is in turn perturbed, and the effect of the weight perturbation on the output error is calculated. The weight is then modified slightly so as to decrease the error. Obviously, this is a highly inefficient learning method, even if several weight updates can be made at once. Nevertheless, the advantage of this scheme is that all time-invariant noise and other nonideal hardware behavior is taken into account, including even altogether malfunctioning circuits.

Other investigators have included circuits for on-chip learning. A computer may still be necessary to apply training vectors, but learning can usually proceed much more rapidly due to higher weight-update parallelism and faster learning cycles. While many investigators have designed and even partially implemented analog networks with on-chip learning, using supervised learning algorithms such as EBP [29, 48–52] and other gradient-descent techniques [53], or unsupervised learning algorithms such as Oja's rule [54] and Kohonen networks [55–57], relatively few functional analog on-chip learning systems (beyond limited prototypes) have been reported. Pioneering experiments with small networks capable of learning were pursued starting in the 1950s by Widrow [58], using his madaline learning mechanisms. Alspector et al. have successfully executed several designs, using (stochastic) Boltzmann learning [59]. Alspector's more recent stochastic system used controlled noise sources in the form of digital circuits that generated random bit streams with low correlation [60, 61], rather than the uncontrolled sources inherent in the analog circuitry. Finally, a more specialized analog implementation used Grossberg self-organized learning [62]. Digital on-chip learning networks have also been implemented, generally with EBP learning variants [3, 19, 63]. One noteworthy neural chip with a measured time for a feedforward pass of only 104 ns used a variant of *restricted-Coulomb energy* (*RCE*) learning [64].

27.6 SELF-EVOLVING ARCHITECTURES

Most learning algorithms operate on a fixed architecture that has been predetermined, often using little more than guesswork. The problem is that the network size required for a given problem is dependent on the complexity of the input data set and the structure of the patterns to be extracted. These factors are generally unknown. If the selected architecture is larger than required for a particular problem, learning may take longer than necessary; and if the selected architecture is too small, the network will not adequately learn the task at hand. To avoid the necessity of fixing a network architecture and to obtain higher efficiency in learning, a new class of learning architecture has been proposed in which a network evolves out of a simple two-layer precursor architecture. Hidden units are added as necessary until the network performs adequately.

The first such architecture appears to be Scott Fahlman's *cascade correlation* (*CC*) learning scheme [65]. The precursor network has no hidden units, and weights are adjusted by using the gradient descent (or one of its variants). Then, in each subsequent operation, a new single-neuron layer is added, with the neuron's inputs connecting to the network inputs as well as all hidden-unit neuron outputs. Initially, a new neuron's output is not connected, and the input weights are set so as to maximize the covariance between the new neuron's output and the residual error of the network output. These input weights are not altered after this. Finally, all output layer weights are retrained by using the delta rule. In this way, each new neuron serves as a feature detector which is likely to reduce the output error and which can be used by subsequent neurons for more sophisticated features. A final advantage is that the rate of decrease of error with each new hidden-unit addition can indicate the utility of adding further units.

Such an architecture has a number of attractive features for use with hardware implementations. Besides the advantages deriving from architectural efficiency, such as efficient network size and use of a small network for at least part of the training task, each of the two steps of the learning algorithm requires updating of relatively few synapses. Furthermore, an error signal does not need to be propagated back across multiple layers—a process that is highly noise-prone in analog implementations.

A study of the sensitivity of CC learning to reduced-dynamic-range variables and weights has shown that while the algorithm is relatively insensitive to representing neuron activation by even as few as 5 bits of precision, weights must be represented with a much greater dynamic range [41]. The 6-bit parity was one among various problems studied in simulation, where the limited weight precision led first to an increase in network size, then to catastrophic failure below about 12 bits as weight updates were mostly truncated to zero. Modifications of the algorithm that included probabilistic weight update resulted in successful learning with as few as 7 bits [41]. However, these modifications would be expensive to implement in hardware.

27.6.1 Cascade Back Propagation Learning Architecture

In this section we develop a new self-evolving architecture that is highly efficient with respect to hardware implementations, and we demonstrate its ability to learn with reduced synaptic weight dynamic range. This new learning architecture is termed *CBP* (cascade back propagation), and it is shown in Fig. 27.9. In comparison with EBP, CBP was designed with a clear motivation to avoid the arbitrary and predetermined assignment of hidden units and thus avoid identical subspaces in weight space that may cause convergence problems [66]. In addition, its most important feature is the capability to reduce the weight resolution requirement of EBP, which is particularly costly to implement in hardware [42]. Further, the theory of self-evolving architecture shows that each added hidden unit potentially reduces the energy level, which continuously moves the network toward the minimum energy level [67].

CBP uses the stochastic gradient-descent technique and the self-evolving architecture [65]. The process of adding a new hidden unit is based on a number of fixed iterations. Learning is required for the synaptic weights that are related to the new hidden unit and the output bias weights only. However, in this study, we have not optimized the number of iterations that may be required to learn the input-output relationship for the particular problem.

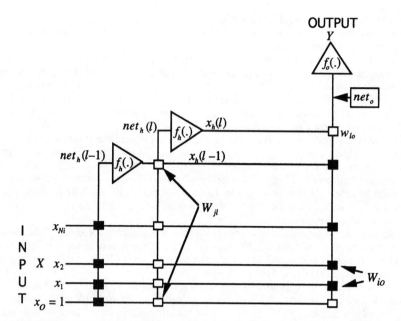

FIGURE 27.9   Schematic diagram of a cascade back propagation architecture showing added hidden units. Synaptic weights are shown as small rectangles where the filled rectangles signify that they are frozen after completion of training, before the next hidden unit is added.

27.6.2   Mathematical Model

First we define some variables:

p is the variable for the number of training patterns, where $p = \{1, \ldots, P\}$.

o is the variable for the output components with $o = \{1, \ldots, O\}$.

x_0 is the bias input which is kept fixed at 1.

x_j is the input signal with $j = \{1, \ldots, Ni\}$.

$x_h(l)$ is the output from hidden unit l with $l = \{Ni + 1, \ldots, Ni + n\}$.

Here Ni represents the input dimension, O is the output dimension, and n is the number of added hidden units (or the expanded input space). The energy function can therefore be written as

$$E = \sum_{p=1}^{P} E^p = \sum_{p=1}^{P} \sum_{o=1}^{O} (t_o^p - y_o^p)^2 \qquad (27.1)$$

Let T be the target matrix, with a column for each input target pattern, given by

$$T = \begin{bmatrix} t_1^1 \, t_1^2 \cdots t_1^P \\ \cdots \cdots \cdots \\ t_O^1 \, t_O^2 \cdots t_O^P \end{bmatrix}$$

and the corresponding actual output matrix is

$$Y = \begin{bmatrix} y_1^1\, y_1^2 \cdots y_1^P \\ \cdot\,\cdot\,\cdot\,\cdot\,\cdot\,\cdot \\ y_o^1\, y_o^2 \cdots y_o^P \end{bmatrix}$$

Then, with no hidden units in the network, one can calculate the output as

$$Y = F(WX) \tag{27.2}$$

and let W_{io} be the set of weights between input and output matrices. The best-estimation weight set of the given energy function l in affine space is calculated as

$$W_{io} = F^{-1}(T)X^+ \tag{27.3}$$

with X^+ as the pseudo-inverse of X [68] and F^{-1} as an inverse transformation matrix given by

$$F^{-1}(T) = \begin{bmatrix} f^{-1}(t_1^1)\, f^{-1}(t_1^2) \cdots f^{-1}(t_1^P) \\ \cdot\,\cdot\,\cdot\,\cdot\,\cdot\,\cdot\,\cdot\,\cdot \\ f^{-1}(t_o^1)\, f^{-1}(t_o^2) \cdots f^{-1}(t_o^P) \end{bmatrix}$$

The set of weights W_{io} is then kept frozen. Assume that n hidden units are added, and the output is calculated as follows:

$$y_o = f(\text{net}_o) \tag{27.4}$$

where

$$\text{net}_o = \sum_{l = Ni + 1}^{Ni + n} x_h(l)w_{lo} + \sum_{j = 0}^{Ni} x_j w_{jo}$$

and f is the transfer function of the output neuron (termed f_o). Further,

$$x_h(l) = f(\text{net}_h(l)) \tag{27.5}$$

where f is the transfer function of the current hidden neuron (termed f_h and identical to f_o),

$$\text{net}_h(l) = \sum_{k = Ni + 1}^{Ni + l - 1} x_h(k)w_{kl} + \sum_{j = 0}^{Ni} x_j w_{jl}$$

and

$$x_i = \begin{cases} 1 & \text{if } i = 0 \\ x_j & \text{if } i < Ni + 1 \\ x_h(l) & \text{if } i \geq Ni + 1 \end{cases}$$

Let us define

$$f_h'(l) = \frac{df(\text{net}_h(l))}{d\text{net}_h(l)}$$

and

$$f_o' = \frac{df(\text{net}_o)}{d\text{net}_o}$$

With η as the learning rate, the stochastic gradient descent gives the weight update as

$$\Delta w_{ij} = -\eta \, \frac{\partial E^p}{\partial w_{ij}} \tag{27.6}$$

where i and j denote the starting node i and the destination node j. And applying the chain rule to Eq. (27.6) for the weights between the hidden and the output neurons, and the bias synapses connected to the output, we get

$$\frac{\partial E^p}{\partial w_{ij}} = \frac{\partial E^p}{\partial y_o^p} \, \frac{\partial y_o^p}{\partial \mathrm{net}_o^p} \, \frac{\partial \mathrm{net}_o^p}{\partial w_{ij}}$$

which can be written as (we are only interested in the new hidden unit)

$$\frac{\partial E^p}{\partial w_{ij}} = -2(t_o^p - y_o^p) f_o'^p x_h^p(n) \tag{27.7}$$

Using Eq. (27.7), we can rewrite Eq. (27.6) explicitly with a first-order and a second-order term [69] as

$$\Delta w_{no}(k) = \eta x_h^p(n)(t_o^p - o_o^p) f_o'^p - \alpha \, \Delta w_{no}(k-1) \qquad \text{with } 0 < \alpha < 1 \tag{27.8}$$

which gives the weight updates for the synaptic components between the currently added hidden unit n and the output o, as shown in Fig. 27.10. Similarly, the updates for the weights between the inputs (including expanded inputs and the bias weight at the currently added hidden unit) and the current hidden unit are given by

$$\frac{\partial E^p}{\partial w_{ij}} = \frac{\partial \mathrm{net}_h^p}{\partial w_{ij}} \, \frac{\partial f_h(\mathrm{net}_h^p)}{\partial \mathrm{net}_h^p} \sum_{o=0}^{O} \frac{\partial \mathrm{net}_o^p}{\partial f_h(\mathrm{net}_h^p)} \, \frac{\partial y_o^p}{\partial \mathrm{net}_o^p} \, \frac{dE^p}{dy_o^p}$$

which then can be written as

$$\frac{\partial E^p}{\partial w_{ij}} = -2x_i^p f_h'^p(n) \sum_{o=1}^{O} w_{no} f_o'^p (t_o^p - y_o^p)$$

This equation is similarly written in an explicit form with a first-order and a second-order term as

$$\Delta w_{in}(k) = \eta x_i^p f_h^p(n) \sum_{o=1}^{m} w_{no}(t_o^p - y_o^p) f_o^p + \alpha \, \Delta w_{in}(k-1) \qquad \text{with } 0 < \alpha < 1 \tag{27.9}$$

for the weight components. The change in learning rate after addition of each new hidden unit is given by

$$\eta_{\mathrm{new}} = \eta_{\mathrm{old}} - \frac{c}{\text{no. of iterations}} \tag{27.10}$$

with η_{new} as the current learning rate, η_{old} as the previous learning rate, and c as a constant. When α is zero, we obtain the first-order gradient descent; and if α is a nonzero constant, then the two terms in both the Eqs. (27.8) and (27.9) contribute to the weight updates, and the second-order gradient descent is obtained.

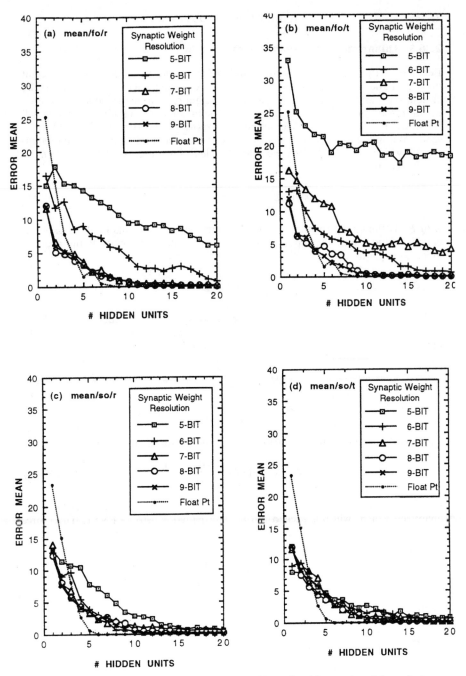

FIGURE 27.10 Mean error as a function of added hidden units with synaptic weight resolution as a parameter for the cascade back propagation learning simulation for hardware with (*a*) only the first-order weight-update term and roundoff (fo/r) conversion; (*b*) first-order term and truncation (fo/t) conversion, (*c*) second-order term and round-off (so/r) conversion; and (*d*) second-order term and truncation (so/t) conversion methods.

27.6.3 Quantization of Weight Space

Because of the limited quantization weight space, the value ΔW_{ij} of the weight update will have to be modified to ΔW_{ij}^{*} to fit with the available quantization. The closeness between them will depend on the weight resolution available. Let $n$bit be the bit resolution of the weight space. Then the maximum level of weight space will be MAXLEVEL = $2^{n\text{bit}} - 1$. We define stepsize(n) to be a step size for the weight space of a hidden unit n. The stepsize(n) can be generated from a constant stepsize(0) which is fixed before we start the learning process. The stepsize(n) is obtained as follows:

$$\text{stepsize}(n) = \text{stepsize}(0)\frac{E_{n-1}}{E_0} \tag{27.11}$$

with E_0 as the energy of the network without any hidden units or the bias input added (includes only the input-to-output weights calculated by using the pseudo-inverse technique), i.e.,

$$E_0 = \sum_{p=1}^{P} E^p(W_{io}; X^p; Y^p)$$

and the energy E_{n-1} is the energy of the network with $n - 1$ hidden units added. There are two ways to obtain the number of steps for ΔW_{ij}: One is the roundoff technique where the number of steps is calculated as follows

$$\#\text{step}i = \begin{cases} (\text{int}) \left[\dfrac{\Delta W_{ij}}{\text{stepsize}(n)} + 0.5 \right] & \text{if } \Delta W_{ij} > 0 \\[3ex] (\text{int}) \left[\dfrac{\Delta W_{ij}}{\text{stepsize}(n)} - 0.5 \right] & \text{if } \Delta W_{ij} < 0 \end{cases} \tag{27.12}$$

and the other is the truncation technique for calculation of the number of steps:

$$\#\text{step}i = (\text{int}) \left[\frac{\Delta W_{ij}}{\text{stepsize}(n)} \right] \tag{27.13}$$

Before updating the candidate weight using ΔW_{ij}^{*}, one must ensure that the final quantized weight will not exceed the limit provided as MAXLEVEL. Therefore, first the previously stored weight is converted to an equivalent number of steps, given by

$$\#\text{step}a = (\text{int}) \left[\frac{W_{ij}}{\text{stepsize}(n)} \right] \tag{27.14}$$

Then

$$\Delta W_{ij}^{*} = \begin{cases} 0 & \text{if } (\#\text{step}i + \#\text{step}a) > \text{MAXLEVEL} \\ \text{stepsize}(n)(\#\text{step}i) & \text{otherwise} \end{cases} \tag{27.15}$$

27.6.4 Procedure for Learning in Hardware

A clear procedure for the learning algorithm, used for solution of a 6-bit parity problem, as an illustrative example, is presented below.

Based on the mathematical analysis of the EBP learning algorithm [69], the weight update (consisting of the first- and second-order terms) can be performed by incorporating (1) either the first-order term only or (2) the summation of the two terms to obtain the second-order effect as well. The idea of this development effort, of course, is to make the algorithm implementable in hardware given the limited synaptic weight resolution.

When the transfer characteristics of a neuron are considered, a mathematical equivalent of a sigmoidal function such as a logistic function is considered or a lookup table is constructed. A lookup table requires step updates and hence a quantization of the values. It has been shown that such a neuron quantization is not as sensitive as synaptic equalization [41, 42] for the convergence properties of the circuit. In addition, the density of synapse on a chip is much higher than that of neurons. Thus, it is important to keep the synapse quantization as low as possible, commensurate with proper learning. Therefore, in our study, the effect of neuron quantization has not been considered. On the other hand, synaptic weight quantization is known to affect the sensitivity of learning to a larger extent, and the synaptic weights in hardware may be limited in their resolution anywhere from 5 to 10 bits.

27.6.5   Weight Update Issues

The weight update Δw_{ij} is obtained as an analog number. However, the weight space is discrete in a hardware based on hybrid digital-analog synapse designs, as is the case with our MDAC approach, described earlier in Sec. 27.4.1. Therefore, to update the weight, the value Δw_{ij} must be converted to the number of steps by which the weight is to be updated before it is summed into the weight component. The conversion from an analog level to the respective discrete level results in some losses due to quantization.

In A/D conversion techniques, typically, there are two conversion schemes: *roundoff* and *truncation*. In our simulation, we have compared these two schemes for their effectiveness in learning. We find that the roundoff scheme works better in terms of convergence, especially when only the first-order term in the weight update is considered. During the learning phase, one must also consider the constraint of discrete levels limited by the available weight resolution. For example, with an 8-bit synapse, the number of discrete levels should not exceed 255.

Some of the salient features of our new learning algorithm are as follows:

1. The step size is dynamically changed after addition of each hidden unit. The change is based on the level of energy left over in the previous hidden unit (as a ratio of the original level of energy). In general, with the addition of a new hidden unit and subsequent training of the respective weights, the energy of the network decreases, resulting in smaller step size for the next stage of added hidden unit. However, in the present simulation for the 6-bit parity problem, the maximum number of hidden units added was limited to 20 irrespective of whether each additional hidden unit decreased the energy or not, or whether the network converged to the right solution.

2. The input to a neuron can be adjusted by using two variables besides the input to the synapse itself. One is the weight value, which can be updated during training, and the other is the bias itself to the synapse. It is this latter feature that allows for easy adjustment of the step size and, more importantly, promotes convergence with lower quantization of synaptic weights. Furthermore, this new design will provide independent, programmable bias voltages to rows of synapses connected to each hidden unit.

27.7 THE 6-BIT PARITY PROBLEM

To assess the effectiveness of our methodology, and for easy comparison with other work reported in literature, we selected to study the 6-bit parity problem, using our new CBP learning algorithm. The 6-bit parity problem has 64 discrete patterns to be classified. The neural network architecture has six inputs and one bias line directly connected to one output line through seven programmable weights. The procedure used for training is as follows:

1. Calculate the six weight values for the input-output connection weights, using the pseudo-inverse relationship. In this particular case, the solution of the pseudo-inverse calculation is very close to zero. Therefore, we have arbitrarily set all the weights to 0.5. These weights are then kept frozen throughout.

2. Provide the input patterns (with bias weights not connected), evaluate the respective output errors, and calculate the energy $E(0)$. If the errors are within a given tolerance, then the training is complete. If not, proceed further.

3. Set a learning rate $\eta = 3.5$ and $\alpha = 0.9$ for second-order effects and $\alpha = 0$ for first-order effects and a weight step size given by

$$stepsize(0) = 0.015*2^{8-nbit}$$

where $nbit$ = synaptic weight resolution in bits.

4. Add a new hidden unit along with randomly selected input and output weights, including the bias weights. These weights have to be converted to quantized levels of weights where each weight = stepsize(n) * (#step$a$.) Further, #step$a$ should be an integer given by either the roundoff or truncation method.

5. Again provide the inputs, measure the output, and evaluate the new error values for all the input patterns to ascertain if training is complete. Otherwise, continue the training process.

6. $\eta = \eta - 3.5/10{,}000$, and stepsize($n$) is given by Eq. (27.11).

7. Apply a random input pattern to the network.

8. Calculate the change in weights ΔW_{ij}, using Eqs. (27.8) and (27.9).

9. Calculate the number of steps required #step$i$, using Eqs. (27.12) or (27.13).

10. The total number of steps #step(total) = #step$a$ + #step$i$. If #step(total) > MAXLEVEL, then set $\Delta W_{ij}^{\ *}$ [= #step$i$ * stepsize(n)] to 0. Otherwise, update W_{ij} and #step$a$. This procedure will update all the weights for the added hidden neurons and the output bias weights.

11. Go to step 7, until the required applications of the number of iterations of the random patterns are completed. The number of iterations can be decided depending upon the requirement of the problem and the time available. In our case, we used 6000 iterations as an outer loop and 64 iterations as an inner loop for each pattern.

12. Calculate the error for all the patterns, and evaluate for completion of training. If complete, stop training; otherwise, calculate the energy $E(n)$ and go to step 4.

13. If the number of added hidden units is greater than 20, give up and quit.

27.7.1   Cascade Back Propagation Simulations

Using the above procedure, simulations for hardware were performed, and the mean error and the standard deviation of the error were obtained for the four cases, two with only the first-order term, with both roundoff and truncation methods of conversion, and similarly the other two cases with the second-order term included. As expected, the simulation showed that including the second-order term made the errors go down considerably compared to those with just the first-order term. As a result, this led to an acceptable solution with reduced synaptic weight resolutions. The mean error and the standard deviation curves for these four cases as an average of 10 runs are shown in Figs. 27.10a to d and 27.11a to d, respectively. Overall, the method showed tremendous tolerance to reduced weight resolution, and with second-order term included, the hardware with ≥7-bit resolution performed as well as that with full floating-point accuracy with about 12 neurons added as hidden units. In addition, with the second-order term included, the results with 6- and 7-bit resolution had close to 100 percent correctness, and even 5-bit resolution weights provided 80 to 90 percent correctness. Table 27.2 summarizes these results of weight quantization and the correctness of the solution in the four cases (out of 64 patterns).

27.8   HARDWARE IMPLEMENTATION WITH LEARNING

A neural network hardware system was assembled from the analog neuron and synapse building-block chips described in Sec. 27.4.1, a computer interface, and CBP learning algorithm (Fig. 27.12). The hardware consisted of eight building-block chips: two synapse-neuron hybrid chips gave a maximum of 64 neurons, two synapse-only chips completed this fully parallel 64×64 architecture's first 7 bits of synaptic precision. The last four synapse chips paralleled the first set of synapses in this network to allow larger dynamic range in the weights (13 bits). A schematic diagram showing the chip arrangement is given in Fig. 27.13. The system was connected to a personal computer, with parallel ports to access the digital weights and analog converters to program inputs and read outputs. An early version of the CBP algorithm was used, with first-order learning dynamics and truncation of weights. The learning algorithm used all 13 bits of precision (with the sign bits of each paralleled synapse pair tied together). Although the 13 bits thus obtained did not necessarily increase monotonically, the stochastic nature of the analog hardware evidently served to bridge nonmonotonicities sufficiently that learning could proceed. The measured input-output characteristic of one synapse-neuron pair is shown in Fig. 27.14.

Two applications were tested: parity and a computation-intensive feature classification problem. The 2-bit parity problem was taught to the network by adding hidden units until the outputs were correct, exceeding a threshold of three-fifths full range for a true and measuring below two-fifths full range for a false. This substantial noise margin at the output made it unlikely that noise levels would cause a false reading. After each hidden unit was added, 3000 back propagation trials were executed, and the network function was tested for correctness. A scatter plot of (binary) output as a function of (analog) inputs showed a marked bias toward "true" outputs overall, although the output was correct for the binary input representations ($-V_{max}$, $+ V_{max}$) [24]. In most cases, 2 to 4 neurons were required as hidden units for all outputs to reach the criterion threshold levels.

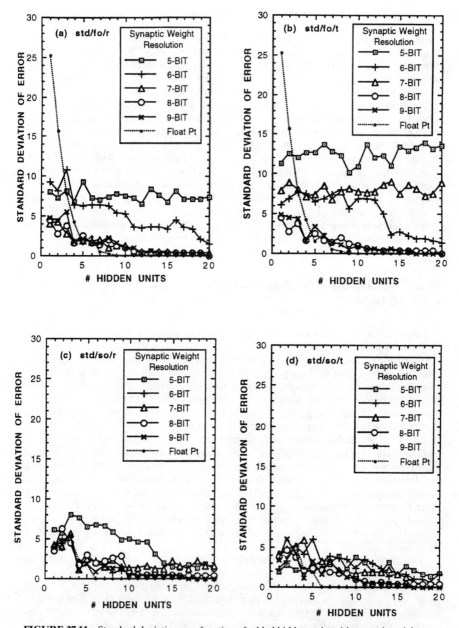

FIGURE 27.11 Standard deviation as a function of added hidden units with synaptic weight resolution as a parameter for the cascade back propagation (CBP) learning simulation for hardware with (*a*) only the first-order weight-update term and roundoff (fo/r) conversion, (*b*) first-order term and truncation (fo/t) conversion, (*c*) second-order term and roundoff (so/r) conversion, and (*d*) second-order term and truncation (so/t) conversion methods.

TABLE 27.2 Summary of Solution Results

Percentage of correct CBP learning runs for 6-bit parity problem with variation of synaptic weight resolution, using first-order and second-order terms in learning algorithm, with roundoff (RO) and truncation (Tr) modes of weight value conversion

	Percentage correct, first-order RO	Percentage correct, first-order Tr	Percentage correct, second-order RO	Percentage correct, second-order Tr
5-bit weight Q	40	10	90	80
6-bit weight Q	90	80	100	90
7-bit weight Q	100	80	90	100
8-bit weight Q	100	100	100	100
9-bit weight Q	100	100	100	100
Floating point	100	100	100	100

FIGURE 27.12 A photograph of an eight-chip board with 64×64, 13-bit synaptic array and 64 neurons connected to a host computer and configured as a feedforward network for solution of a map data classification problem with hardware-in-the-loop CBP learning.

The classification task—map separates—involves processing color map data (similar to roadmaps)—sampled at 24 bits per pixel—in order to determine the primary colors at each pixel. Representing maps with 24 bits per pixel is grossly wasteful, since a map is printed with only about eight colors and thus each pixel could be represented fully by either an 8-bit vector (if more than one color can be associated with a pixel) or a 3-bit color identifier (if each pixel is to be classified as only one color). Not only can storage requirements of maps thus be reduced, but also automatic and manual operations applied to the map would be greatly simplified if individual colors

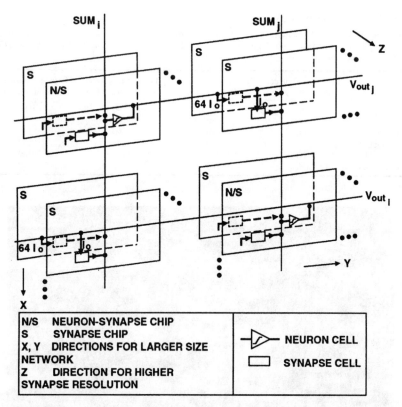

FIGURE 27.13 A schematic diagram showing two neuron-synapse and six synapse chips cascaded to form a 64×64 reconfigurable neural network with nominally 13 bits of synaptic resolution.

(such as black and red, mostly representing roads) could be independently extracted for display or processing. This task is more difficult than it may appear, since large variations in hue and intensity exist between maps and even over one map. Furthermore, noise in the form of small dots may need to be filtered. Thus, a network must take as input a window of pixels centered on the particular pixel currently being processed. This application is well suited to a fully parallel neural network due to the massive number of maps (currently stored on videodisk and CD-ROM memory) and the large number of pixels that need to be processed per map [70, 71].

To map this problem into our hardware, a 3×3 window with three analog color intensities (i.e., red, green, and blue) per pixel was applied to the 27 inputs of the network, once for each pixel in our 305×200 map segment. The system was trained on a subset of the pixels that had been classified by hand, using a precursor of the CBP algorithm in which first-order truncation dynamics were used for weight mappings and error back propagation and all weights were adjusted at each step (rather than freezing all but the output layer). To validate the results, the error was compared with alternative classification methods, as shown in Table 27.3. Figure 27.15 shows the original map data and the neural network hardware output after completion of

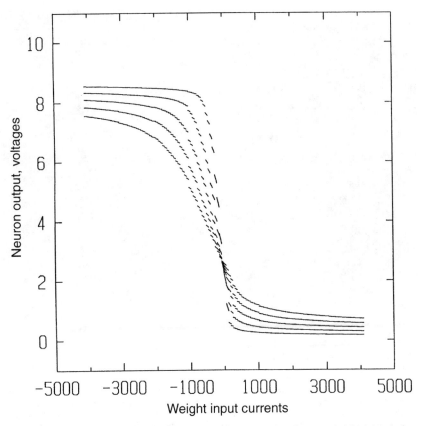

FIGURE 27.14 Synapse-neuron sigmoidal transfer curves for the cascaded high-resolution synapse arrangement with ±4096 levels.

TABLE 27.3 A Comparison of Accuracy of Various Data Classification Methods for Given Map Data Classification Problem

Classifier method	Accuracy, %
Neural network simulation	91.2
Neural network hardware	89.3
K nearest neighbors	91.9
Baysian-unimodal gaussian	89.8

hardware-in-the-loop training. The hardware performed as well as the alternate classification algorithms running in software [70, 71].

The primary limitation to processing speed in this application was the conversion between analog and digital domains at network input and output. Analog-to-digital conversion has frequently been the primary limiting factor in throughput, although

FIGURE 27.15 Map data input (left) and feature classified output (right) for a 305 × 200 pixel map segment using the setup shown in Fig. 27.13. A training set of 2000 data points was used, and the neural network architecture consisted of 27 analog inputs for each 3 × 3 pixel window, each pixel with three colors (RGB), each color with 8 bits of resolution (256 levels). The output consisted of seven different color outputs (< 3 bits) assigned to each central pixel of the 3 × 3 window representing as many different features on the map. The hardware solution with 89.3 percent accuracy was nearly as good as that obtained by using other feature classification methods in software (Table 27.3).

one can expect that low-cost, high-speed video converters with sufficient dynamic range will soon become available.

27.9 CONCLUSIONS

Custom neural network hardware is appropriate, and in many cases required, for certain applications. When the application requires real-time response that exceeds the capability of high-end workstations, or when a mass-produced system that is not computer-based requires nontrivial data processing, custom neural hardware may be highly cost-effective. Furthermore, there are particular applications such as biological neural subsystem emulation [18], associative memory [72], and pattern matching [35] which beg a neural solution. But many general tasks can also be carried out by neural systems. Indeed, we look forward to the day when easy-to-use neural hardware black boxes, each appropriate for certain classes and sizes of architecture, are available in much the same way as software objects capable of executing common (but perhaps specialized) tasks are coming into use today.

Both analog and digital implementations have their place in today's neural milieu. Digital designs allow a greater flexibility in mapping arbitrary or extremely large problems onto a limited number of time-multiplexed processing circuits, and no analog conversion is needed if inputs and outputs are already in binary representations. Also, advances in fabrication technologies may benefit digital implementations more so than analog. Analog circuits can be much smaller in size than digital, making it feasible to implement a fully parallel system of moderate size on one chip or a chip set. By taking advantage of physics, the circuits that aggregate signals at neuron inputs, which are space-consuming in digital technologies, can be implemented essentially as wires in analog technology. Also, while circuit noise may be considered by some to be the bane of analog implementations, many learning algorithms benefit from a noise component that can shake the weight configuration out of local minima. New techniques for obtaining larger silicon real estate show promise for constructing very large networks. Wafer-scale neural networks have already been successfully constructed. It is only a matter of time until chip stacking, which can be used to efficiently implement three-dimensional topologies, is used for neural networks.

Control of the network is usually relegated to a general-purpose computer. This allows generality at a high level—the particular training set, learning algorithm, compensation for network flaws (such as malfunctioning output units), and the architecture that is mapped onto the resources available in the custom hardware can all be fine-tuned by the user. However, the greater the required learning and operation throughput, the costlier this processing overhead becomes (a phenomenon reminiscent of Amdahl's law in computer engineering [73]). Thus, the highest throughput can be obtained only by directly interfacing the hardware to the external inputs and outputs and implementing feedforward pass (and learning, if learning speed is critical) into a custom hardware, at the cost of generality. This unfortunate tradeoff of generality for throughput may be somewhat ameliorated by implementing programmable data paths and multiple learning algorithms in digital implementations (at a significant space penalty), or by using chip sets that allow a user wired-in flexibility over architecture in analog implementations.

The current state of custom neural hardware technology allows single-chip systems to be fabricated that have dozens of neurons and up to tens of thousands of synapses. A few specialized wafer-scale systems have exceeded these numbers by an order of magnitude. While such systems have been used to demonstrate a variety of interesting applications, only a handful of such networks have been commercialized for specific applications. Much application development work has yet to be done before a niche for custom hardware can be carved out. It is likely that a good deal of this work must center on learning.

Learning algorithms are perhaps the "missing link" in the development of custom hardware implementations. While much effort has gone into the analysis and development of learning algorithms for computer-based neural simulations, relatively little work has been directed toward developing or adapting learning algorithms to be compatible with the limited precision (and analog system noise) inherent in hardware. Almost certainly, more work is needed in this direction before custom neural hardware can become mainstream. It can be anticipated that the learning algorithms used by biological systems will soon be more fully teased out, and that these algorithms will be profitably applied to hardware, especially to analog circuits.

Most learning algorithms in use today require a user to select the network architecture before learning commences. In looking toward the goal of semiautonomous black box networks, we see that algorithms that automatically configure the network until a criterion level of performance is reached would be highly advantageous for hardware implementations. Two feedforward learning algorithms that add hidden-unit layers automatically are CC and our CBP method. We developed CBP to simplify the hardware required for on-chip learning and to allow learning with as few bits of synaptic precision as possible. We have shown that CBP can work reliably with as few as 5 bits of weight precision. To achieve this, a method for associating dynamic weight-update steps was developed that may be applied to any cascade learning algorithm, as long as each layer can learn independently of the others.

ACKNOWLEDGMENTS

The research described herein was performed by the Center for Space Microelectronics Technology, Jet Propulsion Laboratory, California Institute of Technology, and was jointly sponsored by the Ballistic Missile Defense Organization/Innovative Science and Technology Office (BMDO/IST), the Office of Naval Research (ONR), the Advanced Research Projects Agency (ARPA), and the National Aeronautics and Space Administration (NASA). The authors thank Drs. A. Stubberud, S. Kemeny, R. Tawel, and S. Gulati for useful discussions. Authors also acknowledge M. Tran and H. Langenbacher for technical assistance.

REFERENCES

1. M. Holler, S. Tam, H. Castro, and R. Benson, "An Electrically Trainable Artificial Neural Network (ETANN) with 10,240 "Floating Gate" Synapses," *Proceedings IEEE International Joint Conference on Neural Networks,* vol. 2, June 18–22, Washington, 1989, pp. 191–196.

2. Y. Arima, M. Murasaki, T. Yamada, A. Maeda, and H. Shinohara, "A Refreshable Analog VLSI Neural Network Chip with 400 Neurons and 40K Synapses," *IEEE Journal of Solid-State Circuits,* vol. 27, no. 12, pp. 1854–1861, December, 1992.

3. D. Hammerstrom, "A Massively Parallel Architecture for Cost-Effective Neural Network Pattern Recognition, Image Processing, and Signal Processing Applications," *Digest of Papers in Government Microcircuit Applications Conference,* Las Vegas, NV, 1992, pp. 281–284.

4. C. Grove, Ni1000 Recognition Accelerator Chip, Netstor, Inc., One Richmond Square, Providence, RI 02906.

5. N. H. Farhat, "Optoelectronic Neural Networks and Learning Machines," *IEEE Circuits and Devices Magazine,* September 1989, pp. 32–41.

6. T. Daud, A. Moopenn, J. Lamb, A. Thakoor, and S. Khanna, "Feedforward, High Density, Programmable Read Only Neural Network Based Memory System," *Society of Photo-Optical Instrumentation Engineers/High Speed Computing,* D. P. Cassasent, ed., vol. 880, January 11–12, 1988, Los Angeles, pp. 76–84.

7. A. P. Thakoor, A. Moopenn, J. Lambe, and S. K. Khanna, "Electronic Hardware Implementations of Neural Networks," *Applied Optics,* vol. 26, pp. 5085–5092, 1987.

8. R. Ramesham, T. Daud, A. Moopenn, A. P. Thakoor, and S. K. Khanna, "Manganese Oxide Microswitch for Electronic Memory Based on Neural Networks," *Journal of Vacuum Science Technology,* series B, vol. 7, no. 3, pp. 450–454, 1989.

9. S. Thakoor, A. Moopenn, T. Daud, and A. P. Thakoor, "Solid State Thin Film Memistor for Electronic Neural Networks," *Journal Applied Physics,* vol. 67, p. 3132, 1990.

10. A. J. Agranat, C. F. Neugebauer, R. B. Nelson, and A. Yariv, "The CCD Neural Processor: A Neural Network Integrated Circuit with 65,536 Programmable Analog Synapses," *IEEE Transactions on Circuits Systems,* vol. 37, no. 8, pp. 1073–1075, August 1990.

11. A. M. Chiang and J. R. LaFranchise, "Real-Time CCD-Based Neural Network Systems for Pattern Recognition Applications," *Digest of Papers in* Government Microcircuit Applications Conference, Las Vegas, NV, 1992, pp. 285–288.

12. A. F. Murray, "Pulse Arithmetic in VLSI Neural Networks," *Micro Magazine,* pp. 64–74, December 1989.

13. J. E. Tomberg and K. K. K. Kaski, "Pulse-Density Modulation Technique in VLSI Implementations of Neural Network Algorithms," *IEEE Journal of Solid-State Circuits,* vol. 25, no. 5, pp. 1277–1286, October 1990.

14. S. Churcher, D. J. Baxter and A. Hamilton, A. F. Murray, and H. M. Reekie, "Generic Analog Neural Computation—The EPSILON Chip," in *Advances in Neural Information Processing Systems,* vol. 5, Morgan Kaufmann, San Mateo, CA, 1993, pp. 773–780.

15. R. Sarpeshkar, W. Bair, and C. Koch, "Visual Motion Computation in Analog VLSI Using Pulses," in *Advances in Neural Information Processing Systems,* vol. 5, Morgan Kaufmann, San Mateo, CA, 1993, pp. 781–788.

16. A. Hamilton, A. F. Murray, D. J. Baxter, S. Churcher, H. M. Reekie, et al., "Integrated Pulse Stream Neural Networks: Results, Issues and Pointers," *IEEE Transactions on Neural Networks,* vol. 3, no. 3, pp. 385–393, 1992.

17. J. J. Hopfield, "The Effectiveness of Analogue 'Neural Network' Hardware," *Network,* vol. 1, pp. 27–40 (1990) (IOP Publ. Ltd., U.K.).

18. C. Mead, *Analog VLSI and Neural Systems,* Addison-Wesley, Reading, MA, 1989.

19. S. Schoenung, B. S. Papadales, and T. A. Tibbetts, data compiled by W. J. Schafer Associates in conjunction with a study jointly funded by Jet Propulsion Laboratory and Ballistic Missile Defense Organization.

20. M. Yasunaga, N. Masuda, M. Yagyu, M. Asai, K. Shibata, et al., "A Self-Learning Digital Neural Network Using Wafer-Scale LSI," *IEEE Journal of Solid-State Circuits,* vol. 28, no. 2, pp. 106–114, 1993.

21. M. Masaki, Y. Hirai, and M. Yamada, "Neural Networks in CMOS: A Case Study," *IEEE Circuits and Devices Magazine,* vol. 6, no. 4, pp. 13–17, 1990.

22. R. C. Frye, E. A. Rietman, and C. C. Wong, "Back-Propagation Learning and Nonidealities in Analog Neural Network Hardware," *IEEE Transactions on Neural Networks,* vol. 2, no. 1, pp. 110–117, January 1991.

23. L. R. Carley, "Trimming Analog Circuits Using Floating-Gate Analog MOS Memory," *IEEE Journal of Solid-State Circuits,* vol. 24, no. 6, pp. 1569–1575, 1989.

24. T. A. Duong, S. P. Eberhardt, M. D. Tran, T. Daud, and A. P. Thakoor, "Learning and Optimization with Cascaded VLSI Neural Network Building-Block Chips," *Proceedings of IEEE International Neural Network Society International Joint Conference on Neural Networks,* vol. 1, June 7–11, 1992, Baltimore, MD, pp. 184–189.

25. S. P. Eberhardt, T. A. Duong, and A. P. Thakoor, "Design of Parallel Hardware Neural Network Systems from Custom Analog VLSI 'Building-Block' Chips," *IEEE International Neural Network Society Proceedings International Joint Conference on Neural Networks,* vol. 2, June 18–22, 1989, Washington, p. 183.

26. A. P. Moopenn, T. A. Duong, and A. P. Thakoor, "Digital-Analog Hybrid Synapse Chips for Electronic Neural Networks," *Advances in Neural Information Processing Systems,* vol. 2, D. S. Touretzky, ed., Morgan Kaufmann, San Mateo, CA, 1990, pp. 769–776.

27. F. Kub, I. Mack, K. Moon, C. Yao, and J. Modolo, "Programmable Analog Synapses for Microelectronic Neural Networks Using a Hybrid Digital-Analog Approach," poster presented at IEEE International Conference on Neural Networks, San Diego, CA, July 24–27, 1988.

28. M. Jabri and B. Flower, "Weight Perturbation: An Optimal Architecture and Learning Technique for Analog VLSI Feedforward and Recurrent Multilayer Networks," *IEEE Transactions on Neural Networks*, vol. 3, no. 1, pp. 154–157, January 1992.

29. T. A. Duong, "On-Chip Learning in VLSI Hardware," *NASA Technology Briefs*, to be published.

30. S. P. Eberhardt, T. A. Duong, and A. P. Thakoor, "A VLSI Synapse 'Building-Block' Chip for Hardware Neural Network Implementations," *Proceedings of Third Annual Parallel Processing Symposium*, vol. 1, March 1989, Fullerton, CA, IEEE Orange County Computer Society, 1989, pp. 257–267.

31. R. G. Benson and D. A. Kerns, "UV-Activated Conductances Allow for Multiple Time Scale Learning," *IEEE Transactions on Neural Networks*, vol. 4, no. 3, pp. 434–440, 1993.

32. K. Madani, P. Garda, E. Belhaire, and F. Devos, "Two Analog Counters for Neural Network Implementation," *IEEE Journal of Solid-State Circuits*, vol. 26, no. 7, pp. 966–974, 1991.

33. J. Ghosh, P. Lacour, and S. Jackson, "OTA-Based Neural Network Architectures with On-Chip Tuning of Synapses," *IEEE Transactions on Circuits and Systems 2: Analog and Digital Signal Processing*, vol. 41, no. 1, pp. 50–57, 1994.

34. B. W. Lee and B. J. Sheu, "General-Purpose Neural Chips with Electrically Programmable Synapses and Gain-Adjustable Neurons," *IEEE Journal of Solid-State Circuits*, vol. 27, no. 9, pp. 1299–1302, 1992.

35. B. E. Boser, E. Sackinger, J. Bromley, Y. LeCun, and L. D. Jackel, "An Analog Neural Network Processor with Programmable Topology," *IEEE Journal of Solid State Circuits*, vol. 26, no. 12, December 1991.

36. 80170NW Electrically Trainable Neural Network Specification Sheet, USA/E358/0590/2k/GF/CC, Intel Corp., Santa Clara, CA, 1990.

37. S. P. Eberhardt, T. A. Duong, R. Tawel, F. J. Pineda, and A. P. Thakoor, "A Robotic Inverse Kinematics Problem Implemented on Neural Network Hardware with Gradient-Descent Learning," *Proceedings of the Second ISTED International Symposium on Expert Systems and Neural Networks*, M. H. Hamza, ed., Hawaii, August 15–17, 1990, pp. 70–73.

38. T. A. Duong, T. X. Brown, M. D. Tran, S. P. Eberhardt, T. Daud, et al., "Cascaded VLSI Neural Network Building-Block Chips for Map Classification," *Digest of Papers in Government Microcircuit Applications Conference*, Las Vegas, NV, November 10–12, 1992, pp. 145–146.

39. S. Kemeny, T. Duong, M. Tran, T. Daud, D. Ludwig, et al., "Low Power Analog Neurosynapse Chips for a 3-D 'Sugarcube' Neuroprocessor," *Proceedings of IEEE International Conference on Neural Networks* (ICNN/WCCI), vol. 3, Orlando, FL, June 28–July 2, 1994, pp. 1907–1911.

40. S. N. Shanken, "3-D Processor Packaging and Interconnect," *Proceedings of the Government Microcircuits Applications Conference*, vol. 17, pp. 151–154, 1991.

41. M. Hoehfeld and S. Fahlman, "Learning with Limited Numerical Precision Using the Cascade-Correlation Algorithm," *IEEE Transactions on Neural Networks*, vol. 3, no. 4, pp. 602–611, July 1992.

42. P. W. Hollis, J. S. Harper, and J. J. Paulos, "The Effects of Precision Constraints in a Backpropagation Learning Network," *Neural Computation*, vol. 2, pp. 363–373, 1990.

43. S. Sakaue, T. Kohda, H. Yamamoto, S. Maruno, and Y. Shimeki, "Reduction of Required Precision Bits for Back Propagation Applied to Pattern Recognition," *IEEE Transactions on Neural Networks*, vol. 4, no. 2, pp. 270–275, March 1993.

44. R. Tawel, "Learning in Analog Neural Network Hardware," *Computers and Electrical Engineering*, vol. 19, no. 6, pp. 453–467, 1993.

45. S. P. Eberhardt, R. Tawel, T. X. Brown, T. Daud, and A. P. Thakoor, "Analog VLSI Neural Networks: Implementation Issues and Examples in Optimization and Supervised Learning," *IEEE Transactions on Industrial Electronics*, vol. 39, no. 6, pp. 552–564, December 1992.

46. D. Andes, B. Widrow, M. Lehr, and E. Wan, "MRIII: A Robust Algorithm for Training Analog Neural Networks," *Proceedings International Joint Neural Networks Conference*, vol. 1, Washington, January 15–19, 1990, pp. 533–536.

47. T. Duong, T. Daud, and A. Thakoor, "Cascaded VLSI Neural Network Architecture for On-Line Learning," *NASA Technical Brief*, vol. 17, no. 12, December 1993.

48. B. Furman and A. Abidi, "A CMOS Backward Error Propagation LSI," *Proceedings of the Twenty-Second Asilomar Conference on Signals, Systems, and Computers*, Pacific Grove, CA, November 1988.

49. S. P. Eberhardt, "Analog Hardware for Delta-Backpropagation Neural Networks," U.S. patent 5,101,361, 1992.

50. T. Morie and Y. Amemiya, "An All-Analog Expandable Neural Network LSI with On-Chip Backpropagation Learning," *IEEE Journal of Solid-State Circuits*, vol. 29, no. 9, pp. 1086–1093, 1994.

51. J. B. Lont and W. Guggenbuehl, "Analog CMOS Implementation of a Multilayer Perceptron with Nonlinear Synapses," *IEEE Transactions on Neural Networks*, vol. 3, no. 3, pp. 457–465, 1992.

52. T. Shima, T. Kimura, Y. Kamatani, T. Itakura, Y. Fujita, et al., "Neuro Chips with On-Chip Back-Propagation and/or Hebbian Learning," *IEEE Journal of Solid-State Circuits*, vol. 27, no. 12, pp. 1868–1876, 1992.

53. D. B. Kirk, D. Kerns, K. Fleischer, and A. H. Barr, "Analog VLSI Implementation of Multidimensional Gradient Descent," in *Advances in Neural Information Processing Systems*, vol. 5, Morgan Kaufmann, San Mateo, CA, 1993, pp. 789–796.

54. J. Donald and L. Akers, "An Adaptive Neural Processing Node," *IEEE Transactions on Neural Networks*, vol. 4, no. 3, pp. 413–426, 1993.

55. Y. He and U. Cilingiroglu, "A Charge-Based On-Chip Adaptation Kohonen Neural Network," *IEEE Transactions on Neural Networks*, vol. 4, no. 3, pp. 462–469, 1993.

56. P. Heim and E. A. Vittoz, "Precise Analog Synapse for Kohonen Feature Maps," *IEEE Journal of Solid-State Circuits*, vol. 29, no. 18, pp. 982–985, 1994.

57. D. Macq, M. Verleysen, P. Jespers, and J.-D. Legat, "Analog Implementation of a Kohonen Map with On-Chip Learning," *IEEE Transactions on Neural Networks*, vol. 4, no. 3, pp. 456–461, 1993.

58. B. Widrow, "Generalization and Information Storage in Networks of Adaline 'Neurons,' " in *Self-Organizing Systems*, M. Yovitz, G. Jacobi, and G. Goldstein, eds., Spartan Books, Washington, 1962, pp. 435–461.

59. J. Alspector, J. W. Gannett, S. Haber, M. B. Parker, and R. Chu, "A VLSI-Efficient Technique for Generating Multiple Uncorrelated Noise Sources and Its Application to Stochastic Neural Networks," *IEEE Transactions on Circuits and Systems*, vol. 38, no. 1, pp. 109–123, January 1991.

60. J. Alspector, R. Meir, B. Yuhas, A. Jayakumar, and D. Lippe, "A Parallel Gradient Descent Method for Learning in Analog VLSI Neural Networks," in *Advances in Neural Information Processing Systems*, vol. 5, Morgan Kaufmann, San Mateo, CA, 1993, pp. 836–844.

61. A. Jayakumar and J. Alspector, "On-Chip Learning in Analog VLSI Using Simulated Annealing," *Digest of Papers in Government Microcircuit Applications Conference*, Las Vegas, NV, 1992, pp. 277–280.

62. W.-C. Fang, B. J. Sheu, O. T.-C. Chen, and J. Choi, "A VLSI Neural Processor for Image Data Compression Using Self-Organizing Networks," *IEEE Transactions on Neural Networks*, vol. 3, no. 3, pp. 506–518, 1992.

63. C. G. Kirkpatrick, R. C. Kezer, and G. A. Works, "Intelligent Gradient Descent IC with On-Chip Learning," *Digest of Papers in Government Microcircuit Applications Conference*, Las Vegas, NV, 1992, pp. 273–276.

64. K. Uchimura, O. Saito, and Y. Amemiya, "A High-Speed Digital Neural Network Chip with Low-Power Chain-Reaction Architecture," *IEEE Transactions on Solid-State Circuits,* vol. 27, no. 12, pp. 1862–1867, 1992.

65. S. E. Fahlman and C. Lebiere, "The Cascade Correlation Learning Architecture," in *Advances in Neural Information Processing Systems,* vol. 2, D. Touretzky, ed., Morgan Kaufmann, San Mateo, CA, 1990, pp. 524–532.

66. A. M. Chen and R. Hecht-Neilsen, "On the Geometry of Feedforward Neural Network of Weight Spaces," in *Proceedings of the Second IEE Conference on Artificial Neural Networks,* IEE Press, London, England, 1991, pp. 1–4.

67. T. A. Duong, "An Analysis of Cascade Architecture in Neural Network Learning," in preparation.

68. G. Strang, *Linear Algebra and Its Applications,* 3d ed., Harcourt Brace Jovanovich, San Diego, CA, 1988.

69. D. B. Parker, "Optimal Algorithms for Adaptive Networks: Second Order Back Propagation, Second Order Direct Propagation, and Second Order Hebbian Learning," *Proceedings of IEEE First Intel Conference on Neural Networks,* vol. 2, San Diego, CA, 1987, pp. 593–600.

70. T. X. Brown, M. D. Tran, T. Duong, T. Daud, and A. P. Thakoor, "Cascaded VLSI Neural Network Chips: Hardware Learning for Pattern Recognition and Classification," *Simulation,* vol. 58, no. 5, pp. 340–346, 1992.

71. T. A. Duong, T. Brown, M. Tran, H. Langenbacher, and T. Daud, "Analog VLSI Neural Network Building Block Chips for Hardware-in-the-Loop Learning," *Proceedings of IEEE International Neural Network Society International Joint Conference on Neural Networks,* Beijing, China, November 3–6, 1992.

72. M. Verleysen, B. Sirletti, A. M. Vandemeulebroecke, and P. G. A. Jespers, "Neural Networks for High-Storage Content-Addressable Memory: VLSI Circuit and Learning Algorithm," *IEEE Journal of Solid-State Circuits,* vol. 24, no. 3, pp. 562–569, 1989.

73. J. Wawrzinek, K. Asanovic, and N. Morgan, "The Design of a Neuro-Microprocessor," *IEEE Transactions on Neural Networks,* vol. 4, no. 3, pp. 394–399, 1993.

CHAPTER 28
MORPHOLOGICAL NETWORKS

Stephen S. Wilson
Applied Intelligent Systems, Inc.
Ann Arbor, Michigan

Mathematical morphology refers to a class of nonlinear operators that analyze patterns in images. Sequences of morphological operators on multivalued images give rise to complex networks that are closely related to the usual form of neural networks. Morphological networks consist of a massive number of signals input to a massive number of very simple cells. The computational requirements and programming strategies of morphological networks differ from those which are generally encountered in the commonly used network architectures. In this chapter morphology will be introduced, and special computational techniques will be developed that require massively parallel computer architectures composed of simple bit-serial processing elements.

28.1 MATHEMATICAL MORPHOLOGY

28.1.1 Basis of Morphology

Mathematical morphology involves logical operations on images and is based on set theory. The operations are characterized by structuring elements which are small two-dimensional shapes that act as probes that transform the image in a variety of ways. Since the relationships of shapes in an image are often more logical and geometric than arithmetic, the logical sequences of morphological image operations using various structuring elements have been found to be very effective in analyzing or filtering images.

Sequences of Morphological Operations. Very robust applications result from sequences of operations on images that generate several intermediate images. These secondary images represent perceptions of different features, each resulting from a different set of morphology operations. These images can be separately filtered to reduce noise by using optimal structuring elements appropriate to each feature image. Further morphology operations combine the various features that exist in various geometrical relationships to realize the desired objective such as pattern recognition, object location, or noise reduction.

Certain classes of morphological sequences that involve a multiplicity of operations on a multiplicity of images are called *morphological networks* [1]. The mathematical structure of these networks is captured in a concise unified theory called *matrix morphology* [2, 3]. Morphological networks are translation-invariant, which means that an operation has the same effect on a local pattern no matter where it is located in the image.

Neural Networks in Imaging. Most often in neural imaging applications, a preliminary screening of the image isolates an object of interest, and the full power of the network is focused on a smaller area. For example, the NeoCognitron [4] segments an image into individual characters and operates on the image one character at a time. In many industrial applications, the object of interest is imbedded in a noisy or confusing background so that a preliminary screening is impossible without some sophisticated scheme, such as a neural network. In morphological networks there is an identical set of neurons at each pixel site and the network operates equally on every pixel. Some work has been done to teach translation invariance in neural networks [5]. Morphological networks are designed to be used with images and have translation invariance built into the structure. Translation-invariant networks on image spaces have been called *iconic networks* [6].

28.1.2 Erosion, Dilations

Mathematical morphology was developed by Matheron [7] and Serra [8]. Rigorous mathematical developments and a deeper insight into the significance of the theory have been given in the literature [8, 9]. A brief overview will be given here.

Binary Operations. The two simplest operations in mathematical morphology are *erosion* and *dilation*. Simple, informal pictorial definitions can be given as shown in Fig. 28.1. A structuring element B, shown in Fig. 28.1a, acts as a probe and is moved throughout the image. The cross in the center of the structuring element B is its coordinate reference point. An image is shown in Fig. 28.1b. An erosion is defined as follows. Wherever all points of B contact the foreground members of a shape in image X, the reference point of B marks a pixel to be contained in the output eroded image as shown in Fig. 28.1c. A dilation is shown in Fig. 28.1d. Wherever at least one point of the probe B contacts the image, the reference point of B marks a pixel to be contained in the output dilated image.

In a more formal manner, the *erosion* of image X by structuring element B is written as $X \ominus B$ and defined in terms of logical AND or set intersection operations of various translations of the image. Image X is a set defined in a two-dimensional (2-D) Euclidean space. The vectors $\mathbf{u}$ are members of structuring element B. E is the eroded image.

$$E = X \ominus B = \bigcap_{\mathbf{u} \in B} X_{-\mathbf{u}} \tag{28.1}$$

where $X_{-\mathbf{u}}$ denotes a translation of the image X by vector $\mathbf{u}$.

Dilation is defined in terms of logical OR or set union operations:

$$D = X \oplus B = \bigcup_{\mathbf{u} \in B} X_{\mathbf{u}} \tag{28.2}$$

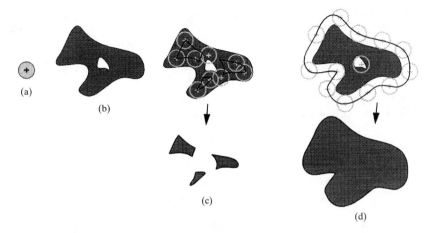

FIGURE 28.1 Erosion and dilation examples: (*a*) structuring element, (*b*) image, (*c*) use of probe for an erosion, (*d*) use of probe for a dilation.

The example in Fig. 28.1 is extremely simple. The structuring elements in practice can be much more complex. In morphological networks, erosions are used as a method for pattern recognition. Objects in an image similar to the structuring element shape appear as small blobs after an erosion. Dilation by small shapes is used as a relaxation between erosions.

Binary Matrix Morphology. In this section, definitions that provide the basis for *matrix morphology* will be given. The usual form of morphology will sometimes be called *scalar morphology* to prevent confusion.

Image Matrix. An *image matrix* is a finite two-dimensional array of sets defined in 2-D euclidean space and represented by a boldface character. It is easiest to think of A as a number of separate pictures, $A_{11}, A_{12}, A_{13}, \ldots$, where each picture is a binary silhouette bit plane and is a member of a set $\{A_{ik}\}$ with a matrix indexing. A matrix of structuring elements has the same definition, e.g., $B = \{B_{ki}\}$. Figure 28.2 shows an example of a matrix in a symbolic and pictorial form to emphasize the image nature of the matrices. A matrix dilation will consist of a number of dilations of the various components of A by various components of the B array. The rules of matrix operations will tell precisely which of the A elements are dilated by which of the B elements, and how the results are combined into a new array.

$$
A = \begin{bmatrix} A_{11} & A_{12} \\ A_{21} & A_{22} \end{bmatrix} =
$$

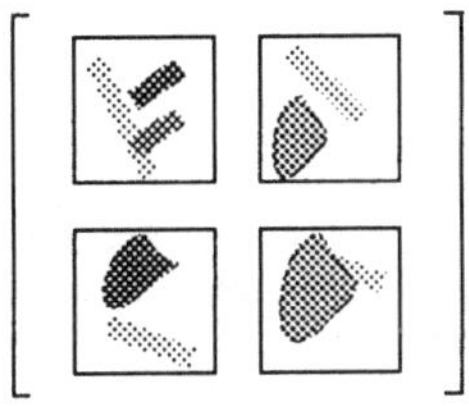

FIGURE 28.2 Example of a 2×2 image matrix in symbolic and pictorial form.

Matrix Erosion.   If the number of columns of the matrix of images is equal to the number of rows of the matrix of structuring elements, then an erosion of the image matrix by the structuring element matrix is defined as a new set of images given by an intersection over the index k:

$$E = \{E_{ij}\} = \{\bigcap_k A_{ik} \ominus B_{kj}\}$$

Matrix Dilation.   A matrix dilation is defined as $D = \{D_{ij}\} = \{\bigcup_k A_{ik} \oplus B_{kj}\}$. The following is an example of a matrix dilation:

$$
\begin{aligned}
A \oplus B &= \begin{bmatrix} A_{11} & A_{12} \\ A_{21} & A_{22} \end{bmatrix} \oplus \begin{bmatrix} B_{11} & B_{12} \\ B_{21} & B_{22} \end{bmatrix} \\[2mm]
&= \begin{bmatrix} ((A_{11} \oplus B_{11}) \cup (A_{12} \oplus B_{21})) & ((A_{11} \oplus B_{12}) \cup (A_{12} \oplus B_{22})) \\ ((A_{21} \oplus B_{11}) \cup (A_{22} \oplus B_{21})) & ((A_{21} \oplus B_{12}) \cup (A_{22} \oplus B_{22})) \end{bmatrix}
\end{aligned}
$$

Matrix erosions and dilations are analogous to matrix multiplication. Unions and intersections of image matrices are analogous to matrix addition. In most applications the image A is a row vector $\{A_1, A_2, A_3, \ldots\}$ and the structuring element is a rectangular matrix. Complex applications using chains of matrix structuring elements operating on image vectors are given in Refs. 3, 10, and 11.

Gray-Level Morphology

Threshold Decomposition.   Binary scalar morphology operations have been extended to gray-level images by use of a *threshold decomposition* [12]. An example gray-level image shown in Fig. 28.3a is broken into a large number of binary images by a sequence of threshold or cross-section operations and is shown in Fig. 28.3b as a stack of binary images.

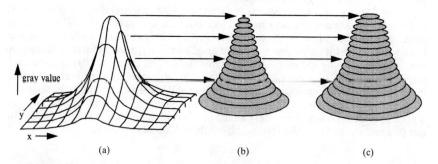

FIGURE 28.3   Gray-level generalization. (*a*) Gray-level image; (*b*) threshold decomposition; (*c*) stack filter operation.

Stack Filters.   A binary morphology operation such as a dilation is applied separately to each binary image in the stack as shown in Fig. 28.3c, and then reassembled into a gray-level image. The gray-level operators defined from binary operators using this method are called *stack filters* [13]. It has been shown that a gray-level erosion is equivalent to a minimum operation over the neighborhood defined by the structuring element, and a gray-level dilation is equivalent to a maximum [14].

Gray-Level Morphology as Fuzzy Logic. It is obvious that the stack filter definition in this case is equivalent to a fuzzy logic extension of the erosion and dilation operations as defined in Eqs. (28.1) and (28.2). The gray level erosion is a minimum of various translations of the image X by the various vectors $\mathbf{u}$ which are members of the structuring element B. The dilation is a maximum.

$$\text{Fuzzy erosion:} \qquad E = \text{MIN}\{X_{-\mathbf{u}} : \mathbf{u} \in B\}$$

$$\text{Fuzzy dilation:} \qquad D = \text{MAX}\{X_{\mathbf{u}} : \mathbf{u} \in B\}$$

Threshold Logic. *Threshold logic* is a general computational model that can simplify some complex classes of boolean logic decompositions [15]. Threshold logic should not be confused with the threshold decomposition.

Definition. Suppose there are N boolean variables $x_1, \ldots, x_N$ represented by a characteristic binary 1 or 0. A threshold logic gate passes a binary 1 if the sum of the binary values is greater or equal to some threshold t. A logical AND of N variables is equivalent to threshold logic with a threshold set to N, and a logical OR function has a threshold set to 1. Threshold logic is further extended to include weights where the general expression is given by

$$Y = \text{Th}_t(\Sigma\, w_i\, x_i) \tag{28.3}$$

where $\text{Th}_t(n)$ is 0 if $n < t$, and 1 if $n \geq t$. Threshold logic is weaker than boolean logic since any threshold function can be represented by some logical expression, but the opposite is not true. Threshold logic can easily be applied to binary erosions and dilations which both become expressions of the same form.

Morphology Extended by Threshold Logic. The images in the following definitions are spatial functions with a characteristic binary range 0 or 1. Given spatial coordinates x and y, input image $A(x, y)$, output image $C(x, y)$, and structuring element $B(x, y)$, a general morphological operation using threshold logic is expressed as

$$C(x, y) = \text{Th}_t(\sum_{u,v} B(u, v) \times A(x - u, y - v)) \tag{28.4}$$

where $B(u, v) = 1$ for all points in the structuring element and 0 otherwise. Morphology using threshold logic is nothing more than thresholded convolutions with unit weights in the kernel $B(u, v)$.

Since B is 0 or 1 in morphology, it is a faster computational model to sum over the points defining B and ignore points where B is zero. Suppose B is composed of the set of points $\{u_i, v_i\}, i = 1, N$. Then Eq. (28.4) becomes

$$C(x, y) = \text{Th}_t(\sum_{i = 1, N} A(x - u_i, y - v_i)) \tag{28.5}$$

Equations (28.4) and (28.5) are erosions if $t = N$ and dilations if $t = 1$. A more robust form than the erosion results if t is slightly less than N because the effect of the erosion is not destroyed if one or two pixels of the input image are missing due to noise.

Gray-Level Threshold Logic. Threshold logic can easily be extended to gray-level images by using threshold logic in each bit plane of a threshold decomposition. The use of threshold logic as a stack filter gives rise to a class of operators called *rank-order* or *order-statistic* filters. Equivalence between the rank-order filter and the stack filter defined by threshold logic has been shown in Ref. 12. The most well-known rank-order operator is called the *moving median filter*, where N is odd and the threshold (or rank) is set to $(N + 1)/2$. Rank-order filters are a generalization of erosions and dilations using fuzzy logic over neighborhoods and include fuzzy logic as extreme values of the threshold or rank (1 or N). In theory, all rank-order filters can be expressed in terms of complex decompositions involving only minimum and maximum functions [16].

28.1.3   Network Model of Morphology

From the sum of products in Eq. (28.4) it is easy to see how scalar erosions and dilations are translation-invariant artificial neural networks (ANNs) [17], where the connection pattern is given by B. There is a neural cell at each pixel site with an identical pattern of connections, and a hard limiting threshold. In scalar morphology a hit or miss transform is defined [8] and is equivalent to Eq. (28.4) where negative unit weights are allowed. In the neural model of Eq. (28.4), inputs to cells are connected from a neighborhood of pixels defined by the nonzero values of the structuring element. Neural weights are the weights of the structuring element viewed as a convolution kernel. Figure 28.4 is an illustration of the network model of a simple scalar erosion.

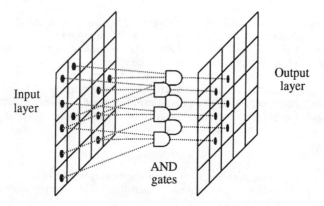

Input layer

AND gates

Output layer

FIGURE 28.4   Erosion as a network of AND gates.

Example Application.   In general, the input image is not a single binary image plane, but an M component vector space of M bit planes, where the value at each pixel site $p(x, y)$ is an ordered set of points $p(x, y) = [p_1(x, y), p_2(x, y), \ldots, p_M(x, y)]$. Structuring elements are generally rectangular matrices. The model for the connection patterns for a sequence of matrix morphology operators $(X\ OP1\ B1)\ OP2\ B2$ is shown in Fig. 28.5 and is much more complex than that shown in Fig. 28.4. Connections for only one cell in each layer are shown. The example in Fig. 28.5 is taken from a character recognition application [3] where the input image is a thresholded gradient vector. Gradients in four directions are north, south, east, and west image bit planes. The operation $OP1$ and $B1$ is a matrix erosion that computes eight different planes (only three are shown in Fig. 28.5) given by features that are line segments in four different directions, and corner segments in four directions. The last layer defined by $OP2$ and $B2$ recognizes one specific character. In practice, the final layer is a vector with one component layer for each of the characters in the set to be rec-

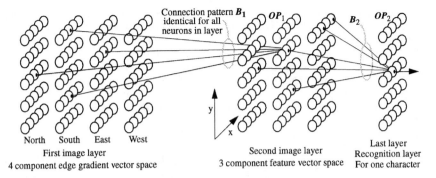

North   South   East   West
First image layer
4 component edge gradient vector space

Second image layer
3 component feature vector space

Last layer
Recognition layer
For one character

FIGURE 28.5   Matrix network.

ognized. After the sequence of matrix operations that define this application are executed, there will be a response from one of the output component planes only where a corresponding character is present.

Differences.   There are several major differences between morphological networks and other networks:

1. There is a massive number of very simple neural cells.
2. The weights are +1, −1, or 0.
3. Connection patterns are image based and are identical for each neural layer.
4. Gray-level threshold logic is generated by using a threshold decomposition and a stack operator.
5. The generalization leads to rank-order operators, not to a sum of products.

Another type of morphological network is based on a representation of the Hopfield net [18] and is used for image enhancement and filtering. The binary form of the Hopfield net and the morphological realization are identical. Differences occur in the gray-level form where the morphological model is defined by the application of the threshold decomposition and stack filters, and leads to Hopfield cells based on the rank-order operation.

28.1.4   Training Structuring Elements

Since the matrix structuring element is equivalent to a network connection pattern, there should exist training techniques analogous to those in a neural network. The major difficulty is that the weights are +1, −1, or 0. Thus, methods that use a fractional change of weights during training cannot be used. Automated methods for training structuring elements are generally statistical in nature. The major problem is reducing the size of an intractable search space so that an optimal set of structuring elements can be found according to some optimizing criteria in a reasonable amount of time.

Hebbian Learning.   The final layer of structuring elements in a character recognition application can be trained by a hebbian learning method similar to the delta rule used in neural training [3]. The network starts out with all connections having a zero weight (unconnected). Sample images of the entire character set are compared to a desired output image template for a specific character. A training rule is applied to the differences between the teach image and the ensemble of samples. The rule consists of looking for that connection point that will give the lowest false alarm rate if added to the structuring element. Every time the training rule is applied, another point that minimizes the error is added to the structuring element of the layer being trained, and the error decreases. The training rule is cycled a predetermined number of times to build up a specified number of points. This method, called the *morphological training rule,* requires about one minute per character.

Simulated Annealing.   Simulated annealing has been used to train a system to locate the surface of an IC chip [10]. A thermodynamic model is developed by defining molecules as connection points. The neighborhood of allowed molecular movement during one time cycle is represented as temperature. The connection pattern at each cycle is used to define the potential energy as the largest convolution output other than that at the point being trained and is related directly to the false alarm rate. At a high temperature, the connection patterns are almost random and search the space globally for a minimum energy. As the energy is lowered during annealing, false recognitions decrease in intensity. At low temperature, the connections move very little and search for a local minimum. A new part can be trained in about 45 seconds.

Unsupervised Learning.   An unsupervised competitive learning technique has been developed to train hidden layers in a morphological network [11]. First a training image that has a representative sample of all the image patterns that are important is input to the system. All layers are processed up to, but not including, the hidden layer. The layer that is input to the hidden layer is a vector space with several components corresponding to the several layers. A random search takes place for sets of connections that define features that are orthogonal and complete. The definition of orthogonality and completeness force the system to adopt features that are independent and span the space of possible features, otherwise information that may be critical to the final layer may be lost. Orthogonality is a uniqueness criterion that attempts to minimize the number of cases that two different features respond at the same pixel site. The completeness criterion attempts to maximize the total number of pixels responding to at least one feature.

Conditional Expectation.   One major area of interest is filtering out noise in an image. In the following method, morphological operators are interpreted as statistical estimators [19]. On the basis of the neighborhood about a pixel site, sets of connections are adopted if the expectation of the morphological estimator using those connections favors a specific pixel value (1 or 0 for binary images). The morphological operator defines an expected pixel value, and may switch the value of the pixel in the input image. The training goal is to minimize the switching error. Noise is introduced into the system for training, and the positions of the noise sites are recorded. Structuring elements are chosen that result in the minimum mean squared error, i.e., those that eliminate noise while minimizing the disturbance to the original image. The search for structuring elements that have the highest unambiguous expectations is narrowed down by using neighborhood segments in the image itself as candidate structuring elements.

28.2   HARDWARE ARCHITECTURES

Because of the massive number of neural cells, a serial processor or workstation cannot handle real-time computations. If a practical cost-effective application is not important, a supercomputer or massively parallel serial computer can be used and is much faster, although the architecture is not necessarily set up to work efficiently on the small word sizes. The data input/output (I/O) bottleneck is significant because the data is massive and the computation is simple. The computation pace of a supercomputer is much faster than the I/O pace needed for morphological networks.

There are two types of parallelism to be discussed in this section: multiple instruction, multiple data (MIMD) and single instruction, multiple data (SIMD) architectures. In a SIMD architecture there are multiple data paths connected to a multiplicity of identical processing elements, all operating with the same instruction. The focus here is on systems that are designed for handling images and have provisions for high-speed camera inputs and monitor outputs.

28.2.1   MIMD Pipeline Architectures

CytoComputer.   One of the original pipeline systems for morphology was developed at the Environment Research Institute of Michigan. The system, called a Cyto-Computer [20], consists of a chain of identical programmable stages that are optimized for binary and gray level morphology. One stage consists of a neighborhood memory and a processing section, as illustrated in Fig. 28.6. The neighborhood memory contains a backlog of two input image rows and presents a 3×3 neighborhood to the processing section which provides the output computation in one clock cycle. As the image data flow into a stage, the output flows out at the same rate.

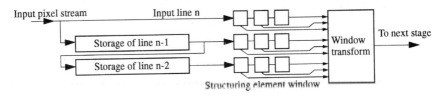

FIGURE 28.6   Block diagram of CytoComputer.

Heterogeneous Pipeline Systems.   Unlike the CytoComputer, most pipeline architectures are heterogeneous systems. For example, DataCube (Danvers, Mass.) and Imaging Technology, Inc. (Huntington Beach, Calif.) offer systems with a wide variety of stages that can be arbitrarily intermixed. Separate sections provide binary versus gray-scale operations. The basic architecture of pipeline systems for imaging is the same as that given in Fig. 28.6, although the window transform section can be different from one stage to the next. Pipelines are limited directly to small neighborhoods. However, larger neighborhoods can be built up by sequences of operations. Simple convex structuring elements can be built up from the 3×3 neighborhoods supported in hardware by chaining. For example, an ero-

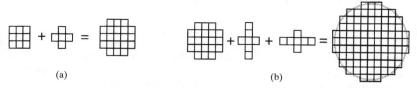

FIGURE 28.7   Example of chaining structuring elements to generate (*a*) octagon, (*b*) circle.

sion by an octagon is equivalent to chaining an erosion of a box followed by a diamond, as shown in Fig. 28.7. An erosion by a circle is derived by following an erosion by an octagon by two other elements. Threshold logic cannot be done with chaining.

Sparse Structuring Elements. Pipeline systems offer good support for thresholded convolutions and morphology with convex structuring elements, and less support for general morphological network models with sparse structuring elements that are composed of disconnected points. The difficulty with the pipelined systems is that they are specifically designed to efficiently handle simple convex structuring elements such as squares, ellipses, and octagons. Pipelines support the three popular types of rank-order filters—minimum, maximum, and median—but few pipeline systems directly support arbitrary rank-order filters.

Many important applications require large sparse structuring elements with, for example, 35 disconnected points in a 30 × 30 pixel area [3]. Pipeline systems generally allow large neighborhood structuring elements to be constructed point by point by large displacements of the pixel addressing circuits at a rate of one frame time per pixel, or faster if the region of interest is small. In order to handle the multitude of connections that arise from complex but robust systems at a faster rate, a massively parallel system is the only recourse.

28.2.2 SIMD Architectures

At one time, massive parallelism also implied the usage of fine-grained (bit-serial) processing elements, but that has changed in the '90s. Now massive parallelism is generally understood to mean supercomputing with a large number of serial processors. However, there are a number of massively parallel systems where the architecture is designed specifically to handle the type of data movement and simple processing that is required by morphological networks.

Custom Neural Chips. There are a number of SIMD digital neural chips available such as the CNAPS (Adaptive Solutions Inc., Beaverton, Ore.) with 64 processors per chip and the Intel Ni1000 with 1024 neurons per chip. Systems with these chips are massively parallel and very high in performance for many network paradigms. Although they are designed to allow imaging applications, they do not necessarily have a built-in translation-invariant structure, type of data communication, or processing element design that is geared toward morphological networks. Neural chips cannot handle the rank-order operators that arise from gray-level signals. However, the performance of these types of chips is so high as to be worthy of consideration for binary signals.

Commercial Mesh-Connected Systems. Historically, the most popular interconnection scheme is the mesh-connected architecture shown in Fig. 28.8. The processing elements (PEs) are arranged in a two-dimensional array and are interconnected to nearest neighbors. The first realization of this architecture is a research system built by Goodyear and called the massively parallel processor (MPP) [21] with a 128×128 array of 16K PEs. The BLITZEN chip [22] is an outgrowth of the MPP and has 128 PEs in a 8×16 array. Each PE contains 32-bit cache and a 1024-bit random access memory. Adaptive Memory Technology, Inc. (AMT), Irvine, Calif., also manufactures a mesh-connected system that uses the DAP architecture [23]. Word-wide coprocessors accelerate arithmetic computations. National Cash Register, Inc. (NCR), Fort Collins, Colo., builds a chip called the GAPP. An early version (NCR45CG72) contains 72 bit-serial PEs. In this chip there are two communication layers, horizontal and vertical. There are a number of lesser known realizations of mesh-connected architectures surveyed by Fountain [24]. Most of these are one-of-a-kind research systems.

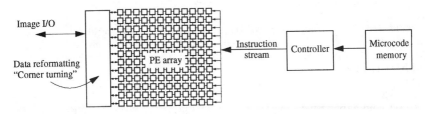

FIGURE 28.8   Mesh-connected SIMD system.

Example of Mesh Architecture.   In a typical mesh-connected system as shown in Fig. 28.8, an array of processing elements is connected so that each PE communicates data directly to its vertical and horizontal neighbors. The digitized data from a camera comes in serial words row by row. The mesh system requires an entire plane in the form of some significant bit. For example, the most significant bits of a whole image might be stored first. Since the usual memory systems do not read out data in this fashion, a special interface circuit for "corner turning" the data is provided. After the data are present at the processing elements, the controller broadcasts a single instruction that transforms all the data simultaneously and writes data back to the local memory associated with each processing element. Subsequent instructions are broadcast at the clock rate of the system as an algorithm proceeds.

Example of Mesh Processing Element.   A single processing element in the GAPP chip is shown in Fig. 28.9. Processing elements in mesh systems are very simple because the architecture tradeoff favors massive parallelism on a chip at the expense of PE complexity. Also there are a limited number of pins that can be devoted to the updating of instructions that must occur at high speed. Each PE contains four single-bit registers, an adder-subtracter, a 128-bit RAM, and multiplexers that switch data into the various registers and memory. As is typical in this type of PE, the instruction bits are devoted to switching the input multiplexers and addressing the memory. The limited on-board memory is supplemented by an external memory that can feed into the system via the registers that are linked to adjacent PEs in both the vertical and horizontal.

Addition on a Mesh.   Addition is a bit-serial operation, where the sum and carry for each successive bit are generated simultaneously and stored in the registers. Sub-

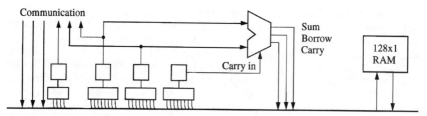

FIGURE 28.9   GAP processing element.

traction is also directly supported. The borrow or carry is stored on board the chip, since it is immediately used in the next operation. Any word sizes can be efficiently accommodated. Processing speed is proportional to the word size, and offers a trade-off for speed against precision. Other logic operations are available by switching the appropriate signals into the adder-subtracter.

Linear Arrays.   A linear array SIMD architecture is a long one-dimensional chain of processors, each communicating data to the nearest processors on the right and left. Each PE processes image data in the column associated with it. Data interact with the chain of PEs one row at a time.

   Commercial Systems.   The most popular example of the bit-serial linear connected SIMD processor, shown in Fig. 28.10, is the Applied Intelligent Systems Inc. (AISI), Ann Arbor, Mich., series of computers using the Pixie [25], Firefly, and Centipede chips [26]. These systems are 10 times lower in cost than mesh systems, and are the only examples of SIMD architectures used in widespread turnkey applications. In some systems (AIS-4000) there are 512 PEs, one for each column in the image. Other systems (AIS-3000 and AIS-3500) divide the processing into smaller ribbons of images of 64 and 128 PEs. The image memories are on separate chips and are large enough to hold several image frames. Other examples of linear SIMD arrays used in research are the scan line array processor (SLAP) [27] developed at Carnegie Mellon, and the VIP developed at the University of Linkoping [28]. The Texas Instruments PVP [29] processor is primarily for digital television. The TI system differs from most other linear arrays in that the local tightly coupled memory is on board the chip, and large enough to hold a backlog of a few lines rather than a few frames. The system operates in a mode that is similar to mesh systems, in that a controller broadcasts a new instruction every clock cycle.

The AISI Architecture

   The System.   There are several components to the AISI processing system shown in Fig. 28.10. A general-purpose host microcomputer generally controls the

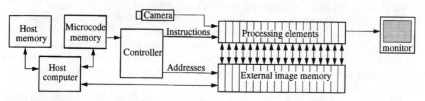

FIGURE 28.10   Firefly system.

sequence of the image processing functions. The host can also read or write data directly in the image memory. A controller is connected to a small memory that contains microcode instructions and general data for support of the parallel processing array. The controller has several functions:

1. Transmit instructions to the parallel processor array.
2. Supply a high-speed address pattern to the image memory so that the processor array reads and writes the rows of image data according to the address pattern.
3. Handle image I/O on an interrupt basis.
4. Directly read or write pixels for operations that do not easily lend themselves to parallel processing. As a hardware background task, a camera may be inputting data to a separate buffer in the chip. When an entire line of data has been captured, the processor is interrupted and those data are sent to the external image memory.

SIMD Operation. There is enough memory directly connected to each PE to hold the entire column of image data for several distinct images. The image storage is such that typically 128 bit planes (512×512 binary images), or 16 gray-level images, or any combination of various image word sizes can be saved. A single image operation is processed by first broadcasting an instruction to all PEs. The image data are sent row by row to the processing elements, and results are returned row by row back to the memory. Nearest neighbor information is exchanged between adjacent processors during the processing. Details of this architecture for an earlier system can be found in Ref. 25. Since each instruction is valid for all rows of an entire image, the instructions are loaded at a much lower rate than the clock rate of the system. The controller needs only to update the address pattern of the external memories at high speed. Thus the real-time control of a linear system is much simpler than that of a mesh system where the entire instruction must be updated at high speed. Furthermore, the instruction can be loaded serially into the PEs and can consist of much longer instruction words than the chip pins can directly accommodate.

Firefly Processing Element. Figure 28.11 shows details of a single processing element separated into three parts for clarity. The controller first transmits an instruction to registers in the processor chip. The instruction merely sets up internal data pathways, and sets values in a truth table. The controller then sends a sequence of addresses to the image memory along with read or write enable signals. The processor functions are

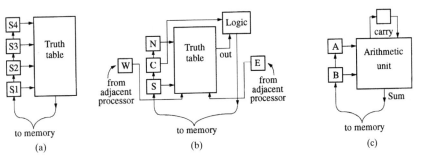

FIGURE 28.11 Firefly processing element. (*a*) Four-input boolean truth table; (*b*) neighborhood transform; (*c*) bit-serial arithmetic unit.

Boolean function. Internal data pathways for the Boolean function are shown in Fig. 28.11a. Four rows of binary data from the image memory corresponding to the controller address are sequentially sent to shift registers S1 to S4. The truth table defines an output for each possible combination of the four sources S1 to S4. The output of the truth table is read back to the image memory according to the controller-generated address.

Neighborhood function. The pathways defined by a controller instruction that sets up a north (N), south (S), east (E), west (W) neighborhood function are shown in Fig. 28.11b. The PEs are programmed with a truth table that defines the neighbor transformation. The W and E data come from adjacent PEs. The shape of the neighborhood is directly limited to the close horizontal and vertical neighbors.

Arithmetic operations. The pathways for an arithmetic add are shown in Fig. 28.11c. They are similar to those in the GAPP chip.

28.3 COMPUTATIONAL METHODS FOR SIMD SYSTEMS

For morphological networks, a serial processor would be programmed with three nested loops: the x and y spatial dimensions and the list of points of the structuring element given by the summation in Eq. (28.5). A multiprocessor consisting of many serial processors would have a similar algorithm, but different regions of the image would be assigned to the different processors. An additional task is to sort out the flow of data at the boundaries of each region.

Since ordinary languages and compilers are not designed to handle massively parallel systems, the nature of the hardware system is generally built into a language by the use of function calls that initiate logical or arithmetic operations between a set of images in the image memory directly coupled to the PEs. The function itself does no image processing but is written to construct the microcode that is stored in the microcode memory to be later used by the controller during run time. Microcode contains the states of switches in the processor array and address patterns for the image memory. During run time the controller decodes microcode and transfers signals to the processor array at an uninterrupted high speed.

In a SIMD or pipeline system the programming of an application involves a different level of detail than a serial program. The x, y spatial loops are done in hardware. Conditional branching is not allowed at the pixel level, and substitutes for these operations must be provided. Examples of techniques for SIMD systems are described in the following sections. Library functions are used to set up the hardware and direct the flow of data from image memories. With a serial computer there is some leeway as to how the software loops can be set up to provide sparse connections and unusual shapes in an erosion. In a SIMD or pipeline system the techniques to provide various operations such as sparse erosions and threshold logic and rank-order operators are not always obvious because algorithms using these systems must always be constructed so that the x, y spatial loops are the innermost nested loops. Operations and function calls must reference image spaces and not individual pixels.

28.3.1 Binary Morphology

The following methods for binary morphology involve translating a copy of an image by some vector, and then performing an accumulation type operation between the translated image and a stationary accumulator plane. An example of this technique is illustrated in Fig. 28.12 and is described in detail in the following.

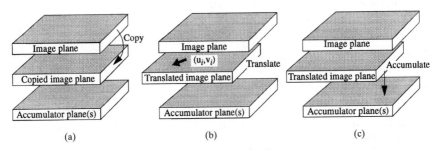

FIGURE 28.12 Sparse structuring element algorithm. (*a*) Copy image to temporary plane; (*b*) translate temporary plane; (*c*) accumulate temporary plane into accumulator plane.

Sparse Dilations

1. Set all pixels in accumulator to binary 0.
2. Write input image into memory A.
3. Copy image A into memory B.
4. Translate B by vector (u_i, v_i) as in Eq. (28.5).
5. Move logical OR of image B and accumulator image C into image C.
6. Repeat steps 3, 4, and 5 for all (u_i, v_i).

Sparse Erosions. These are the same as dilations except that in step 1 the accumulator is set to a logic 1, and step 5 involves a logical AND.

Sparse Threshold Logic Operators. These are the same as dilations except that the accumulator image C is a multibit word plane with enough bit planes to handle the maximum sum of the M structuring element points (or connections). Step 5 involves a sum of the single-bit B image plane to the accumulator plane. There is one further, final step:

7. Subtract accumulator image C from a constant t. The final "borrow plane" resulting from the subtraction is the output and represents those image regions that have gray levels greater than the threshold t.

Soft-Limited Outputs. In the terminology of ANNs, threshold logic has unit weights and is a hard-limited output function. Other, soft-limited output functions are possible. One popular soft-limited function is to set any output that is at threshold t to a binary 0, and to set any output that is n units above the threshold to n. In other words, the output is the sum of inputs minus the threshold where underflows are truncated to zero. However, for a fine-grained array processor that handles bit-serial arithmetic, any reduction in precision saves time. It is more efficient to start with an accumulator of, say, only three bit planes and count down whenever some point in a displaced plane is zero. Although there may be many connections, the accumulator can be quite small. In the case of a seven-level span (3 bits) above the threshold, the following procedure is used.

Sparse Threshold Logic Operator with Soft-Limited Output

1. Set the three bit planes of the accumulator to binary 1.
2. Complement input binary image and write into memory A.
3. Copy image A into memory B.
4. Translate B by vector (u_i, v_i) as in Eq. (28.5)
5. Subtract image B from accumulator image C (three bit planes). Set all pixels in image C that underflow to zero.
6. Repeat steps 3, 4, and 5 for all (u_i, v_i).

On a SIMD processor step 5 is executed by logic equations after every subtraction. Let the three bit planes that define accumulator C be designated as C_i and the "borrow plane" as C_b. Those pixels that underflow will have a binary 1 in C_b. Truncation after the subtraction is executed by $C_i = C_i$ AND (NOT C_b), $i = 0, 1, 2$. An underflow means that too few connections respond for the cell to have an output.

28.3.2   Gray-Level Erosions and Dilations

In gray-level morphology the AND and OR are replaced by the minimum or maximum functions in the procedure for sparse erosions or dilations given above. To find the maximum of a displaced plane B compared with an accumulator plane C, first subtract C from B and store the final borrow bits into a plane C_b. At those points where B is larger than C, the value for all significant bits C_i must be replaced by the value for B_i. This is executed by the following logic equations on image planes: $C_i = (C_i$ AND $C_b)$ OR $(B_i$ AND NOT $C_b)$.

28.3.3   Gray Level Rank-Order Algorithms

Rank-Order Algorithms in a Serial Processor.   Rank-order algorithms are much harder to program, especially in a SIMD processor. For a serial processor, one technique involves sliding the structuring element window to some pixel site, listing and ordering the N neighboring pixel values contacted by the structuring element from lowest to highest, and picking the rth element in the list as the output of the operator for that pixel site. The ordering and ranking must be repeated hundreds of thousands of times to transform all pixels. For the two extreme special cases where the rank r is respectively 1 or N, it is obvious that the operator is the minimum, or maximum, although this method is not ideal for those two cases. Ordering arbitrary values is a formidable task in a SIMD system where the neighbors of every pixel site have a unique ordering.

Danielsson's Algorithm.   The following rank-order algorithm is adopted from Danielsson [30], where it is specifically designed to be efficient for massively parallel bit-serial processors. The cycle time for Danielsson's algorithm is proportional to the number of bits in the gray-level image times the number of connections. The cycle time for the usual rank-order algorithms that depend on sorting and ordering data is proportional to the square of the number of connections. The algorithm is described for the case of 15 neighboring points in the structuring element. Let A_0 to A_7 be the significant bit planes of an input image to the rank-order operator of rank r. In Danielsson's algorithm, the image A is processed from the most significant bit plane A_7 to the least significant A_0. The rth element is found not by ordering, but by successively screening out candidates.

Image Planes Required. Several types of temporary image planes must first be defined:

1. S_0 to S_{15} are defined as 16 planes, where each plane is associated to a unique neighbor. The S_i planes act as screening planes. Candidate neighboring values of pixels that are not the rth element in the list will be successively screened out and tagged by the S_i "image" planes. The condition that some neighbor at displacement (u_i, v_i) is potentially at the desired rank r is represented by $S_i = 1$. If that neighbor is definitely not at the rank r then S_i is set to zero. Initially, all S_i are set to 1 at all pixel sites.
2. T is a 4-bit nibble plane that counts the number of neighbors that are definitely above the rank. Initially T is set to zero.
3. B is a temporary plane to hold one of the significant bits A_j of the input image displaced by vector (u_i, v_i).
4. C is a 4-bit nibble plane that counts the number of neighbors with unscreened zeros.
5. O is an 8-bit output plane.

The Procedure. The algorithm is shown as a flowchart in Fig. 28.13. A detailed explanation follows.

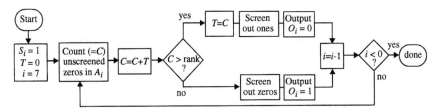

FIGURE 28.13 Flowchart of Danielsson's method

1. First count the number of zeros in A_7 that the structuring element contacts in a manner similar to sparse threshold logic operators previously discussed. For those pixel locations where the count of zeros C exceeds the rank, then:
   a. One of those neighbors that was counted must be the rth element.
   b. The most significant bit of the rank-order operator O_7 must be zero.
   c. Those neighbors with the most significant bit equal to 1 must be screened out and are not candidates (set $S_i = 0$).
2. For those pixel locations where the count of zeros C is less than the rank, then:
   a. None of the neighbors that were counted can be the rth element.
   b. The most significant bit of the rank-order operator must be 1.
   c. Those neighbors with the most significant bit equal to 0 must be screened out and are not candidates. In this case the count of unscreened zeros has exceeded the target count and must revert back to 0.

3. Next the remaining unscreened zeros of A_6 in the neighborhood defined by the structuring element are counted. If the total count $C + T$ of unscreened neighbors exceeds the rank, then:
   a. One of the unscreened neighbors in the new total count must be the rth element.
   b. The sixth significant bit of the rank-order O_6 operator must be zero.
   c. Those neighbors with the sixth significant bit equal to 1 must be screened out and are not candidates.
4. For those pixel locations where the total count C including the zeros of A_6 is less than the rank, then:
   a. None of the neighbors that were counted in plane A_6 can be the rth element.
   b. The sixth significant bit O_6 of the rank-order operator must be 1.
   c. Those neighbors with the sixth significant bit equal to zero must be screened out and are not candidates. In this case the count of unscreened zeros has exceeded the target count and must revert back to the previous count.
5. The algorithm continues in this manner to the least significant bit plane A_0.

Branching in a SIMD System.   SIMD processors are not able to individually execute conditional branches that are data-dependent since all processors receive the same instructions. The section of the flowchart that screens out ones or zeros is represented as a branch that depends on the count; however, the branch logic is simulated using the boolean truth table in the Firefly chip and is not actually a computational branch.

28.3.4 Binary Matrix Morphology

Although there is considerable added network complexity in the transition from scalar morphology to matrix morphology, there is no added computational complexity except that there are generally more connections in the loops. Modification of the scalar algorithms is very straightforward and consists of the following conceptual changes to Fig. 28.12:

1. Instead of one binary image plane, there are as many planes as there components in the input vector image.
2. One of the components of the vector image plane is selected, copied, and translated.
3. There are as many accumulators as there are vector components in the output image.
4. For each cycle only one is selected for accumulation.

28.4 CONCLUSIONS

Properties of Morphological Networks

Morphological networks operate on image spaces and consist of a massive number of inputs to a massive network of iconic cells, each with 10 to 30 connections with unit signals and weights. In contrast, many neural systems use much smaller input vectors and a much smaller number of cells with complex output functions and floating-point weights having a high dynamic range. It is clear that a large amount of system "intelligence" can exist in either type of network, but a morphological network is geared toward simple cells.

The use of these networks in translation-invariant image spaces with a perhaps quarter of a million or more input signals at each layer forces us to use a very simple neural cell because in industrial applications processing time is limited to 50 milliseconds for some applications and up to around 2 seconds for others.

There is a fundamental equivalence between binary morphology using hit-and-miss transforms, thresholded convolutions with binary signals, and weights of ±1 and 0, and translation-invariant networks on image spaces (iconic networks). However, thresholded convolutions and iconic networks are generalized to multivalued signals (i.e., gray-level images) by simple arithmetic (sum of products of words), whereas in morphological networks, the generalization uses threshold decompositions and stack filters and leads to nonlinear rank-order operators.

Advantages of SIMD Systems.   Neural chips are generally committed to a small class of operations such as a sum of products, and would not work at all for other classes of operations such as fuzzy networks. A SIMD hardware system is not committed to any particular class of operations, but is committed only to array operations in general. Thus a SIMD system can combine any functions that occur in the software library such as linear convolutions, Hough transforms, fast Fourier transforms, image rotations, and fuzzy operations or sums of products in networks. There are many signal conditioning, noise filtering, segmentation, and feature extraction methods in the literature that are very useful for preconditioning image inputs to a network that would not be addressed by a special neural chip.

Linear SIMD systems are one or two orders of magnitude faster than pipeline systems for sparse structuring elements. On a linear SIMD system operating on a 512×512 image, the time for a binary network operation with 35 connection points within a 20×20 neighborhood window is about 8.5 milliseconds. Mesh systems are an order of magnitude faster than linear SIMD systems. Linear SIMD systems are low enough in cost for widespread industrial applications.

Thinking Parallel.   Looping computations of neural outputs on a SIMD system is different than that for a serial system. A serial system would complete the computation of each neural output before going to the next cell. In a SIMD system the output values are built up gradually for all cells in a layer as the computation progresses because each single instruction operates on a multiplicity of cells assigned to a multiplicity of processing elements. Data-dependent branching at the pixel level is not possible as a SIMD operation because all PEs receive the same instruction. However, it is always possible to simulate branching using SIMD logic equations. Some SIMD algorithms are fairly straightforward, such as the erosion algorithm. Other algorithms, such as a general rank-order filter, are very abstract. Algorithms that are perceived to be efficient are often only efficient on a serial system.

REFERENCES

1. Wilson, S. S., "Morphological Networks," *SPIE Conference, Visual Communications and Image Processing '89*, vol. 1199, pp. 483–493, November 5–10, 1989.

2. Wilson, S. S., "Theory of matrix morphology," *IEEE Trans. on Pattern Analysis and Machine Intelligence*, vol. 14, no. 6, pp. 636–652, June 1992.

3. Wilson, S. S., "Training structuring elements in morphological networks," in *Mathematical Morphology in Image Processing*, E. R. Dougherty (ed.), pp. 1–41, 1992.

4. Fukushima, K., "Neocognitron: a hierarchical neural network capable of visual pattern recognition," *Neural Networks*, vol. 1, pp. 119–130, 1988.

5. Hinton, G. E., "Learning translation invariant recognition in a massively parallel network," in *PARLE: Parallel Architectures and Languages, Europe. Lecture Notes in Computer Science*, G. Goos and J. Hartmanis (eds.), Springer-Verlag, Berlin, 1987.

6. Wilson, S. S., "Vector morphology and iconic neural networks," *IEEE Trans. on Systems, Man, and Cybernetics*, vol. SMC-19, no. 6, pp. 1636–1644, November/December 1989.

7. Matheron, G., *Random Sets and Integral Geometry*, Wiley, New York, 1975.

8. Serra, J., *Image Analysis and Mathematical Morphology*, Academic Press, London, 1982.

9. Haralick, R. M., S. R. Sternberg, and X. Zhuang, "Image analysis using mathematical morphology," *IEEE Trans. on Pattern Analysis and Machine Intelligence*, vol. PAMI-9, no. 4, pp. 532–550, 1988.

10. Wilson, S. S., "Teaching network connections for real time object recognition," *Neural and Intelligent Systems Integration*, B. Soucek (ed.), Wiley Series in Sixth Generation Computer Technologies, Wiley, New York, pp. 135–160, 1991.

11. Wilson, S. S., "Unsupervised training of structuring elements," *Proc. SPIE 36th Annual Symposium on Optical and Optoelectronic Applied Science and Engineering*, vol. 1568, pp. 189–199, San Diego, July 21–26, 1991.

12. Fitch, J. P., E. J. Coyle, and N. C. Gallagher, "Threshold decomposition of multidimensional ranked order operations," *IEEE Trans. on Circuits and Systems*, vol. CAS-32, pp. 445–450, May 1985.

13. Wendt, P. D., E. J. Coyle, and N. C. Gallagher, "Stack filters," *IEEE Trans. on Acoustics, Speech, and Signal Processing*, vol. ASSP-34, pp. 898–911, August 1986.

14. Nakagawa, Y., and A. Rosenfeld, "A note on the use of the local min and max operations in digital picture processing," *IEEE Trans. on Systems, Man, and Cybernetics*, vol. SMC-8, no. 8, pp. 632–637, 1978.

15. Muroga, S., *Threshold Logic and Its Applications*, Wiley, New York, 1967.

16. Maragos, P., and R. W. Schafer, "Morphological filters—Part II: Their relations to median, order-statistics, and stack filters," *IEEE Trans. on Acoustics, Speech, and Signal Processing*, vol. ASSP-35, no. 8, pp. 1170–1184, August 1987*b*.

17. Wilson, S. S., "Neural Network Computations On A Fine Grain Array Processor," *Neural Networks for Perception*, Harry Wechsler (ed.), vol. 2, pp. 335–359, Academic Press, New York, 1992.

18. Wilson, S. S., "Morphological Hopfield nets," *Proc. SPIE 2300*, pp. 323–330, 1994.

19. Dougherty, E. R., A. Mathew, and V. Swarnakar, "A conditional-expectation-based implementation of the optimal mean-square binary morphological filter," *Proc. SPIE*, vol. 1451, pp. 137–147, 1991.

20. R. M. Lougheed and D. L. McCubbrey, "The cytocomputer: a practical pipelined image processor," *Proc. 7th Annual International Symp. on Computer Architecture*, May 1980.

21. Batcher, K. E., "Design of a massively parallel processor," *IEEE Trans. on Computers*, vol. C-31, pp. 377–384, 1982.

22. Davis, E. W., and J. H. Reif, "Architecture and operation of the BLITZEN processing element," *Proc. Third International Conf. on Supercomputing*, L. P. Kartashev, and S. I. Kartashev (eds.), vol. III, pp. 128–137, 1988.

23. Parkinson, D., and J. Litt, "Massively parallel computing with the DAP," in *Research Monographs in Parallel and Distributed Computing*, MIT Press, Cambridge, Mass., 1990.

24. Fountain, T. J., "A review of SIMD architectures," *Image Processing System Architectures*, J. Kittler, and M. J. B. Duff (eds.), Research Studies Press Ltd., England, pp. 3–22, 1985.

25. Schmitt, L. A., and S. S. Wilson, "The AIS-5000 parallel processor," *IEEE Trans. on Pattern Analysis and Machine Intelligence,* vol. 10, no. 3, pp. 320–330, May 1988.

26. Wilson, S. S., "One dimensional SIMD architectures—the AIS-5000," In *Multicomputer Vision,* S. Levialdi (ed.), Academic Press, London, pp. 131–149, 1988.

27. Fisher, A. L., "Scan line array processors for image computation," *The 13th Annual International Symp. on Computer Architecture,* Tokyo, pp. 338–345, June 2–5 1986.

28. Chen, K., and C. Svensson, "A 512-processor array chip for video/image processing," *From Pixels to Features,* H. Burkhardt, Y. Neuvo, and J. C. Simon (eds.), North-Holland, pp. 187–199, 1990.

29. Miyaguchi, H., et al., "Digital TV with serial video processor," *IEEE Trans. on Consumer Electronics,* vol. 36, no. 3, pp. 318–326, 1990.

30. Danielsson, P-E., "Getting the median faster," *Computer Graphics and Image Processing,* vol. 17, pp. 71–78, 1981.

CHAPTER 29
CHAOTIC NEURAL NETWORK ARCHITECTURE

Harold Szu*
Naval Surface Warfare Center
Silver Spring, Maryland

Charles Hsu
Mona Zaghloul
Department of Electrical Engineering and Computer Science
The George Washington University, Washington, D.C. 20052

In this chapter, we discuss the relationship between fuzzy logic (FL) and the chaotic neural network (CNN) as well as chaotic neural network architecture. An application of two-scale multiresolution analysis to the fuzzy membership function (FMF) is suggested by the bifurcation route to chaos, which is generated by our chaotic neuron model. Two applications are given:

- The mean synaptic weight field plays an important role for fast pattern recognition capability in examples of both habituation and novelty detections [1].

- Another novel usage of the chaotic neural network and fuzzy logic is that of sharpening of FMF.

The design of a chaotic neuron model is developed and implemented by a complementary metal-oxide semiconductor (CMOS) voltage-mode circuit. A CMOS very large scale integration (VLSI) chaotic chip was fabricated as well. The transfer function of neurons is expressed by a piecewise linear (PWL) N-shaped function. An output-to-input inverse weight mapping is the baseline introduced to control the chaotic behavior of neurons. For simplicity, the chaotic behavior of two neurons is demonstrated in term of Lyapunov exponents. The image process using the N-shaped function is simulated and displayed. The Spice simulations of the CMOS circuit are demonstrated and the measurement diagnoses of the chip are included.

---

* Now with The Center for Advanced Computer Studies, University of Louisiana, Lafayette.

29.1 INTRODUCTION

There has been an explosion of interest in chaotic behavior. This is because non-linearity is inherent in almost any artificial or natural system. Chaotic dynamics can be investigated by continuous flows of nonlinear differential equations and discrete maps of difference equations. All these become possible with powerful computers that provide the insight of chaos. Chaotic neural networks play an important role in information processing [1–4]. Recently, many electrical circuits that display chaotic behavior have been reported [5–11] and used to demonstrate chaos through experiments.

Fuzzy logic is useful in industrial engineering because it is simple (if-then rule-based) and provides us with the capability to "explore the tolerance of imprecision," according to L. Zadeh [12]. We studied the fuzzy membership functions through the chaos bifurcation. We wish to point out that the chaotic neural network can help to analyze the membership function easily.

In this chapter, we will study the multiresolution analyses of fuzzy logic membership functions by means of the chaotic neural network. Secondly, we will develop the chaotic neuron model which was modified from Aihara et al. [13]. For easy hardware implementations, we will consider the case of a piecewise linear output function. The chaotic behavior of neurons with a feedback baseline function will be analyzed. We will discuss the case of two chaotic neurons and verify the chaotic behavior of neurons by the Lyapunov exponents. In addition, the behavior of a neural network composed of 256×256 fully connected N-shaped function neurons governed by hebbian learning is illustrated by image processing. A CMOS voltage-mode circuit to implement the model is introduced, and the Spice simulations used to verify the chaotic behavior of the neurons are described. The CMOS circuit was fabricated using 2-μm technology through the MOSIS program. The chip measurement is included to verify the chaotic neuron model.

29.2 MULTIRESOLUTION ANALYSES OF FUZZY LOGIC MEMBERSHIP FUNCTIONS BY MEANS OF CHAOTIC NEURAL NETWORKS

Artificial neural networks have been used to learn the classifier variances having major and minor axes with respect to the (*If* (INPUTS), *then* (OUTPUTS)) rule domain. The variances, when projected along the output and input axes, give the respective fuzzy membership functions [14]. To change the rule, it is more important to change the FMFs [15]. It is often assumed that such membership functions are described by triangles with obvious centroids (rather than crisp rectangles for numerical values) [16, 17]. Automatic optimal splitting and combining of membership functions, as well as the shape of those functions, can be determined from the data fed into a neural network. This paper addresses such a possibility through chaos bifurcation.

For instance, as one can vaguely recollect from past decades (in the spirit of "exploiting the tolerance of imprecision"), the peak weekend of the cherry blossom (CB) bloom in Washington, D.C., is very difficult to predict. Since Washington is located close to the Appalachian ridge in an unstable region where weather systems from Canada and the Gulf of Mexico converge, the weather chaotically fluctuates from year to year. In addition, the full CB bloom does not last long (having a life span, Δt, of about 5 to 10 days), making it more difficult to predict the exact peak. How does one then treat such a chaotic time series?

It is intuitively clear that chaos provides a deterministic possibility useful for fuzzy logic. The computational basis of fuzzy logic is the rule and the FMF. The FMF is often chosen in the shape of a triangle for a clear centroid and is expressed as

$$\Phi(t) = \begin{cases} 1 - |t| & 0 \le |t| \le 1 \\ 0 & \text{otherwise} \end{cases}$$

It turns out that the triangle is equivalent to a low-pass scaling function used for multiple-resolution high-pass wavelet analysis:

$$\Phi(t) = \frac{\Phi(2t+1)}{2} + \Phi(2t) + \frac{\Phi(2t-1)}{2}$$

Figure 29.1 shows the two-scaling relationship [18] illustrating a special case of the collage theorem [19].

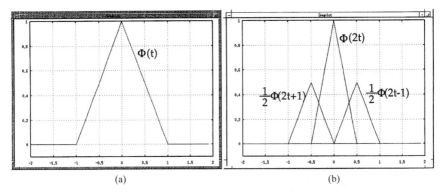

(a)   (b)

FIGURE 29.1   A hat scaling function relation useful for fuzzy membership functions. (*a*) Function $\Phi(t)$; (*b*) functions $\Phi(2t)$, $\Phi(2t-1)$, and $\Phi(2t+1)$.

If the underlying fuzzy dynamics is a bifurcation route toward chaos, then we expand the chaotic data set efficiently on this set of nesting triangular membership functions (MFs), regressing from a nonoverlapping crisp MF to an overlapping fuzzy MF, as schematically shown in Fig. 29.2. Note that Fig. 29.2 has taken into account the standard FMF overlapping and complementing characteristics, but without the details of the CB ratio $\Delta T / \Delta t$ shown in Fig. 29.3.

If we assume the triangle envelope covering a typical bifurcation cascade spectrum is the FMF, then the bifurcation to chaos suggests a multiresolution FMF analysis as follows. We introduce an average file span, Δt, say $\Delta t = 7$ days, with a standard deviation σ_t of 3 days. We also introduce the time resolution scale length Δt in the analysis of the periodic CB event. One can trivially forecast every year with the absolute certainty, "crisp or sharp," that CBs will surely peak sometimes during the $\Delta T^{(0)} =$ spring time of the year. A factor of 2 increase in the precision, $\Delta T^{(1)} = \Delta T^{(0)}/2$, corresponds to a decrease in the certainty in the unit of a 2-week period at the end of March or at the beginning of April. Likewise, for $\Delta T^{(2)} = \Delta T^{(1)}/2$, there is still less

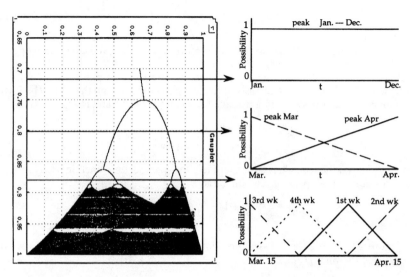

FIGURE 29.2 Analogy between the bifurcation route to chaos (left) and the crisp route to fuzzy overlapping membership functions (right)

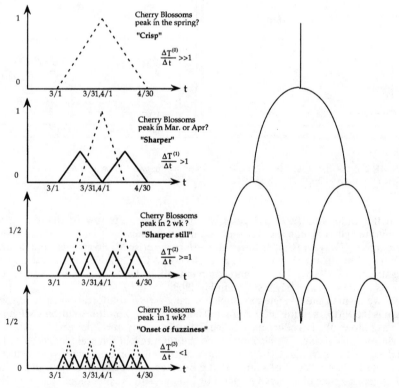

FIGURE 29.3 The dashed triangles indicate the differences between two adjacent resolutions of the bifurcated membership functions in terms of the resolution scales $\Delta T^{(n)}$ toward overlap with the mean event life span Δt.

certainty in the unit of a 2-week period at the end of March or at the beginning of April. However, this nonoverlapping MF can not be extended indefinitely. This is because, when $\Delta T^{(3)} = \Delta T^{(2)}/2$, the subtriangle becomes overlapping, thus marking the onset of FMF when the resolution scale $\Delta T^{(3)}$ for a week approaches the average CB event span Δt.

We have presented the relationship between the fuzzy logic membership function and the chaos bifurcation. In the following sections, a chaotic neural model will be introduced. The chaotic behavior can be controlled by the proposed chaotic neural model. The numerical simulation and the circuit design are also included in the next sections.

29.3 THEORETICAL BACKGROUND OF CHAOTIC NEURAL MODEL

A classical model is the McCulloch-Pitts neuron [20], for which Caianiello introduces a refractory version [21]. The neuron models are further modified by Nagumo and Sato with a step function [22] due to a past firing of a neuron. Aihara et al. [13] next suggests that the output function of the artificial neuron should be replaced by a continuous increasing function. They propose a chaotic neuron model defined by the following difference equation:

$$x(n + 1) = kx(n) - \beta f(x(n)) + B$$
$$y(n + 1) = f(x(n + 1))$$
(29.1)

where $\quad x(n + 1)$ = internal state
$\qquad y(n + 1)$ = output of the neuron at the discrete time $n + 1$
$\qquad\quad f$ = continuous nonlinear output function of the chaotic neuron
$\qquad\quad B$ = sum of all input excitations
$\qquad\quad \beta$ = parameter for refractoriness
$\qquad\quad k$ = damping factor of the refractoriness

In Ref. 13, $f(x)$ has been suggested to be the logistic sigmoidal function, where ε is the steepness parameter:

$$f(x) = \frac{1}{1 + e^{-x/\varepsilon}}$$
(29.2)

In our analysis we will reexpress the set of equations (29.1) as

$$y(n + 1) = f(kx(n) - \beta f(x(n)) + B)$$
$$= f(kx(n) + (\beta - \beta f(x(n))) + (B - \beta)) = f(g(x(n)) + \theta) = F(x(n))$$
(29.3)

The expression in Eq. (29.3) above has been decomposed so that parts of the function can be easily identified. The nonlinear function $(\beta - \beta f(x))$ (shown in Fig. 29.4a) and the summation of two functions kx and $(\beta - \beta f(x))$ yields an N-shaped function $kx + (\beta - \beta f(x))$ (shown in Fig. 29.4b). The sigmoidal function $f(g(x) + \theta)$ (shown in Fig. 29.4c) yields an overall sigmoidal N-shaped function $F(x(n))$.

The above analysis will yield the output of the neuron at discrete time $n + 1$ as

$$y(n + 1) = F(x(n))$$
(29.4a)

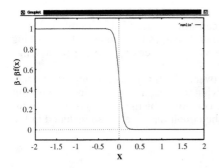

FIGURE 29.4a Nonlinear function $b - bf(x)$, where $\beta = 1$ and $f(x)$ is a sigmoidal function with $\varepsilon = 0.15$.

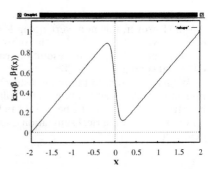

FIGURE 29.4b N-shaped function, $kx + \beta - \beta f(x)$, where $\beta = 1, k = 0.5$ and $f(x)$ is a sigmoidal function with $\varepsilon = 0.15$.

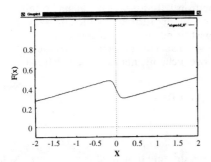

FIGURE 29.4c Sigmoidal N-shaped function, where $\beta = 1$ and $f(x)$ is a sigmoidal function with $\varepsilon = 0.15$.

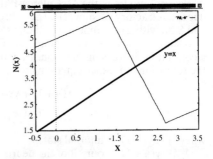

FIGURE 29.4d PWL N-shaped function $N(x)$, defined by Eq. (29.5), which approximates function $F(x)$ in Eq. (29.3).

Let the internal state $x(n + 1)$ be:

$$x(n + 1) = y(n + 1) \qquad (29.4b)$$

For simplicity, we approximate the sigmoidal N-shaped function $F(x(n))$ of Eq. (29.4) by a piecewise linear approximation function denoted as $N(x)$, shown in Fig. 29.4d and described by the following expression (where $m_2 < 0$ and $\delta_2 > \delta_1$):

$$N(x) = \begin{cases} m_1 x + b_1 & x \leq \delta_1 \\ m_2 x + b_2 & \delta_1 < x \leq \delta_2 \\ m_3 x + b_3 & \delta_2 < x \end{cases} \qquad (29.5)$$

Hence, the neuron model of Eq. (29.4) becomes:

$$\begin{aligned} y(n + 1) &= N(x(n)) \\ x(n + 1) &= y(n + 1) \end{aligned} \qquad (29.6)$$

Map $N(x)$ of Eq. (29.6) has two critical turning points associated with the piecewise linear mapping studied in Refs. 23 and 24. Corollary 2.1 in Ref. 24 states the conditions for the existence of the chaotic behavior of concave-up and concave-down functions. By applying their criterion, Bailleul and coauthors concluded that mapping $N(x)$ is chaotic if and only if $m_2 < -1$ and either set of Eq. (29.7) is satisfied.

Set A:

1. $m_3(1 + m_2) \le -1$

2. $(1 - m_2)b_3 < (1 - m_3)b_2$ (29.7a)

3. $\dfrac{m_2^2 b_3 + m_2 b_2 + b_2}{1 - m_2^2 m_3} \le \dfrac{m_2 b_1 - m_1 b_2}{m_2 - m_1}$

Set B:

1. $m_1(1 + m_2) \le -1$

2. $(1 - m_1)b_2 < (1 - m_2)b_1$ (29.7b)

3. $\dfrac{m_2^2 b_1 + m_2 b_2 + b_2}{1 - m_2^2 m_1} \le \dfrac{m_3 b_2 - m_2 b_3}{m_3 - m_2}$

The above conditions can be interpreted as follows [23, 24]:

1. This condition states that when the map has one critical turning point (a cone), there exists at least one period 3 orbit. (Proof of the theorem that the existence of period 3 implies chaos can be found in Ref. 25.)

2. This simple condition means that the diagonal mapping line (line $y = x$ in Fig. 29.4d) crosses the decreasing part of the map.

3. This condition guarantees that at least one period 3 exists when the map is truly bimodal (i.e., both critical turning points of the bimodal map are involved in the mapping).

Another way to indicate that the system may show chaos is to apply Lyapunov exponent theory. The Lyapunov exponent is a fast quantitative estimation of the local stability of an attractor. For a discrete map, $N(x)$ on the one-dimensional interval, the Lyapunov exponent is defined as [26]

$$\lambda = \lim_{n \to \infty} \frac{1}{n} \sum_{k=0}^{n-1} \ln |N'(x_k)| \tag{29.8}$$

where $x_k = N^{(k)}(x_0)$ and x_0 is some initial value in the basin of the attractor under consideration. Positive Lyapunov exponents measure the average exponential spreading of nearby trajectories, and negative Lyapunov exponents measure the average (exponential) convergence of the trajectories onto the attractor [26]. The average of the Lyapunov exponents for a dissipative system possessing an attractor must be always negative.

Next, we show that one single neuron with a PWL N-shaped function exhibits the chaotic behavior when conditions of Eq. (29.7) are satisfied. In our circuit realization, we assume the PWL N-shaped function $N(x)$ as

$$N(x) = \begin{cases} \alpha x + 5 & x \le 1.33 \\ (\alpha - 3.65)x + 9.85 & 1.33 < x \le 2.7 \\ \alpha x & 2.7 < x \end{cases} \tag{29.9}$$

Comparing Eq. (29.9) to Eq. (29.5), we have $m_1 = \alpha$, $m_2 = \alpha - 3.65$, $m_3 = \alpha$, $b_1 = 5$, $b_2 = 9.85$, and $b_3 = 0$. And substituting these parameters into Eq. (29.7), we found out it satisfies the conditions when $0.4 \gtrsim \alpha \gtrsim 0.5$ and $0.6 \gtrsim \alpha \gtrsim 1.0$. The cascade spectrum of PWL N-shaped $N(x)$ as a function of α is shown in Fig. 29.5a. The Lyapunov exponents of PWL N-shaped $N(x)$ as a function of α is shown in Fig. 29.5b. Both diagrams show that the chaotic behavior appears for $0.4 \gtrsim \alpha \gtrsim 0.5$ and $0.6 \gtrsim \alpha \gtrsim 1.0$. Thus, we select α as 0.65 and find that the parameters in Eq. (29.9) satisfy the conditions of Eq. (29.7). The chaotic behavior of the bimodal mapping defined by Eqs. (29.5) and (29.6) is observed in Fig. 29.6. The single chaotic neuron model has been analyzed and the conditions of the chaotic behavior have been established by Lyapunov exponents and verified.

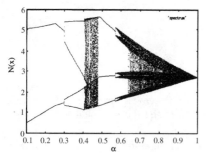

FIGURE 29.5a Cascade spectrum of PWL N-shaped function $N(x)$ as a function of α.

FIGURE 29.5b Lyapunov exponents of PWL N-shaped function as a function of α.

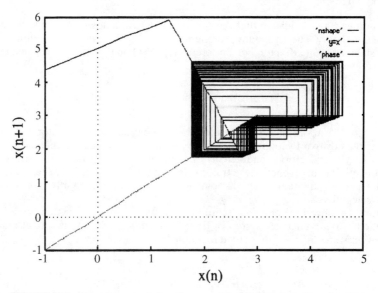

FIGURE 29.6 Phase diagram of $x(n+1)$ versus $x(n)$ of PWL N-shaped function $N(x)$.

29.4 CHAOTIC BEHAVIOR OF COLLECTIVE NEURONS

In this section we extend the single chaotic neuron to a collection of many interactive chaotic neurons. A proposed neural network model is shown in Fig. 29.7. The dynamics of a neural network composed of M neurons is described by a set of difference equations:

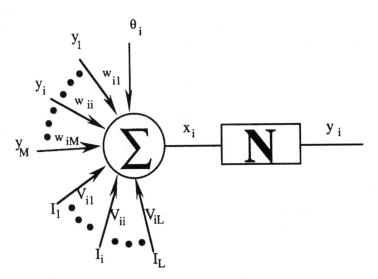

FIGURE 29.7 A model of a collective neural network.

$$y_i(n+1) = N(x_i(n)) \tag{29.10a}$$

$$x_i(n+1) = w_{ii}\, y_i(n+1) + \sum_{j \neq i}^{M} w_{ij}\, y_j(n+1) + \sum_{j=1}^{L} V_{ij}\, I_j + \theta_i \tag{29.10b}$$

where $x_i(n+1)$ = neuron state
          $y_i(n+1)$ = its output at the discrete time $n+1$
            $N(x_i)$ = neuron transfer characteristic function described by Eq. (29.9)
              w_{ij} = connection weight from the jth neuron to the ith neuron
               M = number of neurons
               L = number of external inputs
             V_{ij} = connection weight from the jth external input to the ith neuron
              I_j = jth external input

Equation (29.10b) can also be written as

$$x_i(n+1) = w_{ii} N(x_i(n)) + A_i(n) \tag{29.11}$$

$$A_i(n) = \sum_{j \neq i}^{M} w_{ij}\, N(x_j(n)) + \sum_{j=1}^{L} V_{ij}\, I_j + \theta_i \tag{29.12}$$

$A_i(n)$ is the contribution to the state of the ith neuron from all other neurons and external sources.

In order to understand the collective chaos, we consider neuron 1 and rewrite its dynamic equation as

$$y_1(n+1) = N(x_1(n)) \tag{29.13a}$$

$$x_1(n+1) = w_{11}y_1(n+1) + A_1(n) \tag{29.13b}$$

From Eq. (29.13b), the feedback mapping line may be rewritten as $y(n+1) = ax(n+1) + c$, where a and c are scalar parameters. This mapping line is named the *baseline*. The parameters a and c of the baseline function are determined from Eq. (29.13b), which can be rewritten as:

$$y_1(n+1) = \frac{1}{w_{11}} x_1(n+1) - \frac{A_1(n)}{w_{11}}$$

$$= ax_1(n+1) + c$$

where

$$a = \frac{1}{w_{11}} \quad \text{and} \quad c = -\frac{A_1(n)}{w_{11}}$$

Thus the neuron model at discrete time $n+1$ is described by

$$y_1(n+1) \Leftarrow N(x_1(n))$$

$$y_1(n+1) \Rightarrow ax_1(n+1) + c \tag{29.14}$$

where the symbols $\Rightarrow$ and $\Leftarrow$ indicate the direction of mapping.

Figure 29.8 shows two iterations of the discrete mapping described by Eqs. (29.13a) and (29.14). A mapping from x_0 to x_1 is shown.

In this interpretation of the mapping, the N-shaped characteristic of the neuron is fixed while the baseline changes with each iteration. The conditions of Eq. (29.7)

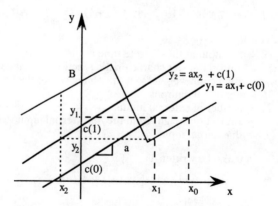

FIGURE 29.8 Two iterations of the discrete mapping function described in Eqs. (29.13a) and (29.14).

can be expressed in terms of the parameters a and c of Eq. (29.14) and the parameters in Eq. (29.9) which define the N-shaped function. The first two conditions from Eq. (29.7), which guarantee that the baseline crossing is at the decreasing part of the N-shaped function and that at least one period 3 oscillation exists in a unimodal map, can be expressed in terms of a and c. For $0 < a < 3.65 - \alpha$:

Sets A and B: **1.** $\alpha(a - 3.65 + \alpha) \leq - a^2$ (29.15a)

Condition A: **2.** $(a + 3.65 - \alpha)c > (a - \alpha)(c - 9.85)$ (29.15b)

Condition B: **3.** $(a - \alpha)(c - 9.85) < (a + 3.65 - \alpha)(5 - c)$ (29.15c)

As an example, consider a neuron with no contribution of other neurons or external inputs, i.e., $c = 0$. From Eq. (29.9), with $\alpha = 0.65$, it can be found that the neuron displays chaos for $0.65 < a < 1.108$. This condition can be observed also from the cascade spectrum diagram of this case ($c = 0$) shown in Fig. 29.9. It can be observed that the conditions of Eq. (29.15) do not cover the chaotic region, $1.108 < a \lesssim 1.45$, which is obtained by period doubling. The chaotic region can be also obtained on the space diagram of the parameters a and c as plotted in Fig. 29.10. It also shows that the neuron exhibits chaotic behavior in the range of $0.65 < a < 1.45$. This result may be expressed in terms of the self-weight of neuron 1: $0.69 < w_{11} < 1.54$. This is a very useful result for learning the weights in a neural network that will drive a neuron to chaos.

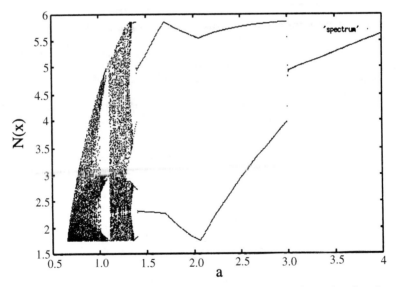

FIGURE 29.9 Cascade spectrum diagram of mapping Eq. (29.15) as a function of a when $c = 0$.

Consider now another case where the neuron receives a chaotic input from another neuron. This corresponds to a value $A_i(n)$ that is chaotic and therefore to a chaotic shift of the baseline ($c = -A_i(n)/w_{ii}$). The state x_i of a neuron that receives

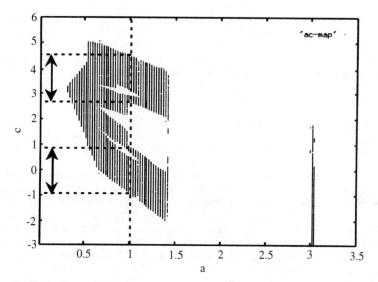

FIGURE 29.10   Chaotic region of map Eqs. (29.13) and (29.14) in space of parameters a and c.

the chaotic input from another neuron ($w_{ij} \neq 0$) will be most probably chaotic. Assume for a moment that the baseline slope is fixed to 1 ($a = 1$, that is, $w_{11} = 1$), and the N-shaped function is defined as Eq. (29.9). The neuron exhibits chaotic behavior for the range $-0.944 < c < 0.737$ and $2.85 < c < 4.53$, from Eq. (29.15). These results are also observed in Fig. 29.10, where the full region of chaos of map Eqs. (29.13) and (29.14) in the space of parameters a and c is shown.

The above theory is illustrated by a neural network of two connected neurons. The neurons' N-shaped transfer function is defined by Eq. (29.9) with $\alpha = 0.65$ and $m_0 = -3.65$. Two cases are considered:

Case 1.   Neuron 1 becomes chaotic itself because its characteristic function satisfies the conditions of Eq. (29.7). Neuron 2 is not chaotic. The weights are selected as $w_{12} = 0.1$, $w_{21} = 0.0$, $w_{22} = 0.2$, and w_{11} of neuron 1 is assumed to be a parameter. The Lyapunov exponents and the cascade spectrum of neuron 1, shown in Fig. 29.11a and b, define the region of w_{11} for which neuron 1 can be chaotic. The other weights are selected so that neuron 2 cannot become chaotic. This is because w_{22} is out of the chaotic region and $w_{21} = 0.0$, i.e., $c_2 = 0.0$, therefore the chaotic behavior of neuron 1 cannot influence neuron 2. Nonchaotic behavior of neuron 2 for this case is shown in Fig. 29.11c and d.

Case 2.   Neuron 1 is chaotic. Neuron 2 receives chaotic input from neuron 1. The neural network weights are $w_{12} = 0.1$, $w_{21} = 0.25$, $w_{22} = 0.69$, and a_2 is fixed at $a_2 = 1/w_{22}$. Neuron 2, for which $c_2 = -A_2(n)/w_{22}$, may exhibit chaotic behavior if c_2 falls in the range of chaos shown in Fig. 29.10. Since $A_2(n)$ depends on w_{11} of the first neuron, w_{11} may be considered as the parameter to drive neuron 2 into chaos. The Lyapunov exponents and the cascade spectrum of two neurons are shown in Fig. 29.12. The diagrams show the same chaotic region for both neurons.

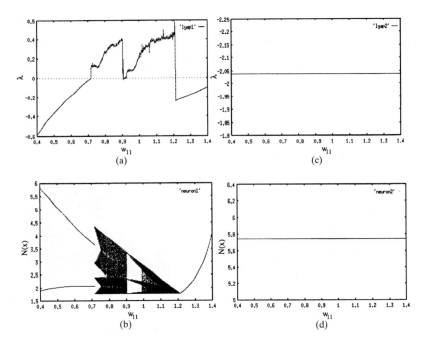

FIGURE 29.11 The chaotic behavior of two neurons as a function of w_{11} when $w_{12} = 0.1$, $w_{21} = 0.0$, $w_{22} = 0.2$, and $\alpha = 0.65$. (a) Lyapunov exponents of neuron 1 in space of w_{11}; (b) cascade spectrum of neuron 1 as a function of w_{11}; (c) Lyapunov exponents of neuron 2 in space of w_{11}; (d) cascade spectrum of neuron 2 as a function of w_{11}.

Next, we extend the two chaotic neurons model into a chaotic neural network [1]. The behavior of a chaotic neural network composed of 256×256 fully connected neurons with the N-shaped function governed by hebbian learning is illustrated by image processing. We study the perception habituation. For simplicity, we denote as **I** and **P** the images in Fig. 29.13a and b. Simulation steps are given as follows:

1. Initiation of bipolar memory:

$$W_{ij} = (X(\mathbf{I})_i X(\mathbf{I})_j - \delta_{ij} X(\mathbf{I})_i X(\mathbf{I})_j) = [(X(\mathbf{I})_i X(\mathbf{I})_j]$$

2. N-shaped transfer function of the image (top left, Fig. 29.14):

$$V_i = N(\Sigma \, W_{ij} X(\mathbf{P}))$$

3. Updated W'_{ij} as the average between current W_{ij} and image **P** (Fig. 29.13b):

$$W'_{ij} = \{W_{ij} + [X(\mathbf{P})_i X(\mathbf{P})_j]\}/2$$

4. N-shaped output of image (top left third of Fig. 29.14)

$$V_i = N(\Sigma \, W'_{ij} X(V))$$

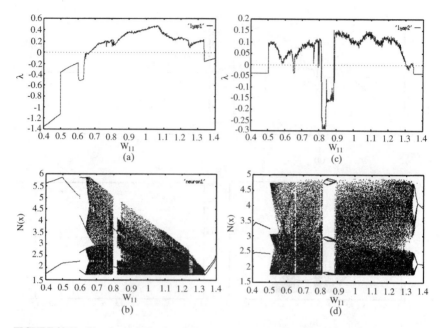

FIGURE 29.12 The chaotic behavior of two neurons as a function of w_{11} when $w_{12} = 0.1$, $w_{21} = 0.25$, $w_{22} = 0.69$, and $\alpha = 0.65$. (a) Lyapunov exponents of neuron 1 in space of w_{11}; (b) cascade spectrum of neuron 1 as a function of w_{11}; (c) Lyapunov exponents of neuron 2 in space of w_{11}; (d) Cascade spectrum of neuron 2 in function of w_{11}.

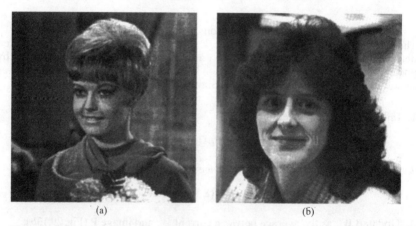

FIGURE 29.13 Two face images: (a) image **I**; (b) image **P**. *(Courtesy of Purdue University Image Laboratory.)*

FIGURE 29.14   Perception habituation in 15 steps.

5. Updated W'_{ij} for iterations between steps 4 and 5:

$$W'_{ij} = \{W_{ij} + [X(V)_i X(V)_j]\}/2$$

6. Go back to step 4 for output of image (top left four).

We observe that after 15 steps in Fig. 29.14, the image has suffered a contrast reversal of those pixels which have the middle gray scale value below 0.5. This can be explained by the effect of the negative logic located below the middle gray scale value. The final weight W_{ij} can be read as the outer product of the final image pixels, denoted by IP_i. All dark pixels are converted to about -1 values for the inhibition memory, except those brightest pixels that have $+1$ values contributing to the excitation memory. More analyses related to the chaotic neural network can be studied through the image process. More detailed descriptions of the chaotic neural network with the N-shaped function are given in Ref. 1.

29.5 CMOS CIRCUIT IMPLEMENTATION OF THE CHAOTIC NEURON

In this section, we show that it is possible to implement a chaotic neuron as a CMOS inverter and a linear resistor. There are three elements in a chaotic neuron: the PWL N-shaped function, sample-and-hold, and the feedback baseline function. The piece-

wise linear map $N(x)$ defined in Eq. (29.9) can be realized by the transfer characteristic of a CMOS inverter circuitry and a linear resistor, as shown in Fig. 29.15a. The
Spice simulation of this transfer characteristic is shown in Fig. 29.15b. In Fig. 29.15a
the PWL N-shaped function is obtained as the graphical composition of an inverter
characteristic function and a linear resistor characteristic. From Fig. 29.15, we note
that the slopes and constants of the three piecewise linear maps $N(x)$ are functions
of the physical parameter α:

$$m_1 = \alpha \qquad m_2 = -3.65 + \alpha \qquad m_3 = \alpha$$
$$b_1 = 5 \qquad b_2 = 9.85 \qquad b_3 = 0 \tag{29.16}$$

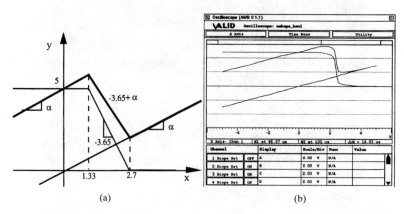

(a)   (b)

FIGURE 29.15 Piecewise linear N-shaped function. (a) Graphical composition; (b) Spice
simulation.

The neuron model of the PWL N-shaped map of Eq. (29.13) is represented by the
block diagram of Fig. 29.16, and its possible realization using a CMOS inverter and
operational amplifiers and sample-and-hold circuitry is shown in Fig. 29.17. V_n in Fig.
29.17 is the control voltage to change α, which is the linear function. V_c and V_a are
the control voltages to change the parameters a and c, which are the scalar elements
of the baseline function. The circuit may be easily implemented in CMOS technology for possible integration as shown in Fig. 29.18.

In our circuit realization, parameter a of the baseline function is fixed at value 1,
while parameter c is varied by the voltage V_c, which represents external inputs to the
neuron from the other neurons. V_n is developed by a variable resistor in series of a
passive resistor (Fig. 29.19). Figures 29.20 to 29.22 show Spice simulations of the
variable resistor.

Spice simulations of phase diagrams for some chosen cases are shown in Figs.
29.23 to 29.25. Figure 29.23 shows the phase diagram of a chaotic neuron with $\alpha =$
0.65, $a = 1$, and $c = 0$, when $V_n = 6.2$ V, and $V_c = 0.0$ V. This chaotic result can be easily
observed in Fig. 29.5a, the cascade spectrum of a PWL N-shaped function. Figure
29.24 shows the phase diagram of three fixed points of a chaotic neuron with $\alpha = 0.5$,
$a = 1$, and $c = 0$, when $V_n = 8.5$ V, and $V_c = 0.0$ V. This result also can be obtained from
Fig. 29.5a. Figure 29.25 shows the phase diagram of the convergent region of a

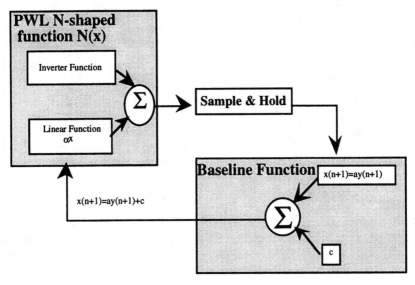

FIGURE 29.16   Conceptual block diagram of one chaotic neuron.

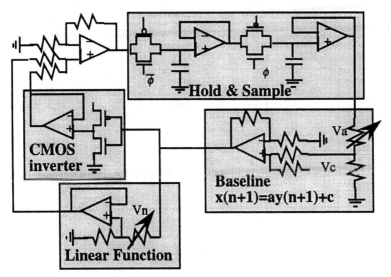

FIGURE 29.17   Circuit realization of one chaotic neuron, where V_a, V_n, V_c are controlled voltages.

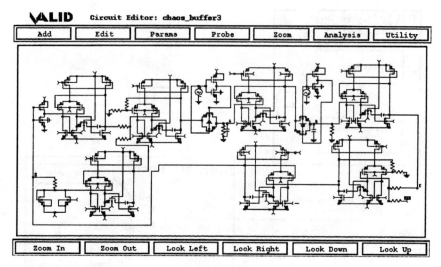

FIGURE 29.18   CMOS voltage-mode circuit for chaotic neuron model.

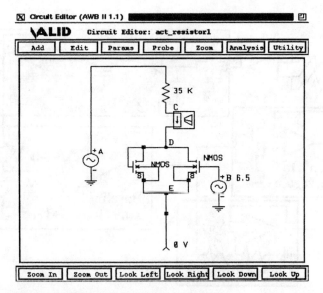

FIGURE 29.19   The circuit of the variable resistor.

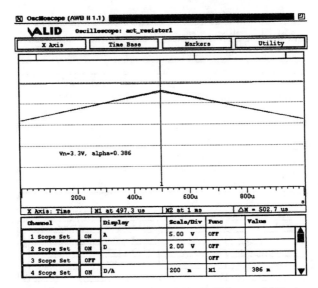

FIGURE 29.20 Spice simulation of Fig. 29.17 for $\alpha = 0.386$ when $V_n = 3.3$ V.

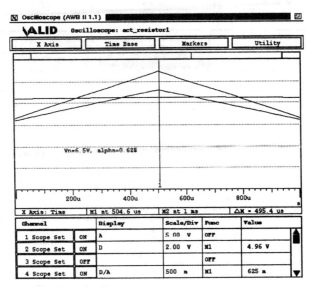

FIGURE 29.21 Spice simulation of Fig. 29.17 for $\alpha = 0.645$ when $V_n = 6.5$ V.

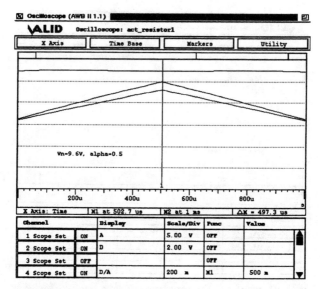

FIGURE 29.22 SPICE simulation of Fig. 29.17 for $\alpha = 0.5$ when $V_n = 5.6$ V.

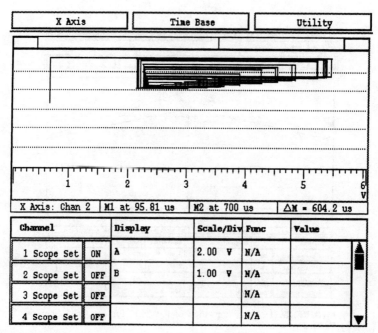

FIGURE 29.23 Phase diagram of a chaotic neuron in chaotic region with $\alpha = 0.65$, $a = 1$, and $c = 0$, where $V_n = 6.2$ V and $V_c = 0$ V.

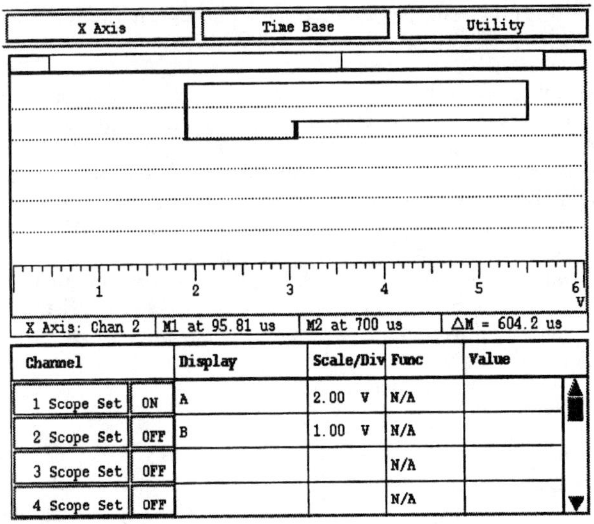

X Axis	Time Base	Utility

1	2	3	4	5	6

X Axis: Chan 2 | M1 at 95.81 us | M2 at 700 us | ΔM = 604.2 us

Channel		Display	Scale/Div	Func	Value
1 Scope Set	ON	A	2.00 V	N/A	
2 Scope Set	OFF	B	1.00 V	N/A	
3 Scope Set	OFF			N/A	
4 Scope Set	OFF			N/A	

FIGURE 29.24 Phase diagram of a chaotic neuron in oscillation region with $\alpha = 0.5$, $a = 1$, and $c = 0$, where $V_n = 8.5$ V and $V_c = 0$ V.

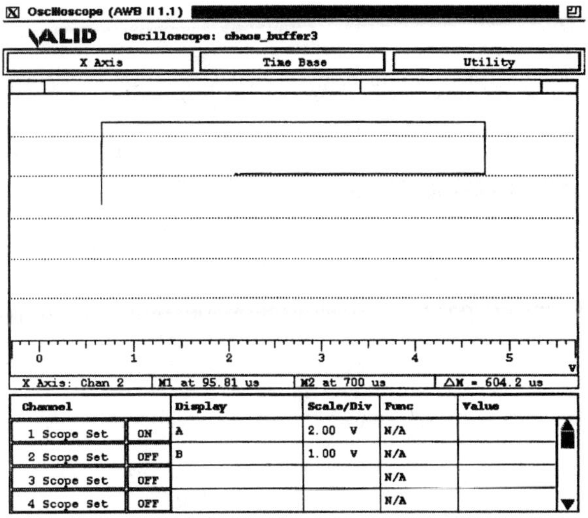

Oscilloscope (AWB II 1.1)

VALID Oscilloscope: chaos_buffer3

X Axis	Time Base	Utility

0	1	2	3	4	5

X Axis: Chan 2 | M1 at 95.81 us | M2 at 700 us | ΔM = 604.2 us

Channel		Display	Scale/Div	Func	Value
1 Scope Set	ON	A	2.00 V	N/A	
2 Scope Set	OFF	B	1.00 V	N/A	
3 Scope Set	OFF			N/A	
4 Scope Set	OFF			N/A	

FIGURE 29.25 Phase diagram of a chaotic neuron in convergent region with $\alpha = 0.65$, $a = 1$, and $c = 0.5$, where $V_n = 6.2$ V and $V_c = 0.5$ V.

chaotic neuron with $\alpha = 0.65$, $a = 1$, and $c = 0.5$ in the baseline function, where $V_n = 6.2$ and $V_c = 0.5$. This result can be found in Fig. 29.10, which shows that it is not in the chaotic region when $a = 1$ and $c = 0.5$.

It is important to note that the N-shaped transfer characteristic of the neuron model can be easily modified by changing the voltage supply of the inverter. This corresponds to changing the value 5 as B in the function $N(x)$ of Eq. (29.9), or changing the parameter b in the neuron model Eq. (29.1). Figure 29.26 shows the N-piecewise linear characteristic of the real electronic circuit with power supply $B \neq 0$. The limits $\pm\delta$ are due to the operational amplifier saturation. Those limits play no role in the above chaos analysis. However, we note that when $B = 0$ (there is no power supply to the inverter), the N-piecewise linear characteristic will convert into a linear characteristic, as shown in Fig. 29.27, which is a characteristic of the classical neuron. Although the above circuit is designed for voltage-mode operation, A current-mode circuit is also possible with CMOS technology [27].

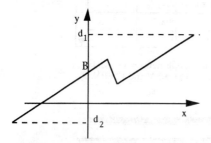

FIGURE 29.26   PWL N-shaped characteristic with $B \neq 0$.

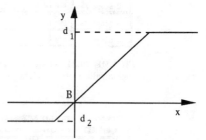

FIGURE 29.27   PWL N-shaped characteristic with $B = 0$.

29.6 CHIP MEASUREMENTS

The voltage-mode CMOS chaotic neuron was fabricated in a VLSI chip through the MOSIS program. The layout of the whole chip is shown in Fig. 29.28. The Spice simulation was demonstrated in the previous section. The active resistor is the dominant element in changing the PWL N-shaped function in this chip. The value of a is determined by the active resistor in series with a passive resistor. The value of the active resistance is defined by the controlled voltage V_n.

Three measurements for the chaotic chip are included in this section:

1. $V_n = 3.3$ V and $a = 0.386$. The Spice simulation is shown in Fig. 29.21. From Fig. 29.5a, a two-square-dance result will be obtained if $0.3 < \alpha < 0.4$. The two "square dances" of the chaotic chip are shown in Fig. 29.29.

2. $V_n = 6.5$ V, $\alpha = 0.645$. The Spice simulation is shown in Fig. 29.21. From Fig. 29.5a, the behavior of the neuron should be chaotic if $0.6 < \alpha$. The measured chaotic behavior of the neuron is shown in Fig. 29.30.

3. $V_n = 5.6$ V, $\alpha = 0.51$. The Spice simulation is shown in Fig. 29.22. From Fig. 29.5a, the three fixed points will be obtained if $0.5 < \alpha < 0.6$. The measurement of three fixed points of the chaotic chip is shown in Fig. 29.31.

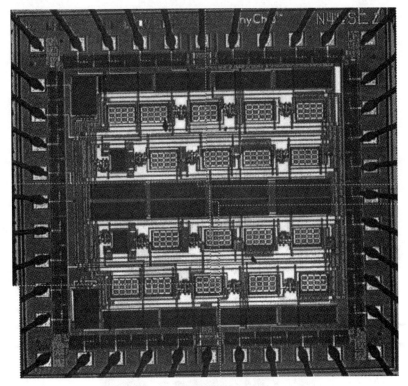

FIGURE 29.28　Layout of the chaotic neuron chip.

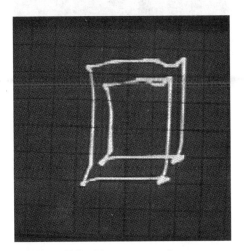

FIGURE 29.29 Measurement of two square dances in the chaotic chip when $V_n = 3.3$ V. X axis is $V(n)$, and Y axis shows $V(n + 1)$; one square is 500 mV × 500 mV.

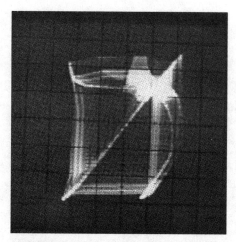

FIGURE 29.30 Measurement of chaotic result in the chaotic chip when $V_n = 6.5$ V. X axis is $V(n)$, and Y axis shows $V(n + 1)$; one square is 500 mV × 500 mV.

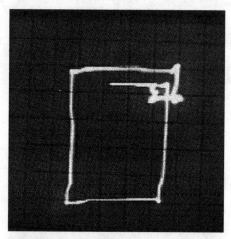

FIGURE 29.31 Measurement of three fixed points in the chaotic chip when $V_n = 5.6$ V. X axis is $V(n)$, and Y axis shows $V(n + 1)$, one square is 500 mV × 500 mV.

The above measurements show that the chaotic neural network behaves in the theoretically expected way.

29.7 CONCLUSION

A piecewise negative logic neuron model that displays chaos is introduced. The model is derived without delay from the well-known Nagumo-Sato and Aihara neuron model. The neuron dynamics are described by a one-dimensional nonlinear mapping. Conditions for the chaotic behavior are also given. An electronic circuit realization of a neuron model is proposed. The chaotic behavior of the neuron model is simulated numerically, and the chaotic behavior of the neuron circuit is verified by Spice simulation. The proposed circuit model gives a wide flexibility of hardware for building single neurons having a variety of transfer characteristics and for supporting any neural network structure. The piecewise negative logic neuron model can be used to develop a data-coding scheme that may ease crowding on the airwaves. In addition, some applications of chaotic neurons such as fuzzy logic and predicting sunspots and chemical reactions have been announced. Chaos, neural networks, and fuzzy logic can be combined as future research work. The chaotic chip can be applied to washing machines, for example, because of the nonidentical water currents it generates. Many applications of the chaotic neuron can and should be the subject of further research.

REFERENCES

1. H. Szu, B. Telfer, G. Rogers, D. Gobovic, C. Hsu, M. Zaghloul, and W. Freeman, "Spatio-temporal Chaos Information Processing in Neural Networks—Electronic Implementation," *WCNN*, vol. 4, pp. 758–774, Portland, Ore., July 1993.

2. Harold Szu, "A Dynamic Reconfigurable Neural Network," annotated by Walter Freeman, *J. Neural Network Computing*, vol. 1 pp. 3–23, 1989.

3. H. Szu, B. Telfer, G. Rogers, Kyoung Lee, Gyu Moon, M. Zaghloul, and M. Loew, "Collective Chaos in Neural Networks," *Proc. Int. Joint Conf. Neural Networks*, IJCNN-92, Beijing, November 1–6, 1992.

4. H. Szu, R. Yentis, C. Hsu, D. Gobovic, and M. Zaghloul, "Chaotic Neuron Model and Neural Networks," *Proc. IJCNN*, Nagoya, Japan, October 1993.

5. Charles C. Hsu, Mona E. Zaghloul, and Harald H. Szu, "CMOS Circuit Implementation to Control Chaotic Neurons," *Proc. WCNN*, pp. 684–689, San Diego, June 1994.

6. H. Szu et al., "Chaotic Neurochip for Fuzzy Computing," *SPIE*, vol. 2037–18, San Diego, July 1993.

7. T. Matsumoto, L. O. Chua, and M. Komuro, "The Double Scroll," *IEEE Trans. Circuits and Systems*, vol. CAS-32, no. 8, August 1985, pp. 798–818.

8. N. Kanou, Y. Horio, K. Aihara, and S. Nakamura, "A Current-Mode Circuit of a Chaotic Neuron Model," *Proc. 35th Midwest Symp. Circuits and Systems*, Washington, D.C., August 1992, pp. 1530–1533.

9. T. Yamakawa, T. Miki, and E. Uchino, "A Chaotic Chip for Analyzing Nonlinear Discrete Dynamical Network Systems," *Proc. 2d Int. Conf. Fuzzy Logic and Neural Networks*, Iizuka, Japan, July 1992, pp. 563–566.

10. A. Rodriguez-Vazquez, J. L. Huertas, A. Rueda, B. Perez-Verdu, and L. O. Chua, "Chaos from Switched-Capacitor Circuits: Discrete Maps," *Proc. IEEE*, vol. 75, no. 8, August 1987, pp. 1090–1106.

11. Y. Horio and K. Suyama, "Switched-Capacitor Chaotic Neuron for Chaotic Neuron Networks," *Proc. Int. Symp. Circuits and Systems,* Chicago, 1993, pp. 1018–1021.

12. L. Zadeh, "Fuzzy Sets," *Information and Control,* vol. 8, pp. 338–353, 1965.

13. K. Aihara, T. Takbe, and M. Toyoda, "Chaotic Neural Networks," *Physics Letters A,* vol. 144, no. 6, 7, March 1990, pp. 333–340.

14. J. Dickerson and B. Kosko, "Fuzzy Function Approximation with Supervised Ellipsoidal Learning," *WCNN-1993,* vol. 2, pp. 9–17, Portland, Ore., July 1993.

15. P. Werbos, "Elastic Fuzzy Logic: A better way to combine Neural and Fuzzy Capabilities," *WCNN,* vol. 2, pp. 623–626, Portland, Ore., July 1993.

16. E. Cox, "Fuzzy Fundamentals," *IEEE Spectrum,* pp. 58–61, October 1992.

17. E. Cox, "Adaptive Fuzzy Systems," *IEEE Spectrum,* pp. 27–31, February 1993.

18. I. Daubechies, "Ten Lectures on Wavelets," SIAM, p. 146, 1992.

19. M. Barnsley and L. Hurd, "Fractal Image Compression," A. K. Peters, Wellesley, Mass., p. 100, 1993.

20. W. S. McCulloch and W. H. Pitts, "A Logical Calculus of Ideas Immanent in Nervous Activity," pp. 115–133, 1963, *Bull. Mathematical Biophysics,* vol. 5, pp. 115–133, 1943.

21. E. R. Caianiello, "Outline of a Theory of Thought-Process and Thinking Machines," *J. Theoretical Biology,* vol. 2, pp. 204–235, 1961.

22. J. Nagumo and S. Sato, "On a Response Characteristic of Mathematical Neuron Model," *Kybernetik,* vol. 10, pp. 155–164, 1972.

23. D. Veitch, "Windows of Stability in Control Chaos," *IEEE Trans. Circuits and Systems,* vol. 38, no. 10, pp. 808–819, October 1992.

24. J. Baillieul, R. W. Brocket, and R. B. Washburn, "Chaotic Motion in Nonlinear Feedback Systems," *IEEE Trans. Circuits and Systems,* vol. CAS-27, no. 11, pp. 990–997, November 1980.

25. T.-Y. Li and J. A. Yorke, "Period Three Implies Chaos," *American Mathematics Monthly,* vol. 82, pp. 985–992, 1985.

26. John S. Nicolis, "Chaos and Information Processing," World Science Publishing Co., Singapore, 1991.

27. Charles Hsu, Mona Zaghloul, and Harold Szu, "CMOS Current Mode Circuit to Control Chaos," *Proc. Int. Symp. Circuits and Systems,* Seattle, 1995.

CHAPTER 30

ARTIFICIAL NEURAL SYSTEMS BASED ON FREE-SPACE OPTICAL INTERCONNECTS

Ashok V. Krishnamoorthy

Advanced Photonics Research Department
AT&T Bell Laboratories, Holmdel, New Jersey

Gokce Yayla
Matthias Blume
Sadik C. Esener

Department of Electrical and Computer Engineering
University of California, San Diego

30.1 INTRODUCTION

Artificial neural networks have emerged as powerful, massively parallel computational paradigms. However, the application of neural network techniques to real-world problems has been restricted by a lack of large-scale, parallel implementations. In addition, the development and analysis of neural learning algorithms and their application to large-size problems has been hampered by the inordinate training times required by these algorithms and the limitations of available simulation tools [1]. Physical simulation of large-scale neural networks imposes serious challenges even to our most sophisticated computers, while special-purpose VLSI systems are not well-suited to implement highly interconnected neural architectures [2]. Consequently, there exists a need to develop scalable neural network systems with parallel learning capabilities which can be tailored to a variety of neural network models, including the popular multilayer feedforward networks, recurrent networks, and self-organizing systems.

In this chapter we describe how free-space optoelectronic technology can be used to implement artificial neural networks. We begin by discussing the device and system requirements for neural networks in Sec. 30.2. Interconnections are arguably the single most important component of a neural net system, since intelligence and memory in neurocomputing paradigms reside primarily in the connections and their weights, rather than the neurons themselves. The choice of the connection technology is therefore critical. As we will discuss in Sec. 30.3, free-space optical communications and optical storage techniques can be used to augment electronic processing in large, densely interconnected optoelectronic neural network systems. In Sec. 30.4, we discuss the key technologies required for implementing scalable optoelectronic neural networks. These include smart pixels, diffractive optical interconnects, photorefractive interconnects, and parallel optical storage devices. In Sec. 30.5, we describe several examples of architectures and systems for implementing specific neural network models using these optoelectronic devices.

30.2   HARDWARE REQUIREMENTS FOR ARTIFICIAL NEURAL NETS

The functional requirements of a single layer of a feedforward network (or an iteration step of a recurrent network) can be described in broad terms as a generalized inner-product, or a matrix-vector, multiplication with a nonlinearity. The process consists of a distribution of the neuron outputs; a local operation, typically multiplication, at each synaptic element; a global operation, typically summation of the resultant synaptic outputs; followed by a nonlinear squashing function:

$$Y_i = f\left\{ \sum_j W_{ij} X_j \right\}$$

The local and global operations can be generalized to other boolean operations. The critical issues in determining the suitability of a particular technology for implementing a large-scale neural network are the connectivity requirements and the precision needed in the synaptic connections, which in turn depends on the choice of network structure and learning rule. While the general problem of training a neural net is NP-complete [3], there is evidence that useful subclasses of the general learning problem are probably convergent in polynomial time [4]. For large neural network implementations, parallel learning capabilities can therefore provide substantial savings in learning times. Empirical results indicate that the learning time (for backpropagation learning) of a network with N weights is approximately $O(N^3)$ time steps when implemented on a serial machine. This is because the minimum number of samples needed to train the network is approximately $O(N)$ [5] and because the number of cycles is also $O(N)$ [1]. Thus an $O(N)$ speedup can be achieved via the use of dedicated hardware for each synapse. In practice, the speedup will depend on the specific network model and learning rule and on the amount of parallelism that is technologically feasible. Reinforcement learning methods [6], for instance, require only a single scalar value to be broadcast to all synapses at each iteration, making the update procedure relatively simple and readily parallelizable.

Implementation of a general-purpose neural network places stringent demands on the connection system. For random input/output mappings, if each neuron must learn its function from examples when it is constrained to see only its own bits and the bits of the neurons it is connected to, the minimum number of connections it must have is determined by the amount of information needed to specify the environment that generates the examples. Since the overwhelming majority of functions of N variables (where N is large) are of a random or unstructured nature [7], a high degree of connectivity may, therefore, be needed if the network architecture is to be applicable to a variety of "hard" problems. Hence, the system must be able to distribute the signals to many neurons (fan-out) and collect many inputs to each neuron (fan-in). In some special cases, this requirement can be relaxed to a certain extent and the network can be given structure suited to the specific task [8]. Furthermore, the learning process necessitates that the connection weights between neurons be iteratively modified so that the network can learn to solve new problems. The consequent demands on the computational resources in terms of memory, logic, and connectivity depend on the particular learning rule used.

It should be noted that not all artificial neural networks may require fully parallel learning. Certain applications may allow the connections to be developed by off-line training of a general-purpose machine, which might be slow or expensive. Once the weights of the network are known, unnecessary connections may be "pruned" so as to reduce the hardware cost and obtain improved performance [9]. Simpler machines preprogrammed with the set of useful connection patterns could then be mass-produced at low cost. However, this approach is of limited use for larger networks, particularly when the network comprises nonideal components. An alternative is to decouple the forward-operating network from the learning hardware, but allow the error outputs from the operating forward-network to feed the learning hardware [10, 11]. In this architecture, the network is given the opportunity to learn the nonuniform characteristics of the constituent components and can therefore compensate for them. This allows the learning hardware to be implemented digitally with double-precision arithmetic and with an appropriate amount of parallelism, depending on the specific learning rule used. New weights may be calculated each cycle, then transferred to the fully parallel (and possibly analog) forward-operating network. Simulations of such a system have shown that the network was able to compensate for up to 30 percent component variations using backpropagation learning [11].

In addition to the connectivity and learning issues, there is the precision issue. It is reasonable to expect that the precision required for neural network implementations is considerably less than that used in conventional digital computers (32-bit floating-point operations) since there is substantial biological evidence that a network built with imprecise components can produce an accurate, reliable response to a set of stimuli. In fact it has been proven that the synaptic weights for a Hopfield network can be completely "diluted" so that only sign information remains, without significantly affecting network capacity [12]. For networks that learn or self-organize, the amount of precision needed in the synaptic connections is still an open area of research, but in general depends on the particular neural network model, type of learning rule, and size of the network. For feedforward networks, an approximate estimate is that the number of useful bits of precision scales as the logarithm of the number of synapses per neuron [13]; i.e., the number of useful gray levels grows linearly with the number of synapses. This does not, however, indicate what the necessary precision is, which is of paramount importance to the hardware designer because it may preclude the use of certain devices, storage mechanisms, and data-encoding methods. A theoretical analysis of multilayer feedforward networks indicates a general tradeoff between the size of the network (number of neurons) needed to solve a particular problem and the resolution of weights (number of functions each neuron can implement). Indeed, it was shown that a multilayer perceptron with weights assuming one of k values must have at least $Ne/(\log_2 k)$ weights and $Ne/(d \log_2 k)$ hidden units in order to implement an arbitrary dichotomy of N points, where d and e are the number of input and output units respectively [14]. In order to minimize the number of hidden units, at least $\log_2 N$ weight values were needed. This result, however, does not include the precision requirements imposed by the dynamic nature of the learning process. Gradient descent procedures such as backpropagation often require higher precision since the network must often work its way down relatively shallow error surfaces. Simulations of backpropagation learning have shown that a minimum precision of 6 to 8 bits for the synaptic weights and 6 bits for the neuron outputs is required to train a network to learn a function with low output error [10, 15]. Since these results are specific to the network architectures and problems considered, they can provide the hardware designer with only a rough estimate of the required precision.

In summary, the usefulness of a particular technology for implementing neural networks depends on the extent to which it can meet the functional, connectivity, and precision requirements; these requirements should drive the design of appropriate systems. In order to achieve large highly connected neural networks with parallel learning capabilities, it therefore becomes essential to develop low-area/ low-power techniques to implement the primitive neural functions such as storage, multiplication, summation, thresholding, derivative, etc. In the following, we discuss why optoelectronic technology is better suited to meet these challenges.

30.3 ADVANTAGES OF FREE-SPACE OPTICAL INTERCONNECTS

In this section we discuss the solutions optoelectronic technology offers to interconnection problems. Our arguments will be based on topological suitability, achievable interconnection density, power dissipation, scalability, fault tolerance, modularity, and suitability to evolving neural systems.

30.3.1 Topological Considerations and Interconnection Density

It is widely recognized that the performance of very large scale integrated circuit (VLSI) electronic systems is limited by their planar nature. VLSI electronics suffers from severe electrical interconnection limitations which makes it ill-suited for implementing highly parallel computing architectures, that is, VLSI systems are governed by the principle of locality. Communication is expensive with VLSI. Chip floorplanning is usually optimized for minimum interconnection lengths, leading to localized communication in the chip. In addition, reconfigurable communication (e.g., communication switching networks) is very expensive in terms of area utilization. Communication in sending signals between chips is even more costly in terms of power dissipation and delay due to pin-out and packaging limitations. Consequently, with the present VLSI technology, only locally interconnected and/or nonscalable connectionist architectures with a limited number of neural processing elements can be implemented. Large-scale electronic neural network systems typically require that the connectivity between neurons be limited or that connection multiplexing be used [2, 16].

The connectivity and pin-out restrictions of VLSI can be alleviated by introducing optical inputs and outputs via the integration of optical transmitters and receivers onto a VLSI chip. In an optoelectronic module (Fig. 30.1), the connections between the optical transmitters and the optical receivers are realized in free space with arrays of lenses and holographic optical elements. The advantage of this approach stems from its three-dimensional (3-D) globally connected topology. By using the third dimension normal to the processing plane where the processing elements (PEs) reside, free-space optical interconnects offer the advantage of high-speed parallel and global interconnections between different PEs, as well as

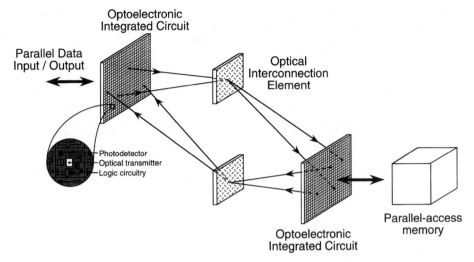

FIGURE 30.1 Conceptual view of a free-space interconnected optoelectronic multiprocessor system.

between different PE planes [17]. No crosstalk occurs between intersecting light beams. This is in contrast to a multichip electronic module where the interconnections are distributed in many planar interconnection layers. Vias allow for vertical communication between layers only at distinct regions. In a free-space optoelectronic module, interconnections can be truly distributed throughout a volume since the interconnection optics can overlap.

It can also be shown that the area taken in an optical interconnect medium to implement highly interconnected architectures is considerably less than the area taken by the electrical interconnects on a VLSI chip [18, 19, 20]. That is, optical interconnects area scale far better than electrical interconnects for connectionist architectures. In a VLSI-based two-dimensional (2-D) system, the number of communication channels n is governed by a one-dimensional (1-D) communication bisectrix, which grows in proportion to the side of the chip. That is, $n = O(\sqrt{A})$, where A is the chip area. In the case of a 3-D system as shown in Fig. 30.1, the communication takes place through a planar bisectrix of area A ($n = O(A)$) rather than a 1-D bisectrix of length $\sqrt{A}$. As a result, the communication capacity of a 3-D optoelectronic system asymptotically exceeds that of an electronic system.

30.3.2 Interconnect Delay and Energy Considerations

In order to demonstrate the scalability of optoelectronic systems, several researchers have compared the energy dissipation of an optical interconnect to that of an electrical interconnect [21, 22] and demonstrated that for interconnections longer than a certain break-even length, free-space optical interconnects consume less energy and are faster than their electrical counterparts [22]. The delay of an interconnection line of length L (without repeaters) can be shown to approximate [23]

$$T_{90\%} = 2.3(R_O C_{\text{int}} L + R_O C_O + R_{\text{int}} C_O L) + R_{\text{int}} C_{\text{int}} L^2 \qquad (30.1)$$

where R_O and C_O are the output resistance and load capacitance of a minimum size gate and R_{int} and C_{int} are the resistance and capacitance per unit length of the interconnecting line, respectively. The second term on the right is small for typical on-chip wire lengths, and therefore the delay grows approximately linearly with interconnection length. According to Eq. (30.1), any increase in the interconnection complexity (i.e., the length and number of parallel interconnection lines) of the chip must be followed by a decrease in the resistance and the capacitance of the interconnects to keep the delay constant. This is in contrast to optical interconnects, where the interconnect delay is independent of the interconnect length at typical VLSI lengths and switching speeds. It follows that for highly interconnected neural architectures, the use of optical interconnects can lead to systems that have lower delays and higher throughputs. It is also instructive to examine the ratio of the energy dissipated in an optical link connecting a light transmitter to a light detector to that dissipated in an electrical interconnect [22]

$$\frac{E_o}{E_e} = \frac{h\nu}{qV}\frac{C_o}{\eta C_e(L)} + \frac{2P_{di}}{fC_e(L)V^2} \tag{30.2}$$

where

$h\nu$ = photon energy
q = electronic charge
V = power supply voltage
η = optical link efficiency
L = electrical interconnection length
C_o and C_e = capacitance associated with the optical and electrical interconnects, respectively
f = speed of operation
P_{di} = threshold power (for lasers only)

In a system, C_o could be the sum of the transmitter and detector capacitance in the link, while capacitance C_e could include the electrical line capacitance as well as the input and output capacitance of electronic inverters. In the above equation, the first term is the ratio of the capacitance associated with electrical and optical interconnections. This term also takes into account the efficiencies of the detector, the optical interconnection, and the optical transmitter. The second term is associated with light transmitters, such as laser diodes, that exhibit a threshold. This term dominates at low speeds. For light modulators, this term vanishes. Note that the communication energy overhead associated with electronics grows with increasing interconnection length, while the overhead associated with optical interconnects is independent of the length of the interconnection. At the module level, the high capacitance of the pins and the board-level interconnections further increase C_e, thereby further increasing the energy advantage of optics. As will be discussed in Sec. 30.5, these energy considerations will have direct consequences on optoelectronic system designs.

In summary, the potential advantages of optoelectronic computing for connectionist computing systems can be enumerated as follows. Optical interconnections can be realized in the third dimension and hence the silicon integrated circuit can be more effectively used to host a denser, globally connected array of PEs. From a topological argument, a level of connectivity that is otherwise impossible to achieve for large networks can be realized. Interconnection among PEs between wafers is not limited by pin-out problems, allowing a modular approach. Optical interconnects are superior to electrical interconnects for global communication in terms of energy consumption. Optical interconnects enable communication and processing to be decoupled, and can provide tolerance to defects in the interconnection medium when holographic techniques are used. These interconnections may also be designed to avoid faulty processing elements. As discussed in the next section, free-space optoelectronic technology has the necessary generality and flexibility to implement modular connectionist systems.

30.4 TECHNOLOGY DESCRIPTION

In this section we describe the individual components required for implementing optoelectronic neural networks: smart pixels, free-space diffractive optical interconnects, and parallel-accessed optical storage devices.

30.4.1 Smart Pixels

One of the key components of optoelectronic computing modules is the smart-spatial light modulator (S-SLM) [24], otherwise known as the *smart pixels* [25]. Smart pixels can be regarded as an evolution of conventional electrooptic spatial light modulators (SLMs) [26]. Conventional SLMs are devices in which one two-dimensional optical field modulates a certain characteristic of another two-dimensional optical field (usually phase, polarization, or intensity). In most SLMs, however, the interaction between the two optical fields requires optical-to-electrical and electrical-to-optical energy conversions. An important class of electrooptic SLMs is spatially segmented. In such SLMs the input and output optical fields are pixelated. Smart SLMs or smart pixels differ from conventional spatially segmented SLMs in that some information processing can be carried out electronically in each pixel of the SLM [27]. In a smart pixel implementation of neural networks, the neuron (and possibly the synaptic) function is realized within each smart pixel or optoelectronic processing element. Figure 30.2 depicts an array of smart pixels. In each pixel or PE, incoming optical data are sensed by light detectors. These detectors con-

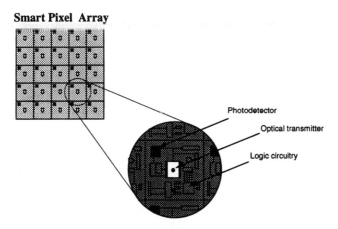

FIGURE 30.2   Schematic of a smart pixel.

vert the data into electronic form that is then fed to an electronic circuit for local processing. The control signals for the electronic circuit can also be received optically. In principle, the electronic circuit of the PE can be as simple as a logic gate with a few transistors or as complex as a programmable processor with a few thousand logic gates. Information processing in each PE can be carried out in a digital as well as analog fashion. At the output of the PE, the processed data are converted back into optical form via light transmitters (sources or modulators) and then routed to another PE with free-space interconnection optics. It should be noted that the optoelectronic data conversions in the operation of a smart pixel do not need to be as frequent as in a conventional SLM. The data in a smart pixel remain in electronic form while being processed locally. Local electrical interconnections to other pixels are possible. Data are in the optical form only when global transmission to other smart pixels is necessary. This considerably reduces the rate of energy conversions and allows the optoelectronic parallel computers to outperform all electronic and very fine grain optical parallel computers.

Smart pixels employ materials with widely different properties for logic, light detection, and light transmission. Various smart pixel technologies are presently under development. Most smart pixels are based on substrates such as silicon, silicon on sapphire, gallium arsenide, indium phosphide, or ferroelectric material. The contemplated logic technologies vary from silicon complementary metal oxide semiconductor (CMOS) to group III-V metal-semiconductor field-effect transistors (MESFETs). Various light detectors and detection circuits have also been proposed. Similarly, several light transmitter device technologies have been suggested for use in smart pixels. In the following section, we summarize some of the considerations involved in selecting suitable smart pixel technologies for neural network applications.

Light Transmitter Technology.   A key factor in determining the suitability of a smart pixel technology to a given application is the light transmitter technology that is adopted. Two approaches are presently under investigation: light sources and light modulators. The former approach has a major advantage in that active light sources such as laser diodes can be fast (subnanosecond) and provide large dynamic range and high contrast ratios. The optical system can be simplified because no external laser is required. Surface-emitting laser diodes that can efficiently direct the laser beam out of the smart pixel plane have been developed [28]. Vertical-cavity surface-emitting lasers (VCSELs) currently require relatively large threshold currents (about 100 μA to 1 mA). At a high level of integration, this results in large on-chip power dissipation. Thus, for high-density point-to-point interconnects, VCSELs are less advantageous. On the other hand, when operating with a large fan-out, the threshold current of an individual VCSEL can effectively be amortized over a larger number of interconnects. For architectures that do not require high-density integration of transmitters or mutually coherent transmitters (see Sec. 30.5.2), VCSELs are a good candidate. It is expected that by the end of this decade, threshold currents will be reduced by an order of magnitude, making laser diodes very attractive for neural net applications.

Light-emitting diodes (LEDs) can presently be integrated on a large scale with gallium arsenide (GaAs) logic. Like semiconductor lasers, they benefit from large dynamic ranges but suffer from high on-chip power dissipation. Their main limitation is the large spectral width of their emission; this precludes their use with volume holographic interconnections. Since most neural net architectures require large fan-out, the proper utilization of LEDs for this application requires their integration with very high sensitivity detectors.

The electrooptic light modulator approach has significant near-term advantages over lasers diodes and LEDs. There exists a larger variety of materials capable of light modulation. Therefore, material integration requirements can be more easily met. Compared to laser diode fabrication, modulator fabrication processes are simpler and more consistent with logic technology. Light modulators are capacitive; they therefore require little current and reduce the on-chip dissipated power. The excess heat dissipation due to the inefficiency associated with electrical-to-optical conversion in the lasers is kept away from the smart pixel array. This is especially important for implementing architectures that require high fan-out.

Multiple-quantum-well absorption modulators [29], as well as ferroelectric liquid crystal [30] and lead lanthanum zirconate titanate (PLZT) polarization modulators [31] based on smart pixels have been suggested for neural network applications. We first note that for GaAs/A1GaAs (aluminum gallium arsenide) multiple quantum well (MQW) and PLZT modulators the switching speed is limited by electronic effects; that is, they can operate at high speeds if enough drive power can be provided. Of the two technologies, MQW absorption modulators have an order of magnitude lower capacitance, and can be modulated at gigahertz rates. The small switching energy of an MQW is achieved at the expense of narrow spectral bandwidth. On the other hand, ferroelectric liquid crystal (FLC) modulators have a switching time of about a microsecond. For neural network applications an important consideration for MQW modulators arises from their absorptive nature; their on-chip power dissipation increases with fan-out. Hence, they are best-suited for high-speed point-to-point optical interconnects with low fan-out per device.

Both FLC and PLZT polarization-based modulators can provide large fan-out because of their nonabsorptive nature. For example, a fan-out of up to 1000 should be achievable with 100 μm^2 PLZT modulators, with 20-mW modulated output power and 10-μW detector power (assuming 50 percent optical losses). The major difference between FLC and PLZT modulators is in their switching time (in favor of PLZT) and in the required switching energy (in favor of FLCs). Thus, for applications requiring dense arrays of light modulators operating at 10-μs switching times or higher, FLC-based smart pixels will be preferable; for higher-speed, high–fan-out, lower-density transmitter applications, PLZT-based smart pixels should be used. Applications of silicon/FLC smart pixels to a competitive-learning neural system have been reported [32]. Other applications in early vision, image-processing displays are being actively investigated.

Electronic Logic Technology. The second consideration in the choice of smart pixels for neural network implementations is the electronic technology. Presently, the electronic chip market is shared by various electronic logic families. However, the consumer market is dominated by silicon CMOS devices which have a wide range of applications. Other technologies are expected to remain limited to niche applications. CMOS gates have negligible static power dissipation, large noise margins, and can operate with high reliability. This technology also allows for high device density and speed of operation. Consequently, CMOS technology has become universal, and there are also strong indications that the supremacy of CMOS will continue. It is expected that metal-oxide-semiconductor field-effect transistor (MOSFET) feature sizes will continue to be reduced, possibly down to 0.1 μm by the end of this decade, further increasing device densities and achievable circuit complexities by a factor of 100. During this decade, it has been established that silicon CMOS VLSI is, and will continue to be, the leading technology for integrated circuits.

CMOS technology, however, suffers most from interconnection problems in comparison to other existing logic families precisely because of its high level of integration. This limitation of CMOS is expected to become more severe with the scaling-down of device dimensions [17]. Therefore, CMOS is a logic technology that should be targeted for optoelectronic neural networks. We believe the favorable attributes of CMOS logic technology will be the driving force behind silicon-based smart pixels. For neural network implementations, MOSFETs possess useful physical characteristics (e.g., low power dissipation and subthreshold operation) that match the needs of artificial neural networks [33]. Much of the pioneering experimental research on neural network implementations has been carried out in CMOS VLSI. Novel circuit techniques for weight storage [e.g., dynamic random-access memories (DRAMs) and electrically erasable/programmable read-only memories (EEPROMs)] and multiplication (e.g., the switched-capacitor synapse in Sec. 30.5) have been developed. Silicon-CMOS–based smart pixels will benefit from this work, and will enable efficient implementations of various key functions necessary for neural net algorithms. Thus, the overwhelming advantages of CMOS-based smart pixel technology favors its use in free-space optoelectronic neural networks.

Smart Pixel Integration Techniques.   Smart pixels employ materials with widely different properties for logic, light detection, and light modulation. In the following section, we review some of the integration approaches that are currently being investigated for the development of smart pixels. These approaches can be classified as *hybrid* and *monolithic*.

Hybrid Integration.   A straightforward approach is to use a hybrid integration technique, such as flip-chip bonding. Flip-chip bonding, currently used for silicon packaging, is a mature and well-developed technique that can also be used advantageously to realize smart pixels. This technique has been studied with different materials and devices for smart pixels [34]. Figure 30.3 illustrates this approach, and shows the cross-section of a PE in a hybrid silicon/PLZT smart pixel array. The PLZT wafer is used to support the PLZT modulators. The modulator is used in a reflective configuration and is connected electrically using flip-chip bonding to the output of the silicon circuit in the PE with an indium bump. More recently, a technique for flip-chip bonding MQW modulators operating at 850 nm [35] to prefabricated silicon circuits has been demonstrated. The size of the bump which can be made as small as 10 μm is governed by the warpage of the wafers and the desired dis-

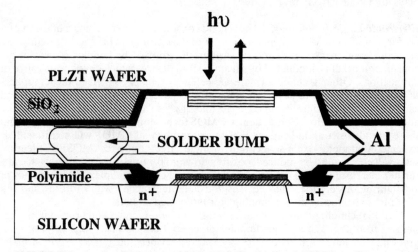

FIGURE 30.3   A unit cell of a smart pixel based on flip-chip-bonded PLZT on silicon.

tance between wafers. This approach can be used to increase smart pixel yield by bonding pretested operational silicon chips one at a time. It is expected that 100 by 100 arrays of smart pixels can be readily produced with this hybrid integration technique. It should be noted that the flip-chip bonding technique can also be used for integrating VCSELs as well as LEDs with silicon circuits.

Monolithic Integration.   The performance of smart pixels can be improved with monolithic integration techniques. Monolithic integration will ensure the manufacturability of large smart pixel arrays at lower cost than the hybrid approach. Apart from cost, the parasitic capacitance associated with the hybrid approach can also be eliminated. The growth or deposition of desired optical materials on an appropriate substrate (silicon, sapphire, or gallium arsenide) must be developed, however. Accordingly, most of the present research effort on monolithic smart pixels is focused on growth techniques for optical materials of interest.

Currently, the leading approach for monolithic realization of smart pixels is the FET-SEED (self-electrooptic-effect device) approach, which uses a GaAs/AlGaAs MQW for optical modulation and a GaAs MESFET for electronic logic [36].

At this point in time, major research issues for the monolithic integration of smart pixels still remain, although we believe that these issues can and will eventually be resolved. Until then, hybrid integration techniques will be the preferred manufacturing method and we expect that most early optoelectronic neural net systems will be assembled from hybrid smart pixels.

Smart Pixel Partitioning and Grain Size.   A limit on the size of a smart pixel array stems from the device fabrication yield, the integration method, the maximum power dissipation and area, the optical power requirements, and the partitioning of the circuit. The *grain size* of the circuit, defined as the number of electronic devices per optical input/output (I/O), is a useful metric to describe the partitioning of the smart pixel array. The grain size may vary considerably from one smart pixel array to another, depending on the application needs and the specific device technology used. A general guideline in determining an efficient grain size for a particular smart pixel array comes from energy considerations. To determine this, we return to the comparison of the energy dissipation of an optical link to that of an electrical link. Note that for communication distances longer than a certain break-even length, free-space optical interconnects consume less energy and are faster than their electrical counterparts. The break-even length L can be computed directly from Eq. (30.2) by setting $E_o = E_e$. This break-even length is strongly affected by the electrical and optoelectronic device technology of the smart pixel array through the capacitances C_e and C_o and the optical interconnect technology through the efficiency η. Presently, the break-even length ranges from a few hundred micrometers to about a centimeter, depending on the particular smart pixel technology. It follows that the longest electrical interconnections within a pixel in a smart pixel array should be less than this break-even length for an energy-efficient system. For a smart pixel array coupled with optical interconnections, this break-even length provides a rough guideline for the optimal size of a pixel from an energy dissipation point of view. For a more precise estimate, a detailed engineering study can be performed to optimize the grain size for each specific smart pixel system [37, 38].

30.4.2   Free-Space Optical Interconnection

The connections between neurons are perhaps the most important components of a connectionist system, since they govern both the performance of such a network and the cost of the network in terms of space, time, and power. The choice of the connection topology and technology is therefore critical. Interconnection topologies can be classified in terms of their regularity (space invariance or variance), density (fan-out, fan-in), and degree to which they can be reconfigured. The least general systems are fixed, with a single, built-in connection pattern. Programmable systems are more general; the system can select any one among a limited set of prestored connections. Depending on the technology, the time required to change patterns can be small. Still more general are reprogrammable interconnection systems, which can interrupt processing and reset to any desired connection pattern. The time required to reset the connection depends again on the technology. Finally, there are adaptive systems, in which the connection patterns are continuously changing as the system operates.

In general, the choice of the appropriate free-space optical interconnect technology is strongly dependent on the required regularity and reconfigurability. Each type of connection system has potential applications. Neural networks in biological organisms use adaptive connections, and so these are of greatest interest. However, many artificial neural learning algorithms (such as Kohonen, Widrow-Hoff, and hebbian learning) can be implemented using reprogrammable interconnects. Nonlearning systems with predetermined connection patterns can use fixed or programmable optical interconnects.

In terms of implementation, free-space optical interconnects can be classified as refractive or holographic, the latter including both "thin" diffractive optical elements such as computer-generated holograms (CGHs) and "thick" holographic interconnects using photorefractive materials.

Fixed Optical Interconnection. In general, refractive optical components such as lenses, prisms, and gratings are well-suited for implementing regular, fixed interconnection networks [39]. Such implementations may be very useful for specific neural network systems (see Sec. 30.5.2). It is also possible to implement a space-variant interconnection by implementing a space-invariant superset interconnection with refractive optics and masking out the unwanted interconnections, at the expense of larger optical power loss.

Holographic techniques are well-suited for implementing regular as well as irregular, fixed as well as programmable, interconnects. An optical hologram is made by interfering two wavefronts in a medium, which records the intensity and phase distribution. A wavefront from each PE (or neuron) is interfered with the wavefronts from the connecting PEs (or neurons) to record a hologram component. When the hologram consisting of N component holograms for a network of N neurons is made and illuminated by the input PEs, the output is holographically recalled, and the connection to output PEs is made. This hologram allows an output PE to collect signals from several input PEs (fan-in) and distribute the output to various output PEs (fan-out) simultaneously. By individually setting the intensity of each wavefront component of the hologram, the strength of each connection can be given an analog weight. This exactly matches the needs of neural systems. The hologram is used to store the synaptic weights, thus reducing the storage requirements on the electronic processing elements.

Two types of holograms can be distinguished: thin (or planar) holograms and thick (or volume) holograms. When the thickness T of the holographic storage media is less than or comparable to the average interference fringe spacing ($\Lambda = 1$ to 10 μm), the hologram is defined as thin. Thin (planar) holograms can be permanently optically recorded on photographic or thermoplastic films, or can be computer-generated and fabricated using microelectronic lithography techniques for fixed interconnection patterns. Thick ($T \gg \Lambda$) (volume) holograms can be optically recorded in dichromated gelatin or photorefractive crystals [e.g., lithium niobate ($LiNbO_3$)]. Generally, thick phase holograms can offer higher storage capacities and diffraction efficiencies and/or better signal-to-noise ratios than thin phase holograms.

The set of N component holograms for a network of N neurons can be multiplexed in several ways. Each can be given a separate area or volume, or they can be superimposed in the same area or volume by multiple exposures, or a combination of both methods can be used. Generally, superimposing holograms in the same area or volume requires less recording area, but the signal-to-noise ratio of the reconstruction will be reduced because recalling any one hologram may also recall weak distorted reconstructions from other holograms. For programmable interconnections, a limited number of holograms can be prestored in the same area or volume by using orthogonal phase codes or different wavelengths of light. To select one among a set of prestored interconnections, the proper phase code or wavelength can be selected for reconstruction. When multiple subholograms or holograms are superimposed in the same medium, the optical experiment can become quite complicated. For this reason, computer-aided design methods for multiple exposure holograms have been studied [40]. If the connection patterns required are both known and fixed, the necessary multiplexed hologram can be computed off-line and fabricated using, for instance, electron-beam lithography methods that are fully compatible with VLSI in terms of fabrication characteristics and physical dimensions. Computer-generated holograms may sometimes require long and expensive computations, but they can be made with lower aberration and higher diffraction efficiency (by adopting multilevel phase) than thin optical holograms [41]. Limitations on fabrication technology (both the writing resolution and storage capacity) determine the quality of reconstruction (spot size and signal-to-noise level) and the maximum interconnection distance, density, and complexity. In any case, CGHs are well-suited to systems requiring known and fixed interconnections.

Unlike electronic, fiber-optic, or integrated optics connections, holographic storage distributes the information throughout the medium, so that a local defect cannot destroy the connection. This dramatically increases the fault tolerance of the network's connection. A single volume hologram effectively records a stack of thin holograms so that the reconstructed image must fulfill the phase-matching condition at each plane. As a result, noise is suppressed and diffraction efficiency improved. These characteristics are highly desirable for programmable connection applications, since energy throughput and connection density should be maximized.

Reprogrammable and Adaptive Optical Interconnects. The development of reprogrammable optical interconnects is still largely at the research stage. Many researchers are still investigating new photorefractive materials (e.g., semiconductor photorefractives) and various multiplexing techniques to store volume holograms (e.g., using orthogonal phase codes or color). Volume holograms are characterized, in general, by high diffraction efficiencies and good superposition properties. In addition to their thickness, holograms in photorefractive crystals (e.g., SBN:60) differ from thin holograms in film or dichromated gelatin, in an important respect. That is, it is not necessary to remove them from their recording position in order to develop them. In photorefractive crystals, the refractive index responds continuously to the incident light, allowing the crystal to remain in place while the hologram is continuously stored. The hologram can be written, erased, and rewritten in situ, thus allowing reprogrammable or adaptive connections to be made. In many photorefractive materials, the stored holograms suffer a slight degradation (erasure) during readout unless they are permanently fixed by some means. Also, when new holograms are written for multiplexing purposes, the previously recorded holograms are slightly erased. This effect can be reduced by applying a voltage across the crystal, which increases the asymmetry between the writing time and the erasure time, and using a recording schedule [42]. Another method is to use an incremental recording procedure [43] so that each hologram is written incrementally over several cycles. For parallel learning networks, this degradation process can be used to advantage as many neural algorithms use a "forgetting" term in the connection update algorithm to improve learning [44]. If the connection patterns are instead to remain constant, a processing cycle can be used to refresh the stored holograms [45]. Alternatively, the stored pattern might be frozen by using a type of photorefractive fixation [46]. For example, temperature can be used as a control parameter (in $LiNbO_3$) to first free, and then fix, the positive ions in the crystal. Once the ionic hologram is fixed, it is undisturbed by readout. As many as 5000 distinct volume holograms, each recreating a desired output with the readout beams propagating at different angles, have been superimposed in a single photorefractive crystal [47]. In Sec. 30.5, we review several holographic neural network systems that rely on multiple exposure holography in photorefractive materials.

30.4.3 Parallel-Accessed Optical Storage Devices

As discussed in Sec. 30.2, the emergence of artificial neural network algorithms has brought about a need not only for massively parallel processing systems, but also storage systems with enormous capacities and memory bandwidths. Although in biological networks, storage and interconnections are indistinguishable, artificial neural networks may augment their storage capacity by using separate memory devices. Progress in VLSI electronic neural networks and the advent of optoelectronic technology now allow large arrays of highly integrated and very high speed computing devices for parallel processing to be built. However, this has created a demand for low-cost, high-capacity, and high-bandwidth memory subsystems that are compatible with optoelectronic systems. Existing semiconductor or magnetic memory technologies, being essentially serial or semiparallel in nature, cannot meet this demand without having the memory subsystem dominate the processors themselves in terms of overall cost, power consumption, and volume. The need for low-cost, high-performance memories and compatibility with optical interconnections can best be satisfied by parallel accessed optical storage devices.

The parallel-accessed optical storage system may be either binary or analog, depending on the particular optoelectronic architecture. If electronic synapses are used for the multiplication and summation operations (Sec. 30.5.2), binary bit planes from the optical storage device may be used to load new connection weights in parallel; weights with K gray levels can be implemented using $\log_2 K$ bit planes. This technique effectively increases the connection capacity of the network and enables larger networks to be emulated by the parallel hardware. If the synaptic function is implemented optically, analog optical storage devices can provide the interconnection and weighting operations simultaneously. Various schemes for parallel accessed memories are presently being developed. These include both planar media such as optical disks as well as volume media such as two-photon and photorefractive materials.

Motionless-Head Parallel-Readout System for Optical Disk. A near-term solution to parallel-accessed optical storage is optical disk systems modified for parallel readout. Such systems leverage on existing optical disk technology. Optical disks are good candidates for this application because they combine high capacity (900

Mbytes for a 5¼ in-diameter disk), low cost (1 dollar/Gbyte), and robustness (no head-crash risk). It has also been shown that optical disks can be read in parallel. Several parallel readout systems have been proposed. For instance, some of the earliest work involved the recording of one-dimensional Fourier transform holograms along radial lines of the disk and reading them out in parallel [48, 49]. More recently, it was demonstrated that binarized versions of 2-D Fourier transform holograms of images can be recorded onto a glass disk [50]. Alternatively, analog 2-D images can be stored by using an area-modulation technique together with an imaging system to obtain a high-performance spatial light modulator [51].

Generally, there are three distinct limitations to high-speed operation of parallel accessed optical disks: the tracking, focusing, and addressing mechanisms. Traditionally, all these functions require mechanical motions of the head which slow down the disk operation. The method presented below uses a hybrid Fourier transform/imaging technique to eliminate the need for any mechanical motion of the readout head. This makes parallel accessed optical disk systems well-suited to optoelectronic associative memories and neural networks.

The optical disk readout system [52] is designed to read data blocks laid out radially on the active disk surface, as illustrated in Fig. 30.4. The 128×128 image to be stored is first sliced into columns. These columns are then 1-D Fourier-transformed to form computer-generated holograms calculated to reconstruct one column of an

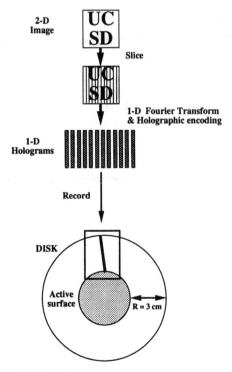

FIGURE 30.4 Data-encoding method for motionless-head parallel-readout optical disk.

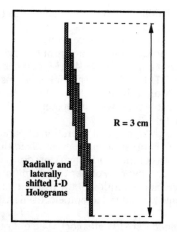

FIGURE 30.5 Disk data layout. Data blocks of each image are radially shifted from each other.

image. The CGH encoding method developed specifically for the disk holograms is based on a gray-level encoding scheme [52, 53]. These CGHs are then shifted radially with respect to each other such that the data associated with one image spans the radius of the active disk surface (Fig. 30.5). During readout, an area on the disk whose length is equal to an entire radial line of the active disk surface is illuminated (Fig. 30.6). A cylindrical lens is used to perform a Fourier transform of the illuminated disk area along the radial direction, and another cylindrical lens images and magnifies the data along the tangential direction. In practice, these last two lenses may be combined into one custom optical element. Since Fourier transform holograms are shift-invariant, the radial shifts of different columns and eccentricity of the spinning disk does not affect the reconstruction of the data. Therefore, a 2-D binary image is reconstructed on the output plane and no tracking servo is needed. Since the entire content of the disk can be retrieved in one rotation, no mechanical motion of the head is required to access the data stored on any location of the disk surface. Finally, the wobble of the disk is overcome by slightly underillu-

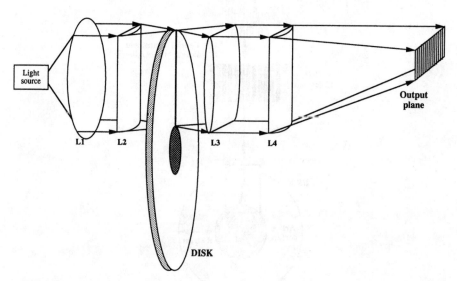

FIGURE 30.6 Optical disk readout system. Light is collimated by lens L1 and focused onto the disk by cylindrical lens L2. Cylindrical lens L3 performs the Fourier transform of the data along the radial direction and cylindrical lens L4 images and magnifies the data along the tangential direction. In practice, L3 and L4 may be replaced by a single custom optical element [53].

minating the 1-D holograms (relying on the information redundancy of holographic storage) and using an illumination lens with a large depth of focus. Note that, because of the hologram information redundancy, even partially illuminated holograms reconstruct the entire data; a loss of 10 percent of the hologram information induces a loss of only 10 percent in the reconstruction signal amplitude [50].

An experimental feasibility analysis of such a system was recently performed [53]. From this analysis one can project that 15,000 images, each of 128×128 bits, can be stored on a disk. Assuming a conservative rotation speed of 2400 r/min, such a disk could be capable of achieving an I/O bandwidth in excess of half a million images per second, or 10 Gbit/s, with an average image access time (random access) of 12.5 ms. One may expect that such a parallel-readout optical disk system with a motionless readout head will find numerous applications in the implementation of optoelectronic neural networks. In Sec. 30.5.1, an optoelectronic associative memory system that takes full advantage of this disk system is presented.

3-D Memories.   To meet increasing demands on storage systems, researchers have been seeking three-dimensional optical memory devices as an alternative means to achieve low-cost, high-performance memory systems [54]. Present memory devices store information on a two-dimensional surface. A 3-D memory is a single memory unit where three independent coordinates are used to specify the location of the information. Such a device would allow the storage of two-dimensional information (bit planes) stacked in the third dimension, thereby achieving higher theoretical storage capacities. For example, the maximum theoretical storage density for an optical disk is $\rho_{2\text{-}D} = 1/\lambda^2 = 3.5 \times 10^8$ bit/cm^2 assuming that a 0.5-μm wavelength of light is used to access the information. On the other hand, the maximum theoretical storage density of a volume 3-D memory device is $\rho_{3\text{-}D} = 1/\lambda^3 = 6.5 \times 10^{12}$ bits/cm^3, assuming the same wavelength of light. In practice, the capacity is limited by the devices used to access the bit planes to and from the memory. Three-dimensional optical memory devices also have the potential for parallel access, because an entire bit plane can be read or written in a single memory access cycle.

Three-dimensional memories are generally classified as bit-plane oriented and holographic. Bit-oriented memories generally use amplitude recording media. In bit-oriented 3-D memories, each bit occupies a specific location. The coordinates that specify the location of the information can be spatial, spectral, or temporal, giving rise to a variety of 3-D memory concepts that use different materials with different properties. For example, materials that exhibit two-photon absorption, which refers to the excitation of a molecule to an electronic state of higher energy by simultaneous absorption of two photons of different energy, can provide 3-D storage capability [55]. Two optical beams must temporally and spatially overlap in order for two-photon absorption to result. This allows true volume storage, since the beams can penetrate the material to record, read, or erase information without affecting it except in the regions where they overlap. In contrast, materials wherein spectral holes are burnt can provide spectral/spatial storage [56], while materials that exhibit the photon echo effect [57] could, in principle, provide temporal/spatial storage.

Three-dimensional holographic storage differs from bit-plane-oriented memories in that the information associated with the stored bits is distributed throughout the memory space. Hence, 3-D holographic storage in phase recording media (e.g., photorefractive crystals) is tolerant to point defects in the storage medium [58]. To multiplex the information about many different bit planes, angle, wavelength, or orthogonal phase codes can be used.

In summary, information about many binary planes can be stored in the volume of 3-D memory. One memory I/O operation is performed on the entire plane of bits, thus achieving a tremendous memory bandwidth increase over conventional bit-oriented serial memories. These considerations make 3D memories very compatible to the needs of optoelectronic neural network requirements and, in the long term, a strong competitor to parallel-accessed optical disks.

30.5 OPTOELECTRONIC NEURAL NET EXAMPLES

This section presents a few optoelectronic neural network system design examples. These examples illustrate that the performance of neural net systems can be improved by increasing the amount of optoelectronic devices and optical interconnects in the systems. The first example is an associative memory system that uses a parallel-accessed optical disk together with a silicon chip for detection and processing. This simple associative memory system can achieve significantly better performance than its all-electronic counterparts. The second example, the D-STOP system, relies on a smart pixel technology where silicon processing, light detectors, and a small number of light modulators per unit area are used to create a scalable optoelectronic neural system, capable of fully parallel learning. Finally, we review several prototype systems that implement the synapse function optically, in a photorefractive crystal, which may allow the implementation of very large optical neural networks.

30.5.1 Optoelectronic Associative Memory

There has been considerable interest over the past two decades in the ability to achieve recall of an item stored in a memory device based on a partial query, namely an associative memory [44]. The characteristic that distinguishes an associative memory is its ability to recall the correct output pattern even when the input is distorted or incomplete. Associative memories are also robust, in the sense that information is stored in a distributed, redundant manner, and that the system degrades gracefully when too many patterns are stored in the memory, or when too much noise is introduced in the input query.

The key performance measures for a hardware implementation of an associative memory or content-addressable memory (CAM) are its capacity (number of stored bits) and its search rate [bit-operations per second (bit-ops/s)]. In general, both the capacity and the search rate are limited by the particular technology used for storage/processing and by the choice of algorithm.

For purely electronic CAM implementations, there exists a tradeoff between the storage capacity and the maximum search rate. While high speed, pipelined VLSI chips (10^9 bit-ops/s) have been demonstrated [59, 60, 61], their capacity is limited (10 to 20 Kbits) because the entire memory resides on chip and because each cell includes some matching circuitry. Current high-capacity secondary storage systems have low transfer rates relative to these processing speeds. For instance, solid-state disk drives, with capacities of 100 Mbytes, can provide data rates on the order of 10 Mbyte/s [62]. Although projected development in main memory technologies such as SRAM and DRAM (static and dynamic random-access memory, respectively) could provide bandwidths of 100 Mbyte/s, their capacity will be limited to a few hundred megabits for the remainder of this century [63]. This fact combined with the limited pin-out and I/O bandwidth available on a VLSI chip creates a performance bottleneck for associative memory applications, since the serial (or semiparallel) I/O

subsystem forces the processing units to wait for new data. An optoelectronic associative memory system can remove this limitation by using a parallel-accessed optical memory (Sec. 30.4.3, under "Motionless-Head Parallel-Readout System for
Optical Disk") and a custom-designed integrated circuit modified for parallel optical input.

Associative Memory Algorithms.   Several algorithmic approaches to associative
memory using 2-D bit-plane storage have been investigated. These fall into two
broad categories. The first is an outer product algorithm using matrix-tensor multiplication. The second is an inner-product scheme based on bitwise matching. In
outer-product-based associative memory algorithms, the memories are distributed
in the storage medium via an outer-product construction. If X_m represents one of M
two-dimensional images to be stored and Y_m the desired output, a fourth-rank ten-
sor must be stored:

$$W = \sum_m Y_m X_m^Y$$

For autoassociative memories, $Y_m = X_m$. Outputs are obtained by iteratively performing matrix-tensor multiplication on the input followed by thresholding and
feedback.

For inner-product-based algorithms such as the Hamming network [64], the data
(X_m's) are stored explicitly. Inner products between the input and all the X_m's are
calculated and the output is the corresponding Y_m associated with the largest inner
product. The inner products may be calculated in parallel, in which case a maximum-
selector network is needed, and the capacity of the associative memory is limited by
the size of this network. Alternatively, inner products may be calculated page-
serially (Fig. 30.7), for each X_m, which does not require maximum selector network
to be implemented in hardware.

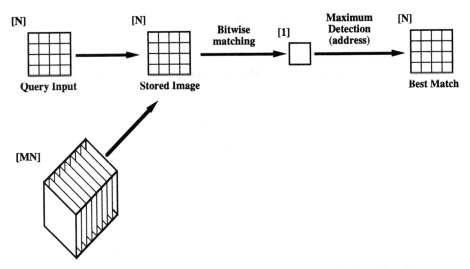

FIGURE 30.7   Page-serial, bit-parallel associative memory algorithm. M is the number of memory
pages, and N is the number of bits per page.

For an optoelectronic implementation, the storage requirements, system complexity, search times, and fault tolerance of these algorithms determine the optimal design. Outer-product neural network algorithms such as the Hopfield network and its variants have several disadvantages when compared to parallel inner-product methods [65, 66]. Outer-product-based associative memories provide robust storage and fast convergence when a small number of very large memory pages are used [67]. However, inner-product methods provide significant hardware savings when a large number of pages must be stored. For parallel-accessed optical storage devices such as the parallel optical disk ($M = 14,500$ images of $N = 128 \times 128$ bits each) [68], the page-serial, bit-parallel inner-product method has the least storage requirements as well as the lowest system complexity because no maximum selector network is needed. For this same reason, the method does not place an upper limit on the number of memories that can be searched. Because of the high data rate achievable with the parallel readout optical disk, this method can lead to a system with a high search rate when combined with the optoelectronic integrated circuit described below. Finally, as discussed previously, robustness to point defects can be traded in for disk capacity. For these reasons, the page-serial, bit-parallel inner-product algorithm is well-suited to implementation with parallel-accessed optical storage devices such as the parallel optical disk.

Associative Memory System Design. The optoelectronic associative memory system [69] consists of the parallel-readout optical disk, a photodetector array, and a silicon optoelectronic integrated circuit (OEIC) with fast local exclusive-nor (XNOR) circuitry (Fig. 30.8). A 2-D query from the host computer is electronically loaded onto the OEIC. The query image is then compared serially to the binary images from the optical disk (bitwise matching operations), which are optically loaded onto the OEIC. The output of the OEIC is fed into a decision circuit which controls the data flow between the photodetector array and the host computer. The

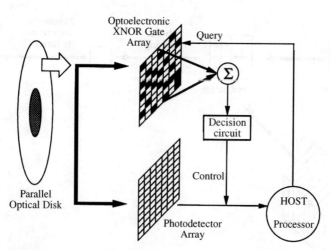

FIGURE 30.8 Optoelectronic associative memory system consisting of the host computer, the parallel-readout optical disk, a photodetector array, and a silicon optoelectronic integrated circuit with fast local XNOR and decision circuitry.

OEIC, described below, incorporates an electronic tree-based fan-in structure for high-accuracy associative search, high-speed pipelined operations, and a reconfigurable architecture which enables search operations to be performed on variable-size subfields [68, 69].

The optoelectronic integrated circuit consists of an array (128×128) of unit cells, each having a light detector and local silicon circuitry that performs the exclusive-nor function. Each unit cell receives three inputs as well as control information. The query bit is electronically loaded from the host computer. The corresponding bits from the stored images arrive from the disk at the detector. The third input is a clock obtained from the disk that signals when a complete image is under observation. The detector circuits of the optoelectronic XNOR gate array are designed to maximize noise margins for the detected input bits. The XNOR logic circuits produce a high output only when a bit match occurs. The signal-to-noise ratios achievable with the disk holograms can therefore be tolerated, since each detector circuit restores logic levels. In Fig. 30.9, raw 16×16 images obtained from the experimental optical disk by a charge-coupled device (CCD) camera and their thresholded and pixelated versions are shown. The outputs of the unit cells are then summed electronically by a tree fan-in structure (Fig. 30.10). Each fan-in unit adds the inputs it receives and sends the result up the tree. The Hamming distance between the query image and a stored image is obtained in $\log_k N$ stages, where k is the fan-in per stage ($k = 2$ in Fig. 30.10). Operations are pipelined in order to increase the system throughput. The

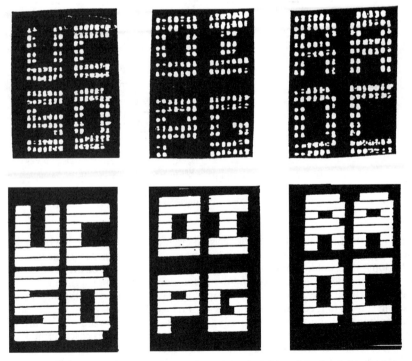

FIGURE 30.9   Raw 16×16 image obtained from the optical disk and the thresholded and pixelated version.

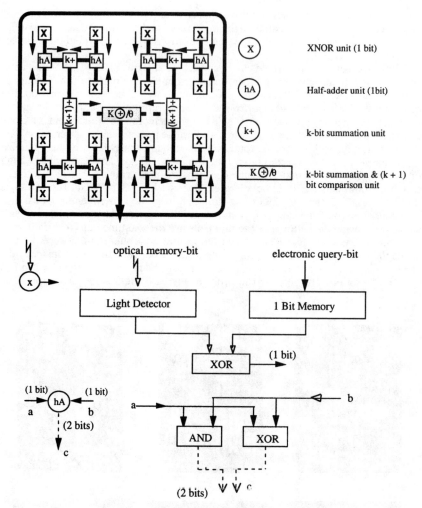

FIGURE 30.10 Architecture of the optoelectronic associative memory circuit.

output of the final stage is fed to a decision circuit that determines the best matching image. Search operations can also be performed on subimages by incorporating additional thresholding circuitry at the fan-in nodes. The size of the subfield to be searched can be varied by enabling the fan-in units at the appropriate level of the tree to perform thresholding. For example, in Fig. 30.11, a preset threshold can be used in stage 3 to recognize a particular 4×4 image. In this case, the fan-in nodes in earlier stages of the tree perform 1-bit additions. But, if threshold units are used in Stage 2, it becomes possible to search for 2×2 images. In this case, fan-in units in higher levels (after thresholding) can be used either to count the number of matched subimages or to find the best matching subimage by addressing the individual fan-in nodes. The ability to perform a correlation between the disk images and the query

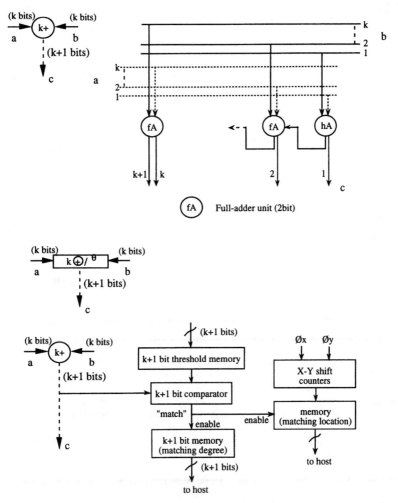

FIGURE 30.10 (*Continued*) Architecture of the optoelectronic associative memory circuit.

can also be achieved by electronically shifting the disk images between successive XNOR/summation operations.

The system can support several operation modes. In the first mode, a threshold value is selected prior to the search. All images that are sufficiently close to the query are retrieved by the host computer via the photodetector array. The second mode finds the best match to the query image. On the first rotation, the Hamming distance detected for each image is input to the decision circuit (page-serial, bit-parallel search). The best match is identified and retrieved on the subsequent rotation. By reconfiguring the functionality of the fan-in nodes, associative search can be achieved with variable-size fields while retaining the parallelism and high data rate provided by the disk images. The maximum search rate is estimated to be 10^{11} bit-

FIGURE 30.11 Principle of subfield search using a tree-based architecture.

ops/s using a custom-designed silicon OEIC [69]. A prototype of the system is currently under development.

30.5.2 Dual-Scale Topology Optoelectronic Neural System

In this section the simple associative memory OEIC design is extended to a more general 3-D optoelectronic neural system that uses a hybrid silicon VLSI based optoelectronic integrated circuit (OEIC) technology to implement the neurons and their associated synapses, and fixed, free-space optical diffractive elements to interconnect the neurons. The optoelectronic architecture has a number of applications in neural [70] and fuzzy systems. The architecture provides full connectivity between neurons, flexible functionality of neurons and synapses, accurate electronic fan-in, and biologically inspired dendritic-type fan-in processing.

System Architecture. The dual-scale topology optoelectronic processor architecture [70] (D-STOP) consists of arrays of N processing elements arranged in a 2-D topology. Each PE consists of a neuron with a light modulator for optical output and an array of N synapses which have optical inputs and electronic outputs. The schematic of a typical PE consisting of the central neuron (modulator) unit surrounded by its synapse (detector) units is shown in Fig. 30.12. In each synapse, incoming optical data is sensed by light detectors. These detectors convert the data into electronic form that is then fed to an electronic circuit for local synaptic processing. At the output of the PE, the processed data is converted back into optical form via light modulators, and is then routed to another PE using free-space interconnection optics. The detector units of one PE are placed in the same pattern as the modulator units of the PE array (Fig. 30.13). This dual-scale invariant layout has the property that full connectivity can be achieved optically with space-invariant optical elements by first demagnifying the image of the modulators to the scale of the detector units of one PE, then replicating this demagnified image over the PE array (Fig. 30.13). Multiple planes may be cascaded in this manner with a variable number of neurons in each layer. Alternatively, a feedback configuration may be used. Once the

Neuron Layout

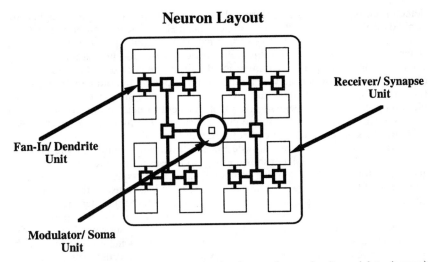

FIGURE 30.12   Optoelectronic PE layout showing detector (synapse) units, modulator (neuron) unit, and fan-in (dendrite) units. Detector units of one neuron are placed in the same pattern as the modulator units of the neuron array.

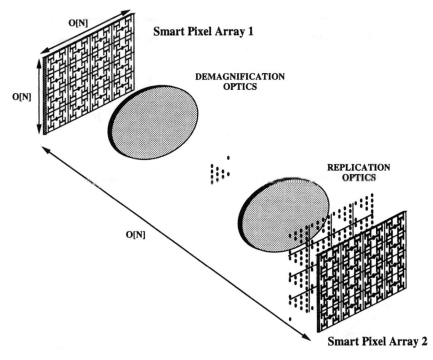

FIGURE 30.13   Schematic of optoelectronic neural system. The image of the modulators is demagnified to the scale of a single neuron and replicated over the neuron array to achieve full connectivity.

detector units receive the corresponding neuron outputs, synaptic weights are applied locally and the results are summed via an electronic tree-based fan-in structure. Therefore, accurate electronic summation with both positive and negative synaptic values is possible with this architecture. Additional information processing can be performed by placing computational units at the intermediate dendrite units of the H tree. The timing skew resulting from the optical fan-out can be neglected (about 10^{-10} s). Since the electronic line lengths of the tree are equal there is negligible timing skew between signals arriving at the central neuron unit from different synapses. This feature can be used to preserve precise timing relationships between firing neurons or to implement controlled dendritic delays.

Several optical systems can provide the full broadcast required by the D-STOP architecture. The optical system shown in Fig. 30.14 uses a computer-generated hologram to perform the beam-splitting function [70]. The first two lenses form a demagnified image of the input array of transmitters. The third lens transfers this image to the output plane. A holographic beam splitter in contact with the third lens performs the replication and can also provide aberration correction. This system was experimentally demonstrated for a 64×64 output array (8×8 input array) as shown in Fig. 30.15. The 8×8 input displayed the letter A. The input (modulator) spacing was 675 μm and the output spacing was 85 μm. On the right an expanded view of a central A is shown.

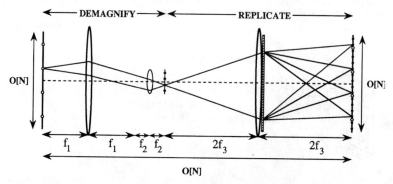

FIGURE 30.14 The D-STOP optical system using separate demagnification and replication optics.

The D-STOP system was designed to take full advantage of both fixed, free-space optical interconnections and electronic VLSI systems. The fan-in is electronic and the fan-out is performed with a planar holographic element. This allows the freedom to use either coherent or mutually incoherent sources such as laser diodes or even narrow linewidth LEDs. The design minimizes the number of required light transmitters, allowing the silicon ICs and the light transmitters to be fabricated on separate chips (or wafers) and later bonded face to face by a hybrid integration technique described in Sec. 30.4.1 under "Hybrid Integration." The system achieves high-density optical interconnection (more than 10^4 interconnections/cm² using the circuits described in Sec. 5.2.3) limited only by the synapse circuit area and not by the resolution of the optical system or the power dissipation of the modulator and detector units. The yield of the electronic circuitry does not limit the system size, since no interneuron electronic communications are necessary. The PEs can therefore be implemented in a modular fashion on separate chips, which can then be placed on a multichip carrier that can house several hundred such chips [23].

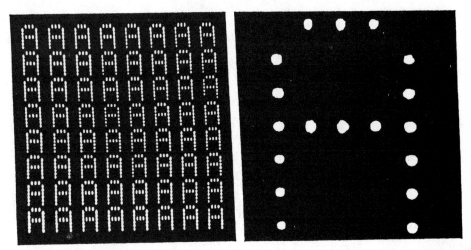

FIGURE 30.15 Demonstration of the optical system using Burch-encoded binary phase hologram showing demagnified and replicated 8×8 input. Output spot size = 14 µm; output spot spacing = 85 µm; output field size = 5 mm [70].

Data-Encoding Method. A critical issue for an artificial neural network implementation is the method of data representation, which should be chosen to minimize the silicon area and on-chip power dissipation while providing the precision necessitated by the application in question. Note that a simple digital pulse-code modulation technique would require an excessive number of digital multiply-accumulate circuits, which tend to be quite expensive in terms of silicon area. More efficient data-encoding methods for communication between electronic neuron modules have been suggested, including pulse-amplitude modulation (PAM), pulse-frequency modulation (PFM), and pulse-width modulation (PWM) [72, 73, 74, 75]. In this section we argue that the data-encoding method best suited to the D-STOP neural system is a combination of the pulse-width modulating optical neurons and pulse-amplitude modulating electronic synapses [76, 77].

For the optical neuron-to-synapse channel, PAM schemes require high-contrast-ratio light modulators and optical interconnects with tightly controlled uniform losses in order to provide accurate analog intensity information. Although electrically addressed light modulators with high contrast ratios are achievable, binary-encoding schemes such as PFM and PWM demand the detection of only two light-intensity levels and are more immune to parameter variations and system noise. Hence, they are more suitable for fast light modulators with lower contrast ratios such as flip-chip-bonded Si/PLZT modulators, where compatibility with VLSI dictates that low modulation voltages be used.

Another important consideration is the power consumption. PAM methods require analog voltage states to be detected, which necessitates a linear resistive load at the detector sites. This causes a short-circuit current to flow at the synapse level during the detection process. This direct current results in static power dissipation which may be quite high, since large-value resistors are difficult to implement in VLSI. These problems can severely limit synaptic resolution and/or integration density.

With PFM or PWM methods, the detected voltage V_{DET} has binary values as stable states. In these cases, the driver circuitry can be designed as a simple CMOS

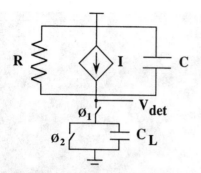

FIGURE 30.16 Equivalent circuit of a binary light detector with a capacitive load.

buffer with negligible static power consumption. The detector circuit can be designed using a switched-capacitor technique eliminating any static power dissipation (Fig. 30.16) [77].

Among the binary-encoding methods, PFM methods require high-speed modulators and generally result in higher dynamic power consumption than PWM methods, since the modulator capacitance C_{MOD} and the detector capacitance C_{DET} must be charged and discharged at higher frequencies. For GaAs/AlGaAs-MQW based smart pixels, these capacitances can be very low, so PFM methods can be used effectively. For modulators with larger intrinsic capacitance, such as PLZT, a PWM method is best suited for optical neuron-to-synapse communication.

For the electronic synapse-to-neuron channel, available VLSI devices and circuit techniques can provide the required precision for PAM methods to be used with high integration densities. The use of time-domain encoding methods, such as voltage-controlled frequency oscillators, at the synapse level may lead to excessive area requirements. Furthermore, the problem of linear dynamic range can be alleviated if the synapses modulate the neuron signal in a different dimension (a lesson learned from biological neurons). This suggests that a PAM method be used for the synapse-to-neuron communication in conjunction with a pulse-width modulating neuron.

Synapse and Neuron Design. In this section, circuit designs for pulse-width-modulating optical neurons and pulse-amplitude-modulating electronic synapses are described. The two important considerations in synapse design are the storage mechanism and the devices and circuit techniques to be used for implementing synaptic multiplication.

The design combines a novel synaptic multiplication principle [78] with capacitive-load light detection. A low-power, high-dynamic-range, switched-capacitor technique is combined with a low-area analog storage technique (in this case an EEPROM) to achieve a simple synapse circuit. Synaptic multiplication is obtained by using a time-domain multiplication technique. The synapse and neuron circuits are shown in Fig. 30.17. $X_j(t)$ is the PWM light output signal of the jth neuron received by synapse ij. During the ON state of neuron X_j, the illuminated photodiode D connects the floating gate transistor FG to the node ij. Thus, the capacitor C_{ij} periodically switched between ground (during ϕ^e) and $V_{ij} = V_{DD} - V_{Tij}$ (during ϕ^o), where VT_{ij} is the adaptive threshold voltage of the transistor FG. This periodical switching of the synaptic capacitors results in a pumping of either negative or positive charge packets to the common node 1 depending on the sign of the synapse. When the input illumination ceases, that is, when $X_j(t)$ drops to the zero state, the transistor FG is disconnected from C_{ij}. Therefore the synapse becomes neutral and does not contribute to the charge injection. The injected charge, i.e., the synaptic strength, is determined by the product $C_j = V_{DD} - V_{Tij}$. Therefore, either C_{ij} or V_{Tij} (or both) can be used for synaptic adaptation. For example, the analog floating-gate storage device FG may be replaced with a simple switch, and a binary array of capacitors can be used for C_{ij}, with digital storage to form a capacitance-based multiplying digital-to-analog converter (MDAC) configuration. In this manner, accu-

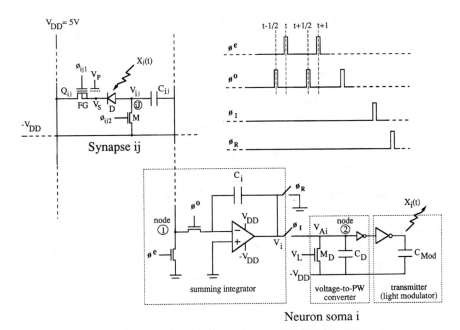

FIGURE 30.17 PAM synapse and PWM neuron circuits and timing diagrams. C_{ij} represents C_L in Fig. 30.16; the floating-gate transistor *FG* and the transistor *M* represent the switches ϕ_1 and ϕ_2 respectively.

racy can be traded in for circuit area and vice versa, depending on application requirements.

Multiplication of the neuron output and the synaptic strength is achieved thus through the periodical switching of C_{ij} in the time window defined by $X_j(t)$. Several circuit techniques can be used to introduce synaptic sign programmability. In one method (which the presented circuit assumes), the synapse sign is determined by the temporal sequence of the clock phases ϕ_1 and ϕ_2: In the excitatory synapses ϕ' is ϕ_1 and ϕ'' is ϕ_2, and vice versa in the inhibitory ones. This selectivity can be easily achieved using a 1-bit memory cell to store the sign. This approach renders the entire supply voltage range available for either positive or negative weight adaptation. Another method could be to add a second capacitor to each synapse, which, as long as the input is ON, subtracts a constant amount of charge from the dendrite. By properly adjusting the ratio of capacitor values, the supply range can be divided into excitatory and inhibitory programming regions. This method halves the synapse programming window, but since it eliminates the need for digital storage of the sign bit, the synapse addressing/programming procedure is simplified and possibly some area is saved.

In the circuit of Fig. 30.17, the excitatory and inhibitory synaptic charges injected to the dendrite are spatially summed at node 1 and temporally integrated at the neuron body. When the integration is complete, V_{Ai}, representing the total input activity of the neuron, is transferred to node 2 for further processing. The high-resistance transistor discharges the capacitor C_D from V_{Ai} to below the threshold voltage V_{Th} of the n-channel MOS (NMOS) inverter. For a larger value of V_{Ai} the discharge time will be longer, thereby widening the output pulse $X_i(t)$. This scheme allows a small-value capacitor C_{ij} to be used, since the synapse does not integrate the incoming neuron signal before fully processing it, but rather, processes it in incremental time steps. The integration process is then left to the neuron body. The operational amplifier with the capacitive load reduces to two gain stages in CMOS technology.

The dynamic synapse described above uses the programmable threshold voltage of the transistor *FG* directly as a multiplicand. In the proposed circuit, the source and the substrate of the transistor *FG* are short-circuited making the entire voltage range 0 to V_{DD} available for linear threshold adaptation. This fact, together with the time-domain multiplication technique, results in a close-to-perfect synaptic linearity for the entire design range. Spice simulations indicate that the synaptic resolution can be as high as 8 bits ($V_{DD} = 5V$) [77]. With these synapse and neuron circuit designs, a system with over 1000 fully connected neurons with more than 10^6 weighted interconnections and 10^{12} interconnections per second seems feasible in the near term. The memory capacity of the system can be increased to more than 10^8 interconnections by using parallel accessed memory devices as described in Sec. 30.4.3.

D-STOP Neural System Prototype. We have recently implemented a prototype D-STOP neural system consisting of a 16-node input layer, 4-neuron hidden layer, and a single-neuron output layer [79]. The input layer consists of a 4×4 array of integrated PLZT modulators. The image of the modulators is distributed optically to the 64 synapses of the 4 hidden-layer neurons which are electrically connected to the output neuron. As described above, the system uses pulse-width-modulating neuron outputs to achieve low modulation voltages and low dynamic power consumption. The prototype chip uses amplitude modulation at the synapses based on well-known current summing circuits. The synapse circuit consists of a 5-bit current-scaling multiplying digital-to-analog converter controlled by a light detector. While the presynaptic input incident on the detector is ON, the MDAC is enabled and a synaptic current (controlled by a 5-bit weight value) is generated. Depending on the sign of the synapse, this current is sent to either the excitatory or the inhibitory input of a fan-in unit where two regulated-cascade current mirrors subtract the total inhibitory current from the total excitatory current. One fan-in unit per four synapses is used. Bipolar outputs of four fan-in units are summed via an H tree and temporally integrated at the neuron soma. A controllable resistor-capacitor delay circuit converts the integrated input activity to a pulse, during which the neuron nonlinearity is applied. The differencing fan-in units allow the use of a source-only MDAC at the synapses which reduces the synapse area and removes any mismatch error between current-sourcing and current-sinking mechanisms. The fan-in unit also acts as a buffer between the synapses and the neuron body. This greatly improves the output resistance of the synapses. Measured synapse and fan-in unit characteristics exhibit high linearity with low power consumption. Test results revealed an 8-bit fan-in precision and a 100-ns minimum pulse width for neural outputs. This allows a prototype system speed of up to 640 million interconnections per second [79]. System scalability is limited by the large synapse circuit (200 μm on a side in a 2-μm CMOS technology). The switched-capacitor circuits of the previous section would reduce this area by an order of magnitude by directly storing analog weights. With these circuits, a 1000-neuron multichip system seems feasible in the near future.

30.5.3 Tandem D-STOP

The D-STOP system provides full unidirectional connectivity from one layer of PEs to another. However, many neural algorithms, such as backpropagation and recurrent multilayer perceptrons, require bidirectional communication. This may be implemented by placing two D-STOP systems side by side in such a way that the directions of light propagation in the two systems are opposite, and adding beam splitters and mirrors which align the output pattern of the first system to the detector array of the second and vice versa. This general scheme, which provides full bidirectional connectivity between two layers of PEs, is termed tandem D-STOP (TDS) [80].

N modules, each containing one D-STOP optical system, may be abutted to form an N-layer system in which every PE of a layer l is fully connected to every PE of layers $l-1$ and $l+1$ (Fig. 30.18). As in the simple D-STOP system, the detector units of one PE (in layer l) are placed in the same pattern as the modulator units of the PE array (in layers $l-1$ and $l+1$). The first two lenses through which the light from a modulator array passes form a demagnified image of the modulators, and the CGH replicates this image onto the detector plane in conjunction with the third lens. Consequently, the TDS system has the same advantageous properties as D-STOP, such as requiring only one transmitter per PE, negligible timing skew, compatibility with analog and digital electronics for computing any generalized matrix-vector product, and the option of performing dendritic processing. Each optical path in the TDS configuration is used twice—for the connections from layer l to $l-1$ and for the connections from layer l to $l+1$. This makes efficient use of the optical hardware and reduces the number of components that must be aligned.

The remainder of this section describes how gradient-descent learning algorithms, such as error-backpropagation and its variants, may be mapped onto TDS (shown schematically in Fig. 30.19). The architecture allows all weights in a given layer to be updated simultaneously during learning. Furthermore, training examples may be pipelined through the system if each PE has the ability to store $O(L)$ output values, where L is the total number of layers in the system.

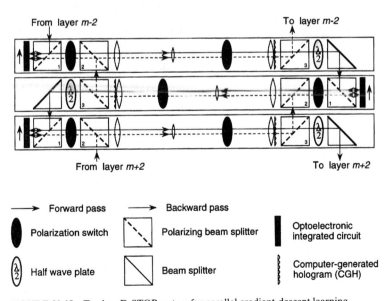

FIGURE 30.18 Tandem D-STOP system for parallel gradient-descent learning.

The method we consider is the original triphase backpropagation algorithm [81] (or simply *backprop*) with the following notation:

w_{lij} Connection weight from PE j in layer $l-1$ to PE i in layer l

$s()$ Nonlinear "squashing" function.

z_{li} Output of ith PE in layer l

δ_{li} Error of ith PE in layer l

The equations governing the PE outputs and the weight updates are as follows:

Forward pass:

$$zli = s(\sum_j w_{lij}z(l-1)j) = s(I_{li}) \qquad (30.3)$$

Backward pass:

$$\delta_{li} = s'(I_{li})\sum_k w_{(l+1)ki}\delta_{(l+1)k} \qquad (30.4)$$

$$\Delta w_{lij} = \alpha\delta_{li}z_{(l-1)j} \qquad (30.5)$$

Notice that backprop requires the transposition of the input weight matrix of layer $l+1$, $w_{(l+1)ki}$, to compute the scaled error terms of layer l, δ_{li}. This is accomplished by storing and locally updating each weight w_{lij} in two locations: near detector j of PE li and near detector i of PE $(l-1)j$ (Fig. 30.19). Thus all information required to calculate the above equations is available locally in each PE.

The forward propagation phase [Eq. (30.3)] is implemented by using optical fan-out of the previous layer's outputs, $z_{(l-1)j}$, and electronic fan-in of the synaptic outputs, $w_{lij}z_{(l-1)j}$. Calculation of the scaled error terms δ_{li} [Eq. (30.4)] is implemented by using optical fan-out of the following layer's scaled error terms $\delta_{(l+1)k}$, and electronic fan-in of the unscaled error terms, $w_{(l+1)ki}\delta_{(l+1)k}$. The backward pass weights associated with PE li, $w_{(l+1)ki}$, are updated by using electronic fan-out of the locally stored z_{li} and optical fan-out of the $\delta_{(l+1)k}$ [Eq. (30.6)]

$$\Delta w_{(l+1)ki} = \alpha\delta_{(l+1)k}zli \qquad (30.6)$$

Finally, the forward pass weights associated with PE li, w_{lij}, are updated using electronic fan-out of the just-calculated δ_{li} and optical fan-out of the $z_{(l-1)j}$ stored in the previous layer [Eq. (30.5)]. Thus, the same detectors, H-tree

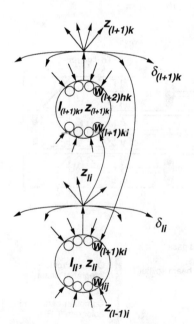

FIGURE 30.19 Mapping of gradient-descent algorithms onto the tandem D-STOP system.

fan-in structure, and dendrite units are multiplexed for the forward and backward phases. Note that the same scaled error terms are sent to both the forward and transposed weights. The TDS architecture achieves fully parallel learning without having to resort to bidirectional synapses or to $O[N^2]$ modulators.

A major practical difficulty for parallel implementations of backprop is that the algorithm requires a great deal of weight precision during learning [10]. This necessitates digital electronics for the computations and weight storage, which implies a large circuit for every synapse. The result is a system with large circuit area (i.e., expensive) which places stringent requirements on the precision of the optics and the optical alignment. In general, algorithms requiring less precision (and therefore less circuit area), such as binary back propagation [82] and back propagation with trinary quantization of weight updates [83], are better-suited to parallel optoelectronic implementations. We have recently shown that a binary version of the backpropagation algorithm can be mapped onto the tandem D-STOP system [84].

30.5.4 Optoelectronic Neural Systems Based on Holographic Synaptic Storage and Processing

The D-STOP system previously discussed uses electronic storage and processing of synaptic weights, possibly augmented with optically loaded weights from a digital optical memory. One method of increasing the size of the network, in terms of the number of neurons per layer and the number of weights per neuron, is to use a nonlinear optical crystal such as a photorefractive, wherein a weighted connection between an input light transmitter array and an associated output optical receiver array is established via a holographic grating. As discussed in Sec. 30.4.2, superimposing many such gratings in the crystal can allow large numbers of connection patterns (i.e., one per neuron) between input/output arrays. Angle-multiplexing techniques are typically used to superimpose multiple volume holograms in a photorefractive crystal, that is, each separate connection pattern is stored by using a reference beam at a slightly different angle. In readout, a light beam must match one of the original writing beams to satisfy the Bragg condition and form a clean reconstruction. Multiplexing techniques that seek to minimize the crosstalk between the stored holograms, while maximizing the number of stored holograms and their readout diffraction efficiency, have been the subject of much attention. Angle multiplexing is often combined with spatial multiplexing to obtain very large storage capacities. For instance, Owechko and Soffer at Hughes Labs have recently achieved up to 10^4 neurons, 2×10^7 weights, and learning rates of 2×10^7 connection updates per second, with the potential to increase the number of weights by a factor of 1000 and the processing rate by a factor of a million [85]. They achieve this by using a technique known as *cascaded grating holography* that removes crosstalk due to Bragg degeneracy by forcing a reference beam to match the Bragg condition at multiple locations with a series of cascaded gratings [85]. The system uses a single spatially segmented, electrically addressed spatial light modulator to provide both the data and the reference beams which record the desired connection patterns in the crystal during the learning phase. During operation, the SLM modulates the reference beam, and the reconstruction, representing the weighted connection pattern of a 2-D input plane to a 2-D output plane, is collected on a CCD camera. Several learning algorithms, including backpropagation, have been successfully mapped onto the holographic neural network.

Another interesting approach, being pursued by Psaltis et al. at Caltech, involves the use of a 3-D photorefractive disk, wherein the holograms are both spatially and angularly multiplexed [86, 87]. Access to a particular area follows from a linear movement of the readout head and the rotation of the disk. Once the head is at a particular location (about 2 mm × 2 mm), angle multiplexing is used to store approximately 1000 holograms per location. Up to 10^{12} weights can be stored on a 3-D disk. This technique has been applied to the task of face recognition. Templates corresponding to a large number of faces are stored on a photorefractive 3-D disk, which represents the hidden-layer weights. A 2-D disk is used for the lower-density hidden-layer to output-layer weights. An experimental prototype of the face-recognition system was recently demonstrated [88].

Another holographic system for matrix-vector multiplication has been proposed by researchers at the University of Southern California [89, 90]. This design is conceptually similar to the previous two designs. One SLM is used for the input pattern and another is used for the training pattern. The light transmitted through the input SLM constitutes the reference beams, light transmitted through the training SLM constitutes the object beams, and the two together record the interconnection weights in the hologram. The distinctive property of this system is that an array of individually coherent but mutually incoherent sources is used. This source array is imaged onto the input SLM and Fourier-transformed onto the training SLM. Since the reference beams (one per input pixel) are mutually incoherent, the reconstructed (output) beams due to different input pixels are also mutually incoherent and add linearly in intensity, as is desired in the summation process. Furthermore, only one of the reconstructions of a given object beam will be Bragg-matched to each reference beam, eliminating beam degeneracy. The additional angular multiplexing of the set of object beams breaks the Bragg degeneracy of the set of readout beams that result from simultaneous readout of the full contents of the volume holographic element. The result is a system with low interchannel crosstalk and high optical throughput.

30.6 CONCLUSIONS

In this article, we have described how optoelectronic technology can provide the high-density interconnects required for hardware implementations of parallel artificial neural networks with learning capabilities. We began by considering hardware requirements imposed by large-scale neural network paradigms. We then examined the key optoelectronic system components, including smart pixels, free-space optical interconnects, and parallel-accessed optical storage devices, and analyzed their potential use for scalable neural systems. Next, we then provided specific examples of optically interconnected neural systems. All these systems could, in principle, interface to a workstation-type processor as a high-performance neural coprocessor engine.

The first system was an associative memory system that capitalized on the high data-transfer rate available from a parallel optical memory such as a holographic optical disk. A custom VLSI integrated circuit with a large number of silicon-compatible optical receivers and processing circuitry was used to perform fast comparisons between a loaded query and the stored data on the disk. This is an example of a simple design that performs content-based data reduction on a large memory; because only the matched image data are retrieved, the system could readily interface to a standard computer.

The next example utilized high-density optical inputs and lower-density optical outputs from a VLSI chip. All processing was performed electronically; optical interconnection was used between layers for high-density interconnection (greater than 10^4 interconnections per square centimeter). This structure was more general in that it enabled general feedforward and recurrent artificial networks to be constructed. The D-STOP optoelectronic hardware design used a combination of pulse-width-modulating neurons and pulse-amplitude-modulating synapses. Analog storage techniques together with switched-capacitor circuit designs provided low-area synapses with large linear dynamic range (greater than 8 bits). The design minimized the number of light transmitters needed (one per neuron); this allowed the silicon ICs and the light modulators to be fabricated separately, and later bonded face to face by hybrid flip-chip packaging techniques. With current silicon VLSI feature sizes and off-the-shelf optical laser sources, a neural system with up to 10^6 synapses should be achievable. To increase the synaptic capacity of the system to 10^8 weights and beyond, optical memories with parallel-access capability would be needed. The D-STOP system was nominally designed for full connectivity between layers. In reference 80, we show how the system can achieve an arbitrary connectivity per layer with a similar optical system, with the restriction that neurons in the same layer have the same fan-out.

Finally, we reviewed several examples of very large optical neural networks that rely entirely on optical storage and processing of synaptic weights. These systems use volume holographic techniques to superimpose a large number of images, representing synaptic weights, in a nonlinear optical device such as a photorefractive crystal. Large-scale optical neural networks are constructed by combining these optical synapses with smart-pixel circuits that provide the optoelectronic neuron function. Important issues of reducing the size, volume, and cost of these systems are currently being researched.

ACKNOWLEDGMENTS

The authors express their gratitude to Gary Marsden, Joseph Ford, Philippe Marchand, Jean Mercklé, Volkan Ozguz, S. H. Lee, and other members of the Electrical and Computer Engineering Department at the University of California, San Diego, who have made valuable comments and contributions to this manuscript.

REFERENCES

1. G. E. Hinton, "Connectionist learning procedures," *Artificial Intelligence,* vol. 40, pp. 185–234, 1989.

2. J. Bailey and D. Hammerstrom, "Why VLSI implementations of associative VLCNs require connection multiplexing," *Proc. IJCNN 1988,* II, pp. 173–180.

3. S. Judd, "On the complexity of loading shallow networks," *Journal of Complexity,* vol. 4, pp. 177–192, 1988.

4. L. G. Valiant, "Learning Disjunctions of Conjunctions," *Proc. 9th IJCAI,* pp. 550–556, August 1985.

5. E. B. Baum and D. Haussler, "What size net gives valid generalization?," *Neural Computation,* vol. 1, pp. 151–160, 1989.

6. A. Barto, R. Sutton, and C. Anderson, "Neuron-like adaptive elements that can solve difficult learning control problems," *IEEE Trans. Systems, Man and Cybernetics,* vol. 13, no. 5, pp. 834–846, 1983.

7. Y. S. Abu-Mostafa, "Random problems," *Journal of Complexity,* vol. 4, pp. 277–284, 1988.

8. A. Krishnamoorthy et al., "Hardware Tradeoffs for Boolean Concept Learning," *Proc. World Congress on Neural Networks,* San Diego, June 1994.

9. J. Sietsma, "Neural network pruning: why and how," *Proc. ICNN 1988,* vol. I, pp. 325–333.

10. P. W. Hollis, J. S. Harper, and J. J. Paulos, "The Effects of Precision Constraints in a Back-propagation Learning Network," *Neural Computation,* vol. 2, no. 3, pp. 363–373, Fall 1990.

11. R. C. Frye, E. A. Rietman, and C. C. Wong, "Backpropagation learning and nonidealities in analog neural network hardware," *IEEE Trans. Neural Networks,* vol. 2, no. 1, pp. 110–117, January 1991.

12. D. J. Amit, *Modeling Brain Function,* Chap. 7, Cambridge University Press, 1989.

13. J. S. Denker and B. S. Wittner, "Network generality, training required, and precision required," *AIP Proc.,* pp. 219–222, 1988.

14. E. B. Baum, "On the capabilities of multilayer perceptrons," *Journal of Complexity,* vol. B4, pp. 193–215, 1988.

15. E. A. Rietman, R. C. Frye, and C. C. Wong, "Signal prediction by an optically controlled neural network," *Applied Optics,* vol. 30, no. 8, pp. 950–957, March 1991.

16. A. Masaki, Y. Hirai, and M. Yamada, "Neural Networks in CMOS: A Case Study," *IEEE Circuits and Devices,* pp. 13–17, 1990.

17. J. W. Goodman, F. J. Leonberger, S. Y. Kung, and R. A. Athale, "Optical interconnections for VLSI systems," *Proc. IEEE,* vol. 72, p. 850, 1984.

18. M. R. Feldman, C. C. Guest, T. J. Drabik, and S. C. Esener, "Comparison between electrical and free-space optical interconnects based on interconnect density capabilities," *Applied Optics,* vol. 28, no. 18, p. 3820, September 15, 1989.

19. F. Kiamilev, P. Marchand, A. V. Krishnamoorthy, S. Esener, and S. H. Lee, "Performance comparison between VLSI and optoelectronic multistage interconnection networks," *IEEE J. Lightwave Technology,* vol. 9, no. 12, pp. 1674–1692, December 1991.

20. R. Bakarat and J. Reif, "Lower bounds on the computational efficiency of optical computing systems," *Applied Optics,* vol. 26, no. 6, p. 1015, March 1987.

21. R. K. Kostuk, J. W. Goodman, and L. Hesselink, "Optical imaging applied to microelectronic chip-to-chip interconnections," *Applied Optics,* vol. 24, no. 17, pp. 2851–2858, September 1985.

22. M. R. Feldman, S. C. Esener, C. C. Guest, and S. H. Lee, "Comparison between optical and electrical interconnects based on power and speed considerations," *Applied Optics,* vol. 27, no. 9, pp. 1742–1751, May 1, 1988.

23. H. B. Bakoglu, *Circuits, Interconnections and Packaging for VLSI,* Addison Wesley, 1990.

24. S. C. Esener, "Silicon based smart spatial light modulators technology and application to parallel computers," *Critical Review of Optical Science and Technology: Digital Optical Computing,* vol. CR-35, R. Athale (ed.), SPIE Optical Engineering Press, pp. 100–125, 1990.

25. *Proc. IEEE LEOS Summer Topical Meeting on Smart Pixels,* Santa Barbara, Calif., August 1992.

26. J. A. Neff, R. A. Athale, and S. H. Lee, "Two-Dimensional Spatial Light Modulators: A Tutorial," *Proc. IEEE,* vol. 78, pp. 826–855, May 5, 1990.

27. F. Kiamilev et al., "Programmable optoelectronic multiprocessors and their comparison with symbolic substitution for digital optical computing," *Optical Engineering,* vol. 28, no. 4, pp. 396–409, 1989.

28. (a) J. L. Jewell et al., "Vertical Cavity Single Quantum Well Laser," *Applied Physics Letters,* vol. 55, pp. 424–426, 1989. (b) R. Geels, S. Corzine, and L. Coldren, "InGaAs Vertical-Cavity Surface Emitting Lasers," *IEEE J. Quantum Electronics,* vol. 27, no. 6, June 1991.

29. (a) D. S. Chemla, D. A. B. Miller, and P. W. Smith, "Nonlinear optical properties of GaAs/GaAlAs multiple quantum well materials: Phenomena and applications," *Optical Engineering,* vol. 24, no. 4, pp. 556–564, 1985. (b) D. A. B. Miller et al., "Novel hybrid optically bistable switch: The quantum well self-electro-optic effect device," *Applied Physics Letters,* vol. 45, no. 1, pp. 13–15, 1984.

30. (a) K. M. Johnson, M. A. Handschy, and L. A. Pagano-Stauffer, "Optical computing and image processing with ferroelectric liquid crystal," *Optical Engineering*, vol. 26, no. 5, pp. 385–391, 1987. (b) T. J. Drabik, L. K. Cotter, and M. A. Handschy, "Ferroelectric liquid crystal/silicon VLSI spatial light modulator," paper ThS3, presented at *Annual Meeting of Optical Society of America*, 15–20 October 1989, Orlando.

31. (a) S. H. Lee, S. C. Esener, M. A. Title, and T. J. Drabik, "Two-dimensional silicon-PLZT spatial light modulator," *Optical Engineering*, vol. 25, p. 250, 1986. (b) T. H. Lin et al., "Two-dimensional spatial light modulators fabricated in Si/PLZT," *Applied Optics*, vol. 29, pp. 1595–1603, April 1990.

32. K. Wagner and T. M. Slagle, "Optical competitive learning with VLSI/liquid-crystal winner-take-all modulators," *Applied Optics*, vol. 32, no. 8, pp. 1408–35, March 10, 1993.

33. C. Mead, *Analog VLSI and Neural Systems*, Addison-Wesley, 1989.

34. B. Mansoorian, V. Ozguz, C. Fan, and S. Esener, "Design and implementation of flip-chip bonded Si/PLZT smart pixels," *Proc. IEEE LEOS Summer Topical Meeting on Smart Pixels*, paper MC2, Santa Barbara, Calif., August 1992.

35. (a) K. W. Goossen, J. E. Cunningham, and W. Y. Jan, "GaAs 850 nm modulators solder-bonded to silicon," *IEEE Photonics Technology Letters*, vol. 5, no. 7, pp. 776–778, July 1993. (b) K. W. Goossen et al., "GaAs MQW modulators integrated with silicon CMOS," *IEEE Photonics Technology Letters*, vol. 7, no. 4, pp. 360–362. April 1995. (c) A. V. Krishnamoorthy et al., "3-D integration of MQW modulators over active submicron CMOS circuits: 375 Mb/s transimpedance receiver-transmitter circuit," *IEEE Photonics Technology Letters*, vol. 7, no. 11, November 1995.

36. T. K. Woodward et al., "Operation of a fully integrated GaAs-Al/subx/Ga/sub 1-x/As FET-SEED: a basic optically addressed integrated circuit," *IEEE Photonics Technology Letters*, vol. 4, no. 6, pp. 614–617, June 1992.

37. A. Krishnamoorthy, P. Marchand, F. Kiamilev, and S. Esener, "Grain size considerations for optoelectronic multistage interconnection networks," *Applied Optics*, vol. 31, no. 26, pp. 5480–5506, September 1992.

38. D. T. Lu et al., "Design trade-offs in optoelectronic parallel processing systems using smart-SLMs," *Optical and Quantum Electronics*, vol. 24, pp. S379–S403, 1992.

39. A. W. Lohmann, "What Classical Optics can do for the digital optical computer," *Applied Optics*, vol. 25, pp. 1543–1549, 1986.

40. K. S. Urquhart, S. H. Lee, C. C. Guest, M. R. Feldman, and H. Farhoosh, "Computer aided design of computer generated holograms for electron beam fabrication," *Applied Optics*, vol. 28, p. 3387, 1989.

41. G. J. Swanson, "Binary Optics Technology: the theory and design of multi-level diffractive optical elements," DARPA technical report.

42. J. E. Ford, J. Ma, Y. Fainman, S. H. Lee, Y. Taketomi, D. Bize, and R. R. Neurgaonkar, "Multiplex holography in Strontium Barium Niobate with Applied Field," in Special Issue on Progress in Holography, *Journal of the Optical Society of America (JOSA)*, vol. 9, no. 7, July 1992, pp. 1183–1192.

43. Y. Taketomi et al., "Incremental recording for photorefractive hologram multiplexing," *Optics Letters*, vol. 17, 1992.

44. T. Kohonen, *Self-Organization*, Springer-Verlag, Berlin, p. 97, 1984.

45. H. Sasaki, Y. Fainman, J. E. Ford, Y. Taketomi, and S. H. Lee, "Dynamic photorefractive optical memory," *Optics Letters*, vol. 16, no. 23, pp. 1874–1876, December 1, 1991.

46. D. L. Staebler, W. J. Burke, W. Phillips, and J. J. Amodei, "Multiple storage and erasure of fixed holograms in Fe-doped $LiNbO_3$," *Applied Physics Letters*, vol. 26, no. 4, pp. 182–184, February 15, 1989.

47. F. H. Mok, "Angle multiplexed storage of 5000 holograms in lithium niobate," *Optics Letters*, vol. 18, no. 11, pp. 915–917, June 1, 1993.

48. K. Kubota et al., "Holographic disk with high transfer rate: its application to an audio response memory," *Applied Optics,* vol. 19, no. 6, pp. 944–951, March 1980.
49. A. Mikaelian et al., "Digital signal recording and readout system using one-dimensional hologram technology," *Int. J. Optical Computing,* vol. 1, pp. 93–100, 1990.
50. D. Psaltis, M. Neifeld, A. Yamamura, and S. Kobayashi, "Optical memory disk in optical information processing," *Applied Optics,* vol. 29, no. 14, pp. 2038–2057, May 1990.
51. J. Rilum and A. Tanguay, "Utilization of optical memory disk for optical information processing," *Technical Digest, OSA* annual meeting 1988, paper M15.
52. P. Marchand, A. V. Krishnamoorthy, P. Ambs, and S. Esener, "Optoelectronic associative recall using motionless-head parallel readout optical disk," *SPIE Proc.,* 1347-10, San Diego, pp. 86–97, July, 1990.
53. P. Marchand et al., "Motionless-head parallel readout optical disk system," *Applied Optics,* vol. 32, no. 2, pp. 190–203, January 10, 1993.
54. S. Esener, "3-D optical memories for high performance computing," *SPIE Critical Reviews,* vol. 1150, p. 113, August 1989.
55. S. Hunter, F. Kiamilev, S. Esener, D. Parthenopoules, and P. Rentzepis, "Potentials of two-photon based 3-D optical memories for high performance computing," *Applied Optics,* vol. 29, no. 14, p. 2058, May 1990.
56. U. P. Wild, S. E. Bucher, and F. A. Burkhalter, "Holeburning, Stark effect, and data storage," *Applied Optics,* vol. 24, p. 1526, 1985.
57. N. W. Carlson, L. J. Rothberg, and A. G. Yodh, "Storage and time reversal of light pulses using photon echoes," *Optics Letters,* vol. 8, p. 483, 1983.
58. J. E. Weaver and T. K. Gaylord, "Evaluation experiments on holographic storage of binary data in electro-optic crystals," *Optical Engineering,* vol. 20, p. 404, 1981.
59. T. Ogura, J. Yamada, S. Yamada, and M. Tan-no, "A 20-Kbit associative memory LSI for artificial intelligence machines," *IEEE J. Solid State Circuits,* vol. 24, no. 4, pp. 1014–1020, August 1989.
60. H. Takata et al., "A 100-mega-access per second matching memory for a data driven microprocessor," *IEEE J. Solid State Circuits,* vol. 25, no. 1, pp. 95–99, February 1990.
61. H. Bergh, J. Eneland, and L. Lundstrom, "A fault tolerant associative memory with high speed operation," *IEEE J. Solid State Circuits,* vol. 25, no. 4, pp. 912–919, August 1990.
62. L. Curran, "Wafer scale integration arrives in disk form," *Electronic Design,* Vol. 26, October 1989.
63. Reports of the SIA Semiconductor Technology Workshop, Irving, Texas, November 1992.
64. R. P. Lippmann, "An introduction to computing with neural nets," *IEEE ASSP* magazine, pp. 4–22, April 1987.
65. B. L. Montgomery and B. V. K. Vijaya Kumar, "Evaluation of the Hopfield neural network as a nearest neighbor algorithms," *Appl. Opt.,* Vol. 25, pp. 3759–3766, October 1986.
66. E. B. Baum, J. Moody, and F. Wilczek, "Internal representations for associative memory," *Biological Cybernetics,* vol. 59, pp. 217–228, 1988.
67. J. Komlos and R. Paturi, "Convergence results in an associative memory," *Neural Networks,* vol. 1, pp. 239–250, 1998.
68. A. V. Krishnamoorthy, P. Marchand, G. Yayla, and S. Esener, "Optoelectronic associative memory using a parallel readout optical disk," in *Technical Digest OSA Annual Meeting '90,* paper MJ5, Boston, November 1990.
69. A. V. Krishnamoorthy, P. Marchand, G. Yayla, and S. Esener, "Photonic content-addressable memory system that uses a parallel-readout optical disk," *Applied Optics,* vol. 29, no. 31, November 1995.
70. (*a*) G. C. Marsden, A. V. Krishnamoorthy, S. C. Esener, and S. H. Lee, "Dual-Scale Topology Optoelectronic Processor," *Optics Letters,* vol. 16, no. 24, p. 1970, December 15, 1991. (*b*)

A. V. Krishnamoorthy et al., "D-STOP: scalability analysis and technological feasibility," *Proc. OSA Topical Meeting Optical Computing*, Salt Lake City, p. 244, March 1991.

71. (*a*) G. C. Marsden, B. Olsen, S. Esener, and S. H. Lee, "Optoelectronic fuzzy logic system," *Proc. OSA Topical Meeting Optical Computing*, Salt Lake City, p. 212, March 1991. (*b*) M. Blume and S. Esener, "Optoelectronic Fuzzy Artmap processor," *Proc. OSA Topical Meeting Optical Computing*, Salt Lake City, p. 213, March 1995.

72. J. J. Hopfield, "Neurons With Graded Response Have Collective Computational Properties Like Those Of Two-State neurons," *Proc. National Academy of Sciences U.S.A.*, vol. 81, pp. 3088–3092, May 1984.

73. A. F. Murray, "Pulse Arithmetic In VLSI Neural Networks," *IEEE Micro,* pp. 64–74, December 1989.

74. D. Del Corso, F. Gregoretti, C. Pellegrini, and L. Reyneri, "An artificial neural network based on multiplexed pulse streams," *Proc. Workshop on Microelectronics for Neural Networks,* Dortmund, June 1990.

75. O. N. Mian and N. E. Cotter, "Convergence Properties of a Pulsed Neural Network," *Proc. IJCNN 1990,* San Diego, pp. 599–609.

76. A. V. Krishnamoorthy, G. Yayla, and S. Esener, "Design of a scalable optoelectronic neural system using free-space optical interconnects," *Proceedings Int. Joint Conf. Neural Networks,* pp. 527–534, Seattle, July 1991.

77. A. V. Krishnamoorthy, G. Yayla, and S. Esener, "Scalable optoelectronic neural system using free-space optical interconnects," *IEEE Trans. Neural Networks,* vol. 3, no. 3, p. 404, special issue on hardware implementations, May 1992.

78. G. Yayla, A. V. Krishnamoorthy, and S. C. Esener, "Switched capacitor synapses using analog storage," U.S. Patent no. 5,343,555, August 30, 1994.

79. G. Yayla, A. V. Krishnamoorthy, G. Marsden, and S. C. Esener, *Proc. SPIE,* San Diego, July 1992, and "A prototype 3D optically interconnected neural network," *Proc. IEEE,* special issue on optical interconnections, vol. 82, no. 11, pp. 1749–1762, November 1994.

80. A. V. Krishnamoorthy et al., "New dimensions in D-STOP neural systems," *SPIE Proc.,* vol. 2026, San Diego, pp. 416–36, July 1993.

81. D. Rumelhart, G. Hinton, and R. Williams, in *Parallel Distributed Processing,* vol. 1, MIT Press, 1986.

82. S. A. Brodsky, and C. C. Guest, "Binary backpropagation in content addressable memory," *Proc. IJCNN 1990,* San Diego, III, pp. 205–10.

83. P. A. Shoemaker, M. J. Carlin, and R. L. Shimabukuro, "Back propagation learning with trinary quantization of weight updates," *Neural Networks,* vol. 4, no. 2, pp. 231–41, 1991.

84. A. Krishnamoorthy et al., "Hardware-Efficient Learning on a 3-D Optoelectronic Neural System," *Proc. World Congress on Computational Intelligence,* Orlando, July 1994.

85. Y. Owechko and B. H. Soffer, "Holographic neurocomputer for backpropagation based on cascaded-grating holography," *SPIE Proc.,* vol. 2026, San Diego, pp. 464–471, July 1993.

86. D. Psaltis, H. S. Li, and X. Ann, "Image processing application of optical neural networks," *SPIE Proc.,* vol. 2026, San Diego, pp. 492–496, July 1993.

87. D. Psaltis, Y. Qiao, and H. Li, "Optical face-recognition system," *SPIE Proc.,* vol. 1773, San Diego, pp. 59–62, July 1992.

88. H. Li, Y. Qiao, and D. Psaltis, "Optical network for real-time face recognition," *Applied Optics,* vol. 32, no. 8, pp. 5026–5035, September 10, 1993.

89. G. C. Petrisor et al., "Volume holographic interconnection and copying architectures based on incoherent/coherent source arrays," *Fourth Int. Conf. Holographic Systems, Components and Applications,* Neuchatel, Switzerland, pp. 21–26, September 1993.

90. P. Asthana, G. P. Nordin, A. R. Tanguay, Jr., and B. K. Jenkins, "Analysis of weighted fan-out/fan-in volume holographic optical interconnections," *Applied Optics,* vol. 32, no. 8, pp. 1441–1469, March 10, 1993.

CHAPTER 31

A GENERAL-PURPOSE ANALOG NEURAL COMPUTER FOR REAL-TIME SPATIOTEMPORAL PATTERN ANALYSIS: VISUAL MOTION ESTIMATION

Jan Van der Spiegel
Ralph Etienne-Cummings
Christopher Donham
Alyssa Apsel
Moore School of Electrical Engineering
Center for Sensor Technologies
University of Pennsylvania, Philadelphia

Paul Mueller
David Blackman
Corticon Incorporated, Philadelphia

31.1 INTRODUCTION

Visual processing is known for requiring large amounts of computation, spanning multiple spatial and temporal dimensions. The serial nature of traditional von Neumann machines, which have been the preferred computational platform, introduces bottlenecks in data flow and computational speed. Hence, it has become obvious that machines with parallel processing capabilities are better equipped for dealing with vision problems since they can perform multidimensional computations simultaneously and can share information from each dimension synchronously or asynchronously [1, 2]. However, pure parallelism would require vast numbers of processing elements, hence rendering the computer impractically large [3]. Therefore, there is a need for a "divide-and-conquer" approach to visual processing which requires processing at the sensor level followed by processing in a parallel computer [4]. Furthermore, continuous time analog processing is attractive since it allows truly simultaneous propagation of information, and offers the temporal domain as a continuous computational dimension. This is reminiscent of biological systems, on which the computational hardware being presented is based.

Over the last 40 years it has become clear that neural networks offer an efficient and effective method for implementing solutions to many real-world problems. Traditionally, neural networks have been simulated in software, and through rigorous mathematical modeling, their computational power has been demonstrated clearly. However, despite their success, these simulations fall short when real-time interaction with the environment is required. That is, when inputs from external sensors are presented to the neural simulator and the simulation outputs are used to drive external actuators, the computational time is usually much more than real time. Fortunately, the development of very large scale integrated circuits (VLSI) has provided a means to obtain real-time performance from neural networks. Conventionally, digital hardware has been used to model neural components in much the same manner as the software simulations. Inherently, this approach has speed limitations associated with the conversion of real-world inputs into digital formats [analog-to-digital (A/D) conversion] and the sequential nature of communication and processing in digital machines. On the other hand, analog neural computers can receive direct inputs from the world, and can perform continuous time, fully parallel communication and processing. Furthermore, analog neural networks offer the temporal domain as a continuous computational variable. Hence, analog networks can better handle real-world inputs since these inputs are naturally analog and span multiple spatial and temporal dimensions.

Visual motion estimation is an area where spatiotemporal computation is of fundamental importance. It is intuitively obvious that the motion of an object is described by its position in space over time. This observation leads to the representation of the motion as features in the space-time domain. Each distinct motion vector exhibits a unique contour in the space-time domain. Hence, the problem of visual motion estimation reduces to a feature extraction task, with each feature extractor tuned to a particular motion vector. As neural networks are particularly efficient feature extractors, they can be used to implement these visual motion estimators [5]. Such neural circuits are believed to be present in area MT of macaque monkeys, where cells are selective to stimulus direction and speed [6].

In this chapter, a hardware implementation of visual motion estimation with spatiotemporal feature extractors is presented. The motion detection neural networks are implemented on a general-purpose analog neural computer which is composed of programmable analog neurons, synapses, axon/dendrites, and synaptic time constants [7-10]. The additional computational freedom introduced by the synaptic time constants, which are unique to this neural computer, is required to realize the spatiotemporal motion estimators. The visual motion vector is implicitly coded as a distribution of neural activity. This approach for image motion estimation is believed to be employed by the visual cortex in the later processing stages [6, 11]. However, because of its complexity, this method of image motion estimation has not been attempted in discrete or VLSI hardware. The general-purpose analog neural computer offers a unique avenue for the real-time implementation and investigation of the spatiotemporal feature extraction method for visual motion estimation. The analysis, implementation, and performance of these motion estimators are discussed [12].

31.2 GENERAL-PURPOSE ANALOG NEURAL COMPUTER

31.2.1 System Overview

A 1024-neuron general-purpose analog neural computer (GPANC), based on a 72-neuron prototype, has been designed and fabricated [7, 8]. The GPANC is composed of modules which model neurons (neuron chip), synapses (synapse chip), and synaptic time constant and axon/dendrites (switch chip). These VLSI modules have been fabricated in a 1.5-μm n-well CMOS process through NCR's silicon foundry. Figure 31.1 shows the architecture of the neural computer. In addition to the features of the prototype, the new computer exhibits vast improvements such as an expandable architecture, improved and fully reconfigurable processing elements, variable processing speeds of the elements up to 1 MHz, and an improved software interface. The system is composed of an array of cascadable macrocells, and can be expanded to any arbitrary size. Each macrocell consists of 1 neuron chip, 3 synapse chips, and 8 switch chips. Each of the elements operates in a continuous time and analog mode. The GPANC has 3072 external inputs/outputs and offers distributed spatiotemporal computations through the use of the approximately 10^3 neurons, 10^5 synapses, 6×10^5 switches, and 7×10^3 synaptic time constants. Each neuron can receive up to 96 synaptic inputs. While it does not have enough neurons to handle high-definition vision problems, the neural computer does provide a real avenue where feasibility tests for such problems can be performed. Furthermore, expansion of the system to more neurons does not pose any limitation on its computational bandwidth. This neural computer has a maximum computational speed of 10^{11} cycles per second, or

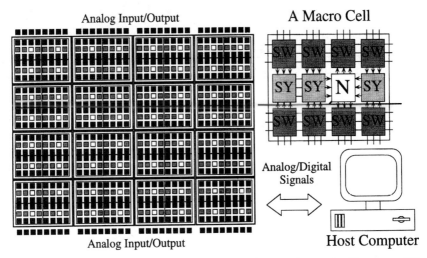

FIGURE 31.1 Architecture of the general-purpose analog neural computer. The neuron (N), synapse (SY), and switch (SW) modules model biological neurons, synapses, and axon/dendrites, respectively. The output of the neurons is multiplexed onto one line and sampled by the host computer. The chips are arranged into macrocells, and there are four macrocells per board. All elements are individually programmable and reconfigurable. This system is expandable to any arbitrary size.

it can solve 10^3 nonlinear functions of 10^4 coupled first-order differential equations in real time [14]. A host digital computer is used to configure the architecture and attributes of the computational elements of the GPANC. Once the network has been loaded, it operates in full analog, parallel, and real-time mode.

31.2.2   The Neuron Chip

The neuron chip contains circuits which model biological neurons, neuron's time response control circuits, and other peripheral circuits. Figure 31.2 shows a block diagram of the neuron chip, neuron schematic, and transfer function. The neuron sums its total input currents and produces an output voltage according to its transfer function. The transfer function of the neurons, which is a piecewise linear function, is programmable [8]. The piecewise linear function is produced by summing rectified ramp and step functions. The neuron does not include a sigmoidal transfer function, but sigmoids of various slopes can be approximated with the piecewise linear transfer function. Furthermore, the speed of these neurons can also be varied between 4 Hz and 1 MHz. This is achieved with the use of fully integrated modifiable resistance-capacitance (R-C) circuits. Moreover, these neurons can be used in conjunction with the synaptic time constants to simulate biological "spiking" neurons [15]. The 16 outputs of the neurons are presented in parallel to the neighboring chips. To monitor the state of the neurons, a multiplexer is included on the chip. Additional circuits are present to mediate the loading of the digital memories, and to control whether certain chips are sampled. This helps control the amount of information

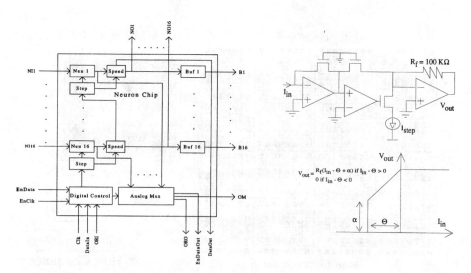

FIGURE 31.2   The neuron chip. Block diagram of the chip, neuron schematic, and transfer function are shown. The neuron is a piecewise linear transimpedance element. This chip has neurons which handle large input and output capacitive loads, have variable speeds and fine transfer function control, and are digitally controlled. The digital controls allow parts of the computer to be reprogrammed without disturbing other parts. Furthermore, entire chips can be bypassed in the output monitor (OM) mode if their outputs are deemed irrelevant. They also have additional outputs for probing and external use.

that the host computer has to handle and also increases the frequency at which each relevant neuron is sampled. The area of the chip is 25 mm², and it dissipates 175 mW.

31.2.3 The Synapse Chip

The synapse chip provides weighted inputs to the neurons [13]. Through an array of voltage-to-current converters and current scalers, an input voltage is transformed into an output current. This current can then be scaled over three orders of magnitude under the control of local programmable memories. The outputs of multiple synapses are connected, and thereby added to produce the input to the neuron. Each 8-bit memory is divided into a mantissa, characteristic, and sign reminiscent of a floating-point representation in a digital computer. The sign bit allows both positive and negative currents to be produced. Positive currents lead to an increased neuron output similar to the operation of excitatory synapses. Likewise, negative currents suppress the neuron output, like inhibitory synapses. Each 54.4-mm² synapse chip has 64 inputs and 16 outputs for a total of 512 synapses (see Fig. 31.3). The synapses can respond to inputs as fast as 1 MHz, which makes them well-suited for the operating range of the neurons.

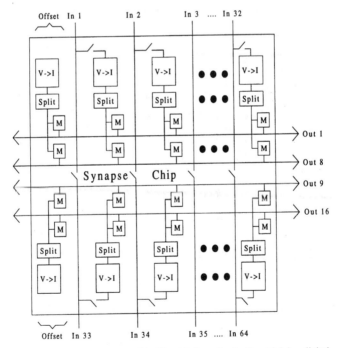

FIGURE 31.3   The synapse chip. The chip has a bank of multiplying digital-to-analog converters with voltage inputs (0 to 2.5 V) and current outputs. Transresistance settings from 6.66 kΩ to 10 MΩ can be programmed into each synapse. This chip includes simple routing capabilities (the switches in the diagram) and 16 × 32 synapses (to accommodate the 16 neurons in each neuron chip).

31.2.4   The Switch Chip

The switch chip is composed of elements that model biological axons, dendrites, and synaptic time constants. In biological systems, the axons and dendrites are used to route neuron outputs to and from other neurons, sensors, and actuators. However, they are not simply passive wires. They also have computational properties. In this system, the abundance of time constants in the switch chips allows us to also endow the interconnections with computational properties. Hence, the GPANC offers the temporal domain as a computational dimension.

The interconnections are made by simple crosspoint switches, implemented with transmission gates, which are arranged in a 32×32 array [8]. This allows any horizontal line to be connected to any vertical line, as can be seen in Fig. 31.4. Additional cut switches are included to facilitate complex routing and to allow maximum usage of lines. The on resistance of the switches is approximately 1.5 kΩ and the off resistance is in the terohm range. The synaptic time constants are implemented with load-compensated operational transconductance amplifiers [16]. The essential components of the time-constant circuit are shown in Fig. 31.4. This circuit allows very large time constants to be integrated in small silicon areas. These time constants have 32 programmable values from 1 ms to 1 s. Furthermore, a bypass state also exists to create a zero delay path. Moreover, since the positions of the time constants are fixed in the chip, the time constants are bidirectional so that they can handle both incoming and outgoing signals. Additional digital circuits are present on the

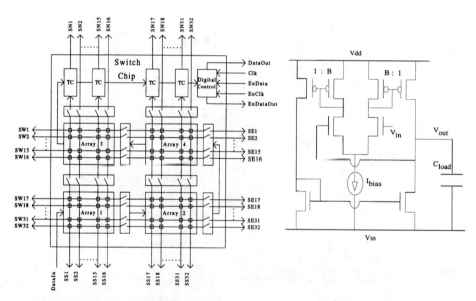

FIGURE 31.4   The switch chip. Block diagram of the chip and simplified schematic of the time constants are shown. The switches, which are used to interconnect neurons, are implemented as crosspoint switches. In this system, they have on resistances of 1.5 kΩ. Also included on every other line are programmable RC time constants which have values logarithmically distributed from 1 μs to 1 s. These values are realized by varying I_{bias}, B, and C_{load}. The switch chips perform as the axons, dendrites, and synaptic time constants of the neural computer.

chip to program the switch configuration and time-constant values. The chip occupies an area of 48.5 μm².

31.2.5   The Software Organization

The software for programming the neural computer is designed to allow the operator to conceptualize the network at many different levels [13]. At the most abstract level, a logical neural network consisting of circles representing neurons, and arrows representing interconnections can be drawn on a freeform work sheet. This network representation can also be entered as an ASCII netlist file which describes the neurons and their associated interconnections, as shown in Fig. 31.5. Placement and routing software then assigns each neuron to a real (physical) neuron in a neuron chip, and determines the necessary switch and synapse settings to create the desired interconnections. The network can then be viewed or changed on a physical level where chip settings are displayed graphically on a workstation. Finally, the chip settings are programmed into the neurocomputer via serializing first-in, first-out registers (FIFOs) which are interfaced to the various synapse, switch, and neuron chips.

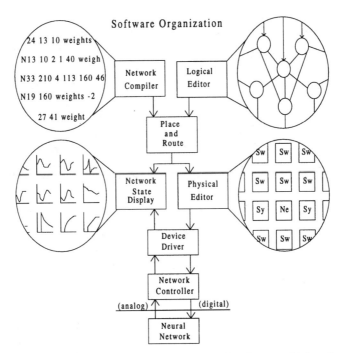

FIGURE 31.5 In this system, the software contains a sophisticated X-Windows interface that allows access to the neural computer across the Ethernet. The software allows a run-time definition of the neural network architecture, thus allowing the user to explore novel network topologies, macrocell configurations, and network sizes.

Programming the system can proceed at rates up to 1Mb/s. The entire neurocomputer can be reprogrammed in approximately 2 s.

31.3 THEORY OF SPATIOTEMPORAL MOTION ESTIMATION

The technique of estimating motion with spatiotemporal filters was concurrently proposed by Watson and Ahumada [17] and Adelson and Bergen [18] in 1985. It emerged out of the observation that a point moving with constant velocity traces a line in the space-time domain. The one-dimensional case is shown in Fig. 31.6. This chapter will deal primarily with the one-dimensional case; the extension to the two-dimensional case, which will be briefly discussed, requires some nontrivial modifications to the theory as discussed in references [11, 19]. The slope of the line is proportional to the velocity of the point. Hence, the velocity is represented as the orientation of the line. Therefore, spatiotemporal orientation detection units, similar to those proposed by Hubel and Wiesel for spatial orientation detection, can be used for detecting motion [20, 21].

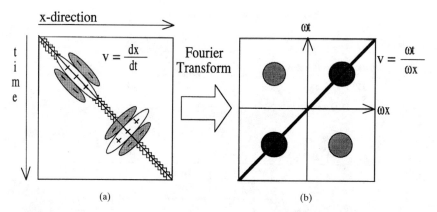

FIGURE 31.6 Motion detection with oriented spatiotemporal filters. (*a*) The locus of a point moving in +x. Also shown are two orientation detectors, i.e., the convolution kernel, tuned to +x and –x motion. The unshaded part is $+v_e$ while the shaded is $-v_e$. (*b*) The circles show the frequency representation of the two types of motion detectors in *a*, and the solid line is the Fourier transform of the motion. The detector which is aligned with the motion overlaps the frequency response of the motion, while the other detector does not.

The construction of the spatiotemporal detection units is based on the frequency domain representation of visual motion. In the frequency domain, constant motion of a point is represented as a line through the origin with a slope $\mathbf{v} = \omega/\nu$, where $\mathbf{v}$ is the velocity, ω is the temporal frequency, and ν is the spatial frequency. That is, the Fourier transform of $\delta(x - v_x t)$ is $\delta(v_x v_x - \omega_t)$. Therefore, spatiotemporal filters which lie on the line will be responsive to the motion represented by that line, as shown in Fig. 31.6. To create the filter response as shown in the figure, Adelson and Bergen proposed using quadrature pairs of spatial and temporal bandpass filters

[18]. The $\pi/2$ phase relationship between the filters allows the filters to be combined such that they cancel in opposite quadrants, leaving the desired oriented filter. Figure 31.7 shows a schematic of this process. One example from the family of these filters, employed by D. Heeger, is given in Eqs. (31.1) and (31.2) [19].

$$g_o(t) = \frac{1}{\sqrt{2\pi}\sigma_t} \exp\left(\frac{-t^2}{2\sigma_t^2}\right) \sin(2\pi\omega t) \tag{31.1a}$$

$$g_e(t) = \frac{1}{\sqrt{2\pi}\sigma_t} \exp\left(\frac{-t^2}{2\sigma_t^2}\right) \cos(2\pi\omega t) \tag{31.1b}$$

$$g_o(x) = \frac{1}{\sqrt{2\pi}\sigma_x} \exp\left(\frac{-x^2}{2\sigma_x^2}\right) \sin(2\pi v x) \tag{31.2a}$$

$$g_e(x) = \frac{1}{\sqrt{2\pi}\sigma_x} \exp\left(\frac{-x^2}{2\sigma_x^2}\right) \cos(2\pi v x) \tag{31.2b}$$

$$g_e(t)g_e(x) + g_o(t)g_o(x) \rightarrow \text{left motion} \tag{31.3a}$$

$$g_e(t)g_e(x) - g_o(t)g_o(x) \rightarrow \text{right motion} \tag{31.3b}$$

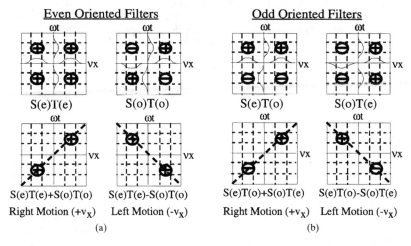

FIGURE 31.7   Frequency domain construction of oriented spatiotemporal filters. Shows the construction of two quadrature pairs of oriented spatiotemporal filters from the odd and even pairs of separable spatial and temporal filters. An even (*a*) and odd (*b*) pair of oriented filters is obtained for each direction of motion.

The only requirements for successful candidate functions are that they should be matched, band-limited, and quadrature counterparts. Equation (31.3) shows how they are combined to realize even-oriented spatiotemporal filters; other combinations, as shown in Fig. 31.7, can be used to realize the odd-oriented filters. Although the hardware implemented and discussed here uses a single type (odd) of oriented filters for simplicity, the complete velocity-selective filter is constructed by combining the even- and odd-oriented filters, i.e., $\text{Right}^2 = (\text{Right}_{\text{even}})^2 + (\text{Right}_{\text{odd}})^2$. Hence, the energy in the filters is obtained. Since this technique measures the energy of the input signal about the preferred orientation of the filter, it suffers from speed/contrast ambiguity. To eliminate this effect, contrast is normalized by using a filter tuned for a static input, effecting a gain-control mechanism [18]. The final representation of the method is then given by Eq. (31.4):

$$\mathbf{v} = \frac{L^2 - R^2}{S^2} \tag{31.4}$$

where $\mathbf{v}$ is the output of the filter and is a bipolar representation of velocity and L, R, and S are the outputs of the left motion, right motion, and static contrast measurements, respectively. The complete model is then composed of a population of these detectors with various spatiotemporal tunings, and velocity is represented as the distributed outputs of each filter, much like the motion-sensitive cells from area MT of macaque monkeys [6, 21].

31.4 NEURAL IMPLEMENTATION OF SPATIOTEMPORAL MOTION DETECTORS

Since the problem of motion estimation has been translated into a feature extraction task, neural networks offer a powerful platform for implementing motion detectors. However, the technique, as presented above, depends on multiplications and divisions which are not easily cast into neural fabric. This statement is by no means implying that these operations are not performed by biological neural systems. Nonlinear units have been recorded which behave quadratically, and automatic gain control systems exist in biology [22, 23]. However, for artificial neural networks, and especially analog neural networks, these functions are difficult. (Nonetheless, Heeger has proposed a neurologically plausible model for implementing the square and automatic gain control required by the model [24]). Hence, the model has to be modified to become compatible with the allowed computations of the neural platform being used.

The spatiotemporal orientation detector filters will be implemented on the general-purpose analog neural computer that was described earlier. The inclusion of the temporal domain computational capabilities of this neural computer, represented by the synaptic time constants, is an important departure from conventional hardware implementation of neural networks, and is one which is of vital importance to many tasks such as speech processing, motor controls, and motion estimation, to name a few. These time constants are used extensively in realizing the spatiotemporal filters, which allow for real-time estimation of visual motion.

The neural computer can perform rectification, weighted summing, and temporal smoothing, but not squaring and division. Using these tools, spatiotemporal filters can be implemented by replacing the squares with rectifications and eliminating the need for the gain control. The gain control is realized by using a silicon retina that serves as a front-end to the neural computer. It convolutes the input image with a difference-of-gaussian operator and threshold [12]. Hence, only the binary representation of the image edges is presented to the motion estimation networks. The retina has the additional benefit of band limiting the image so the motion detection network always operates in the baseband and limits spatial aliasing.

The first stage of the spatiotemporal filter is composed of the odd and even pair of spatial filters. The first and second derivatives of gaussian functions are chosen to implement the spatial filters. They are realized by using an input layer of neurons which are fed forward into a second layer of neurons with appropriate weights. The connection weights are computed by spatially sampling first- and second-order derivatives of a gaussian function. Since the spatial sampling rate of the silicon retina is fixed, by taking more or less samples (while keeping the areas under each filter equal), the scale of the spatial filters can be varied. The first-order derivative supplies the odd spatial filters, while the even filter is obtained from the second-order derivatives. Figure 31.8 shows schematically how the spatial filters are constructed. The weights are normalized so that all the filters have equal positive and negative areas. Clearly, as the scale of these spatial filters increases, they utilize increasingly larger numbers of circuit components (i.e., large die areas), which make them impossible to implement using single-chip or small-scale systems. On the other hand, the scale and architecture of the GPANC allows these filters to be easily realized.

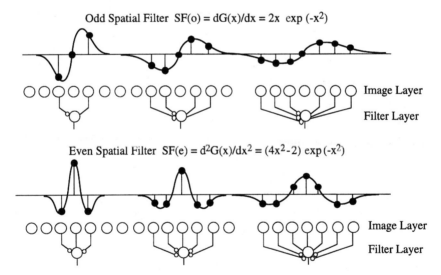

Odd Spatial Filter $SF(o) = dG(x)/dx = 2x \ exp \ (-x^2)$

Even Spatial Filter $SF(e) = d^2G(x)/dx^2 = (4x^2-2) \ exp \ (-x^2)$

FIGURE 31.8 Neuromorphic construction of the spatial filters. Shows schematically how the odd and even spatial filters are constructed from the first- and second-order derivatives of a gaussian function, respectively. The weights are normalized so that the areas under all the filters are identical.

Three parallel channels are implemented with varying spatial scales. The connection weights for the three pairs of spatial filters are given in Table 31.1. The Fourier transforms of the spatial filters from this table are given by Eq. (31.5), where m is the number of taps in the half kernel. Hence, the highest frequency filters, which are designated as channel 3, are given by Eq. (31.6).

TABLE 31.1 Connection Weights of the
Three Spatial Filters

Channel	Even	Odd
1	−0.080	0.125
	−0.160	0.250
	0.125	0.150
	0.250	0
	0.125	−0.125
	−0.160	−0.250
	−0.080	−0.125
2	−0.090	0.160
	−0.160	0.330
	0.500	0
	−0.160	−0.160
	−0.090	−0.330
3	−0.250	0.500
	0.500	0
	−0.250	−0.500

$$\mathrm{SF}_{2m-1}(e) = 2a_m \cos [mv] + 2a_{m-1} \cos [(m-1)v] + \cdots + a_0 \qquad (31.5a)$$

$$\mathrm{SF}_{2m-1}(o) = -2j(a_m \sin [mv] + a_{m-1} \sin [(m-1)v] + \cdots + a_1 \sin [v]) \quad (31.5b)$$

$$\mathrm{SF}_3(e) = 0.5 - 0.5 \cos (v) \qquad (31.6a)$$

$$\mathrm{SF}_3(e) = 0.5 - 0.5 \cos (v) \qquad (31.6b)$$

The spatial frequency v has been normalized by the sampling distance of the retina, which is 0.11 mm. Notice that Eq. (31.6a) is always real, while Eq. (31.6b) is always imaginary. Hence these filters are $\pi/2$ out of phase. The magnitude responses are not identical, but are sufficiently close to perform the necessary function. Similar transforms can be calculated for the other two channels.

For implementing the temporal filters, the time constants are used. Figure 31.9 shows a schematic of the neural schematic containing the silicon retina as the imaging layer, the spatial filters SF(e) and SF(o), the temporal filters T(e) and T(o), and their combination to create the oriented filters. The pair of temporal filters must be band-passed. Hence, the odd filter (top branch) and the first stage of the even filter (lower branch) are realized with a band-limited neural differentiator by feeding the output of one neuron into another with an excitatory synapse and delayed inhibitory synapse. For the odd temporal filter, the output of the bandpass filter is then low-passed, as seen in Fig. 31.9. All neurons are activated to half full scale so they operate in their linear range. The frequency domain representation of the odd temporal filters is

$$T(o) = \frac{j\omega \delta_1 \delta_2}{(j\omega + \alpha)(j\omega + \delta_1)(j\omega + \delta_2)} \qquad \alpha \ll \delta_1 \approx \delta_2 \qquad (31.7)$$

$$T(e) = \frac{-\omega^2 \delta_2}{(j\omega + \alpha)(j\omega + \delta_1)(j\omega + \delta_2)} \qquad \alpha \ll \delta_1 \approx \delta_2 \qquad (31.8)$$

The low-pass cutoff frequencies δ_1 and δ_2 are 20 and 40 times larger than α, respectively. To create the even filter, a phase of $\pi/2$ is added to the odd filter using a

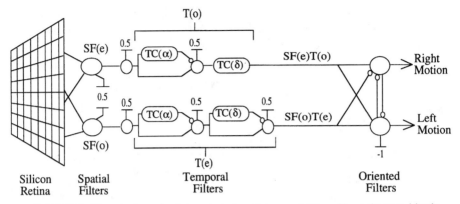

FIGURE 31.9 Neural schematic of the oriented spatiotemporal filters. Shows the neural implementation of the spatiotemporal filters. The transfer function at each stage coincides with Eqs. (31.6) through (31.9). The neurons' offset of 0.5 of full scale is required for them to operate in their linear region.

second bandpass filter which replaces the first low-pass filter, δ_1, in Eq. (31.7). Since these even and odd temporal filters must interact to produce the oriented filters, their respective delays, given by the derivative of the phase with respect to frequency, must also be matched. This is achieved by making the pole locations for both even and odd temporal filters identical. (The zeros of the temporal transfer functions are nonconsequential since they are at the origin.) Hence, by using δ_1 as the cutoff pole location of the second bandpass filter used to realize the even filter, delay matching is obtained. The even filter is then given by Eqs. (31.8). Equations (31.7) and (31.8) have an additional low-pass filter, whose cutoff frequency is δ_2, which is lumped into the temporal filter transfer functions (not shown in Fig. 31.9). This second low-pass filter is included at the outputs of both spatial filters to limit the temporal bandwidth of the spatiotemporal filters. However, the poles for both even and odd filters are still identical, resulting in equal delays. Like the spatial filters, the odd filter has an imaginary numerator while that of the even filter is real. Hence, the phase difference of $\pi/2$ is realized since their denominators are identical. Figure 31.10 shows plots of the magnitude and phase of the temporal filters with $\alpha = 11.11$ rad/s. Since there is a relationship between α and δ, by varying α the tuning of the temporal filters can be varied. Three temporal filters have been implemented for each spatial channel, setting $\alpha = 33.33, 11.11,$ and 2.29 rads/s with time constants of 30, 90, and 375 ms, respectively.

The spatial and temporal components are next combined to produce the oriented filters. First the output of the spatial filter is fed into the temporal filters, as shown in Fig. 31.9. As can be seen from the transfer functions, the spatial and temporal filters are separable. Hence, the convolution of the spatial and temporal filters will be zero unless the input to the spatial filters changes position over time. Therefore, the spatiotemporal filter is insensitive to spatially and temporally static inputs. Furthermore, the spatiotemporal filter is also insensitive to temporally modulating spatially static inputs, provided that the modulation does not cause the output of the edge detection circuit on the silicon retina to decrease beyond its threshold. With the retina used, the contrast can be changed by an order of magnitude without affecting the output. For spatially varying inputs over time, i.e., motion, the output of the spa-

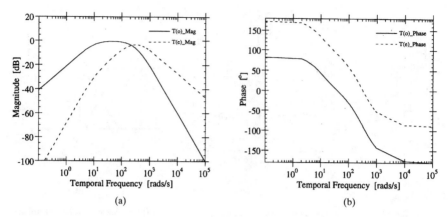

FIGURE 31.10 (a) The magnitude and (b) phase plots for the even and odd temporal filters for $\alpha = 11.11$ rad/s. The magnitude responses are not identical (but close enough for our purpose), but the phase difference is always $\pi/2$.

tial filter becomes time varying, and hence the convolution with the temporal filters becomes nonzero. In the frequency domain, because of their separability, the spatial and temporal responses can be multiplied, which results in responses similar to those shown in Fig. 31.7. The even spatial filter and odd temporal filter in each channel at every scale are cascaded. This is also done for the antisymmetric pair. The output of the cascaded pairs is summed or differenced (as is shown in Fig. 31.9) and then rectified. The output of the summer is maximally responsive to motion in one direction at a specific speed while the output of the differencer responds maximally to the opposite direction motion at the same speed. Equation (31.9) shows the transfer functions of channel 2.

$$SF_5(e)T(o) = [0.5 - 0.32 \cos(v) - 0.18 \cos(2v)]T(o) \qquad (31.9a)$$

$$SF_5(o)T(e) = [-0.32j \sin(2v) - 0.66j \sin(v)]T(e) \qquad (31.9b)$$

$$Left_5(\omega, v) = SF_5(e)T(o) + SF_5(o)T(e) \qquad (31.9c)$$

$$Right_5(\omega, v) = SF_5(e)T(o) - SF_5(o)T(e) \qquad (31.9d)$$

In Eq. (31.9), *left* and *right* correspond to leftward and rightward motion, respectively. However, Eq. (31.9) gives only the odd-oriented filter, which is the only one implemented in this work. Figure 31.11 shows a contour plot of the power spectrum for rightward motion for channel 2 with $\alpha = 11.11$ rad/s. The spatial frequency is plotted from $[-\pi, \pi]$ to coincide with the band limit imposed by the optical system and the silicon retina. To further improve the tuning of the filters, competition through delayed lateral inhibition is also used in the neural implementation, as shown in Fig.

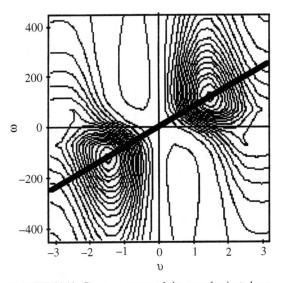

FIGURE 31.11 Power spectrum of the neural oriented spatiotemporal filter. Shows a plot of power spectrum of Right$_5$ in Eq. (31.9) for channel 2 and $\alpha = 11.11$ rads/s. The slope of the line through the peaks gives the velocity to which this filter is tuned.

31.9. The lateral inhibition is included between opposite motions at the same scale in each channel. Further lateral inhibition between all the channels at every scale may improve the tuning further, but was not investigated here. The activity of the motion filters for various stimuli is measured as the peak value over time. For slow speeds, the spatially sampled property of the silicon retina produces multiple peaks as the stimuli passed through the receptive field of the spatial filters. In this case, an average of the peak values over the time corresponding to the time spent by the stimuli in the filters' receptive field is used. Figure 31.12 shows schematically the distribution of the power spectrums of the 9 oriented spatiotemporal neural filters implemented in this work. The shaded ellipses show the location of the maximum magnitude of the filters (see Fig. 31.11), while the surrounding unshaded ellipses show their bandwidths. There is significant overlap between the various filters, which helps reduce the number of filters required to uniquely determine motion over a wide range.

31.5 RESULTS

Within each channel the scale of the spatial filter is constant. Hence, the speed of tuning of each of the filters is governed by their temporal tuning. According to theory, as the passband of temporal filters shifts to higher values, the preferred speed of the filters increases. The outputs of the neural spatiotemporal motion detectors are found to be consistent with the theoretical prediction. Figure 31.13 shows a plot of the output of channel 2 for a light bar moving both left and right. The responses of the three filters are shown for both directions of motion. As can be seen, there is a

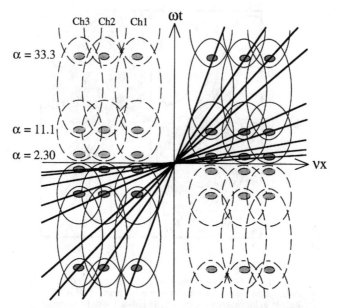

FIGURE 31.12 Distribution of the neural oriented spatiotemporal filters. Shows schematically the location in the frequency domain of the nine neural oriented spatiotemporal filters. The filters for left and right motion are represented with dotted and solid lines, respectively. The shaded ellipse corresponds to the maximum of the power spectrum (see Fig. 31.11), while the unshaded surrounding ellipse shows the spatiotemporal bandwidth.

decrease in the preferred speed as α is decreased, which corresponds to a shift to lower passband frequencies. In the frequency domain, this is represented by a decrease in the slope of the line through the origin, which passes through both peaks of Fig. 10.11.

On the other hand, for a constant temporal tuning, decreasing the spatial tuning will also increase the speed at which the filter is tuned. The spatiotemporal motion estimator is again found to be consistent with this expectation. Figure 31.14 shows a plot for all the channels for $\alpha = 33.33$. Clearly, the preferred value of motion decreases from channel 1 to channel 3, as this corresponds to an increase in spatial tuning frequency.

Table 31.2 shows a comparison between the theoretical speed tuning and the measured tuning of the neural filters. The variables v_x, ω_t, v_t, and v_m correspond to the tuned spatial frequency, tuned temporal frequency, theoretical tuned velocity, and measured tuned velocity. There is good agreement between the experimental results and the theoretical results. The theoretical results were generated by measuring the slope of the line joining the peaks in the frequency domain plots, as in Fig. 31.11, and converting to millimeters per second. The experimental results are obtained by measuring the time taken for the light bar to translate between two photoreceptors on the retina with a known separation; the exact on-chip speed thus is obtained. Plots similar to Figs. 31.13 and 31.14 are generated and used to determine the preferred velocity. The discrepancies can easily be accounted for by considering analog variations of the filters and peak location in the measured data.

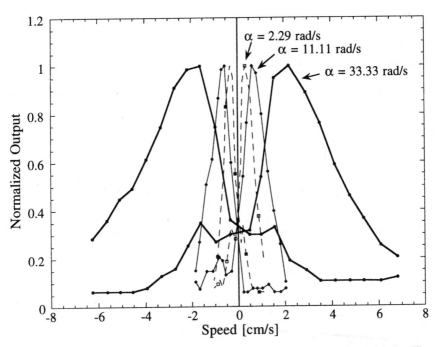

FIGURE 31.13 A plot of the responses of all the filters in channel 2 to a moving bright line. The preferred speeds for $\alpha = 33.33, 11.11$, and 2.29 rad/s are approximately 20, 6, and 3 mm/s, respectively.

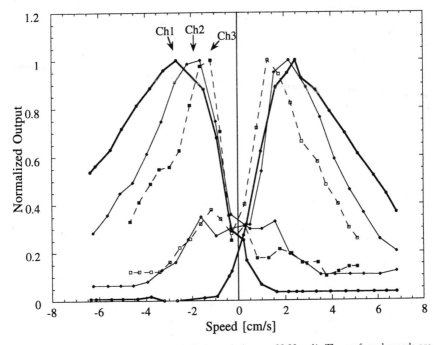

FIGURE 31.14 A plot of responses of all channels for $\alpha = 33.33$ rad/s. The preferred speeds are approximately 30, 20, and 13 mm/s for channels 1, 2, and 3, respectively.

TABLE 31.2 Comparison of Theoretic and Measured Tuned Velocity

Shows the spatial tuning v_x, temporal tuning ω_t, theoretical tuned speed v_t, and measured tuned speed v_m for all the filters.

Channel	α, rad/s	v_x, 1/mm	ωt, Hz	v_t, mm/s	v_m, mm/s
1	33.3	1.24	53	42.7	30.4
	11.1	1.24	18.43	14.86	9.1
	2.3	1.24	3.98	3.21	4.75
2	33.3	2.33	53	23	20.0
	11.1	2.33	18.43	7.9	6.0
	2.3	2.33	3.98	1.71	3.0
3	33.3	3.18	53	16.5	13.3
	11.1	3.18	18.43	6.3	5.53
	2.3	3.18	3.98	1.25	2.1

To measure the speed of stimuli from outputs of the motion filters, consideration of the ensemble of activity must be used. This is obvious since a nonmaximal output of any of the filters corresponds to two distinct speeds. However, by considering the activity of all the detectors together, the speed can be disambiguated. By taking an average of the predicted velocity of each filter, a more accurate result can be obtained. Furthermore, the broad tuning of the filters results in the possibility of using few filters at each scale to cover a wide range of motion without ambiguity.

Because of the edge detection operation performed by the silicon retina, the responses of the motion detection for light and dark bars are similar. The response for moving gratings is also consistent with the expected results. The output of the filters increases as the spatial frequency of the grating and its speed become more aligned with the tuning of the filter. For a moving square wave grating with an on-chip grating frequency of 2 cycles/mm and moving at a speed of 10 mm/s, the average normalized outputs of channel 1 = {0.82, 0.91, 0.37}, channel 2 = {0.55, 0.71, 0.0935}, and channel 3 = {0.95, 0.82, 0.21} for α = 33.33, 11.11, and 2.3 rad/s, respectively. The predicted average speed is 1.1 cm/s. This estimation is in good agreement with the real speed. Figure 31.15 shows a plot of all nine tuning curves for the left direction, and their measured output for the square grating moving at 1.0 cm/s are depicted by the black circles. The vertical line at 1.1 cm/s shows the average of the reported speed.

31.6 SUMMARY AND CONCLUSION

A large-scale analog neural computer with programmable architecture has been presented. The network contains 1024 neurons with 64 synaptic inputs per neuron. Among its unique features is the programmability of the architecture and its neural components, allowing it to be used as a research tool for a variety of applications. The incorporation of programmable time constants makes the network particularly well-suited for real-time dynamic pattern analysis, such as acoustical pattern decomposition, pattern recognition, and motion estimation. This chapter concentrated on using the computer for visual motion estimation.

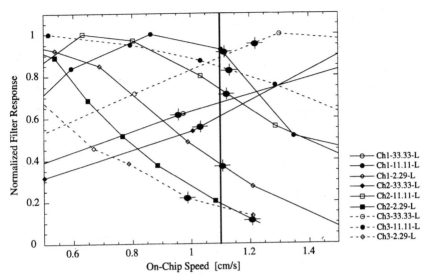

FIGURE 31.15   A plot of all nine filters in the left direction centered around 1 cm/s. The circles with crosshairs indicate the output of each filter for a stimulus moving at 1 cm/s. The average value is 1.1 cm/s.

Spatiotemporal filters have been implemented by exploiting the temporal processing capabilities of a general-purpose analog neural computer. Using spatial and temporal filters implemented with analog neurons, synapses, and synaptic time constants, filters with nine different spatiotemporal tunings have been constructed. The model of the filters, proposed by Adelson and Bergen, requires the computation of motion energy and contrast normalization. The absence of multipliers and dividers in the neural computer led to the replacement of squares with rectification and contrast normalization with thresholds. This did not affect the performance of motion detectors. These filters represent the velocities of the stimuli as a distribution of activity. The average value of the distribution is found to be consistent with the actual velocity of the stimuli. Theoretical analysis of the motion filters is also found to agree well with the measured data.

The input image is presented to the neural computer in parallel and analog mode via a silicon retina. The retina performed the contrast normalization with an edge detection and threshold operation. The synaptic time constants of the neural computer, which are unique to this machine, are crucial for the implementation of any temporal pattern analysis. This has been exemplified with this implementation of real-time visual motion estimation.

ACKNOWLEDGMENTS

The authors would like to thank R. Villegas, D. Koffa, and D. Williams for their help in building interface circuits, and J. Kinner for his contribution to the software development. The work was in part sponsored by the Office of Naval Research and the Ben Franklin Center of Southeastern Pennsylvania.

REFERENCES

1. Cypher, R., and J. Sanz, "SIMD Architectures and Algorithms for Image Processing and Computer Vision," *IEEE Transactions on Acoustics, Speech, and Signal Processing* **37**(12): 2158–74 (1989).

2. Jeschke, H., H. Volkers, and T. Wehberg, "A Multiprocessor System for Real-Time Image Processing Based on a MIMD Architecture," in Burkhardt, Neuvo, and Simon (eds.), *From Pixels to Features II,* North-Holland, New York, 1991.

3. Tsotsos, J., D. Fleet, and A. Jepson, "Towards a Theory of Motion Understanding in Man and Machine," in Martin and Aggarwal (eds.), *Motion Understanding: Robot and Human Vision,* Kluwer Academic Publishers, Boston, 1988.

4. Van der Spiegel, J., "Computational Sensors," in H. Yamasaki (ed.), *Intelligent Sensors,* Elsevier Science Publisher, Amsterdam, 1996.

5. Hertz, J., A. Krogh, and R. Palmer, *Introduction to the Theory of Neural Computation,* Addison-Wesley, Redwood City, Calif., 1991.

6. Maunsell, J., and D. Van Essen, "Functional Properties of Neurons in Middle Temporal Visual Area of the Macaque Monkey. I. Selectivity for Stimulus Direction, Speed and Orientation," *J. Neurophysiology,* **49**(5): 1127–47 (1983).

7. Mueller, P., et al., "Design and Performance of a Prototype General Purpose Analog Neural Computer," *IJCNN,* **I:** 463 (1991).

8. Van der Spiegel, J., et al., "An Analog Neural Computer with Modular Architecture for Real-Time Dynamic Computations," *IEEE J. Solid-State Circuits,* **27**(1): 82–92, (1992).

9. Van der Spiegel, J., et al., "Large Scale Analog Neural Computer with Programmable Architecture and Programmable Time Constants for Temporal Pattern Analysis," *Proc. IEEE ICNN:* 1830–1835 (1994).

10. Etienne-Cummings, R. et al., "A General Purpose Analog Neural Computer and a Silicon Retina for Real Time Target Acquisition, Recognition and Tracking," in M. Bayoumi, L. Davis, and K. Valavanis (eds.), *Proc. CAMP* 93: 48–58 (1993).

11. Simoncelli, E., "Distributed Representation and Analysis of Visual Motion," Ph.D. thesis, Department of Electrical Engineering, Massachusetts Institute of Technology, Cambridge (1993).

12. Etienne-Cummings, R., "Biologically Motivated Analog VLSI Systems for Optomotor Tasks," Ph.D. thesis, Department of Electrical Engineering, University of Pennsylvania (1994).

13. Donham, C., "Design, Implementation and Application of a General Purpose Analog Neural Computer," Ph.D. thesis, Department of Electrical Engineering, University of Pennsylvania (1994).

14. The computational speed of 10^{11} cycles per second is given by the 10^{-6}-second response time of the 10^3 neurons, each receiving 10^2 parallel inputs. When the time constants are added onto the inputs of the neurons, the system then computes 10^3 (number of neurons) nonlinear functions of 10^4 (number of time constants) coupled first-order differential equations.

15. Mueller, P., et al., "Real Time Decomposition of Acoustical Patterns with an Analog Neural Computer," *SPIE Conf. on Applications of Artificial Neural Networks III,* Orlando, April 20–24, 1992.

16. Steyaert, M., P. Kinget, W. Sansen, and J. Van der Spiegel, "Full Integration of Extremely Large Time Constants in CMOS," *Electronics Letters,* **27**(10): 790–91 (1991).

17. Watson, A., and A. Ahumada, "Model of Human Visual-Motion Sensing," *J. Optical Society of America,* **A2:** 322–41 (1985).

18. Adelson, E., and J. Bergen, "Spatiotemporal Energy Models for the Perception of Motion," *J. Optical Society of America,* **A2:** 284–99 (1985).

19. Heeger, D., "Model for the Extraction of Image Flow," *J. Optical Society of America,* **4**(8): 1455–71 (1987).

20. Hubel, D., and T. Wiesel, "Receptive Fields, Binocular Interaction and Functional Architecture in the Cat's Visual Cortex," *J. Physiology,* **160:** 106–154 (1962).

21. Grzywacz, N., and A. Yuille, "A Model for the Estimate of Local Image Velocity by Cells in the Cortex," *Proc. R. Soc. London B,* **239:** 129–161 (1990).

22. Heeger, D., "Half-Squaring in Responses of Cat Simple Cells," *Visual Neurophysiology* **9:** 427–43 (1992).

23. Heeger, D., "Normalization of Cell Responses in Cat Striate Cortex," *Visual Neurophysiology,* **9:** 181–98 (1992).

24. Heeger, D., "Modeling Simple Cell Direction Selectivity with Normalized, Half-Squared Linear Operators," *Investigative Ophthalmology and Visual Science Supplement,* **33:** 953 (1992).

INDEX

ABOUT THE EDITOR IN CHIEF

C.H. Chen is professor of electrical and computer engineering at the University of Massachusetts Dartmouth. His areas of specialization include signal processing and pattern recognition with applications to ultrasonic nondestructive evaluation; sonar, radar, and seismic problems; image processing and computer vision; and neural networks. A Fellow of the IEEE, Dr. Chen is a member of numerous other professional organizations. He is a prolific writer, with hundreds of research papers to his credit. Among his 17 previous books, he is editor of the *Computer Engineering Handbook* (McGraw-Hill, 1992).